S0-BAF-752

ADDISON WESLEY

Physics 11

Addison Wesley Science Authors

Ray Bowers
Eric Brown
Sadru Damji
Dean Eichorn
Ute Goering-Boone
Art Last
Frank Mustoe
Dale Parker
Robert Perkins
Geoff Rayner-Canham
Mark van Roode
Len Silverman
Gail de Souza
Elgin Wolfe
Rob Young

Advisory Panel

Ray Bowers
Shawna Hopkins
Heather Mace
Philip Marsh
Graham Satterthwaite
Gail de Souza
Elgin Wolfe

Elgin Wolfe

Ontario Institute for Studies in Education
University of Toronto
Toronto, Ontario

Eric Brown

Peel District School Board (Retired)
Mississauga, Ontario
Seneca College
Toronto, Ontario

Dale Parker

Halton District School Board (Retired)
Burlington, Ontario

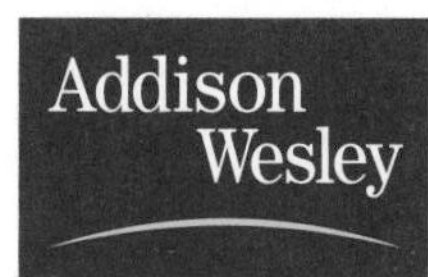

Toronto

The publisher has taken every care to meet or exceed industry specifications for the manufacturing of textbooks. The spine and the endpapers of this sewn book have been reinforced with special fabric for extra binding strength. The cover is a premium, polymer-reinforced material designed to provide long life and withstand rugged use. Mylar gloss lamination has been applied for further durability.

Publisher Susan Green
Managing Editor Cecilia Chan
Product Manager Donna Picheca
Developmental Editors Julia Hubble, Jodi Webber
Coordinating Editor Lynne Gulliver
Editorial Team Kate Baltais, Keith Lennox, Harold Otto, David Peebles, Cynthia Young
Editorial Assistant Judy Wilson
Indexers Kate Baltais, Harold Otto

Marketing Manager Dawna Day-Harris

Production Manager Theresa Thomas
Production Coordinator Sandra Magill

Art Direction
Alex Li

Cover Design
Anthony Leung

Interior Design
Anthony Leung
Alex Li

Page Layout
Valerie Bateman/ArtPlus Limited

Photo Research
Paulee Kestin

Illustration
ArtPlus Limited
Imagineering Scientific and Technical Artworks Inc.

Cover Image: Digital Vision
Cover picture shows fibre optics.

ISBN 0-201-70792-6

Printed and bound in Canada

1 2 3 4 5 – TCP – 05 04 03 02 01

Acknowledgements

Curriculum and Assessment Consultant

Marietta (Mars) Bloch
Toronto District School Board

Senior Science Consultant

Philip Marsh
Peel District School Board

Technology Consultant

Mike Newnham
Thames Valley District School Board

Accuracy Reviewers

Marko Horbatsch, Dr. phil. nat.
Department of Physics & Astronomy, York University

Nutakki D. Rao, B.E., M.E., Ph.D., P. Eng.
Department of Electrical and Computer Engineering, University of Calgary

Peter J. Simpson, B.Sc., M.Sc., Ph.D.
Department of Physics & Astronomy, University of Western Ontario

Safety Reviewer

Ralf Gmell
Hamilton-Wentworth District School Board (Retired)

Catholicity Reviewer

John McParland
Brother Edmund Rice S.S., Toronto

Review Panel

Steve Alsop
York University

David Doucette
Dr. G.W. Williams S.S., Aurora

Dennis Karasek
Westminster S.S., London

John Mrmak
Brock University

Christine Renaud
Lively D.S.S., Lively

Reviewers

Dan Blanchard
Middlefield C.I., Markham

David Collins
St. Joan of Arc C.H.S., Maple

Paul Inwood
Marathon S.S., Marathon

Bryan Kearney
Tagwi S.S., Avonmore

Rob Lenters
Cobourg D.C.I. West, Cobourg

Janice Longo
North Dundas D.H.S., Chesterville

Dermot O'Hara
Mother Teresa C.S.S., Scarborough

Maya Rao
Agincourt C.I., Agincourt

Renita Roxburgh
St. Anne's C.S.S., Clinton

Graham Satterthwaite
Sir Robert Borden H.S., Nepean

Jacqueline Shaver
Branksome Hall, Toronto

Contributing Writers

Gabriel Roman Ayyavoo, M.Ed.
Francis Libermann C.H.S., Scarborough

Julie Czerneda
Professional Writer

David Doucette
Dr. G.W. Williams S.S., Aurora

Neil Dyal
Birchmount Park C.I., Scarborough

Heather Mace
Ottawa-Carleton District School Board

Contents

UNIT

1 Forces and Motion

OVERALL EXPECTATIONS

By the end of this unit, you will be able to:

- demonstrate an understanding of the relationship between forces and the acceleration of an object in linear motion
- investigate, through experimentation, the effect of a net force on the linear motion of an object, and analyze the effect in quantitative terms, using graphs, free-body diagrams, and vector diagrams
- describe the contributions of Galileo and Newton to the understanding of dynamics; evaluate and describe technological advances related to motion; and identify the effects of societal influences on transportation and safety issues

You slowly rise up to the top of the first crest. Suddenly, gravity pulls you down the other side. Your velocity increases rapidly. Within seconds you are plummeting downward at over 95 km/h. When you reach the bottom of the hill, you are forced down into your seat so hard that it feels like you weigh 2000 N (200 kg). Then a hairpin turn slams you to one side. Before you can react, you are hurled into a death-defying loop and find yourself upside down! After another minute of terrifying hills, curves, dips, and loops the ride is over.

To understand what happens when any object moves—whether it be a roller coaster, a snowboarder careening down a slope, or a satellite circling Earth—requires a knowledge of the basic laws governing forces and motion. Scientists Galileo and Sir Isaac Newton first formulated the basic laws that describe how different forces act on objects in motion. Ride designers today use their knowledge of these principles to make sure that your ride experience is sufficiently terrifying but still safe.

In this unit, you will study concepts related to forces and motion such as displacement, velocity, and acceleration. You will examine the relationship between mass and the force of gravity. You will take a look at Galileo's famous thought experiment, and you will investigate different types of friction and how they affect horizontal motion. Finally, you will study Newton's three laws of motion, which explain the forces and motions of all mechanical systems. As you proceed through the unit, you will get a good sense of how the use of that knowledge in the development of various technologies affects your daily life.

PHYSICS HEADLINES

- **Dangers of Prolonged Weightlessness**

  The weightlessness of space is detrimental to muscles and bones, especially the pelvis and vertebrae. Without the pull of gravity, bones deteriorate at 1–3% per month, and muscles, in one case, up to 40% on an extended visit to Mir. Scientists don't know if the deterioration stops. Astronauts arriving on Mars may not be strong enough to walk.

- **Motion Sensors Border U.S.A. and Canada**

  Motion sensors and sophisticated spy cameras are being installed along a 50-km stretch between Washington State and British Columbia after a man was caught taking bomb-making materials from British Columbia into the U.S.A. in December 1999.

- **Melting Ice Will Lead to Lower Sea Levels**

  The gravitational pull from polar ice sheets is so strong that if the ice sheet melts the sea levels nearby will actually fall. For instance, researchers at the University of Toronto claim that if the Greenland icecap melts, places like Newfoundland and Great Britain will actually see sea levels fall. The reason is simple: the Greenland ice sheet exerts a strong gravitational pull on the sea; as it melts the pull will be less and the sea level will drop.

- **The Moon May Have Helped Create Life**

  Life on Earth may be due in part to Earth's and the Moon's gravitational influences. Recent studies show that after Earth cooled, the Moon's gravitational pull helped create tidal pools where it's been suggested much of life began. The Moon also helps keep Earth's axis stable.

- **Virtual Test Dummies**

  Each year, crash testing helps reduce injury and death, but physical testing is expensive and time consuming. Now, computer programs can perform virtual crashes. This saves time and money, and allows investigators more options in studying crash scenarios—to repeatedly replay the "accident" to better see structural damage.

ACHIEVEMENT TASK PREVIEW

At the end of this unit, you will demonstrate your learning by completing the task "Are Amber Light Times Set Correctly?"

CHAPTER 1

Displacement, Velocity, and Acceleration

SPECIFIC EXPECTATIONS

By the end of this chapter, you will be able to:

- define and describe concepts and units related to force and motion (1.1, 1.2, 1.3, 1.4, 1.5)
- describe and explain different kinds of motion, and apply quantitatively the relationships among displacement, velocity, and acceleration in specific contexts (1.1, 1.2, 1.3, 1.4, 1.5, 1.6)
- analyze uniform motion in the horizontal plane in a variety of situations using vector diagrams (1.1, 1.2, 1.3, Investigation 1, Investigation 2)
- interpret patterns and trends in data by means of graphs drawn by hand or by computer, and infer or calculate linear and nonlinear relationships among variables (1.3, 1.5, Investigation 1, Investigation 2)
- evaluate the design of technological solutions to transportation needs and, using scientific principles, explain the way they function (1.1, 1.2, 1.3, 1.4, 1.5, 1.6)

It seems as if every hour is rush hour as traffic gridlock on Canada's streets and highways continues to get worse. Some people think we should simply build more highways to solve the problem, but this is expensive and could encourage more car use and its accompanying pollution. Others feel that we should increase public transit, but this is also expensive and offers no guarantee that drivers will abandon the convenience of their cars. Still others argue that increasing the speed limit would enable more traffic to travel from one point to another in a given time interval.

FIGURE 1.1 How might an understanding of displacement, velocity, and acceleration have helped these drivers avoid a crash?

Solving complex difficult problems like this one starts with the ability to measure and analyze the movement of objects. For example, the faster a car goes, the longer it takes to stop. At a speed of 80 km/h it can take over 80 m for a car to decelerate to 0 km/h. Therefore, for safety's sake, higher speeds require drivers to leave more space between vehicles. This means fewer cars per kilometre of highway.

In this chapter, you will study the motion of objects using vector quantities. These are quantities that consist of three parts: a numeral, a unit, and a direction. Common vector quantities include position, displacement, velocity, and acceleration. These quantities can be used to analyze more than just traffic flow. They can be used to analyze everything from the performance of Olympic athletes to the trajectory of missiles. The knowledge you gain in this chapter can be applied anytime a precise measurement of motion is needed.

CHECK**POINT**

What does the area under a velocity–time graph give for a moving object?

a) travel time
b) average velocity
c) displacement
d) acceleration
e) position

Sketch a velocity–time graph and use it to explain your answer.

Discovering Physics

Creating a Position–Time Graph

What do you think the position–time graph of a dropped coffee filter will look like? Make a prediction, and then follow the steps below.

You will need graph paper, some large paper coffee filters, a metre-stick or measuring tape, and a stopwatch.

1. Record your prediction by sketching a graph and explain your reasoning.
2. Drop one coffee filter from different heights up to a maximum of 2 m and time its fall (Figure 1.2).
3. Plot a position–time graph of the results. (If you have a motion sensor, interface, and computer, repeat the experiment to see what the position–time graph generated by the computer looks like.)

- Describe the position–time graphs for the single coffee filter dropped from different heights.
- What kind of motion did the coffee filter have for most of its trips?
- Design an indirect way to use a coffee filter, a stopwatch, and what you learned from this experiment to determine the height of a stairwell.

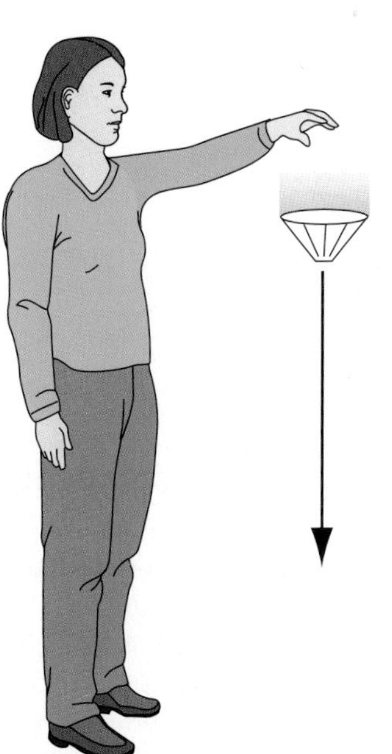

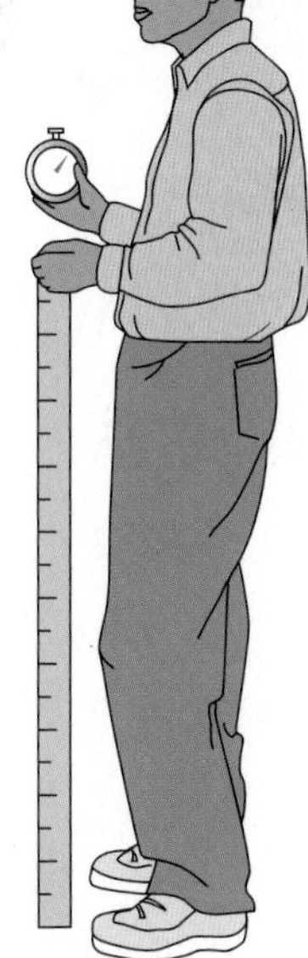

FIGURE 1.2 Dropping a coffee filter

1.1 Displacement and Position Vectors

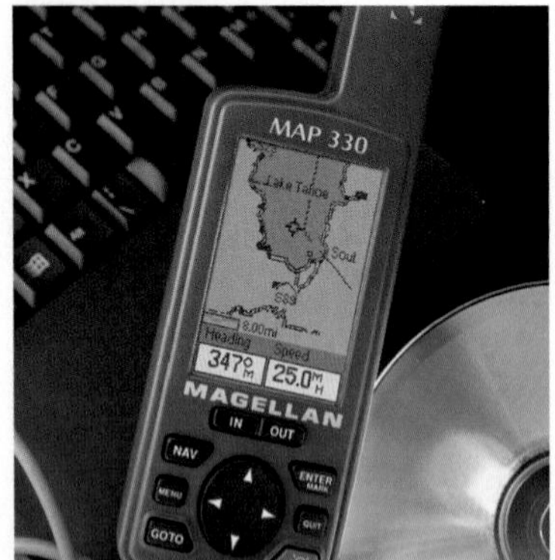

FIGURE 1.3 A GPS receiver

Key Understandings

When you have completed this section, you will be able to:

- describe the difference between a scalar and a vector quantity
- describe and name the different parts of a vector
- distinguish between displacement and position
- draw position vectors and displacement vectors
- distinguish between and add collinear and non-collinear vectors

Many things that you do can be measured and described (e.g. how much time you spend in school, or how heavy your backpack is). Time and mass are examples of physical quantities. Physical quantities can be classified as either scalars or vectors.

A **scalar quantity** is any physical quantity that can be completely described by a single numeral and the correct unit of measurement. For instance, a red blood cell lives, on average, 120 d. Other examples of scalar quantities are distance, speed, mass, and volume.

However, many physical quantities cannot be described using only a numeral and a unit; a direction must also be included. For example, to tell a hiker the position of a campsite with reference to the park office you need to know how far away it is and in what direction. A **vector quantity** is any quantity that is completely described by a numeral, a unit, and a direction. Some common vector quantities are displacement, velocity, and acceleration.

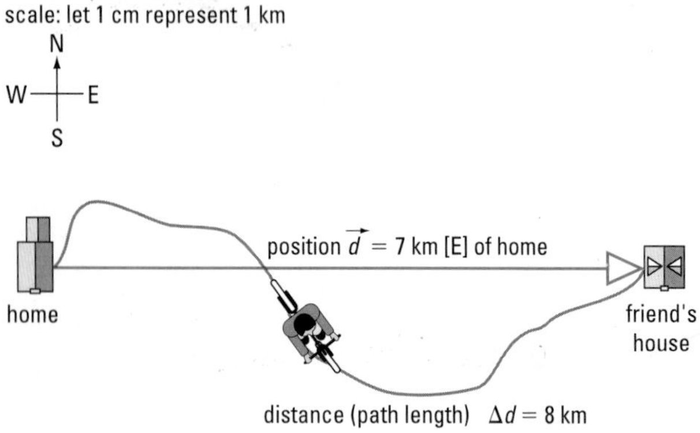

Position

Position is the location of an object relative to a reference point. It is a vector quantity since a direction must be specified. The symbol for position is $\vec{d}$ and its SI unit is the metre (m). An arrow is placed over the symbol to show that it is a vector quantity. Imagine you go to visit a friend. You leave home and cycle along a winding path (Figure 1.4). You travel a total distance of 8 km, but you are not 8 km from home as the crow flies. The shortest distance from your home to your friend's house is 7 km. The position of your friend's house is $\vec{d}$ = 7 km [E] of your home. Note that to describe a position you must state a magnitude (7 km), a direction ([E]), and a reference point (home).

scale: let 1 cm represent 1 km

N

W E

S

position $\vec{d}$ = 7 km [E] of home

home

friend's house

distance (path length) Δd = 8 km

FIGURE 1.4 The difference between distance and position

Displacement

Displacement is the change in position of an object. It is a vector quantity that represents the length of a straight line segment directed from the initial position to the final position. If the initial position is $\vec{d}_i$ and the final position is $\vec{d}_f$ then the change in position is $\vec{d}_f - \vec{d}_i$. The symbol for displacement is $\Delta\vec{d}$ and its SI unit is the metre. Displacement differs from position in that a displacement does not need a reference point. A displacement of 100 km [N] from an airport in British Columbia and a displacement of 100 km [N] from an airport in New Brunswick are equivalent.

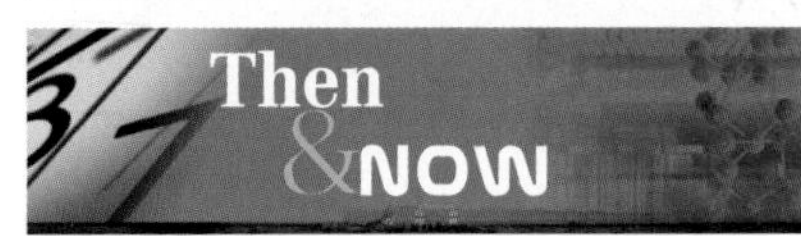

Where am I?

Imagine that you are on a sailboat. You scan the horizon, but all you see is water. No land is in sight. How would you figure out where you are? In the past, one of your only options was a method called celestial navigation. Celestial navigation works on the principle that if you know the exact location of a celestial body such as the Sun, Moon or a star and can measure a relationship between it and your boat, you can calculate your craft's position.

First you would measure the angle between a celestial body and the horizon using a sextant. Then you record the exact time of day using an extremely accurate clock called a chronometer. Most celestial bodies change position in the sky as Earth rotates. Referring to the Nautical Almanac you would find a cross-reference of the celestial body and the time. Using this information and some math, you can calculate your position. To get the most accurate position, you would repeat with at least one other celestial body.

Modern sailors rarely rely on only their own calculations to pinpoint their position. Instead, they use the global positioning system, commonly know as GPS. The GPS navigation system consists of 24 satellites orbiting Earth. The satellites continuously broadcast signals of their exact location. A receiver on the ground picks up these signals and its internal computer calculates the receiver's position and displays it for the user to see.

GPS receivers are small, lightweight, portable, and relatively inexpensive. They are becoming extremely popular with boaters, pilots, hikers, mountain climbers and anyone who needs to keep track of where they are. Civilian GPS receivers are accurate to about 100 m, but military GPS receivers are accurate to about 9 m.

Consider the trip to see your friend: your displacement is $\Delta\vec{d} = 7$ km [E]. Note that to specify a displacement you must indicate a magnitude (7 km) and a direction ([E]). Unlike position, displacement does not require a reference point.

The directions that accompany vector quantities are enclosed within square brackets [ ]. A displacement of twenty kilometres north would be written $\Delta\vec{d} = 20$ km [N]. Directions between the north, south, east, and west reference coordinates are usually given in terms of degrees measured from north or south toward the east or west. For example, sixty degrees east of south is measured by first facing south, and then by rotating sixty degrees toward the east. It is written [S 60° E]. Thus, a displacement of fifty metres, sixty degrees east of south would be written $\Delta\vec{d} = 50$ m [S 60° E].

Representing Vector Quantities

A vector quantity is represented on a diagram by a line segment with an arrowhead at one end. This directed line segment is called a **vector**. The length of the vector represents its magnitude and the direction of the arrowhead shows its direction. The **tail** of the vector is called the **origin**, and the **tip** is called the **terminal point**. Two pieces of information are essential to interpret a vector diagram. First, the scale, or relationship, between the vector and the physical quantity must be indicated. Second, **reference coordinates** or the points of a compass must be included to show the direction. Figure 1.5 shows several different displacement vectors, all drawn to the same scale. To draw a vector:

1. Choose a suitable scale.
2. Draw the reference coordinates or compass points.
3. Draw a line segment in the appropriate direction.
4. Measure off the vector along the line segment according to the scale.
5. Draw the arrowhead at the terminal point.
6. Finally, label the vector.

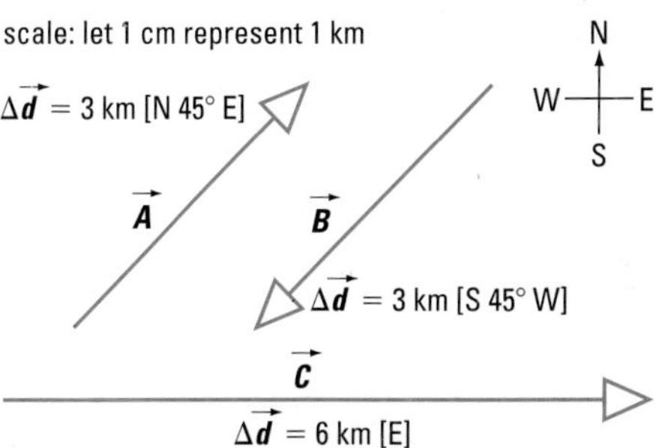

FIGURE 1.5 Several different displacement vectors drawn to the same scale. Vector B has the same magnitude as vector A, but opposite direction. Vector C differs in both magnitude and direction.

EXAMPLE 1 CONCEPTUAL

Draw a vector to represent the position of a snowmobile located 30 km [N 45° E] of a cottage near Huntsville, Ontario.

Reasoning and Solution

Start by drawing the reference coordinates. Because each centimetre of the directed line segment in Figure 1.6 represents 5 km, the vector representing the position of the snowmobile is 6 cm long. The arrowhead points 45° east of north, showing that the displacement is directly northeast. The origin of the vector is the cottage, and the terminal point of the vector is the final position of the snowmobile with reference to the cottage. Both the scale and the reference coordinates are shown beside the diagram.

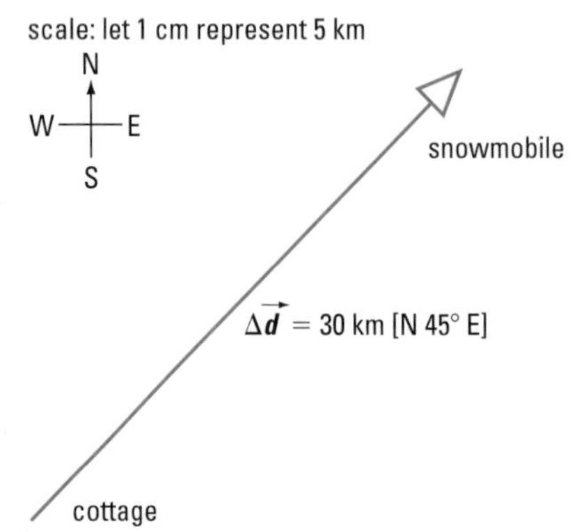

FIGURE 1.6

CHALLENGE

Draw a vector to represent the position of a windsurfer located 80 m [S 30° E] of a dock. Show both the scale and the reference coordinates.

Adding Collinear Vectors

If vectors are directed along the same straight line then they are said to be **collinear**. They can be either in the same direction (parallel), or in the opposite direction (anti-parallel). Collinear vectors can be added algebraically. There is a simple strategy for doing this:

1. First, label the direction of the larger vector quantity as the positive direction.
2. Give any vector quantities in the opposite direction negative signs and then reverse them so that they now follow the same direction as the larger value.
3. Add the values of the vector quantities.

If a vector quantity is negative, then this indicates that its true direction is opposite to the specified direction. For example, a displacement of 7 km [E] is equal to a displacement of −7 km [W] (Figure 1.7). Before the vector quantities can be added, the specified directions must be the same. By reversing both the sign and the direction, the vector quantities have the same specified direction and can be added.

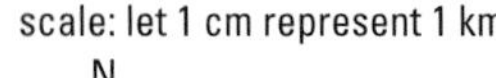

N
W
E
S

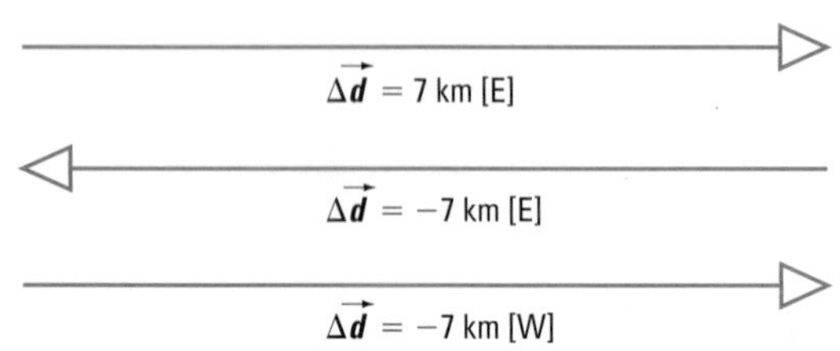

FIGURE 1.7 A negative displacement of −7 km [E] is opposite in direction to a positive displacement of +7 km [E].

EXAMPLE 2 NUMERICAL

A shopper walks 800 m [W] from her home to the bank, then 500 m to the store. Call the first displacement $\Delta\vec{d}_1$ and the second displacement $\Delta\vec{d}_2$. What is the shopper's final position from home $\vec{d}_f$ if the store is: a) due west of the bank? b) due east of the bank?

Given

$\Delta\vec{d}_1 = 800$ m [W]

a) $\Delta\vec{d}_2 = 500$ m [W]

b) $\Delta\vec{d}_2 = 500$ m [E]

Required

$\vec{d}_f$

Analysis

The displacements are collinear, so apply the steps for adding collinear vector quantities.

Solution

a) $\vec{d}_f = \Delta\vec{d}_1 + \Delta\vec{d}_2$
$= 800$ m [W] $+ 500$ m [W]
$= 1300$ m [W] of home

b) $\vec{d}_f = \Delta\vec{d}_1 + \Delta\vec{d}_2$
$= 800$ m [W] $+ 500$ m [E]
$= 800$ m [W] $+ (-500$ m [W])
$= 300$ m [W] of home

Statement

If the store is west of the bank, the final position is 1.30×10^3 m [W] of home. If the store is east of the bank, the final position is 3.00×10^2 m [W] of home.

INSIGHT

Note that the answer has three significant digits. For more information on significant digits, mathematical operations, rounding off numbers, and standard form see Appendixes H–K.

PRACTICE PROBLEMS

1. A camper kayaks 13 km [E] from a camping site, stops, has lunch, and then paddles 20 km [W]. What is the kayaker's final position with reference to the camping site?
2. A boat sails 4.0 km [N 45° E]. It then changes direction and sails 6 km [S 45° W]. Where does the boat end up with reference to its starting point?

Adding Non-Collinear Vectors

Vectors located along different straight lines are called **non-collinear vectors**. Algebraic addition cannot be used for non-collinear vectors because their different directions must be considered. For example, suppose that a rancher searching for a lost calf travelled two consecutive displacements along two different directions: 4 km [E], followed by 3 km [N]. The rancher would have travelled a total distance of 7 km. However, the rancher would not be 7 km from home. How can we find the rancher's resultant displacement and then his final position?

Vectors that have different directions can be added using a graphical strategy called the **tail-to-tip** strategy. To do this:

1. Choose a suitable scale.
2. Draw the reference coordinates.
3. Draw one of the vectors to scale and call it the first vector.

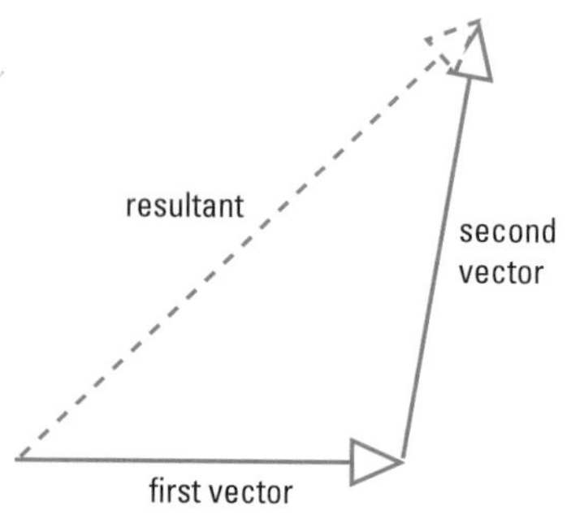

FIGURE 1.8 Adding vectors

4. Dot in a line from the tip of the first vector in the direction of the second vector.
5. Draw the second vector to the same scale as the first, with the tail of the second vector at the tip of the first.
6. Dot in another vector from the tail of the first vector to the tip of the second vector. This new vector represents the sum (resultant) of the first two vectors (Figure 1.8).
7. Measure the length and direction of the resultant.
8. Compare the length of the resultant with the scale.
9. Finally, state the magnitude and direction of the resultant.

The vectors can be added in any order, and the tail-to-tip method can be used for any number of vectors. The method also works for collinear vectors, and for all kinds of vector quantities.

INFOBIT

Non-collinear vectors that form two arms of a triangle can also be added using the trigonometric sine law:

$$\frac{a}{\sin A} = \frac{b}{\sin B} = \frac{c}{\sin C}$$

and the cosine law:

$c^2 = a^2 + b^2 - 2ab \cos C$, where A, B, and C are the angles of a triangle and a, b, and c are the sides opposite the corresponding angles.

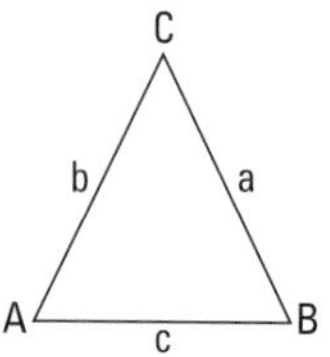

EXAMPLE 3 NUMERICAL

A prospector left her cabin to look for gold. She walked 8 km [S], then 12 km [E], and finally 3 km [N]. Calculate her resultant displacement.

Given

$\Delta\vec{d}_1 = 8$ km [S]

$\Delta\vec{d}_2 = 12$ km [E]

$\Delta\vec{d}_3 = 3$ km [N]

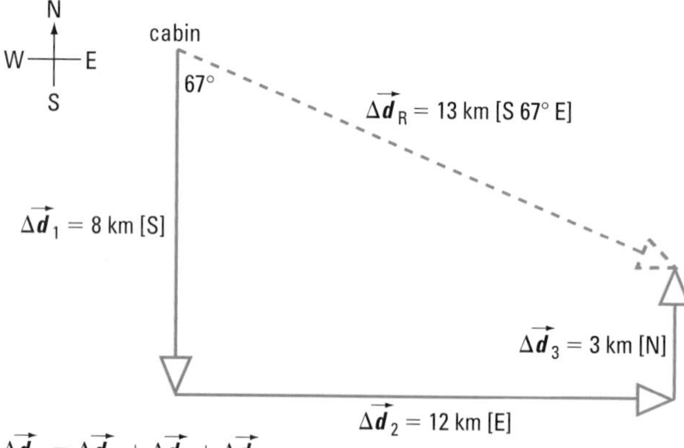

FIGURE 1.9

Required

$\Delta\vec{d}_R$

Analysis

The three vectors are non-collinear. Use the tail-to-tip strategy to add the vectors.

Solution

See Figure 1.9.

Statement

The prospector's resultant displacement is 13 km [S 67° E].

Try adding the vectors for the trip in a different order. Is the answer the same?

PRACTICE PROBLEMS

1. A canoeist paddles 4.0 km [E], 5.0 km [N], 7.0 km [W], and 6.0 km [S]. What is the canoeist's final position with reference to where he started?
2. Starting from her home, a student roller-bladed 200 m [W], 100 m [S], and 500 m [S 30° E] to pick up a video. Where is the video store with reference to home?

Discovering Physics — Distance, Displacement, and Position

Figure 1.10 shows the distances a letter carrier travelled in going along the path from A to D passing through B and C on the way. Use the information in the diagram, a ruler calibrated in mm, and a protractor to complete the distance, displacement, and position information required in Table 1.1. Assume the letter carrier's reference point is A. Complete Table 1.1, then draw and label the displacement vectors AB, BC, and CD, and the position vectors AB, AC, and AD.

TABLE 1.1 Distance, Displacement, and Position

	Distance Δd (m)	Final Position $\vec{d}$ (m) [direction] reference point	Displacement $\Delta\vec{d}$ (m) [direction]
AB			
BC			
CD			
AC			
AD			

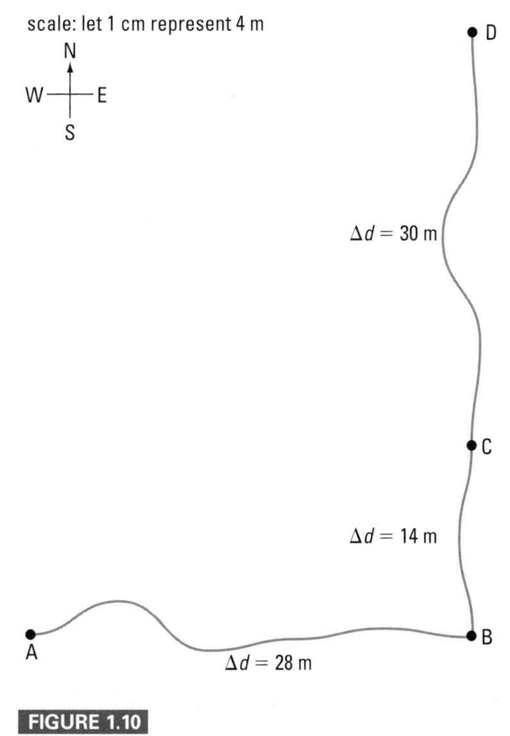

FIGURE 1.10

Section 1.1 Review

Understanding Concepts

1. Draw a Venn diagram to show the similarities and differences between position and displacement.
2. Using symbols, write the direction "forty degrees west of south." Show this direction using reference coordinates.
3. Symbols and scientific terms are used to communicate information precisely and accurately. In your own words, define $\vec{d}$ and $\Delta\vec{d}$.
4. Choose a suitable scale, draw the reference coordinates, and draw the following position vectors:
   a) 5 m [N] of A
   b) 10 km [W] of home
   c) 20 m [N 45° E] of the goal post
5. Draw vectors to represent the following displacements. Use an appropriate scale and reference coordinates.
   a) 4 m [N]
   b) 8 km [E]
   c) 6 cm [S 60° W]
6. A competitor in an international bike race pedalled 35 km [E] followed by 40 km [S 45° E]. Calculate
   a) the total distance travelled
   b) the resultant displacement
   c) the competitor's final position

Applying Inquiry/ Communication Skills

7. Design a procedure to determine the displacement between two trees on opposite banks of a river. You cannot get across the river to measure it directly. You have a 10-m tape calibrated in mm, a protractor, a compass, and five sharp stakes. Test your procedure by using two markers 10 m apart.
8. Describe a procedure for determining the position of the entrance to the school library relative to the entrance to the physics classroom. Carry out your procedure and report the results.

Making Connections

9. Research to find out what reference direction air traffic controllers use to keep track of the position of the airplane? How would they write the direction [S 45°W]?
10. A straight level highway is to be constructed between two cities. One city is located 40 km [S] and 75 km [E] of the other. How long will the highway be? Draw a sketch to show the new highway. Show displacement and direction.

1.2 Velocity and Uniform Motion

Key Understandings

When you have completed this section, you will be able to:

- distinguish between constant, average, and instantaneous velocity
- calculate the average velocity and the constant velocity of an object

The 100-m Olympic event is run along a straight course. The concepts of displacement and time are used in calculating the velocity for the race. Maurice Green of the U.S.A. won the gold medal at the 2000 Sydney Olympics with a time of 9.87 s (Figure 1.11). He covered a greater displacement per unit time than the nearest rival, Ato Boldon of Trinidad and Tobago.

Velocity is a vector quantity that describes both how fast an object is moving and its direction. **Velocity** is defined as the displacement (change in position) of an object per unit time, and the symbol for velocity is $\vec{v}$. If an object moving in a straight line covers equal displacements in equal times then it has **constant velocity**. We can also say that it has **uniform motion**.

However, objects seldom move at constant velocity: a rocket speeds up as it leaves the launching pad; a train slows down as it enters the station; a person may walk quickly, slow down to avoid a child on a bike, or change direction to avoid construction on the sidewalk. How can we calculate the average velocity when the velocity changes in size or direction?

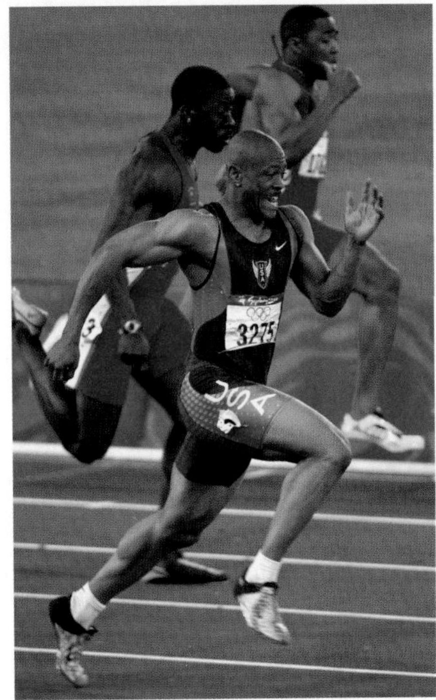

FIGURE 1.11 Gold medal winner Maurice Green at the 2000 Olympics

Average Velocity

Average speed is calculated by dividing the total distance travelled by the elapsed time. Since both distance and speed are scalar quantities, speed is a scalar quantity. The **average velocity** of an object is calculated by dividing the change in position, or the displacement, by the elapsed time. Thus

$$\text{average velocity} = \frac{\text{change in position}}{\text{elapsed time}}$$

$$= \frac{\text{displacement}}{\text{elapsed time}}$$

The symbol for average velocity is $\vec{v}_{av}$. Thus, the equation for average velocity, in terms of the initial and final positions, $\vec{d}_1$ and $\vec{d}_2$, and the initial and final times, t_1 and t_2, is

$$\vec{v}_{av} = \frac{(\vec{d}_2 - \vec{d}_1)}{(t_2 - t_1)}$$

Since $\vec{d}_2 - \vec{d}_1$ is the displacement $\Delta\vec{d}$ and $t_2 - t_1$ is the elapsed time Δt, then

$$\vec{v}_{av} = \frac{\Delta\vec{d}}{\Delta t}$$

The average velocity for an object is the same as the constant velocity it must have in order to cover the same displacement in the same time. Both these equations can be used to calculate constant and average velocity.

INSIGHT

Use the first equation if the problem involves positions and times. Use the second equation if the problem involves a displacement and a time interval.

EXAMPLE 4 NUMERICAL

A student decides to go hiking. First he walks 6.0 km [E] in 2.0 h, then he walks 8.0 km [N] in 4.0 h. Because he is tired, he takes the bus home. Calculate his average velocity while walking.

Given

$\Delta\vec{d}_1 = 6.0$ km [E]
$\Delta t_1 = 2.0$ h

$\Delta\vec{d}_2 = 8.0$ km [N]
$\Delta t_2 = 4.0$ h

Required

$\vec{v}_{av}$

Analysis

- Displacement is a vector quantity.
- Use the tail-to-tip strategy of vector addition to find the total displacement.
- The elapsed time is the sum of the two given times.
- Apply the equation
$$\vec{v}_{t_{av}} = \frac{\Delta\vec{d}_t}{\Delta t_t}$$

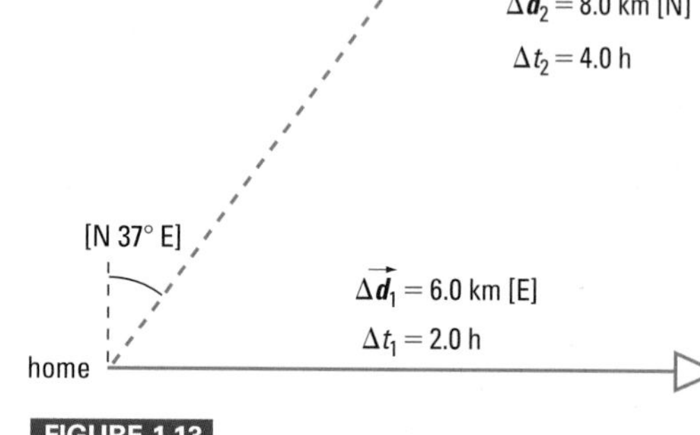

FIGURE 1.13

Solution

Figure 1.13 shows the vector addition of the two displacements to get the total displacement. The total displacement $\Delta\vec{d}_t$ = 10 km [N 37° E].

$$\vec{v}_{t_{av}} = \frac{\Delta\vec{d}_t}{\Delta t_t}$$

$$= \frac{10 \text{ km [N37° E]}}{6.0 \text{ h}}$$

$$= 1.7 \text{ km/h [N 37° E]}$$

Statement

The average velocity for the hike is 1.7 km/h [N 37° E]. Note that the average velocity is the same as the constant velocity that the student would need to reach the final position in 6.0 h by *the most direct path*, which would be a straight line between the initial and final positions.

The average velocity for the whole trip is zero. Can you explain why?

WEBLINK

To explore displacement and velocity further, go to **www.pearsoned.ca/physics11.**

PRACTICE PROBLEMS

1. A cyclist covers 20 km [W] in 1.5 h and then 15 km [S] in 2.0 h to reach a rest area. Calculate the average velocity.
2. A circus van moves 50 km [E] in the first hour, 40 km [W] in the second hour, and 30 km [N] in the next half hour. Calculate the average velocity of the travelling circus van.

Instantaneous Velocity

Instantaneous velocity is the velocity an object has at a specific instant of time. The symbol for instantaneous velocity $\vec{v}$ is the same as for constant velocity. If an object is in uniform motion, then its instantaneous velocity is equal to its constant velocity. But what happens if the velocity is changing in magnitude or direction, or both? For example, suppose that over a two-second time interval an object increases its velocity in a uniform way from 10 m/s [N] to 20 m/s [N]. At half-time (one second into the trip) it will have an instantaneous velocity of 15 m/s [N].

Consider a Ferris wheel revolving at a constant speed (Figure 1.14). At any one instant a rider at the top has the same speed as a rider at the bottom. However, the instantaneous velocities are in opposite directions. If the rider at the top has an instantaneous velocity of 4 m/s [E], then the rider at the bottom has an instantaneous velocity of 4 m/s [W].

FIGURE 1.14 Is the velocity of the top of the Ferris wheel the same as the velocity of the bottom?

Section 1.2 Review

Understanding Concepts

1. Re-arrange the formula for average velocity to solve for
   a) $\vec{d}_2$ in terms of $\vec{v}_{av}$, $\vec{d}_1$ and Δt.
   b) Δt in terms of $\Delta\vec{d}$ and $\vec{v}_{av}$.
2. Explain the terms average velocity and constant velocity in your own words.
3. Which of the following describe uniform motion?
   a) a child on a merry-go-round
   b) a ball rolling down a ramp
   c) a car driving west at 100 km/h

   Explain your answer.
4. A delivery van, parked 200 m [E] of a police car, moves to a position 600 m [E] of the police car in 18 s. What was the average velocity of the delivery van in km/h?
5. An amateur ball player runs at an average speed of 6.0 m/s between home plate and first base and 9.0 m/s between first and second. If the distance between the bases is 27.4 m and the base lines form an angle of 90°, calculate his average velocity. Include reference coordinates in your answer.

Applying Inquiry/Communication Skills

6. Design a procedure to determine whether the average velocity of a cart up a ramp is the same magnitude as its average velocity down the ramp. Pay close attention to the control of variables. Make a prediction, explain your prediction, and, if you have time, check the prediction by implementing the procedure.

Making Connections

7. In the past, some cameras used bursts of ultrasound to focus the lens on the object to be photographed. The camera recorded the time between the emission of the ultrasound and the return of its echo. Explain how this information could be used by the camera to determine the distance to the object. Include any assumptions that must be made, and show and explain the equation used by the camera to calculate the displacement.

1.3 Position–Time Graphs

Key Understandings

When you have completed this section, you will be able to:

- describe position–time graphs for constant velocity and changing velocity
- describe the relationship between the slope of a graph and constant velocity
- use a position–time graph showing different constant velocities to calculate the average velocity for any interval from the graph
- describe the change in the slope of a position–time graph as the velocity increases and decreases
- state and apply the relationship between the slope of a position–time graph and the average and instantaneous velocity

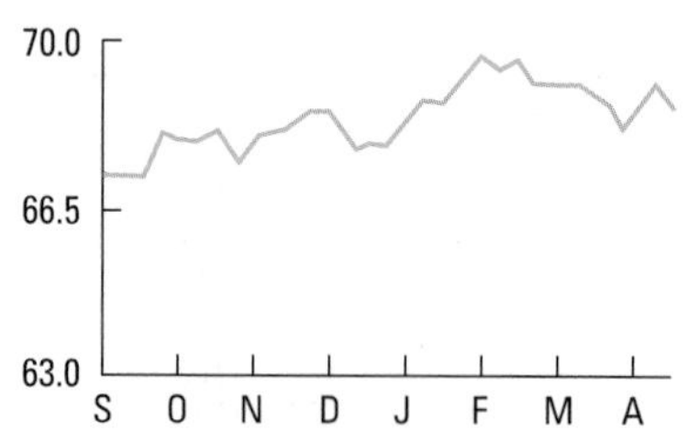

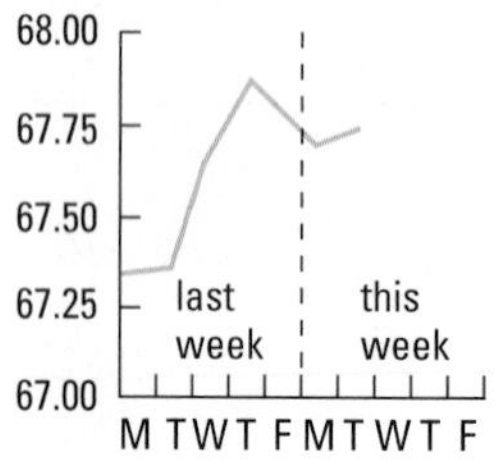

FIGURE 1.15 Graphs communicate quantitative information efficiently.

A graph is a diagram that depicts the relationship between two or more variables. A relationship may be known mathematically (e.g. the graph of the equation $y = mx + b$ is a straight line with constant slope and a y-intercept) or it may be unknown (e.g. a graph of the value of the Canadian dollar as a function of time, Figure 1.15). Businesses, governments, scientists, and engineers make extensive use of graphs to communicate information visually. Graphs show trends better than tables, summarize a lot of data, and are often easier to understand.

Graphical Analysis

René Descartes (1596–1650) was a French philosopher and mathematician who made important contributions to science. He was the first to use the letters near the beginning of the alphabet for constants and those near the end for variables. He also introduced the use of exponents and the square root sign.

Descartes devised the Cartesian system of coordinates while lying in bed. As he watched a fly hovering in the air Descartes realized that the fly's position could be described at every moment by locating three mutually perpendicular planes that intersect at the position occupied by the fly. This led him to realize that every point in a plane could be represented by a system of two numbers.

Furthermore, every curve on a Cartesian coordinate system represents a particular equation and every equation represents a particular curve. Thus, it is to Descartes that we owe the use of graphical analysis techniques in physics.

Graphical analysis techniques play a major role in business, industry, and science today. Financial analysts plot graphs of stock fluctuations used by investment counsellors. Architects interpret charts and graphs of beam strength as a function of cross-sectional areas for new materials when designing buildings. Scientists measure light intensity as a function of temperature for various kinds of light sources.

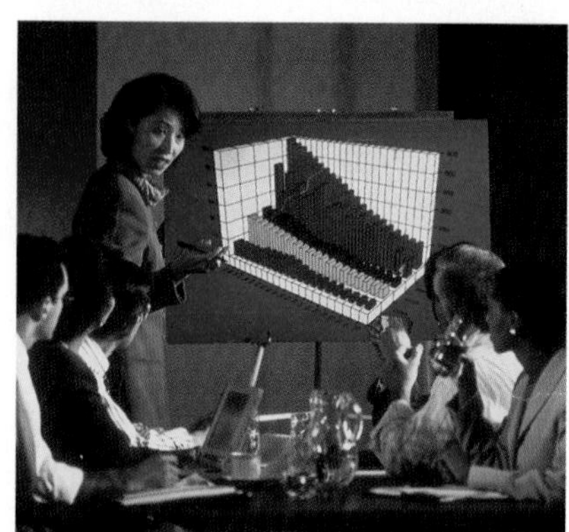

FIGURE 1.16

Position–Time Graphs for Constant Velocity

Any object is moving at constant velocity if it covers equal displacements in equal intervals of time. For example, a woman drives east at constant velocity along a straight level road. She records her position, from the start, at various times during the trip. The data are given in Table 1.2.

The driver travels 40 km [E] every half hour, or 80 km [E] every hour. The car therefore has a constant velocity of 80 km/h [E]. Figure 1.17 shows the position–time graph for the constant velocity.

TABLE 1.2 Position–Time Data for a Car Travelling at Constant Velocity

Time t (h)	Position $\vec{d}$ (km [E])
0	0
0.25	20
0.50	40
1.00	80
1.50	120
2.00	160
3.00	240

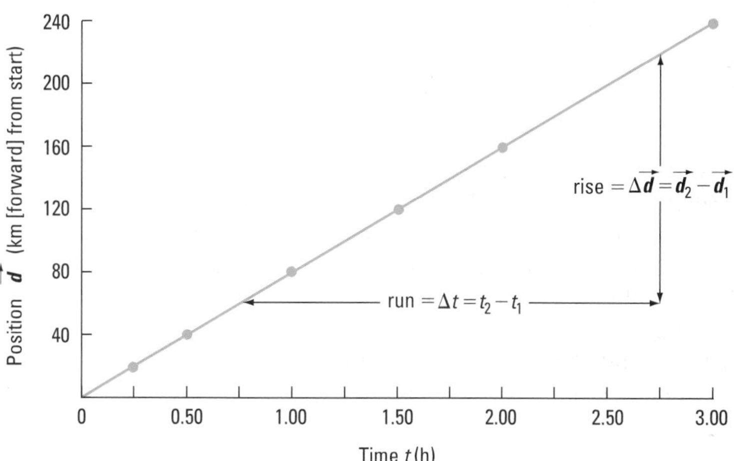

FIGURE 1.17 A position–time graph for constant velocity

The position–time graph for an object moving at constant velocity is a straight line with constant slope. If the object starts at position zero, the line passes through the origin. Calculate the slope of the line shown in Figure 1.17. The **slope** is equal to the rise divided by the run.

$$\begin{aligned}\text{slope} &= \frac{\text{rise}}{\text{run}}\\ &= \frac{\text{position 2} - \text{position 1}}{\text{time 2} - \text{time 1}}\\ &= \frac{\vec{d}_2 - \vec{d}_1}{t_2 - t_1}\\ &= \frac{220\text{ km [E]} - 60\text{ km [E]}}{2.75\text{ h} - 0.75\text{ h}}\\ &= \frac{160\text{ km [E]}}{2.00\text{ h}}\\ &= 80\text{ km/h [E]}\end{aligned}$$

Thus, **the slope of the position–time graph for an object moving at constant velocity gives the value of the constant velocity.**

INSIGHT

Calculating the slope of a position–time graph will give the same value for constant velocity even if the object starts at a position other than zero.

Investigation 1

Refer to page 48, Investigation 1

TABLE 1.3 Position–Time Data for Two Walks

Time Δt (s)	Position $\vec{d}$ (m) [from start]	
	Slow	Fast
0	0	5.0
5	2.3	11.2
10	4.5	17.0
15	6.8	23.9
20	9.0	29.9
25	11.2	35.1
30	13.5	41.4
35	15.8	46.7
40	18.0	53.0
45	20.3	58.6
50	22.5	65.2

Exploration Using a Graphing Calculator

Position–Time Graphs for Two Walks

The equation for finding constant velocity is $\vec{v} = \frac{\Delta\vec{d}}{\Delta t}$. This can be re-arranged to $\Delta\vec{d} = \vec{v}\Delta t$. You can use a graphing calculator to determine whether a set of data yields a straight-line position–time graph and, if so, to find the slope.

A student walked for 50 s in a straight line at a slow steady velocity. The student then repeated the walk at a faster steady velocity. At 5-s time intervals a signal was given and the student dropped a sandbag to mark the position. The positions of the sandbags, from the starting point, were measured and are summarized in Table 1.3. Use the graphing calculator to determine whether the motions are uniform and, if so, find the values of the constant velocities.

Use the graphing calculator to plot both position–time graphs on the same axes. Then use it to identify the function that best models the data and to plot the line graphs of the functions.

Discussion

1. What physical quantities do x and y represent?
2. Write the equation that best models the relationship between position and time for both sets of data.
3. What are the slopes? What property of the graph do they represent?
4. Do the data support constant velocity for both graphs?
5. What are the units of the slope?
6. What are the y-intercepts? (one should be close to zero and the other not)
7. Why is one y-intercept not zero? What does this mean?
8. Calculate the position that corresponds to a time of 28 s for both graphs using the equation.
9. Calculate the time that corresponds to a position of 17 m forward for both graphs using the equation.
10. Compare the coordinates of these points with the coordinates you determined by interpolating using the graphing calculator.

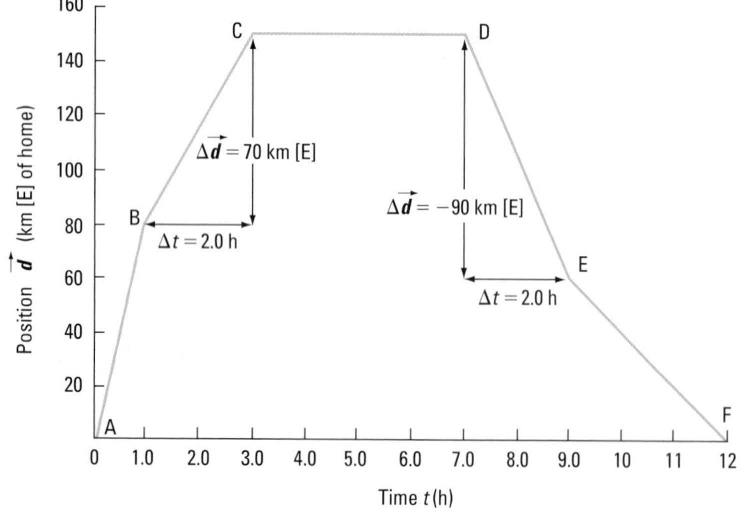

FIGURE 1.18 A position–time graph for a round trip on a motorcycle

Position–Time Graph for a Round Trip

Figure 1.18 shows the position–time graph for a round trip on a motorcycle. What information can be determined from the graph?

We can tell that the destination is 150 km [E] of home and that it takes 3.0 h to get there. Also, the first part of the trip (interval AB) takes 1.0 h. The speed is less during the second part (interval BC). Four hours are spent at the destination (interval CD) and it takes 5.0 h to return home. The first 2.0 h of the return trip (interval DE) are made at a faster constant velocity than the last 3.0 h (interval EF). Also, the velocity coming back is in the opposite direction to the velocity going away.

Discovering Physics — *Matching a Position–Time Graph*

Match your motion to the points plotted on a position–time graph. Is it as easy as it sounds?

You will need a data logger interface, a motion sensor, and a computer.

1. Connect the computer, interface, and motion sensor as directed by the manufacturer.
2. Position the motion sensor as shown in Figure 1.19.
3. Turn on the computer and upload the experiment for matching a position–time graph.
4. Study the position–time graph on the monitor and discuss how you will move to exactly match the graph.
5. Clear a safe walking path in front of the sensor. Begin collecting data and move to match the graph. Repeat the walk several times.
6. Work together in groups of three or four to prepare a position–time graph that occupies about 10 s of time. Show your graph to another group and have them try to match the graph using the motion sensor.
   - How did your initial position compare with that expected by the computer program?
   - How well were you able to match the sloping portion of the graph?
   - Did you stop on time and at the correct position? Did practice help?
   - How well were other students able to match your group's graph?
   - Why might they have found it more difficult to match your paper graph than to match the graph on the computer monitor?

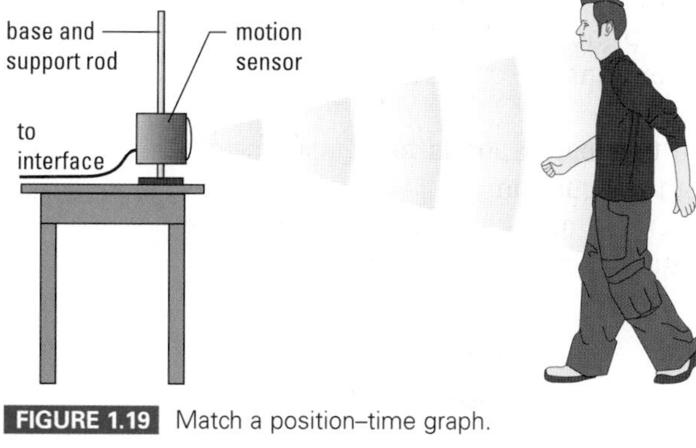

FIGURE 1.19 Match a position–time graph.

You can calculate the velocity of the motorcycle during each interval of the trip. The constant velocity during interval AB can be found directly from the graph. It took 1.0 h to travel 80 km [E]. Thus, the velocity was 80 km/h [E]. Interval BC is more difficult to interpret. Calculate the slope of the line:

$$\text{velocity during interval BC} = \text{slope} = \frac{\text{rise}}{\text{run}} = \frac{\vec{d}_2 - \vec{d}_1}{t_2 - t_1}$$

$$= \frac{150\text{ km [E]} - 80\text{ km [E]}}{3.0\text{ h} - 1.0\text{ h}}$$

$$= \frac{70\text{ km [E]}}{2.0\text{ h}}$$

$$= 35\text{ km/h [E]}$$

INSIGHT

When calculating slopes, always retain the units of the rise and run as well as the direction. This will give you the units and the direction for the final answer.

The constant velocity during interval BC of the trip was 35 km/h [E]. This example shows that **a positive constant slope on a position–time graph represents a constant positive velocity**.

Note the horizontal line on the position–time graph during interval CD. During this time interval the position of the motorcycle stays constant. The motorcycle stops at a position 150 m [E] of the start for 4.0 h. Thus, **a horizontal line on a position–time graph has zero slope and represents zero velocity**.

The slope of the line during interval DE is negative. What is the velocity during interval DE of the trip?

$$\text{velocity during interval DE} = \text{slope} = \frac{\text{rise}}{\text{run}} = \frac{\vec{d}_2 - \vec{d}_1}{t_2 - t_1}$$

$$= \frac{60 \text{ km [E]} - 150 \text{ km [E]}}{9.0 - 7.0 \text{ h}}$$

$$= \frac{-90 \text{ km [E]}}{2.0 \text{ h}}$$

$$= -45 \text{ km/h [E]}$$

$$= 45 \text{ km/h [W]}$$

WEBLINK

To explore position-time graphs further, go to **www.pearsoned.ca/physics11.**

The velocity during interval DE is 45 km/h [W].

Likewise, by calculating the slope of the graph during interval EF, we can see that the velocity during this interval is −20 km/h [E] or 20 km/h [W]. These calculations demonstrate that **a straight line with a negative slope on a position–time graph represents a negative constant velocity**. A negative slope on a position–time graph indicates that the object has a velocity opposite in direction to that chosen as positive.

Finding Average Velocity Suppose we wish to calculate the average velocity for two different parts of a round trip. How can we determine the average velocity of the motorcycle during the combined intervals BC and CD? This is the interval BD, from time t = 1.0 h to t = 7.0 h (see Figure 1.20).

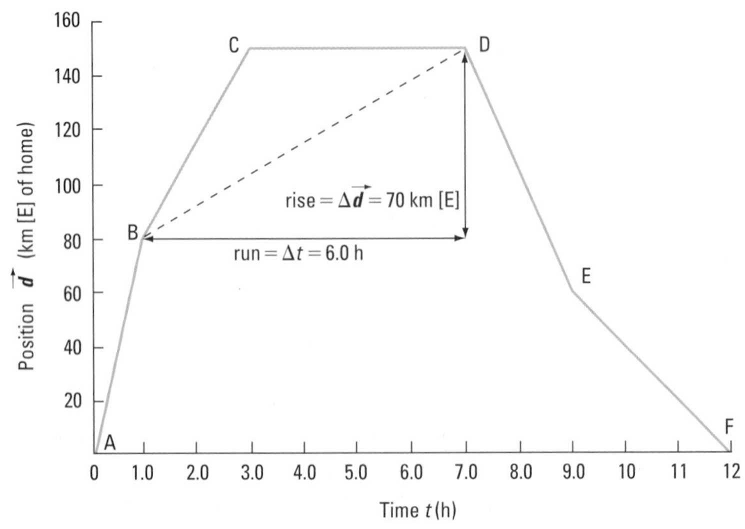

FIGURE 1.20 Determining average velocity from a position–time graph

$$\text{average velocity for interval BD} = \frac{\text{change in position}}{\text{elapsed time}}$$

$$\vec{v}_{av} = \frac{\vec{d}_2 - \vec{d}_1}{t_2 - t_1}$$

$$= \frac{150 \text{ km [E]} - 80 \text{ km [E]}}{7.0 \text{ h} - 1.0 \text{ h}}$$

$$= \frac{70 \text{ km [E]}}{6.0 \text{ h}}$$

$$= 12 \text{ km/h [E]}$$

How does the velocity 12 km/h [E] compare with the slope of the straight line between $t = 1.0$ h and $t = 7.0$ h in Figure 1.20? The velocity represents the slope of the straight line joining the two points B and D on the graph. Therefore, **the average velocity between any two points on a position–time graph is equal to the slope of the line joining the two points**.

INSIGHT

A positive slope between two points on a position–time graph indicates that the average velocity is positive. What would a negative slope indicate and what does it mean in real life?

Position–Time Graphs for Changing Velocity

Figure 1.21 shows a cart released from the top of a ramp. At the bottom of the ramp the cart collides with a perfectly elastic spring that instantly bounces the cart back up the ramp. Table 1.4 shows the ideal position–time data for the motion. In reality, it takes some time for the cart to change direction, but to simplify the discussion assume that this occurs instantaneously and ignore friction.

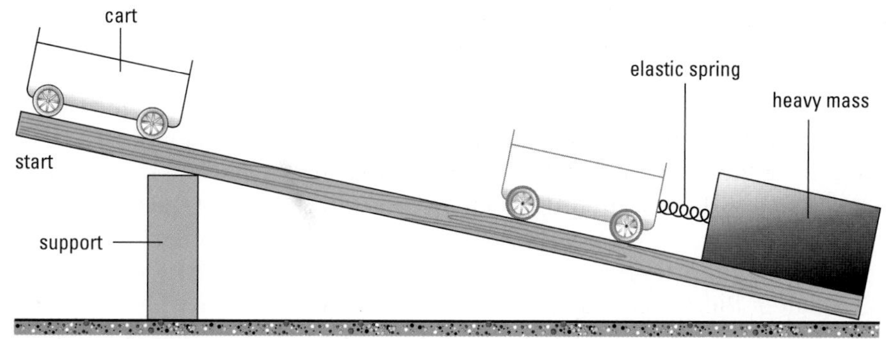

FIGURE 1.21 A cart rolling down a ramp and being reflected by an elastic spring

TABLE 1.4 The Motion of a Cart on a Ramp

Time t (s)	0.0	0.1	0.2	0.4	0.6	0.8	1.0	1.2	1.4	1.5	1.6
Position $\vec{d}$ (m) [Down Ramp]	0.0	0.02	0.08	0.32	0.72	1.28	0.72	0.32	0.08	0.02	0.0

Figure 1.22 shows the position–time graph for the cart. At $\Delta t = 0.0$ the cart is at rest. The line is horizontal, so its slope is zero. Then, as the cart speeds up, the positive slope increases. The graph has its steepest slope at 0.80 s. This

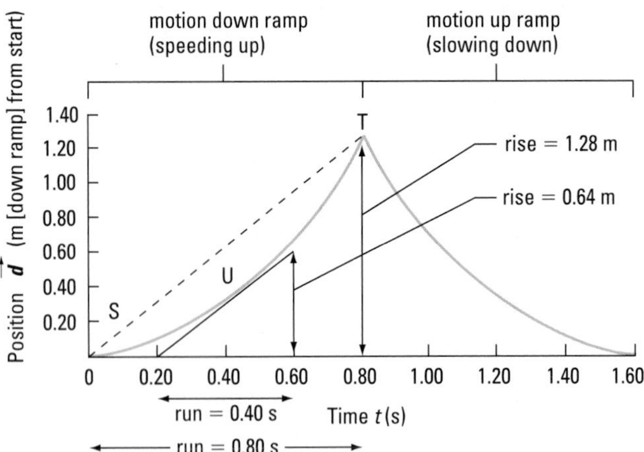

FIGURE 1.22 The position–time graph for a cart rolling down and back up a ramp

occurs just as the cart reaches the bottom of the ramp and hits the spring. The spring instantaneously reverses the motion of the cart. As a result, the slope of the graph changes from its maximum positive value to its maximum negative value. Then the cart slows down as it moves up the ramp. This is shown by the decreasing negative slope of the graph. Finally, at a time of 1.60 s, the slope is again zero because the cart has stopped at the top of the ramp.

Finding Average Velocity A position–time graph for changing velocity looks more complicated than one for constant velocity. However, the same basic rules apply for finding velocity from the graph. Begin by finding the average velocity of the cart for the time during which it is rolling down the ramp. Remember that average velocity is the total displacement divided by the elapsed time. The displacement for the first half of the trip is 1.28 m [down] and the elapsed time is 0.80 s. The average velocity is

$$\vec{v}_{av} = \frac{\text{displacement}}{\text{elapsed time}} = \frac{\Delta\vec{d}}{\Delta t} = \frac{1.28 \text{ m [down]}}{0.80 \text{ s}} = 1.6 \text{ m/s [down]}$$

The calculations show that the average velocity for the trip down the ramp is 1.6 m/s [down]. This is also the slope of the straight line dotted between the initial point S (0,0) and the final point T (0.80 s, 1.28 m [down]) on the first half of the graph. This means that **the average velocity between any two points on a position–time graph for any kind of motion is equal to the slope of the line joining the two points**.

INFO BIT

The slope of the tangent at the mid-point of an interval (in this example $\Delta t = 0.40$ s) is equal to the slope of the average velocity for the total interval (in this example $\Delta t = 0.80$ s).

Finding Instantaneous Velocity How can we find the instantaneous velocity at a specific time, for example, at 0.40 s? We cannot take the slope of the line because it is curved. However, we can draw a straight line, called a tangent, touching the curve at the 0.40 s point. This point is labelled U on the graph. A **tangent** is a straight line that touches a curve at only one point and does not cross the curve. The slope of the tangent drawn at $\Delta t = 0.40$ s is

$$\text{slope} = \frac{\text{rise}}{\text{run}} = \frac{\Delta\vec{d}}{\Delta t} = \frac{0.64 \text{ m [down]}}{0.40 \text{ s}} = 1.6 \text{ m/s [down]}$$

The instantaneous velocity at a time of 0.40 s is 1.6 m/s [down]. This demonstrates that **the instantaneous velocity, at a point on a position–time graph, is the slope of the tangent drawn to the curve at that point**.

Exploration Using a Graphing Calculator

Position–Time Graph for Changing Velocities

Two top sprinters ran in a 100-m final. Sprinter B won the race with a time of 9.83 s. Their official times for various positions from the time the starter gave the signal are summarized in Table 1.5. Use your graphing calculator to plot position–time graphs of their motion. Then compare their graphs with an idealized position–time graph for constant velocity.

TABLE 1.5 Position–Time Data for a World Championship Race

Position $\vec{d}$ (m [forward])	Time Δt (s)	
	Sprinter A	Sprinter B
0	0	0
0	0.145	0.123
10	1.94	1.84
20	2.96	2.86
30	3.91	3.80
40	4.78	4.67
50	5.64	5.53
60	6.50	6.38
70	7.36	7.23
80	8.22	8.10
90	9.07	8.96
100	9.93	9.83

Discussion

1. Which sprinter had a faster reaction time? By how much?
2. Describe the shape of both graphs near the beginning of the race. What does the shape imply about the motion of the runners during this time interval?
3. How does a position–time graph for increasing velocity differ from a position–time graph for constant velocity?
4. Did the sprinters reach constant velocity? If so, when?
5. How do you think the position–time graph for a novice sprinter would differ from these graphs? Why?

Section 1.3 Review

Understanding Concepts

1. Sketch a position–time graph for a student who is

a) walking home with a constant positive velocity

b) stopping at the mall 5 km from home

c) cycling to school with constant velocity

2. Explain how you would use a position–time graph to determine the average velocity for a specified interval.

3. Describe briefly the kind of motion that is taking place in each lettered stage of the situations represented by the position–time graphs in Figure 1.23.

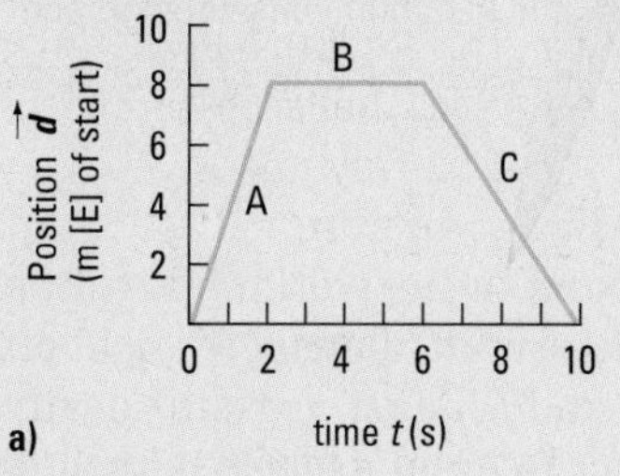

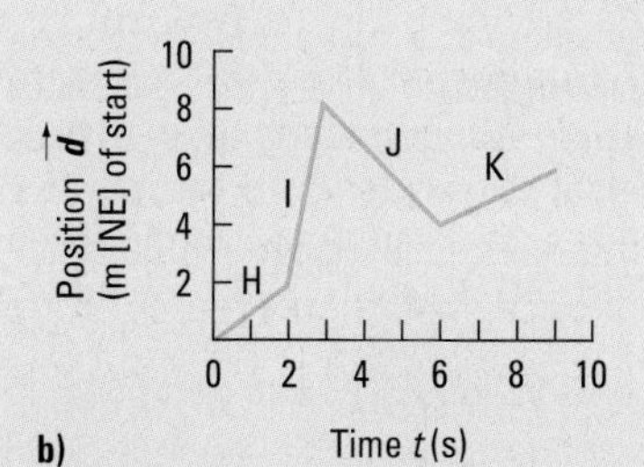

FIGURE 1.23 Describe the motion at each of the stages.

Refer to Figure 1.24 (overleaf) to answer questions 4 to 8. An efficiency expert has been hired by a company to analyze the process of assembling the parts of a refrigerator. Figure 1.24 shows the motion of an inspector on an automated refrigerator assembly line. Position zero is the start of the assembly line.

4. How far is the inspector from the starting point after 40.0 s?

5. When is the inspector at a position of 150 m?

6. What is the inspector's velocity during each of the lettered intervals?

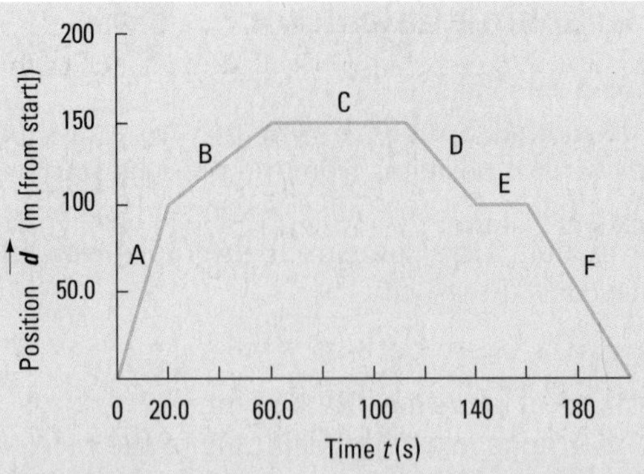

FIGURE 1.24 Inspecting a refrigerator assembly line

7. Calculate the average velocity for the 60-s to 160-s time intervals.
8. With reference to his position at 10.0 s, when is the inspector's average velocity zero?

Applying Inquiry/ Communication Skills

9. Predict the shape of and sketch a position–time graph for a person starting 0.40 m from a reference point, walking slowly away at constant velocity for 3.0 s, stopping for 4.0 s, backing up at half the speed for 5.0 s, and finally stopping. Design an activity using a motion sensor, interface, and computer to check the shape of your graph. What information would you need to exactly model the graph?

Making Connections

10. It is claimed that if drivers keep their eyes on the road for long straight stretches of highway, their minds adjust to the motion. This causes them to underestimate their speed and to drive faster. Also, drivers overestimate the time to collision when approaching or overtaking other cars. Describe a method of collecting data that could be used to test these claims.

1.4 Acceleration

Key Understandings

When you have completed this section, you will be able to:

- distinguish between velocity and acceleration
- distinguish between constant, average, and instantaneous acceleration
- solve problems involving initial and final velocity, initial and final or elapsed time, and average acceleration

FIGURE 1.25 Skydivers

Skydiving is one of the most exciting sports in the world. It involves stepping into space from the open door of an aircraft flying at a height of 3 km. The only barrier between survival and almost certain death is a knowledge of physics, raw courage, a rip cord, and a folded parachute. The skydiver accelerates toward the ground, reaching a speed of 175 km/h in a little over 30 s. When the rip cord is pulled, the parachute unfurls and the skydiver decelerates rapidly to a final speed of about 7 km/h. A skilled skydiver can navigate the parachute through horizontal winds as high as 15 km/h to a safe landing spot.

The motion of the skydiver is very complex: it includes the rapid vertical and sideways deceleration on leaving the airplane, the vertical acceleration during free fall, the jarring deceleration when the parachute opens, and the unpredictable sideways accelerations caused by gusting winds near the ground.

Whether we move by the power of our own legs, or by a train, plane, or car, we seldom move at a constant velocity; either the speed changes or the direction changes. When the speed or direction of an object changes, the object is accelerating.

Acceleration is the rate of change of velocity. It is calculated by dividing the change in velocity by the time taken to make this change. Thus

$$\text{acceleration} = \frac{\text{change in velocity}}{\text{elapsed time}}$$

Acceleration is a vector quantity because it is derived from velocity, which involves direction. The symbol for acceleration is $\vec{a}$. The acceleration of an object travelling in a curved path is more complicated, so we will consider only accelerations that result from a change in velocity along a straight line.

Units of Acceleration

The SI unit for change in velocity is the metre per second (m/s), and the unit for elapsed time is the second (s). The SI unit of acceleration is, therefore, metres per second per second, or metres per second squared (m/s^2). An acceleration of 5 m/s^2 [E] is read as "five metres per second squared east" or "five metres per second per second east." This means that the velocity changes in magnitude by an average of five metres per second every second in an easterly direction. For example, if the velocity of an object changes from 10 m/s to 20 m/s in two seconds then the average acceleration is 5 (m/s)/s = 5 m/s^2.

FIGURE 1.26 What range of speeds will a speedometer on a motorcycle read?

Cars, trucks, and motorcycles have speedometers calibrated in kilometres per hour (km/h) (Figure 1.26). When the change in velocity is in kilometres per hour and the elapsed time is in seconds, the unit of acceleration is the kilometre per hour per second (km/h)/s. An acceleration of 6 (km/h)/s [N] is read as "six kilometres per hour per second north." This means that the velocity changes by an average of six kilometres per hour each second in a northerly direction. As you can see, it is important to take careful note of both the units and the direction of acceleration.

Constant Acceleration

The motion of a pear falling from a tree is an example of constant acceleration. An object has **constant acceleration** if its velocity changes by equal amounts in equal intervals of time.

Table 1.6 shows the velocity–time data for a helicopter with a constant acceleration of 3.0 m/s^2 [E]. Note that the velocity of the helicopter increases by 3 m/s [E] every second. If this trend continues, what would be the velocity of the helicopter after 8.0 s? What would it be after 12 s?

TABLE 1.6 Velocity–Time Data for a Helicopter with Constant Acceleration

Time t (s)	0	1.0	2.0	3.0	4.0	5.0
Velocity $\vec{v}$ (m/s [E])	0	3.0	6.0	9.0	12.0	15.0

Discovering Physics — *Simulating an Elevator and a Projectile*

1. You will need a stopwatch and two 14-m lengths of string.
2. Starting at one end, tie knots in the first string to mark off six 2-m intervals. Knot the second string at 0, 0.25, 1.00, 2.25, 4.00, 6.25, 9.00, and 12.25 m. (Note that the longer displacement intervals are near the start for the "projectile" string.)
3. Stretch the strings out in straight lines and parallel to one another in a suitable walking location as shown in Figure 1.27.

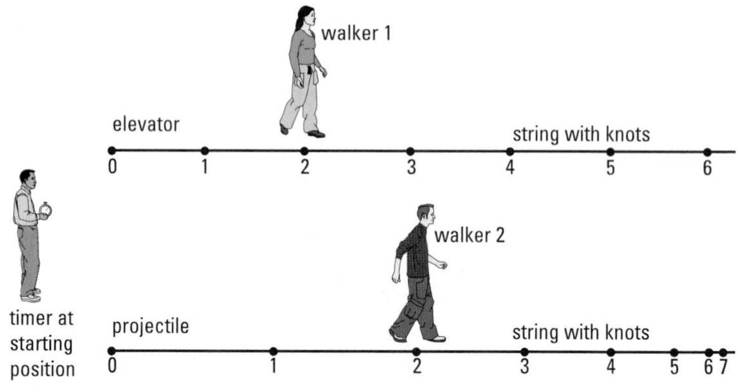

FIGURE 1.27

3. Choose two walkers and one timer. Have the timer call "knot" at equal time intervals; say every 3.0 s.
4. Have the first walker move with constant speed down and back along the path beside the string with equally spaced knots so that a knot is passed every time the time calls out "knot."
5. Have the second walker move with uniformly changing speed down and back along the path beside the unequally spaced knots so that a knot is passed each time the timer calls out "knot." (This may take some practice.)
6. Have both walkers repeat their motions at the same time. This will give you a chance to compare the motions.
   - Describe the motion of the walker moving at constant speed. How does this motion model the motion of an elevator?
   - Describe the motion of the walker moving at a uniformly changing speed. In what ways does this walker model the motion of ball thrown upward?

For the time intervals called out, what value of acceleration was used for determining the spacing of the knots for the "projectile" string?

WEBLINK

To explore displacement, velocity, and constant acceleration, go to **www.pearsoned.ca/physics11.**

Average Acceleration

Few objects undergo constant acceleration for very long. A sports car that accelerates to a velocity of 50 km/h [W] from a traffic light has its greatest acceleration at the start. As the car goes faster, its acceleration decreases until the velocity reaches the constant value of 50 km/h [W], then the acceleration drops to zero.

Average acceleration is used to describe acceleration when the velocity changes in a non-uniform way. Average acceleration is found by calculating the change in velocity during an interval and dividing it by the time taken for the change.

The symbol for average acceleration is $\vec{a}_{av}$. The equation for calculating average acceleration in terms of the change in velocity $\Delta\vec{v}$ and the elapsed time Δt is

$$\vec{a}_{av} = \frac{\Delta\vec{v}}{\Delta t}$$

but

$$\Delta\vec{v} = \vec{v}_2 - \vec{v}_1 \text{ and } \Delta t = t_2 - t_1$$

therefore

$$\vec{a}_{av} = \frac{\vec{v}_2 - \vec{v}_1}{t_2 - t_1}$$

Average acceleration and constant acceleration are related. The average acceleration for a time interval is the same as the constant acceleration an object would need if it were to change velocity by an equal amount in an equal interval of time.

Consider the helicopter you studied in Table 1.6. Suppose that, instead of changing velocity by 3 m/s [E] each second, it changed velocity by 2 m/s [E] in the first second, and 4 m/s [E] in the next second. The change in velocity during the first two seconds would be 6 m/s [E]. The average acceleration during the first two seconds would be 6 m/s [E]/2.0 s = 3 m/s^2 [E]. This average acceleration would yield the same final velocity after two seconds as when the helicopter had a constant acceleration of 3.0 m/s^2 [E]. The above equations therefore apply to both constant and non-uniform (average) acceleration.

EXAMPLE 5 NUMERICAL

Table 1.7 shows the velocity–time data for a motorcycle with changing acceleration. Calculate a) the average acceleration for the five-second interval and b) the average acceleration of the motorcycle during the fifth second.

Given

TABLE 1.7 Velocity–Time Data for a Motorcycle with Changing Acceleration

Time t (s)	0	1.0	2.0	3.0	4.0	5.0
Velocity $\vec{v}$ (m/s [E])	0	4.0	7.8	11.0	13.0	14.0

Required

a) $\vec{a}_{av}$ for the five-second interval
b) $\vec{a}_{av}$ for the fifth second

INSIGHT

When we refer to the fifth second we mean the one-second time interval between $t = 4.0$ s and $t = 5.0$ s.

Analysis

a) Acceleration equals change in velocity divided by the elapsed time.

$$\vec{a}_{av} = \frac{\Delta\vec{v}}{\Delta t}$$

b)

- The fifth second is the time interval from $t = 4.0$ s to $t = 5.0$ s.
- $\vec{v}_1 = 13$ m/s [E] $t_1 = 4.0$ s
- $\vec{v}_2 = 14$ m/s [E] $t_2 = 5.0$ s
- $\vec{a}_{av} = \dfrac{\vec{v}_2 - \vec{v}_1}{t_2 - t_1}$

Solution

a) $$\vec{a}_{av} = \frac{\Delta\vec{v}}{\Delta t} = \frac{14 \text{ m/s [E]}}{5.0 \text{ s}} = 2.8 \text{ m/s}^2 \text{ [E]}$$

b) $$\vec{a}_{av} = \frac{\vec{v}_2 - \vec{v}_1}{t_2 - t_1} = \frac{14 \text{ m/s [E]} - 13 \text{ m/s [E]}}{5.0 \text{ s} - 4.0 \text{ s}} = \frac{1 \text{ m/s [E]}}{1.0 \text{ s}} = 1 \text{ m/s}^2 \text{ [E]}$$

Statement

The average acceleration of the motorcycle for the five-second interval is 2.8 m/s^2 [E]. The average acceleration for the fifth second is 1 m/s^2 [E].

PRACTICE PROBLEMS

1. A runner takes 0.123 s to get off the blocks after the starting signal. He rapidly accelerates to top speed. Velocity–time data for the first six seconds of the race are summarized in Table 1.8. Use the data to calculate his average acceleration.
   a) between $\Delta t = 0.123$ s and $\Delta t = 0.50$ s.
   b) between $\Delta t = 3.0$ s and $\Delta t = 4.0$ s.
   c) What happened to his acceleration over the first five seconds?
   d) What is his acceleration during the fifth second?
   e) Describe his motion during the fifth second.

TABLE 1.8 Velocity–Time Data for a Sprinter

Time t (s)	0	0.123	0.50	1.00	1.50	2.0	3.0	4.0	5.0	6.0
Velocity $\vec{v}$ (m/s [forward])	0	0	2.4	4.8	6.6	8.2	10.5	11.8	12.0	12.0

2. A van is moving east at 80 km/h when the driver sees a problem ahead and slows down to a speed of 50 km/h in 5.0 s.
   a) Calculate the acceleration of the van in km/h/s and in m/s^2. In your own words, describe the meaning of both answers.
   b) Account for the negative sign in the answer.

Exploration Using a Graphing Calculator

Velocity–Time Graph for Changing Acceleration

Two top sprinters ran in a 100-m final. Sprinter B won the race with a time of 9.83 s. Their estimated velocities at various times are summarized in Table 1.9.

Use your graphing calculator to plot a velocity–time graph of their motions. Then compare their graphs with a velocity–time graph for constant velocity.

TABLE 1.9 Velocity–Time Data for a World Championship Race

Time Δt (s)	Velocity $\vec{v}$ (m/s [forward])	
	Sprinter A	Sprinter B
0.0	0	0
0.123	0	0
0.145	0	1.40
0.50	2.80	3.10
1.00	5.00	5.70
2.00	8.00	8.50
3.00	9.80	10.10
4.00	10.80	10.90
5.00	11.30	11.30
6.00	11.60	11.60
7.00	11.70	11.60
8.00	11.80	11.55
9.00	11.90	11.50
9.83	11.95	11.40
9.93	11.97	

Discussion

1. Which sprinter had a faster reaction time? What advantage does this give the sprinter?
2. Describe the shape of both graphs near the beginning of the race. How are the shapes the same? How are they different? What does this imply about their relative motions?
3. Over what period of time does the acceleration appear to be fairly constant? How do you know?
4. Which runner accelerates right to the end of the race?
5. Which runner begins to decelerate and at what time?
6. How do you think the velocity–time graph for a novice sprinter might differ from these graphs? Why?

Instantaneous Acceleration

From Table 1.7 it can be seen that the average acceleration of the motorcycle during each second, beginning with the first, is 4.0 m/s^2 [E], 3.8 m/s^2 [E], 3.2 m/s^2 [E], 2.0 m/s^2 [E], and 1.0 m/s^2 [E]. Can you explain how these values were obtained? The acceleration decreases during the five-second trip.

If we calculate the average acceleration for smaller and smaller intervals of time, we eventually obtain the acceleration at an instant. Acceleration at a specific instant of time is called **instantaneous acceleration** and is given the symbol $\vec{a}$. Just as a speedometer measures the instantaneous speed, an instrument called an accelerometer registers instantaneous acceleration.

Discovering Physics — *Making an Accelerometer*

Find a transparent bottle with parallel sides. Half fill the bottle with coloured water, screw on the top, and hold the bottle horizontally (Figure 1.28). Observe the level of the liquid inside the bottle as you stay at rest, move forward at constant velocity, accelerate forward by speeding up, and decelerate forward by slowing down. Try spinning the bottle horizontally and observe the shape of the surface. Explain how the bottle can be used to sense acceleration.

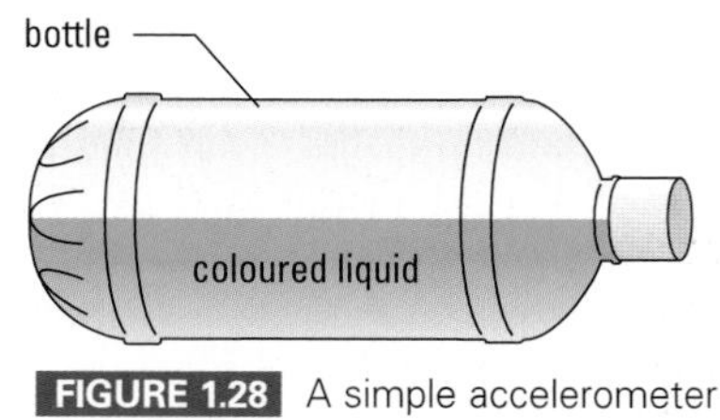

FIGURE 1.28 A simple accelerometer

Section 1.4 Review

Understanding Concepts

1. Define acceleration.
2. Compare the meaning of the terms constant velocity and constant acceleration.
3. Distinguish between constant and average acceleration.
4. Re-arrange the formulas for average acceleration to solve for
   a) $\Delta\vec{v}$
   b) Δt
   c) $\vec{v}_2$
   d) $\vec{v}_1$
5. A motorcyclist changes velocity from 80 km/h [N] to 100 km/h [N] in 5.0 s. Calculate her average acceleration.
6. A sprinter on a school track team, has a velocity of 6.0 m/s [S] at $t = 3.0$ s. Five seconds later he is moving north with a speed of 4.0 m/s. Calculate the sprinter's average acceleration.

Applying Inquiry/ Communication Skills

7. Design a procedure to determine the deceleration of a tennis ball rolling along the school hallway. Assume that the deceleration is uniform and that you have some masking tape, a measuring tape, two stopwatches, and at least two other people to work with. (Hint: For uniform acceleration, the average velocity for an interval is equal to the instantaneous velocity at half-time in the interval.)

1.5 Velocity–Time Graphs

Key Understandings

When you have completed this section, you will be able to:

- describe the velocity–time graph for constant velocity (uniform motion)
- describe the velocity–time graph for constant acceleration
- determine constant acceleration from a velocity–time graph
- determine displacement from a velocity–time graph

Dragonflies are amazing insects. They are fiercely carnivorous and consume vast numbers of insects, including mosquitoes, black-flies, deer flies, and horseflies. They are able to accelerate to speeds close to 50 km/h, decelerate rapidly, hover, and even fly backward (Figure 1.29). In addition to their amazing speed, they are stealthy hunters. Their wings beat with a lower frequency than other flies and bees. As a result they can pursue a quarry without being detected.

Dragonflies are also equipped with superb eyesight and powerful flight muscles to enhance their hunting skill. What would a velocity–time graph look like for an accelerating, decelerating, and hovering dragonfly?

FIGURE 1.29 Dragonflies—winged warriors of the wetlands

Velocity–Time Graphs for Constant Velocity

An object that travels at a constant speed in a straight line has a constant velocity. The position–time graph for constant velocity (uniform motion) is a straight line. It therefore has a constant slope. Table 1.10 shows the position–time data for a lion moving at constant velocity toward its prey (Figure 1.30).

TABLE 1.10 Position–Time Data for a Lion Moving at Constant Velocity

Time t (s)	0	1.0	2.0	3.0	4.0	5.0	6.0
Position $\vec{d}$ (m [E] of start)	0	14	31	44	61	75	90

FIGURE 1.30 A lion has a top speed of 80 km/h.

Figure 1.31 shows the position–time graph for constant velocity. Note that the graph is a straight line with a constant slope. Figure 1.32 shows the corresponding velocity–time graph. Since the velocity is the same at every instant, **the velocity–time graph for constant velocity is a horizontal straight line**. The point at which the line crosses the y-axis (y-intercept) gives the value of the constant velocity. The constant velocity of the lion in this example is 15 m/s [E].

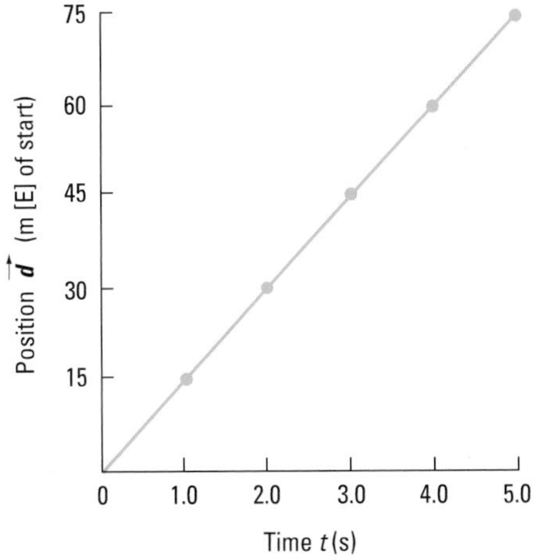

FIGURE 1.31 Position–time graph for a lion moving with a constant velocity

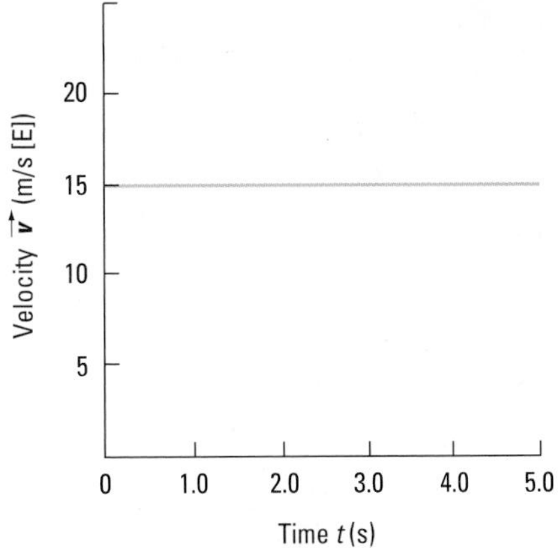

FIGURE 1.32 Velocity–time graph for a lion moving with a constant velocity

FIGURE 1.33 A hawk can focus on its prey from a great height.

Velocity–Time Graphs for Constant Acceleration

Table 1.11 shows what the velocity–time graph would look like for an object whose velocity changes in a uniform way. It shows position–time data for a hawk (Figure 1.33) that has a constant positive acceleration as it dives toward its prey.

TABLE 1.11 Position–Time Data for a Hawk Diving with Constant Acceleration

Time t (s)	0	1.0	2.0	3.0	4.0	5.0	6.0
Position $\vec{d}$ (m [down] from start)	0	2	8	18	32	50	72

Figure 1.34 shows the corresponding position–time graph. A position–time graph for constant positive acceleration has the shape of a parabola.

You have seen that the average velocity for an interval is equal to the displacement divided by the elapsed time. Scientists have also found that, **during constant acceleration, the average velocity for an interval is equal to the instantaneous velocity at half-time in the interval**. For example, the average velocity of the hawk for the time interval from 4.0 s to 6.0 s is equal to its instantaneous velocity at 5.0 s.

You can use this technique to find the instantaneous velocity of the hawk at each second during the first five seconds that are shown in Table 1.12.

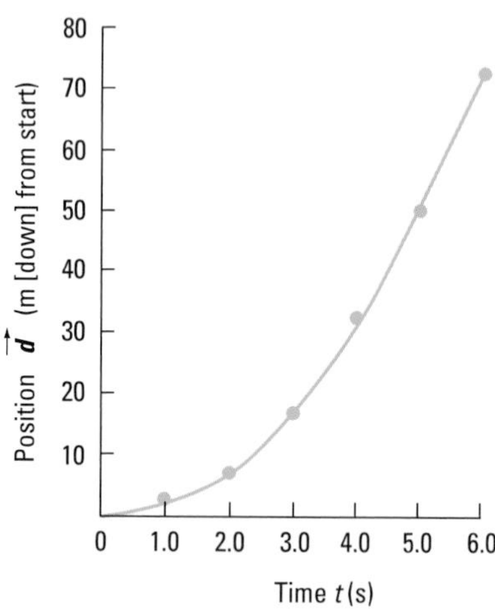

FIGURE 1.34 Position–time graph for a hawk that has a constant positive acceleration

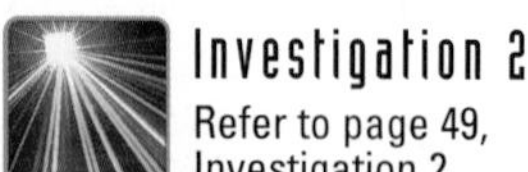

Investigation 2

Refer to page 49, Investigation 2

TABLE 1.12 Calculating the Hawk's Instantaneous Velocity Using Position–Time Data from Table 1.11

Time Interval Δt (s)	Elapsed Time Δt (s)	Half-time t (s)	Displacement $\Delta\vec{d}$ (m [down])	Average Velocity $\vec{v}_{av} = \Delta\vec{d}/\Delta t$ (m/s [down])	Velocity at Half-time $\vec{v}$ (m/s [down])
0 to 2.0	2.0	1.0	8.0	8.0/2.0=4.0	4.0
0 to 4.0	4.0	2.0	32	32/4.0=8.0	8.0
0 to 6.0	6.0	3.0	72	72/6.0=12	12
3.0 to 5.0	2.0	4.0	50−18=32	32/2.0=16	16
4.0 to 6.0	2.0	5.0	72−32=40	40/2.0=20	20

EXAMPLE 6 NUMERICAL

Find the instantaneous velocity of the hawk at $t = 5.0$ s.

Given

$t_1 = 4.0$ s

$\vec{d}_1 = 32$ m [down] from start

$t_2 = 6.0$ s

$\vec{d}_2 = 72$ m [down] from start

Required

$\vec{v}$ at $t = 5.0$ s

Analysis

Since the hawk has constant acceleration, the instantaneous velocity at $t = 5.0$ s is equal to the average velocity for the interval from $t = 4.0$ s to $t = 6.0$ s. For convenience we have defined down as positive.

Solution

$$\vec{v} = \frac{\Delta\vec{d}}{\Delta t}$$

$$= \frac{72 \text{ m [down]} - 32 \text{ m [down]}}{6.0 \text{ s} - 4.0 \text{ s}}$$

$$= \frac{40 \text{ m [down]}}{2.0 \text{ s}}$$

$$= 20 \text{ m/s [down]}$$

Statement

The instantaneous velocity of the hawk at 5.0 s is 20 m/s [down].

PRACTICE PROBLEMS

1. Determine the instantaneous velocity of the hawk at $t = 4.5$ s by calculating the average velocity between $t = 3.0$ s and $t = 6.0$ s. Compare this with the slope of the tangent drawn at $t = 4.5$ s.
2. Determine the instantaneous velocity of the hawk at $t = 2.5$ s by calculating the average velocity of the hawk between $t = 1.0$ s and $t = 4.0$ s. Compare this with the slope of the tangent drawn at $t = 2.5$ s.

The last column of Table 1.12 shows the instantaneous velocity of the hawk at 1.0, 2.0, 3.0, 4.0, and 5.0 s. You cannot calculate the values for $t = 0$ and $t = 6.0$ s using this technique. Can you explain why? Figure 1.35 shows the velocity–time graph for these data. As you can see, **the velocity–time graph for constant nonzero acceleration is a straight line with some slope**.

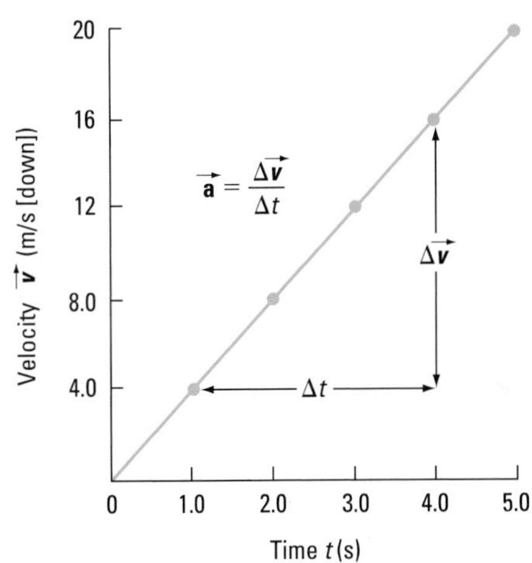

FIGURE 1.35 Velocity–time graph for a hawk that has a constant positive acceleration

Calculating Constant Acceleration

You have already seen that acceleration is equal to the change in velocity divided by the elapsed time. This is the same as the slope of a velocity–time graph (Figure 1.35). Thus, **constant acceleration is the slope of the straight line on a velocity–time graph**. Remember that the slope of a straight-line graph is calculated by finding the ratio of the rise to the run; in this case the rise is $\Delta\vec{v}$ and the run is Δt. If the slope of the velocity–time graph is constant, we know that the acceleration is constant.

EXAMPLE 7 NUMERICAL

Use Figure 1.36 to find the acceleration of the hawk during the first 5.0 s of its dive.

Given
Figure 1.36

Required
$\vec{a}$

Analysis
- The graph is a straight line.
- $\vec{a} = \text{slope} = \dfrac{\Delta\vec{v}}{\Delta t}$

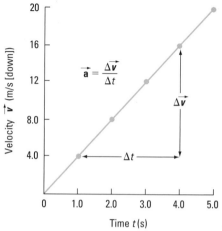

Solution

$$\begin{aligned}\vec{a} &= \frac{\Delta\vec{v}}{\Delta t}\\ &= \frac{\vec{v}_2 - \vec{v}_1}{t_2 - t_1}\\ &= \frac{16\ \text{m/s [down]} - 4.0\ \text{m/s [down]}}{4.0\ \text{s} - 1.0\ \text{s}}\\ &= \frac{12\ \text{m/s [down]}}{3.0\ \text{s}}\\ &= 4.0\ \text{m/s}^2\ \text{[down]}\end{aligned}$$

FIGURE 1.36

Statement
The acceleration of the hawk is 4.0 m/s² [down].

PRACTICE PROBLEMS

1. Use the graph to find the acceleration of the hawk between $t = 2.0$ s and $t = 5.0$ s. How does it compare with the acceleration calculated from $t = 1.0$ s to $t = 4.0$ s? How should it compare?
2. Figure 1.37 shows the idealized velocity–time graph of a greyhound accelerating out of the starting gate at a dog race to its top velocity of 63 km/h [forward]. Calculate the acceleration of the greyhound in m/s².

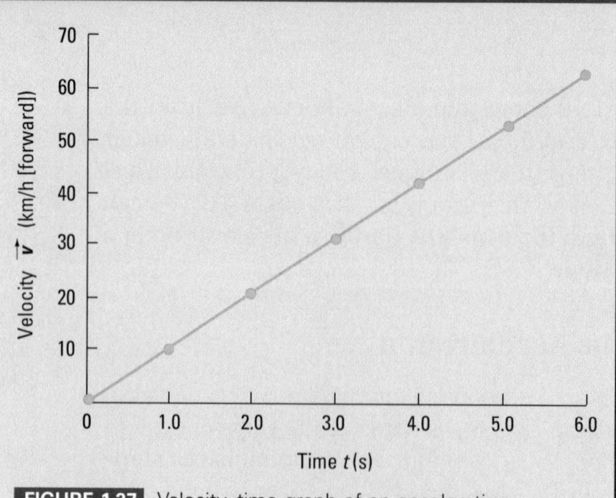

FIGURE 1.37 Velocity–time graph of an accelerating greyhound

Calculating Displacement

How can you find displacement from a velocity–time graph? Rearranging the equation $\vec{v}_{av} = \Delta\vec{d}/\Delta t$ to solve for $\Delta\vec{d}$ gives $\Delta\vec{d} = \vec{v}_{av}\Delta t$. This shows that displacement is equal to the average velocity multiplied by the elapsed time. By looking at Figure 1.38, we can see that this product is the same as the area beneath a velocity–time graph. Therefore, **displacement is equal to the area beneath a velocity–time graph**. In Figure 1.37a), displacement is the area of a rectangle. In Figure 1.37 b), displacement is the area of a triangle.

Look again at Figure 1.32. The area beneath the velocity–time graph is a rectangle. The height h of the rectangle is 15 m/s [E] and the base b is 5.0 s. The area of this rectangle is

$$\Delta\vec{d} = \text{area} = h{\cdot}b = 15\text{ m/s [E]} \times 5.0\text{ s} = 75\text{ m [E]}$$

This area gives the displacement of the lion during the first 5.0 s of its dash.

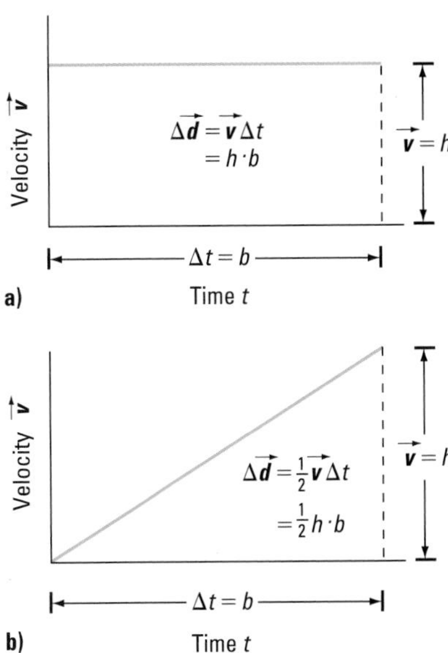

FIGURE 1.38 The area beneath a velocity–time graph is equal to displacement.

EXAMPLE 8 NUMERICAL

Use the velocity–time graph in Figure 1.39 to find the displacement of the hawk during the first 5.0 s of its dive.

Given

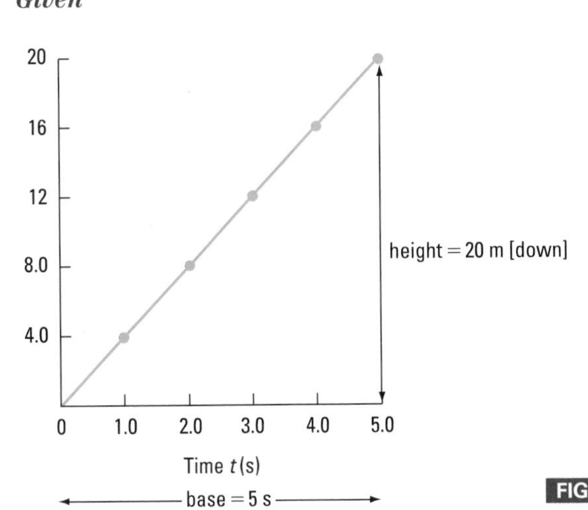

FIGURE 1.39

Required

$\Delta\vec{d}$ after 5.0 s

Analysis

- Displacement is the area beneath a velocity–time graph. The area in Figure 1.39 is a triangle.
- The height h of the triangle is 20 m/s [down] and the base b is 5.0 s.
- The area of a triangle $= \frac{1}{2}hb$

PRACTICE PROBLEMS

1. Refer to Figure 1.39. Use the graph to find the displacement of the hawk during the two-second interval from $t = 3.0$ s to $t = 5.0$ s.
2. Refer back to Figure 1.37 and use the graph to calculate the displacement, in metres, of the greyhound during the six-second interval.

Solution

$$\Delta\vec{d} = \text{area} = \frac{1}{2}hb$$
$$= \frac{1}{2} \times 20 \text{ m/s [down]} \times 5.0 \text{ s}$$
$$= 50 \text{ m [down]}$$

Statement

The displacement of the hawk during the first 5.0 s is 50 m [down]. By referring to Table 1.12 you can see that the displacement of the hawk during the first 5.0 s is indeed 50 m [down].

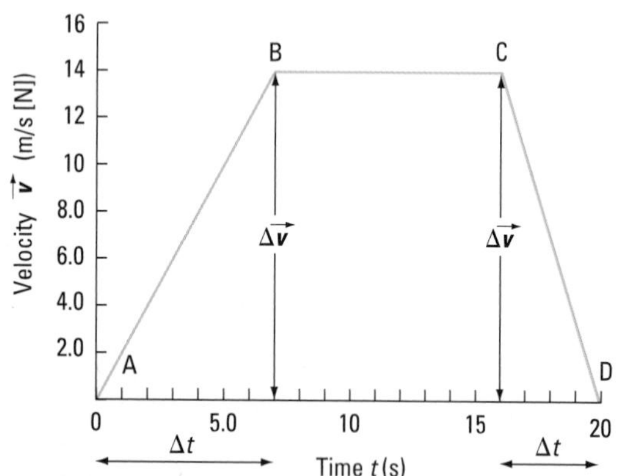

FIGURE 1.40 Positive, zero, and negative acceleration of a subway train

Positive, Negative, and Zero Accelerations

Sometimes an object speeds up, stays at constant speed, and then slows down. Consider the following example. A subway train speeds up as it moves north out of a station. It reaches a maximum speed, and then slows down as it approaches the next station on the line. Figure 1.40 shows a velocity–time graph for the total trip.

The subway train has three different kinds of acceleration. During interval AB, when the velocity is increasing, the velocity–time graph has a constant positive slope. Therefore, the train has a constant positive acceleration. During interval BC, when the velocity is constant, the slope of the velocity–time graph is zero, showing that the acceleration is zero. During interval CD, when the train is slowing down, the slope of the graph is negative. As a result, the acceleration is negative. A **negative acceleration** is sometimes called a **deceleration**. An object is decelerating if it is still moving, but slowing down.

We can find the acceleration of the subway train during intervals AB, BC, and CD from the graph by calculating the slopes for these intervals.

INSIGHT

If the numerator of a ratio is zero, then the ratio is equal to zero.

TABLE 1.13 Data from Figure 1.40

Interval AB	Interval BC	Interval CD
Rise $= \Delta\vec{v}$ $= 14$ m/s [N] Run $= \Delta t = 7.0$ s Slope $= \vec{a} = \frac{\Delta\vec{v}}{\Delta t}$ $= \frac{14 \text{ m/s [N]}}{7.0 \text{ s}}$ $= 2.0$ m/s^2 [N]	Rise $= \Delta\vec{v}$ $= 0$ Run $= \Delta t = 9.0$ s Slope $= \vec{a} = \frac{\Delta\vec{v}}{\Delta t}$ $= \frac{0}{9.0 \text{ s}}$ $= 0$	Rise $= \Delta\vec{v}$ $= -14$ m/s [N] Run $= \Delta t = 4.0$ s Slope $= \vec{a} = \frac{\Delta\vec{v}}{\Delta t}$ $= \frac{-14 \text{ m/s [N]}}{4.0 \text{ s}}$ $= -3.5$ m/s^2 [N] $= 3.5$ m/s^2 [S]

This example shows that on a velocity–time graph, a positive slope represents positive acceleration, a zero slope represents zero acceleration or constant velocity, and a negative slope represents negative acceleration. The slope of interval CD illustrates that a negative acceleration in one direction [N] is equal to a positive acceleration of the same magnitude in the opposite direction [S].

EXAMPLE 9 NUMERICAL

Use the graph in Figure 1.40 (opposite) to find the displacement of the subway train during the 20-s interval.

Given
Figure 1.40 and $\Delta t = 20$ s

Required
Total displacement

Analysis

- Displacement is the area beneath a velocity–time graph. The area in Figure 1.40 consists of the triangle beneath AB, the rectangle beneath BC, and the triangle beneath CD.
- The height of the triangle beneath AB is 14 m/s, the base is 7.0 s, and the area of a triangle = $1/2hb$.
- The height of the rectangle beneath BC is 14 m/s and the base is 9.0 s. The area of a rectangle = hb.
- The height of the triangle beneath CD is 14 m/s and the base is 4.0 s.
- The total displacement is the sum of the three separate displacements.

Solution

$$\Delta\vec{d}_{AB} = \frac{1}{2}hb$$
$$= \frac{1}{2} \times 14 \text{ m/s [N]} \times 7.0 \text{ s}$$
$$= 49 \text{ m [N]}$$

$$\Delta\vec{d}_{BC} = hb$$
$$= 14 \text{ m/s [N]} \times 9.0 \text{ s}$$
$$= 126 \text{ m [N]}$$

$$\Delta\vec{d}_{CD} = \frac{1}{2}hb$$
$$= \frac{1}{2} \times 14 \text{ m/s [N]} \times 4.0 \text{ s}$$
$$= 28 \text{ m [N]}$$

$$\Delta\vec{d}_{T} = \Delta\vec{d}_{AB} + \Delta\vec{d}_{BC} + \Delta\vec{d}_{CD}$$
$$= 49 \text{ m [N]} + 126 \text{ m [N]} + 28 \text{ m [N]}$$
$$= 203 \text{ m [N]}$$
$$= 2.0 \times 10^2 \text{ m [N]}$$

Statement
The total displacement of the subway train is 2.0×10^2 m [N].

PRACTICE PROBLEMS

The cheetah is the fastest land animal. It can reach a speed of 112 km/h in short sprints, but it can only maintain this speed for short distances. Figure 1.41 shows the velocity–time graph for a cheetah chasing its prey.

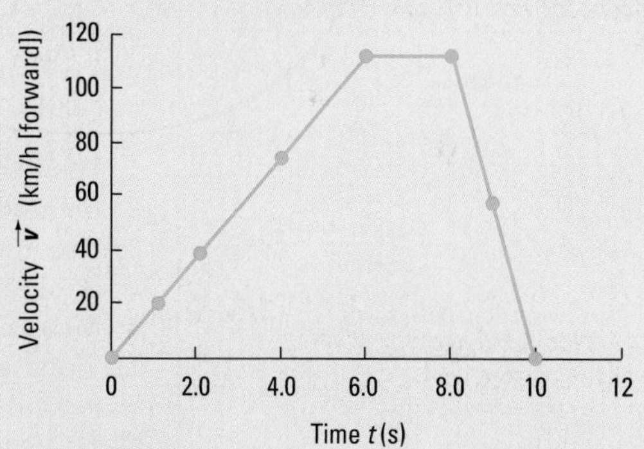

FIGURE 1.41 Velocity–time graph for a cheetah

1. Determine the acceleration of the cheetah during the first 6.0 s.
2. Determine the acceleration of the cheetah during the final 2.0 s.
3. Determine the displacement travelled in metres by the cheetah from 0 to 10.0 s.

Accidents and Vehicle Following Distances The speed limit on Ontario roads varies from 40 km/h to 100 km/h. However, many drivers travel over the speed limit, sometimes at speeds in excess of 120 km/h. Driving too close to the car ahead is called tailgating and can lead to rear-end collisions. If a car slows down suddenly, it can be rammed from behind and a chain reaction can result. Rear-end collisions happen often on roads where the speed limit is in excess of 90 km/h. Foggy conditions, night driving, or cars stalled on highways are frequent causes.

The two-second rule is often used as a guideline for the safe distance to leave between moving vehicles, i.e. "The minimum time allowed for a car to travel to the position that the car ahead occupies is two seconds." In other words, a safe following distance is one where, at the speed you are travelling, it would take at least two seconds to reach the vehicle ahead if it were to stop.

The problem with this rule is that the distance a vehicle travels is directly proportional to its speed. Doubling the speed doubles the distance travelled in two seconds. Research shows that it takes about 0.75 s for a driver to react to a dangerous situation. The greater the speed, the farther the car travels during this reaction time before braking begins. An average braking deceleration is about 6.0 m/s^2. For decelerated motion, the distance needed for a car to stop varies as the square of the speed. At 40 km/h the two-second rule recommends a stopping distance of about 22 m. At 80 km/h it recommends about 44 m. But the braking distance at 80 km/h is about four times that at 40 km/h.

So the two-second rule may be safe for city driving but not for higher speed highway driving.

Discovering Physics — *Stopping Distances*

Is there a relationship between speed and stopping distances? To find out, you will need a photogate, a cylindrical mass with a smaller diameter than the width of the photogate, a metre-stick, and a graphing calculator.

1. Position the photogate on the surface of the lab table (Figure 1.42).
2. Slide the cylindrical mass through the photogate at various speeds.
3. Use the diameter of the cylinder and the time to pass through the photogate to calculate the initial speed of the cylinder.
4. Measure the stopping distance with the metre-stick.
5. Plot a graph of stopping distance against initial speed. Use your graphing calculator to find the equation of best fit for the graph.
   - Describe the graph. What is the equation of best fit?
   - How do your findings relate to tailgating?
   - How do you think police determine the speed that a car was travelling at the scene of an accident?
   - What other driver-related factors would affect the stopping distance for a vehicle?

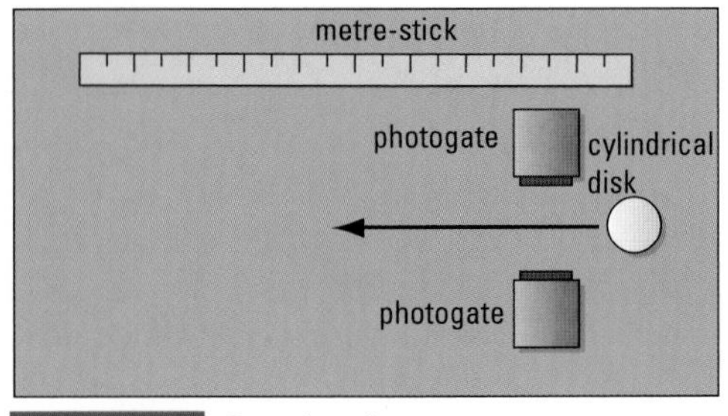

FIGURE 1.42 Stopping distances

INSIGHT

You can calculate the average speed of the cylinderical mass as it travels through the photogate and use this as its initial speed.

Section 1.5 Review

Understanding Concepts

1. Sketch a position–time graph and a velocity–time graph for constant velocity.
2. Sketch a position–time graph and a velocity–time graph for constant acceleration.
3. How is acceleration found from a straight-line velocity–time graph? Include an example.
4. How is displacement found from a velocity–time graph? Include an example.
5. Sketch and label a velocity–time graph showing positive, negative, and zero acceleration.

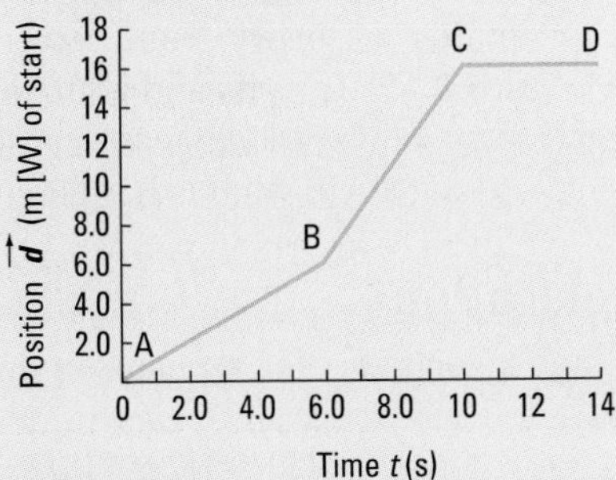

FIGURE 1.43 Position–time graph for a squirrel

6. Figure 1.43 shows the positions of a squirrel as it climbs a tree.
   a) Calculate the velocity of the squirrel during intervals AB, BC, and CD.
   b) Draw a velocity–time graph of the squirrel's motion.
   c) Explain how you would calculate the average acceleration for an interval.
7. Figure 1.44 shows the velocity–time graph for a dandelion seed blown by the wind. The seed's velocity changes during the four intervals AB, BC, CD, and DE. Calculate
   a) the acceleration during each interval
   b) the displacement during each interval
   c) the final position of the dandelion seed

Applying Inquiry/ Communication Skills

8. Design a procedure to collect velocity–time data for a vehicle coasting to rest from a speed of 50 km/h on a straight level road. Predict the shape of the graph and give reasons for your answer.

Making Connections

9. Explain why driving too close to the car in front (tailgating) is a safety issue.
10. Car manufacturers claim that automatic braking system technologies reduce stopping distance, oversteering, and understeering. But do they reduce accidents, even for unsafe drivers? Research the Internet and other sources and talk to car dealers and insurance adjusters. Write a short position paper on your findings.

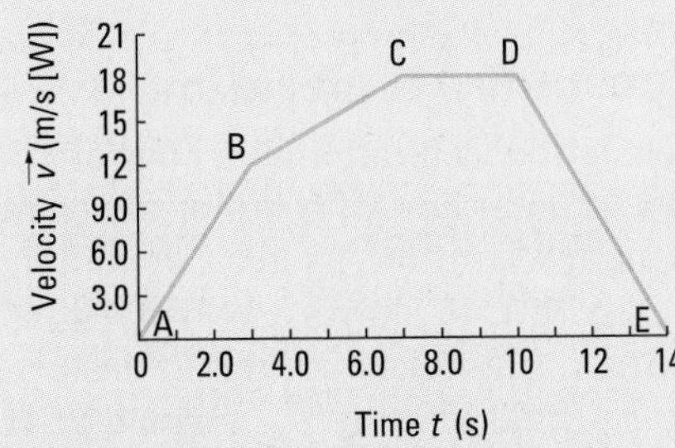

FIGURE 1.44 Velocity–time graph for a dandelion seed blown by the wind

1.6 Equations for Uniformly Accelerated Motion

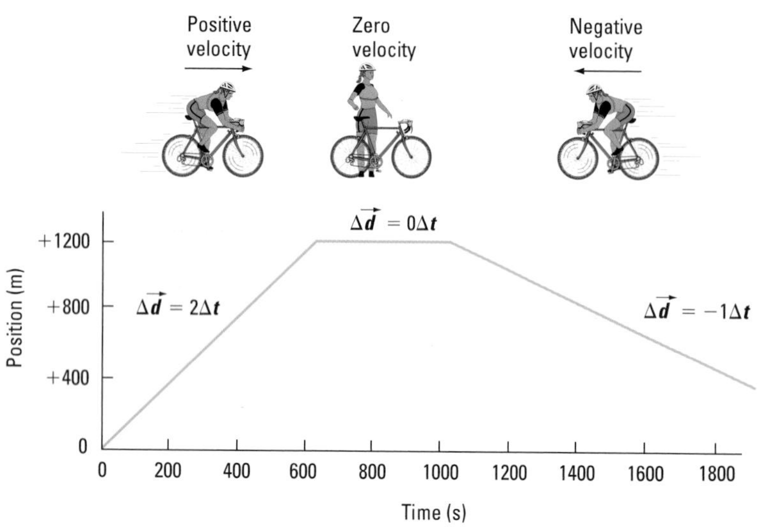

FIGURE 1.45 Graphs and equations are ways of describing the world of motion

Key Understandings

When you have completed this section, you will be able to:

- write and apply two kinematics equations applicable to any kind of motion
- derive and apply three of the kinematics equations for uniformly accelerated motion

So far you have looked at some of the ways to describe motion. Many of the relationships you have discovered can be expressed as equations. An equation for a curve describes a relationship satisfied by the coordinates of every point on the curve (Figure 1.45). Graphs and equations are both very powerful tools that allow you to see, at a glance, what is happening.

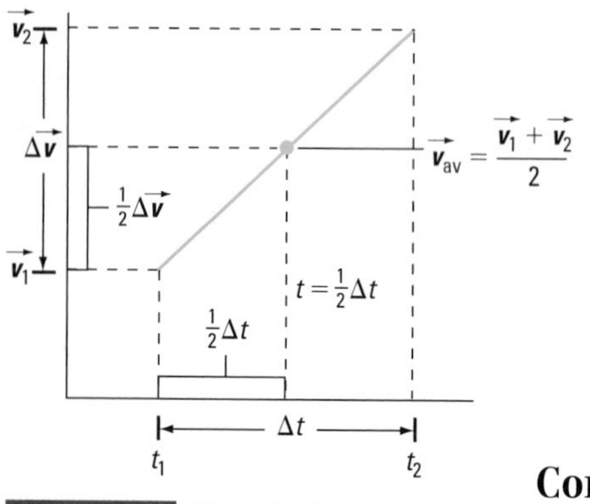

FIGURE 1.46 The velocity–time graph for an interval of constant acceleration showing that

$$\vec{v}_{av} = \frac{\vec{v}_1 + \vec{v}_2}{2}$$

Changing or Constant Acceleration

When an object travels with an average velocity $\vec{v}_{av}$ for an elapsed time Δt, its displacement is

$$\Delta\vec{d} = \vec{v}_{av}\,\Delta t \qquad \text{(equation 1)}$$

If the average acceleration is $\vec{a}_{av}$, in a time interval Δt, the change in velocity is

$$\Delta\vec{v} = \vec{a}_{av}\,\Delta t \qquad \text{(equation 2)}$$

Both equations apply to constant velocity, constant acceleration, and variable acceleration.

Constant Acceleration

Constant acceleration is a special kind of motion in which an object travels in a straight line with uniformly changing speed. When an object has a constant acceleration, its average and instantaneous accelerations are equal.

Figure 1.46 shows a velocity–time graph for an interval of uniform acceleration. The following quantities are labelled on the diagram: initial velocity $\vec{v}_1$, final velocity $\vec{v}_2$, change in velocity $\Delta\vec{v}$, initial time t_1, final time t_2, and the elapsed time Δt. The graph shows that for constant acceleration, the average velocity $\vec{v}_{av}$ is the mid-velocity between the initial velocity $\vec{v}_1$ and the final velocity $\vec{v}_2$. Also, the average velocity occurs at half-time in the interval. Since the average velocity is the average between the initial velocity and the final velocity, therefore, for constant acceleration

$$\vec{v}_{av} = \frac{\vec{v}_1 + \vec{v}_2}{2} \qquad \text{(equation 3)}$$

You can verify this equation by drawing any velocity–time graph for constant acceleration.

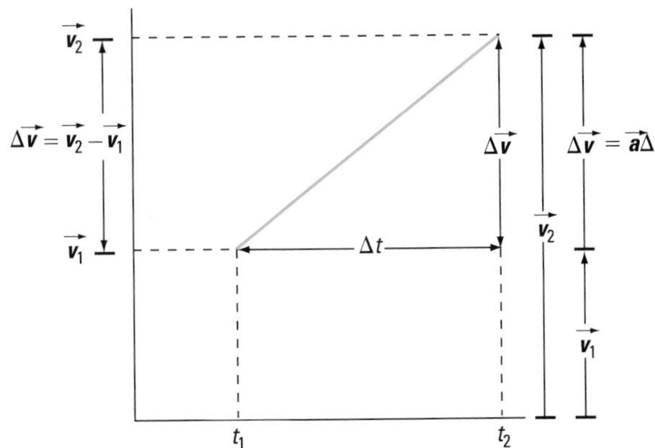

FIGURE 1.47 The slope of the velocity–time graph is the change in velocity divided by the elapsed time. The vectors at the right of the graph show that $\vec{v}_2 = \vec{v}_1 + \vec{a}\Delta t$.

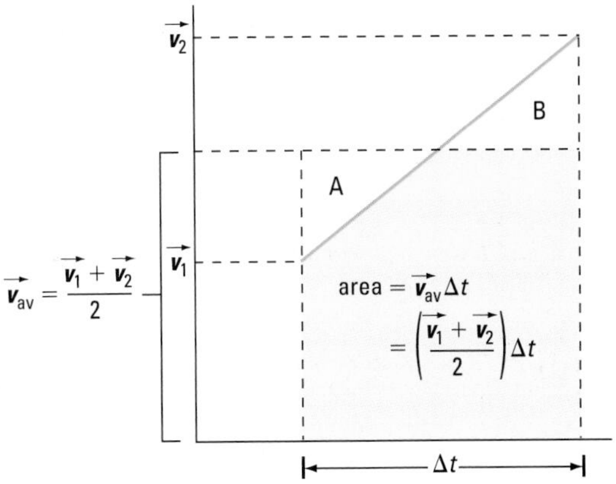

FIGURE 1.48 The area beneath a velocity–time graph is the average velocity multiplied by the elapsed time.

We know from previous work that acceleration is equal to the slope of a velocity–time graph.

Recall that slope $= \dfrac{\text{rise}}{\text{run}}$ which in this case is $\dfrac{\Delta\vec{v}}{\Delta t}$.

Therefore, from Figure 1.46,

$$\vec{a} = \frac{\vec{v}_2 - \vec{v}_1}{\Delta t}$$

Re-arranging the equation to find the final velocity we obtain

$$\vec{v}_2 = \vec{v}_1 + \vec{a}\Delta t \qquad \text{(equation 4)}$$

The velocity vectors drawn to the right of the diagram in Figure 1.47 verify this equation.

From Section 1.3, we know that displacement equals the area beneath a velocity–time graph. Figure 1.48 shows that displacement is equal to the area of a rectangle whose height is equal to the average velocity $\vec{v}_{av}$, and whose base is the elapsed time Δt. Therefore, displacement is given by the equation

$$\Delta\vec{d} = \frac{(\vec{v}_1 + \vec{v}_2)}{2}\Delta t \qquad \text{(equation 5)}$$

An indication that this equation represents the area beneath the graph is that the area of triangle A, included as part of the rectangle, is equal to the area of triangle B, excluded from the rectangle.

Figure 1.49 shows that displacement is also equal to the sum of the area of the small rectangle and the triangle beneath the graph. The area of the small rectangle represents the displacement of an object travelling with a constant velocity $\vec{v}_1$. The height of the rectangle is $\vec{v}_1$ and the base is Δt. Therefore, the area of the rectangle is equal to $\vec{v}_1\Delta t$. The area of the triangle represents the additional

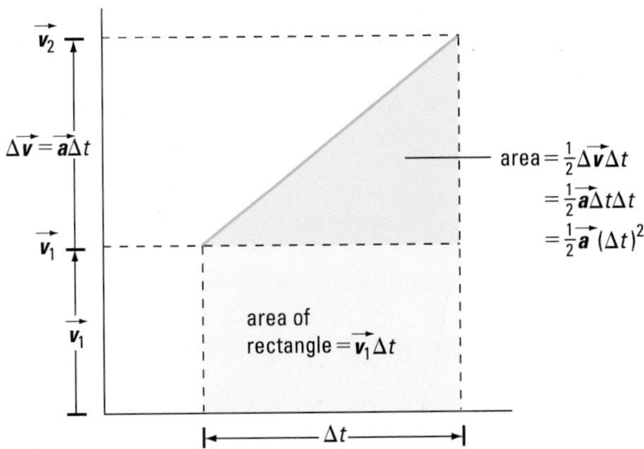

FIGURE 1.49 The area beneath the velocity–time graph is the area of the small rectangle plus the area of the triangle.

displacement resulting from the change in velocity. The height of the triangle is $\Delta\vec{v}$ and the base is Δt. The area of the triangle is equal to $\frac{1}{2}(\Delta\vec{v})\Delta t$. But, $\Delta\vec{v} = \vec{a}\Delta t$. Therefore, the area of the triangle is equal to $\frac{1}{2}(\vec{a}\Delta t) = \frac{1}{2}\vec{a}(\Delta t)^2$. By adding these two displacements we obtain

$$\Delta\vec{d} = \vec{v}_1\Delta t + \frac{1}{2}\vec{a}(\Delta t)^2 \qquad \text{equation 6}$$

Choosing the Correct Equation

The six equations that can be used to solve constant (uniform) acceleration problems are summarized in Table 1.14.

TABLE 1.14 Equations for Constant Acceleration

	Equation	Quantities Given or Required
1	$\Delta\vec{d} = \vec{v}_{av}\Delta t$	$\Delta\vec{d}, \vec{v}_{av}, \Delta t$
2	$\Delta\vec{v} = \vec{a}_{av}\Delta t$	$\Delta\vec{v}, \vec{a}_{av}, \Delta t$
3	$\vec{v}_{av} = \frac{\vec{v}_1 + \vec{v}_2}{2}$	$\vec{v}_{av}, \vec{v}_1, \vec{v}_2$
4	$\vec{v}_2 = \vec{v}_1 + \vec{a}\Delta t$	$\vec{v}_1, \vec{v}_2, \Delta t, \vec{a}$
5	$\Delta\vec{d} = \frac{(\vec{v}_1 + \vec{v}_2)}{2}\Delta t$	$\vec{v}_1, \vec{v}_2, \Delta t, \Delta\vec{d}$
6	$\Delta\vec{d} = \vec{v}_1\Delta t + \frac{1}{2}\vec{a}(\Delta t)^2$	$\vec{v}_1, t, \Delta\vec{d}, \vec{a}$

The last column in Table 1.14 summarizes the variables in each equation. The equation you choose is determined by two factors: the information you are given in the problem and what you are required to find. For example, if you are given $\vec{v}_1$, $\vec{v}_2$, and $\vec{a}$ and need to find Δt, then use equation 4.

When solving problems, it is often useful to sketch a simple **displacement diagram**. A displacement diagram helps you visualize the problem and identify what you are asked to find. Figure 1.50 shows an example of a displacement diagram in which the initial velocity, acceleration, and final velocity are given, and the elapsed time is required. Note that the car is shown at two positions.

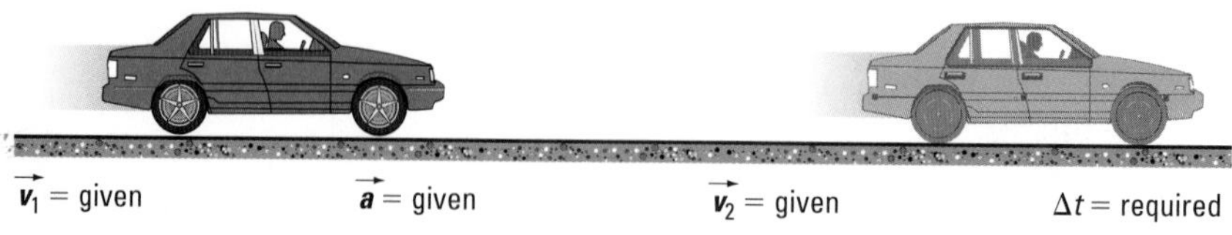

FIGURE 1.50 A typical displacement diagram

EXAMPLE 10 — NUMERICAL

A helicopter accelerates uniformly from 20 m/s [W] to 50 m/s [E] in 9.0 s. Find the average velocity of the helicopter for the 9.0-s interval.

Given

$\vec{v}_1 = 20$ m/s [W]

$\vec{v}_2 = 50$ m/s [E]

$\Delta t = 9.0$ s

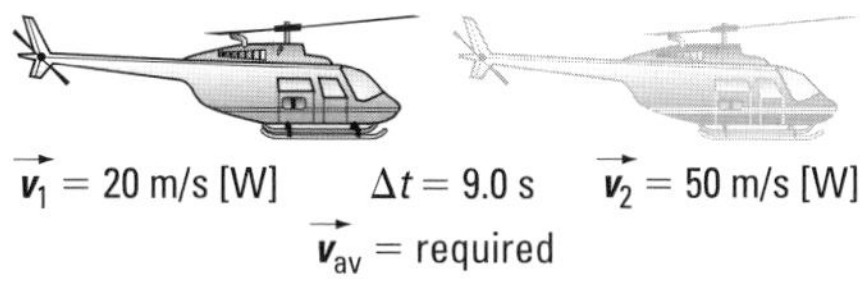

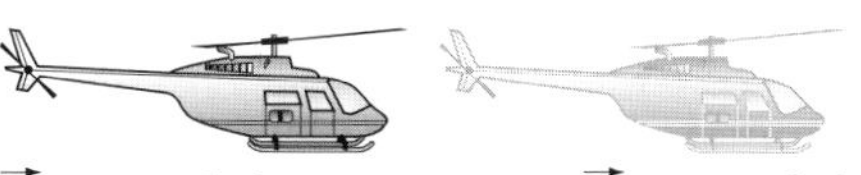

FIGURE 1.51

Required

$\vec{v}_{av}$

Analysis

- The acceleration is uniform, therefore equation 3 can be used.
- Since the initial and final velocities are in opposite directions, change the direction of the smaller velocity before adding.

Solution

$$\vec{v}_{av} = \frac{\vec{v}_1 + \vec{v}_2}{2}$$

$$= \frac{20 \text{ m/s [W]} + 50 \text{ m/s [E]}}{2}$$

$$= \frac{-20 \text{ m/s [E]} + 50 \text{ m/s [E]}}{2}$$

$$= \frac{30 \text{ m/s [E]}}{2}$$

$$= 15 \text{ m/s [E]}$$

Statement

The average velocity of the helicopter for the 9.0-s interval is 15 m/s [E].

INSIGHT

Check that the stated directions are the same before adding the vector quantities.

PRACTICE PROBLEMS

1. A Black Mamba snake has a top speed of 32 km/h. If a Black Mamba snake moving east at top speed decelerates uniformly to 20 km/h in 8.0 s, find its average velocity.
2. A domestic cat moving at a velocity of 7.0 m/s [N] accelerates uniformly in a time of 4.0 s to a top velocity of 13 m/s [S]. What is the cat's average velocity?

EXAMPLE 11 — NUMERICAL

A subway train travelling west at 20 m/s is brought to rest in 10 s. Find the displacement of the subway train while it is coming to a stop. Assume uniform deceleration.

Given

$\vec{v}_1 = 20$ m/s [W]

$\vec{v}_2 = 0$ m/s [W]

$\Delta t = 10$ s

INSIGHT

Since the deceleration is uniform, an alternative solution is to sketch a velocity–time graph and find the area beneath the graph. In this case the area takes the form of a triangle.

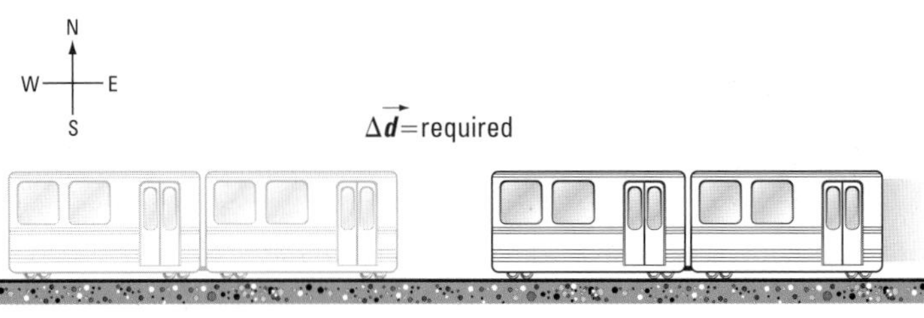

FIGURE 1.52

Required

$\Delta\vec{d}$

Analysis

Use equation 5 and solve for $\Delta\vec{d}$.

Solution

$$\Delta\vec{d} = \frac{(\vec{v}_1 + \vec{v}_2)}{2}\Delta t$$

$$= \frac{(20 \text{ m/s [W]} + 0 \text{ m/s [W]})}{2} \times 10 \text{ s}$$

$$= (10 \text{ m/s [W]}) \times 10 \text{ s}$$

$$= 100 \text{ m [W]}$$

$$= 1.0 \times 10^2 \text{ m [W]}$$

Statement

The subway train travels 1.0×10^2 m [W] before it stops.

PRACTICE PROBLEMS

1. A jackal travelling at its top velocity of 16 m/s [W] slows down uniformly to a velocity of 4.0 m/s [W] in 5.0 s. What is the displacement of the jackal during this time?
2. A ball moves up a long ramp with an initial velocity of 5.0 m/s. Four seconds later it is moving down the ramp at 10 m/s. Find the first position of the ball from its release point.

EXAMPLE 12 NUMERICAL

A sport utility vehicle (SUV) with an initial velocity of 10 m/s [E] accelerates at 5.0 m/s^2 [E]. How long will it take the SUV to acquire a final velocity of 25 m/s [E]?

Given

$\vec{v}_1 = 10$ m/s [E]

$\vec{v}_2 = 25$ m/s [E]

$\vec{a} = 5.0$ m/s^2 [E]

Required

Δt

Analysis

(See Figure 1.53). Use equation 4 and solve for Δt.

FIGURE 1.53

Solution

$\vec{v}_2 = \vec{v}_1 + \vec{a}\Delta t$

Therefore

$$\begin{aligned}\Delta t &= \frac{\vec{v}_2 - \vec{v}_1}{\vec{a}} \\ &= \frac{25\text{ m/s [E]} - 10\text{ m/s [E]}}{5.0\text{ m/s}^2\text{ [E]}} \\ &= \frac{15\text{ m/s [E]}}{5.0\text{ m/s}^2\text{ [E]}} \\ &= 3.0\text{ s}\end{aligned}$$

Statement

It will take 3.0 s for the SUV to reach the velocity of 25 m/s [E].

PRACTICE PROBLEMS

1. Describe in words and using velocity values, the change in velocity of the SUV during the 3.0-s time interval.
2. A motorcycle with an initial velocity of 3.0 m/s [NE] accelerates at 4.0 m/s² [NE]. How long will it take the motorcycle to reach a final velocity of 33 m/s [NE]?
3. An elk moving at a velocity of 18 km/h [N] accelerates at 1.5 m/s² [N]. How long will it take the elk to reach its top velocity of 72 km/h [N]?

EXAMPLE 13 NUMERICAL

A golf ball rolls up a steep hill. It is initially travelling at 25 m/s and slows down with an acceleration of -5.0 m/s². Find its displacement after 15 s.

Given

$\vec{v}_1 = +25\text{ m/s}$

$\vec{a} = -5.0\text{ m/s}^2$

$\Delta t = 15\text{ s}$

Required

$\Delta\vec{d}$

Analysis

- Use equation 6 and solve for $\Delta\vec{d}$.
- Assign a positive direction for uphill and a negative direction for downhill.

Solution

$$\begin{aligned}\Delta\vec{d} &= \vec{v}_1\Delta t + \frac{1}{2}\vec{a}(\Delta t)^2 \\ &= (25\text{ m/s}^2)(15\text{ s}) + \frac{1}{2}(-5.0\text{ m/s}^2)(15\text{ s})^2\end{aligned}$$

PRACTICE PROBLEMS

1. A skier is moving down a uniform slope at 2.0 m/s. If the acceleration down the hill is 3.0 m/s^2, find the skier's displacement after 6.0 s.
2. A bus travelling at 100 km/h reaches a steep hill and decelerates at 0.40 m/s^2 for 1.0 min. How far up the hill did the bus travel in this time?

$= 375 \text{ m} + \frac{1}{2}(-5.0 \text{ m/s}^2)(225 \text{ s}^2)$

$= 375 \text{ m} - 562.5 \text{ m}$

$= -187.5 \text{ m}$

$= -1.9 \times 10^2 \text{ m}$

Statement

The displacement of the golf ball is -1.9×10^2 m [uphill] or 1.9×10^2 m [downhill] from its starting point.

INSIGHT

Always check for consistency of units.

Note that the acceleration in this problem is in the opposite direction to the original motion. The golf ball slows down as it moves up the hill, stops for an instant, and then accelerates as it moves down the hill. However, the acceleration remains unchanged during the entire trip; it is always 5.0 m/s^2 directed down the hill. A common difficulty in solving problems of this nature is realizing that an object can have an acceleration and yet be at rest for an instant of time. When the object is at rest the velocity is zero as it changes direction, but there is still an acceleration present. In this case the acceleration is 5.0 m/s^2 [down the hill] even when the golf ball is stopped for an instant at the top.

Section 1.6 Review

Understanding Concepts

1. Write the two equations that apply to both changing and constant acceleration and define the variables in the equations.
2. Sketch a velocity–time graph for constant acceleration.
   a) Locate and label on the graph the initial velocity, the final velocity, and the average velocity for an interval of time.
   b) Write the equation for the average velocity for the interval in terms of the initial and final velocity.
3. In the equation $\Delta\vec{d} = \vec{v}_1\Delta t + \frac{1}{2}\vec{a}(\Delta t)^2$
   a) what does $\vec{v}_1\Delta t$ represent?
   b) what does $\frac{1}{2}\vec{a}(\Delta t)^2$ represent?
   c) what does $\vec{a}\Delta t$ represent?
4. An airplane maintains a constant acceleration of 4.0 m/s^2 [E] as it speeds up from 16 m/s [E] to 28 m/s [E].
   a) What is the average velocity?
   b) How long does the airplane accelerate?
   c) When is the instantaneous velocity equal to the average velocity for the interval?
   d) What is the displacement?
5. A dune buggy accelerates from rest to a velocity of 26 m/s [S] in a time of 6.0 s. Assuming that the acceleration is constant,
   a) how far does the buggy travel?
   b) what is the buggy's acceleration?
   c) what is the buggy's average velocity?
   d) when does the buggy have the velocity calculated in c)?

e) solve a), b), c), and d) graphically. Which is easier, using the equations or using the graph?

6. An avalanche sliding down a mountain has a constant acceleration of 3.0 m/s^2 [W]. It takes 6.0 s to cover a displacement of 78 m [W].

a) Calculate its initial velocity.

b) Calculate its final velocity.

c) When did the avalanche have a velocity equal to the average velocity for the interval?

Applying Inquiry/ Communication Skills

7. Use a sentence that contains the words "speed" and "direction" to describe constant acceleration.

8. Write a letter to the editor of your local newspaper supporting or opposing the use of photo radar to identify motorists who speed on provincial highways. Use your knowledge of the time it takes to stop at speeds greater than 100 km/h to support your opinion.

9. Design a procedure to verify the equation $\Delta\vec{d} = \frac{1}{2}\vec{a}t^2$. You can use a length of drapery track, a marble, a metre-stick and a stopwatch. Check the procedure with your teacher and do the experiment if you have time.

10. Design an experiment using a motion sensor to verify the claim that the average velocity for an interval is equal to the instantaneous velocity at half-time in the interval.

Making Connections

11. A ride on the "Demo Drop" at an amusement park is a heart-stopping thrill. You are held in place by shoulder straps and taken to the top of the tower in an enclosed car. At the top the supports under the car are suddenly released and you are in free fall until the brakes are applied.

a) Suppose you want to determine the acceleration you will undergo before taking the ride. You know the distance of the fall. What other measurement would you need to make to determine the acceleration?

b) From a safety standpoint, should rides like this be permitted at amusement parks? Discuss.

Investigation 1 (Section 1.3)

Inquiry Skills

- Initiating and Planning
- Applying Technical Skills
- Using Tools, Materials, Equipment
- Conducting and Recording
- Analyzing and Interpreting
- Concluding and Communicating

Walking Trips

In this investigation a person in your class will walk four different trips. The class will work together to collect position–time data for the walks. Then you will use the data to plot position–time graphs, analyze the graphs and calculate a variety of velocities.

Problem

What is the relationship between the slope of a position–time graph and velocity?

Materials

- string marked off into 10 two–metre intervals
- 10 stopwatches

Important: Review the procedure for zeroing a stopwatch between walks.

Experimental Design

1. Design a procedure for collecting position–time data for a person walking the following trips along the string (Figure 1.54):
   a) Move forward with a slow constant velocity throughout the trip.
   b) Move forward with a fast constant velocity throughout the trip.
   c) Move forward with a slow constant velocity for half the trip. Stop for about 5 s. Then move forward with a faster constant velocity for the remainder of the trip.
   d) Move forward with a slow constant velocity for 6 m. Stop for about 5 s. Then move forward with a faster constant velocity to the farthest position. Stop for about 10 s, then return to the starting point with a medium constant velocity.

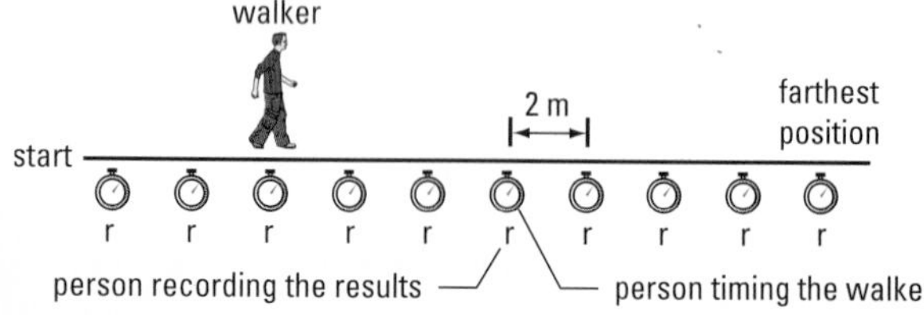

FIGURE 1.54 Four walking trips

2. Design a data table to record your measurements.
3. As a class, collect the data and plot the position–time graph for each trip.
4. Use the graphs to calculate the different constant velocities for each nonzero constant-velocity interval.

Analyzing and Interpreting

1. Describe the graph for each trip. How are they similar? How are they different?
2. What values were obtained for the different constant nonzero velocities? Why was one of these values negative?

Concluding and Communicating

3. What does a zero slope on a position–time graph represent?
4. What does a positive slope on a position–time graph represent?
5. What does a negative slope on a position–time graph represent?
6. Describe three uses for position–time graphs for constant velocity.

Extending

7. Sketch a position–time graph for a walker starting from rest and moving with uniformly increasing velocity from the initial position to the final position along the string. Collect real data for the walk and compare the real graph with the predicted graph. How can you calculate the average velocity for the trip from the graph?

Investigation 2 (Section 1.5)

Inquiry Skills

- Initiating and Planning
- Applying Technical Skills
- Using Tools, Materials, Equipment
- Conducting and Recording
- Analyzing and Interpreting
- Concluding and Communicating

Motion Down a Ramp

As a youngster you were probably introduced to motion as you coasted down a hill on a sleigh. In this activity, you will study quantitatively the motion of a cart that has been released from the top of a ramp. Before you begin, sketch the shape of the velocity–time graph you expect for the motion. Give reasons for the shape of your sketch.

Problem

What does the velocity–time graph look like for a cart rolling down a ramp? How can you determine displacement and acceleration from a velocity–time graph?

Materials

- C-clamp
- ramp
- masking tape
- recording tape
- ruler
- graph paper
- loaded cart
- power supply
- recording timer

Procedure

1. Draw a table in your notebook to record time, displacement, and average velocity.
2. Set up the ramp, recording timer, and cart as shown in Figure 1.55.

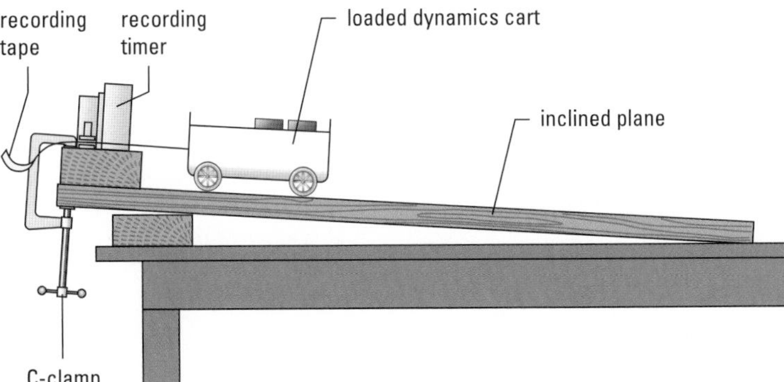

FIGURE 1.55 Recording motion down an incline

3. Attach a length of recording tape to the cart. Thread it through the timer as shown.
4. Start the timer and release the cart down the ramp so that the recording tape is pulled through the timer.
5. Repeat steps 3 and 4 until each person in your group has a tape of the motion.
6. Analyze the tape by marking the starting dot $t = 0$ and dividing the tape into equal time intervals, as shown in Figure 1.56. If the period of the timer is 1/60 s, each six-interval frame will be 0.10 s.

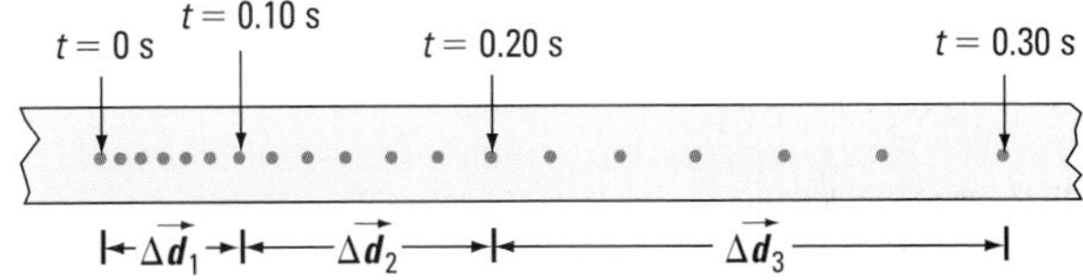

FIGURE 1.56 Analyzing a ticker tape

7. Measure and record in your table the displacements (such as $\Delta\vec{d}_1$, $\Delta\vec{d}_2$, $\Delta\vec{d}_3$, etc.) corresponding to each time interval.
8. Calculate and record the average velocity for each time interval.
9. Plot a graph of velocity against time for the cart by plotting the average velocities at half-time intervals (0.05 s, 0.15 s, etc.).
10. Draw the straight line of best fit from the origin through the points.
11. Calculate the average acceleration of the cart in cm/s^2 by finding the slope of the velocity–time graph.

12. Calculate the displacement of the cart by finding the area of the triangle beneath the velocity–time graph. Be sure to include the units. Compare this with the displacement of the cart by measuring the length of the recording tape for the same part of the trip.

Analyzing and Interpreting

1. Describe how to calculate the average velocity for an interval.
2. For constant acceleration, how does the average velocity for an interval compare with the instantaneous velocity at half-time in the interval?
3. Where must the average velocity for an interval be plotted on a velocity–time graph to represent an instantaneous velocity?
4. Describe the shape of the velocity–time graph for an object accelerating down a ramp.
5. From the velocity–time graph, what kind of motion was the cart experiencing?
6. What was the average acceleration of the cart in cm/s^2?
7. For the same time interval, how did the area beneath the velocity–time graph compare with the displacement of the cart? How should it compare?

Concluding and Communicating

8. Sketch the shapes of the position–time, velocity–time, and acceleration–time graphs for the cart rolling down a ramp.
9. Explain how to generate
   a) a velocity–time graph from a position–time graph
   b) a position–time graph from a velocity–time graph.
   c) an acceleration–time graph from a velocity–time graph
   d) a velocity–time graph from an acceleration–time graph
10. Describe the acceleration of the cart including its magnitude.

Extending

11. If your school has a motion sensor, use it to measure the position of the cart at specific times as it moves down the ramp. Have the computer draw position–time, velocity–time, and acceleration–time graphs for the cart. Analyze how you can generate a position–time graph and an acceleration–time graph from the velocity–time graph.

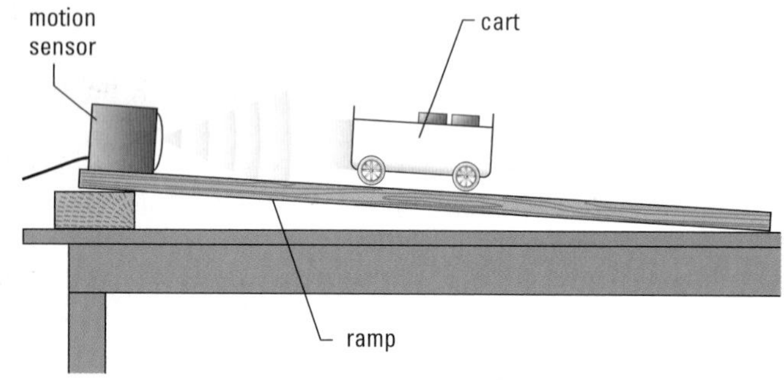

FIGURE 1.57

CHAPTER SUMMARY

Key Terms

acceleration
average acceleration
average velocity
collinear vectors
constant acceleration
constant velocity
deceleration
displacement
displacement diagram
instantaneous acceleration
instantaneous velocity
negative acceleration
non-collinear vectors
origin
position
reference coordinates
scalar
uniform motion
vector
velocity

Key Equations

$\vec{v}_{av} = \frac{\vec{v}_1 + \vec{v}_2}{2}$ $\Delta\vec{d} = \frac{(\vec{v}_1 + \vec{v}_2)}{2}\Delta t$ $\vec{v}_2 = \vec{v}_1 + \vec{a}\Delta t$ $\Delta\vec{d} = \vec{v}_1\Delta t + \frac{1}{2}\vec{a}(\Delta t)^2$

Essential Understandings

- A vector quantity can be completely described by stating a numeral, a unit, and a direction.
- A vector is a directed line segment whose length represents the size of a vector quantity and whose arrowhead represents the direction.
- Collinear vector quantities are added in the same way as positive and negative numbers.
- Non-collinear vector quantities are added by drawing vectors and using the tail-to-tip strategy of vector addition. Collinear vectors can also be added this way.
- Velocity is the change in position, or displacement, per unit time.
- An object that has a constant speed and a constant direction has constant velocity (uniform motion).
- The position–time graph for an object with constant velocity is a straight line with a constant slope.
- The slope of the position–time graph of an object moving at constant velocity gives the value of the constant velocity.
- The position–time graph for an object that is changing velocity is a curve.
- The average velocity between any two points on a position–time graph is equal to the slope of the straight line joining the two points.
- The instantaneous velocity at a point on a position–time graph is equal to the slope of the tangent at that point.
- Acceleration is the rate of change of velocity and is measured in m/s^2.
- If the acceleration of an object changes, we can find the average acceleration by dividing the change in velocity by the elapsed time.
- Instantaneous acceleration is the acceleration of an object during a very short interval of time.
- The velocity–time graph for constant velocity is a straight, horizontal line with zero slope.
- The position–time graph for constant positive acceleration is a parabola.
- The velocity–time graph for constant acceleration is a straight line with constant slope.
- The value for the constant acceleration is the slope of the straight line on a velocity–time graph.
- Displacement can be determined by calculating the area beneath a velocity–time graph.
- An object has a negative acceleration if it slows down in the direction of the initial velocity or speeds up in the opposite direction.

Consolidate Your Understanding

1. Look back to your answer for the Checkpoint on page 5 What answer would you give now? Explain why are each of the other answers is incorrect?
   Describe, using an example, what the area under a velocity–time graph represents for a moving object.
2. Create a concept map to be used as a study map for displacement, velocity and acceleration. Consult the Key Terms provided above and include as many as possible in your concept map. Include at least one of the Key Equations and an example problem solved using the GRASS strategy.
3. Write a paragraph explaining the role of graphs and graphical analysis techniques in interpreting patterns and trends in experimental data. Prepare an example graph. Teach the technique involved in interpreting the graph to another student. Summarize the strengths and weaknesses of your lesson.

CHAPTER 1 REVIEW

Understanding Concepts

1. Which statement about distance, displacement, and position is true?
   a) The position of an object includes a direction and a reference point.
   b) The displacement of an object is the path of the length travelled.
   c) The distance travelled by an object is equal to its change in position.
   d) The position of an object is exactly the same as its displacement.
   e) The distance an object travels can be less than its displacement.

Refer to Figure 1.58 for questions 2, 3, and 4. The graph shows the motion of a speeding car and a police car going the same direction in a 50 km/h zone. The speeding car passes the police car at time $t = 0$ and continues at a constant velocity. The police car immediately accelerates at a constant rate to catch the speeding car.

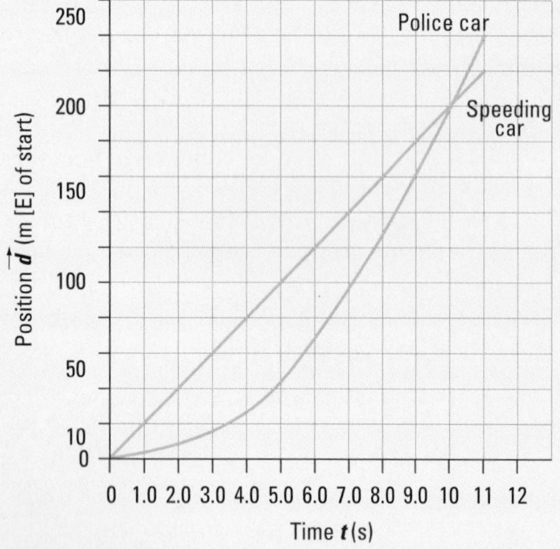

FIGURE 1.58

2. The speeding car is exceeding the speed limit by
   a) 22 km/h b) 28 km/h c) 50 km/h
   d) 60 km/h e) 72 km/h

3. What is the velocity of the police car at the instant it overtakes the speeding car?
   a) 10 m/s [E] b) 20 m/s [E] c) 30 m/s [E]
   d) 40 m/s [E] e) 50 m/s [E]

4. What is the constant acceleration of the police car?
   a) 2.0 m/s^2 [E] b) 4.0 m/s^2 [E] c) 8.0 m/s^2 [E]
   d) 20 m/s^2 [E] e) 40 m/s^2 [E]

Use Figure 1.59 to answer questions 5 and 6. The graph shows eight seconds of the velocity–time graph of a marble rolling down a ramp of constant slope.

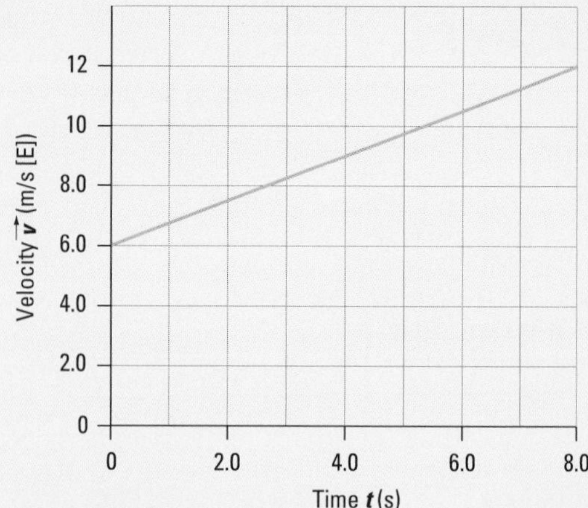

FIGURE 1.59

5. What was the average velocity of the marble during this time?
   a) 12 m/s [E] b) 9.0 m/s [E] c) 6.0 m/s [E]
   d) 1.5 m/s [E] e) 0.75 m/s [E]

6. What displacement did the marble travel during the 8.0-s interval?
   a) 96 m [E] b) 72 m [E] c) 48 m [E]
   d) 24 m [E] e) 12 m [E]

7. Explain, using examples, why there are many equivalent displacements but only one position.

8. A student claims that the distance and displacement of a moving object may or may not be equal after a specific time interval. Is she correct? Why?

9. Explain why you get the same resultant displacement if two displacements are added in the reverse order. Include diagrams to support your answer.

10. What is the difference between adding scalar quantities and adding non-collinear vector quantities? Include an example.

11. Derive the conversion factor between m/s and km/h. Include an example and show your work.

12. The minute hand of a clock makes one complete revolution in 1 min. Is the tip of the hand in uniform motion? Discuss.

13. a) Describe in words what a position–time graph would look like for an object moving toward the reference point at constant velocity.
    b) Explain how to find, using the graph, the value of velocity in part a).

14. a) Use sketches to explain the differences between a position–time graph for a one-way trip and a round trip.
    b) You have the position–time graph for a round trip. Explain how to calculate the average speed and the average velocity for the trip from the graph.

15. For uniformly accelerated motion, the average acceleration is equal to the constant acceleration. Explain why.

16. Describe a situation where both the velocity of a squirrel and its acceleration are negative.

17. Can the position–time graph for uniform motion have the same shape as the velocity–time graph for uniform acceleration? Explain.

18. Draw an acceleration–time graph for constant acceleration. Show that the area beneath an acceleration–time graph for an interval is the change in velocity for the interval.

19. The equation $\Delta\vec{d} = \vec{v}_2\Delta t - 1/2\,\vec{a}(\Delta t)^2$ can be used if you are given final velocity and need to find displacement. What does $1/2\,\vec{a}(\Delta t)^2$ represent?

20. Calculate the change in velocity of an eagle that accelerates downward at 4.6 m/s^2 for a time of 5.0 s.

21. A snow avalanche moving with a velocity of 8.0 m/s [S] undergoes an acceleration of 1.5 m/s^2 [S] for 6.0 s. What is the final velocity of the avalanche?

22. A curling stone travels 28 m in 22 s. Assuming uniform deceleration, calculate
    a) the initial velocity of the stone
    b) the deceleration of the stone

23. A competitor is aiming to complete a 1500-m wheelchair race in less than 4.0 min. After moving at a constant speed for exactly 3.5 min, there were still 240 m to go. What must his acceleration be for the remaining distance if he were to finish the race on time?

24. Find the resultant of the following displacements: 40 m [S], then 50 m [W] followed by 30 m [N 45° E].

25. Sketch a velocity–time graph for a deer starting from rest, $\vec{v}_1 = 0$, and undergoing a constant positive acceleration. Use the graph to derive:
    a) the equation for the displacement $\Delta\vec{d}$ of the deer in terms of only the acceleration $\vec{a}$ and the elapsed time Δt
    b) the equation for the acceleration $\vec{a}$ of the deer in terms of only the final velocity $\vec{v}_2$ and the elapsed time Δt
    c) the equation for the average velocity $\vec{v}_{av}$ of the deer in terms of only the final velocity $\vec{v}_2$

Applying Inquiry/ Communication Skills

26. Suppose you are walking downtown in a large city where all the streets run north–south and all the avenues run east–west. The blocks are rectangles with the street sides being longer than the avenue sides. You have to walk from a corner bus stop to a corner store several blocks away.
    a) Is it shorter to walk along a street first and then along an avenue, or does it matter? Use a diagram in your explanation.
    b) Should you zigzag along the streets and avenues, or go as far as you have to in one direction before walking in the other direction? Does it matter? Explain using a diagram.

27. Can three or more displacement vectors with unequal magnitudes be added together using the tail-to-tip strategy so that their vector sum is zero? Use an example to explain your answer.

28. Sketch a position–time graph of a person who walks one city block at a slow constant velocity, waits for the light to change, walks across the intersection at a fast constant velocity, continues for another city block at a moderate velocity, and returns home at a very fast constant velocity. Assume the two blocks are the same length and that the intersection is one-tenth of a city block.

29. Superwoman is flying at 108 km/h [N]. She decelerates at a constant rate to 36 km/h [N] in 8.0 s, then travels at 36 km/h [N] for 10 s, and finally accelerates at a constant rate of 9.0 km/h/s [N] to a final speed of 90 km/h [N].
    a) Draw the position–time graph.
    b) How far in metres did Superwoman travel during the first 8.0 s?
    c) What is Superwoman's initial acceleration during the first 8.0 s in km/h/s?

Making Connections

30. On some major highways lines are painted at regular intervals, and drivers are instructed to leave a space between cars equal to the space between two consecutive sets of lines. Explain why these lines should be farther apart on highways with a 100 km/h speed limit than on highways with an 80 km/h speed limit.

31. Highway 407 is an Express Toll Route (ETR) located across the north perimeter of Toronto. When cars enter and exit the highway photographs are taken of the licence plate. The entrance and exit locations and times are also recorded. Research how police could use the information to monitor and charge speeders for violating the traffic act.

32. Look up data for two of your favourite cars by researching in the library or on the Internet. Use the kinematics data to help you decide which car you would rather buy. Submit a report which includes the criteria used in reaching your decision.

CHAPTER 2

Acceleration and the Force of Gravity

SPECIFIC EXPECTATIONS

By the end of this chapter, you will be able to:

- define and describe concepts and units related to force (2.1, 2.2)
- identify and describe the fundamental forces of nature (2.1)
- analyze and describe the gravitational force acting on an object near, and at a distance from, the surface of Earth (2.3)
- analyze and describe the forces acting on an object, using free-body diagrams, and determine the acceleration of the object (2.1)
- analyze the motion of objects, using vector diagrams, free-body diagrams, uniform acceleration equations (2.1)
- analyze and explain the relationship between an understanding of forces and motion and an understanding of political, economic, environmental, and safety issues in the development and use of transportation technologies (2.1)
- explain how the contributions of Galileo and Newton revolutionized the scientific thinking of their time and provided the foundation for understanding the relationship between motion and force (2.4)

What do a skydiver, hang-glider pilot, bungee jumper, and hot-air balloonist have in common? They all use specialized equipment in an attempt to defy the laws of gravity. Gravity is a force that attracts all objects in the universe. It holds you to the planet Earth. It holds the planet Earth to its orbit around the sun. People have been trying to defy the law of gravity for years. It is now a major pastime and is the main feature of many recreational sports like the ones mentioned above.

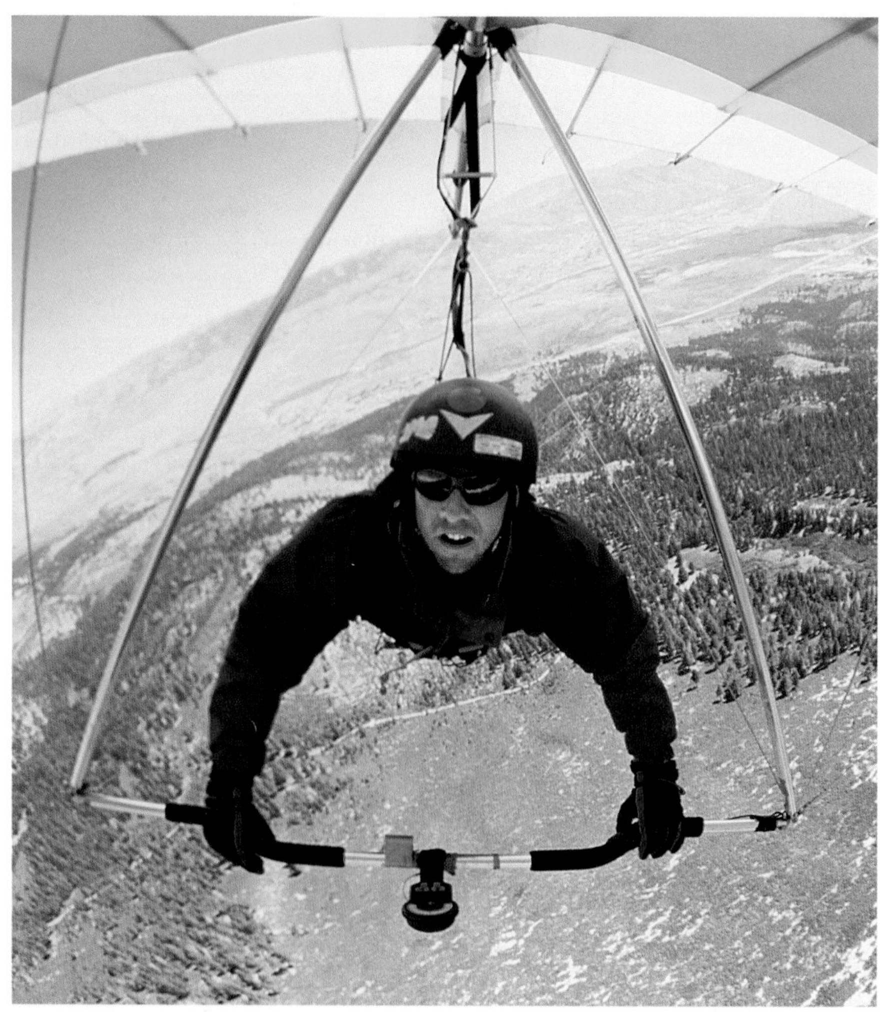

FIGURE 2.1

The equipment these gravity-defying daredevils use must be designed with a sound knowledge of the law of gravity. The length and elasticity of a bungee cord, the precise shape of a hang-glider wing, and the volume of a hot-air balloon must all be carefully considered. The successful daredevils do not actually defy the law of gravity at all. Instead, they strive to understand it and then work within those limits. Those who do not, face the obvious consequences.

In this chapter, you will study the interaction between mass and and the force of gravity. You will see how the strength of the gravitational attraction between two objects is completely dependent on their masses and their distance from one another. You will discover some interesting quirks about gravity, such as the fact that it is not constant everywhere on Earth's surface. You will examine an important principle, which states that all objects near the surface of Earth (and in the absence of friction) fall at the same rate regardless of size, shape, or mass.

By the end of the chapter, you will see that these basic principles apply to any activity, whether it be launching a satellite into space or climbing a set of stairs.

Discovering Physics

Coins in Free Fall

Do coins of different sizes and shapes such as those in Figure 2.2 fall through air at the same rate?

Take some coins of different sizes and shapes—a dime, a quarter, a loonie, a toonie, etc. Choose any two different coins and place them at the edge of a table above an uncarpeted floor. Using a ruler, push the coins off the table so that they leave at the same time. Listen carefully for the sound(s) of the coins as they hit the floor. Repeat this experiment with different combinations of two coins and record your results.

- When the coins landed, did you hear one sound or two? Did all combinations of coins give the same result?
- If the coins all fall at the same rate, how many sounds should you hear when they land?
- How would the results compare if the different coins were released at the same time from a greater height, say 10 m?

FIGURE 2.2 Falling coins

CHECKPOINT

A baseball is thrown vertically into the air. The instantaneous acceleration of the ball at the highest point in its travel is

a) 9.8 m/s^2 [up]
b) 9.8 m/s^2 [down]
c) changing from 9.8 m/s^2 [up] to 9.8 m/s^2 [down]
d) changing from 9.8 m/s^2 [up] to zero to 9.8 m/s^2 [down]
e) zero

Explain your answer. Use a sketch if necessary

2.1 The Vector Nature of Force

Key Understandings

When you have completed this section, you will be able to:

- identify and describe the fundamental forces of nature
- define and describe the meaning of force
- describe the following forces: net, resultant, unbalanced, normal, friction, collinear, non-collinear
- analyze and describe forces using free-body diagrams
- add collinear and non-collinear forces to find the net force

Fundamental Forces

Science is a body of knowledge, but it is also an active ongoing process. Scientists have learned, over the past several hundred years, that there seem to be only four fundamental forces in the universe.

Gravity is the weakest of the four fundamental forces. It is a force of attraction between objects that have mass. The Sun exerts a force of attraction on the Earth. This force keeps Earth in orbit around the Sun. You even exert a gravitational force of attraction on the person sitting next to you. But this force is very small compared with the force exerted by Earth on you.

There are two types of nuclear force. The **strong nuclear force** binds atomic nuclei together. The **weak nuclear force** is responsible for the fact that some nuclei are radioactive. The fourth fundamental force is the **electromagnetic force**. It is a combination of the electrical force between two charged particles at rest and the magnetic force produced when charged particles move.

Scientists have been studying these four fundamental forces to find out if they are different versions of one kind of force, or if they are separate and distinct and hence fundamental. For example, it is now thought that the electromagnetic and the weak nuclear forces are forms of one force, recently called the **electroweak force**. Some scientists have found evidence for the existence of other smaller forces that are difficult to detect and may depend on properties of matter as yet undiscovered.

Force Is a Vector

FIGURE 2.3 Large, machines must exert huge forces to move soil, rocks, or snow.

Athletes, such as weightlifters, can lift and move amazingly large masses. Their muscles, exercised and nourished for years, are used to overcome the force of gravity. Heavy machinery can exert huge forces (Figure 2.3). Children apply small forces to form modelling clay into interesting shapes. What are the other kinds of forces? How do these forces differ from the force of gravity? What effects do forces have on objects?

Force is defined as a push or a pull on an object. A force applied to an object will sometimes change the shape and/or motion of the object (Figure 2.4).

Force is a **vector quantity**. It therefore has a size, or **magnitude**, and a direction. The sizes of forces can be described using adjectives like large, small, huge, and insignificant. Scientists describe the size of a force with a numeral and a unit, e.g. 10 N. The direction is given by using adjectives such as [forward], [backward], [up], and [down] to state directions. Compass directions,

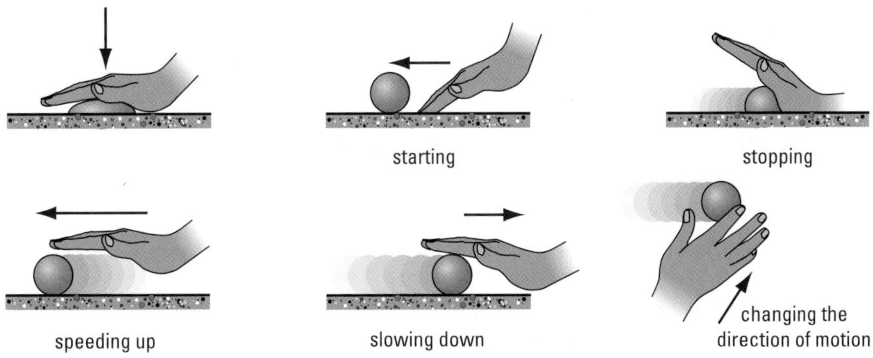

FIGURE 2.4 The effects of a force on an object. Here the hand is appying the force on a ball.

such as north [N], south [S], and 30 degrees east of north [N 30° E], are also accepted ways of describing the direction of a force.

The symbol for force is $\vec{F}$ and its SI unit is the **newton** (N), named in honour of Sir Isaac Newton, the famous English physicist. In base units, a newton is equal to a kilogram metre per second squared ($1 \text{ N} = 1 \text{ kg·m/s}^2$). One newton is the amount of force required to accelerate a one-kilogram object at one metre per second squared.

Force can be measured using a spring scale. A force, such as a weight applied to an elastic spring, causes it to stretch. As it stretches, the elastic force exerted by the spring increases. When the applied force is balanced by the elastic force (Figure 2.5) the spring scale stops stretching and the applied force can be read from the calibrated scale.

Similarly, if you see the spring triple its stretch you can assume the force on the spring has tripled. Before the spring scale can be used to measure force it needs to be calibrated with known forces.

For instance, a 100-g mass exerts twice the force of a 50-g mass on the spring. Thus, a relative scale of forces can be used. For example, if the 50-g mass exerts a force of 1 unit, the 100-g mass exerts a forces of 2 units, 150 g would exerts 3 units, and so on.

The relationship between the stretch of an elastic spring and the restoring force is called Hooke's law after Robert Hooke (1635–1703) who

Discovering Physics — *The Stretch of a Spring*

Study how a spring scale measures force.

You will need an elastic spring, a set of hooked masses, and a metre-stick. Suspend the spring so that it hangs in front of a blackboard or a bulletin board. Mark the initial position of the lower end of the spring. This is the zero stretch point. Hang various masses and combinations of masses on the spring and measure the stretch (change in length from the zero point) in each case.

Record your results for force and stretch and use them to plot a graph of force exerted on the spring (in relative units) against the stretch of the spring in centimetres. When the force doubles, what happens to the stretch of the spring? Does this pattern continue when the force triples, etc.? Should the origin be a point on your graph?

INFO**BIT**

One newton is roughly equal to the force of gravity exerted by Earth on a medium-sized apple or on two golf balls.

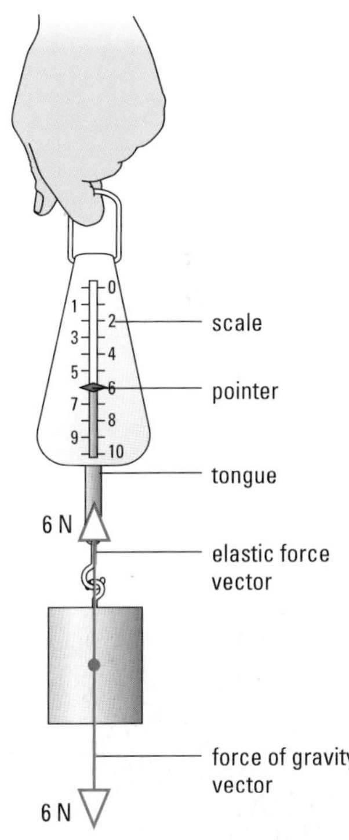

FIGURE 2.5 A spring scale. The elastic force exerted by the spring scale on the mass balances the force of gravity exerted by Earth on the mass.

began his career in science by making vacuum pumps. Hooke made significant contributions to several fields of science. In physics, he found that the period of a vibrating string is the same regardless of the extent of the vibrations.

The cord used in a bungee jump is elastic, like the spring of a newton spring scale. But, unlike a spring, this cord can stretch to several times its free length. During the first part of a jump, the person is in free fall and accelerates downward at 9.8 m/s^2. The downward acceleration decreases as the bungee cord reaches its natural extension and begins to be stretched by the jumper. The bungee cord pulls upward on the jumper. The net force is still less than the force of gravity. The bungee cord continues stretching and its upward force increases, until it exceeds the force of gravity. At this point the net acceleration is upward. As the cord reaches its maximum extension the force up reaches a maximum.

The jumper begins to accelerate upward. When the cord is back to its original length then the elastic force is no longer present. The jumper continues to the top of the first cycle at which point the instantaneous velocity is zero again, and the jumper falls back down in free fall.

Several more exciting vibrations occur. When the jumper finally stops vibrating, the force of gravity of Earth acting down on the jumper is equal to the elastic force exerted upward by the stretched cord. The person can then be lowered to safety.

INFOBIT

Robert Hooke was the first to use the name "cells" (for the rectangular structures in cork seen under a microscope). He discovered that Gamma Arietis is a double star, and he predicted that earthquakes are caused by the cooling and contraction of Earth.

Free-Body Diagrams

A force can be represented in a diagram by a directed line segment called a **vector**. The length of the line segment represents the magnitude or size of the force, and the arrowhead shows the direction. A scale and reference coordinates are included in the diagram.

In reality, an object seldom has only one force acting on it. So it is helpful to draw a vector diagram showing all the forces acting simultaneously on an object. This helps to picture and analyze the situation. Such a diagram is called a **free-body diagram** because the object is shown isolated from its surroundings. The following strategy will help you draw a free-body diagram:

1. First draw the compass points and decide on a suitable scale.
2. Then draw a sketch of the object isolated from its surroundings.
3. Locate, with a point, the approximate centre of the object.
4. From the point, draw a force vector to represent each force acting on the object.
5. Note: do ***not*** include forces that the object exerts on other objects.

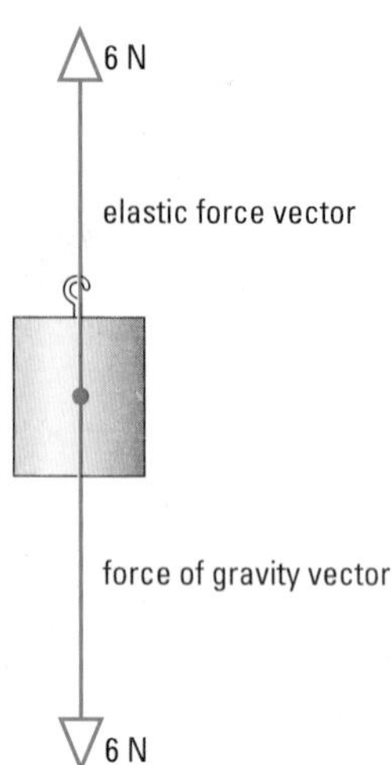

FIGURE 2.6 A typical free-body diagram

The free-body diagram for the mass suspended from the spring in Figure 2.5 is shown in Figure 2.6. Note that two equal-sized forces (the force of gravity and the elastic force) act in opposite directions on the mass. The spring scale is not shown because we are drawing a free-body diagram for the mass, not the spring scale. But the reference coordinates and a scale are always included.

Two other forces commonly act on an object. First, the **normal force** is the force that acts on an object perpendicular to the surface on which it is resting. For example, if you are sitting in a chair, the normal force acting on you is the upward force exerted by the chair on you. Another force, the **force of friction** acts opposite to the direction the object is moving or is tending to move. For example, if a person pushes to the right on a large box but the object does not move, the object still tends to move to the right and the force of friction is directed to the left. The force of friction prevents the box from sliding to the right.

EXAMPLE 1 CONCEPTUAL

Draw a free-body diagram to show the following forces acting on a coasting car on a level road: a force of gravity $\vec{F}_G$ of 10 000 N [down]; a normal force exerted by the road $\vec{F}_N$ of 10 000 N [up]; a force of friction $\vec{F}_f$ of 3000 N [back]. What kind of motion would the object be exhibiting?

Reasoning and Solution

A free-body diagram shows the car isolated from its surroundings. The coasting car has three forces acting on it. The car is in neutral so there is no force exerted forward by the road on the tires. But there is a backward force of friction. The other two forces are balanced; the normal force exerted upward by the road and the force of gravity exerted by Earth downward.

A free-body diagram shows all the forces (drawn to scale) that are acting on an object and helps us to analyze the situation (Figure 2.7). The free-body diagram shows that the object will slow down as it moves to the right because the force of friction acts opposite to its direction of motion.

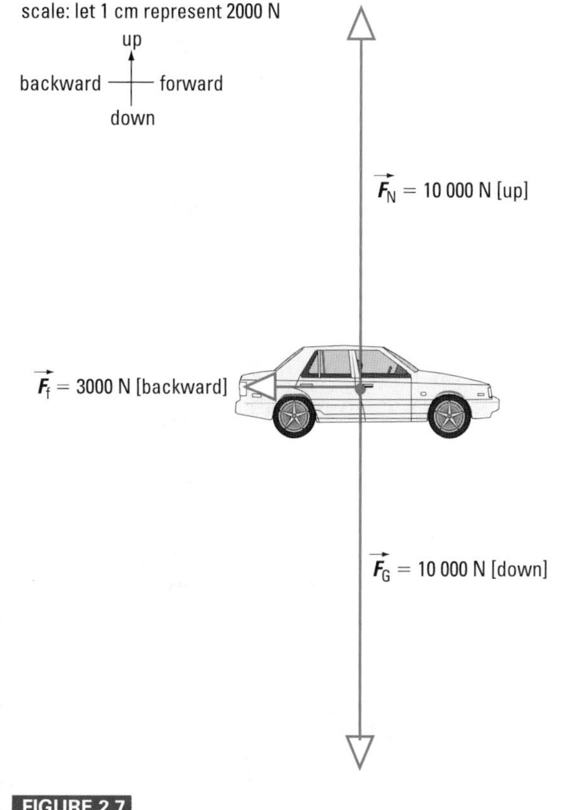

FIGURE 2.7

CHALLENGE

Suppose the driver of the coasting car sees a pedestrian ahead and applies the brakes. This results in an additional backward force of 5000 N. Draw the free-body diagram for this situation.

It is often necessary to find the sum of several forces acting on an object. The total force is called the **net force**. The net force is a single force that will have the same effect as several forces acting simultaneously. You can determine the net force by finding the vector sum of all the forces acting on the object. Other names for the net force are the **unbalanced force** or the **resultant force**.

Adding Collinear Forces

As with other vector quantities, forces that are along the same straight line (**collinear**) are added by finding their algebraic sum in the direction chosen to be positive. The following example shows how.

EXAMPLE 2 NUMERICAL

A tow truck is starting to tow a damaged car and exerts a force $\vec{F}$ of 4000 N [E] on the car. A 1500-N [W] force of friction $\vec{F}_f$ opposes the car's motion. The force of gravity on the car $\vec{F}_G$ is 8000 N [down].

a) Draw a free-body diagram for the car.
b) Calculate the net force on the car.

Given

$\vec{F}$ = 4000 N [E]

$\vec{F}_f$ = 1500 N [W]

$\vec{F}_G$ = 8000 N [down]

Required

a) Free-body diagram for the car

b) Net force on the car ($\vec{F}_{net}$)

Analysis

a)

- Since the car moves neither up nor down, the road must exert a normal force $\vec{F}_N$ = 8000 N [up].
- This free-body diagram must show four forces.

b)

- The horizontal forces are collinear because they are along the same straight line.
- Choose the direction of the larger horizontal force as positive.
- Give a negative to the force in the opposite direction and reverse its designated direction.
- Add the quantities algebraically.

Solution

a) See Figure 2.8.

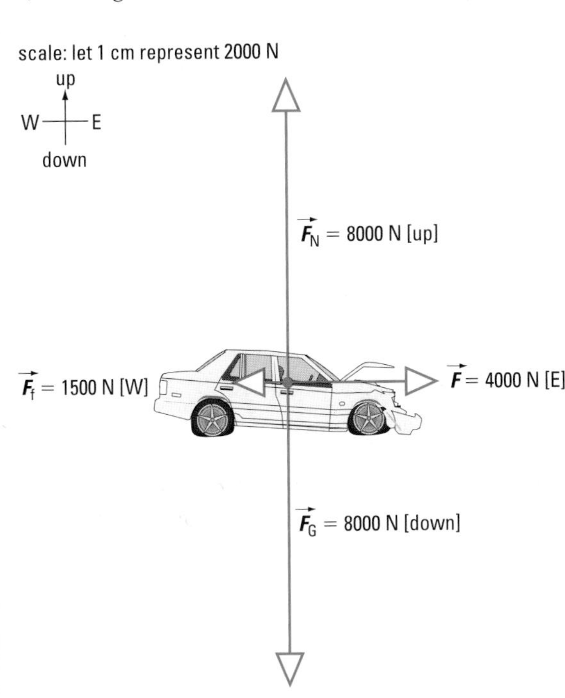

FIGURE 2.8

b)
$$\begin{aligned}\vec{F}_{net} &= \vec{F} + \vec{F}_f \\ &= 4000\text{ N [E]} + 1500\text{ N [W]} \\ &= 4000\text{ N [E]} + (-1500\text{ N [E]}) \\ &= 4000\text{ N [E]} - 1500\text{ N [E]} \\ &= 2500\text{ N [E]}\end{aligned}$$

Statement

The single force that could replace the two horizontal forces and have the same effect is 2500 N [E].

PRACTICE PROBLEMS

1. The cable of an elevator exerts an upward force of 12 000 N, while gravity pulls down on the elevator with a force of 10 000 N. Draw a free-body diagram of the forces on the elevator and find the net force acting on it.
2. Suppose that the only horizontal forces acting on a 120-N pumpkin on a table are 36 N [right] and 52 N [left]. Draw a free-body diagram to show all four forces, and state the net force acting on the pumpkin.

Adding Non-Collinear Forces

Since force is a vector quantity, forces can be added using the tail-to-tip strategy covered in Chapter 1. Sometimes forces are **non-collinear**. This means they do not act along the same straight line. For example, a football player may be tackled by several opposing players at the same time. How can we find the net horizontal force on the player? Both **collinear** and non-collinear forces can be added using a graphical method called the **tail-to-tip** strategy.

To use the tail-to-tip strategy of vector addition for forces:

1. First draw the compass points and choose a suitable scale.
2. Then draw one of the force vectors to scale and call it the first force vector.
3. Dot in a line from the tip of the first force vector in the direction of the second force vector.

4. Draw, with a solid line, the second force vector to the same scale as the first, with the tail of the second force vector at the tip of the first.
5. Dot in another force vector from the tail of the first force vector to the tip of the second force vector. This new force vector represents the sum or resultant of the first two force vectors.
6. Now measure the length and direction of the resultant force vector.
7. Compare the length of the resultant force vector with the scale.
8. Finally, record the magnitude and the direction of the resultant force vector.

Note: The tail-to-tip strategy can be used to add any number of vectors in any order.

INSIGHT

Although there are vertical forces acting on the football player (gravity and the normal force), this problem focusses on the horizontal forces. The vertical forces can be ignored in this problem if we assume that the force of gravity and the normal force balance each other.

INSIGHT

The two forces could be replaced by a single force of 360 N [N 34° W]. This single force, called the net force, will have the same effect on the fullback's motion as the two original forces acting together.

EXAMPLE 3 NUMERICAL

Two football players tackle a rival fullback, exerting two horizontal forces on him at the same time. The forces are 300 N [N] and 200 N [W]. What is the net horizontal force on the fullback?

Predict the likely effect of the net force on the motion of the fullback.

Given

$\vec{F}_1 = 300$ N [N]

$\vec{F}_2 = 200$ N [W]

Required

$\vec{F}_{net}$

Analysis

- The two forces are not parallel and are therefore non-collinear.
- Use the tail-to-tip strategy.

Solution

See Figure 2.9.

Statement

The net force on the fullback is 3.60×10^2 N [N 34° W]. The net force will change the velocity of the fullback. The net force might actually cause the fullback to speed up, depending on the direction of his initial velocity.

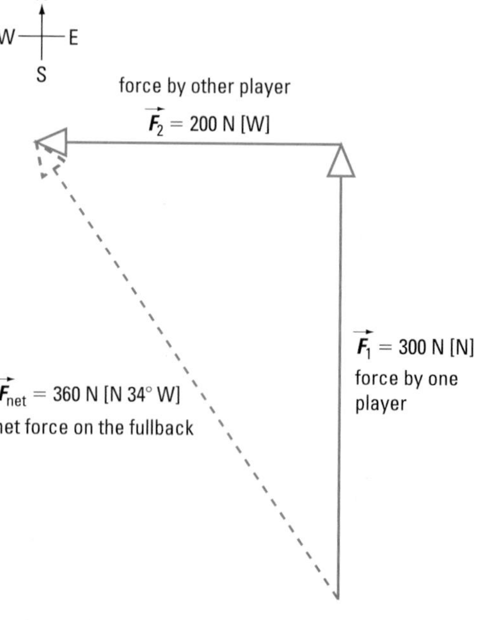

FIGURE 2.9

PRACTICE PROBLEMS

1. Two horizontal forces act on an object. One is 10 N [W] while the other is 20 N [E 30°N]. Calculate the net force on the object.
2. A paddler in a canoe paddles with a force of 200 N [E] while the current exerts a force of 100 N [E 45° S] on the canoe. Use the tail-to-tip strategy to calculate the net horizontal force on the canoe.

Adding Non-Collinear Forces Using Trigonometry

Non-collinear forces that form two arms of a triangle can also be added using the trigonometric sine law $\frac{a}{\sin A} = \frac{b}{\sin B} = \frac{c}{\sin C}$ and cosine law $c^2 = a^2 + b^2 - 2ab \cos C$, where A, B, and C are the angles of a triangle and a, b, and c are the sides opposite the corresponding angles.

EXAMPLE 4 CONCEPTUAL

Consider the football players in Example 3. Find the net horizontal force on the fullback using the sine and cosine laws.

Reasoning and Solution

The sine and cosine laws enable us to find the magnitude of the net force and its direction for two forces at any angle to one another.

Sketch the two given forces and the net force. Label the diagram as shown in Figure 2.10.

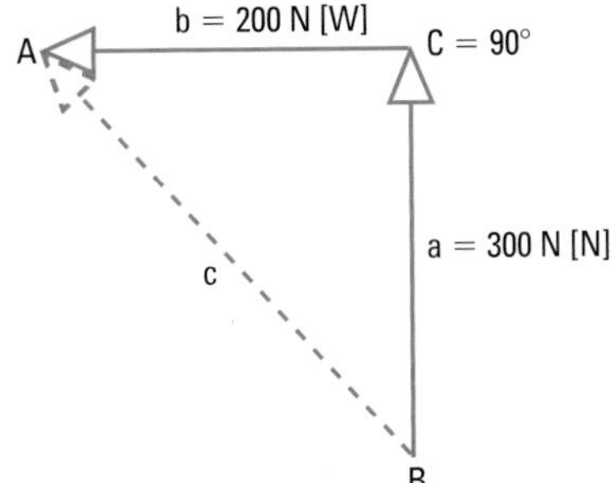

FIGURE 2.10

According to the cosine law $c^2 = a^2 + b^2 - 2ab \cos C$. Substituting into this law we obtain $c^2 = (300)^2 + (200)^2 - 2 \times 300 \times 200 \cos 90°$. But the cosine of 90° is zero. Simplifying, we obtain $c^2 = (300)^2 + (200)^2$. Therefore $c = 360.6$ N.

Now that we know the value of c we can use the sine law

$$\frac{a}{\sin A} = \frac{b}{\sin B} = \frac{c}{\sin C}$$

to determine the angle B.

Substituting into this law we obtain

$$\frac{\sin B}{200} = \frac{\sin 90°}{360.6}$$

But the sin of 90° is one. Simplifying and re-arranging we obtain

$\sin B = \frac{200}{360.6} = 0.554631$. Therefore $B = 33.7°$.

Referring back to the sketch and rounding off, the net force on the fullback is 3.61×10^2 N [N 34° W], almost the same as before.

INSIGHT

The trigonometric solution is usually more accurate than drawing and adding the vectors. Can you explain why?

INSIGHT

The cosine law simplifies to the Pythagorean theorem if the two vectors are at 90° to one another.

CHALLENGE

Two hockey defence players exert a body check on a centre at the same time. The horizontal forces are 400 N [N 45° W] and 300 N [S 30° W]. Use the sine and cosine laws to determine the net horizontal force on the centre.

Should Bungee Jumping Be Banned?

Decision-Making Skills

- Defining the Issue
- Developing Assessment Criteria
- Researching the Issue
- Analyzing Data and Information
- Proposing a Course of Action
- Justifying the Course of Action
- Communicating Your Proposal

BACKGROUND INFORMATION

Bungee jumping originated with the centuries-old ritual of the land divers of Pentecost Island in the Pacific. The modern sport of bungee jumping started with a jump from a high bridge near Bristol, England in 1979.

Bungee jumpers launch themselves backward off an elevated platform, such as a crane, tower, or even a hot-air balloon (Figure 2.11). Only an elastic cord saves a jumper from certain injury or possible death. One end of the cord is attached to the platform and the other is connected to a harness worn by the jumper. The elastic cord can stretch to several times its full length.

There are a number of safety issues in bungee jumping. It is important to match the elasticity of the cord to the weight of the jumper and to the jump height. If the cord is too long or not stiff enough the jumper will hit the ground during the fall. Several people have been killed and others injured, mostly because of human error. Some cords were improperly matched. Others were connected incorrectly to the jumper's harness or the platform. In some cases mathematical errors crept into the height calculation or operators did not consider all of the physics involved. Bungee jumping was banned in France after three deaths in 1989. Should it be banned everywhere?

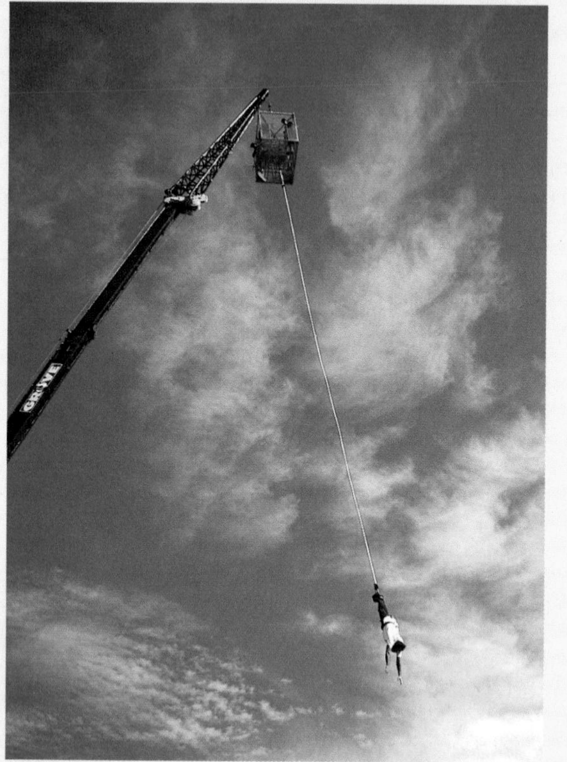

FIGURE 2.11

Analyzing the Issue

1. Research the sport of bungee-jumping. Describe the procedure involved in preparing the equipment for a jump.
2. Based on your research, what do you think are the most important factors for a person to consider if he or she wants to try bungee-jumping?
3. If you were the owner of a bungee-jumping business, in what ways would you think you could be most responsible to your customers? Provide a written customer hand-out to explain the physical forces involved in a bungee jump.
4. What role does society play as bungee-jumping continues to be a popular sport for some enthusiasts?
5. Write a letter to the editor to express your personal opinion about whether bungee jumping should be banned. Consider your research and understanding of the physical forces involved.

Section 2.1 Review

Understanding Concepts

1. List the four fundamental forces of nature.
2. Define force, and state the unit of force.
3. Draw a separate vector diagram for each of the following forces:
   a) 20 N [W] b) 850 N [S]
   c) 1500 N [E 30° S] d) 25 N [E]
4. The total force of gravity on a biker and her motorbike is 1800 N [down]. The engine exerts a force of 600 N [forward]. The air resistance acting on the rider and bike is 200 N [backward]. The friction between the tires and the road is 100 N [backward]. The normal force exerted by the road is 1800 N [up].
   a) Draw a free-body diagram for the system which includes both biker and bike.
   b) Calculate the net force.
5. A person is pulling a heavy wagon along the sidewalk by exerting a force of 12 N [E] on it. A force of friction of 10 N opposes the motion. The force of gravity on the wagon is 100 N.
   a) Draw a free-body diagram showing all the forces acting on the wagon.
   b) Determine the net force on the wagon.
6. How could your knowledge of the vector nature of force affect the techniques you might use while shovelling snow?
7. Three children are tugging a rubber tube in shallow water. One exerts a force of 40 N [N 30° E], another a force of 30 N [W], and the third a force of 50 N [S 45° W].
   a) Draw a free-body diagram showing the three horizontal forces acting on the tube. (Ignore any vertical forces.)
   b) What is the net horizontal force acting on the tube?

Applying Inquiry/ Communication Skills

8. Sketch a graph showing what you think the force–stretch graph of an elastic band will look like. Explain your prediction. Then design and perform an experiment to test your prediction. Based on your results, explain why elastic bands are not used in the construction of instruments used to measure newton force.
9. How does the deflection of the end of a diving board depend on the mass of the diver standing at the end? Make a prediction and explain your reasoning to another student.
   a) Design an experiment to check your hypothesis using a metre-stick as the diving board, a C-clamp to attach the metre-stick so that it extends about 90 cm over the edge of the desk, a set of masses as divers, and some string to hang the masses from the end.
   b) Use a graphing calculator or a spreadsheet program to plot a graph of deflection against mass. How well did your results support your hypothesis?

Making Connections

10. Use your research skills to find the meaning of "elastic limit" as it applies to springs.
11. Imagine you are a scientist studying the fundamental forces of nature. Write a one-page proposal to the Federal Government describing the benefits you feel your research will have.

2.2 Mass and the Force of Gravity

FIGURE 2.12 Counteracting gravity

Key Understandings

When you have completed this section, you will be able to:

- distinguish between mass, force of gravity, and weight
- list the factors that affect the force of gravity on an object
- use Newton's law of universal gravitation to analyze and describe the gravitational force acting on an object near to and at a distance from the surface of Earth

You have probably heard about Newton and the apple. In the seventeenth century, Sir Isaac Newton realized that the force of gravity which pulls a falling apple toward Earth is the same force that keeps the Moon in orbit around Earth. Other people had seen apples fall, but Newton had the vision to link this to orbital motion. He saw what everyone else saw, but thought what no other person thought. What is the force of gravity? How does this force vary throughout the universe?

Mass

Mass is defined as the amount of material in an object. Two objects have the same mass if they have the same amount of matter in them. The SI unit of mass is the kilogram. For 106 years, a single precious platinum-iridium cylinder in Sèvres, France, has served reliably as the kilogram standard. The mass of an object is often measured using an equal arm balance (Figure 2.13). The object with unknown mass is placed on one pan and standard masses are added to the other pan until they balance. The force of gravity acting on the unknown mass is balanced against the force of gravity acting on the standard masses.

FIGURE 2.13 An equal arm balance

When the mass of an object is measured using an equal arm balance, the same value is obtained whether the measurement is made on Earth, the Moon, or any other planet or Moon. The force of gravity exerted by the Moon on the unknown mass is less than that exerted by Earth on the mass. But the force of gravity exerted by the moon on the standard masses on the other side of the balance is also less. The mass of an object never changes unless, of course, some matter is added to or removed from it.

Force of Gravity and Weight

The **force of gravity** is defined as the force of attraction between any two masses in the universe. For example, at its surface, Earth attracts a 60-kg person with a certain force. The Moon, at its surface, attracts the same 60-kg person with only about one-sixth of Earth's force. **Weight** is the term that is used to describe the force of gravity that a celestial body, such as Earth, exerts on a mass. When we say that a person weighs 800 N on Earth we mean that the force of gravity exerted by Earth on the person is 800 N.

Although the mass of an object is always the same, the force of gravity can change. The force of gravity between an object and a planet depends on the mass of the planet, the mass of the object, and the distance between the two. Larger masses mean larger forces, while greater distances between the masses mean smaller forces of gravity.

For instance, a 1-kg mass at a certain distance from the centre of Earth would weigh more than it would weigh at that same distance from the centre of the Moon. This is because Earth has more mass than the Moon.

In addition, the further an object is from the centre of Earth, the less it weighs. If you were on top of Mount Everest you would actually weigh slightly less than you would at sea level, because you would be farther from the centre of Earth. Also, since the radius of Earth is greater at the equator than at the poles, you would weigh less at the equator. In each case the difference in weight is not much (about 0.5%). But these factors could matter if you are a weightlifter or a high jumper trying to set a new world record. When the force of gravity is measured at the surface of Earth and again one Earth radius above Earth, the force of gravitational attraction is one-quarter as great as the first—a significant difference.

The forces of gravity between any two objects always come in pairs. If Earth exerts a force of gravity on you of 700 N, then you also exert a force of gravity on Earth of 700 N. Earth attracts you and you attract Earth. Your force on Earth doesn't affect it much because of its huge mass. The Earth is hard to push around. However, Earth's force of gravity on you affects you because of your relatively small mass.

WEBLINK

To explore how mass and weight are measured, go to **www.pearsoned.ca/physics11.**

EXAMPLE 5 CONCEPTUAL

Gravity is the major factor in producing ocean tides. But where do the high and low tides occur? And why are there two high tides and two low tides each day at a given location?

Reasoning and Solution

FIGURE 2.14 The oceans' waters at A and B are at high tide, at the same time.

The major force that causes the tides is the pull of gravity exerted by the Moon on Earth and its oceans. We know that the force of gravity between two masses depends on the distance between these masses. The farther apart they are, the smaller the force of gravity. As you can see in Figure 2.14, the water on the side of Earth marked A is closest to the Moon, so it experiences the largest force of gravity. This causes the water to bulge and produces a high tide.

Earth rotates on its axis once every 24 h. The same side of Earth is nearest the Moon only once a day. Then why are there two high tides at location A each day? Sir Isaac Newton was the first to explain this. The explanation is complex, but one way to think of it is to say that the Moon

WEBLINK

Newspapers in cities like Halifax, near an ocean, often publish tidal charts which show the times of local high and low tides. Search the web for an example of a tide chart and suggest possible uses of the chart by a variety of people. Begin your research at **www.pearsoned.ca/physics11.**

INFOBIT

The tides in the Bay of Fundy are the highest in the world. In some places, the water level rises up to 18 m between low and high tides.

also pulls on Earth itself. In a sense it pulls it slightly away from the water on the far side of Earth at B. This causes the high tide bulge at B. Thus, there are two high tides and two low tides at any given location each day. Although there are other factors affecting tides (the rotation of Earth, the gravitational pull of the Sun, and friction between Earth and the water), gravity is the major cause of the tides.

FIGURE 2.15

CHALLENGE

Sometimes the tides are higher than normal and sometimes they are lower than normal. These tides are called spring tides and neap tides. Use your research skills to find out what causes spring tides and neap tides.

WEBLINK

An associate of Newton's, Sir Edmund Halley, actually paid for the publication of some of Newton's famous work. Search the web for information about Edmund Halley and use the information to write an obituary that could have been used all those years ago. Begin your research at **www.pearsoned.ca/physics11.**

Newton's Law of Universal Gravitation

Newton showed that **the force of gravity between two masses in the universe is directly proportional to the product of the masses and inversely proportional to the square of the distance between their centres**. This statement is now called **Newton's law of universal gravitation** and it can be written as an equation if we introduce a constant G called the **universal gravitational constant**. Why do you think it is called a universal constant?

$$F_G = \frac{Gm_1m_2}{\Delta d^2}$$

where F_G is the magnitude of the force of gravitational attraction between any two objects, in newtons

m_1 is the mass of one object, in kilograms

m_2 is the mass of the other object, in kilograms

Δd is the distance between the centres of the objects, in metres

G is the universal gravitational constant, 6.67×10^{-11} N·m^2/kg^2

Newton estimated an approximate value for G, using the mass of Earth, the mass of the moon, and the distance between their centres. Cavendish, an English chemist and physicist, verified Newton's law of universal gravitation in 1778. But it was about a century before an accurate value for G was found.

Newton and Gravity

Sir Isaac Newton (1642–1727) proposed the law of universal gravitation in 1665. Legend has it that as Newton sat beneath an apple tree pondering the motion of the Moon, he saw an apple fall to the ground. He wondered whether the same force that holds the Moon in its orbit also attracts the apple. He predicted that the rate of fall of an object is directly proportional to the force of gravity. He hypothesized that the force of gravity, and hence the rate of fall, are inversely proportional to the square of the distance from the centre of Earth. Newton used the available figures for the radius of Earth, and the distance from the centre of Earth to the Moon, to calculate what the rate of fall of the Moon as it orbits Earth should be. Because his calculations were only seven-eighths accurate when compared with the observed rate of fall, he set the problem to one side.

Over 20 years later, Newton was encouraged by Sir Edmund Halley to revisit the problem. The law of universal gravitation was then published, but only because Halley paid for the publication.

EXAMPLE 6 NUMERICAL

Two people are sitting on a bench 0.60 m apart. If one has a mass of 80 kg and the other a mass of 55 kg, what is the force of gravitational attraction between them?

Given
$m_1 = 80$ kg, $m_2 = 55$ kg, $\Delta d = 0.60$ m

Required
F_G

Analysis
- Assume that their centre of masses are separated by 0.60 m.
- Use the value of G as 6.67×10^{-11} N·m²/kg².
- Substitute the data into the equation for the law of universal gravitation.
- Solve for the force of gravity.

Solution

$$F_G = \frac{Gm_1m_2}{\Delta d^2}$$

$$= \frac{(6.67 \times 10^{-11}\ \text{N·m}^2/\text{kg}^2)\ (80\ \text{kg})\ (55\ \text{kg})}{(0.60\ \text{m})^2}$$

$$= 8.2 \times 10^{-7}\ \text{N}$$

Statement
The force of gravitational attraction between the two people is only 8.2×10^{-7} N.

PRACTICE PROBLEMS

1. Earth has a mass of 5.98×10^{24} kg. The mass of the moon is 7.34×10^{22} kg, and the mean radius of its orbit is 3.8×10^{8} m. Calculate the force of gravity between Earth and the moon.
2. Assume the force of gravitational attraction between the fatal iceberg and the *Titanic* was 61 N when their centres were separated by 100 m. The *Titanic* had a mass of 4.6×10^{7} kg. What was the mass of the iceberg?

As you can see, the force of gravity between everyday things at normal distances is very small. Note that every other object (person, etc.) around the two people is pulling on them too. But the only force of gravity they will notice is the one exerted by Earth.

INSIGHT

Sometimes problems on the topic of universal gravitation can be solved quickly by using proportionalities. For example, doubling one of the masses in the problem would simply double the force of gravity between the two. It is a little trickier working with the term for distance, because it is squared. This means that when the distance is doubled, the force is 1/4 of the original value. When the distance is tripled, the force is 1/9 of the original value, and so on.

Section 2.2 Review

Understanding Concepts

1. Distinguish between the terms mass and weight.
2. Explain why an easy way to lose weight would be to travel from the north pole to the equator.
3. Suppose the force of gravity between two people 1.0 m apart is F. How would the force change if
   a) they moved to a distance of 2.0 m apart?
   b) one of them was joined by an equally massive friend while at this 2.0-m separation?
4. The mass of the Moon is 7.34×10^{22} kg and its radius is 1.74×10^{6} m. Earth has a mass of 5.98×10^{24} kg and a radius of 6.38×10^{6} m.
   a) Calculate the gravitational force of the moon on a 100 kg astronaut standing on the moon's surface.
   b) Compare this force with Earth's gravitational force on that same astronaut standing on Earth.

Applying Inquiry/ Communication Skills

5. One person says that an astronaut in orbit is weightless. Another person disagrees. In a paragraph, outline your answer to your classmates. Now revise your paragraph so that it could be understood by a student in grade 5.
6. What is the relationship between the mass of an object in kilograms and the force of gravity acting on it in newtons? Make a prediction and do an activity to find out. You will need a set of standard masses, a newton spring scale with a range of 0 to 10 N, and a sheet of rectangular coordinate graph paper, or a graphing calculator or spreadsheet program. Plot a graph of force of gravity against mass and find the slope of the graph. What does this tell you about the relationship between the force of gravity and mass? If you know the mass of an object in kilograms, how can you find the force of gravity acting on it in newtons? How can you calibrate a spring scale to read a force in newtons?

Making Connections

7. Science was done differently 350 years ago in Newton's era. Three big differences between then and now are:
   a) Scientists often worked alone and contact with other scientists working on the same ideas was difficult.
   b) Many scientists often had very strong religious beliefs and studied religious writings.
   c) Scientists were often knowledgeable in many different fields. Newton, for example, spent many years doing chemistry.

   In paragraph form, assess the impacts that these factors might have had on science in Newton's day and evaluate the effects these factors might have on scientists today.

2.3 Gravitational Field Intensity

Key Understandings

When you have completed this section, you will be able to:

- analyze and describe the gravitational force acting on an object
- define gravitational field intensity
- given any two of gravitational field intensity, force of gravity (i.e. weight), and mass, determine the third

Did you know that a javelin can be thrown farther in Banff, Alberta, than it can in Brussels, Belgium? There is also more chance of breaking the high-jump record in Banff. It all has to do with gravity, or more precisely, with gravitational field intensity. How does gravity change around Earth? How strong is gravitational field intensity at other places in the solar system?

FIGURE 2.16 Working against gravity

Gravitational Field Intensity

Earth exerts a force of gravity on every mass. The result is that everything on or near Earth is pulled toward the centre of Earth. The greater the mass, the stronger the pull. Table 2.1 shows the force of gravity measured in Toronto for different masses.

TABLE 2.1 Force of Gravity and Mass in Toronto

Mass *m* (kg)	0	1.50	3.00	4.50	6.00	7.50	10.0
Force $\vec{F}_G$ (N [down])	0	14.7	29.4	44.1	58.9	73.6	98.1

Figure 2.17 is a graph of the force of gravity plotted against mass for the data in Table 2.1. The data and graph show that the force of gravity is directly proportional to the mass. If the mass is doubled, the force of gravity doubles. If the mass is tripled, the force of gravity triples. Let's calculate the slope of the graph.

$$\text{Slope} = \frac{\text{rise}}{\text{run}} = \frac{80.1\text{ N [down]}}{8.14\text{ kg}} = 9.84\text{ N/kg [down]}$$

The slope of the straight line is 9.84 N/kg [down]. Thus, the ratio of the force of gravity to the mass is constant. The ratio of the force of gravity to mass at a specific location is called the **gravitational field intensity**, and the equation for this relationship is:

$$\vec{g} = \frac{\vec{F}_G}{m}$$

where $\vec{g}$ is the gravitational field intensity in newtons per kilogram

$\vec{F}_G$ is the force of gravity on an object, in newtons

m is the mass of the object, in kilograms

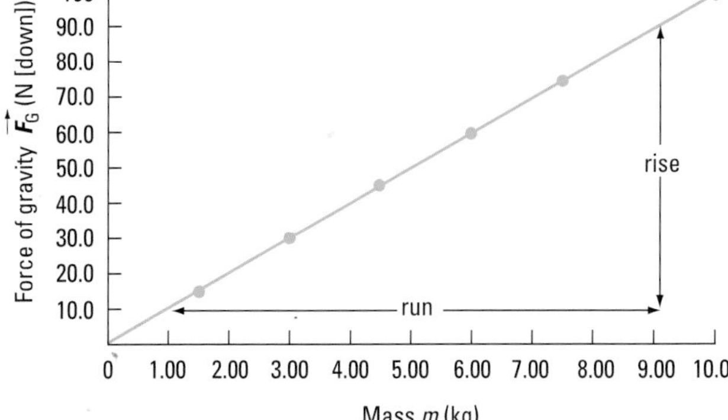

FIGURE 2.17 Force of gravity against mass in Toronto

We can use this formula to solve problems involving force of gravity, mass, and gravitational field intensity. Although $\vec{g}$ varies slightly over Earth, use $\vec{g}$ = 9.8 N/kg [down] unless otherwise stated. Down, in the case of gravitational field intensity, means toward the centre of the celestial body.

Refer to page 84, Investigation 1

PRACTICE PROBLEMS

1. Calculate the mass of an object on Earth if the downward force of gravity on it is 1.2×10^3 N.
2. The gravitational field intensity on the surface of Mars is 3.61 N/kg. How much would a 3.0×10^3 kg space vehicle weigh on Mars?

EXAMPLE 7 NUMERICAL

What is the force of gravity on an elephant with a mass of 1365 kg?

Given

$m = 1365$ kg

Required

$\vec{F}_G$

Analysis

- Re-arrange the equation $\vec{g} = \dfrac{\vec{F}_G}{m}$ to solve for the force of gravity.
- Use 9.8 N/kg [down] as the value of the gravitational field intensity.

Solution

$$\vec{g} = \frac{\vec{F}_G}{m}$$

therefore, $\vec{F}_G = m\vec{g}$

$= (1365 \text{ kg})\ (9.8 \text{ N/kg [down]})$

$= 13\ 377$ N [down]

$= 1.3 \times 10^4$ N [down]

Statement

The force of gravity on the elephant is 1.3×10^4 N [down].

Gravitational Field Intensity on Earth's Surface

For a long time people thought that gravitational field intensity was constant at a specific location. However, scientists, using sophisticated equipment able to detect tiny variations in $\vec{g}$, have found that $\vec{g}$ varies slightly with time. To date, we do not know why this happens.

On Earth, the gravitational field intensity varies with latitude and altitude. Latitude is the angular distance north or south of the equator, whereas altitude is the elevation of an object above sea level. Values of $\vec{g}$ for different latitudes and altitudes are shown in Table 2.2.

The data show that the gravitational field intensity increases as we move away from the equator, either north or south. This is because Earth is not quite a sphere; it bulges out slightly at the equator. In fact, the distance from the centre of Earth to the surface is 21 km greater at the equator than at the poles. The greater the distance from the exact centre of Earth, the smaller $\vec{g}$ becomes. Remember that according to Newton's law of universal gravitation, the force of gravity varies inversely as the square of the distance from the centre of Earth.

TABLE 2.2 Gravitational Field Intensity on Earth

Place	Latitude (degrees)	Altitude (metres)	Magnitude of the Gravitational Field Intensity $\vec{g}$ (newtons per kilogram)
North Pole	90 [N]	0	9.832
Greenland	70 [N]	20	9.825
Stockholm	59 [N]	45	9.818
Brussels	51 [N]	102	9.811
Banff	51 [N]	1 376	9.808
Toronto	44 [N]	162	9.805
Dead Sea	32 [N]	−397	9.796
Mount Everest	28 [N]	8 848	9.796
Canal Zone	9 [N]	6	9.782
Equator	0	0	9.781
New Zealand	37 [S]	3	9.800

Applications of Gravitational Field Intensity

Local variations in the gravitational field intensity are due to the irregularities in the land and the variation in the density of the rocks and gases beneath the surface. Geophysicists and geologists use sensitive **gravimeters** to detect small variations in $\vec{g}$ when they search for minerals, oil, and natural gas. Dense mineral deposits near the surface, such as gold and silver, increase the value of $\vec{g}$. Oil and natural gas in the ground decrease $\vec{g}$. Gravitational field intensity maps and core samples are very important in geology (Figure 2.18).

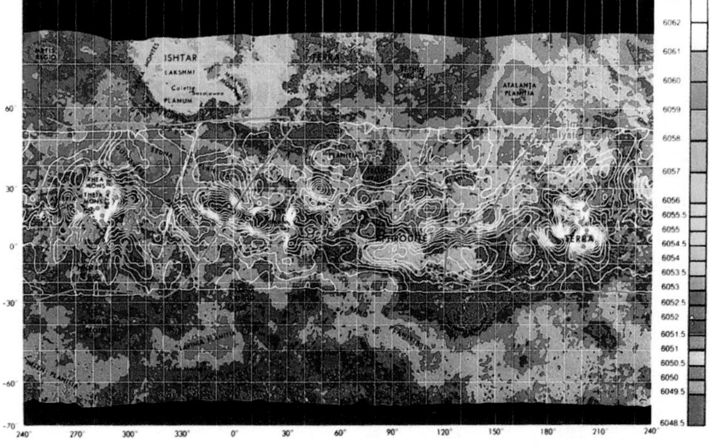

FIGURE 2.18 Coloured contours show surface elevations on Venus.

Changes in the gravitational field intensity around Earth also have implications for athletic records. The Olympics are held in a new location every four years. These different locations are at a variety of latitudes and altitudes, and therefore the gravitational field intensities are often different in these various cities. Even the rotation of Earth contributes to different values for $\vec{g}$. In addition, at higher altitudes the air is less dense and distance runners have difficulty getting enough oxygen. For example, the 1968 Olympics in Mexico City (elevation 2300 m) produced record times in the short races (100 m, 200 m, 400 m), and very poor times in the 5000-m, 10 000-m, and marathon races. A record was set in the long jump, partly due to the lower value for $\vec{g}$ and the thin air, but mainly due to the excellence of the athlete. A javelin can be thrown 35 cm farther in Mexico City than in Moscow (elevation 150 m) because of low $\vec{g}$ and thin air. So, location is an important factor to consider when comparing athletic records.

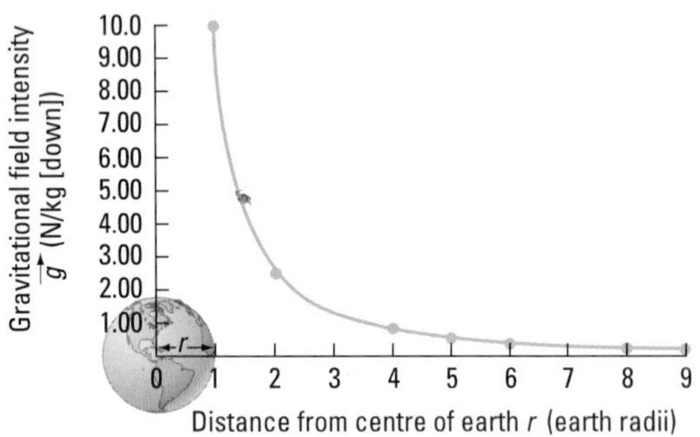

FIGURE 2.19 Gravitational field intensity decreases as the distance from the centre of Earth increases.

Gravitational Field Intensity above Earth's Surface

We know that gravitational field intensity decreases as we move away from the centre of Earth. However, for very small changes in altitude, the change in gravitational field intensity is very small. That is why we can use $\vec{g}$ = 9.8 N/kg [down] for problems that involve objects near Earth's surface. However, farther away from Earth in orbit $\vec{g}$ is noticeably less. For the Hubble Space Telescope in orbit at an altitude of 596 km above Earth's surface, $\vec{g}$ is about 9.1 N/kg [down]. At twice the distance from the centre of Earth, $\vec{g}$ decreases to one-quarter the value at the surface. At three times the distance from the centre of Earth, $\vec{g}$ becomes one-ninth as large. Figure 2.19 shows how $\vec{g}$ varies with distance. Using the value of $\vec{g}$ from the graph, we can calculate the force of gravity at a specific altitude.

INSIGHT

Once you know that the astronaut is five Earth radii from the centre of Earth, another way to find $\vec{g}$ is to use the inverse square law for the force of gravity. Remember that when r doubles, $\vec{g}$ becomes 1/4 $\vec{g}$. When r triples, $\vec{g}$ becomes 1/9 $\vec{g}$. So at five Earth radii, $\vec{g}$ becomes 1/25 $\vec{g}$ = (9.8 N/kg [down])/25 = 0.39 N/kg [down]

EXAMPLE 8 NUMERICAL

The average radius of Earth is about 6.40×10^3 km. What is the force of gravity acting on an 80.0-kg astronaut in orbit 3.20×10^4 km from the centre of Earth?

Given

$r_1 = 6.40 \times 10^3$ km

$r_2 = 3.20 \times 10^4$ km

$m = 80.0$ kg

Required

$\vec{F}_G$

Analysis

- $\vec{g}$ decreases with altitude
- Find out how many Earth radii the astronaut is from the centre of Earth.
- Use Figure 2.19 to find $\vec{g}$.
- Use $\vec{F}_G = m\vec{g}$ to solve the problem.

Solution

Number of Earth radii $\frac{r_2}{r_1}$

$= \frac{3.20 \times 10^4 \text{ km}}{6.40 \times 10^3 \text{ km}}$

$= 5.00/1.00$

From Figure 2.19, at this altitude, $\vec{g}$ is 0.39 N/kg [down].

$\vec{F}_G = m\vec{g}$

$= 80.0 \text{ kg} \times 0.39 \text{ N/kg [down]}$

$= 31 \text{ N [down]}$

Statement

The force of gravity on the astronaut at this altitude is 31 N [down].

PRACTICE PROBLEMS

1. A satellite travels in orbit around Earth at a distance of three Earth radii above Earth's surface.
   a) How many Earth radii is it from Earth's centre?
   b) What is the value of $\vec{g}$ at this location?
2. The highest satellites are about 6.6 Earth radii from the centre of Earth. This is about a tenth of the way to the Moon. What would the force of gravity be on a 70-kg astronaut at this location?

Gravitational Field Intensity and the Solar System

Every planet, star, and moon has its own gravitational field. We know that the gravitational field intensity at the surface depends on the mass of the celestial body and its radius. The greater the mass, the greater $\vec{g}$ becomes. But the greater the radius of the planet, the smaller $\vec{g}$ is at the planet's surface. Table 2.3 shows some of the known values of $\vec{g}$ for our solar system. Considering $\vec{g}$, do you think your skeleton could support your weight on Jupiter? How much stronger would your bones need to be?

TABLE 2.3 Gravitational Field Intensities in the Solar System

Celestial Object	Mass (kg)	Radius (m)	Gravitational Field Intensity at the Surface $\vec{g}$ (N/kg) [down]
Sun	1.98×10^{30}	6.95×10^{8}	270.0
Jupiter	1.90×10^{27}	7.18×10^{7}	24.6
Neptune	1.03×10^{26}	2.48×10^{7}	11.2
Saturn	5.67×10^{26}	6.03×10^{7}	10.4
Earth	5.98×10^{24}	6.38×10^{6}	9.80
Uranus	8.80×10^{25}	2.67×10^{7}	8.23
Venus	4.83×10^{24}	6.32×10^{6}	8.09
Mars	6.37×10^{23}	3.43×10^{6}	3.61
Mercury	3.28×10^{23}	2.57×10^{6}	3.31
Moon	7.34×10^{22}	1.74×10^{6}	1.62
Pluto	6.00×10^{23}	3.00×10^{6}	unknown

INSIGHT

Example 8 shows that a force of gravity is exerted on an object even when the object appears to be "weightless." In reality astronauts are not weightless, they just appear to be because they are in free fall.

Exploration Using a Graphing Calculator

Gravitational Field Intensity

The equation for determining the value of gravitational field intensity g at a distance Δd from the centre of a specific celestial body of mass M is $g = \frac{GM}{\Delta d^2}$. Graph this equation for the Moon using the graphing calculator. The universal gravitational constant $G = 6.67 \times 10^{-11}$ N·m²/kg², and the mass and radius of the Moon are 7.34×10^{22} kg and 1.74×10^{6} m, respectively (Table 2.3). Plot g on the y-axis (with a range of 0 N/kg to 2.0 N/Kg) and Δd on the x-axis (with a range of 1 to 5 Moon radii). After plotting the graph, toggle through to read values of g corresponding to specific values of Moon radii Δd, referred to in the discussion below.

Discussion

1. Describe the graph of g against Δd for the Moon. How is it similar to Figure 2.19?

WEBLINK

To explore the effects of gravitational field intensity, go to **www.pearsoned.ca/physics11.**

INFOBIT

You can get dizzy or even faint if you stand up too quickly. When you sit down or stand still for a long period of time, your blood tends to pool in the veins of your feet and legs. Veins are very stretchy compared with arteries, and so they cannot exert enough force to return the blood to the top part of your body. In fact, if you take your shoes off while you are sitting, your feet will likely swell up, and you may have trouble getting your shoes back on again! You can help prevent this by moving your toes, feet, and legs a bit while you are sitting. Fidgeting helps squeeze the blood back up to your heart.

2. What is the value of g
   a) at the surface of the Moon?
   b) half a Moon radius from the surface?
   c) one Moon radius above the surface?
3. At what distance from the Moon's surface do you think you could ignore g? Test your hypothesis with the graph generated using the graphing calculator.

Section 2.3 Review

Understanding Concepts

1. a) Define gravitational field intensity, state its units, and symbol.
b) List two factors that affect the gravitational field intensity on Earth.

2. a) Assuming that the radius stays constant, how does gravitational field intensity vary with the mass of a planet?
b) Use Table 2.3 to determine the ratio of the force of gravity on a 1-kg mass on Jupiter and on Earth.

3. At the top of Mount Robson in British Columbia, the force of gravity on a 7.5-kg turkey is 73.6 N [down]. Calculate the gravitational field intensity at this location.

4. If $\vec{g}$ is 9.8 N/kg [down] at the surface of Earth, what is its magnitude 1.6 Earth radii from Earth's centre?

5. Calculate the force of gravity on a 70-kg astronaut 2.0 Earth radii from the centre of Earth. (Refer to Figure 2.19.)

Applying Inquiry/ Communication Skills

6. Write a short paragraph explaining why astronauts do exercises in space and why they experience difficulty in walking when they return to Earth.

7. Do you think the gravitational field intensity will be different at the bottom of the CN Tower in Toronto from at the top? Make a prediction and give your reasons. Describe an experiment you could do to test your prediction.

Making Connections

8. Research how geophysicists and geologists use sensitive gravimeters and an undertanding of gravitational field intensity to search for minerals, oil, and natural gas in Canada. Submit a half-page report on your findings.

9. One issue today is whether athletic records should be adjusted for the local value of g and other factors such as oxygen levels and air density at different locations. What course of action would you suggest to an Olympic committee responsible for addressing this issue and why?

2.4 Acceleration Due to Gravity

Key Understandings

When you have completed this section, you will be able to:

- compare acceleration due to gravity and gravitational field intensity
- solve problems involving force of gravity, acceleration due to gravity or gravitational field intensity, and mass
- solve problems involving displacement, acceleration due to gravity, initial velocity, final velocity, and elapsed time

Aristotle (384–322 B.C.), an early Greek philosopher, thought that heavy objects fell faster than lighter ones. In fact, he believed that the rate of fall was directly proportional to the mass. What do you think? Will a bowling ball fall faster than a billiard ball? Will a stone fall faster than a feather (Figure 2.20a))?

Galileo (1564–1642), the Italian astronomer and physicist, predicted that heavy objects and light ones would fall at the same rate if there were no air resistance. Galileo was not content to base his theories on logic alone, as the Greek philosophers had done. Instead, he constantly searched for crucial experiments that would provide data to test his theories. His approach revolutionized science. Legend has it that Galileo dropped stones of various sizes from the leaning tower of Pisa to test his hypothesis, although it is not clear if he really did this experiment. Modern experiments show that Galileo's hypothesis was correct. Without friction, all objects near the surface of Earth at the same location do fall with the same constant acceleration (Figure 2.20b)). This acceleration is called the **acceleration due to gravity**. The magnitude of the acceleration due to gravity is very nearly 9.8 m/s^2 anywhere near the surface of Earth. In free fall, an object accelerates downward at this rate whether it is dropped straight downward or thrown vertically or horizontally.

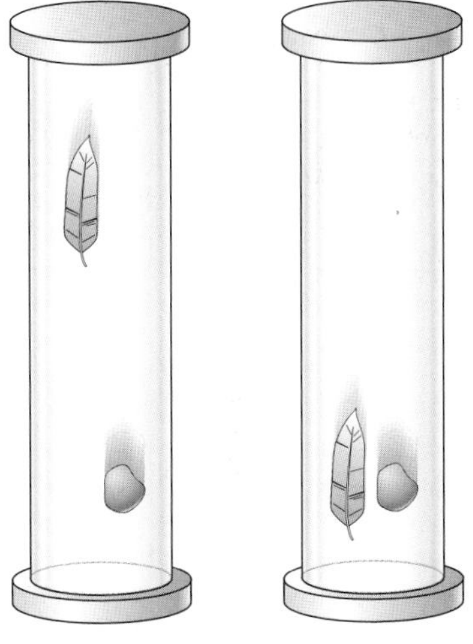

FIGURE 2.20 A stone and a feather are dropped at the same time in a) air and b) a partial vacuum. Note the effect of friction.

Refer to page 85, Investigation 2

Analysis of Experimental Data

Scientists frequently check the experimental data collected by other scientists and the claims they make based on their data. You can do this too. Figure 2.21 shows the data from a multiple-exposure photograph. It shows the positions of a falling sphere at 0.040-s intervals. The original photograph was taken in a darkened room with the shutter of the camera kept

Discovering Physics *Free Fall*

What happens when you drop a book and a sheet of paper from the same height at the same time?

Hold a heavy book beside a sheet of paper about shoulder high. Drop them and see which one lands first. Try it again but see if you can reduce air friction on the piece of paper. What conclusion do you make after this second try?

Now use a fresh piece of paper that is smaller than the book front cover. Place the paper on top of the book and drop them together. Why do you think they stay together as they fall? Will they stay together if the paper is placed under the book?

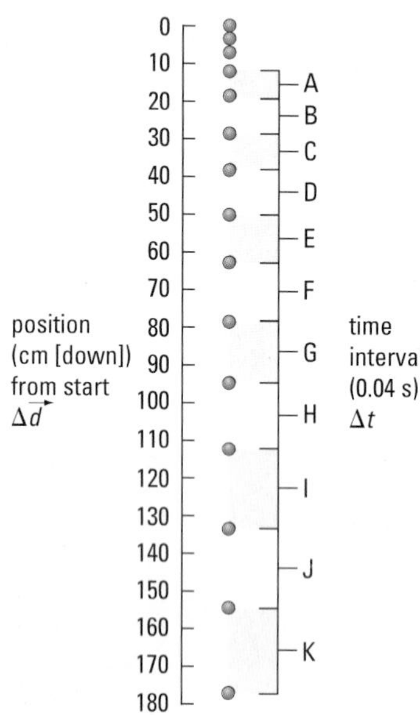

FIGURE 2.21 A reproduction of a flash photograph of a falling sphere

open. A stroboscope was adjusted so that the light flashed on 25 times every second (i.e. the light flashed every 0.040 s) on the same piece of film. The sphere fell in front of a grid, and measurements were made from the photograph to yield the displacements given in Table 2.4. The first three positions were discounted to improve the precision of the measurements. Because it was difficult to measure the displacements accurately, the last digit in the displacement column is very uncertain. It was retained to decrease the errors that would accumulate if the figures were rounded off early.

TABLE 2.4 Acceleration Due to Gravity

Interval	Elapsed Time Δt (s)	Displacement $\Delta\vec{d}$ (cm [down])	Average Velocity $\vec{v}_{av}$ (cm/s [down])	Change in Average Velocity $\Delta\vec{v}_{av}$ (cm/s [down])	Acceleration $\vec{a}$ (m/s^2 [down])
A	0.040	7.06	176		
				40	10.0
B	0.040	8.63	216		
				39	9.8
C	0.040	10.20	255		
				39	9.8
D	0.040	11.76	294		
				40	10.0
E	0.040	13.34	334		
				38	9.5
F	0.040	14.88	372		
				39	9.8
G	0.040	16.45	411		
				40	10.0
H	0.040	18.03	451		
				40	10.0
I	0.040	19.62	491		
				38	9.5
J	0.040	21.17	529		
				39	9.8
K	0.040	22.71	568		
				Average acceleration	9.8

The average velocity during each 0.040-s interval is calculated using the equation $\vec{v}_{av} = \frac{\Delta\vec{d}}{\Delta t}$. For example, the average velocity during interval A is (7.06 cm [down])/0.040 s or 176 cm/s [down]. Likewise, the average velocity during interval B is 216 cm/s [down]. Recall that for constant acceleration, the average velocity for an interval is equal to the instantaneous velocity at half-time in the interval. As a result, it takes 0.040 s for the average velocity to change from 176 cm/s [down] to 216 cm/s [down]; a change in velocity of 40 cm/s [down]. The acceleration for each interval is calculated using the equation $\vec{a} = \frac{\Delta\vec{v}}{\Delta t}$. The acceleration from the mid-time of interval A to the mid-time of interval B is (40 cm/s [down])/0.040 s = 1000 cm/s^2 [down], or 10 m/s^2 [down].

This process was used to complete Table 2.4. The measurements and calculations show that, on average, the acceleration due to gravity at Earth's surface is 9.8 m/s^2 [down]. You can check this by finding the average of the accelerations in the last column.

WEBLINK

One method of studying what happens to objects in free fall is to photograph them during their fall. For example, what happens to a drop of milk as it falls into a pan of milk? To try to capture these images on film the stroboscope was invented by Dr. Harold Edgerton. Search the web to find out about the action of a stroboscope and produce a photo essay that illustrates some applications of this device. Begin your research at **www.pearsoned.ca/physics11.**

The Leaning Tower of Pisa

Galileo may have dropped stones from the leaning tower of Pisa to test his theories. The foundation stones for the bell tower next to the church in Pisa, a town near Rome, Italy, had been laid 400 years earlier. The seven-storey structure was built on the shifting sands of a former flood plain and is believed to have begun to tilt before it was officially completed in 1370.

By 1990, the leaning tower of Pisa was leaning a full 4.5 m. It was in serious danger of either falling over or collapsing due to extra pressure at the second level caused by the lean. As a result, the Italian government closed the tower.

In the following years, a number of state-of-the-art technologies and simple mechanical principles were used to save the tower. In 1992, engineers wrapped 18 narrow steel belts around the tower up to the second storey. This closed many cracks and reduced the chances of a buckling collapse. In 1993, workers inserted lead counterweights at the base of the north side to try and pull the north side down. As an extra precaution, large steel cables were loosely attached to the north side. The cables could be tightened if any unwanted movements occurred during the straightening efforts.

These efforts were successful at reducing the risk of collapse, but unfortunately all of the cables and counterweights spoiled the tower's appearance. In 1999, a more aesthetically pleasing solution was found. Engineers used an inclined drill to remove soil from under the north side of the tower and successfully reduced the lean by 38 cm. But don't worry, the tower still retains most of its famous tilt. The 38-cm reduction was enough to eliminate the threat of collapse, but not enough to be noticed by the naked eye.

The soil-removing technique was so successful that, in early 2001, the unsightly lead counterweights and steel cables were removed. As a precautionary measure, a new set of extremely thin, almost invisible cables were installed. After being closed for more than a decade, the famous tower was able to re-open to the public in June of 2001.

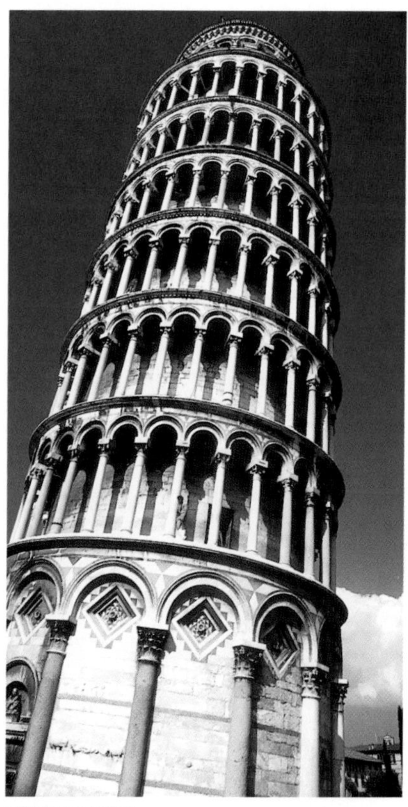

FIGURE 2.22 The leaning tower of Pisa

Acceleration Due to Gravity and Gravitational Field Intensity

Without air resistance, the magnitude of the acceleration due to gravity at Earth's surface is 9.8 m/s^2. The magnitude of the gravitational field intensity at this location is 9.8 N/kg. Are these two quantities equivalent? The answer is yes. Everything that affects the gravitational field intensity also affects the acceleration of a freely falling object. Imagine that you are somewhere in space, two Earth radii from the centre of Earth, where the gravitational field intensity is 2.5 N/kg. An object dropped from this point will accelerate toward the centre of Earth at 2.5 m/s^2. If the gravitational field intensity on the Moon's surface is 1.62 N/kg, then an object released just a little above the surface will accelerate toward the Moon's centre at 1.62 m/s^2. Since the acceleration due to gravity and the gravitational field intensity are equivalent, we can use the same symbol $\vec{g}$ for both. As a result, we can use the two quantities interchangeably. For example, if we know the mass of an object and either the acceleration due to gravity or the gravitational field intensity, we can find the force of gravity acting on the object.

INSIGHT

When simplified to base units, the units for acceleration due to gravity and gravitational field intensity are equal.

Since $1\text{ N} = 1\text{ kg}\cdot\text{m/s}^2$

$$1\text{ N/kg} = \frac{1\text{ kg}\cdot\text{m/s}^2}{1\text{ kg}} = 1\text{ m/s}^2$$

Free Fall and Kinematics Equations

If friction is ignored, the kinematics equations, which we developed and used in Chapter 1 for constant acceleration, can be used for free fall. To do this, simply replace $\vec{a}$ with the appropriate value for $\vec{g}$.

INSIGHT

When choosing a direction as positive, it is wise to select the direction that most frequently occurs in the problem. For example, if most initial motions are in the downward direction, then call [down] positive. Then give a positive sign to those in the downward direction and a negative sign to those in the upward direction.

EXAMPLE 9 NUMERICAL

A football is thrown straight up with a speed of 39.2 m/s where the gravitational field intensity $\vec{g}$ is 9.80 N/kg [down]. In the absence of air friction due to wind resistance, how long would it take the football to slow down to a velocity of 4.90 m/s [up]?

Given

$\vec{v}_1 = 39.2$ m/s [up]

$\vec{v}_2 = 4.90$ m/s [up]

$\vec{g} = 9.80$ N/kg [down]

Required

Δt

Analysis

- Choose [up] as positive.
- Use $\vec{g}$ as the acceleration due to gravity.
- Make $\vec{g} = -9.80$ m/s^2.
- Use the kinematics equation $\vec{v}_2 = \vec{v}_1 + \vec{a}\Delta t$ and replace $\vec{a}$ with $\vec{g}$.
- Re-arrange the equation to solve for elapsed time Δt.

Solution

$$\Delta t = \frac{\vec{v}_2 - \vec{v}_1}{\vec{g}}$$

$$= \frac{4.90 \text{ m/s [up]} - 39.2 \text{ m/s [up]}}{-9.80 \text{ m/s}^2 \text{ [up]}}$$

$$= 3.5 \text{ s}$$

Statement

It took the football 3.5 s to slow down to a velocity of 4.90 m/s [up].

PRACTICE PROBLEMS

1. A stone is thrown at 14 m/s [down] from a bridge over a river. It takes 1.1 s to reach the water. How fast will it be going when it gets there?
2. An astronaut on the Moon, where $\vec{g} = 1.6$ m/s^2 [down], throws a golf ball in the upward direction with a speed of 12 m/s.
   a) How long will it be before it reaches the top of its flight?
   b) How long will it be until it comes back to the astronaut's hand?

INSIGHT

If the direction convention had been reversed so down was chosen as positive, the answer would still be positive. Try it. The key procedure to remember is to be consistent throughout the problem.

Discovering Physics — *Water in Free Fall*

How does water behave during a free fall from a height of several metres? Do this experiment outside. Put two holes on opposite sides of a styrofoam cup near the bottom. Fill the cup with water and observe what happens.

Now block the holes with your thumb and forefinger, fill the cup with water, and then drop the cup of water from a height of several metres. What happens to the water during this free fall? Why do you think the water does this?

EXAMPLE 10 NUMERICAL

A diver jumps with an upward velocity from a 9.0-m diving board. What is her initial velocity if she stays in the air for 1.6 s before reaching the water?

Given
The diving board is 9.0 m above the water.

$\Delta t = 1.6$ s

$\vec{g} = 9.8$ m/s^2 [down]

Required
Initial velocity $\vec{v}_1$

Analysis

- Call [down] positive; therefore [up] is negative.
- $\Delta\vec{d} = +9.0$ m
- $\vec{g} = +9.8$ m/s^2
- Use the equation $\Delta\vec{d} = \vec{v}_1\Delta t + \frac{1}{2}\vec{g}(\Delta t^2)$
- Re-arrange the above equation to solve for $\vec{v}_1$ and substitute.

Solution

$$\vec{v}_1 = \frac{\Delta\vec{d} - 1/2\vec{g}\Delta t^2}{\Delta t}$$

$$= \frac{9.0 \text{ m} - (1/2)(9.8 \text{ m/s}^2)(1.6 \text{ s})^2}{1.6 \text{ s}}$$

$$= -2.2 \text{ m/s}$$

$$= 2.2 \text{ m/s [up]}$$

Statement
The diver's initial velocity is 2.2 m/s [up].

INSIGHT

Once a direction is chosen as positive, you might prefer to omit the directions such as [up] and [down] and replace them with + or − signs. Then after the problem has been solved, re-instate the direction descriptions.

PRACTICE PROBLEMS

1. A pole vaulter leaves the ground to travel 4.0 m up and over the bar, and then another 4.0 m back to the ground. It takes 1.81 s for the whole trip. Calculate the velocity with which she left the ground.
2. A soccer ball is kicked straight up with a speed of 15 m/s.
   a) What will its displacement be after 2.0 s?
   b) Is the ball on the way up or is it on the way down at that time? How do you know?

EXAMPLE 11 CONCEPTUAL

A person throws a smooth ball vertically upward and catches it at the same point on its return (Figure 2.23). How does the release velocity compare with the catch velocity? How does the magnitude of the velocity at the top of the arc compare with the magnitude of the acceleration? How does the acceleration compare just before it reaches the top, at the top, and just after it leaves the top? If air resistance is present, how would your answers change?

Reasoning and Solution
Since the ball is smooth, air resistance can be ignored. The acceleration is caused by the force of gravity, which has the same value throughout the entire flight. Since the force of gravity is always directed downward, the ▶

acceleration due to gravity is always present and directed downward. The acceleration is acting opposite to the direction of motion on the way up and in the same direction as the motion on the way down. On the way up the ball slows down at the same rate as it speeds up on the way down.

Without air resistance, whatever velocity the ball loses on the way up it gains on the way down. Hence, the ball returns to the hand with the same speed as it left, but in the opposite direction. At the top of the arc, the object has a velocity of zero for a small instant of time. At that instant, the force of gravity is still acting and hence the acceleration due to gravity is 9.8 m/s^2, not zero. The force of gravity and hence the acceleration are the same immediately before, during, and after the ball reaches the top.

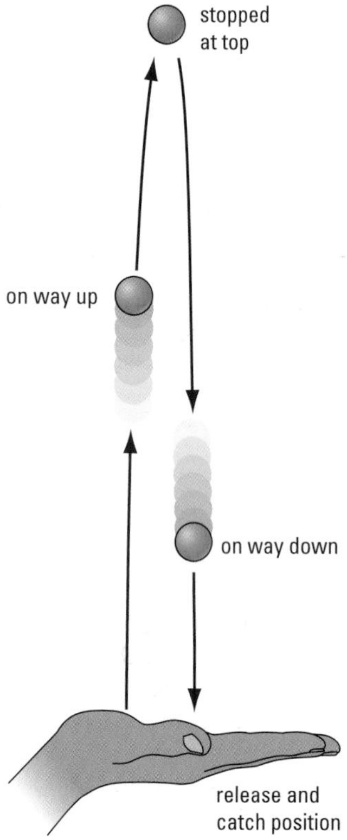

Suppose air friction cannot be ignored. Air resistance always acts opposite to the direction of motion. On the way up, the force of gravity and the force of air resistance both act down. At the top of the arc, the object is stopped and the air resistance is zero. On the way down the air resistance acts up, opposite to the direction of motion. As a result, when air resistance is present, the net force is smaller on the way down than on the way up.

With air resistance present the object slows down at a faster rate on the way up than it speeds up on the way down. In this case the ball returns to the hand moving more slowly than when it left the hand.

FIGURE 2.23

CHALLENGES

1. Describe the motion of a baseball thrown upward on the moon from when it leaves the hand until it returns. Consider velocity and acceleration.
2. Describe the vertical motion (velocity and acceleration) of a skydiver from when she leaves the aircraft to when she opens her parachute and finally lands on the ground.

INFOBIT

Galileo hypothesized that the swing time of the pendulum was independent of its amplitude. He tested this using his pulse as a simple clock, then he devised an experiment to test his hypothesis. Two equal-length pendulums were set vibrating at the same time, one pendulum with a larger amplitude than the other. His hypothesis was proved correct for relatively small amplitudes. Christian Huygens, a Dutch physicist and astronomer, used this principle in the design of the pendulum clock in 1656.

Exploration Using a Graphing Calculator

The Equation for a Pendulum

Enter the equation $T = 2\pi\sqrt{\dfrac{l}{g}}$ for a pendulum of length 1 m.

For this length of pendulum, the equation simplifies to

$$T = \frac{6.28}{\sqrt{g}}.$$

Can you see why?

Plot T on the y-axis (with a range of 1.0 to 5.0 s) and g on the x-axis (with a range from 1.5 to 25 m/s^2). After plotting the graph, toggle along the graph and read values for the period of a one-metre pendulum vibrating on the surface of the planets and the moon. Consult Table 2.3 for values of g.

Discussion

1. What values for the period T did you get for a one-metre-long pendulum located on the surface of
   a) the Moon b) Earth c) Jupiter
2. Provided the pendulum was not destroyed, what would its period be at the surface of the Sun?

INFOBIT

It is a common misconception that the period of a pendulum is independent of its amplitude.

For small amplitudes, the period is reasonably constant, but the period changes significantly as the amplitude is moved to larger angles. That is why the pendulums in grandfather clocks have such small amplitudes and also why the amplitudes are kept constant by the energy from a spring.

Discovering Physics — *Measuring g Using a Pendulum*

You can use a formula to calculate the local value of g. A pendulum swings because of gravity. As the value of g changes, the period T (the time for one vibration of the pendulum) changes. It is known that for a long pendulum, or for one vibrating with a small amplitude, that the following equation applies:

$$T = 2\pi\sqrt{\frac{l}{g}}$$

where T is the period of the pendulum in s, l is the length of the pendulum in cm, and g is the gravitational field strength or the acceleration due to gravity in cm/s^2.

Use the above formula to measure the local value of g. You'll need a pendulum longer than 60 cm, a retort stand, an adjustable clamp, a metre stick, and a stopwatch. Measure and record the length of the pendulum from its pivot to the centre of the bob. Using a small amplitude, release the pendulum and record the time for 10 vibrations. Calculate the time for one vibration. Repeat for two more different lengths greater than 60 cm. Use the equation to calculate three values for g. Convert the values in cm/s^2 to m/s^2. What is the average of your values for g? Identify the variables in this experiment. How could this activity be used to compare the gravitational field intensity at the top and bottom of the CN Tower in Toronto?

Section 2.4 Review

Understanding Concepts

1. a) Compare gravitational field intensity and acceleration due to gravity.
   b) List and describe three factors that affect both.
2. Calculate the force of gravity on an 80-kg astronaut in a space capsule where the acceleration due to gravity is 1.1 m/s^2 [down].
3. The force of gravity on a 5.0-kg boulder on the planet Uranus is 41 N [down]. What is the acceleration due to gravity on Uranus?
4. The force of gravity on a video camera out in space is 29.7 N [down]. What is the mass of the camera if its acceleration in free fall is 3.3 m/s^2 [down]?
5. A worker drops a wrench from the top of a building under construction. If $\vec{g}$ is 9.8 N/kg [down], after 7.0 s
   a) What is the displacement of the wrench?
   b) What is the velocity of the wrench?

Applying Inquiry/ Communication Skills

6. We know that gravity is the force that keeps a pendulum swinging. Construct a pendulum using a pendulum bob and a string. Hold the string as high as you can and start the pendulum swinging. Predict what you will see if you now release the string so that the pendulum falls to the ground. What happens to the swinging pendulum as it falls? Why do you think this happens?

Investigation 1 (Section 2.3)

Inquiry Skills

- Initiating and Planning
- Applying Technical Skills
- Using Tools, Materials, Equipment
- Conducting and Recording
- Analyzing and Interpreting
- Concluding and Communicating

Gravitational Field Intensity

Mass is the quantity of material in an object. The force of gravity of Earth is the attraction between Earth and an object. You have seen that the force of gravity varies with mass. Can one be used to find the other?

Problem

What relationship exists between the mass of an object and Earth's force of gravity on it?

Materials and Cautions

- graph paper
- newton spring scale (0 to 10 N)
- set of hooked standard masses

Experimental Design

1. Design a procedure to determine the force of gravity acting on a series of standard masses.
2. Design a table to record force of gravity, mass, and the ratio of the force of gravity to mass.
3. Calculate the ratio of the force of gravity to the mass for each mass and calculate the average for all masses.
4. Plot a graph of force of gravity against mass and draw a line of best fit though the points. Calculate the slope of the graph.

Analyzing and Interpreting

1. The ratio of the force of gravity to mass is called the gravitational field intensity of Earth and is given the symbol g. How constant is this value?
2. Describe the graph of force of gravity against mass. Compare the slope with the value of the force of gravity-to-mass ratios calculated in step 3, above.

Concluding and Communicating

3. Write an equation relating force of gravity F_G, mass m, and the numerical value of the gravitational field intensity g of Earth from this activity.
4. Suppose you did this activity on the Moon using an appropriate spring scale and the same masses.
   a) Would the graph be a straight line?
   b) Would the line have the same slope?
   c) Would the line go through the origin?
   d) Would the gravitational field intensity be the same?
   e) Why would a 0 to 10 N spring scale not be an appropriate one to use this time?
5. What errors are inherent in your method?

Extending

6. Use the equation $F_G = \frac{Gm_1m_2}{\Delta d^2}$, and what you have learned in this investigation to derive an equation to determine the gravitational field intensity on the surface of a planet from its mass and radius, and the universal gravitational constant G. Use your equation and compare your value to the published value.

Investigation 2 (Section 2.4)

Acceleration Due to Gravity

Inquiry Skills

- Initiating and Planning
- Applying Technical Skills
- Using Tools, Materials, Equipment
- Conducting and Recording
- Analyzing and Interpreting
- Concluding and Communicating

Without friction, two different masses released at the same time from the same height fall through the same vertical distance in the same time. The velocity of both masses increases in the same way. But in what way does the velocity increase? Does the velocity double in twice the distance, or in twice the time? Or does it increase in some other way? Discuss these questions with a partner and make a prediction. Then do the investigation to test your prediction.

Problem

For an object in free fall, how does the increase in velocity vary with the time and the position from the start of the fall?

Materials

- C-clamp
- metre-stick
- clamp
- mass (200 g)
- cushion
- recording timer tape
- graph paper
- recording timer
- power supply
- long retort stand
- masking tape

TABLE 2.5 Motion of an Object in Free Fall

Time Δt (s)	0.1	0.2	0.3
Displacement $\Delta\vec{d}$ (m [down])			
Average Velocity $\vec{v}_{av}$ (m/s [down])			
Time Δt (s)	0.05	0.15	
Position from the start $\vec{d}$ (m [down from start])			

Procedure

1. Use Table 2.5 as a starting point to design a table for your results.
2. Clamp the recording timer in a vertical position about 2.0 m above the floor as shown in Figure 2.24. Place a cushion directly beneath the timer.

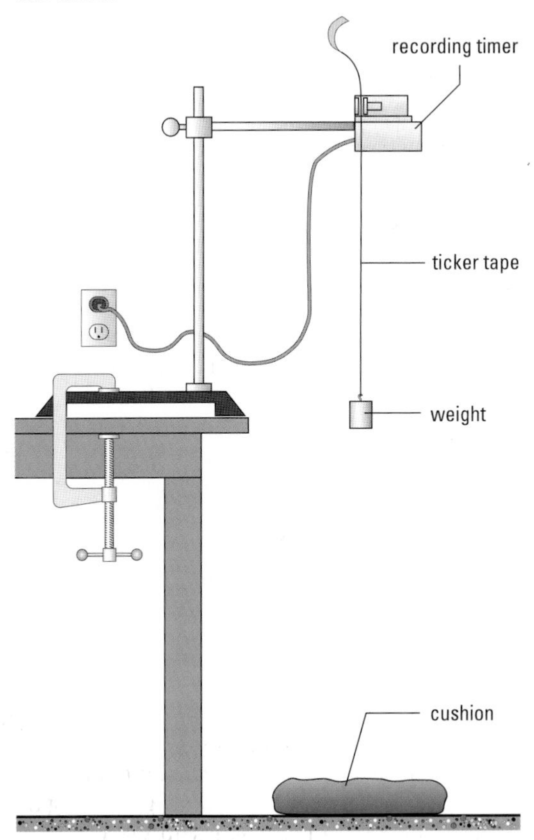

FIGURE 2.24 Measuring the motion of an object in free fall

3. Using masking tape, attach a 200-g mass to the end of a 2.0-m length of recording tape.
4. Thread the recording tape through the timer and hold the upper end vertical to minimize friction between the timer and the tape.
5. Start the timer, then release the 200-g mass.
6. Analyze the tape by marking the starting dot $t = 0$ and dividing the tape into equal time intervals, as shown in Figure 2.25. If the period of the timer is 1/60 s, each 6-dot interval will be 0.10 s. If the period of your timer is not 1/60 s, your teacher will explain how you can analyze the tape.

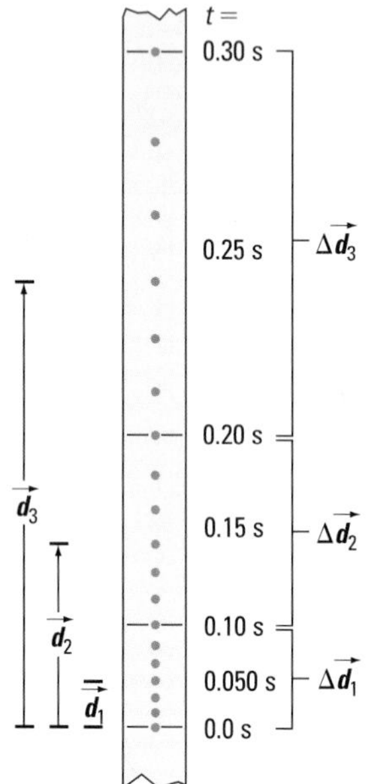

FIGURE 2.25 Analyzing free-fall motion using a recording tape

7. Measure and record the displacements ($\Delta\vec{d}_1$, $\Delta\vec{d}_2$, $\Delta\vec{d}_3$, etc.) corresponding to each 6-dot interval in your table.
8. Calculate and record the average velocity for each 6-dot interval.
9. Plot a graph of velocity against time using the average velocities of the mass at half-time intervals (0.05 s, 0.15 s, etc.).
10. Calculate the slope of the velocity–time graph. This gives you the acceleration in cm/s^2. Convert the acceleration to m/s^2.
11. Measure and record the position from the start of the tape corresponding to each half-time interval (0.05 s, 0.15 s, etc.).
12. Plot a velocity–position graph using the velocities calculated in step 8.

Analyzing and Interpreting

1. Describe the shape of the velocity–time graph.
2. What relationship exists between the change in velocity and the elapsed time?
3. Calculate the slope of the graph in m/s^2. What is the acceleration?
4. Describe the shape of the velocity–position graph.

Concluding and Communicating

5. Is the change in velocity of an object in free fall directly proportional to the time from the start of the fall, or to the displacement? Discuss.

Extending

6. Design and carry out an experiment using a photogate, data logger, computer, and falling picket-fence to measure the acceleration due to gravity in your classroom. How close were your values to the accepted value? What were the sources of error in the experiment, and how did they affect the result? What precautions could you take to reduce these sources of error?

CHAPTER SUMMARY

Key Terms

acceleration due to gravity
collinear forces
force
free-body diagram
gravity
gravimeters
gravitational field intensity
law of universal gravitation
mass
newton
non-collinear forces
normal force
resultant force
unbalanced force
universal gravitational constant
weight

Key Equations

$F_G = \frac{Gm_1m_2}{\Delta d^2}$

$\vec{g} = \frac{\vec{v}_2 - \vec{v}_1}{\Delta t}$

$\Delta\vec{d} = \vec{v}_1\Delta t + \frac{1}{2}\vec{g}(\Delta t^2)$

$\vec{g} = \frac{\vec{F}_G}{m}$

Essential Understandings

- Free-body diagrams can be used to analyze the forces acting on an object.
- The net force is the vector sum of several forces acting on an object. The net force is also called the unbalanced or resultant force.
- The force of gravity is described by Newton's law of universal gravitation as a force of attraction between any two masses in the universe. This force is directly proportional to the product of the masses, and inversely proportional to the square of the distance between their centres.
- The gravitational field intensity is the ratio of the force of gravity to mass at a specific location.
- Gravitational field intensity varies with position, altitude, and the mass and radius of the celestial object on which it is measured.
- Without air friction, heavy and light objects fall with the same acceleration, called the acceleration due to gravity.
- Kinematics equations can be used to solve problems on free fall.
- Acceleration due to gravity and gravitational field intensity are equal.

Consolidate Your Understanding

1. Look back to your answer for the Checkpoint on page 55 What answer would you give now? Explain why each of the other answers is incorrect?

Describe, using an example, the velocity and acceleration of a rock thrown vertically upward on the surface of the Moon. Refer to the magnitudes and directions just after the rock leaves the astronaut's hand, at the top of its arc, and just before it is caught.

2. Create a concept map to be used as a study map of gravitational field intensity, acceleration due to gravity, and the force of gravity. Consult the Key Terms provided above and include as many as possible in your concept map. Include at least one of the Key Equations and an example problem solved using the GRASS strategy.

3. Write a paragraph describing the vector nature of force and the role of free-body diagrams, and vector addition of forces in the study of motion. Prepare an example free-body diagram for a car moving at constant velocity. Teach the technique involved in interpreting the vector diagram to a student who has not studied vectors. Summarize the strengths and weakness of your lesson.

CHAPTER 2 REVIEW

Understanding Concepts

1. Forces of 100 N [N] and 50 N [W] are exerted on an object. The direction of the resultant force on the object is
   a) [NW]
   b) [N 27° W]
   c) [N 63° W]
   d) [N 30° W]
   e) [N 60° W]

2. Which one of the free-body diagrams in Figure 2.26 shows the correct relationship between the force of gravity $\vec{F}_G$ and the elastic force $\vec{F}_e$ when a spring scale is being used to measure the force of gravity?

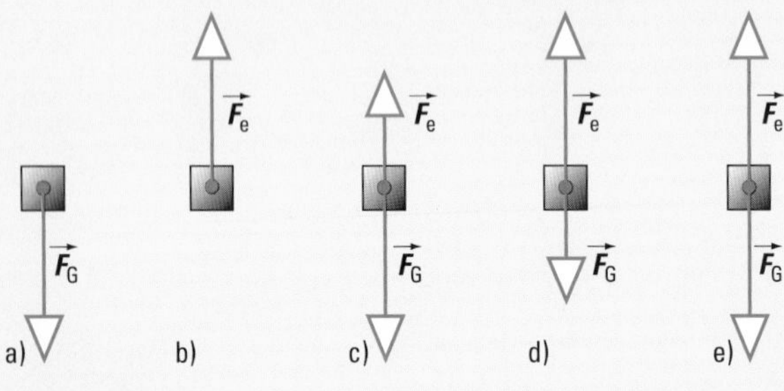

FIGURE 2.26

3. Three forces act at the same time on an object: 2.0 N [E]; 6.0 N [W]; 3.0 N [E]. What is the net force on the object?
   a) 11 N [E]
   b) 11 N [W]
   c) 7.0 N [E]
   d) 1.0 N [W]
   e) 1.0 N [E]

4. Vectors S, T, U, and V in Figure 2.27 represent forces of equal magnitude acting on a tiny sphere P as shown. Which of the single vectors best represents the unbalanced force acting on P?

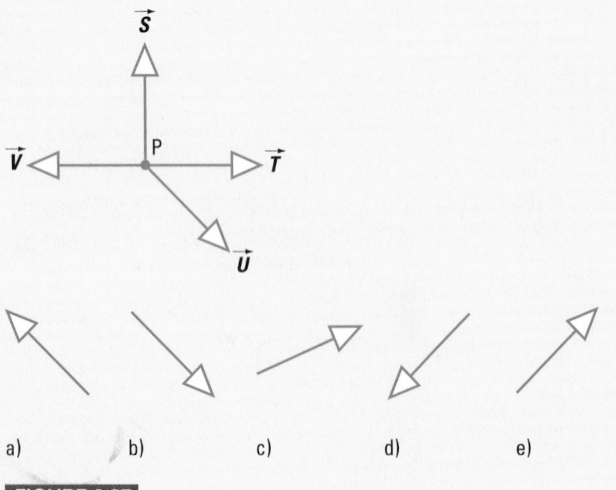

FIGURE 2.27

5. A brick placed on an equal-arm balance requires 5.0 kg to just balance it. When placed on a newton spring scale the brick has a reading of 48 N. The balance, set of masses, spring scale, and brick are moved to a planet where the gravitational field intensity is 2.0 times that on Earth. The new reading on the balance and spring scales will be
   a) balance 5.0 kg, spring scale 48 N
   b) balance 10 kg, spring scale 96 N
   c) balance 5.0 kg, spring scale 96 N
   d) balance 10 kg, spring scale 48 N
   e) balance 5.0 kg, spring scale 24 N

6. Why do scientists use numbers and direction to describe forces rather than adjectives such as "large," "insignificant," etc.?

7. Explain the purpose of drawing free-body diagrams.

8. You are sitting on a chair. Predict what would happen if there was no normal force exerted on you.

9. A spring scale is sometimes used to weigh things and sometimes to pull objects horizontally along a surface. Before using a spring scale, its scale must be set to zero. How would you zero the scale in each of the aforementioned cases?

10. With the aid of a diagram, explain the meaning of the term net force acting on an object.

11. A baseball is dropped from the top of a two-storey building and strikes the ground with a velocity $\vec{v}_2$. At the same time as the ball is dropped, a stone is projected upward with a velocity $\vec{v}_1$. If the magnitudes of the velocities of the two objects are equal, will the stone and ball meet halfway up the building, above halfway up, or below halfway up. Explain.

12. A red ball is thrown vertically downward from a cliff with a velocity $\vec{v}_{red}$. A short time later, a blue ball is thrown downward from the same cliff with a velocity $\vec{v}_{blue}$. If the magnitude of $\vec{v}_{blue} > \vec{v}_{red}$, can both reach the ground at the same time? Explain.

13. A stunt man jumps off the top of a building 99.4 m high. He lands on an airbag with a speed of 39 m/s. If he did the same jump in a vacuum, how much faster would he be travelling when he hit the airbag? Explain in words how to solve this problem.

14. A diver on a high-diving board 3.0 m above the water springs upward with a velocity of 1.6 m/s [up].
    a) With what velocity does she hit the water?
    b) What is the highest point above the water she reaches?
    c) If she walked off the diving board rather than springing up would she be travelling faster, slower, or at the same speed when she hits the water?

15. Two men are bouncing straight up and down on a trampoline. The first bounces twice as high as the second.
   a) Assuming no air resistance, find the ratio of the flight times for them between bounces.
   b) If one has half the mass of the other, will the flight times change? Discuss.

16. A cave explorer drops a pebble into a cavern to find how far down it is to the water. The stone is heard hitting the water 1.8 s after release. If the speed of sound in the air in the cave is 345 m/s, how deep is the cavern?

17. A clay roof tile falls from the top of an office building. It takes 1.5 s to fall from the roof to a window ledge below. The window has a vertical length of 1.5 m. How far above the top of the window is the roof?

18. What is the significance of the term universal in Newton's law of universal gravitation?

19. When solving problems about objects in free fall, why can we replace the $\vec{a}$ term in a kinematics equation with $\vec{g}$?

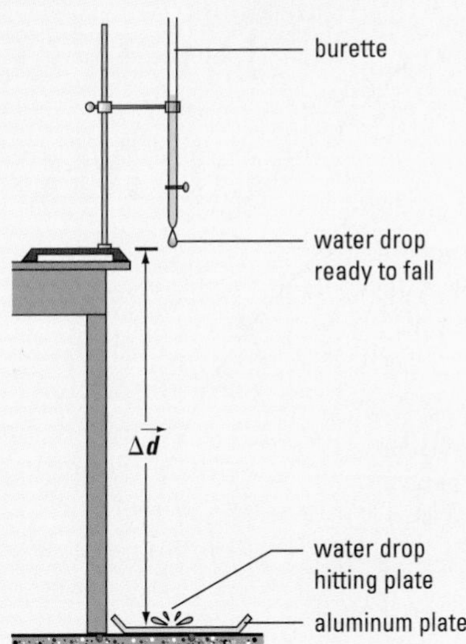

FIGURE 2.28 Apparatus for measuring the acceleration due to gravity

Applying Inquiry/ Communication Skills

20. The numbers on a radio dial are not equally spaced. The numerical divisions on a spring scale are equally spaced. Why?

21. Can two force vectors of different sizes be added to give a net force of zero? Explain.

22. Design a pamphlet that could be used at a science museum to explain to visitors whether an astronaut is weightless when in orbit.

23. Figure 2.28 shows apparatus for measuring the acceleration due to gravity using a burette and an aluminum plate. The burette is filled with water. The tap is slowly opened and adjusted until one drop leaves the burette just as the preceding drop hits the plate. The period between the drops, and the position of the upper drop above the plate, are measured.
   a) Describe how the data can be used to measure g.
   b) Describe the sources of error in this experiment.
   c) Perform the experiment if you have time.

24. Describe a procedure for measuring the height of the CN Tower in Toronto using only a stopwatch and an apple. Will your value for $\vec{g}$ be low or high? Why?

25. Design and perform an experiment with a partner to determine your reaction times. Use only a metre-stick, your knowledge of $\vec{g}$, and the equation $\Delta\vec{d} = \frac{1}{2}\vec{g}\Delta t^2$. In your report, summarize how you controlled all the variables in the experiment.

26. The sum of all the forces acting on a stationary object is zero. Design an experiment using three horizontal newton spring scales and a large force board to verify this for non-collinear forces.

27. Design and perform an experiment using a Polaroid camera, stroboscope light, and accessories to measure the acceleration due to gravity. Include in your report a summary of the sources of error.

28. Design and perform an experiment, using a computer as a timing device, to determine the acceleration due to gravity. Submit a report of your results.

Making Connections

29. Research to find out how forces are used in health sciences such as physiotherapy and sports medicine.

30. Visit a local fitness gymnasium. Find out how athletes use the force of gravity and the force in an elastic spring to improve their fitness. Write a short report.

31. List some occupations that might require a knowledge of how objects accelerate due to gravity.

32. Pilots in high-speed planes are subject to "g forces." Healthy people can withstand up to 3 or 4 "g"s, but after that the blood will pool in the lower half of the body and does not reach the brain, causing the pilot to lose consciousness. Do some research to find out how Dr. Wilbur Franks from Toronto found a solution to this problem. What connection does this problem have to human survival during space flight?

CHAPTER 3

Newton's Laws of Motion

SPECIFIC EXPECTATIONS

By the end of this chapter, you will be able to:

- state Newton's laws, and apply them to explain the motion of objects in a variety of contexts (3.2, 3.3, 3.4, 3.5)
- analyze in quantitative terms, using Newton's laws, the relationships among the net force acting on an object, its mass, and its acceleration (3.1)
- carry out experiments to verify Newton's second law of motion (3.3)
- analyze the motion of objects, using vector diagrams, free-body diagrams, uniform acceleration equations, and Newton's laws of motion (3.5)
- explain how the contributions of Galileo and Newton revolutionized the scientific thinking of their time and provided the foundation for understanding the relationship between motion and force (3.2)

Cars and people, like all objects in the universe, obey Newton's basic laws of motion. When a moving car collides with a large stationary object, such as a wall, the car is stopped very quickly. The driver inside the car, however, continues to move forward until he or she encounters an immovable object such as the steering wheel, dashboard, or windshield. When a stationary car is struck from behind, the car seat moves quickly forward, taking the lower part of the driver's body with it. But the head stays in the same place until it is yanked forward by the neck, causing whiplash.

Car designers are very aware of the laws of motion when they design cars for better safety. That is why they install seatbelts and/or airbags to stop the forward motion of the driver, rather than have the dashboard and windshield do the job. It is also why they install headrests to prevent whiplash by supporting the head. If the car is jolted forward, the head will move forward at the same speed as the rest of the body.

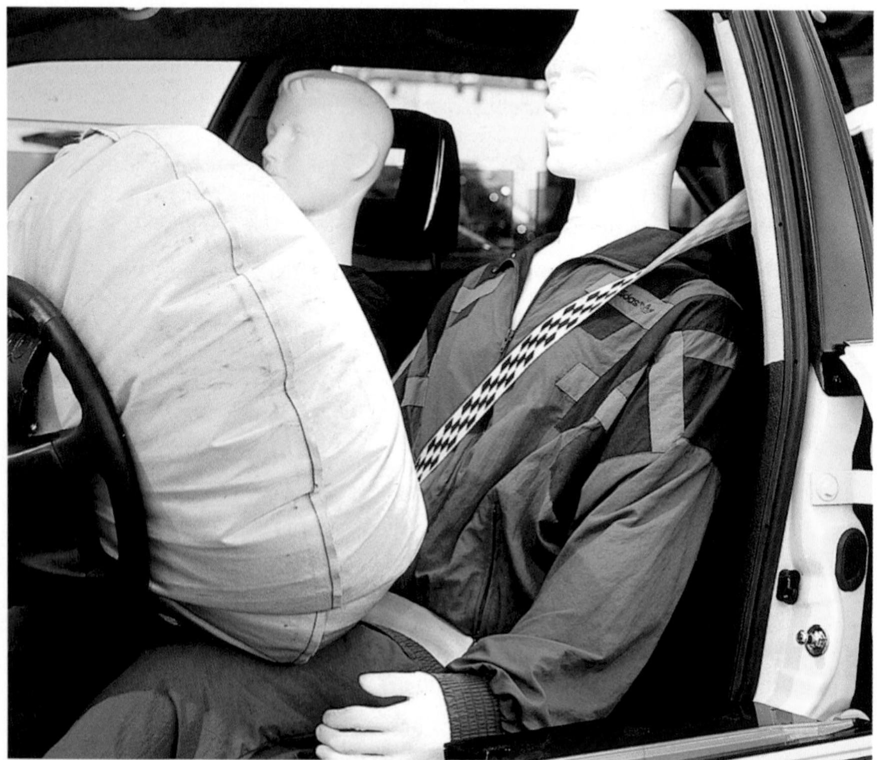

FIGURE 3.1 Accident researchers use dummies to investigate the results of high-speed crashes.

In this chapter, you will investigate Newton's laws of motion. By the time you complete this chapter you will realize that these three laws govern everything from car crashes to throwing a baseball. If you don't understand these laws, you will not be able to understand how the world works.

How much force does it take to start something moving? How much force does it take to keep something moving or even stop something once it has begun to move? What are the laws of motion and how do these laws affect our everyday lives?

CHECKPOINT

Student A with a mass of 90 kg and student B with a mass of 60 kg stand facing each other on in-line skates and toe to toe. Student A suddenly pushes student B causing both to move. In this situation

a) neither student exerts a force on the other

b) student A exerts a force on student B, but B does not exert a force on A

c) each student exerts a force on the other but B exerts the larger force

d) each student exerts a force on the other but A exerts the larger force

e) each student exerts the same amount of force on the other

Explain your answer.

Discovering Physics

Determining Mass in Outer Space

Is there a way to determine the mass of an object out in space where the force of gravity is negligible? Try this to find out. You will need a small can of soup (284 mL), a 200 g mass, a 500-g mass, a stopwatch, some masking tape, and a metre-stick.

1. Measure a displacement of 40 cm along the surface of the lab bench and mark it with two parallel strips of masking tape as shown in Figure 3.2.
2. Rest the 200-g mass on the desk next to one of the markers. The desk will support the mass against the force of gravity.
3. Grasp the mass firmly, keep your arm straight, and accelerate the mass back and forth, parallel to your body, as fast as you can between the marks. Make sure the desk continues to support the mass. ***Caution: Do not release the mass.***
4. Have a partner measure how long it takes you to do 20 complete cycles. Record this time interval.
5. Repeat the experiment using the 500-g mass and, finally the can of soup.

- How did the time intervals compare for the two standard masses and the can of soup?
- How can you use the times to estimate the mass of the can of soup?
- What did you estimate the mass of the can of soup to be?
- Your teacher will tell you the mass of the can of soup after you have given your estimate. How close to the actual value were you?
- Can this method be used to measure mass far out in space? If so how? What additional equipment would you need?
- Which mass was the hardest to accelerate from rest?
- Which mass was the hardest to stop moving?
- Which mass were you able to give the greatest acceleration?
- Which mass pushed back the hardest on your hand and arm?

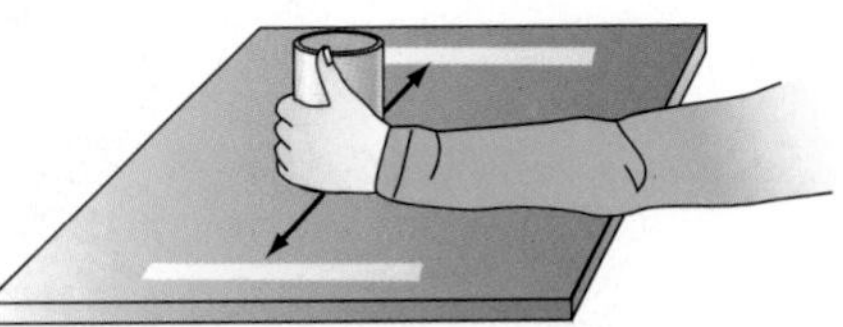

FIGURE 3.2 Estimating an unknown mass

3.1 Horizontal Motion and Friction

FIGURE 3.3 Sweeping a curling stone increases the distance it will travel before stopping. Why?

Key Understandings

When you have completed this section, you will be able to:

- distinguish between Aristotle's and Galileo's explanation of horizontal motion
- define friction and distinguish between limiting static friction and kinetic friction
- solve problems involving the coefficients of friction, the force of friction, and the normal force

The branch of mechanics that describes the motion of an object without considering the cause is called **kinematics**. Displacement, velocity, and acceleration are some quantities used in kinematics. When we investigate the reasons why objects move as they do, we are studying **dynamics**. For example, why does sweeping enable curling stones to slide further (Figure 3.3)? Why do cars skid less on dry pavement than on wet asphalt?

Theories of Motion

Aristotle thought that all matter on and near Earth was a mixture of four elements: earth, water, air, and fire. Each element had its natural place. Fire had the highest place, then air, then water, and finally earth. Each element moved to seek its natural place. Rain fell from the region of air, smoke rose to the region of fire, water in Earth's crust rose to the surface and emerged as springs, and apples fell from trees. Objects exhibited natural motion if they moved to seek their natural place.

Aristotle believed that objects that moved horizontally were in **forced motion** because a force was needed to move the objects. For example, dragging heavy logs and boats horizontally requires a force. If the force is removed, the objects soon stop. Aristotle's theory of forced motion seems to agree with many of our common experiences. Bicycles and cars require a force to keep them moving horizontally. If you stop pedalling a bicycle on a level path, it soon comes to rest. If a car runs out of gas, it quickly coasts to a stop.

Galileo, on the other hand, proposed that a force is only necessary to keep an object in motion because another force is opposing the motion. He named this opposing force, friction. He believed that any time we move or try to move an object we encounter friction. A log is difficult to drag sideways, not because it is in forced motion, but because friction is present. Without friction, an object moving horizontally at constant speed should continue at the same speed forever.

INFOBIT

Aristotle's ideas were based entirely on logic, but Galileo's findings were built and refined on the results of scientific experiments. Galileo ushered in the era of scientific experiment. He challenged the use of pure intellect and logic without experimental support.

Kinds of Friction

Friction is the force that opposes motion whenever one surface moves or tends to move with reference to another. There are different kinds of friction. **Sliding friction** is the force that makes it difficult to slide one surface past another. It is sliding friction that enables us to turn corners. **Rolling friction** is the force that opposes the rolling motion of one surface over another, for example, a train wheel rolling on a steel rail. **Fluid friction** is the force that resists the motion of an object through a fluid. Boats encounter fluid friction as they move through water (Figure 3.4), as do airplanes moving through air.

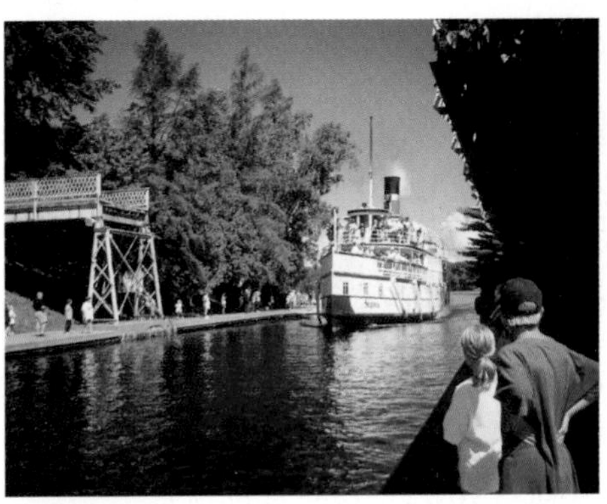

FIGURE 3.4 Boats encounter fluid friction as they move through water.

Force is needed to counteract friction and start an object moving. For example, a horizontal force greater than the force of friction must be applied to a block of wood lying on the table before the block will move. When the force applied increases from zero to the value needed to start the motion, the force of friction opposing the motion must also increase. Otherwise the object will begin to move. The maximum value of the force of friction just before the object starts to move is known as **limiting static friction**. A force is also needed to keep an object on a rough surface moving at constant speed. A block moving at constant speed in a straight line has balanced forces acting on it. The force of friction that opposes the motion of objects once they are moving is called **kinetic friction**.

The frictional forces between the tires on an automobile and the road surface are affected by the road surface conditions and the tire tread design. For example, a ribbed tire increases the sideways friction and helps steer the car, whereas a turf-tread tire provides more traction (Figure 3.5).

FIGURE 3.5 Tire treads

Tire treads are designed for specific purposes. For example, drag racers use tires, called "slicks," that have no tread at all. The frictional force between the tire and the road does not depend on how much of the tire is in contact with the pavement. This means a wide slick tire provides no more friction for drag racers than a narrower one. But, during drag racing the heat is enough to sometimes melt the tire surface. This melting reduces friction because the tire is riding on a layer of liquid rubber. For this reason, drag racers often use wider slicks on the rear wheels because their wider surface spreads the heat, and there is therefore less chance of them melting.

Tires on passenger vehicles have a raised tread. This increases the traction on wet or snowy roads because the grooves in the tire provide places for water and snow to collect without coming between the tire surface and the road. If you are moving at a high speed on a wet road and try to use your brakes to stop the car, the car might act like an aquaplane. That is, the tires slide along on the water's surface without touching the pavement. Some tires are designed to minimize aquaplaning by having grooves in the tire tread that channel the water outward away from the tire.

As tires wear out, the grooves and channels on the tread become smaller and less able to remove water or snow away from the tire. A set of new tires with a tread design appropriately matched to the vehicle is a wise investment.

INFOBIT

Tires that are warm stick to a racing track better than cooler tires. Drag race car drivers often drive on the tires just before their race in order to warm them up for increased traction and, hence, increased forward acceleration.

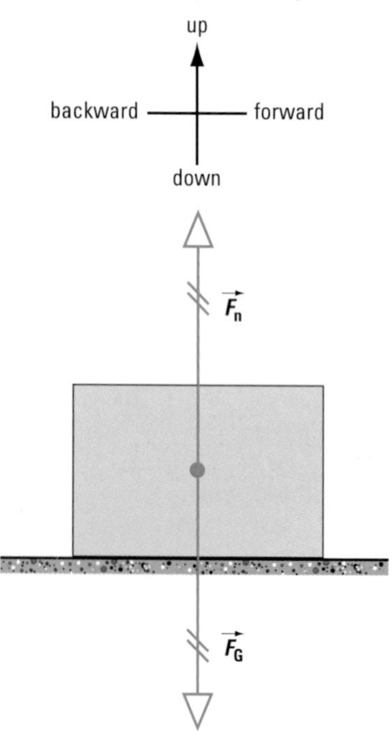

FIGURE 3.6 Free-body diagram for a stationary block of mass ***m*** on a horizontal surface

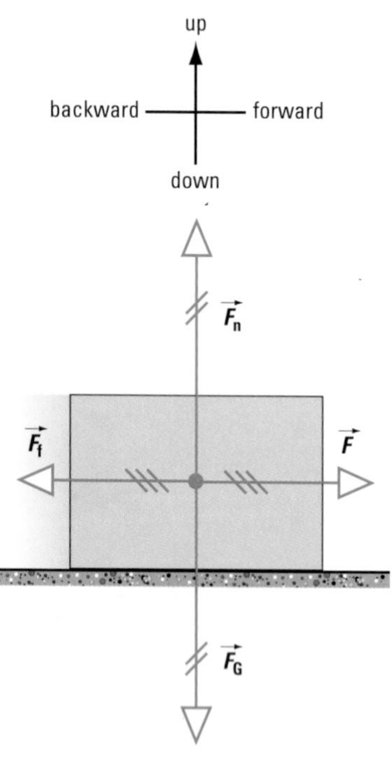

FIGURE 3.7 Free-body diagram for a block of mass ***m*** moving at a constant velocity on a rough level surface

Normal Force

For sliding friction, both limiting static friction and kinetic friction are directly proportional to the size of the force pushing the surfaces together. Figure 3.6 shows a free-body diagram for a stationary block resting on a horizontal surface. The force of gravity $\vec{F}_G$ acting down on the block tends to pull it into the surface. The surface also exerts a force upward on the block. This force is called the **normal force** $\vec{F}_n$ because it is exerted perpendicular to the surfaces in contact. On a level surface, the force of gravity is equal in size but opposite in direction to the normal force provided no other vertical forces act on the block. When the force of gravity doubles, the normal force doubles, and the force of friction between the surfaces doubles. The normal force is smaller than the force of gravity when the block is resting on a sloping surface. Only the component of the force of gravity acting perpendicular to the surface pushes the surfaces together.

Coefficients of Friction

We can find the force of kinetic friction on an object by measuring the force that must be applied to keep an object moving at constant velocity. Figure 3.7 shows the free-body diagram for this situation. Note that when the object is moving at constant velocity, the force of friction $\vec{F}_f$ is equal in size to the applied force $\vec{F}$. The setup shown in Figure 3.8 can be used to find the relationship between the normal force and the force of kinetic friction. Different loads are placed on the block and a newton spring scale is used to drag the block along the horizontal surface at constant velocity.

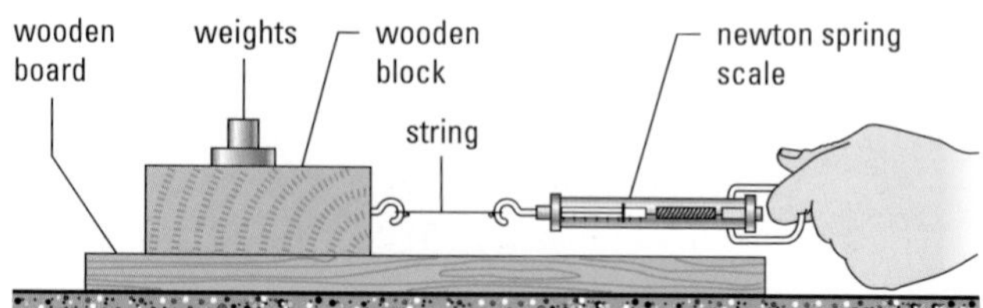

FIGURE 3.8 Measuring the force of friction between a wooden block and a wooden board

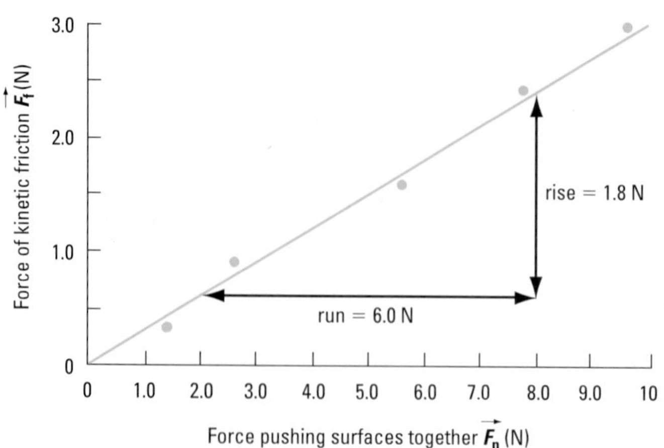

FIGURE 3.9 Finding the coefficient of kinetic friction of wood sliding on wood

A graph of kinetic friction against the force pushing the two wooden surfaces together is shown in Figure 3.9. Note that the force of kinetic friction is directly proportional to the normal force. If the force of gravity doubles, the normal force doubles and the force of kinetic friction doubles. This means that for any two surfaces the ratio of the size of the force of kinetic friction to the size of the normal force is a constant. This constant is called the **coefficient of kinetic friction**. The equation relating the magnitude of the force of friction $\vec{F}_f$, the magnitude of the normal force $\vec{F}_n$, and the coefficient of kinetic friction μ_k is

$$\mu_k = \frac{F_f}{F_n}$$

The coefficient of kinetic friction for the wooden surfaces can be found from Figure 3.9 by calculating the slope of the line.

The formula for slope is

$$\text{Slope} = \frac{\text{rise}}{\text{run}} = \frac{2.4\text{ N} - 0.6\text{ N}}{8.0\text{ N} - 2.0\text{ N}} = \frac{1.8\text{ N}}{6.0\text{ N}} = 0.30$$

The coefficient of kinetic friction does not have units because the units of the rise and the run are the same and divide out. The coefficient is a scalar quantity since it does not have a direction.

The **coefficient of static friction**, μ_s, is the magnitude of the maximum force needed to start an object moving, divided by the magnitude of the normal force.

$$\mu_s = \frac{F_f}{F_n}$$

In most cases, the value of limiting static friction is larger than kinetic friction. As a result, the coefficient of static friction is usually greater than the coefficient of kinetic friction.

INFOBIT

Olympic cyclists now wear slipperier-than-skin suits with seams sewn out of the airflow to reduce friction and improve race times by as much as three seconds.

Investigation

Refer to page 125, Investigation 1

WEBLINK

Some kitchenware is "non-stick." Research the history of how non-stick ware came about and write a short paragraph. Begin your research at **www.pearsoned.ca/physics11**

Discovering Physics *A Brush with Static Friction*

Place a chalk brush with its erasing surface face down on a book cover. Gently tip the book until the brush begins to slide down the book cover. Now, using a second chalk brush, hold the two chalk brushes horizontally with their erasing faces in contact. With your hand holding only the bottom brush, gently tip the two-brush system until the top brush slides along the bottom one (Figure 3.10). In which experiment is the angle at which motion starts greater? In which experiment is the coefficient of static friction greater? Why?

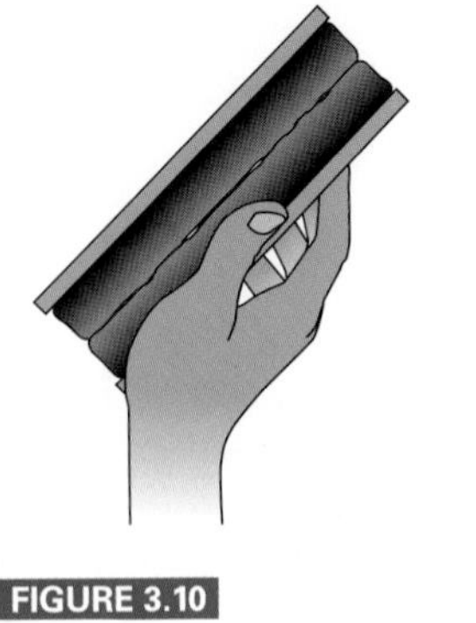

FIGURE 3.10

EXAMPLE 1 NUMERICAL

A skier and her skis have a total weight of 545 N. If it takes a horizontal force of 38 N to start moving on wet snow on level ground, calculate the coefficient of static friction for the skis on wet snow.

Given

$\vec{F}_G = 545$ [down]

$\vec{F} = 38$ N [forward]

Required

μ_s

Analysis

- On the level, the force of gravity down is equal to the normal force up.
- The maximum force needed to start the skier moving forward is equal to the force of static friction opposing the motion.
- Substitute the values for the normal force and the force of static friction into the equation $\mu_s = \dfrac{F_f}{F_n}$ and solve for the coefficient of static friction.

Solution

$$\mu_s = \frac{F_f}{F_n}$$

$$= \frac{38\text{ N}}{545\text{ N}}$$

$$= 0.070$$

Statement

The coefficient of static friction for the skis on wet snow is 0.070.

PRACTICE PROBLEMS

(Refer to Table 3.1)

1. A car of weight 1500 N has its brakes locked. Calculate the force needed to begin to drag the car on dry asphalt. How will the force needed to slide it along the asphalt compare with the force needed to start it sliding? Why?
2. An 80-kg skier is using waxed hickory skis on wet snow. Calculate the force of friction on the skis as the skier glides along on the level.

TABLE 3.1 Typical Values of some Coefficients of Friction

Material	Coefficient of Friction	
	Static μ_s	Kinetic μ_k
Copper on copper	1.6	1.0
Steel on greased steel	0.15	0.09
Steel on dry steel	0.41	0.38
Oak on oak	0.5	0.3
Rubber tire on dry asphalt	1.2	0.8
Rubber tire on wet asphalt	0.6	0.5
Rubber tire on dry concrete	1.0	0.7
Rubber tire on wet concrete	0.7	0.5
Rubber tire on ice	0.006	0.005
Teflon on Teflon	0.04	0.04
Waxed hickory skis on dry snow	0.06	0.04
Waxed hickory skis on wet snow	0.20	0.14

Table 3.1 shows the coefficients of friction between pairs of materials. Note that the coefficient of static friction for copper on copper is 1.6; this is greater than one. In this case, it takes a force greater than the normal force (or the force of gravity) to start a copper block moving along another copper block. From Table 3.1, how does the force needed to keep the copper block moving at constant velocity compare with the normal force?

Friction exists in mammalian joints like the human hip joint (Figure 3.11). How can there be enough friction to keep you from falling down, but not so much friction that you cannot move around? The joints are lubricated with synovial fluid which is squeezed between the cartilage lining the joints when they move. In a healthy hip joint, this synovial fluid reduces the coefficient of static friction to about 0.003. That's less than for a rubber tire sliding on ice! When the joint is stationary, this lubricant is absorbed back into the cartilage so that friction in the joint is increased. This helps you to stand still without falling.

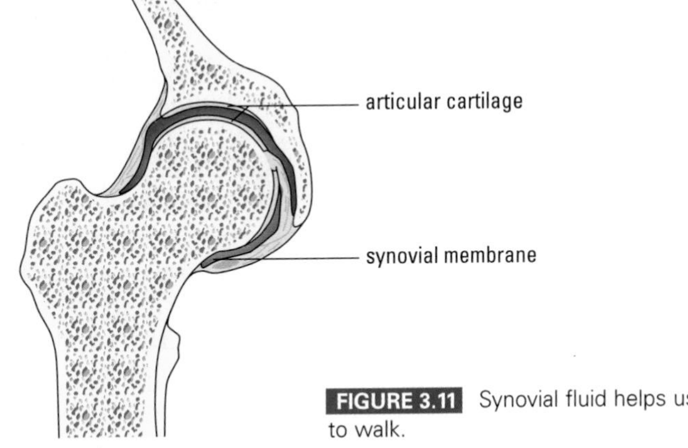

FIGURE 3.11 Synovial fluid helps us to walk.

EXAMPLE 2 NUMERICAL

A lift truck with rubber tires has a mass of 1640 kg. What is the force of kinetic friction when the lift truck skids on wet concrete with all four wheels locked? ($\vec{g}$ = 9.80 N/kg [down])

Given

m = 1640 kg

$\vec{g}$ = 9.80 N/kg [down]

Required

$\vec{F}_f$ for wet concrete

Analysis

- Use Table 3.1 to find μ_k for rubber tires on wet concrete.
- Find the weight of the lift truck using $\vec{F}_G = m\vec{g}$
- Since the lift truck is on the level, this weight is equal in size to the normal force.
- Use the equation $\mu_k = \frac{F_f}{F_n}$ to find the force of kinetic friction.

Solution

$\vec{F}_g = m\vec{g}$

$= 1640 \text{ kg} \times 9.80 \text{ N/kg [down]}$

$= 1.61 \times 10^4 \text{ N [down]}$

therefore

$\vec{F}_n = 1.61 \times 10^4 \text{ N [up]}$

$F_f = \mu_k F_n$

$= 0.5 \times 1.61 \times 10^4 \text{ N}$

$= 8 \times 10^3 \text{ N}$

Statement

The force of kinetic friction of the rubber on wet concrete is 8×10^3 N [opposite to the direction of motion].

HINT

When the term "rough" is used in a problem, it means that friction exists between the surfaces involved. When a problem wants you to ignore friction, the word "smooth" is used.

PRACTICE PROBLEMS

1. A force of gravity of 20 N [down] acts on a book at rest on a rough level table. A horizontal force of 12 N is needed to just start the book moving across the table.
   a) Calculate the coefficient of static friction.
   b) If a second identical book is placed on top of the original book at rest, what horizontal force would be needed to just start the books sliding?
2. A 1000-kg crate is dragged across a rough level floor. A force of 450 N is needed to drag the crate at constant speed. Calculate the coefficient of kinetic friction between the crate and the floor.

Designing Aerodynamic Vehicles

Vast amounts of fossil fuel are used every year to overcome the force of air friction on cars. An average car travelling at 90 km/h uses about 50% of its power just to overcome air drag. The goal of aerodynamic design is to allow the air to flow smoothly over and around the car (Figure 3.13). Sharp corners and gaps force the air to separate from the vehicle's surface forming turbulent eddies. These eddies trap more of the airstream, increasing the drag on the car. At the rear of the car, the turbulence causes a low pressure region that tends to slow the car even more. Can you explain why?

The drag on a car depends on its shape, speed, size, and the density of the air. The drag coefficient is a measure of the effect of the object's shape as it moves through the air. The larger the drag coefficient, the greater the drag. The greater the air pressure, the larger the drag. The faster the speed of the air with reference to the car, the larger the drag. In fact, if the speed of the car doubles, the drag force quadruples, since the drag force varies as the square of the speed. The larger the frontal area, the larger the drag force. A car with twice the frontal area experiences twice the drag force, other features being equal.

The blunt rear end on many cars is designed to reduce air drag. It causes the air to break cleanly from the car and curl around, creating a region of moderate low pressure rather than a very low pressure region. Another way to improve a car's rear airflow is with a spoiler (Figure 3.12). This is a protrusion, jutting up on the rear deck, that slows the air and builds up a high pressure ahead of it. This high pressure decreases lift, reduces drag, and helps hold the car down on the road.

The underside of the car cannot be ignored in the attempt to reduce drag. Car makers attempt to close and smooth the underside without adding additional weight to the car. Surface protrusions like bumpers, windshield wipers, licence plates, door handles, and mud flaps also add drag. Door handles are easy to recess, but for other features the solutions are more difficult to achieve. How has the side mirror in Figure 3.14 been designed to minimize drag?

FIGURE 3.12 This air spoiler decreases lift, increases traction, and reduces drag.

FIGURE 3.13 Computers control temperature, solar heat load, and humidity in a test chamber. Winds of up to 180 km/h can be generated in the chamber to study aerodynamic design.

FIGURE 3.14 The mount of this mirror slopes gently out from the car surface and the mirror is streamlined to conform to the airflow.

Tire Safety

Decision-Making Skills

- Defining the Issue
- Developing Assessment Criteria
- Researching the Issue
- Analyzing Data and Information
- Proposing a Course of Action
- Justifying the Course of Action
- Evaluating the Decision

BACKGROUND INFORMATION

During the summer of 1999, a series of traffic accidents had investigators puzzled. The accidents occurred mainly in the hot climates of the southern United States. What caused these accidents?

The accidents seemed to occur only with one particular vehicle, a popular brand of SUV. Then it was pointed out that the SUV used only one brand of tires. On further investigation, it seemed that the accidents were caused by the tire treads separating from the rest of the tire. The US Government found that these tires had been involved in 193 crashes involving 46 deaths since 1995. Soon after this was reported in the media, there was a voluntary recall of 6.5 million tires, despite the company's report that it found no defects in the tires' production. It was later reported that tests had been conducted that showed a possible link between tire inflation pressure and vehicle roll-over.

Class-action lawsuits are being filed in court against the SUV manufacturers and the tire company. Investigators are trying to determine the reasons for the tread separation. Consumer groups are demanding answers.

Analyzing the Issue

1. Research the factors that affect the manufacture of tires for road travel and the safety-testing process for tires, from the manufacturer's and consumer's points of view.
2. Analyze your research and consider what other factors might influence opinions on tire safety. In a chart, list those factors and how they have an impact on people's opinions.
3. In your opinion, was the tire recall necessary? Propose an alternate response that the tire maker could have had in this situation. Which response do you feel would be more effective? Why?
4. Based on this scenario, work in groups to prepare infomercials. Each group's infomercial should educate the public about the group's new brand of tire. In your presentation, include information on how technological design is based on scientific principles as well as creative marketing strategies.
5. When the presentations are completed, develop criteria for assessing each group's product. Decide as a class which brand will be the best product and discuss the reasons for your decision.

Section 3.1 Review

Understanding Concepts

1. a) Use Aristotle's theory of forced motion to explain the force needed to slide a refrigerator horizontally.

   b) How would Galileo explain the force needed to slide the refrigerator?

2. In your own words

   a) Define friction.

   b) Describe the three kinds of friction.

   c) Distinguish between limiting static friction and kinetic friction.

3. With the tank full of gasoline, a motorcycle and its rider have a weight of 2350 N. Calculate the force of kinetic friction between the rubber tires and dry concrete when the motorcycle skids with both wheels locked. (Refer to Table 3.1.)

4. A force of 31 N pulls an 8.0-kg steel slider at constant speed along a horizontal steel rail. What is the coefficient of kinetic friction of steel on steel? ($\vec{g}$ = 9.8 N/kg [down])

5. Calculate the difference in the force of static friction for waxed hickory skis on wet and dry snow if the skis weigh 15 N.

Applying Inquiry/ Communication Skills

6. A cyclist knows the total mass of herself and her bicycle. She also knows how far she can coast when slowing down from a given speed. How could she use this information to determine the average resistance opposing her motion?

Making Connections

7. During the 2000 Sidney Olympics, some swimmers were wearing special swimsuits that were designed to reduce friction as the swimmers moved through the water. Compare the arguments that people might make to defend or oppose the standardizing of athletic equipment in the interests of fair play.

3.2 Newton's First Law of Motion

Key Understandings

When you have completed this section, you will be able to:

- describe Galileo's thought experiment
- describe and give examples of inertia
- state and apply Newton's first law in everyday situations

All mechanical systems can be explained by Newton's three laws. If you don't know these laws, the way things work will remain a mystery to you. What is Newton's first law? How can it be used for ordinary events, like getting the ketchup out of its bottle? When riding in a car, why do we need to wear seat belts and to position headrests carefully?

Galileo's Thought Experiment

Galileo claimed that a force is needed to keep an object moving on a level surface because the force of friction opposes the motion. Without friction, an

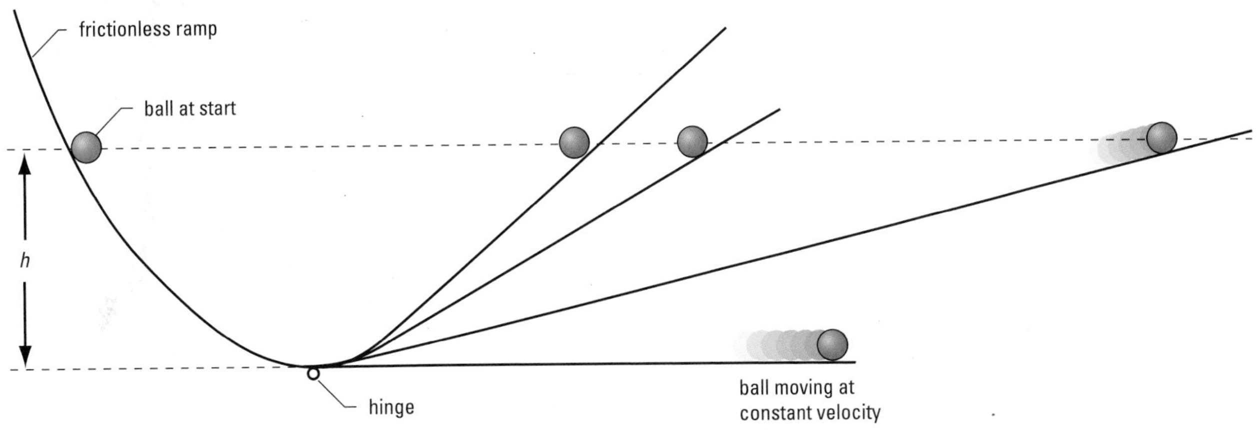

FIGURE 3.15 Galileo's thought experiment

object would keep moving forever. He proposed the following thought experiment to support his claim:

Suppose a ball is rolled down a perfectly frictionless ramp from a height h as shown in Figure 3.15. Without friction, the ball will reach a height h on the ramp on the other side. Suppose that the second ramp is very long and hinged at the bottom. As the slope of the ramp is decreased, the ball moves farther and farther along the ramp to reach the height h. Eventually when the slope of the ramp becomes zero, the ball will continue moving horizontally at constant velocity forever. On a frictionless level surface, there is no push forward, or friction backward, to change the velocity. Thus, the net or unbalanced force on the ball is zero. Contrary to Aristotle's claim, an object moving with constant velocity on the level does not require an unbalanced force. Instead, it has a tendency to keep moving at constant speed in a straight line forever.

Inertia

As a result of his experiments, Galileo claimed that a stationary object tends to stay at rest and a moving object tends to keep moving. **Inertia** is defined as that property of an object that resists changes in its state of rest or motion. Note that inertia is a resistance to a *change* in motion, whereas friction is a resistance to motion.

All objects possess inertia. For example, a stationary curling stone on ice requires a force to start it moving. But once moving, the curling stone is difficult to stop. You experience inertia when riding in a car. If the car accelerates forward, you feel as if your body is being pushed back. Your body resists the increase in speed. Headrests protect you against whiplash during the rapid forward accelerations that occur during a rear-end collision. If the car stops suddenly your body continues to move forward. Seat belts are designed to resist the tendency of your body to keep moving. Airbags provide a protective cushion in a head-on collision. When a car turns a corner, the car seat and door exert an inward force to counteract the tendency of your body to keep moving in a straight line.

Airbags work along with seat belts to bring the driver and passengers to a safe stop during a high-speed collision. When a car is involved in a

INFOBIT

The airbags in a car are designed to deploy in about 40 ms. That's about half the time it takes the average person to blink.

Discovering Physics — *Inertia and Circular Motion*

Many people believe that an object moving inside a circular barrier will continue to move in a circle even when the barrier is removed. What do you think?

Make a prediction and then use an old embroidery hoop or a piece of rubber tubing that can be formed into a circle to test your prediction (Figure 3.16 a). Place the hoop horizontally on a level surface. Roll a marble around inside the loop and observe its motion. Then open up the circle so that about 1/4 of the arc is missing as shown in Figure 3.17 b). Now roll the marble around the inside of the hoop. Observe its path when it leaves the ring.

- Why does the marble follow this path?
- How would this knowledge be useful to a discus thrower who spins in circles to gain speed before hurling the discus?

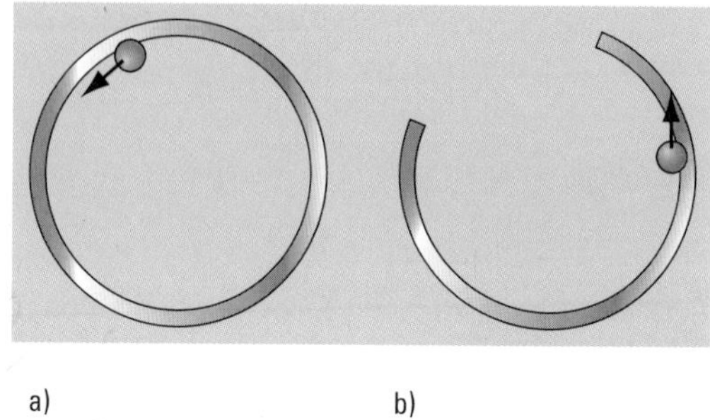

FIGURE 3.16

head-on collision, the car stops but the passengers continue to move forward until acted on by an external net force. This force could be provided by the steering wheel, the dashboard, the windshield, or an airbag. If the collision is violent enough, a sensor system ignites a cartridge of a chemical called sodium azide, which undergoes a rapid chemical reaction to produce nitrogen gas. The airbag inflates with the nitrogen gas and provides a cushion for passengers. This cushion spreads the force over the chest and head so that major injury does not occur. Engineers have designed the cars so that passengers are given a greater distance to travel before coming to a stop in a collision. There are three methods used to provide this extra distance to occupants of the car:

- The front end of the vehicle is designed to crumple so that the vehicle sustains damage while the passenger doesn't.
- The steering column telescopes to collapse and provide an additional 15–20 cm of distance for occupants to travel forward without hitting the steering column.
- The airbag is intentionally designed to leak after inflation so that the fully inflated bag can decrease in thickness from about 30 cm to about 10 cm.

On occasion, airbags have caused injuries. People who sit very close to the steering wheel or dashboard are at higher risk of injury caused by the violent expansion of the airbag. Children under 12 years of age are advised to be seatbelted in the back seat because in the front seat their heads would be in line with the body of the airbag and injury could result. Rear-facing car seats for infants are also a danger if placed in the front seat because the infant's head is too close to the airbag. For safety, vehicle's front seats should be adjusted as far back from the airbags as possible and adjustable steering wheels should be tilted downward so the bag inflates toward the chest and not the head.

INFOBIT

The chemical sodium azide, which reacts to form the nitrogen in airbags, looks like harmless table salt but is, in fact, a deadly poison. Fortunately, this poison reacts to form other substances when the airbag is deployed. Problems arise when cars are sent to the dump with undeployed airbags in them. Environmentalists advocate the simple solution of deploying the airbags of scrapped cars to stop sodium azide from getting into our environment.

Discovering Physics *Tricks with Inertia*

Here are some tricks you can try. They all rely on inertia.

FIGURE 3.17 Can you get the coin into the glass?

Coin in a glass tumbler

Set an empty glass on a level surface. Place a small stiff card over the opening of the glass. Position a small coin directly above the opening as shown in Figure 3.17.

Try to remove the cardboard and have the coin fall into the glass. Were you successful?

Chalk in a Bottle

Cut a flexible plastic hoop about 2 cm wide from an empty cylindrical plastic bottle. Set an empty soft drink bottle on a level surface and place the hoop vertically on the top lip. Very carefully position a small piece of chalk vertically directly above the opening as shown in Figure 3.18.

Try to remove the hoop and end up with the chalk in the bottle.

FIGURE 3.18 Can you get the chalk into the bottle?

Diminishing a Coin Stack

It's possible to use a thin ruler to knock out a coin from the bottom of a stack of coins resting on a horizontal surface. A stack of nickels and a thin ruler will work fine. It's important that the ruler be thinner than the type of coin used.

Slide the ruler quickly along the surface to hit the bottom coin (Figure 3.19). The coin from the bottom will go flying sideways but the stack will drop down. With practice, can you swing the ruler first to the left and then to the right in rapid succession to lower the stack quickly?

- Why doesn't the stack fall over?
- What would happen if you slid the ruler slowly rather than quickly?
- What would happen if you did not continue to move the ruler forward when you hit a coin?

FIGURE 3.19 Can you remove the bottom coin without toppling the stack?

Caution: Keep your eyes well above the coin stack.

Automobile manufacturers are beginning to offer "smart" airbag systems which can detect someone sitting too close to the bag (for example, a sleeping passenger slumped forward in the front seat). Some even have manual shut-off switches to be used at the discretion of the occupants of the car.

The inertia of an object depends on its mass; the greater the mass of the object the more inertia it has. A heavy child on a swing is more difficult to start moving, and to stop, than a light child. Thus, mass is a measure of the inertia of an object. Out in space, the force of gravity on an object is very small. The inertia of the object, however, is the same. This means that mass, rather than force of gravity, affects inertia. It is always more difficult to change the motion of a large mass than of a small mass, even out in space!

If you are trying to get ketchup out of its bottle, you might hold the bottle upside down and hit the bottom of the bottle. Those who are familiar with Newton's first law will realize that this action simply pushes the bottle down and the ketchup further up into the bottle. A more effective method involves the use of inertia. Turn the bottle upside down above the plate. Then move the bottle downward and stop the bottle suddenly. While the bottle stops moving, the ketchup will maintain its downward velocity and, in fact, accelerate after it leaves the bottle until acted on by an upward net force. What provides the net force that finally stops the falling ketchup?

Newton's First Law (Galileo's Principle of Inertia)

FIGURE 3.20

Newton was born in the year that Galileo died. Fifty years after Galileo challenged Aristotle's theory, Newton summarized Galileo's ideas describing the motion of both stationary and moving objects. **Newton's first law of motion** states:

Every object will continue in a state of rest or with constant speed in a straight line unless acted upon by an external unbalanced or net force.

According to this law, every object at rest tends to stay at rest. Every object in motion tends to keep moving in a straight line with constant speed. To change the speed or direction of motion (that is, to change the velocity) requires an external unbalanced force. Because Newton's first law was based on Galileo's findings, it is sometimes called Galileo's principle of inertia.

Anyone who has scored on a lay-up in basketball has used Newton's first law. While moving toward the basket, if you give the basketball a forward velocity with your hand, the ball will likely rebound at high speed from the backboard without going through the hoop. If you release the ball while you are moving toward the basket, it will keep moving forward until a net force (the backboard) acts on it (Figure 3.20). To score on the lay-up shot, an experienced player will take some speed off the ball by exerting a backwards force to reduce the velocity of the ball as it hits the backboard. This leads to a "softer" shot and increases the chance of scoring.

Truck drivers carrying heavy loads are very aware of Newton's first law. Imagine what would happen to a truck and load if the driver attempted to turn a corner too fast. Envisage the result if a truck carrying steel pipe was forced to stop too quickly. Use Newton's first law to explain why a barrier of thick steel usually separates the cab from the load.

Sometimes it is difficult to bring a car to a controlled stop in an emergency. If you jam on the brakes, the wheels will stop turning. The car begins to skid and turning the steering wheel has little effect in changing the direction of the car during the skid. Anti-lock braking systems (ABS) are designed to prevent locking and thus provide a more controlled stop of the vehicle. ABS automatically pumps the brakes at a rate of up to 18 times per second. This pumping action occurs whenever a sensor detects the start of wheel lock. ABS allows the wheels to roll instead of slide even when the driver maintains full brake pressure on the brake pedal. The rolling action helps to regain traction control (stability) and the stopping distance is generally reduced. More importantly, the danger of skidding is decreased.

Intelligent stability and handling systems (ISHS) are even more sophisticated. Most operate under a basic principle of monitoring and comparing the vehicle's movement with the steering direction. That is, if the driver is steering one way but the vehicle is about to head another, such as during a skid, the system automatically causes specific wheels to brake. This allows the driver to regain control and continue in the intended direction.

Section 3.2 Review

Understanding Concepts

1. What did Galileo's thought experiment illustrate?
2. Use Newton's first law to describe the motion of:
   a) dirt on a shovel when the shovel is moving horizontally and is suddenly stopped.
   b) a car that attempts to go around an icy curve too quickly.
   c) a child on a sled that is suddenly jerked forward.
3. a) How are mass and inertia related?
   b) Give some examples, other than those in the text, that illustrate the property of inertia for both a stationary and a moving object.
4. Use Newton's first law and the property of inertia to explain the following:
   a) If the sheet of newsprint shown in Figure 3.23 is pulled slowly, the beaker is pulled off the table. If the newspaper is pulled rapidly, the beaker stays on the table.
   b) While moving horizontally at constant velocity on the snowmobile shown in Figure 3.22, the rider throws a ball vertically upward so that it reaches a height of 5 m. If the snowmobile continues moving at constant velocity, the ball returns to the rider. But if the snowmobile stops, the ball lands ahead of the rider. Draw diagrams to help you explain what is happening.

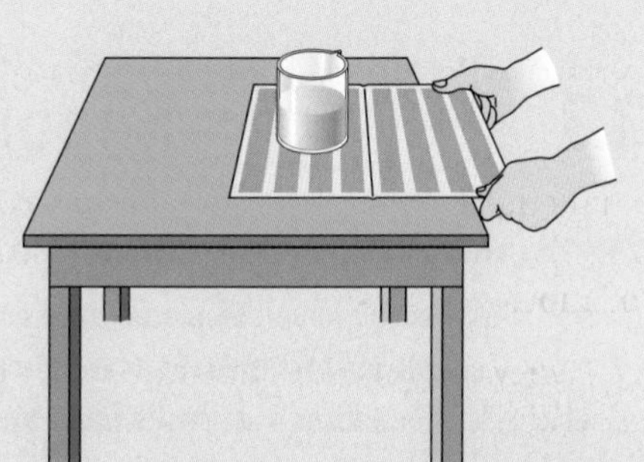

FIGURE 3.21 Can the newspaper be pulled from beneath the beaker without the beaker falling off the table?

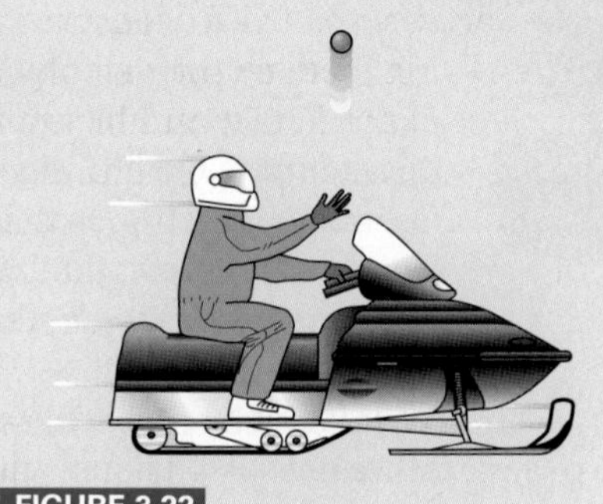

FIGURE 3.22

5. Compare the motion of a hockey puck shot along clean, hard ice, and a sponge of the same size, hit with the same force along the ice.

Applying Inquiry/ Communication Skills

6. Design an experiment using an air table and puck, or a spark table and air puck, to verify Newton's first law using pucks of different mass. Report your findings.
7. You are the coach of a hockey team consisting of ten-year-olds. At a hockey practice, you ask the players to skate across the ice along the blue line and shoot the puck into the empty net. Most of the shots miss the net. The faster the children skate, the more they miss. Newton's first law would help them understand their problem, but a technical explanation might confuse them.
   a) Devise an explanation of this problem that would make sense to the ten-year-olds.
   b) With the aid of a diagram, design a drill for the team that would help them to score on the net in this type of situation.

3.3 Newton's Second Law of Motion

Key Understandings

When you have completed this section, you will be able to:

- state Newton's second law of motion
- define force in terms of mass and acceleration
- solve problems involving net force, mass, and acceleration

If you were to ask scientists or engineers to identify the single most useful physics equation of the hundreds that exist, they would probably say "Newton's second law." What is this law? What makes it so important? Why are free-body diagrams so useful in applying it?

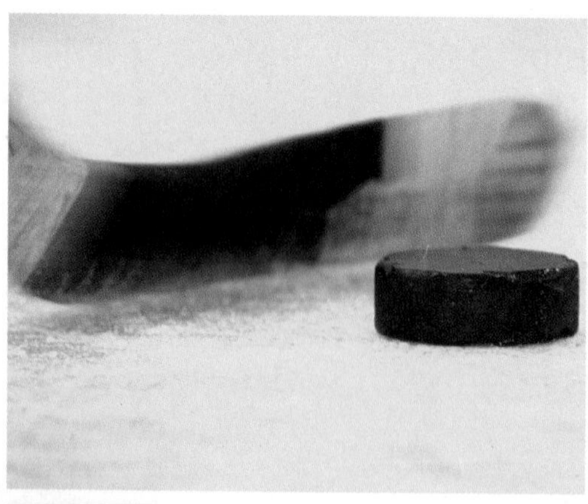

FIGURE 3.23

Acceleration and Net Force for a Constant Mass

According to Newton's first law, when the forces acting on an object are balanced, the object either remains at rest or continues to move at constant speed in a straight line. If an unbalanced net force acts on an object, the object accelerates in the direction of the net force. For example, if the net force on a hockey puck is directed to the right, the puck accelerates to the right. If the puck is initially moving to the right, it speeds up. The greater the net force on the puck, the larger its acceleration. If the puck was initially moving to the left it will decelerate, stop, and then accelerate to the right.

Table 3.2 shows the acceleration of a 10-kg mass under the influence of various applied forces. The table also shows the force of friction and the net force on the mass.

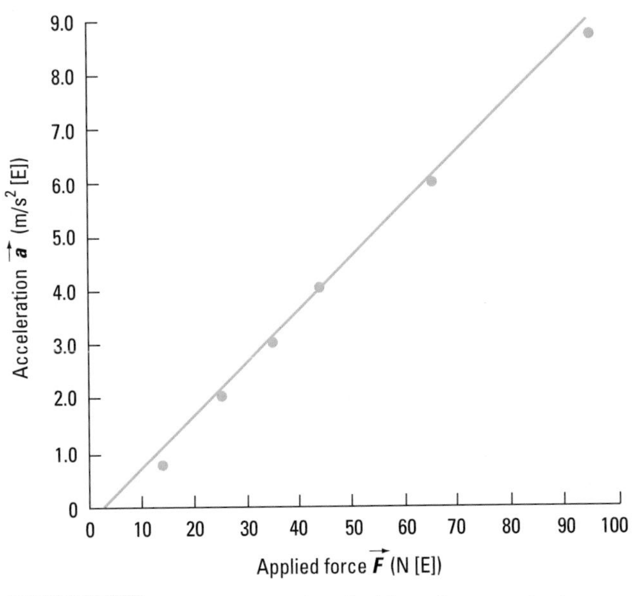

FIGURE 3.24 Acceleration and applied force for a constant mass

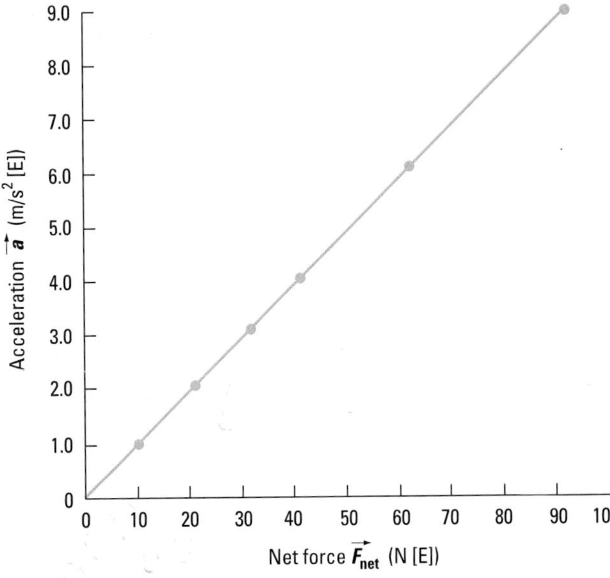

FIGURE 3.25 Acceleration and net force for a constant mass

TABLE 3.2 Acceleration and Force

Applied Force $\vec{F}$ (N [E])	Force of Friction $\vec{F}_f$ (N [W])	Net Force $\vec{F}_{net}$ (N [E])	Mass m (kg)	Acceleration $\vec{a}$ (m/s²[E])
13	3.0	10	10	1.0
23	3.0	20	10	2.0
33	3.0	30	10	3.0
43	3.0	40	10	4.0
63	3.0	60	10	6.0
93	3.0	90	10	9.0

Figure 3.24 shows the graph of acceleration against the applied force. The graph shows a straight line that intercepts the force axis at $\vec{F} = 3.0$ N [W]. This intercept represents the force of kinetic friction.

Figure 3.25 shows the graph of acceleration against the net force. Now the straight line passes through the origin and the slope of the line is constant. Therefore, the acceleration is directly proportional to the net force, provided the mass is constant. If the net force doubles, the acceleration doubles. Triple the acceleration requires triple the net force. Thus

$$\vec{a} \propto \vec{F}_{net} \qquad \text{(if mass is constant)}$$

Acceleration and Mass for a Constant Force

The greater the mass of an object, the smaller its acceleration for a constant force. Table 3.3 shows the acceleration of different masses under the influence of a constant net force of 18 N [E].

TABLE 3.3 Acceleration and Mass

Net Force $\vec{F}_{net}$ (N[E])	Mass m (kg)	Acceleration $\vec{a}$ (m/s² [E])
18	1.0	18
18	2.0	9.0
18	3.0	6.0
18	4.0	4.5
18	6.0	3.0
18	9.0	2.0
18	24	0.75

The data show that as the mass doubles, the acceleration halves. As the mass decreases to one-third, the acceleration triples. Thus, the acceleration is inversely proportional to the mass for a constant force:

$$\vec{a} \propto \frac{1}{m} \qquad \text{(force constant)}$$

Figure 3.26 is a graph of acceleration against mass. This shape is common for an inverse relationship.

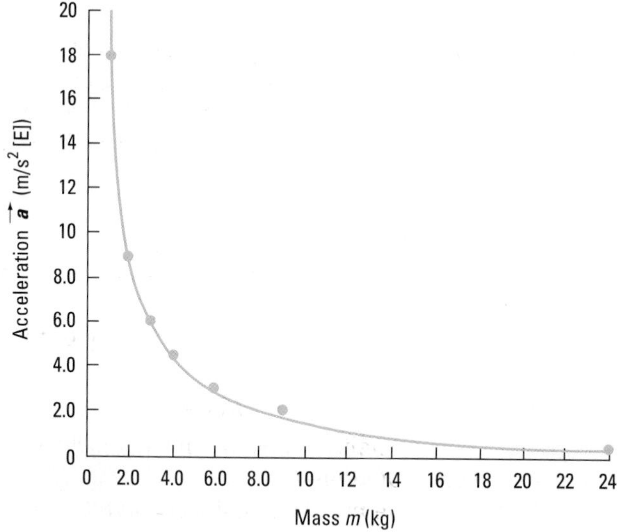

FIGURE 3.26 Acceleration and mass for a constant force

Newton's Second Law

We can combine the two relationships into a single statement relating acceleration, mass, and net or unbalanced force. It is known as **Newton's second law of motion** and states:

When a net force acts on an object, the object accelerates in the direction of the net force. The acceleration is directly proportional to the net force and inversely proportional to the mass. Thus:

$$\vec{a} \propto \frac{\vec{F}_{net}}{m}$$

The general equation for this relationship, where k is a constant, is

$$\vec{a} = \frac{k\vec{F}_{net}}{m}$$

The constant k has been made to equal one by defining the unit of force, the newton, as being a specific size. One newton is that net force which gives a mass of one kilogram an acceleration of one metre per second squared. Substituting k = 1 in the previous equation, we obtain the equation for net force in terms of mass and acceleration:

$$\vec{a} = \frac{\vec{F}_{net}}{m} \text{ or } \vec{F}_{net} = m\vec{a}$$

Where $\vec{F}_{net}$ is the net, unbalanced, or resultant force in newtons, m is the mass in kilograms, and $\vec{a}$ is the acceleration in metres per second squared.

Exploration Using a Graphing Calculator

Finding a Proportionality Constant

Newton's second law states that the acceleration of an object is directly proportional to the net force applied and inversely proportional to the mass. A student reasoned that if this is true then the acceleration must be directly proportional to the unbalanced force divided by the mass. She used a force measurer calibrated in units called "pulls" to accelerate various masses on a smooth surface and measured the accelerations. The data are shown in Table 3.4.

Testing the Hypothesis

To test the student's hypothesis, work out the ratio of net force divided by mass. Then use the graphing calculator to plot the points on a graph of acceleration against this ratio. Next, use the graphing calculator to identify the function that best models the data and to plot the line graph of the function.

Write the Equation

1. What physical quantities do x and y represent?
2. Write the equation that best models the relationship between acceleration and the ratio net force divided by mass.
3. What is the proportionality constant? What property of the graph does it represent?
4. To what extent do the data support Newton's second law?
5. a) Why was the proportionality constant not equal to one as it is in Newton's second law equation?
   b) What are the units of the proportionality constant?
6. Why was the y-intercept so close to zero?

Let's see how Newton's second law equation can be used to find the net force in some common situations.

Investigation
Refer to page 126, Investigation 2

TABLE 3.4 Acceleration, Net Force, and Mass

Acceleration $\vec{a}$, (m/s²) [forward]	Force $\vec{F}$ (Pulls)	Mass m, (kilograms)
1.0	7.5	5.0
2.0	12	4.0
4.0	18	3.0
4.5	47	7.0
5.0	11	1.5
6.0	16	1.8
8.0	54	4.5
10	45	3.0

Discovering Physics — *The Big Rip-Off*

How can you rip off the two sides of an index card at the same time? Cut an index card so that two identical thin strips at each end of the card are almost (but not quite) severed from the rest of the card as shown in Figure 3.27. Rest the card on a level surface. Now hold one thin strip in each hand and try to tear them away from the body of the card at the same time by accelerating your hands outward. If the two strips don't come off at the same time, why don't they? Considering the mass of the card, does it take a very large force to accelerate the card to one side? Try the experiment again with a new card but tape a loonie to the centre portion of the card. Why do the pieces come off at the same time now? Use Newton's second law and inertia to explain your answer.

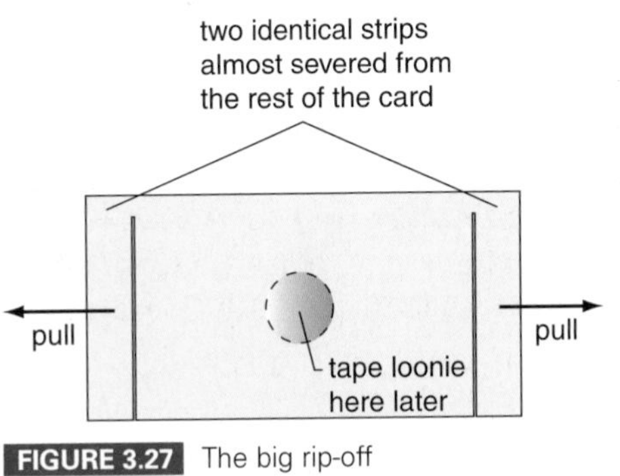

FIGURE 3.27 The big rip-off

EXAMPLE 3 NUMERICAL

A student is ten-pin bowling with her friends. She gives a 7.0-kg bowling ball an acceleration 5.0 m/s² [forward]. Calculate the net force she exerts on the ball.

Given

$m = 7.0$ kg $\quad \vec{a} = 5.0$ m/s² [forward]

Required

$\vec{F}_{net}$

Analysis

- Assume the force of friction is zero.
- The applied force is the only horizontal force acting on the bowling ball, so it is the net force.

Solution

$\vec{F}_{net} = m\vec{a}$

$= 7.0$ kg $\times$ 5.0 m/s² [forward]

$= 35$ kg·m/s² [forward]

$= 35$ N [forward]

Statement

The bowler exerts a net force of 35 N [forward] on the bowling ball.

PRACTICE PROBLEMS

1. A curler exerts a force forward on a 19-kg curling stone and gives it an acceleration of 1.8 m/s² [forward]. The coefficient of kinetic friction of the ice on the curling stone is 0.080 [back]. Calculate the value of the applied force.
2. A truck skidding on wet asphalt has a mass of 2000 kg. The total force of kinetic friction of the asphalt on the tires is 1000 N [back]. Calculate the deceleration of the truck.

The equation for Newton's second law can be adapted to solve problems involving initial velocity, final velocity, and elapsed time.

So if $\vec{F}_{net}$ is the resultant force in newtons, m is the mass in kilograms, and $\vec{a}$ is the acceleration in metres per second squared, then

$$\vec{F}_{net} = m\vec{a}$$

Acceleration can be expressed as

$$\vec{a} = \frac{\vec{v}_2 - \vec{v}_1}{\Delta t}$$

So substituting for $\vec{a}$ gives

$$\vec{F}_{net} = \frac{m(\vec{v}_2 - \vec{v}_1)}{\Delta t}$$

EXAMPLE 4 NUMERICAL

A driver and his motorcycle have a combined mass of 280 kg. They accelerate from 7.0 m/s [E] to 34 m/s [E] in 4.2 s. What is the net force on the driver and his motorcycle?

Given

$m = 280$ kg $\vec{v}_1 = 7.0$ m/s [E] $\vec{v}_2 = 34$ m/s [E] $\Delta t = 4.2$ s

Required

$\vec{F}_{\text{net}}$

Analysis

- The problem gives the initial and final velocity, not the change in velocity.
- The two velocities are in the same direction.
- Use the equation $\vec{F}_{\text{net}} = m\frac{(\vec{v}_2 - \vec{v}_1)}{\Delta t}$ to solve the problem.

Solution

$$\vec{F}_{\text{net}} = \frac{m(\vec{v}_2 - \vec{v}_1)}{\Delta t}$$

$$= \frac{280 \text{ kg } (34 \text{ m/s [E]} - 7.0 \text{ m/s [E]})}{4.2 \text{ s}}$$

$$= \frac{280 \text{ kg } (27.0 \text{ m/s [E]})}{4.2 \text{ s}}$$

$$= 1800 \text{ kg·m/s}^2 \text{ [E]}$$

$$= 1.8 \times 10^3 \text{ N [E]}$$

Statement

A net force of 1.8×10^3 N [E] is exerted on the driver and his motorcycle.

PRACTICE PROBLEMS

1. A net force of 2.2×10^2 N [W] applied to an object increases its velocity from 8.0 m/s [W] to 24 m/s [W] in 5.4 s. What is the mass of the object?
2. A child is riding her bicycle on dry concrete at a velocity of 12 m/s [E] when she puts on her brakes. The bicycle and child have a combined mass of 70 kg, and the friction exerted by the pavement with the brakes locked is 235 N [back]. What is the child's velocity at the end of 2.0 s?

Subtracting Forces

The net force on an object is the vector sum of all the forces. For example, consider a 0.10-kg peach being dragged through an orchard by a squirrel.

The force of gravity downward on the peach is balanced by the normal force of the ground acting upward. Therefore, the resultant vertical force on the peach is zero.

Two horizontal forces act on the peach, a force $\vec{F}$ applied by the squirrel forward, and a force of friction $\vec{F}_f$ exerted by the ground backward. The net or unbalanced horizontal force is the vector sum of the forces and is given by the vector equation:

$$\vec{F}_{\text{net}} = \vec{F} + \vec{F}_f$$

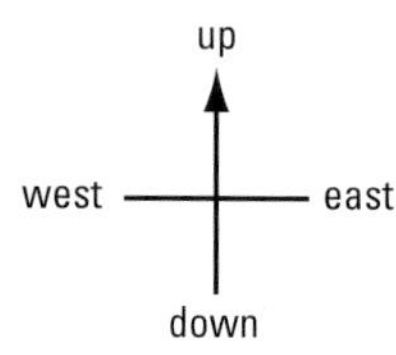

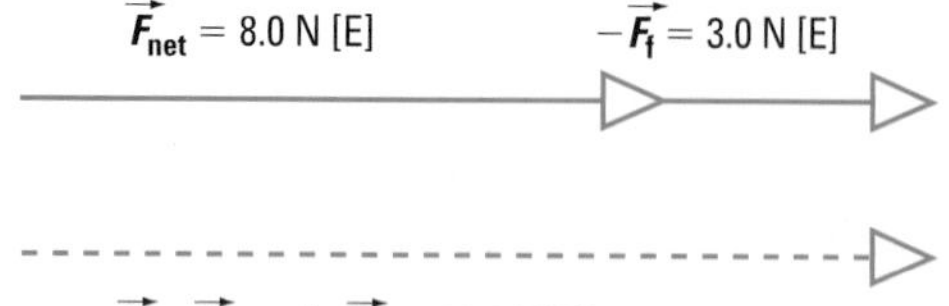

FIGURE 3.28 Subtracting the two collinear forces using the tail-to-tip method.

Suppose you know the net force and the force of friction on the peach and you wish to determine the force applied by the squirrel. Solving for the applied force the equation becomes

$$\vec{F} = \vec{F}_{net} - \vec{F}_f$$

Calculating the applied force $\vec{F}$ involves subtracting the force of friction from the net force. To subtract a vector quantity, we reverse the direction of the vector quantity to be subtracted and add it (Figure 3.28).

EXAMPLE 5 NUMERICAL

A peach that weighs 2.0 N is accelerated by a net force of 8.0 N [E]. The force of friction on the peach is 3.0 N [W]. Find the force that a squirrel applies to the peach to overcome friction and accelerate the peach.

Given

$\vec{F}_{net}$ = 8.0 N [E]

$\vec{F}_f$ = 3.0 N [W]

Required

$\vec{F}$

Analysis

- Sketch a free-body diagram (Figure 3.29)
- $\vec{F} = \vec{F}_{net} + (-\vec{F}_f)$
- To subtract $\vec{F}_f$, reverse its direction and add $-\vec{F}_f$ to $\vec{F}_{net}$

Solution

$\vec{F} = \vec{F}_{net} - \vec{F}_f$

= 8.0 N [E] − (3.0 N [W])

= 8.0 N [E] + (3.0 N [E])

= 11 N [E]

Statement

The squirrel applies a force of 11 N [E] to overcome a friction force of 3.0 N [W] and give a net force of 8.0 N [E] to the peach.

PRACTICE PROBLEMS

1. An elevator (m = 1000 kg) is accelerating up at 3.0 m/s^2.
   a) Make a free-body diagram of the elevator.
   b) Calculate the force in the cable that pulls the elevator up.
2. A 3.0-kg mass is at rest on a horizontal surface. The coefficient of static friction between the mass and the surface is 0.40. A horizontal force of 10 N is applied to the mass.
   a) Calculate the weight of the mass.
   b) Calculate the force of static friction.
   c) Draw a free-body diagram for this mass and use it to explain why the mass does not move.

The Airbag Debate

Decision-Making Skills

- ▶ Defining the Issue
- Developing Assessment Criteria
- ▶ Researching the Issue
- ▶ Analyzing Data and Information
- Proposing a Course of Action
- Justifying the Course of Action
- Evaluating the Decision

BACKGROUND INFORMATION

Airbags, introduced in the 1990s, can help prevent injury to drivers and passengers, especially in head-on collisions. Yet airbags have also been the cause of serious injury, even death. Anti-airbag advocates want greater control and better airbags. Others want airbags out of cars altogether.

Airbags are connected to sensors that detect sudden deceleration. When activated, the sensor sends an electrical signal that ignites a chemical propellant. When ignited, this propellant produces nitrogen gas, which inflates the airbag. The process occurs in less than one-twentieth of a second. But it is in that instant that arms and ribs have been broken and small children, even in car seats, have been killed by the impact of a rushing airbag. Tragically, some of these deaths occurred in very minor accidents.

Manufacturers have placed on/off switches for airbags in some vehicles, but is this the answer? Car manufacturers are now developing "smart" airbags. Engineers are working on an airbag system that senses a car's occupants according to distance from the airbag and adjusts the speed at which the airbag inflates accordingly.

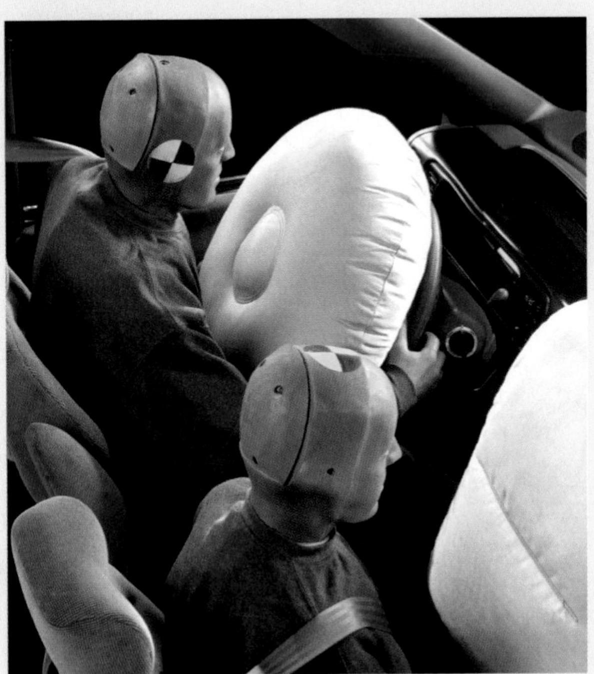

FIGURE 3.29 The role of headrests

Analyzing the Issue

1. Who are the different stakeholders involved in the controversy over airbags?
2. Research the development and safety history of airbags. Analyze your results, and identify any trends in your data. Propose a solution to this issue based on the trends you identified.
3. Propose possible changes to current airbag design that could address the issue of safety.
4. Plan a class debate to argue the pros and cons of airbag use. Identify five stakeholders to represent the "pro-airbag" point of view, and five stakeholders to represent the "anti-airbag" point of view. Support your position with research.

Section 3.3 Review

Understanding Concepts

1. State Newton's second law.
2. Sketch a graph to show the relationship between acceleration and mass for a constant net force.
3. Sketch graphs to show the relationship between acceleration and the applied force for a constant mass when:
   a) friction is present
   b) friction is absent
4. Sketch a graph to show the relationship between the net force and the product of mass and acceleration. What is the slope of this graph when $\vec{F}_{net}$ is in newtons, m is in kilograms, and $\vec{a}$ is in metres per second squared?
5. The net force on a 6.0-kg grocery cart is 12 N [S]. Calculate its acceleration.
6. In a road test, an automobile is given an acceleration of 2.7 m/s^2 [E] by a net force of 4.2×10^3 N [E]. Calculate the mass of the car.
7. What net force is needed to accelerate a 208-kg motorboat at 3.61 m/s^2 [S]?
8. A person applies a force of 8.0 N [S] to give a 2.5-kg sled an acceleration of 3.0 m/s^2 [S]. Calculate the force of kinetic friction.
9. What total force does someone have to apply to accelerate a 2.0-kg steel bolt at 3.0 m/s^2 [forward] along a rough surface against a force of friction of 9.0 N?

Applying Inquiry/ Communication Skills

10. Design an experiment to collect data on acceleration against applied force. You can use a picket fence attached to a rough block of wood resting on a horizontal surface, a newton spring scale, a photogate, an interface, and a computer. Explain how to use an acceleration–force graph to determine the force of friction acting on the block. How could you use the data to determine the coefficient of kinetic friction?

3.4 Newton's Third Law of Motion

Key Understandings

When you have completed this section, you will be able to:

- state Newton's third law
- use Newton's third law to explain common phenomena and solve problems
- use Newton's laws and kinematics equations to solve problems

Newton's third law explains how forces exist in pairs and that these forces are equal in size but opposite in direction. If this is so, why don't these pairs of forces just cancel each other out? How can there ever be a net force and hence an acceleration if forces always exist in pairs?

Newton's Third Law

Newton's second law describes quantitatively the relationship between a net force and the acceleration of a mass. But where does the force come from that is exerted on an object? Newton explained that a force applied to one object

FIGURE 3.30 Which is the action force and which is the reaction force?

always comes from another object. The force of gravity on an apple comes from Earth; the force on a baseball that is struck comes from a bat; the magnetic force on a steel nail comes from a magnet; in atoms, the electric force of attraction on orbiting electrons comes from protons in the nucleus.

Forces always occur in pairs. One is called the **action force** and the other the **reaction force**. If an action force is exerted by object X on object Y, then a reaction force is exerted by object Y back on object X. The falling apple exerts an upwards reaction force on Earth; the baseball pushes backward on the bat; the nail attracts the magnet; and electrons attract protons.

These observations are summarized in **Newton's third law:**

Whenever one object exerts a force on a second object, the second object exerts a force that is equal in magnitude and opposite in direction on the first object.

Newton's third law is often stated as "for every action force there is an equal and opposite reaction force." However, this can lead to a common misconception because it does not emphasize that the action and reaction forces are acting on different objects. The action force that Earth exerts on an apple is equal in size, but opposite in direction, to the reaction force that the apple exerts on Earth. The reason we see the acceleration of the apple, but not Earth, is because the apple has less mass than Earth. In fact, Earth does accelerate but at a rate inversely proportional to its mass. Also, we look at the situation from the point of view of Earth, not the apple.

Examples of Newton's Third Law

There are countless examples of Newton's third law in nature. Try pushing downward on a ball of putty with the palm of your hand. The putty changes shape, indicating that a force is present. But your hand also changes shape (Figure 3.31). Where does the force come from that changes the shape of your hand? From the putty of course!

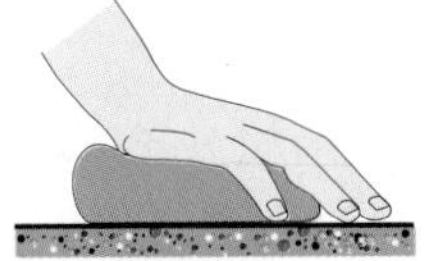

FIGURE 3.31 The hand exerts an action force on the putty. The putty exerts a reaction force on the hand. These forces are on two different bodies.

FIGURE 3.32 Both people move, even though only one person does the pushing. Thus, both an action and a reaction force exist.

With a partner, stand on skateboards on a hard level surface facing each other. Choose a partner with a mass about equal to your own. Give your partner a gentle push (Figure 3.32). What happens? The partner accelerates away from the initial position because of the action force you exert. But you also accelerate in the opposite direction because your partner exerts a reaction force on you. This reaction force has the same magnitude, but is opposite in direction to your action force.

Try another experiment. Stand on the skateboards about 2 m apart (Figure 3.33). Hold a basketball close to your chest. Then pass the basketball toward your partner using a quick chest pass. As you exert a force forward on the ball, you accelerate backward. The ball must exert a force back on you. To catch and stop the ball your partner applies a force opposite to the direction of motion of the ball. The ball exerts a force on your partner in the direction in which it is traveling. This causes your partner to move back. What happens if you throw the ball faster? Both of you move backward at greater speeds than before.

FIGURE 3.33 The person exerts an action force on the ball to start the pass. The basketball exerts a reaction force back on the person.

The motion of a rocket, also illustrates Newton's third law. In order to move, the rocket expels gaseous molecules. The rocket exerts a large force downward on the molecules to expel them at a very high speed. At the same time, the gaseous molecules exert an upward force of equal magnitude on the rocket.

Many people think that the expelled molecules must push against the ground or the atmosphere to propel the rocket. This is not true. If this were the case, then a rocket in space would not be able to accelerate because there would be nothing to push against.

INSIGHT

A rocket accelerates better in outer space because there is no force of friction to oppose the motion.

Discovering Physics *Motion of a Rocket*

Caution: Never point the rocket at anyone. Perform this activity outside.

Add about 2 mL of water to a toy water rocket. Increase the air pressure in the rocket using the hand pump as shown in Figure 3.34. Release the rocket from the pump. Describe the motion of the water and the rocket. Vary the amount of water in the rocket and repeat using the same pressure (same number of pumps). Vary the pressure in the rocket and repeat using the same amount of water. What effect does varying the water have? How does increasing the pressure affect the result? Explain what is happening in terms of Newton's third law.

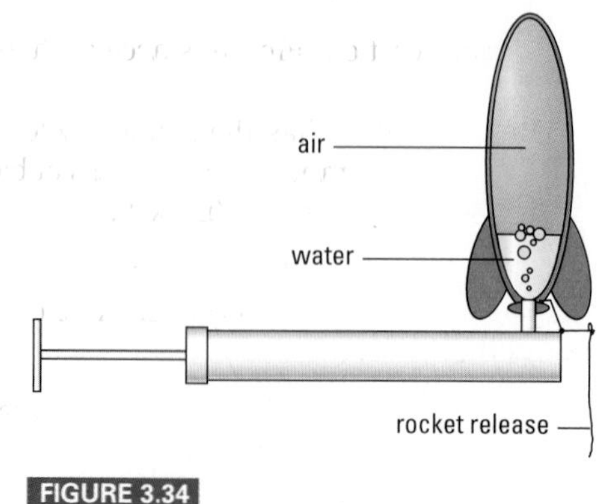

FIGURE 3.34

Discovering Physics — Fan Cart and Sail

Attach a rigid sail to a fan cart as shown in Figure 3.35. Make a prediction concerning the motion of the fan cart if the fan motor is now turned on. Try it. Repeat the activity but without the sail attached to the cart. Explain the motion of the fan cart with and without the sail using Newton's third law.

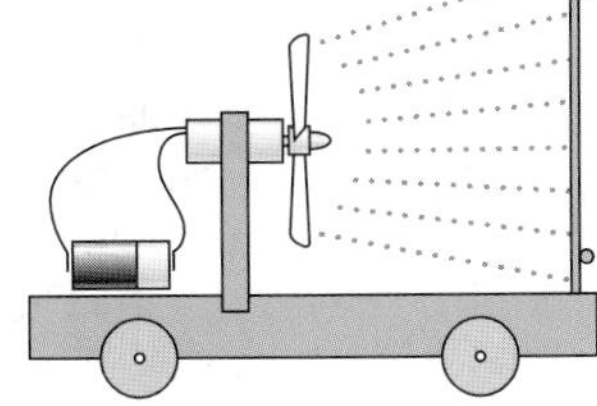

FIGURE 3.35 Fan cart and sail

EXAMPLE 6 NUMERICAL

Two steel blocks rest on a frictionless, horizontal surface. Block X has a mass of 6.0 kg and is attached by means of a light taut string to block Y that has a mass of 12 kg. A force of 36 N [E] is applied to block X, as shown in Figure 3.36. Calculate the force block Y exerts on block X and verify Newton's third law.

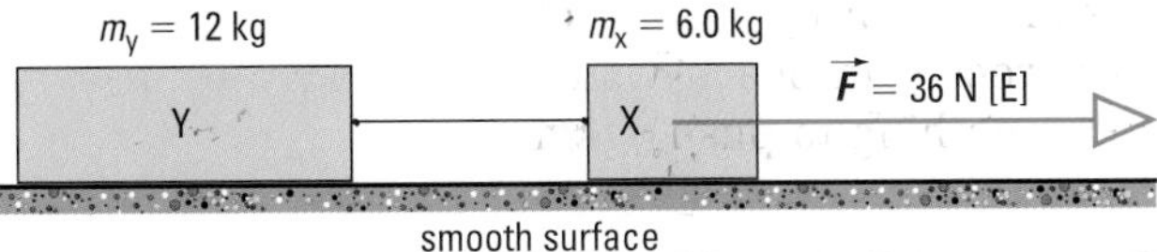

FIGURE 3.36

Given

$m_X = 6.0$ $m_Y = 12$ kg $\vec{F} = 36$ N[E]

Required

Find the force of block Y on block X and verify Newton's third law.

Analysis

- Find the mass of block X plus block Y. Since they are attached together, they have the same acceleration. Find this acceleration using $\vec{a} = \frac{\vec{F}_{net}}{m}$
- Then consider block Y alone. It has the same acceleration as the two blocks together. Use this acceleration and the mass of block Y to find the net force on Y. This force is exerted by block X.
- According to Newton's third law, block Y exerts an identical force back on block X. Calculate the net force on block X and use this force to determine its acceleration.
- Verify Newton's third law by determining if this acceleration is the same as the acceleration of both blocks together.

Solution

Both blocks together

$$m_T = m_X + m_Y = 6.0 \text{ kg} + 12 \text{ kg}$$
$$= 18 \text{ kg}$$
$$\vec{a} = \frac{\vec{F}_{net}}{m_T}$$
$$= 36 \text{ N [E]} / 18 \text{ kg}$$
$$= 2.0 \text{ m/s}^2 \text{ [E]}$$

Block Y alone

$$\vec{F}_{net} = m_Y \vec{a}$$
$$= 12 \text{ kg} \times 2.0 \text{ m/s}^2 \text{ [E]}$$
$$= 24 \text{ N [E]}$$

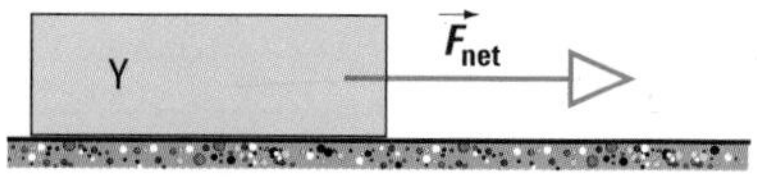

Y $\vec{F}_{net}$

FIGURE 3.37 Block Y alone

Block X alone

$$\vec{F}_{net} = \vec{F} + \vec{F}_{Y on X}$$
$$= 36 \text{ N [E]} + 24 \text{ N [W]}$$
$$= 36 \text{ N [E]} - 24 \text{ N [E]}$$
$$= 12 \text{ N [E]}$$
$$\vec{a} = \frac{\vec{F}_{net}}{m_X}$$
$$= 12 \text{ N [E]} / 6.0 \text{ kg}$$
$$= 2.0 \text{ m/s}^2 \text{ [E]}$$

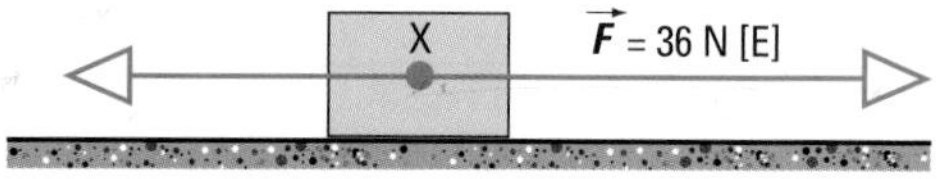

24 N [W] X $\vec{F}$ = 36 N [E]

FIGURE 3.38 Block X alone

Statement

Block X exerts a force on block Y of 24 N [E]. By Newton's third law, Block Y exerts a force of 24 N [W] on block X. The net force on block X is 12 N [E]. This force gives block X the same acceleration as both blocks together, thereby verifying Newton's third law.

PRACTICE PROBLEMS

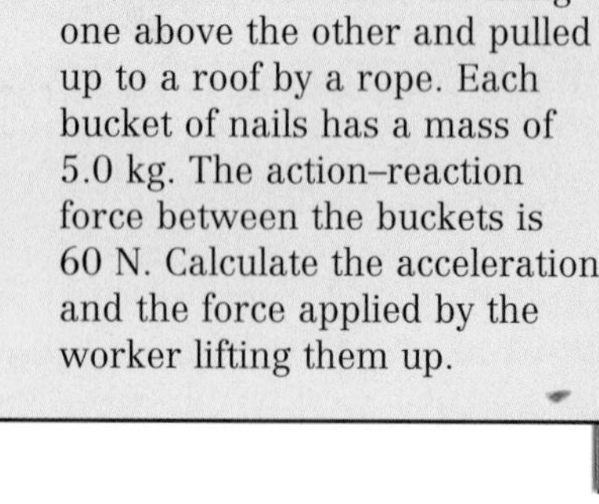

1. A worker applies a small 30-N horizontal force to box A which also pushes onto box B in front. Box A is 25 kg and box B is 15 kg. They sit on a smooth surface. The two-box system accelerates forward at 0.75 m/s^2. What size of forces do the boxes exert on each other? How do their directions compare?
2. Two buckets of nails are hung one above the other and pulled up to a roof by a rope. Each bucket of nails has a mass of 5.0 kg. The action–reaction force between the buckets is 60 N. Calculate the acceleration and the force applied by the worker lifting them up.

FIGURE 3.39 What are the action–reaction forces involved in the operation of a rotary lawn sprinkler?

Applications of Newton's Third Law

Lawn Sprinkler

The motion of some lawn sprinklers involves Newton's third law (Figure 3.39). Can you explain why the water goes in one direction, and the lawn sprinkler head of a rotary sprinkler goes in the opposite direction?

Propeller-Driven Machines

Have you ever wondered what exerts the force to move a propeller-driven machine, such as an airplane, through the air? It's hard to believe that air, thrust backward by the propeller, pushes the propeller and machine forward (Figure 3.40). The blades of the propeller are slanted so that they grab new air during each revolution. This air is accelerated backward by the propeller. But according to Newton's third law, the accelerated air pushes forward on the propeller. The faster the propeller turns, the greater the mass of air directed backward and the faster the machine moves forward.

FIGURE 3.40 Name the action–reaction forces associated with a propeller.

Section 3.4 Review

Understanding Concepts

1. State Newton's third law.
2. Use Newton's third law to explain each of the following:
   a) A walker exerts a force backward on the ground to walk forward.
   b) The larger the bullet fired by a gun, the more the gun recoils.
   c) A swimmer at the edge of a pool pushes backward on the wall to move forward.
   d) When a person throws a package onto the shore from a canoe, the canoe moves away from shore.
3. State the reaction force to each of the following action forces:
   a) Earth attracts the Moon with a force of 9.7×10^{24} N.
   b) A book pushes down on the table with a force of 18 N.
   c) Water pushes sideways on the centre board of a sailboat with a force of 600 N.
   d) The weight of a mass exerts a force of 30 N [down] on a string.
4. An astronaut in outer space is "floating" near a spaceship. How can the astronaut return to the ship using only a cylinder of compressed gas?
5. A 5.0-kg block Y is attached to a 10-kg block X on a smooth level table by a light taut string, as shown in Figure 3.41. Calculate the action and reaction forces on the blocks if a force of 36 N [S] acts on block X.
6. For question 5, assume that the force of friction on the 5.0-kg block is 4.0 N and the force of friction on the 10-kg block is 8.0 N. Calculate the action and reaction forces with friction present. Explain the result.

Applying Inquiry/ Communication Skills

7. Assume that you have two carts with attached spring plungers, C clamps, barriers, and a set of standard masses. Design an experiment to verify Newton's third law. Remember that you can cock each plunger alone or you can cock and release the two plungers at the same time.

Making Connections

8. Injuries can occur in the workplace when parts of the human body are subjected to larger forces than they can handle. Some injuries are due to unsafe actions by workers and some are due to an unsafe working environment. Suppose you are the owner of a small computer business. Using a flow chart, outline a procedure for developing a safety plan that involves both management and workers.

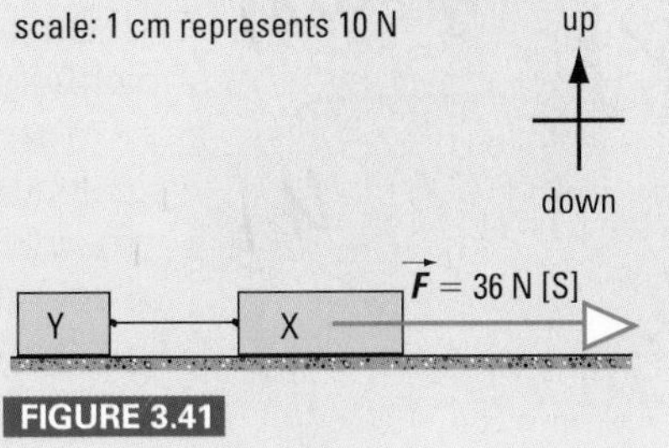

FIGURE 3.41

3.5 Motion Problems and Newton's Laws

Key Understandings

When you have completed this section, you will be able to:

- apply Newton's laws to explain walking
- use Newton's second law to explain why different masses have the same acceleration due to gravity at a given location
- apply Newton's third law to the motion of planets and satellites
- use Newton's laws and kinematics equations to solve problems

Newton's laws give us very powerful ways to solve everyday problems. How can this be if there is only the formula $\vec{F}_{\text{net}} = m\vec{a}$ to use? How can the kinematics equations be used with this important law? The answer lies in the acceleration that an unbalanced force provides.

Newton's Laws and the Kinematics Equations

All of the kinematics equations for constant acceleration can be used with Newton's laws. This provides a very powerful tool for solving everyday problems involving motion. A net force causes a mass to accelerate. The acceleration can be calculated using Newton's second law. This acceleration can be substituted into the kinematics equations and used to find quantities such as displacement and velocity. Alternatively, you can use the kinematics equations to find acceleration. With this acceleration and the mass, you can calculate the net force.

An understanding of Newton's laws and how to use them to solve problems is necessary in the field of gait analysis—the study of human walking. Gait analysis is particularly interesting because it leads to many applications: physical therapy, the design of artificial joints, rehabilitation, orthopedics, and the manufacture of sports and athletic footwear.

The earliest account of gait analysis was in 1682 by Borelli, a student of Galileo. Borelli described how balance is maintained when humans walk by making measurements of the centre of gravity of the body. The earliest measurements were visual. Initially scientists simply watched people walk, and later photography helped in the analysis. Today, the videotaping and digitizing of patterns of movement help scientists to learn more about the mechanics of the gait cycle. Electrical connections directly from the muscles to computers have raised this science to another level by measuring the timing of muscular activity in gait.

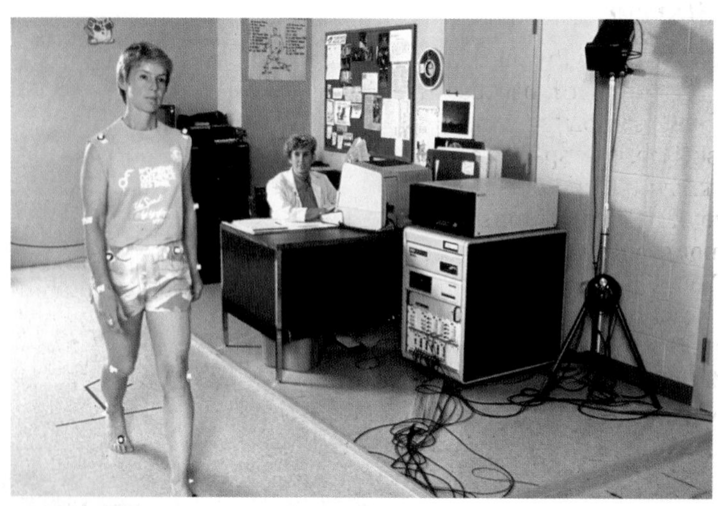

FIGURE 3.42 Walking on a force platform

The fundamentals of gait analysis can be extended to running. When we run our feet hit the ground at just over 1 m/s and compress our shoes about 7–10 mm. Heavier people, or people with heavier running styles, can force their shoes to bottom out, like car springs do when you drive over a speed bump.

Footwear design can change your running profile. Sprinters spend more time on the balls of their feet and need tread and weight distribution to accelerate them. Part of the sole of athletic shoes is for braking and part is for propulsion; so sprinter's shoes should be different from those of a marathon runner.

Newton's Second Law, Acceleration due to Gravity and Mass

Experiments show that when released from the same elevation, and in the absence of air friction, heavy objects reach the ground at the same time as light objects. Remember Galileo's famous experiment at the leaning tower of Pisa. How can Newton's second law and the force of gravity be used to explain this phenomenon?

EXAMPLE 7 CONCEPTUAL

Use Newton's second law and an understanding of the force of gravity to explain why all objects of different mass have the same acceleration due to gravity at the same location.

Reasoning and Solution

Newton's second law expressed in terms of the acceleration due to gravity is $\vec{g} = \frac{\vec{F}_G}{m}$. In the absence of air friction the net force acting on a falling object is equal to the force of gravity. But Newton's law of universal gravitation shows that if the mass of an object doubles from m to $2m$, the force of gravity exerted by Earth doubles from $\vec{F}_G$ to $2\vec{F}_G$. Substituting these into Newton's second law equation we obtain

$$\vec{g} = \frac{\vec{F}_G}{m} = \frac{2\vec{F}_G}{2m}$$

which simplifies to give the same acceleration $\vec{g}$.

CHALLENGE

Experiments show that when released from the same elevation and in the presence of air friction, heavy objects of the same cross-sectional area reach the ground sooner than light objects. Use Newton's second law and free-body diagrams to explain why.

Action Reaction Pairs and the Space Station

The question is sometimes asked, "Why does a satellite such as the space station stay in orbit?" The space station stays in orbit around Earth because of the pull of Earth. This pull is a net force and causes the station to accelerate toward Earth. But instead of falling to Earth's surface, the space station moves in an almost circular (elliptical) orbit. We know the space station is accelerating because its velocity, as it travels around Earth, is constantly changing in direction. In fact, the acceleration is not even constant because the direction of this vector quantity is changing. You will learn more about the acceleration of projectiles and planets in your next physics course.

Earth exerts an action force on the space station. But what is the reaction force to the force Earth exerts on the space station? The space station attracts Earth upward. But the mass of Earth is so large compared with the mass of the space station that the small acceleration Earth undergoes is insignificant. Imagine what would happen if two planets of equal mass orbited one another.

FIGURE 3.43 Space Station Alpha

EXAMPLE 8 NUMERICAL

A driver approaches an intersection at a speed of 14 m/s (50 km/h) when the light turns amber. The driver applies the brakes to get the maximum stopping force without skidding. (Recall that static friction is larger than sliding friction.) The car has a mass of 1500 kg, and the force of limiting static friction between the tires and the road is 1.1×10^4 N. Ignoring the driver's reaction time, calculate:

a) the maximum deceleration of the car, b) the minimum stopping time, and c) the minimum stopping distance.

Given

$\vec{v}_1 = 14$ m/s [forward] $\vec{F}_{\text{static friction}} = 1.1 \times 10^4$ N [back]

$m = 1500$ kg

Required $\vec{a}$

Analysis

- The only horizontal force acting is the force of limiting static friction.
- The force of limiting static friction acting opposite to the direction of motion causes the deceleration.
- Assume the driver's reaction time is zero.

Solution

a) The force of limiting static friction causes the deceleration.

$$\vec{a} = \frac{\vec{F}_{\text{net}}}{m}$$

$$= \frac{1.1 \times 10^4 \text{ N [backward]}}{1500 \text{ kg}} = 7.3 \text{ m/s}^2 \text{ [backward]}$$

b) $$\Delta t = \frac{\vec{v}_2 - \vec{v}_1}{\vec{a}}$$

$$= \frac{0 - 14 \text{ m/s [forward]}}{7.3 \text{ m/s}^2 \text{ [backward]}}$$

$$= \frac{14 \text{ m/s [backward]}}{7.3 \text{ m/s}^2 \text{ [backward]}} = 1.9 \text{ s}$$

c) $$\Delta \vec{d} = \frac{(\vec{v}_1 + \vec{v}_2)}{2} \Delta t$$

$$= \frac{(14 \text{ m/s [forward]} + 0)}{2} \times (1.9 \text{ s}) = 13 \text{ m [forward]}$$

Statement

The driver decelerates at 7.3 m/s^2, stops 1.9 s after she applies the brakes, and travels 13 m in the process.

PRACTICE PROBLEMS

1. Recalculate the stopping distance if the driver jams on the brakes and skids. The force of kinetic friction between the tires and the road decreases to 0.90×10^4 N.
2. What is the stopping distance in practice problem 1 if the driver's reaction time is 0.12 s?

EXAMPLE 9 NUMERICAL

An elevator, including passengers, has a mass of 600 kg. When leaving the first floor, it accelerates upward at 2.0 m/s². What force is the cable exerting on the elevator?

Given

$m = 600$ kg

$\vec{a} = 2.0$ m/s² [up]

Required

$\vec{F}$

Analysis

- Sketch a free-body diagram of the elevator. Since the elevator is accelerating up, the force exerted upward by the cable is larger than the downward force of gravity.
- Use $\vec{F}_{net} = m\vec{a}$ to find the net force up.
- Use $\vec{F}_G = m\vec{g}$ to find the force of gravity down.
- Solve the equation $\vec{F}_{net} = \vec{F} + \vec{F}_G$ for $\vec{F}$.

Solution

$\vec{F}_{net} = m\vec{a}$

$= 600 \text{ kg} \times 2.0 \text{ m/s}^2 \text{ [up]}$

$= 1.2 \times 10^3 \text{ N [up]}$

$\vec{F}_G = m\vec{g}$

$= 600 \text{ kg} \times 9.8 \text{ N/kg [down]}$

$= 5.9 \times 10^3 \text{ N [down]}$

$\vec{F}_{net} = \vec{F} + \vec{F}_G$

therefore

$\vec{F} = \vec{F}_{net} - \vec{F}_G$

$= 1.2 \times 10^3 \text{ N [up]} - 5.9 \times 10^3 \text{ N [down]}$

$= 1.2 \times 10^3 \text{ N [up]} + 5.9 \times 10^3 \text{ N [up]}$

$= 7.1 \times 10^3 \text{ N [up]}$

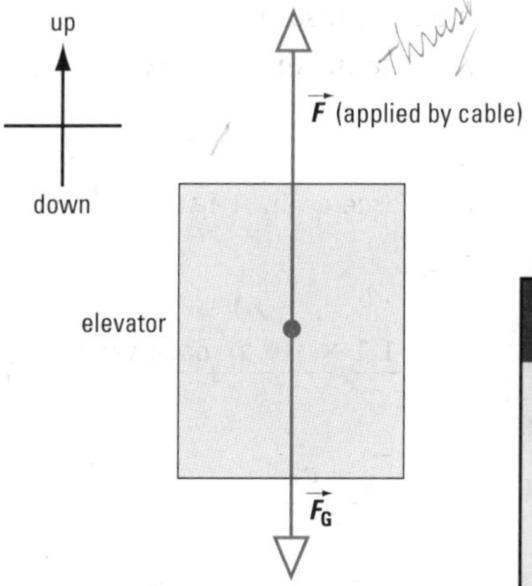

FIGURE 3.45

Statement

The cable exerts a force of 7.1×10^3 N [up]. A force of 5.9×10^3 N [up] is used to support the elevator, and the net force of 1.2×10^3 N [up] causes the acceleration.

PRACTICE PROBLEMS

1. A force of 300 N is applied to a 50-kg box on a rough floor. The frictional force is 200 N.
   a) Calculate the acceleration of the box.
   b) If the 300-N force is removed after 4.0 s, how long will it take the box to come to rest?
2. A 2.0-kg object is moving across a table at constant speed of 2.0 m/s against a force of friction of 6.0 N. The applied force is suddenly increased by 1.0 N. How fast will the object be moving after 3.0 s?

Section 3.5 Review

Understanding Concepts

1. Which of the three terms in the formula for Newton's second law provides the direct link to the formulas for uniformly accelerated motion?
2. A child exerts a force of 2.0 N [forward] on a stationary 4.0-kg tricycle for 1.2 s. Calculate:
   a) the acceleration of the tricycle
   b) how far it travels in this time
   c) the final velocity of the tricycle
3. Two people tug on opposite ends of a 40-kg stationary floating canoe. The first exerts a force of 50 N [E]. The second exerts a force of 60 N [W]. Assuming a force of kinetic friction of 2.0 N, calculate:
   a) the acceleration of the canoe
   b) how long it takes for the canoe to move 4.0 m
   c) the final speed of the canoe after 3.0 s
4. A skydiver, complete with a parachute, has a mass of 65 kg. She opens his parachute when she reaches a velocity of 4.0 m/s [down]. The parachute exerts an upward force of 337 N. After the parachute opens, calculate:
   a) the skydiver's acceleration
   b) her velocity after 2.0 s

Applying Inquiry/ Communication Skills

5. Design an experiment to verify Newton's third law as it applies to blocks being dragged at constant velocity along a level surface.Use two unequal-mass rough wooden blocks, with cup hooks in each end, and two newton spring scales. In your report include a free-body diagram for each block.
6. Design an experiment to verify Newton's third law as it applies to blocks being uniformly accelerated along a level surface. Use two unequal-mass rough wooden blocks with cup hooks on each end, and two newton spring scales, a motion sensor, an interface, and a computer. In your report include a free-body diagram for each block.

Making Connections

7. The distance a car travels before it can be brought to a stop is influenced by many factors. Compare the distances travelled during the stopping process in the following two cases and comment on your observations:
   a) Car A is travelling at 40 km/h. The reaction time of the driver (the time it takes to get a foot on the brake pedal) is 0.75 s. Once the brakes are applied, a frictional force of 1.2×10^4 N slows the 1200-kg car to a stop.
   b) The driver of car B notices that the "WALK–DON'T WALK" sign has changed. She knows that the light is going to turn amber very soon, and she'll likely have to stop. As a result she slows down to 36 km/h and her reaction time is reduced to 0.50 s because she has eased her foot off the gas pedal and is ready to apply the brakes.

Investigation 1 (Section 3.1)

Inquiry Skills

- Initiating and Planning
- Applying Technical Skills
- Using Tools, Materials, Equipment
- Conducting and Recording
- Analyzing and Interpreting
- Concluding and Communicating

Measuring the Coefficient of Kinetic Friction

The acceleration of a block sliding to rest on a level surface can be determined if we know the sliding distance and the time to come to rest. From kinematics, we know that $\Delta\vec{d} = \vec{v}_2\Delta t - 1/2\vec{a}\Delta t^2$ where $\Delta\vec{d}$ is the displacement, $\vec{v}_2$ is the final velocity, $\vec{a}$ is the acceleration, and Δt is the elapsed time. Since $\vec{v}_2 = 0$, this equation simplifies and re-arranges to

$$\vec{a} = -\frac{2\Delta\vec{d}}{\Delta t^2}$$

From the release point to where it stops, the only horizontal force acting on the block (excluding air resistance) is the force of sliding kinetic friction $\vec{F}_k$. Knowing the acceleration of the block and its mass, we can use the equation $\vec{F}_k = m\vec{a}$ to calculate the force of kinetic friction $\vec{F}_k$ for each acceleration measurement. Using this and the equation $\mu_k = \frac{F_k}{\vec{F}_n}$ we can calculate the, coefficient of kinetic friction.

Problem

How consistent is the coefficient of kinetic friction between two surfaces?

Materials

- balance
- masking tape
- metre-stick
- modelling clay
- standard set of masses
- stopwatch
- wooden block

Experimental Design

1. Make a list of the measurements needed to calculate the coefficient of kinetic friction.
2. Write out a list of procedures you will use to obtain the required measurements.
3. Design a data table to record your measurements.
4. When your teacher has approved your procedure, carry out the experiment.

Analyzing and Interpreting

1. Plot a graph of $\Delta\vec{d}$ against Δt^2 and measure its slope.
2. Explain the significance of the negative sign in the formula $\vec{a} = -\frac{2\Delta\vec{d}}{\Delta t^2}$

Concluding and Communicating

3. Are the values for acceleration relatively constant, or do they vary widely?
4. How consistent are the values for the coefficient of kinetic friction?
5. What sources of error are there in this experiment?
6. a) Should the origin be a point on the graph of $\Delta\vec{d}$ against Δt^2? Explain.
   b) When you measured the acceleration of the block, you used the formula $\vec{a} = -\frac{2\Delta\vec{d}}{\Delta t^2}$. This formula re-arranges to become $\Delta\vec{d} = -\frac{\vec{a}\Delta t^2}{2}$. What is the relationship between this formula and the slope of the line on your graph?
7. Describe how you could use the procedure from this experiment to measure the coefficient of rolling friction between the tires of a car and the road surface for different pressures of air in the tires.

Extending

8. What effect will mass have on the coefficient of kinetic friction? For example, if the mass is doubled, what will happen to the coefficient of kinetic friction? Make a prediction. Then repeat this experiment using the same block, but attach modelling clay to its upper surface to increase the mass.
9. What effect will surface area have on the coefficient of kinetic friction? For example, if the surface area is halved, what will happen to the coefficicient? Make a prediction. Then repeat this experiment using the same block, but sliding on a smaller surface with the same smoothness. Are you surprised by the result?

Investigation 2 (Section 3.3)

Inquiry Skills

- Initiating and Planning
- Applying Technical Skills
- Using Tools, Materials, Equipment
- Conducting and Recording
- Analyzing and Interpreting
- Concluding and Communicating

Force, Mass, and Acceleration

From Newton's first law we know that an unbalanced force is needed to accelerate a mass. If a net force of 1 N gives a mass of 1 kg an acceleration of 1 m/s^2, what acceleration will a net force of 2 N produce? If a net force of 1 N is applied to a 2-kg mass, what acceleration will it produce? Before doing this activity, make hypotheses by answering these two questions. Then do the activity to check your hypotheses.

The relationship among the displacement $\Delta\vec{d}$, initial velocity $\vec{v}_1$, the elapsed time Δt, and the acceleration $\vec{a}$ is given by the equation $\Delta\vec{d} = \vec{v}_1\Delta t + \frac{1}{2}\vec{a}(\Delta t^2)$. But, if the initial velocity is zero, the equation simplifies to $\Delta\vec{d} = \frac{1}{2}\vec{a}(\Delta t^2)$. Re-arranging this equation to solve for acceleration we get $\vec{a} = \frac{2\Delta\vec{d}}{\Delta t^2}$. We can use this equation to find the acceleration of carts with different loads under the influence of different net forces.

Problem

What relationship exists between the acceleration of an object, its mass, and the net force applied?

Materials

- C-clamp
- power supply
- masses
- graph paper
- recording timer
- newton spring scales
- masking tape
- cart of known mass
- recording tape
- metre-stick
- long ramp
- wedges

Procedure

1. Copy Table 3.5 (p.127) into your notebook.
2. If the mass of your cart is unknown, use $\vec{g}$ = 9.8 N/kg [down] and a newton spring scale to find it. Record the value in kilograms.
3. Set up the recording timer, cart, and newton spring scale as shown in Figure 3.46. Use wedges to raise one end of the ramp until the cart maintains a constant speed down the incline when given a gentle push. The slope then compensates for friction.
4. Practice pulling the cart down the ramp with a net force of 1 N until you can keep the force fairly constant over a distance of about 1 m.
5. Attach a length of recording tape to the cart and thread it through the timer.
6. Start the timer and pull the cart down the ramp with a net force of 1 N. Label the recording tape "mass = one cart; force = 1 N."
7. Repeat step 6 using a pulling force of 2 N and then 3 N. Label each tape.
8. Now double the mass to be accelerated by placing an identical cart on top of the first, or by adding a brick, sand bag, or standard masses to the cart.
9. Accelerate the new mass by applying a force of 3 N. Label this tape "mass = two carts; force = 3 N."
10. Repeat step 9 using the same force but a mass equal to three carts. Label the tape "mass = three carts; force = 3 N."

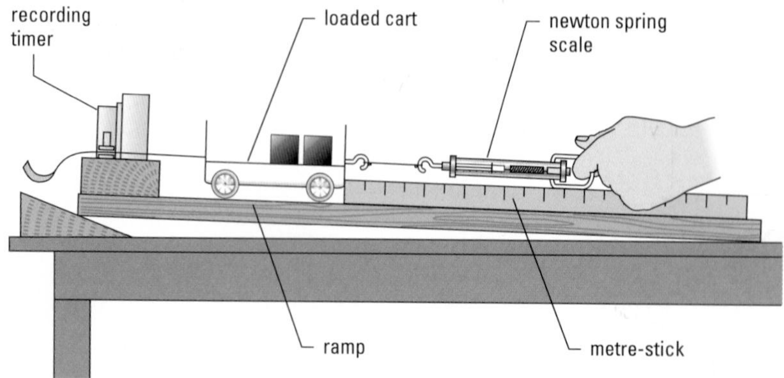

FIGURE 3.44

(continued)

TABLE 3.5 Acceleration, Force, and Mass

Force $\vec{F}_{net}$ (N [F])	Mass m (carts)	Mass m (kg)	Time Δt (s)	Displacement $\Delta\vec{d}$ (m [F])	Acceleration $\vec{a}$ (m/s² [F])	Mass × Acceleration $m \cdot \vec{a}$ (kg m/s² [F])
1	1					
2	1					
3	1					
3	2					
3	3					

11. Go back to the tape labelled "mass = one cart; force = 3 N." Label the starting dot $t = 0$ and mark off a convenient time interval from the start. For example, if the period of your timer is 1/60 s, a time interval of 30 dot spaces would be 0.5 s (30 × 1/60 s = 0.5 s). Record the time interval.
12. Measure and record the displacement travelled in this time interval.
13. Use the equation $\vec{a} = \frac{2\Delta\vec{d}}{\Delta t^2}$ to find the acceleration.
14. Repeat 11, 12, and 13 for the other four tapes, using the same time interval as chosen in 11.
15. Calculate the product of mass and acceleration ($m\vec{a}$) and enter it in the table.
16. For a mass of one cart, plot a graph of acceleration against net force.
17. For a force of 3 N, plot a graph of acceleration against mass.
18. For all the cases, plot a graph of net force against the product of mass and acceleration.

Analyzing and Interpreting

1. Why was the tape labelled "mass = 1 cart; force = 3 N" used to select the time interval?
2. a) Describe the graph of acceleration against net force for a constant mass.
   b) According to Galileo, where should the graph cut the axis? Where does it pass? Why?

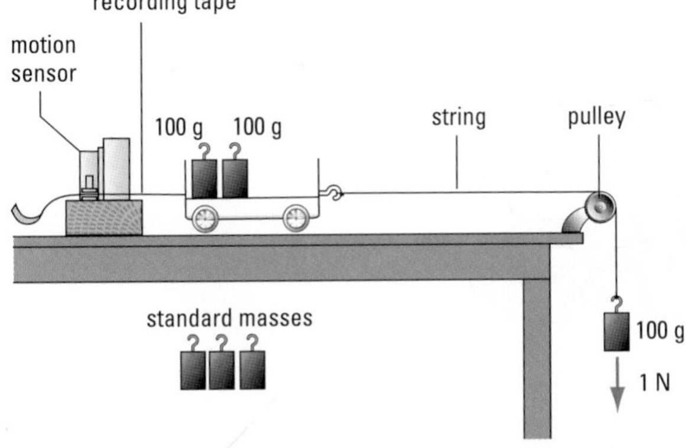

Concluding and Communicating

3. When the net force pulling the cart is doubled, what happens to the acceleration?
4. What is the relationship between acceleration and net force?
5. Describe the graph of acceleration against mass.
6. When the mass being pulled is doubled, what happens to the acceleration?
7. What is the relationship between the acceleration of an object and its mass?
8. Describe the graph of net force against the product of mass and acceleration.
9. What is the relationship between the net force and the product of mass and acceleration?
10. Commercial airlines are becoming stricter about the amount of luggage each passenger is allowed to bring on board. Use Newton's second law to explain why.

Extending

11. Design and do an experiment using a motion sensor and the equipment shown in Figure 3.46 to verify the relationship between the net force, mass and acceleration. Replace the newton spring scale with a thread passing over a pulley to which different hooked masses are attached. Remember that the hooked masses used to provide the force to accelerate the cart are part of the mass of the system. In your report, compare the results from the two activities.

FIGURE 3.46

Design & Build

Collision Test Track

Need

A company wishes to make a model of a test track that will be used to examine the details of various car crashes in order to improve the safety aspects of their car designs.

Proposal

Construct ramps that will allow toy cars to be released from rest and collide head on or at various angles while being recorded on videotape.

Materials

- two toy racing car tracks
- metre-stick
- videotape recorder
- support system for the tracks
- several toy cars and trucks
- triple beam or electronic balance

Specifications

The tracks need to be mounted on some kind of support system. You will need to be able to measure the release heights of the cars so that calculations can be done for the velocities they'll have at the bottom of the ramps. The space at the bottom of the ramps will need to be large enough for the crash to occur and be recorded on videotape. At least one of the ramps will need to be movable so that crashes at various angles can occur.

Plan

Draw up your plans for the design of the system and discuss the features of your plan with classmates so that they can provide input and ask you specific questions about your design. Be sure to use proper drafting procedures including the dimensions of your model.

Construction

1. Construct your model according to the plan.
2. Test the model using various release heights, angles of collision, and types of vehicle.
3. Once you have a feel for the system, videotape a variety of collisions. You might like to include the specifics of release heights (which can be used to calculate speed), relative masses of the vehicles, and angles of the collisions.

Evaluation

Provide a written summary of the operation of your model including any recommendations for changes that might be incorporated in future versions of your model. Include the videotape record as part of your report.

CHAPTER SUMMARY

Key Terms

action force
dynamics
fluid friction
forced motion
friction
inertia
kinematics
kinetic friction
limiting static friction
normal force
reaction force
rolling friction
sliding friction

Key Equations

Coefficient of kinetic friction

$$\mu_k = \frac{F_k}{F_n}$$

Coefficient of static friction

$$\mu_s = \frac{F_k}{F_n}$$

Newton's second law

$$\vec{a} = \frac{\vec{F}_{net}}{m} \text{ or } \vec{F}_{net} = m\vec{a}$$

$$\vec{F}_{net} = \frac{m(\vec{v}_2 - \vec{v}_1)}{\Delta t}$$

Essential Understandings

- Friction is the force that opposes motion when one surface moves or tends to move with respect to another.
- Limiting static friction is the maximum value of the force of friction just before an object starts to move.
- Kinetic friction is the force of friction that opposes the motion of a moving object.
- An object will continue in a state of rest or constant velocity unless acted on by an external net force (Newton's first law).
- Inertia is the property of an object that resists changes in its motion. The larger the mass of an object, the more inertia it has.
- When a net force acts on an object, the object accelerates in the direction of the force with an acceleration that varies directly with the net force and inversely with the mass (Newton's second law).
- When one object exerts a force on a second object, the second object exerts a force that is equal in size and opposite in direction on the first object (Newton's third law).

Consolidate Your Understanding

1. Look back to your answer for the Checkpoint on page 91. What answer would you give now? Explain why each of the other answers is incorrect

An SUV of mass M pushes a small car of mass m from rest and gives it a uniform acceleration along a rough dirt trail. Describe all of the action and reaction pairs of forces involved in this situation.

2. Create a concept map to be used as a study map for friction and Newton's three laws. Consult the Key Terms provided above, and include as many terms as possible in your concept map. Include the equation for Newton's second law and an example problem involving friction. Show a model solution using the GRASS strategy.

3. Write a paragraph explaining the similarities and differences among Newton's three laws. Describe a sports example that involves all three laws and explain how each applies. Use the example to teach the laws to a peer who has not studied dynamics. Summarize the strengths and weaknesses of your lesson.

CHAPTER 3 REVIEW

Understanding Concepts

1. Which one of the following physical quantities did Galileo postulate to explain the motion of a chariot on a level road?
   a) gravity
   b) inertia
   c) friction
   d) action force
   e) reaction force

2. A skater, of mass m, is on a planet where the gravitational field intensity is g and static friction is μ. What is the correct expression for finding the force of limiting static friction F_f?
   a) $F_f = \dfrac{\mu m}{g}$
   b) $F_f = \dfrac{\mu g}{m}$
   c) $F_f = \mu mg$
   d) $F_f = \dfrac{mg}{\mu}$
   e) $F_f = \dfrac{1}{\mu mg}$

3. Table 3.6 shows some coefficients of limiting static friction μ_s, and kinetic friction μ_k for rubber tires in contact with various surfaces.

TABLE 3.6 Coefficients of Friction for a Highway

Surface	Dry Concrete	Dry Asphalt	Wet Concrete	Wet Asphalt
μ_s	1.0	1.2	0.7	0.6
μ_k	0.7	0.6	0.5	0.5

Which of the following statements is/are correct?
I Dry concrete has more static friction than dry asphalt.
II A car slides more easily on wet concrete than on wet asphalt.
III A moving car begins to slide more easily on dry concrete than on dry asphalt.
IV A car with locked brakes slides a shorter distance on dry concrete than on dry asphalt.

Choose your answer from the following:
   a) III only
   b) IV only
   c) I and II only
   d) III and IV only
   e) II, III, and IV only

4. If we know the size and direction of the unbalanced force acting on an object of given mass, Newton's second law allows us to calculate
   a) displacement
   b) position
   c) speed
   d) velocity
   e) acceleration

5. A transport truck pulls on a trailer with a force of 600 N [E]. The trailer pulls on the transport truck with a force of
   a) zero
   b) less than 600 N [W], if the truck is slowing down
   c) 600 N [W], only if the truck is moving at constant velocity
   d) 600 N [W], no matter what the acceleration of the truck
   e) more than 600 N [W], if the truck is accelerating

6. a) An inexperienced driver, stuck in snow, tends to spin the car tires to increase the friction between the snow and the tires. What advice would you give to the driver? Why?
   b) Why is friction increased if a bag of sand is placed in the trunk of a car?
   c) Why is it wise to pay attention to the road sign that states: "Drive carefully—road slippery when wet"?

7. During a parachute jump, the person is initially in free fall and then the parachute is opened. While in free fall, there are two forces acting on the jumper—gravity and air friction. The faster the jumper is falling, the more air friction there is. At a certain speed, the upward force of air friction is just equal in size to the downward pull of gravity. When this happens, the jumper has no net force on her and therefore she falls at a constant velocity. This velocity is called the "terminal velocity." The force of wind friction on a certain 90-kg jumper is calculated using the equation $\vec{F}_f = 0.50v^2$ where the speed is in m/s and the force is in newtons. Calculate the terminal velocity of this parachutist.

8. An 80-kg baseball player slides into third base. The coefficient of kinetic friction between the player and the ground is 0.70. If his speed at the start of the slide is 8.23 m/s,
   a) Calculate his acceleration during the slide.
   b) How long (in time) does he slide until he stops?
   c) You really didn't need to know the mass of the player to solve this problem. Use your knowledge of formulas to show that the time it takes the player to come to a stop is $\Delta t = \dfrac{v_1}{\mu_k g}$.

9. The horse ridden by a member of the Canadian equestrian team stopped suddenly and refused to jump a hurdle. Why might a less skilled rider be pitched forward off the horse when this happens?

10. Explain how a car headrest minimizes injury in a rear end collision.

11. A basketball player starts, stops, and changes direction quickly. Use Newton's second and third laws to identify the sources of the forces that cause his accelerations.

12. An athlete lifting weights exerts an action force on the barbells. What is the source, target, and direction of the reaction force?

13. Two campers discover that the head of their axe is partially off the handle. One camper claims that it is easiest to jar the head back on the handle by holding the axe vertically with the head up while the end of the handle is tapped on a rock. The other claims that the handle should face up while the head of the axe is tapped on the rock. For best results, who is correct and why?

14. The movement of passengers on a bus, particularly during rapid changes in the vehicle's direction, is due to Galileo's law of inertia. Give examples to support this claim.

15. One factor that affects the stopping performance of automobile tires is the mass of the vehicle. For a certain car weighing 8000 N, its acceleration during a stop from 50 km/h is $\vec{a} = -0.87\vec{g}$.
   a) How long would it take this vehicle to come to a stop from 50 km/h?
   b) How far would it travel before stopping?
   c) If the weight of this vehicle were increased to 12 000 N, the stopping acceleration could be given by $\vec{a} = -0.81\vec{g}$. What would be the stopping distance of this same car now that it is heavier?
   d) How does this information affect the safe driving habits of drivers of large, heavy vehicles?

Applying Inquiry/ Communication Skills

16. A knowledge of Newton's laws and of how the human body moves led to the science of ergonomics. Research the topic of ergonomics to find out how it can be useful in the workplace. Detail one specific example that would be useful to you.

17. Punch two holes near the corners on opposite sides of a rectangular cardboard drink box. Hang the box from a rigid support with a string. Predict what will happen if the box is filled with water and then the holes are opened. Use Newton's third law to explain your prediction.

18. Manufacturers of skis recommend different waxes for different snow conditions. Design and carry out an experiment to test these recommendations.

19. Design an experiment using a spark air table and an air puck to verify Newton's second law. Submit a report on your findings. **Caution:** A shock from a spark air table can be dangerous.

20. A 41-kg weather balloon 24 km above Earth is travelling at a constant velocity of 5.0 m/s [W]. If $\vec{g} = 9.7$ m/s^2 [down], draw a free-body diagram for the balloon.

Making Connections

21. One suggestion for managing nuclear waste is to store it below the seabed in the deepest parts of the ocean. One method would be to drop a bullet-shaped canister so that it hits the floor of the ocean at 112 km/h and penetrates the sediment to a depth of 30 m before stopping. If the canister and its contents have a mass of 50 kg
   a) Calculate the average acceleration of the canister from the time it enters the seabed until it stops.
   b) Calculate the average net force exerted on the canister during its acceleration.
   c) What is your opinion on this solution to nuclear waste storage?

22. Research the equation for the relationship between drag D, drag coefficient C_D, air speed v, and frontal area A, for the aerodynamics of cars. Write a report outlining the changes engineers are making in the shape of cars to decrease drag.

23. Urban driving involves shorter trips and lower average speeds with less air friction than highway driving. However, Transport Canada's Fuel Consumption Guide shows a higher fuel consumption for urban driving than for highway driving. Write a report to explain this apparent contradiction.

24. The science of ballistics is useful in criminology. One way to determine the muzzle velocity of a bullet is to fire the bullet into a box of sand. The box of sand then slides along a table. The farther the box slides, the faster the bullet was going when it entered the box. When the bullet is fired into a 1.0-kg box of sand, the box and bullet slide 4.4 cm along the table. The coefficient of friction between the box and the table is 0.42. For this particular bullet and box, ballistics experts know that the speed of the bullet entering the box is $v_b = 501v_1$, where v_1 is the initial speed of the bullet-box system as it begins its slide along the table. Calculate the muzzle velocity of the bullet.

25. Use inertia and Newton's first law to explain how the spin cycle in a washing machine removes water from wet clothes.

Physics—So Much More Than Theory

When students are asked about career choices in science, most can name several in biology or chemistry but get stuck trying to think of what they could do with an interest in physics. In part, this is because physics has an undeserved reputation as being more theoretical than practical. People may view it as the ultimate career choice only for someone interested in developing the next great theory linking everything in the cosmos, hopefully within one easy equation. Many students who enjoy physics in high school end up dismissing their interest in this subject when thinking about a career, simply because they don't see what they can do with it.

While it's true that the theories of physics are important, physics itself is more than theory. Like the other sciences, physics is composed of different fields or specializations. The following table shows some projects underway right now in applied and industrial physics, sorted by field. Some of these terms will be unfamiliar to you. How can you find out what they mean?

What's Happening in Physics

Field	A Project Underway in This Field
acoustics	thermoacoustic refrigeration
biomedical	dental restorative materials
chemical	physics of rocket plume trails
computers	numerical simulations of chemically reactive flows, aerospace navigation systems
electronics	nanoscale self-assembling materials
environmental	assessing buried toxic wastes
fluids	remote sensing of the ocean
geophysics	stimulation technology to improve oil and gas production
manufacturing techniques	alignment and overlay in computer chips
materials	radiation-induced defects in space devices
mechanical systems	aerodynamics of air-bearing sliders
medical physics	diagnostic imaging with positron emission tomography
molecular	adhesion of small particles
nuclear / atomic	nuclear fusion, positron annihilation spectroscopy
optics / photonics	untwinkling starlight using optical phase conjugation / tunable solid-state lasers
plasma	iridescent optical films to prevent counterfeit bills
polymer	conducting polymer light-emitting diodes
semiconductors	artificial neural nets
space	atmospheric reentry testing
telecommunications	superconductors as microwave filters, optical switches
transportation	inertial navigation systems, non-intrusive inspection of trucks and luggage for explosives and contraband

Expanding Your Awareness

Each field in the table represents a specialized area of physics which is, in turn, further divided. In telecommunications, someone may investigate the effect of transmitting signals through water on fish migration, or forecast the impact of solar storms on satellite television. Still within this field, you might find a person designing an interactive television screen or the next wave of cellular phones. So any field in physics, or any other science, is like the tip of an iceberg. There is much more to it than you would think at first sight.

1. Examine the list of fields in the table.
   - Use the table of contents in this text to find out which fields you will be studying in class. If you are interested in a field you will not be studying in class, ask your teacher how you could learn more about it.
   - What are these projects about? Try putting the project description into a search engine and see what you find. Some of the terminology will be unfamiliar. Collect any terms you don't know and challenge yourself to find their meanings.

Choices in Physics

There are more fields within physics than are listed here, and new ones are developing all the time. For example, polymer and plasma physics are relatively recent arrivals. Within any of these fields the number of choices expands again. How can you use these fields to help you think about your career choices?

2. Choose the project from the table that is the closest match to one of your own current interests. Research to find out more about it.

FIGURE 1
Telecommunications is a fast-growing field offering many career opportunities.

For example, if you are interested in marine animals, you might pick remote sensing of the oceans. You may not have considered this project as something to explore, but it could combine your interests very well. Be open-minded and investigate any such matches.

Looking Outward

3. Choose a project from the table that is completely different from anything you can imagine doing in the future.
   - Which field of physics is this part of?
   - What might you enjoy doing within this field?

Be honest and dig a little. You might be pleasantly surprised, or you might be able to eliminate that field as a choice for now. Eliminating choices can be just as useful to your career search as finding interesting options.

Are Amber-Light Times Set Correctly?

Background Information

It is a major offence under the highway traffic act in Ontario to enter a light-controlled intersection after the light turns red. This violation means demerit points and can lead to insurance rate increases. Running the red light can result in a serious collision, as a car waiting to turn left may turn in front of an approaching vehicle because the driver was expecting the approaching vehicle to stop for the red light.

The **amber-light time** depends on two factors: the reaction time of the driver and the braking time. The reaction time is the time that elapses between the driver seeing the amber light and applying the brakes. The Ministry of Transportation of Ontario (MTO) Traffic Branch *Manual of Uniform Traffic Control* allows for a reaction time of 1.0 s for city driving and 1.8 s for provincial highways, where the speeds involved are greater.

The braking time is the time it takes the vehicle to come to a full stop once the brakes are applied. This time depends on the initial speed of the vehicle and negative acceleration of the vehicle. The MTO-predicted braking times are based on the assumption that vehicles are travelling at the posted speed limit and, for most purposes, the MTO uses a uniform acceleration of $-3.0\ \text{m/s}^2$. The actual deceleration is affected by factors such as the coefficient of friction between the road surface and the tires, air resistance, and whether the car is going up or down a hill.

A driver encountering an amber light at a light-controlled intersection must answer two questions: "Am I far enough from the intersection so that I can stop before the amber light turns red?" (stop-distance) and "Is my distance from the intersection such that I have enough time to pass through the intersection during the amber time?" (go distance.)

The **stop-distance** is the sum of the distance travelled during the reaction time and the distance travelled during the braking time. If the vehicle is further from the intersection than the stopping distance it can safely stop before entering the intersection.

The **go-distance** is the maximum distance from the intersection the vehicle can be and still pass through the intersection without encountering a red light. The go distance depends on the speed of the vehicle, the length of the intersection, and the amber-light time.

SCENARIO

You work for MTO on a committee of four people responsible for making recommendations for changes in the Traffic Branch *Manual of Uniform Traffic Control.* Your committee is to investigate the amber-light time settings at different intersections in the city. You are to decide how well the amber-light time is matched to the posted speed limit, the intersection length, the incline of the roadway, and the condition of the road surface. Assume throughout your analysis that drivers are travelling at posted speed limits.

Part A: Research

1. Research or derive equations to determine:
   a) displacement of a car during the reaction time
   b) coefficient of static friction acting on a rubber tire of known weight
   c) force of static friction acting on a car of known weight
   d) deceleration of a vehicle of known mass after the brakes are applied
   e) deceleration time after the brakes are applied
   f) deceleration displacement after the brakes are applied
   g) stop distance
   h) amber light time
   i) go distance

Part B: Design and Analysis

2. Design a survey to measure the amber-light times at ten different intersections near your school.
   - For each intersection record the type of road surface, intersection length, and intersection slope. (Be Careful!)
   - Apply suitable equations from part A to determine appropriate amber times for the ten different intersections.
   - Calculate stop distances and go distances for a range of posted speed limits for each intersection and plot graphs of stop distance and go distance against the posted speed.

3. Design an investigation to measure the coefficients of static friction between a bicycle tire and a level asphalt road surface. Measure the coefficient for both wet and dry conditions. It is important to get approval from your teachers before taking any measurements.

Part C: Making Recommendations

4. Consult the Internet and other sources to research the causes of accidents at light-controlled intersections. Recommend a course of action to educate the public about how these accidents can be prevented.

Part D: Communicating Your Analysis

5. Based on your surveys and investigation, recommend whether existing amber-light times should be increased, decreased, or left the same. Consider posted speeds against actual speeds, level against inclined surfaces, and wet against dry surface conditions in your answer. You may also wish to consider the mass of the vehicle and its load.

6. Prepare a presentation to the other members of your committee. Include graphs and diagrams in your presentation.

UNIT 1 REVIEW

Understanding Concepts

1. A hiker walks 15 km [E], 5.0 km [S], 3.0 km [W], and 5.0 km [N]. The resultant displacement is
a) 12 km b) 12 km [E] c) 15 km [E]
d) 18 km [E] e) 28 km

2. Each side of a square racetrack is 100 m. A runner at the southeast corner starts running northward and runs once around the track in 50 s. The runner's average velocity is
a) zero b) 1.0 m/s [W] c) 2.0 m/s
d) 6.0 m/s e) 8.0 m/s [W]

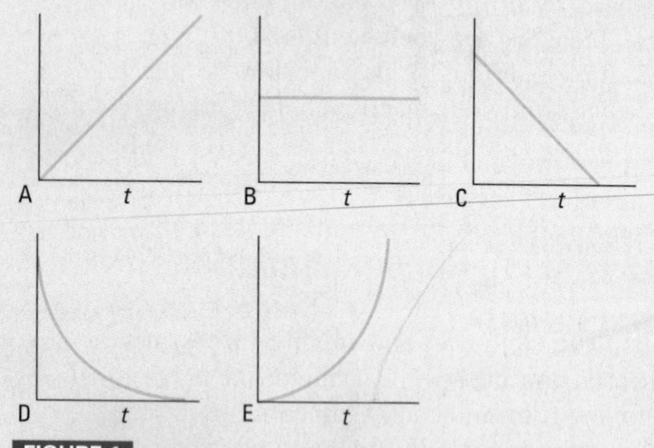

FIGURE 1

Use Figure 1 to answer the next question.

3. If the graph sketches in Figure 1 are position–time graphs, which one(s) represent constant velocity?
a) A only b) A and C only c) D only
d) A, B, and C only e) E only

4. If the graph sketches in Figure 1 are velocity–time graphs, which one(s) represent increasing acceleration?
a) A, B, and C b) E only c) D only
d) A only e) B only

5. If the graph sketches in Figure 1 are velocity–time graphs, which one represents constant positive acceleration?
a) A b) B c) C
d) D e) E

6. A student was working on a satellite problem and had simplified the solution as far as 57.3 N·s²/m. The student was solving for
a) force b) mass c) acceleration
d) period e) radius

7. A northbound train traveling at 30 m/s slows down with a constant acceleration of -4.0 m/s². How long will it take the train to stop?
a) 0.13 s b) -7.5 s c) 7.5 s
d) 34 s e) 120 s

8. A 60-kg skydiver is falling through the air (parachute unopened) and the force of wind resistance is 200 N [up]. The net vertical force on the skydiver is
a) 140 N [down] b) 388 N [down]
c) 588 N [down] d) 788 N [down]
e) 788 N [up]

9. If a small net force acts on an object, the object
a) remains stationary
b) moves at a constant velocity
c) accelerates
d) comes to rest and remains at rest
e) moves with uniform motion

10. Suppose that the only horizontal forces acting on a 12-kg mass are 60 N [W] and 36 N [E]. The acceleration of the mass will be
a) 0.5 m/s² [W] b) 2.0 m/s² [W] c) 5.0 m/s² [W]
d) 8.0 m/s² [W] e) 24 m/s² [W]

11. The force of gravity on a mass at two Earth radii from the centre of Earth is 200 N. The force of gravity on this mass when it moves to a distance of 10 Earth radii from Earth's centre would be
a) 2 N b) 8 N c) 20 N
d) 40 N e) 2000 N

12. An 8-kg body was accelerated from 21 m/s to 29 m/s by a net force of 16 N. The net force was applied for
a) 0.5 s b) 1 s c) 2 s
d) 4 s e) 8 s

13. Galileo's thought experiment was designed to show that an object released down a frictionless ramp
a) returns to the same height on another indentical ramp
b) travels a shorter distance to reach the same height on a steeper ramp
c) travels a longer distance to reach the same height on a less steep ramp
d) has a velocity of zero at the same height on another indentical ramp
e) travels on the level at constant velocity if the unbalanced force is zero

14. A person applies a force of 15 N [E] on an object of weight 20 N If the force of friction has a magnitude of 5.0 N, what is the acceleration of the object?
a) 7.5 m/s² [E] b) 0.13 m/s² [E] c) 0.50 m/s² [E]
d) 5.0 m/s² [E] e) 10 m/s² [E]

15. A book is lying on the table. The table is exerting an upward force on the book which is equal in magnitude to the downward force exerted by the book on the table. This example illustrates
a) Galileo's law of inertia
b) Newton's first law
c) Newton's second law
d) Newton's third law
e) Newton's law of universal gravitation

16. If a driver is pulled over by the police for speeding, which type of speed is in question: instantaneous speed or average speed? Why?

17. How is it possible for a car to be traveling due north while it is accelerating southward?

18. A baseball is thrown straight up in the air. While it is traveling up, what is the direction of its
 a) displacement?
 b) velocity?
 c) acceleration?

19. Suggest two benefits to an engineer of drawing a free-body diagram.

20. The force of gravity on the Moon is less than the pull of gravity on the Earth. As a result, a pendulum on the Moon swings slower than it would on Earth. On the Moon, a pendulum 36 cm long has a period of 3.0 s. Use the pendulum formula $T = 2\pi \frac{\sqrt{l}}{\sqrt{g}}$ to calculate the value of $\vec{g}$ on the Moon.

21. A person wearing a plaster cast on an arm or a leg experiences extra fatigue. Explain this on the basis of Newton's second law.

22. If your pencil exerts a force of 15 N [down] on this paper, what is the reaction force according to Newton's third law?

Applying Inquiry/ Communication Skills

23. In a basketball game, player X_1 passes to X_2 who in turn passes to X_3. The first pass travels 7.1 m [E 45° S] while the second pass goes 7.1 m [S 45° W] as shown in Figure 2. Use a vector diagram or your knowledge of trigonometry to find out the resultant displacement of the ball

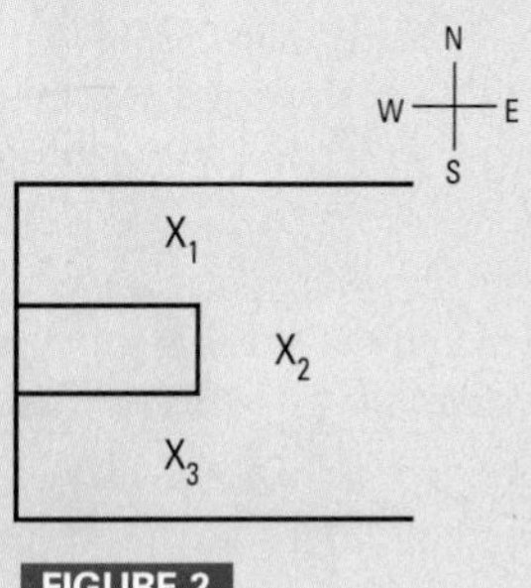

FIGURE 2

24. The position–time data for two walkers, A and B, are shown below.

Time Δt (s)	0	5.0	10	15	20	25	30	35	40	45	50
Position $\vec{d}_A$ (m) [from X]	0	7.5	15	22.5	30	37.5	50	62.5	75	87.5	100
Position $\vec{d}_B$ (m) [from X]	100	87.5	75	62.5	50	37.5	30	22.5	15	7.5	0

Use the graphing calculator or a spreadsheet program to plot both position–time graphs on the same axis. Then answer the following questions using the graph and the data.
 a) From the graph, which person, A or B moved at the highest velocity early in the walk? How do you know?
 b) Where and when did they meet? How do you know?
 c) How many different velocities did each person have? How do you know?
 d) What is the average velocity for each person? How do they compare?
 e) What was the position of each person at a time of 28 s?
 f) When was each person at a position 70 m [from X]?

25. A car is stopped at a stop light facing due east. When the light turns green, the car gradually speeds up from rest to the city speed limit, cruises at the speed limit for a while, then enters a highway on-ramp and gradually speeds up to the highway speed limit all the while heading due east. Sketch a position–time graph and then a velocity–time graph to illustrate the motion of this car.

26. A sprinter ran a race in 12 s. Her velocity-time data are shown below.

Time Δt (s)	0	1.0	2.0	3.0	4.0	5.0	6.0	7.0	8.0	9.0	10	11	12
Velocity $\vec{v}$ (m/s) [forward]	0	0	2.8	4.8	6.2	7.5	8.6	9.6	10.3	10.8	11	10.8	10.6

Use your graphing calculator or a spreadsheet program to plot a velocity–time graph of the motion and use the graph and the data to answer the following questions.
 a) Describe the shape of the graph.
 b) What was the reaction time of the sprinter? How do you know?
 c) When did the sprinter have the greatest acceleration? How do you know?
 d) When did the sprinter reach her maximum velocity? How do you know?
 e) What was the average acceleration of the sprinter for the race?
 f) Explain how to find the length of the race from the graph.

g) What was the velocity of the sprinter at a time of 6.5 s?

h) At what time was the velocity 8.0 m/s [forward]?

27. Explain, using diagrams, why a vector can be subtracted by adding the vector in the opposite direction.

28. Two students investigating the effect of different forces on the acceleration of an object obtained the following data.

Acceleration $\vec{a}$ (m/s²) [forward]	0.0	1.0	2.0	3.0	4.0	5.0
Applied Force $\vec{F}$ (N) [forward]	0.50	5.50	10.5	15.5	20.5	25.5

Plot a graph using the graphing calculator and use it to answer the following questions.

a) What relationship exist between the acceleration and the applied force?

b) What is the equation for the graph?

c) What is the value of the force of friction? How do you know?

d) What is the mass of the object being accelerated? How do you know?

e) What acceleration would result if a force of 12.5 N is applied? Find out using both the equation and by interpolating from the graph.

29. Two students investigating the effect of the same force on the acceleration of different masses obtained the following data.

Acceleration $\vec{a}$ (m/s²) [forward]	10	5.0	3.3	2.5	1.7	1.0
Mass m (kg)	1.0	2.0	3.0	4.0	6.0	10

Plot a graph using a spreadsheet program or the graphing calculator and answer the following questions.

a) What relationship exists between the acceleration and the mass?

b) What is the equation for the curve?

c) What is the value of the net force? How do you know?

d) What would be the acceleration of an object of mass 8.0 kg? Find out using the equation and by interpolating from the graph.

30. The greater the speed of a car, the larger the force required to keep it moving. Write a paragraph outlining the explanations Aristotle and Galileo would have given for this phenomenon. Compare the explanations.

Making Connections

31. The average reaction time of a driver, (i.e. from the time of seeing an object to the instant when brakes are applied) is 0.75 s. This time is the same for all driving speeds. When the brakes are applied, a car typically slows down at the rate of about 12 m/s². Using this information, plot velocity–time graphs to compare a stop being made in a car from 100 km/h to a car stopping from 50 km/h. Include the reaction time and convert all velocities to m/s on your graphs. Use these velocity–time graphs to calculate the distance each car would travel during the stop.

32. Research the nature of the materials being used to make artificial joints like hips and knees. Find out how they are designed to provide enough friction for stability but not so much friction that they can't move.

33. Some swimmers are using the new full-body swimsuits to improve their performance. The makers of the suits contend that they work in two different ways. One way is to compress certain muscle systems to keep them from rippling the water and causing turbulence. The other way they are supposed to work is to reduce friction as the swimmer moves through the water. Some athletes feel that the suits work while others don't feel that they help.

a) Do some research to find out about the difference between streamlined flow and turbulent flow in water.

b) What percentage of medal winners at the 2000 Sidney Olympics were wearing the new body suits.

c) Some critics suggest that the companies who have their logo on the suit are just getting free advertising — using the swimmers as a billboard for their product. Interview a few of your classmates about this idea and report on your findings.

Problem Solving

34. Suppose you drive 120 km [N] and then 50 km [E]. The first part of your trip took 1.5 h while the second part took 0.50 h. Calculate your average speed and your average velocity for the whole trip.

35. A car stopped at a stop light, speeds up from rest to the speed limit of 14 m/s in 2.0 s. If the car is heading east, calculate its average acceleration.

36. How long would it take a truck to increase its velocity from 10 m/s [S] to 30 m/s [S] if it does so with constant acceleration over a displacement of 80 m [S]?

37. In August 1987, Angella Issajenko, a twenty nine year old Canadian sprinter, ran the 100 m dash in Cologne, West Germany in 10.97 s. Her winning time set a new outdoor record for the 100 m dash at normal altitudes.

accelerated uniformly for the first 12.0 m and then travelled at constant velocity to the finish line. If her mass was 50.0 kg,

a) what was her maximum velocity?
b) what average horizontal force did her feet exert on the ground while accelerating? Assume that one foot was always in contact with the ground and that there was no wind resistance opposing her.

38. Three people are trying to cut down a tree. While one does the sawing, the other two pull on the tree with ropes in order that the tree will fall in a certain direction. The horizontal forces they exert on the tree are 400 N [E 30° N] and 300 N [E 45° S]. In what direction will the tree fall if these are the only horizontal forces acting on it?

39. Skylab 1, the first American space station, had a mass of about 68 t and was launched into an orbit 435 km above Earth's surface. Calculate the force of gravity on Skylab1 if g = 8.58 N/kg [down] at this altitude.

40. A newton spring scale is used to measure the force of gravity on a 4.00-kg silver ingot on Earth. If the ingot and spring scale are transported to the surface of Mars, where $\vec{g}$ = 3.61 N/kg [down], by how much does the reading on the spring scale change?

41. A 50-kg diver steps off a 9.0-m diving tower at the same time as a 100-kg diver. Compare the times taken for the two divers to reach the water.

42. A baseball player hits the ball straight up in the air with a velocity of 18.0 m/s. As soon as the ball is hit, the runner on third base dashes at a constant speed of 7.60 m/s toward home plate. The distance between third base and home plate is 27.4 m. Where will the runner be with reference to home plate when the ball returns to its initial height?

43. A stone is dropped down a deep well to determine the distance to the water. The sound of the splash is heard 4.00 s after the stone is released. Calculate

a) the depth of the well if the speed of sound is infinite.
b) the depth of the well if the speed of sound is 335 m/s.

44. Two people on opposite banks, are towing a boat down a narrow river. Each person exerts a force of 65.0 N at an angle of 30° to the bank. A force of friction of 104 N opposes the motion of the boat.

a) Make a free-body diagram showing the horizontal forces on the boat.
b) Calculate the net horizontal force.

45. The coefficient of limiting static friction of a rubber tire on wet concrete is 0.70. What mass of tractor, with its brakes locked, can be dragged by a tow truck that can exert a horizontal force of 1.0×10^4 N?

46. During the last seconds of a hockey game, the losing team replaces their goalie with a good shooter. The other team shoots the 150-g puck with a speed of 7.0 m/s directly toward the unguarded goal from a distance of 32 m. If the coefficient of kinetic friction is 0.08,

a) what is the force of kinetic friction on the puck?
b) what is the deceleration of the puck?
c) how long does the puck take to stop?
d) will the puck reach the goal if no other player touches it?

47. The Soviet Union's G rocket has a mass of about 3.8×10^6 kg and its first stage engines exert a thrust of about 5.0×10^7 N.

a) What is the force of gravity on the rocket at Earth's surface?
b) Calculate the net force on the rocket at lift-off.
c) Calculate the initial acceleration of the rocket.
d) What should happen to the acceleration if the force exerted by the engine remains constant as the fuel burns?
e) Why is the first stage jettisoned after the fuel is consumed?

48. The engine of a train has a mass of 5.0×10^4 kg. It can accelerate six railway cars having a total mass of 3.0×10^5 kg at 0.40 m/s^2. What acceleration can it give four railway cars having a total mass of 2.0×10^5 kg? (ignore friction)

49. A tennis racket, in contact with a 55-g ball for 0.0050 s, changes the ball's velocity from 30 m/s [E] to 40 m/s [W]. What average force does the racket exert on the ball?

50. A drag racing car starting from a standstill can reach a speed of 320 km/h in 6.50 s by exerting an average horizontal force of 1.52×10^4 N on the pavement. If friction equals 5.2×10^3 N, what is the mass of the car?

51. A 0.25-kg model rocket accelerates from 15 m/s [up] to 40 m/s [up] in 0.60 s. Calculate the force the escaping gases exert on the rocket.

52. A 4-kg body was accelerated from 10 m/s to 18 m/s by an unbalanced force of 8 N. for how long was the force applied?

53. Two boxes, one of mass 60 kg and the other 90 kg, are in contact and at rest on a smooth surface. An 800-N force is exerted on the 60-kg box toward the 90-kg box. Calculate:

a) the acceleration of the boxes.
b) the magnitude of the action and reaction forces between the boxes.

54. A 1450-kg car can pull a loaded trailer of mass 454 kg. The car wheels exert a horizontal force of 7.5×10^3 N [backward] against the ground in order to accelerate. If the coefficient of rolling friction on the trailer and car is 0.40, what force does the car exert on the trailer?

UNIT 2 Work, Energy, and Power

OVERALL EXPECTATIONS

By the end of this unit, you will be able to:

- demonstrate an understanding, in qualitative and quantitative terms, of the concepts of work, energy (kinetic energy, gravitational potential energy, and thermal energy and its transfer [heat]), energy transformations, efficiency, and power;
- design and carry out experiments and solve problems involving energy transformations and the law of conservation of energy;
- analyze the costs and benefits of various energy sources and energy-transformation technologies that are used around the world, and explain how the application of scientific principles related to mechanical energy has led to the enhancement of sports and recreational activities.

The solid rocket boosters of the space shuttle ignite, creating a giant fiery plume of hot gas. Cables suspended overhead on huge hydro towers hum loudly. An Indy racecar zooms past, creating a deafening roar that sounds like a jet plane. When we think of energy, these are the kinds of images that come to mind.

Energy comes in many different forms. It is all around you and affects every aspect of your life. The book you are reading right now has energy, the thermal energy created by the random motion of its molecules. The stapler teetering on the edge of your desk has gravitational potential energy, the energy that's released if it falls to the floor. The sandwich in your lunch bag contains the chemical energy stored in its molecules. All of these different forms of energy can be readily converted from one form into another.

For example, when your stapler falls off your desk and hits the floor, some of its gravitational potential energy is converted into sound energy. The sound energy radiates outward and you hear it as a loud irritating clang.

In this unit, you will examine various forms of energy including kinetic, chemical, and electrical energy. You will investigate what happens when work is done to convert one type of energy into another. You will examine various sources of energy and how each of them can be harnessed. You will look at the advantages and disadvantages of using non-renewable energy sources or renewable sources. You will study various machines that use energy to do work. By the time you complete the unit, you will have a better understanding of how your personal energy choices affect not only the environment, but the economy and society as well.

PHYSICS HEADLINES

Fuel-Cell Buses to Hit the Road

The first fuel-cell buses in a UN-funded project will be delivered to Sao Paulo, Brazil in 2002. The project aims to put 40 to 50 fuel-cell-powered buses on the road in major cities and capitals with some of the world's worst air pollution, in Brazil, Mexico, Eygpt, India, and China. At the moment fuel cell buses are not cost competitive with conventional diesel buses, but industry predictions are that the cost of the buses will drop dramatically once more are produced. It is expected that they will become commercially competitive between 2007 and 2010.

Brave Winds on the Prairies

Pincher Creek, Alberta is an ideal place for generating electricity from wind. Winds sweeping down from the Rockies can reach speeds of 170 km/h. If plans to expand two existing wind farms, and construct two new projects, go ahead more than 150 wind turbines could eventually generate 230 MW of electricity—enough to power as many as 70 000 homes.

U.S. Electricity Woes are Canada's Gain

In January, 2001, during a critical 24-h period of electrical shortage in California, B.C. Hydro filled in the gaps. Providing one third of all electricity for California, it's estimated that B.C. Hydro earned approximately $3 million from this one sale.

ACHIEVEMENT TASK PREVIEW

At the end of this unit you will be asked to prepare a position paper, reviewing the current production of primary energy in Canada, evaluate the effects various energy sources are hanving on the environment, identify ways for all Canadians to conserve energy, and, finally, formulate a plan for increasing the percentage of renewable energy in the primary energy source mix.

CHAPTER 4

Work and Energy

SPECIFIC EXPECTATIONS

By the end of this chapter, you will be able to:

- define and describe the concepts and units related to energy and work (4.1, 4.2)
- identify conditions required for work to be done, and apply quantitatively the relationships among work, force, and displacement along the line of the force (4.1)
- analyze, in qualitative and quantitative terms, simple situations involving work, gravitational potential energy, and kinetic energy using the law of conservation of energy (4.3, 4.4, 4.5)
- design and carry out experiments related to energy transformations, identifying and controlling major variables (4.5)
- analyze and interpret experimental data or computer simulations involving work, gravitational potential energy, kinetic energy, and the efficiency of the energy transformation (4.3, 4.4)
- communicate the procedures, data, and conclusions of investigations involving work, mechanical energy, and the law of conservation of energy, using appropriate means (4.5)

Energy is one of the most important concepts in physics. In the world around you there is energy in the food you eat, energy is used to heat or cool your home, energy provides the means to transport people and materials from one place to another. Even the ability to see and hear depends on energy. None of these examples defines energy, but they show that energy is needed to do many jobs. Life would not exist without energy.

FIGURE 4.1 Moving goods takes energy.

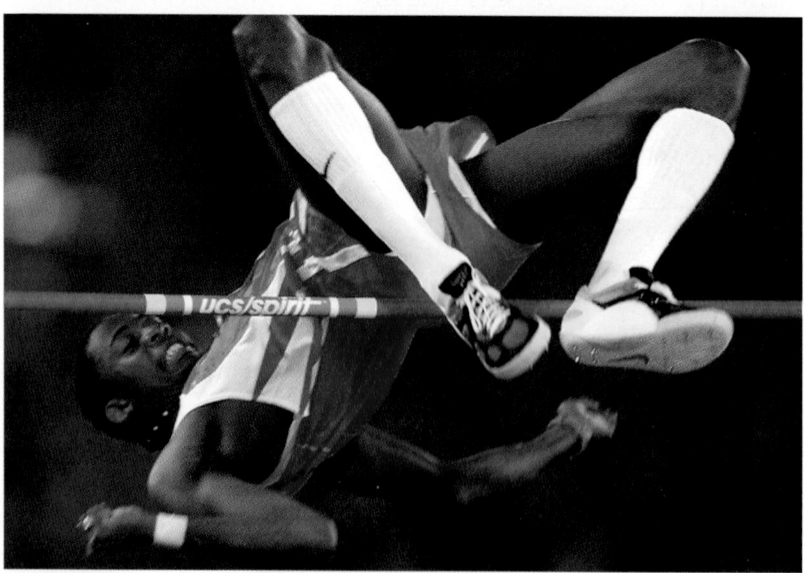

FIGURE 4.2 Mark Boswell jumps 2.31 m to win at the Canadian Olympic trials.

Energy is defined as the ability to do work, and work is done whenever there is a change or transfer of energy. Atheletes, like Canadian high-jumper Mark Boswell, spend years training for competitions. Boswell does work to convert running speed, muscular energy, and technique into height—height of the order of 2.3 m.

Energy comes in many forms and is readily converted from one form to another. It cannot be creatd from nothing; therefore we are constantly searching for new sources of energy. It cannot be destroyed; but when it changes from one form to another some is always converted to heat energy and is widely dispersed.

Knowledge of energy can improve your understanding of nature and allow you to work and play more efficiently. What is work? What is energy? What are the different forms and kinds of energy? Can energy be stored and used at a later time?

Discovering Physics

The Effect of Mass on Work

Raised objects can do work when they fall. How will the mass of an object affect the work done? If the object is released from twice the height will it do twice as much work? Form a hypothesis and predict what will happen if you release a sphere down a ramp from various heights and allow it to collide with a stationary object. Explain your prediction.

You will need the following: a drapery track, some books, a glass marble and a ball bearing with the same diameters (but different masses), a small wooden block or eraser with flat end, and a metre-stick.

1. Measure and record the mass of each sphere.
2. Make a ramp using the drapery track as shown in Figure 4.3.
3. Position the small wooden block or the eraser in the groove on the level part of the track.
4. Release the lightest sphere from a given height on the ramp and measure how far it pushes the wooden block or eraser along the track.
5. Repeat, using the heavier sphere.
6. Repeat, but release the heavier sphere from several different heights.
7. Record your observations.

Analyze your data.

- Which sphere did more work when released from the same height?
- Would a sphere of twice the mass push the block twice as far?
- How did increasing the release height affect the work done?
- What is the relationship between the release height and the displacement of the object?
- What factors affect the work done by an object released from an elevated position?

CHECKPOINT

The work done on an object is calculated by

a) dividing the force applied by the distance travelled
b) dividing the force applied by the distance travelled in the direction of the force
c) multiplying the force applied by the distance travelled
d) multiplying the force applied by the distance travelled and dividing by the time taken
e) multiplying the force applied by the distance travelled in the direction of the force.

Explain your answer using an everyday example.

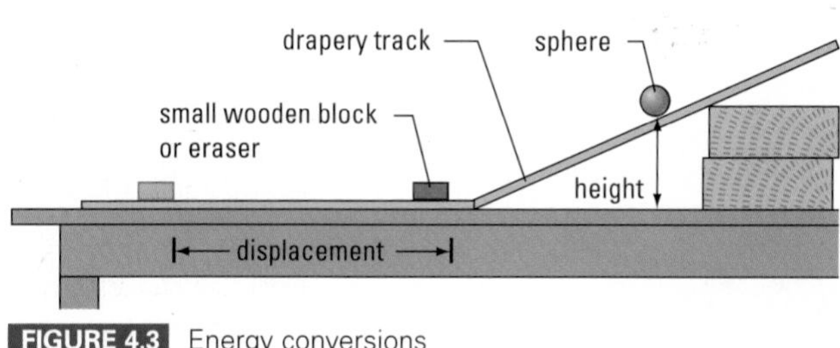

FIGURE 4.3 Energy conversions

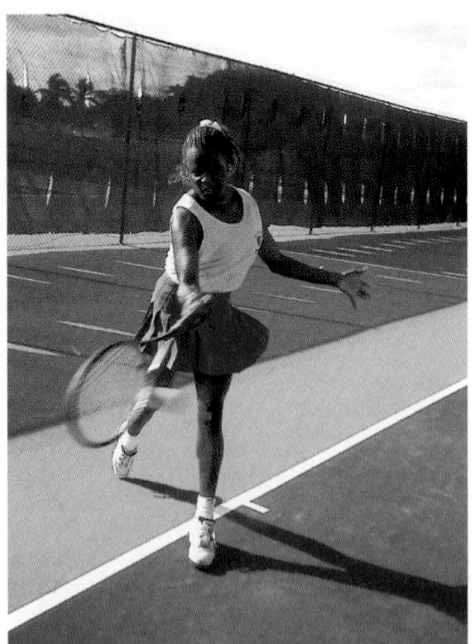

FIGURE 4.4 Work or play?

4.1 Work

Key Understandings

When you have completed this section, you will be able to:

- define and describe work
- identify the conditions required for work to be done
- solve problems involving displacement, force, and work
- interpret force–displacement graphs, and calculate work

The term "work" has different meanings for different people. A student doing homework calls it work. The same student probably calls a game of tennis play. However, a physicist would say the student is doing very little work during homework, but a great deal of work playing tennis. How does a scientist define work? How can we measure the amount of work done?

The Conditions for Mechanical Work

The scientific definition of "work" dictates that three conditions be met before any work is done:

1. A force must be exerted on an object.
2. The object must be displaced by the force.
3. At least part of the force must be in the same direction as the displacement.

In physics, therefore, the term "work" is restricted to activities involving both a force and a displacement. Figure 4.5 shows three examples where work is being done. In each case a force is applied to an object and there is a displacement of the object in the direction of the force.

Figure 4.6 shows three examples where work is not being done. In a), there is a force holding the parcel up, but no displacement. In b), the applied force is perpendicular to the displacement. In c), a space capsule is coasting with its engines off far out in space where the forces of gravity and friction

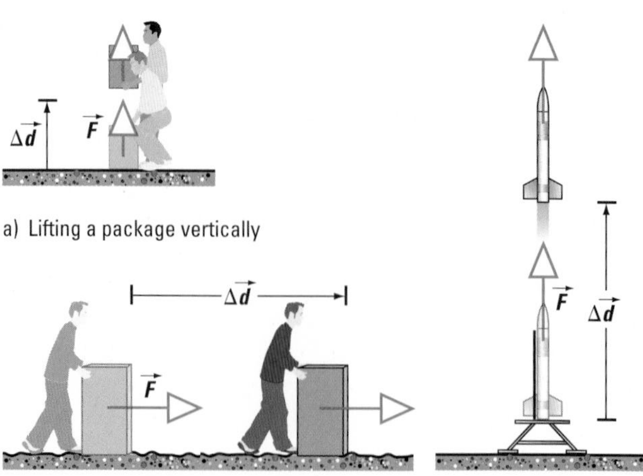

FIGURE 4.5 Work is done in these examples. Why?

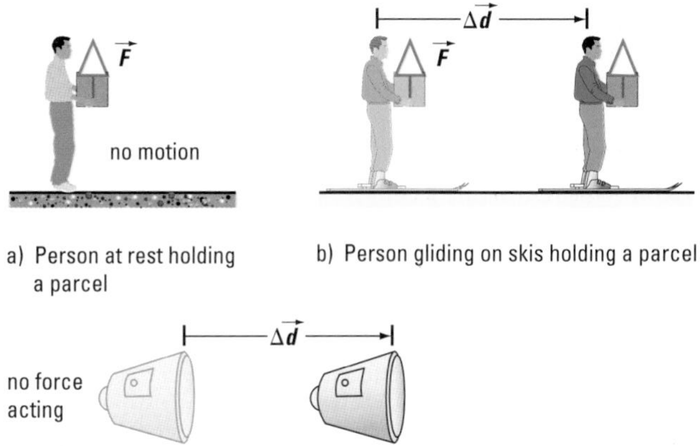

FIGURE 4.6 No work is being done in these examples. Why?

are negligible. Although there is a displacement, there is no force acting on the object, and therefore no work is done.

Work

Work, W, is the product of the magnitudes of the applied force and the displacement of the object in the direction of the force. The larger the applied force and the farther the object moves in the direction of the force, the more work is being done.

If not all of the force is exerted in the direction of the displacement then we have to calculate the part of the force that does act in that direction. Figure 4.7 shows a luggage carrier being pulled to the right by a force exerted along the handle. The handle makes an angle θ relative to to the displacement. We can find the component of the force in the direction of the displacement using trigonometry. This component is $F\cos\theta$.

Work = (magnitude of the force in the direction of the displacement)
× (magnitude of the displacement)

$$W = F\cos\theta\,\Delta d$$

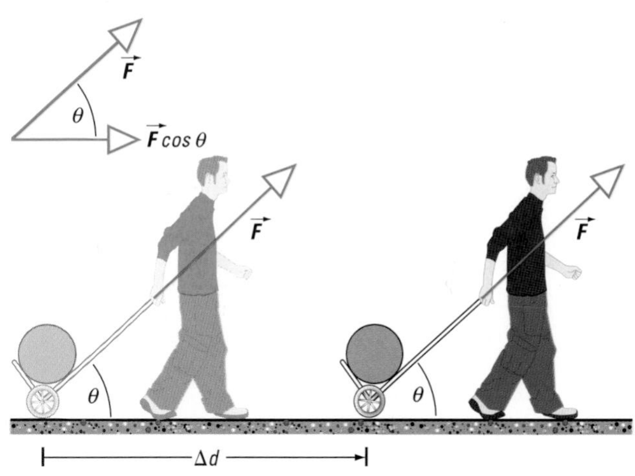

FIGURE 4.7 Finding the component of the force in the direction of the displacement.

where F is the magnitude of the force, Δd is the magnitude of the displacement, and θ is the angle between the force and the displacement. If the applied force is in the same direction as the displacement then the angle θ is zero. Since the cosine of zero is one, the equation simplifies to $W = F\Delta d$.

Since work is the product of the magnitude of the applied force and the displacement, the SI unit of work is the newton metre (N·m). The newton metre has been named the joule (J) in honour of the British physicist James Prescott Joule (1818–89), who studied energy conversions. One **joule** (J) is the work done by a force of one newton (N) applied through a displacement of one metre in the direction of the force:

$$1\ \text{J} = 1\ \text{N·m}$$

INFOBIT

Mathematically, work is defined as the dot product of the force and displacement vectors. The dot product of two vectors gives a scalar quantity in mathematics. Thus, "work" is a scalar quantity.

WEBLINK

To explore the factors affecting work, go to **www.pearsoned.ca/physics11.**

Work is a scalar quantity even though it is the product of two vector quantities—force and displacement. When you are using a force to push a stalled car 10 m, it doesn't matter whether you push the car north or west. As long as the force and displacement are in the same direction, the same amount of work is done. Thus, the vector signs and directions that usually go with force and displacement have been omitted for these physical quantities in this unit.

It is important to realize that there can be positive and negative work. For example, when a pitcher throws a baseball, the force and displacement are in the same direction and the work done on the ball is positive. For a catcher, however, the force exerted on the ball is exactly opposite to the displacement of the ball and so the work done on the ball is negative. Positive work, however, is done on the catcher and glove. Can you explain why?

EXAMPLE 1 NUMERICAL

A worker pulls a heavy cart. He exerts a force of 40 N [E] to pull the cart through a displacement of 5.0 m [E], as shown in Figure 4.8. Calculate the work done.

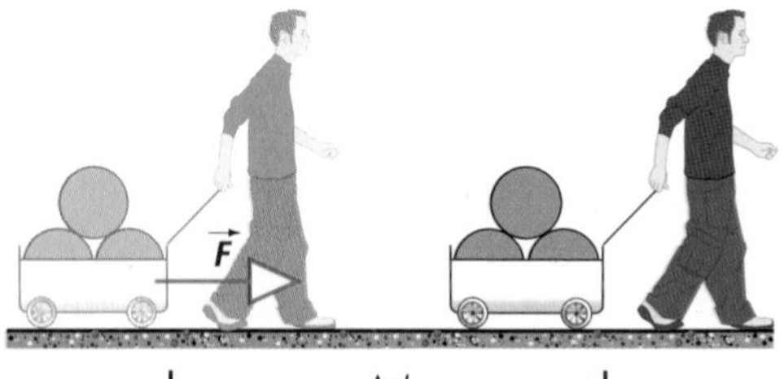

FIGURE 4.8

Given

$F = 40$ N [E]

$\Delta d = 5.0$ m [E]

Required

W

Analysis

Since the force and displacement are in the same direction, the cosine term becomes $\cos 0° = 1$

Solution

$$W = F\Delta d$$
$$= 40 \text{ N} \times 5.0 \text{ m}$$
$$= 200 \text{ N·m}$$
$$= 200 \text{ J}$$
$$= 2.0 \times 10^2 \text{ J}$$

Statement

The worker does 2.0×10^2 J of work in pulling the cart.

PRACTICE PROBLEMS

1. How far could you push a full recycling box along the sidewalk using a horizontal force of 300 N if you do 2.7 kJ of work?
2. What horizontal force would it take to drag a bag of compost 3.2 m along a level driveway using 1200 J of energy?

EXAMPLE 2 CONCEPTUAL

Find the work done when a tourist exerts a 55-N force in pulling a luggage carrier at an angle of 45° to the horizontal through a horizontal displacement of 85 m [E].

Reasoning and Solution

Since the force and the displacement are not in the same direction, to solve this problem we need to find out how much of the 55-N force actually acts in the east direction. The component of the force that acts in the same direction as the displacement is $F\cos 45°$. Then the work done is

$$
\begin{aligned}
W &= F\cos 45°\ \Delta d \\
&= 55\ \text{N} \times \cos 45° \times 85\ \text{m} \\
&= 3305.7\ \text{N·m} \\
&= 3.3 \times 10^3\ \text{J}
\end{aligned}
$$

The tourist does 3.3×10^3 J of work moving the luggage carrier.

CHALLENGE

A householder pushes some snow to the side of her driveway. She exerts a force on the shovel of 200 N at an angle of 30° to the horizontal. If she pushes the snow 1.5 m, how much work does she do?

EXAMPLE 3 CONCEPTUAL

A worker lifts a 10-kg box vertically upwards 95 cm from the floor. He then walks across the room and sets the box back down on the floor. How much work does he do when lifting the box, and when setting it back on the floor?

Reasoning and Solution

If objects are raised or lowered, the gravitational field intensity (9.8 N/kg [down]) comes into play. A force equal in magnitude to the force of gravity is needed to lift or lower the box at constant velocity. The magnitude of the force of gravity on the box is given by the equation $F_G = mg$.

The amount of work done in lifting the box is:

$$
\begin{aligned}
W &= F_G\Delta d \\
&= mg\Delta d \\
&= 10\ \text{kg} \times 9.8\ \text{N/kg} \times 0.95\ \text{m} \\
&= 93\ \text{N·m} \\
&= 93\ \text{J}
\end{aligned}
$$

The worker does 93 J of work when lifting the box and −93 J of work when setting the box back down on the floor.

INSIGHT

When an object is lifted up, the work done on the object by the lifter is positive because the force and displacement are both upwards. When the object is lowered, the work done by the lifter is negative because the force is upwards while the displacement is downwards. However, positive work is done on the person because the force applied on the person's hands is in the same direction as the displacement. How do we know that the box exerts a force on the person's hands? By Newton's third law, of course.

CHALLENGE

A weightlifter raises a 40-kg mass 80 cm up and then lowers the mass back to its starting position. How much work does she do during the lifting and during the lowering?

Discovering Physics — *Measuring Work*

Explore the relationship between force, mass, velocity, and distance.

You will need a table, a metre-stick, a spring scale, and three identical blocks of wood. Using the tape, mark off a 1-m distance on a table. Hold the spring scale horizontally and zero its scale before you start. Attach the spring scale to the first block of wood. Set the block behind the left-hand tape as shown in Figure 4.9. Pull the block with the spring scale until it reaches a constant, slow velocity. Pull the block through the 1-m displacement. Observe and record the average force exerted by the spring scale. Using the values for force and displacement, calculate the work done on the block. Repeat the experiment with a second and then a third wood block piled on the first one. Calculate the work done in each case.

Why is the force needed to pull two and then three blocks different from the force needed to pull one? Does the speed of the block affect the force necessary to pull it? Will the applied force be greater if you accelerate the block? If so, what is the extra work used for? How would you measure the work necessary to lift the block vertically 1 m at constant speed?

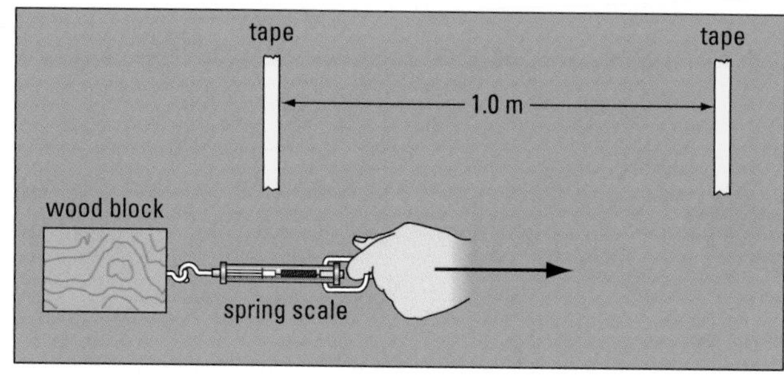

FIGURE 4.9 Measuring work

Calculating Work Graphically

Sometimes a force is applied to an object for one displacement and then replaced by a force of a different size for another displacement. Table 4.1 shows different forces exerted during four intervals, and the resulting displacements. The position from the start is recorded in the fourth column. Because each force and displacement is in the same direction, the work done during each interval is calculated using the formula $W = F\Delta d$.

TABLE 4.1 Different Forces for Different Displacements

Interval	Applied Force $\vec{F}$ (N [E])	Displacement $\Delta\vec{d}$ (m [E])	Position $\vec{d}$ (m [E from Start])	Interval Work W (J)	Total Work W (J)
A	3.0	1.0	1.0	3.0	3.0
B	4.0	3.0	4.0	12.0	15.0
C	2.0	3.0	7.0	6.0	21.0
D	1.0	2.0	9.0	2.0	23.0

Figure 4.10 shows the graph of force against position for the data in Table 4.1. The area beneath a force–displacement graph gives the work done on an object. The product of force and displacement for each interval is the rectangle beneath the line. Calculate the areas and compare them with the values for interval work calculated using $W = F\Delta d$.

In nature, forces frequently change in magnitude or direction or both. For example, the force needed to stretch an elastic spring varies directly with the displacement, or the amount of stretch, as shown in Figure 4.11. The force is zero when the stretch is zero, and increases uniformly to F as it stretches to a displacement of Δd. The work done by the force is equal to the area represented by the triangle beneath the line in Figure 4.11. The formula for calculating this is shown.

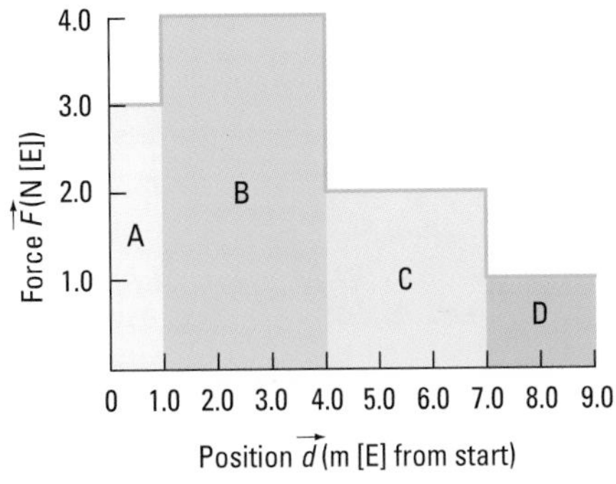

FIGURE 4.10 The area beneath the force–displacement graph represents the work done during each time interval.

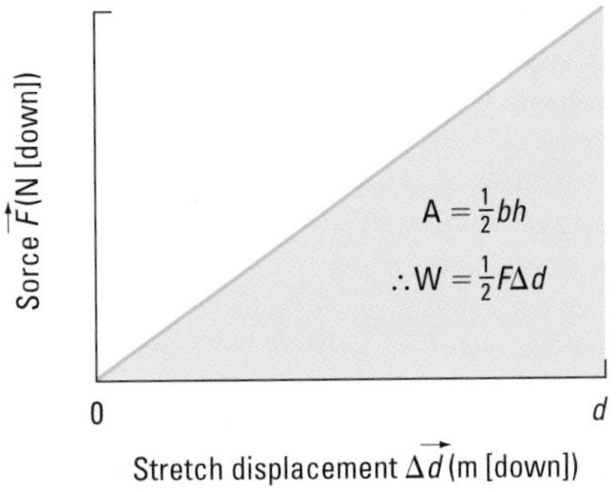

$$A = \frac{1}{2}bh$$

$$\therefore W = \frac{1}{2}F\Delta d$$

FIGURE 4.11 The work done by a uniformly changing force is represented by the area of the triangle under the force–displacement graph.

EXAMPLE 4 NUMERICAL

Figure 4.12 shows the force–extension graph for an elastic spring. Calculate the work done in stretching the spring 8.0 cm.

Given

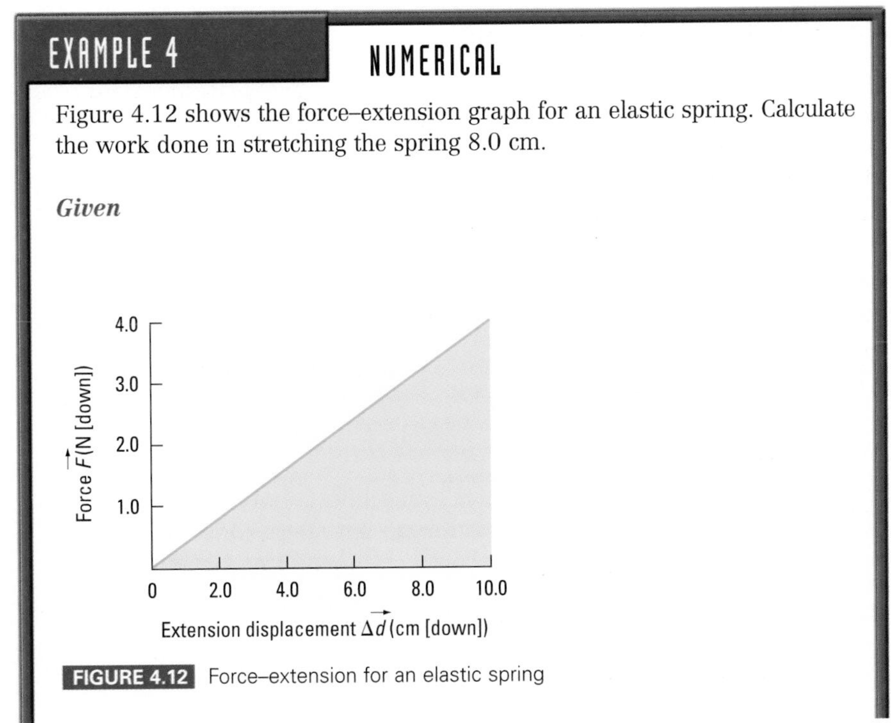

FIGURE 4.12 Force–extension for an elastic spring

Required
W

Analysis
Since the force is changing, find the work by calculating the area of the triangle beneath the graph to 8.0 cm. The units for the extension must be changed from cm to m.

PRACTICE PROBLEMS

1. Use the force–extension graph in Figure 4.12 to calculate the work done in stretching the spring 5.0 cm. Why is it not equal to 5/8 of the work needed to stretch the spring 8.0 cm?
2. Calculate the amount of work represented by one square of the grid on the force–displacement graph of Figure 4.13.

Solution
Base b = 8.0 cm = 0.080 m

Height h = 3.2 N

$$\text{Area} = \frac{1}{2}bh$$
$$= \frac{1}{2} \times 0.080 \text{ m} \times 3.2 \text{ N}$$
$$= 0.13 \text{ N·m}$$
$$= 0.13 \text{ J}$$
$$= 1.3 \times 10^{-1} \text{ J}$$

Statement
The work done in stretching the spring 8.0 cm is 1.3×10^{-1} J.

The graphical method can be used to determine work even if the force is changing in a nonuniform way, as shown in Figure 4.13. However, calculating the area is more difficult for a nonuniform force. It can be done by counting full squares and estimating parts of squares. Try it. You should get a value close to 20 full squares. This translates into a total of 40 J of work.

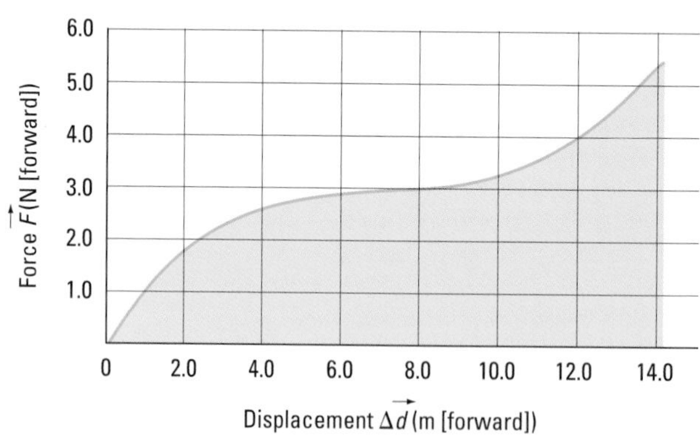

FIGURE 4.13 The area under this graph represents the amount of work done.

Section 4.1 Review

Understanding Concepts

1. a) What three conditions are necessary for work to be done?
   b) Define the joule.
   c) How much work is required to lift a 200-kg mass 2.0 m?
2. How much work is done by a football player pushing an opponent with a force of 700 N [E] for a displacement of 2.0 m [E]?
3. A child applies a force of 8.0 N [W] to pull a toy truck a displacement of 5.0 m [W] along the floor. How much work is done?
4. A plumber uses a rope to drag a heavy box 12 m across the shop. The rope makes an angle of 35° with the horizontal and the force applied is 280 N. How much work is done by the plumber?
5. A weightlifter lifts a 50-kg mass vertically 60 cm at constant velocity and then lowers it back down in the same manner. Calculate the work done
   a) during the lift
   b) during the return

Applying Inquiry/ Communication Skills

6. An archer obtains the force–stretch graph shown in Figure 4.14 for a bow. Calculate the work he did to stretch the bow 7.0 cm.

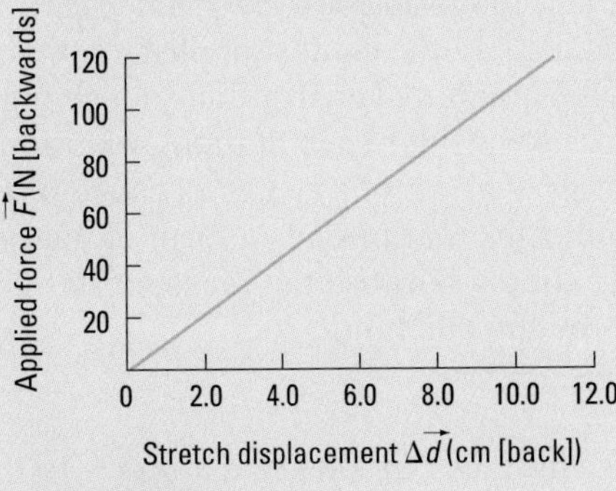

FIGURE 4.14

7. Three different forces are applied to an object, one after the other. The corresponding displacements are shown in Table 4.2.
   a) Calculate the work done by each force and the total work.
   b) Draw a force–position graph for the data.
   c) Calculate the total work using the graph. Compare this with the value obtained in a).

TABLE 4.2 Force–Displacement Data

Interval	Force $\vec{F}$ (N [E])	Displacement $\Delta\vec{d}$ (m [E])
A	4.0	5.0
B	7.0	6.0
C	3.0	2.0

8. For a scientific inquiry into "work," a student wants to use a spring scale first to lift a wooden block up vertically and then to slide the block along a table. Outline the procedure this student should use to set the zero on the spring scale in each part of the inquiry.
9. Prove that one joule is equivalent to 1 $kg{\cdot}m^2/s^2$.

Making Connections

10. Some people suggest that walking for 30 min on a treadmill two or three times a week is enough work to keep a person in good physical shape. What information would you need to find out if this is true?

4.2 The Kinds and Forms of Energy

Key Understandings

When you have completed this section, you will be able to:

- define and state the units of energy
- solve problems involving mass and energy using Einstein's equation
- explain the relationship between work and energy

FIGURE 4.15 Energy conversions take place in the upper atmosphere where highly charged particles collide with nuclei, sometimes producing visible light, the aurora borealis.

When ideas in science are abstract and difficult to understand, we often try to invent more concrete ways to view them. Energy is one of these ideas. Scientists invented the term "energy" to help make an abstract idea more concrete. What is energy? What different forms can it take? How can we use these different forms of energy to help us do work?

Energy and Its Characteristics

Energy is the ability to do work. It has several key characteristics.

- Energy is transferred from one object to another whenever work is done.
- Energy comes in many forms that are interchangeable.
- Energy can be stored and used at a later time to do work.
- Energy is always conserved in a closed system.

Energy can be transferred, changed from one form to another, or stored; but the total energy, including heat, stays the same. Unfortunately, useful energy is not conserved. All energy forms eventually become waste heat, so widely dispersed that it is no longer available for our use.

When we say that energy is conserved, the term *conserved* is not used in the usual sense of "saving" or "not wasting." In the context of physics, to say energy is conserved is to say that the total amount of energy does not change.

There are many kinds of energy. Let us consider each of them separately.

Rest mass energy is the total energy that an object has because of its mass. Einstein's theory of relativity indicates that mass is a form of energy. This means that any mass has energy simply because the mass exists. The total energy of a mass at rest is given by the equation

$$E = mc^2$$

where E is the energy in joules, m is the mass in kilograms, and c is the speed of light in m/s. Einstein predicted that mass can be converted to energy and energy to mass. This has been confirmed experimentally. The energy produced in a nuclear-fission power plant is an example of rest mass energy being converted to thermal energy.

EXAMPLE 5 CONCEPTUAL

How much energy is released if 1.0 g of matter is completely converted into energy?

Reasoning and Solution

It is important to realize that because the speed of light term in Einstein's equation is squared, very small amounts of matter are equivalent to very large amounts of energy.

$$E = mc^2$$

$$= (1.0 \times 10^{-3}\ \text{kg})(3.0 \times 10^{8}\ \text{m/s})^2$$

$$= 9.0 \times 10^{13}\ \text{J}$$

The energy equivalent of 1.0 g of matter is 9.0×10^{13} J. This example shows that very small amounts of matter can yield very large amounts of other forms of energy.

CHALLENGE

The burning of 1.0 kg of coal releases about 10^8 J of heat energy. How much energy could be produced if 1.0 kg of uranium was completely converted to energy?

The Nucleus and Radioactivity

It was discovered in 1896 that some materials radiate energy spontaneously. This energy, called radioactivity, can take several forms. Radium, for example, glows continuously with a bluish light. These radiations, it was later discovered, come from the nuclei of atoms.

Radioactive substances can be put to many uses. Some radiations have enough energy to break chemical bonds and ionize atoms. This means that tissues in our bodies can be damaged by these radiations and normal cells can become cancerous. On the other hand, if these powerful radiations are aimed at cancer cells, they can kill them. Cancer treatment machines are designed to rotate around the patient so that the focus of the radiation is on the cancer cells, while surrounding healthy tissue receives only a minimum dose of radiation (Figure 4.16).

Another cancer treatment is based on the fact that the tissue of the human thyroid gland preferentially absorbs iodine. A patient suffering from cancer of the thyroid gland can be treated with a radioactive form of iodine. The thyroid absorbs the iodine and the concentration of the radiation destroys the cancerous tissues.

Some diseases can be diagnosed using radioactive tracers. The radioactive substance is incorporated into a molecule, like sugar, which is then swallowed or injected into the bloodstream. The path of the radioactive molecules is traced by analyzing the chemical composition of body fluids, such as blood and urine, or tissues, such as bone and muscle. This procedure is used to study diseases such as arthritis, bone cancer, and anemia.

Other applications of energy coming from nuclei include magnetic resonance imaging (MRI), computer axial tomography (CAT) scans, X-ray diagnosis, irradiation of wheat and flour to kill insects, and irradiation of some foods to extend storage life.

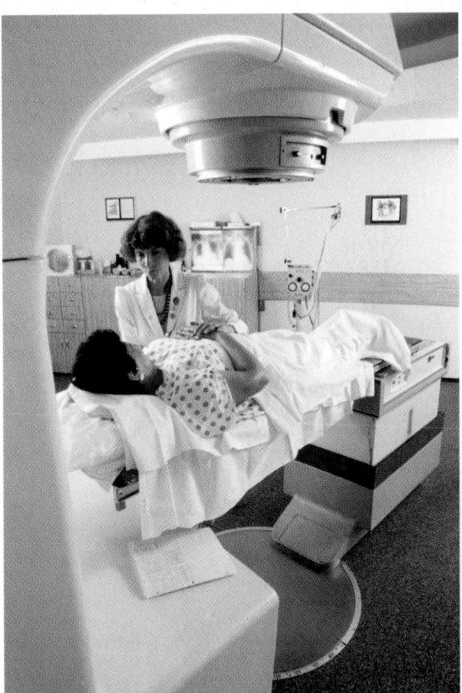

FIGURE 4.16 This machine uses high-energy radiation to kill cancer cells.

Nuclear energy is the energy stored in the nucleus of an atom. It can be released in a number of ways. Sometimes it is released spontaneously in the form of radioactivity. It can also be released when a large nucleus breaks apart during nuclear fission or when two or more small nuclei join together during nuclear fusion. Nuclear fusion is the source of the Sun's radiant energy.

The process of nuclear fission can be used to allow a controlled release of energy. The CANDU reactors near Pickering, Ontario, do this. The energy is released because the total mass of the reactants is slightly greater than the total mass of the products of the nuclear fission reaction. This mass difference is called the **mass defect**, and it is converted to energy according to Einstein's equation.

The energy released by the fission of just one uranium nucleus is 2.8×10^{-11} J. Although this is a small amount of energy, if we consider that there are about 10^{24} nuclei in 1 kg of uranium, the total energy produced is enormous. In fact, the energy released by nuclear fission is about one million times the amount released in a typical chemical reaction. For example, the atoms in 20 kg of uranium can produce as much energy as burning six railroad cars of coal.

EXAMPLE 6 NUMERICAL

When one nucleus of uranium undergoes nuclear fission, the total mass of the reactants is $3.918\ 472\ 839 \times 10^{-25}$ kg, while the total mass of the products is $3.915\ 360\ 617 \times 10^{-25}$ kg.

Calculate the mass defect and the amount of energy released by this nuclear reaction.

Given
The total mass of the reactants and the total mass of the products.

Required
mass defect
energy released

Analysis

- Calculate the mass defect by subtracting the mass of the products from the mass of the reactants.
- Use Einstein's equation to calculate the energy released.

Solution
By subtracting the two masses, the mass defect is $0.311\ 22 \times 10^{-27}$ kg

The energy released is

$$E = mc^2$$
$$= (0.311\ 22 \times 10^{-27}\ \text{kg}) \times (3.0 \times 10^8\ \text{m/s})^2$$
$$= 2.8 \times 10^{-11}\ \text{J}$$

Statement
The energy released by the fission of just one uranium nucleus is 2.8×10^{-11} J.

PRACTICE PROBLEMS

1. How much energy is released in a nuclear fission reaction if the mass defect is 0.20×10^{-27} kg?
2. In a certain nuclear fission reaction an energy of 2.1×10^{-11} J is released. What mass defect could cause the release of this much energy?

Gravitational potential energy is the potential energy that an object has as a result of its distance above a celestial body like Earth. A raised object, such as an axe, stores energy. When released, the axe falls, exerts a force on the block, and splits the block. If the person does additional work by exerting a downward force on the axe handle during the fall, the axe has more energy and is more effective at splitting the wood.

Elastic energy is the energy stored in an object when it is forced out of its normal shape. Elastic materials release the energy when they return to their normal shape. Examples are a stretched bow, a compressed spring, a trampoline, a flexed diving board (Figure 4.17), or an inflated balloon.

FIGURE 4.17 A diving board stores elastic energy.

Kinetic energy is the energy of motion. Since all moving objects, particles, and waves posses kinetic energy, they can do work.

Chemical energy is the potential energy stored in molecules. Foods and fossil fuels such as oil, coal, and natural gas are made of complex molecules. Each molecule has many atoms joined together by chemical bonds. In a chemical reaction the atoms are rearranged into new molecules and some of the chemical energy is released to do useful work. When we eat food, for example, our digestive system breaks down the food and energy is released. This energy is then available to be used by our bodies for everything from maintaining our body temperature at 37°C to playing a game of tennis.

Sound energy is energy that is carried from molecule to molecule by longitudinal vibrations. The vibrations can be detected by the ear. Sound travels from one place to another without the air molecules moving along with it.

Thermal energy is the energy an object has as a result of the random motion of its molecules. The motion is called random because it is unlikely that the molecules are moving in exactly the same direction or with the

Discovering Physics — *Elastic Energy Stored in a Metre-Stick*

In this experiment, you will explore the work done on a metre-stick and how much elastic energy is in the metre stick.

Place a metre stick on a table so that 80 cm project beyond the edge of the table. Measure the vertical height between the metre-stick and the floor. Attach a 200-g mass near the free end of the stick, as shown in Figure 4.18. Lower the weight until the metre stick supports it. Measure the vertical height again. The force of gravity on a 200-g mass is about 2 N. Add weights to the metre stick in steps of 2 N to a maximum of 10 N, measuring and recording the vertical height each time. Determine the vertical depression of the free end from the zero load position under the influence of the various weights.

Plot a graph of vertical depression against the applied force. Describe the shape of the graph. Is it a straight line? Calculate the area under the curve. This represents the work done by Earth to bend the metre-stick. It also represents the elastic energy stored in the bent metre-stick. How much work was done on the metre-stick by Earth through the mass? How much energy is stored in the metre-stick? Discuss the results with a partner and relate this to changes in the gravitational energy of a diver and elastic potential energy of a diving board as an athlete initiates a dive.

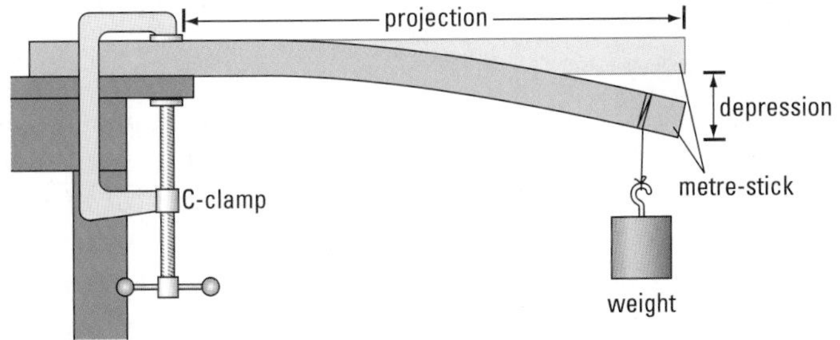

FIGURE 4.18 A metre-stick can store energy like a diving board.

Discovering Physics — Converting Elastic Energy to Kinetic Energy

Construct the following device and use it to observe what happens when elastic energy is converted to kinetic energy.

Use Figure 4.19 as a reference. Drive a medium nail vertically into a block of wood (5 cm × 5 cm × 20 cm) near one end. Obtain a plank of wood (5 cm × 15 cm × 120 cm). At 40 cm from one end, mark a spot near the horizontal edge, where you will drive in a large nail. Put in a second large nail directly across from the first. Stretch an elastic band between these two nails. Slide the block of wood under the elastic band so its nail is in front of the elastic. Pull back on the wooden block to stretch the elastic band.

CAUTION: Do not overstretch the elastic band.

Release the block. The elastic energy stored in the elastic band is converted into kinetic energy of the wooden block. This kinetic energy is dissipated in the surfaces as waste heat. Try changing the stretch and investigate what happens to the kinetic energy produced and the work done against friction as indicated by the distance moved by the block. What do you think a graph of distance moved as a function of stretch would look like?

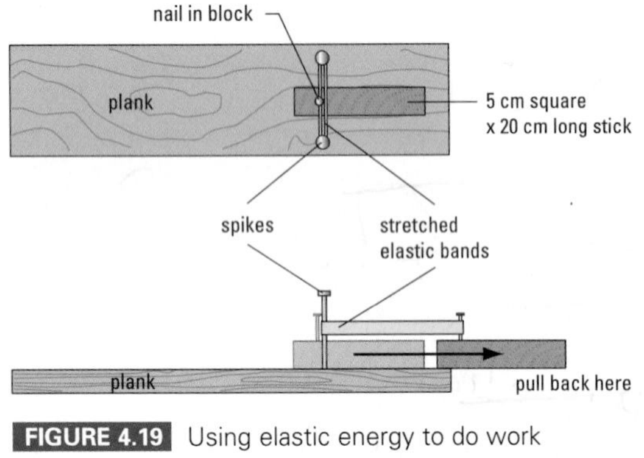

FIGURE 4.19 Using elastic energy to do work

same speed at the same time. The high-speed molecules in a steam-powered electric generator have random motion. So do the molecules of boiling water in a pot.

Radiant energy is energy that travels as electromagnetic waves. The Sun is our largest source of radiant energy. Examples of radiant energy are visible light, ultraviolet, infrared, and radio waves.

Electrical energy is the energy associated with moving electric charges. Lightning is the result of moving electric charges. The energy associated with the electrons forced around the circuit by a large battery can power an electric car.

Measuring Energy

Energy is measured by determining the work done or the heat produced. For example, the kinetic energy of a moving mass can be measured by finding the work that it does in compressing a spring. The more the spring is compressed, the more kinetic energy the moving mass has. The chemical energy in natural gas can be measured by determining how much heat is produced when it burns. Whenever work is done, energy is used. Unfortunately, more energy is always consumed than the useful work accomplished. This is because friction is always present and the energy used to overcome friction becomes waste heat.

Energy is the ability to do work, so it has the same unit as work: the joule (J). The joule is a very small amount of energy, so several larger units are often used. These are the **kilojoule** (kJ), the **megajoule** (MJ), and the **gigajoule** (GJ). The relationship between these units and the joule is shown below.

$$1\ \text{kJ} = 10^3\ \text{J} \qquad 1\ \text{MJ} = 10^6\ \text{J} \qquad 1\ \text{GJ} = 10^9\ \text{J}$$

FIGURE 4.20 A chemical energy of one megajoule.

Another unit of energy, commonly used for measuring the electrical energy consumed in homes, is the **kilowatt hour** (kW·h). Note that 1 kW·h = 3.6 MJ.

Two golf balls raised to chest height have a gravitational potential energy of about one joule. Three Olympic athletes racing at top speed have a combined kinetic energy of about one kilojoule. A 5-cm wedge of double-crusted apple pie (Figure 4.20) has a chemical energy of about one megajoule. When burned, a garbage can filled with oil produces about one gigajoule of thermal energy. A colour television running for three hours uses about one kilowatt hour of electrical energy.

Power from Niagara

Decision-Making Skills

- Defining the Issue
- Developing Assessment Criteria
- Researching the Issue
- Analyzing Data and Information
- Proposing a Course of Action
- Justifying the Course of Action
- Communicating Your Proposal

BACKGROUND INFORMATION

The first recorded use of the energy available in Niagara Falls was in 1759, when Daniel Joncairs dug a narrow ditch on the American side of the falls to drain water to turn a waterwheel, which in turn drove a small sawmill. The first electrical power plant was built in 1881 and provided electrical energy to a few local mills and to light the village of Niagara Falls. Use of the falls increased and by 1896 electrical energy was being provided to the City of Buffalo.

Today, the churning river provides the driving force for almost two million kilowatts of electricity from a number of power plants on the Canadian side. The three largest are Sir Adam Beck Niagara Generating Stations Nos. 1 and 2 and the nearby pumping–generating station. On the American side of the border, down river from the Falls, the Robert Moses Niagara Power Plant and the Lewiston Pump Generating Plant together generate more than 2.4×10^6 kW of electricity, enough to light 24 million 100 W bulbs.

All this activity requires increased diversion of water away from the Falls. Several water use agreements were implemented between Canada and the U.S.A., culminating with the Niagara Diversion Treaty in February, 1950. In it, the USA is limited to 1400 m^3/s while Canada can divert 2800 m^3/s.

But is this enough? Many people wish to reduce our dependence on nuclear power stations. At the same time, electrical energy generation based upon the burning of fossil fuels is creating havoc in our atmosphere. Perhaps we should be expanding our generating plants at Niagara and diverting even more water to produce more electrical power.

FIGURE 4.21

Analyzing the Issue

1. Define the issues relating to the diversion of water from the Niagara River to generate electricity.
2. Research the issue using journals, magazine articles, the Internet, and other electronic resources. Identify the major factors affecting the issue using the following criteria: economic, environmental, technological, political, and social.
3. Describe ways in which the Canadian view on the issue may differ from the American view.
4. You have been asked to provide a Parliamentary Committee with recommendations regarding the advisability of increased diversion of water away from Niagara Falls.Write a position paper to present to the Committee. Support your argument with research and an appendix (or media presentation) of background information.

Section 4.2 Review

Understanding Concepts

1. In your own words, define energy.
2. List three ways in which nuclear energy can be released.
3. In a certain nuclear-fission reaction the mass defect is observed to be 3.3732×10^{-28} kg. How much energy is released in this reaction?
4. What is kinetic energy?
5. Five examples of energy are listed below. Decide which form(s) of energy each has.
   a) a moving hockey puck
   b) a hacksaw blade bent to one side
   c) a bag of peanuts
   d) a stone sitting on a post
   e) a stationary pebble on a beach
6. Consider the relationship between work and energy:
   a) Compare the SI units of energy and work.
   b) Name two units of energy larger than the joule.
   c) How is energy measured?
   d) Why is the energy used always more than the work done?

Applying Inquiry/ Communication Skills

7. As mentioned in this section, when ideas in science are abstract and difficult to understand, we invent more concrete ways to view them. How would you explain the concept of energy to a six-year-old child?
8. Create a concept map to show the different types of energy and their characteristics.

Making Connections

9. Radioactivity can be used to extend the shelf life of food in both grocery stores and the home. The food itself does not become radioactive, but the radiation has enough energy to break some chemical bonds and change the chemistry of the food. What social and economic issues does the raise for conumers?
10. A student eats a candy that contains 200 kJ of energy. He then applies a horizontal force of 50 N to push a cart. How far could he push the cart if he uses only the energy supplied by the candy?

FIGURE 4.22 A water tower

4.3 Gravitational Potential Energy

Key Understandings

When you have completed this section, you will be able to:

- derive the equation for changes in gravitational energy
- solve problems involving changes in gravitational energy, mass, gravitational field intensity, and changes in height

The water supply for towns and villages is often pumped from aquifers and springs deep in the ground and stored in reservoirs towering above the buildings (Figure 4.22). How much work is done in raising the water to these towers? Why is the water raised? How much gravitational potential energy does it have at a given height? How can we derive an equation for this gravitational potential energy?

Changes in Gravitational Energy

Gravitational energy is a very common form of potential energy. This energy is the result of position. We can derive an equation for changes in gravitational energy near the surface of Earth by calculating the work done to raise a mass by a known amount. The force of gravity or weight on the mass is $F_G = mg$. Figure 4.23 a) shows that we must exert a force equal to the weight of the mass to lift it vertically at a constant speed. In Figure 4.23 b), a slightly larger force starts it moving, and a slightly smaller force in Figure 4.23 c) lets it stop. The work done on the mass is

$$\begin{aligned} W &= F\Delta d \\ &= F_G\Delta h \\ &= mg\Delta h \end{aligned}$$

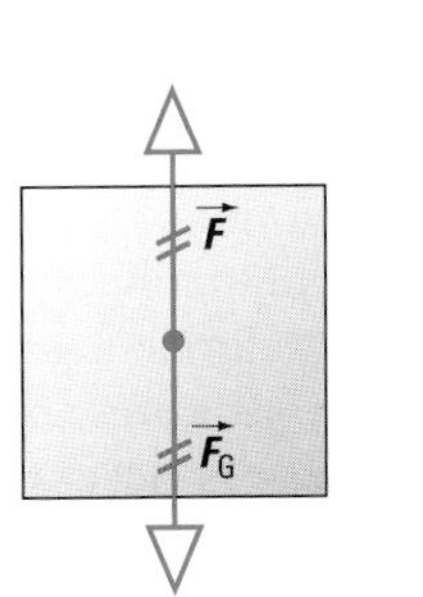

a) Constant speed up

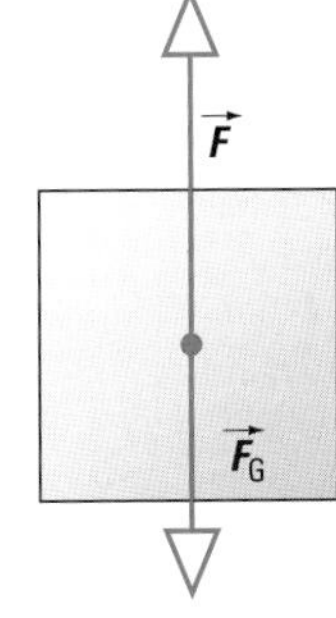

b) Acceleration up

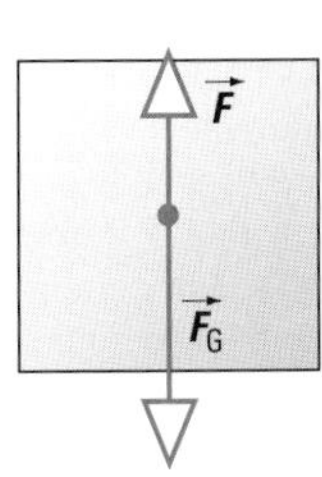

c) Deceleration up (acceleration down)

FIGURE 4.23 To lift an object a force is needed that is equal or greater than to the object's weight

Assuming no friction, the work done is equal to the change in gravitational energy. Thus, the equation for the change in gravitational energy is

$$\Delta E_G = mg\Delta h$$

where m is the mass of the object in kilograms
g is the gravitational field intensity in newtons per kilogram
Δh is the magnitude of the vertical displacement of the object in metres
ΔE_G is the change in gravitational energy of the object in joules.

EXAMPLE 7 CONCEPTUAL

A florist lifts a 2.5-kg pot of poinsettias from the floor to a counter 0.93 m above the floor. Calculate the change in gravitational energy of the pot and its contents. (Recall that g = 9.8 N/kg [down].)

Reasoning and Solution

Since all of the work done to lift a pot gives this pot a gain in its gravitational potential energy and no other form of energy, then the work done is equal to this gain in potential energy.

$$\begin{aligned} \Delta E_G &= mg\Delta h \\ &= 2.5 \text{ kg} \times 9.8 \text{ N/kg} \times 0.93 \text{ m} \\ &= 23 \text{ J} \end{aligned}$$

The florist does 23 J of work to give the flower pot an increase of 23 J of gravitational potential energy.

CHALLENGE

A garage hoist lifts a 1200-kg car vertically 1.7 m. What gain in gravitational potential energy is provided to the car by the hoist?

Relative Gravitational Energy

The change in gravitational energy depends on the vertical height an object is raised above a reference point, and does not depend on the path taken to the new height. In the example above the florist gives the same amount of

INFO**BIT**

Gravitational energy is not a property of a single object, but rather it is a property of a system. This kind of energy depends on the interaction of two bodies. For example, a roller coaster at a certain height above ground has gravitational energy with respect to Earth because Earth exerts a force of gravity on the roller coaster. Thus, it is the Earth–roller coaster system that interacts to produce gravitational potential energy.

INFO**BIT**

The true reference for gravitational potential energy is out in space where the force of gravity approaches zero.

gravitational potential energy to the pot of poinsettias whether the pot is lifted straight up to the counter or along a diagonal path to the same height.

Similarly, if we ignore friction, we see that a pot of poinsettias can do the same amount of work when it falls through a given height, whether it falls vertically or by some other path, such as down a playground slide. Recall that the force of gravity acts downward. Only the displacement in this direction contributes to the work done by Earth on a falling mass.

There is no fixed reference point for gravitational energy. The true zero for energy on Earth is at the centre of Earth, but that is impractical. Many problems ask us to find the gravitational energy at several different heights. It is most convenient to use the lowest position as the reference point and to say that the object has a gravitational energy of zero at this position. Then we can calculate the relative gravitational energy of the object at the different heights. To determine the change in gravitational energy between two points, use the lower of the two points as the reference and measure the vertical displacement from this location.

EXAMPLE 8 NUMERICAL

Figure 4.24 shows a roller coaster with a mass of 220 kg poised at point A. Calculate:

a) the gravitational energy at A with reference to the ground
b) the change in gravitational energy going from B to C

Given

$h_A = 30$ m

$h_B = 20$ m

$h_C = 15$ m

$m = 220$ kg

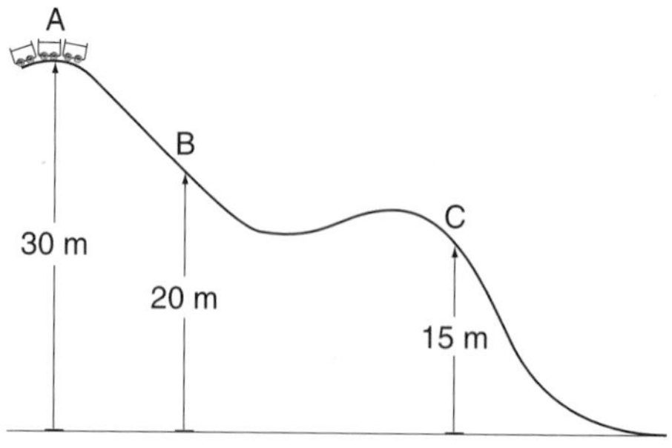

FIGURE 4.24 A roller coaster

Required

E_G at A

ΔE_G from B to C

Analysis

Assume that the gravitational energy at ground level is zero.

Solution

a)
$$\begin{aligned} E_G &= mgh_A \\ &= 220 \text{ kg} \times 9.8 \text{ N/kg} \times 30 \text{ m} \\ &= 6.5 \times 10^4 \text{ J} \end{aligned}$$

b)
$$\begin{aligned} \Delta E_G &= mgh_C - mgh_B \\ &= mg(h_C - h_B) \\ &= 220 \text{ kg} \times 9.8 \text{ N/kg} \times (15 \text{ m} - 20 \text{ m}) \\ &= 220 \text{ kg} \times 9.8 \text{ N/kg} \times (-5 \text{ m}) \\ &= -1 \times 10^4 \text{ J} \end{aligned}$$

Statement

The roller coaster has a gravitational energy of 6.5×10^4 J at A and loses 1×10^4 J of gravitational energy between B and C.

PRACTICE PROBLEMS

1. A hydraulic hoist lifts a 1200-kg car 2.0 m. Calculate:
   a) the change in gravitational energy of the car
   b) the minimum work done by the hoist
2. A 1.5-kg rubber ball released from a height of 6.0 m falls to the pavement and rebounds to a height of 5.5 m. Calculate:
   a) the loss in gravitational energy during the fall
   b) the gain in gravitational energy during the rebound
   c) the net change in gravitational energy

Discovering Physics — Gravitational Energy and Driving Nails

Explore the relationship between mass and work.

Obtain a block of soft wood. Drive in five strong nails so that their heads are all at the same height. Measure and record the height of the nails. Obtain a plastic golf tube insert. Cut the tube into pieces equal in length to the height of the nails plus 5 cm, 10 cm, 15 cm, and 20 cm respectively. Obtain three large bolts with hexagonal flat heads that just fit inside the tubes. Thread nuts onto the bolts so that their masses are in the ration of 1:2:4.

Carefully drop the bolts down the tubes onto the nails as shown in Figure 4.25. Measure the distance the nails are driven farther into the wood. Vary the number of drops from a given height, and vary the mass of the dropped object.

What relationship exists between the mass dropped and the work done driving the nails into the wood? What effect does height have on the work done? Plot a graph of your results using a graphing calculator or a spreadsheet program. What are two factors that affect the gravitational energy of a raised object? What would happen if you did this activity on the moon? Why?

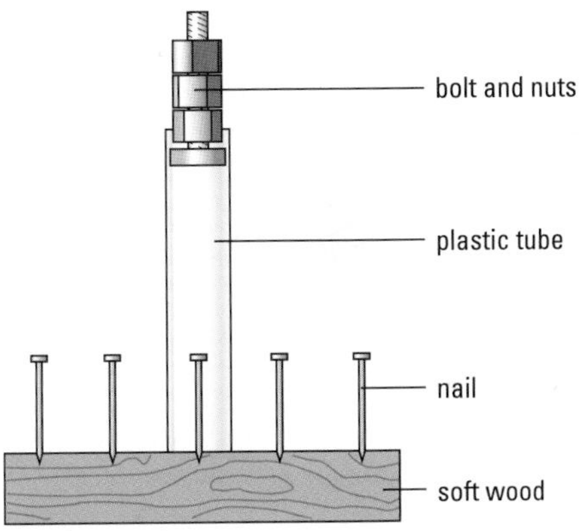

FIGURE 4.25 Gravitational energy can be used to drive nails.

WEBLINK

To explore the affecting gravitational potential energy, including mass, gravitational field intensity, and height, go to **www.pearsoned.ca/physics11.**

Section 4.3 Review

Understanding Concepts

1. What factors affect the gravitational energy of a 10-kg mass on the moon?
2. A boat hoist lifts an 800-kg boat 1.5 m. Calculate:
   a) the change in gravitational energy of the boat
   b) the minimum work done by the boat hoist
3. An inflated car tire of mass 23 kg falls from a height of 2.0 m to the garage floor and rebounds to a height of 1.4 m. Calculate:
   a) the loss in gravitational energy during the fall
   b) the gain in gravitational energy during the rebound
   c) the net change in gravitational energy
   d) What happened to the energy represented by answer c)?
4. A 1300-kg car (Figure 4.26) moves from point A to point B and then to point C. Calculate:
   a) the gravitational energy at B and at C relative to A
   b) the change in gravitational energy between B and C

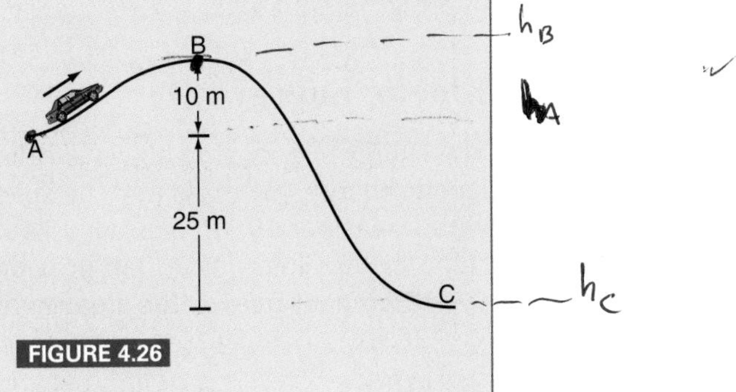

FIGURE 4.26

5. A 70-kg skier is lifted by a chair lift from a height of 700 m above sea level at the bottom of the mountain to a height of 2400 m.
   a) What is the skier's change in gravitational energy?
   b) What is the minimum work done by the chair lift?
   c) How does the actual work to raise the skier compare with the minimum work?

Applying Inquiry/ Communication Skills

6. When water falls from one height to a lower one, the gravitational potential energy lost during the fall can be used. What quantities would you need to measure to determine the amount of energy lost when water falls, and how would you go about measuring these quantities?

Making Connections

7. During construction of a hotel, all the parts of the building that are raised above ground have gravitational potential energy relative to the ground. If, after many years, the hotel is to be demolished, all of this energy can be used to force the building to collapse on itself. If you are the engineer in charge of such a demolition, what course of action would you take to minimize the impact of this demolition on local citizens and ensure their safety?

4.4 Kinetic Energy

Key Understandings

When you have completed this section, you will be able to:

- derive the equation for kinetic energy
- solve problems involving kinetic energy, mass, and speed
- describe the effect of mass and speed on kinetic energy

Sometimes it is not practical to use Newton's laws to solve problems because the forces involved are very difficult to measure. However, Newton's laws, and the concept of work can been used to derive an equation describing the energy of a moving object, such as a roller coaster. What is this equation? How is it derived, and how is the need to know the values of forces eliminated?

Kinetic Energy

The energy of a moving object is called kinetic energy. Two factors affect the kinetic energy: the mass and the speed of the object. A child's curling stone, with a mass of 10 kg, can have as much kinetic energy as a large curling stone, with a mass of 20 kg, provided it is moving fast enough. The extra speed compensates for the smaller mass.

You can derive an equation for changes in kinetic energy by calculating the work done to give an object a known velocity from rest. Imagine that a curler gives a curling stone, of mass m, a constant acceleration $\vec{a}$. This is done by exerting a net force $\vec{F}_{net}$ on it for a displacement $\Delta\vec{d}$, until its final velocity is v_2, as shown in Figure 4.27. Assume that there is no friction. Because the stone is on a level surface, all the work done is used to accelerate the stone and give it kinetic energy. Since the force and displacement are in the same direction, it is not necessary to include the vector signs.

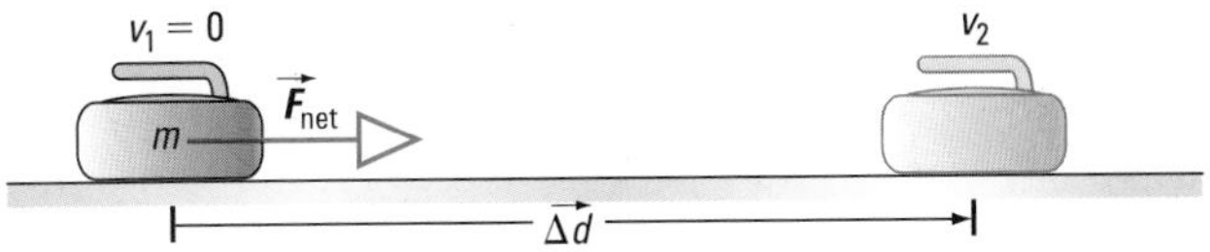

FIGURE 4.27 A net force $\vec{F}_{net}$ acts to move a curling stone.

The work done on the stone is:

$$W = F_{net}\Delta d \qquad \text{(equation 1)}$$

From Newton's second law, the acceleration of the stone is

$$F_{net} = ma \qquad \text{(equation 2)}$$

By substituting for F_{net} in equation 1 from equation 2 we get

$$W = ma\Delta d \qquad \text{(equation 3)}$$

But acceleration is

$$a = \frac{v_2 - v_1}{\Delta t}$$

Since the initial velocity is zero the equation simplifies to:

$$a = \frac{v_2}{\Delta t} \qquad \text{(equation 4)}$$

The displacement is

$$\Delta d = \frac{(v_1 + v_2)}{2}\Delta t$$

Since the initial velocity is zero this equation simplifies to:

$$\Delta d = \frac{v_2}{2}\Delta t \qquad \text{(equation 5)}$$

Substituting the expressions for a from equation 4 and Δd from equation 5 into equation 3 and simplifying we get:

$$\begin{aligned} W &= ma\Delta d \\ &= m\left(\frac{v_2}{\Delta t}\right)\left(\frac{v_2}{2}\right)\Delta t \\ &= \frac{1}{2}m(v_2)^2 \end{aligned}$$

Since there is no friction, all the work done becomes kinetic energy. Therefore, the general expression for kinetic energy is

$$E_k = \frac{1}{2}mv^2$$

where m is the mass of the object in kilograms
v is the velocity of the object in metres per second
E_k is the kinetic energy of the object in joules

INSIGHT

As with gravitational potential energy, the kinetic energy of an object depends on the choice of zero kinetic energy. For example, a person seated on a bus travelling at 50 km/h has kinetic energy relative to someone standing on the sidewalk. But relative to someone sitting next to her on the bus, she has no kinetic energy.

Refer to page 173, Investigation 1.

Exploration Using a Graphing Calculator 

Kinetic Energy and Speed

A four-person bobsled with a mass of 10 kg is accelerating from rest down a steep icy track. The masses of the riders are 80 kg, 80 kg, 90 kg, and 100 kg. The equation for calculating kinetic energy is $E_k = 1/2mv^2$. Graph this equation on a graphing calculator. Plot E_k on the vertical axis (with a range of 0 J to 1.2×10^5 J) and speed on the horizontal axis (with a range of 0 m/s to 25 m/s). Sketch the graph. Use the calculator to read the coordinates of the curve.

Discussion

1. Describe the graph.
2. As the velocity doubles, what happens to the kinetic energy?
3. As the mass triples, what happens to the kinetic energy?
4. Which is the more important factor in the kinetic energy equation: mass or speed? Why?

EXAMPLE 9 NUMERICAL

What is the kinetic energy of a 7.3-kg asteroid moving through space with a speed of 3.0×10^4 m/s?

Given

$m = 7.3$ kg

$v = 3.0 \times 10^4$ m/s

Required

E_k

Analysis

Use the equation $E_k = \frac{1}{2}mv^2$ to solve this problem

Solution

$$E_k = \frac{1}{2}mv^2$$
$$= \frac{1}{2}(7.3 \text{ kg})(3.0 \times 10^4 \text{ m/s})^2$$
$$= 3.3 \times 10^9 \text{ kg·m}^2/\text{s}^2$$
$$= 3.3 \times 10^9 \text{ J}$$

Statement

The asteroid has a kinetic energy of 33×10^9 J

PRACTICE PROBLEMS

1. A boy and his bicycle have a total mass of 60 kg and they are riding at a constant speed of 7.2 m/s. How much kinetic energy do they have?
2. How fast is a 1300-kg car moving if it has a kinetic energy of 127 kJ?

Discovering Physics — *Mass, Speed, Kinetic Energy*

Explore the relationship between mass, speed, and kinetic energy.

You'll need three spherical masses of the same diameter but different weights (e.g., steel ball bearing, glass marble, wooden sphere), a metre stick, modelling clay and a graduated pipette.

1. Record the masses of the spheres.
2. Make a flat, even pad with modelling clay.
3. Drop each sphere from a height of 20 cm so each one lands in a different place. (Note: If the three spheres are dropped from the same height, they will land on the pad at the same speed [neglecting air friction]).
3. Each sphere will make a crater in the modelling clay (Figure4.28). The size of each crater is a measure of the kinetic energy of each sphere. The larger the crater, the more kinetic energy the falling mass has and the more work it does on the clay. Rank the craters from smallest to largest.
4. Measure the volumes of the craters. Use the pipette to fill each crater with water. Compare these volumes with the masses of the spheres.
5. Design an experiment to determine the effect of speed on the kinetic energy of the spheres.

- How much higher do you have to release the sphere in order to double its speed?
- What variable did you control and what did you change?
- What did you find out? Does mass or speed have more effect on kinetic energy?

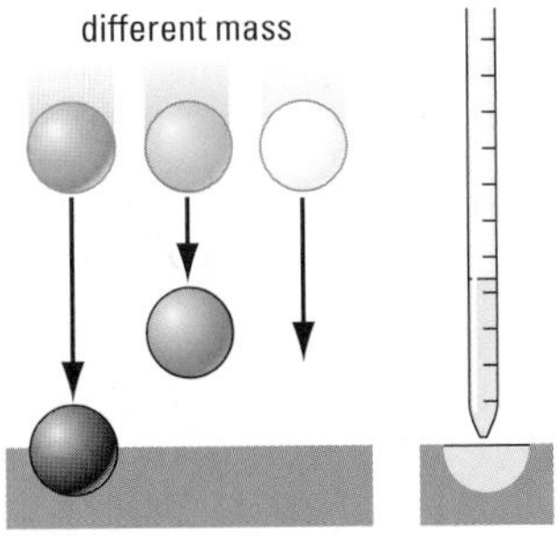

different mass

FIGURE 4.28 Kinetic energy can do work.

WEBLINK

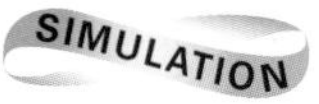

To explore the factors affecting kinetic energy including mass, gravitational field intensity, and height go to **www.pearsoned.ca/physics11.**

EXAMPLE 10 — NUMERICAL

In a demonstration lesson to novice curlers, Sandra Schmirler, the 1996 Canadian women's world curling champion, did the same amount of work on a 20-kg adult's curling stone as on a 10-kg child's curling stone. If she gave the large stone a speed of 2.5 m/s, what speed did she give the small stone?

Given

$m_L = 20$ kg $v_L = 2.5$ m/s $m_s = 10$ kg

Required

v_s

Analysis

- The same work gives the two stones the same kinetic energy.
- Calculate the kinetic energy of the larger stone.
- Assume that the small stone has this energy.
- Use the equation $E_k = \frac{1}{2}m_s v_s^2$ and solve for v_s.

INSIGHT

Note that halving the mass does not double the speed.

Solution

Large Stone

$$E_k = \frac{1}{2}m_L v_L^2$$

$$= \frac{1}{2} \times 20\ \text{kg} \times (2.5\ \text{m/s})^2$$

$$= 62.5\ \text{J}$$

Small stone

$$E_k = \frac{1}{2}m_s v_s^2$$

$$62.5\ \text{J} = \frac{1}{2} \times 10\ \text{kg} \times v_s^2$$

$$v_s^2 = 12.5\ \text{m}^2/\text{s}^2$$

$$v_s = 3.5\ \text{m/s}$$

Statement

The same work gives the small stone a speed of 3.5 m/s.

PRACTICE PROBLEMS

1. How fast is a 1000-kg wrecking ball moving if it has a kinetic energy of 500 kJ?
2. Neglecting friction, how much work would the engine of a 1200-kg car have to do to increase the speed of the car from 14 m/s to 28 m/s?

WEBLINK

Research to find out about meteorites. Make a timeline chart of significant impacts on Earth. Begin you research at **www.pearsoned.ca/physics11.**

Section 4.4 Review

Understanding Concepts

1. Describe the effect of mass and speed on kinetic energy.
2. What is the kinetic energy of a tennis ball with a mass of 0.058 kg moving at a speed of 30 m/s?
3. How fast is a 20-kg curling stone moving if it has a kinetic energy of 32 J?
4. A baseball travelling at a speed of 40.0 m/s has a kinetic energy of 112 J. What is its mass?
5. A shot-put with a mass of 7.3 kg has a horizontal speed of 9.4 m/s at a height of 4.5 m.
   a) Calculate the kinetic energy of the shot-put.
   b) What is the gravitational energy relative to the ground?
   c) Calculate the work done by the competitor in giving the shot both kinetic and potential energy.
   d) Estimate the force that the shot-putter applies to propel the shot-put horizontally. Explain your estimate.

Applying Inquiry/ Communication Skills

6. Use units analysis techniques to show that 1/2 mv^2 can be measured in joules.
7. List the procedural steps you would use in an experiment to measure the kinetic energy of a bicycle and its rider travelling at various speeds.

Making Connections

8. Meteorities are rocks from space that fall to Earth. One such rock was 41 m in diameter and landed in Arizona. It had so much kinetic energy on impact that it made a crater 228 m deep and 1219 m in diameter. Some scientists suggest that we should invest money to locate and track these space rocks, while others think that the money would be better spent on other things. Choose one side of this debate, and list the points that you would make to support your argument.

4.5 Energy Transformations and Conservation

Key Understandings

When you have completed this section, you will be able to:

- describe the energy conversions in a spring pendulum
- state and apply the law of conservation of energy
- solve problems using the law of conservation of energy

A pole vaulter approaches the pit, running very fast. When the pole is jammed into the box, the pole bends, converting the kinetic energy of the vaulter to elastic potential energy stored in the bent pole. As the pole straightens, stored elastic energy is used to help push the vaulter over the bar (Figure 4.29). The pole vaulter makes it over the bar and falls to the mat below. Once over the bar, where does all of this energy go? How can we calculate the speed of the pole vaulter just as she reaches the surface of the mat?

FIGURE 4.29 Elastic potential energy helps the vaulter over the bar.

Energy Conversions in a Spring Pendulum

Figure 4.30 shows a spring pendulum consisting of a mass and a spring. In Figure 4.30a), the mass is resting on the floor and the spring is unstretched. The gravitational energy of the mass and the elastic energy of the spring are zero. Suppose we do work to lift the mass and attach it to the spring, as shown in Figure 4.30b). The work is stored as gravitational energy in the raised mass. If we release the mass, it falls, and the spring stretches. The lost gravitational energy of the mass is converted into kinetic energy and elastic energy in the system. Halfway down, as shown in Figure 4.30c), the system has gravitational energy, elastic energy, and kinetic energy. In Figure 4.30d), the spring is stretched a maximum amount, and the mass is again temporarily at

INSIGHT

In a spring pendulum, the elastic energy is greatest with the spring a at full stretch. For the pole vaulter, the elastic energy is greatest when the pole is bent the most.

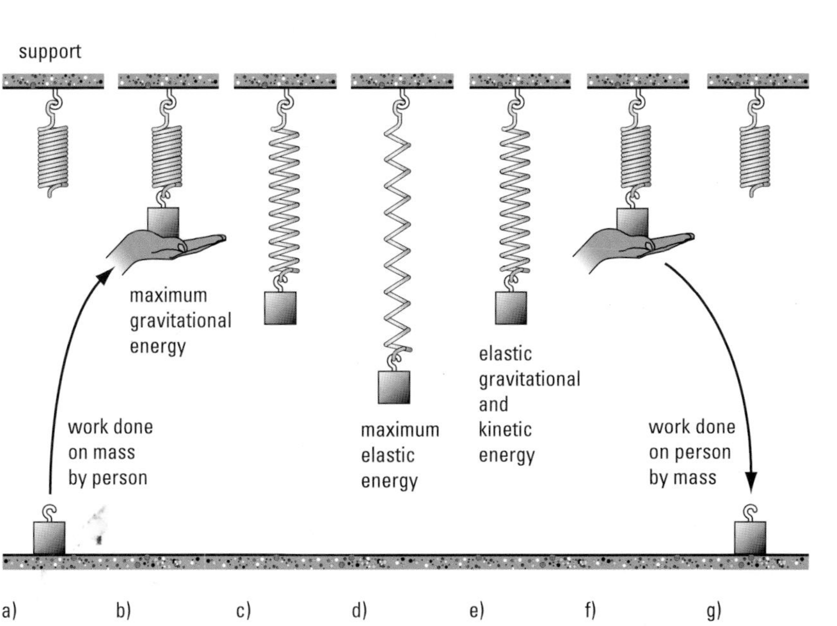

FIGURE 4.30 Energy conservation in a spring pendulum

Refer to page 174 Investigation 2.

rest. All the gravitational energy lost by the mass has been converted to elastic energy in the spring.

As the mass begins to rise, the spring loses elastic energy and the mass gains gravitational potential and kinetic energy. Halfway up, as shown in Figure 4.30e), the energy is shared between elastic, kinetic, and gravitational energy. At the top, the stretch of the spring is zero and the mass is again temporarily at rest. The mass has regained its gravitational energy. If the mass is removed and lowered to its initial position, the gravitational energy lost by the mass on the way down does work on the hand lowering it.

The Law of Conservation of Energy

INFOBIT

Three scientists laid the foundations for the law of conservation of energy. Julius Robert Mayer (1814–78) proposed that when energy is changed from other forms to heat it is neither created or destroyed, but he had difficulty convincing others. James Prescott Joule (1818–89) did many quantitative experiments but did not propose an explicit generalization. Finally, Hermann von Helmholtz (1821–94) proposed the law of conservation of energy in 1847.

Scientists have studied energy conversions in simple machines, such as springs, and in complex machines, such as cars. The results consistently show that we cannot get more useful energy out of a system than we put into it. In fact, we cannot even get the same amount out as we put in. If we had left the spring in Figure 4.30 to vibrate, the vibrations would have stopped eventually. The system would gradually lose the initial energy we gave it. This is because friction limits the efficiency of energy conversions to less than 100%.

The energy that disappears as a result of friction is not destroyed. It becomes thermal energy in nearby molecules. The thermal energy gained by these molecules has been measured and found to be exactly equal to the amount of kinetic, elastic, and gravitational energy that disappears.

The study of the various forms of energy and energy conversions has given us one of the great laws of science. This law, called the **law of conservation of energy**, states:

Energy cannot be created or destroyed. It can be changed from one form to another, but the total amount of energy in the universe stays constant.

Discovering Physics — *Magnets and Potential Energy*

People sometimes say that opposites attract. The expression certainly applies to the south pole of one magnet when it is pointed toward the north pole of another magnet. What happens when you point the same magnetic poles at each other? What indicates that is energy involved?

Place two strong bar magnets far apart from one another on a table so that their north poles are facing each other as shown in Figure 4.31. Slowly push them together and hold them as close together as you can.

- Do you have to do work to push them together?
- Are you doing any work when you are holding them together?
- Now release the magnets to see the results of your work.
- What energy conversions take place?
- When the magnets finally stop, where has the stored energy gone?

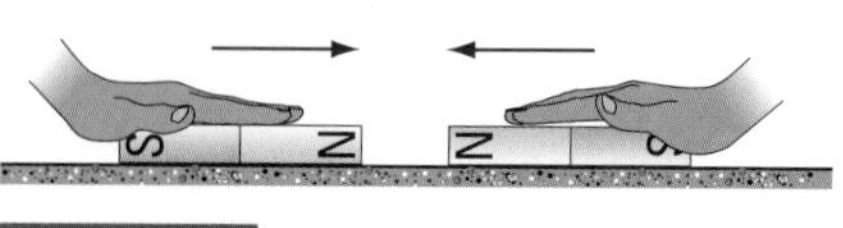

FIGURE 4.31

Discovering Physics *The Stopped Pendulum*

What happens to the energy of a swinging pendulum if you place an obstacle in the path of the pendulum?

1. Use a retort stand, 70-cm length of string, and a mass to set up a pendulum as shown in Figure 4.32 a).
2. Tie a 100-cm piece of string to two other retort stands. Set them on either side of the pendulum so the string is taut. Select a drop height for the pendulum bob and adjust the string to that height. (Refer to Figure 4.32)
3. Let the pendulum swing and observe the highest point it reaches.
4. Fasten the small wooden dowel on the pendulum's retort stand above the release height of the pendulum. The dowel will be an obstacle in the pendulum's path.
5. Release the pendulum again, and observe the highest point the bob reaches.
   - What happened? Why do you think it does this?
   - Does the obstacle do any work ($F\Delta d$) on the pendulum?
6. Try the experiment again, but this time attach some modelling clay to the dowel where the string of the pendulum contacts it.
   - What happened this time?
   - Explain the result in terms of the law of conservation of energy.

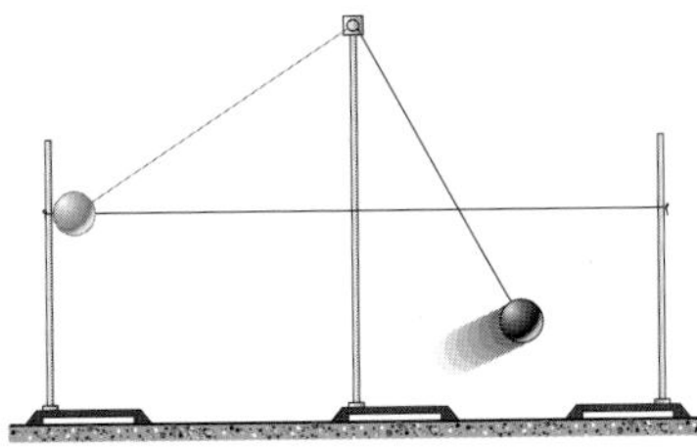

a)

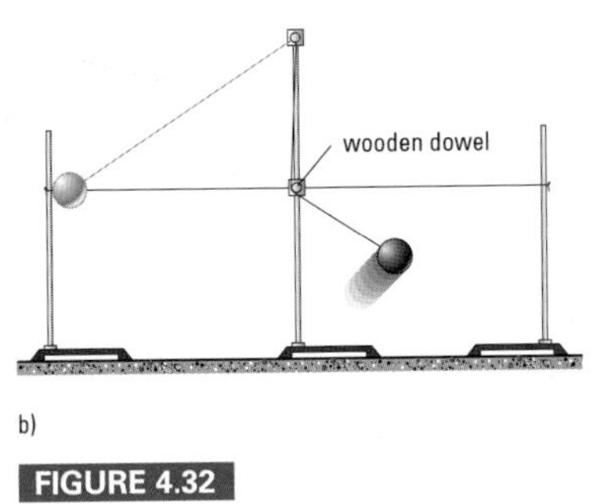

b)

FIGURE 4.32

The law of conservation of energy can be used to solve problems that were previously solved using several kinematics equations. In the example below a problem is solved using both methods. Compare the results.

EXAMPLE 11 NUMERICAL

An astronaut on the moon, where g is 1.6 N/kg, drops a 20-kg boulder from a height of 30 m. Calculate the speed of the boulder, just as it reaches the moon's surface, using:

a) the law of conservation of energy
b) the kinematics equations

Given
$m = 20$ kg $\quad g = 1.6$ N/kg $\quad \Delta h = 30$ m

Required
a) v_2 using energy conversions
b) v_2 using kinematics equations

Analysis

a) Using the law of conservation of energy

- Calculate the initial gravitational energy of the boulder.
- As the boulder falls, it loses gravitational energy and gains kinetic energy.
- There is no air resistance on the moon, so all the gravitational energy lost as the mass falls becomes kinetic energy at the bottom.
- Make $|\Delta E_G| = |\Delta E_k|$ and solve for v.

b) Using kinematics

$g = 1.6 \text{ N/kg} = 1.6 \text{ m/s}^2$

- Since $v_1 = 0$, use $\Delta d = \frac{1}{2} g (\Delta t)^2$ and solve for Δt.
- Then use $v_2 = g\,\Delta t$ and solve for v_2.

Solution

a) Using the law of conservation of energy

$$\begin{aligned}\Delta E_G &= 20 \text{ kg} \times 1.6 \text{ N/kg} \times 30 \text{ m}\\ &= 9.6 \times 10^2 \text{ J}\end{aligned}$$

$$|\Delta E_k| = |\Delta E_G| = 9.6 \times 10^2 \text{ J}$$

$$\Delta E_k = \frac{1}{2}mv^2$$

$$v^2 = \frac{2E_k}{m}$$

$$\begin{aligned}v &= \sqrt{\frac{2E_k}{m}}\\ &= \sqrt{\frac{2 \times (9.6 \times 10^2 \text{ J})}{20 \text{ kg}}}\\ &= \sqrt{96 \text{ J/kg}}\\ &= 9.8 \text{ m/s}\end{aligned}$$

b) Using kinematics

$$\Delta d = \frac{1}{2}g(\Delta t)^2$$

$$\begin{aligned}\Delta t &= \sqrt{\frac{2\Delta d}{g}}\\ &= \sqrt{\frac{2 \times 30 \text{ m}}{1.6 \text{ m/s}^2}}\\ &= 6.1 \text{ s}\end{aligned}$$

$$\begin{aligned}v_2 &= g\Delta t\\ &= 1.6\frac{\text{m}}{\text{s}^2} \times 6.1 \text{ s}\\ &= 9.8 \text{ m/s}\end{aligned}$$

Statement

The boulder reaches a speed of 9.8 m/s. Both methods give the same result.

WEBLINK

Find out about the design of roller coasters such as the Magnum XL-200. Research the heights of the track and the speeds of the cars. Draw a scale diagram of the portion of track where the kinetic energy will be the greatest. Begin your research at **www.pearsoned.ca/physics11.**

INSIGHT

In problems where all the gravitational energy is converted to kinetic energy (or vice-versa), it is possible to solve them without knowing the mass of the object. Since $|mg\Delta h| = \left|\frac{1}{2}mv^2\right|$, the mass term divides out and is not needed to solve the problem!

PRACTICE PROBLEMS

1. At what speed would a 70-kg high jumper have to leave the ground in order to raise his body up to a height of 1.60 m?
2. Neglecting air resistance, how high could a 0.15-kg baseball be thrown if it is thrown straight up at a speed of 25 m/s?

EXAMPLE 12 CONCEPTUAL

An exciting way to dive into water at a safe swimming location is to swing from a rope tied to a high support such as a bridge. By releasing the rope at various locations the swimmer can enter the water at different distances from the shore (Figure 4.33). Does the release point affect the speed with which the swimmer enters the water?

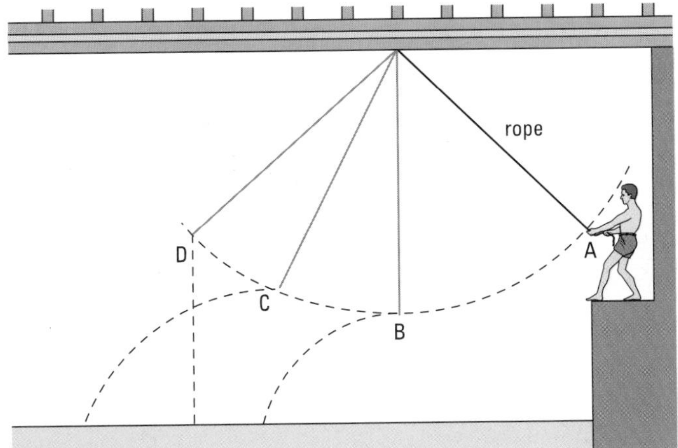

FIGURE 4.33

Reasoning and Solution

This situation involves conversions between gravitational energy and kinetic energy. Assuming negligible air resistance and friction we can apply the law of conservation of energy to answer the question.

The swimmer grasping the rope at A has a certain gravitational energy with reference to the surface of the water. After the person steps off from A, some of this gravitational energy is converted to kinetic energy during the swing to position B. At position B the swimmer still has some potential energy with reference to the surface of the water. If the person lets go at B, the remainder of this potential energy is converted to kinetic energy during the fall along the parabolic path to the surface of the water. At the surface of the water all the original potential energy has been converted to kinetic energy.

If the person hangs on until position C some of the kinetic energy at the bottom of the swing is converted back into gravitational energy. But this kinetic energy is gained back during the fall. At D, the far end of the swing, the swimmer will stop for an instant. At D the swimmer has the same gravitational energy with reference to the water as at A. If the person releases the rope at D all this potential energy will be converted to kinetic energy during the vertical fall to the water. The person's kinetic energy at the surface of the water will be the same in all three cases. The kinetic energy at the surface is always equal to the initial potential energy at A; the law of conservation of energy guarantees it. Because the kinetic energy is the same, the speed is the same. The swimmer's speed will be the same no matter which release point is chosen. But will the velocity be the same? What do you think?

WEBLINK

To explore the energy conversions in a string pendulum go to **www.pearsoned.ca/physics11.**

CHALLENGE

A 45-kg child swings down from a river bank on a rope tied to a tree overhanging the river. He lets go of the rope and falls into the river. If the river bank is 3.0 m above the river, with what speed will the child enter the water?

Section 4.5 Review

Understanding Concepts

1. Explain the energy transformations taking place when a pole vaulter makes a successful jump. Why does the vaulter run rather than walk to the jump?
2. Figure 4.34 shows a pendulum at various points in its swing.

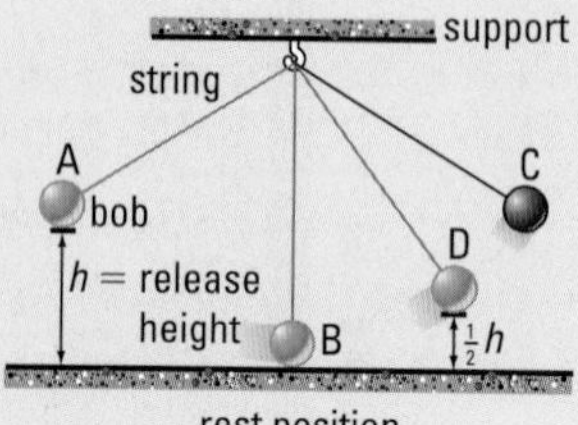

FIGURE 4.34 Energy conversions in a pendulum

   a) Where does the mass have its greatest height, and where does it have its greatest gravitational energy?
   b) Where does the mass have its greatest speed, and where does it have its greatest kinetic energy?
   c) Describe the energy conversion taking place as the mass moves from A to B, and from B to C.
   d) Compare the gravitational energy and the kinetic energy at point D.
   e) Write a word equation for the total energy the mass has at any point in its swing.
3. State the law of conservation of energy, and give an example.
4. Figure 4.35 shows a person demonstrating energy conservation. She is releasing a heavy pendulum mass. The mass has been pulled so it touches her nose. When the mass returns, does she need to move back to be safe? Is it safe to lean forward? Explain your answers.

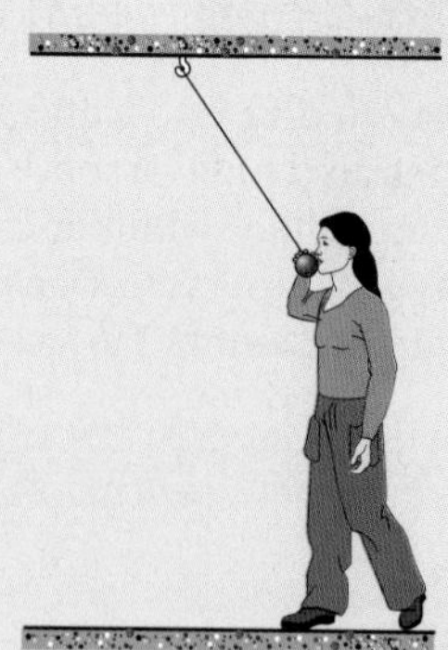

FIGURE 4.35

5. a) A wrecking ball is travelling at 7.0 m/s at the bottom of its swing. How high above the bottom of its swing will it go?
   b) At what speed would the wrecking ball have to be going at the bottom of its swing in order to rise to twice the height it reached in part a) above?
6. A tennis ball is dropped from a height of 2.0 m
   a) At what speed will it strike the ground?
   b) If it loses 20% of its energy when it bounces, how high will it bounce?

Applying Inquiry/ Communication Skills

7. Design an experiment to find out how much energy is lost when a lacrosse ball bounces once.

Making Connections

8. You are to be the chairperson of a committee designing a new, fast, safe roller coaster. You can ask four other people to be on your committee. What expertise would you want each of these people to have and why?

Inquiry Skills

- Initiating and Planning
- Applying Technical Skills
- Using Tools, Materials, Equipment
- Conducting and Recording
- Analyzing and Interpreting
- Concluding and Communicating

Investigation 1 (Section 4.4)

Work, Energy, and Atwood's Machine

Atwood's machine consists of two different masses connected by a long string and suspended from a low friction pulley (Figure 4.36). By using the computer to measure the velocity of the system, it is possible to calculate the changes in energy that occur.

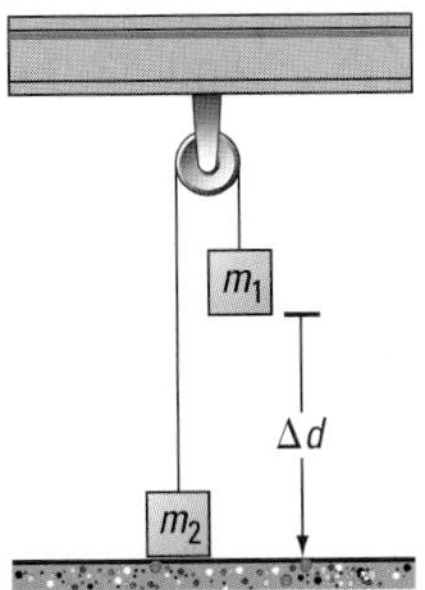

FIGURE 4.36 Atwood's machine

Problem

To compare the work done by gravity on a pulley system to the change in kinetic energy of the system.

Materials

- a set of masses
- smart pulley and computer system
- thin string
- metre-stick

Procedure

1. Connect the computer and smart pulley as instructed by the manufacturer.
2. Choose two masses that differ by only 5 or 10 g (e.g. 95 g and 100 g).
3. Predict the velocity of m_1 when it hits the table. To do this remember that
   $\Delta d = v_1\Delta t + \frac{1}{2}a\Delta t^2$ where $v_1 = 0$ so that
   $a = \frac{2\Delta d}{\Delta t^2}$
   But $v_2 = v_1 + a\Delta t = 0 + a\Delta t$
   So that $v_2 = a\Delta t = \frac{2\Delta d}{\Delta t^2}\Delta t = \frac{2\Delta d}{\Delta t}$.
4. Use the smart pulley system to measure the velocity of the mass as it lands on the table.
5. Repeat the experiment two more times to get the most reliable values you can.
6. Repeat steps 2–5 two more times using different combinations of masses.
7. Calculate the change in kinetic energy of the system $\frac{1}{2}m_1v_1^2 + \frac{1}{2}m_2v_2^2$. Note that both masses have the same *speed* when m_1 hits the table.
8. Calculate the total work done on the system by gravity. Note that gravity does positive work on m_1 ($m_1g\Delta d$) and negative work on m_2 ($-m_2g\Delta d$) so that the total work done by gravity is $m_1g\Delta d - m_2g\Delta d$.

Analyzing and Interpreting

1. How do the predicted velocity values compare to the measured values?
2. The system gained kinetic energy. Where did this energy come from?

Concluding and Communicating

3. How does the total work done by gravity on the system compare to the gain in kinetic energy of the system?
4. This experiment demonstrates the work–energy theorem. Find out what this theorem states and illustrate your grasp of the theorem by applying it to the example of a soccer ball being kicked along the ground.

Extending

5. Use $m_1g\Delta d - m_2g\Delta d = \frac{1}{2}m_1v_1^2 + \frac{1}{2}m_2v_2^2$ to prove that $v_2 = \sqrt{2g\Delta d\frac{(m_1 - m_2)}{(m_1 + m_2)}}$. Use a set of values from your experiment to test this equation.

Investigation 2 (Section 4.5)

Inquiry Skills

- Initiating and Planning
- Applying Technical Skills
- Using Tools, Materials, Equipment
- Conducting and Recording
- Analyzing and Interpreting
- Concluding and Communicating

Energy and the Pendulum

One of the problem-solving advantages when using the law of conservation of energy is that since the total energy stays constant, *you* can choose which places in the motion to do your calculations. In the case of a swinging pendulum, for example, by analyzing the total energy at the top and bottom of the swing, you eliminate some calculations because the kinetic energy at the top of the swing and the potential energy at the bottom of the swing are both zero.

Problem

To calculate and compare the total energy of a pendulum at the top and at the bottom of its swing.

Materials

- computer and photogate
- pendulum bob
- string
- retort apparatus
- calipers (optional)
- metre-stick
- electronic or triple-beam balance
- modelling clay

Experimental Design

1. Make a list of the measurements that must be made to measure the gravitational potential energy at the top of the pendulum swing and the kinetic energy at the bottom of the swing.

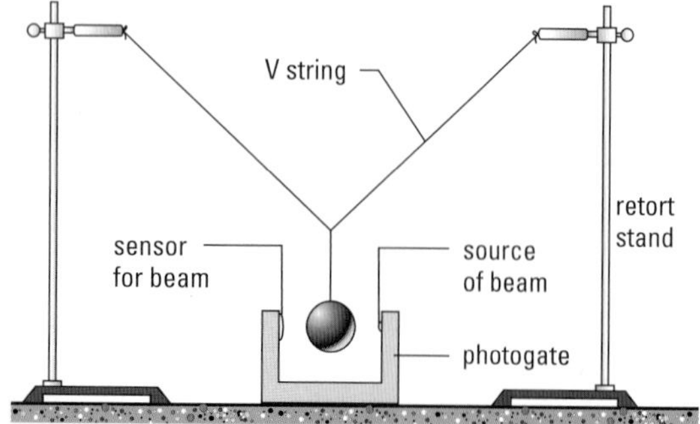

FIGURE 4.37

2. Write out a list of procedures you will use to obtain the required measurements.
3. Design a data table to record your measurements.
4. Discuss with your teacher how the modelling clay can be used to prevent damage to the photogate.
5. When your teacher approves your procedure, carry out the experiment.

Analyzing and Interpreting

1. How does the potential energy at the top of the swing compare with the kinetic energy at the bottom?

Concluding and Communicating

2. Why is the potential energy at the top also the total energy at the top?
3. Why is the kinetic energy at the bottom also the total energy at the bottom?
4. If the photogate were not coated with modelling clay and the pendulum bob hit it, the bob would do work on the photogate (a force acting through a displacement) and possibly break it. In terms of the formula $W = F\Delta d$, what is the function of the modelling clay?

Extending

5. A model of a roller coaster can be constructed out of track for toy racing cars, duct tape, and retort apparatus. Design and build a roller coaster and include information on how kinetic and potential energy can be measured at various points along the track.
6. A construction device used to drive footings into the ground is called a pile driver. Research the specifics of the design of a pile driver and outline the changes in energy that occur during one cycle of its operation.

CHAPTER SUMMARY

Key Terms

chemical energy
elastic energy
electrical energy
energy
gigajoule
gravitational energy
heat energy
joule
kilojoule
kilowatt hour
kinetic energy
law of conservation of energy
megajoule
nuclear energy
potential energy
radiant energy
relative gravitational energy
rest mass energy
sound energy
thermal energy
work

Key Equations

$W = F\Delta d \cos\theta$

$W = F\Delta d$

$E = mc^2$

$E_k = \frac{1}{2}mv^2$

$\Delta E_G = mg\Delta h$

$\Delta E = 0$

Essential Understandings

- Work is the product of the force and the displacement in the direction of the force.
- One joule is the work done by a force of one newton applied through a displacement of one metre in the direction of the force.
- The area beneath a force–displacement graph represents the work done.
- Energy is the ability to do work and, like work, is measured in joules.
- Energy can be stored, transferred from object to object, and converted from one form to another.
- Energy is measured in terms of the work done.
- Gravitational potential energy depends on mass, gravitational field intensity, and vertical height.
- Kinetic energy depends on mass and speed.
- According to the law of conservation of energy, energy is neither created nor destroyed.

Consolidate Your Understanding

1. Look back to your answer for the Checkpoint on page 143. What answer would you give now? Explain why each of the other answers is incorrect.

A person drags a load at constant speed along a rough level floor through a displacement *d* by pulling on a rope with a force *F*. The rope makes an angle of 30° with floor. Explain why the work done is not the product of the force and the displacement.

2. Create a concept map to be used as a study map for work and energy. Consult the Key Terms above, and include as many terms as possible in your concept map. Include the two Key Equations for energy and an example problem involving both. Show a model solution using the GRASS strategy.

3. Write a paragraph describing the law of conservation of energy. Use an example involving a sport and the concepts of potential and kinetic energy to illustrate your understanding of the law and the energy transformations involved. Use the example to teach the law and these concepts to a fellow student who is involved in the chosen sport. Summarize the strengths and weaknesses of your lesson.

CHAPTER 4 REVIEW

Understanding Concepts

1. In which of the following cases is work NOT being done?
a) holding a turkey at chest height
b) pushing a bicycle 0.2 km [E]
c) walking down a flight of stairs
d) playing a violin solo
e) coasting to a stop on ice skates

2. If the speed of an object is quadrupled and the mass decreased by a factor of three, by what factor does the kinetic energy change?
a) $\frac{4}{3}$ b) $\frac{8}{3}$ c) $\frac{16}{3}$
d) 12 e) 36

3. Which of the following is NOT an expression for energy?
a) $\frac{1}{2}mv^2$ b) $F\Delta d$ c) $mg\Delta h$
d) $ma\Delta d$ e) $\frac{F}{\Delta t}$

4. In Figure 4.38, point X indicates the position of the bob of a long pendulum that has been pulled aside. The mass of the bob is m and it is located on a planet that has a gravitational field intensity of g. What is the gravitational energy of the bob at X with respect to the point Y?
a) $4.0m$ b) $4.0mg$ c) $10mg$
d) $11m$ e) $11mg$

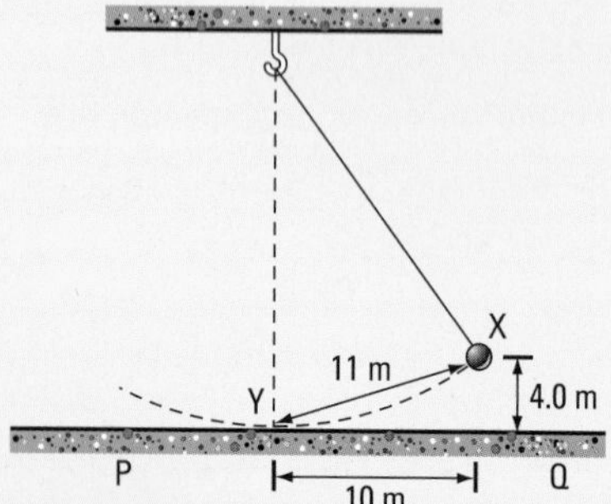

FIGURE 4.38

5. Two boys have the same mass and are riding on identical bicycles. One boy has a speed of 8 m/s and the other a speed of 2 m/s. What is the ratio of the first boy's kinetic energy to the second boy's kinetic energy?
a) 16:1 b) 8:1 c) 4:1
d) 2:1 e) 1:1

6. Use unit analysis to express the joule in SI base units.

7. Use an example to show that the total work done on an object is calculated using the applied force, not the net or unbalanced force.

8. Does Earth do any work on a satellite in a circular orbit? Explain. (Hint: Compare the direction of the applied force with the motion.)

9. How much mechanical work is done by a weightlifter holding a mass of 100 kg, 2.0 m above the floor for 3.0 s? Explain your answer.

10. Calculate the force that does 2.0 kJ of work to push a load of bricks 10 m.

11. What displacement is produced by a force of 80 N [S] which does 240 J of work pushing a wheelbarrow?

12. A carpenter applies a force of 60 N horizontally to push a plane 40 cm along a piece of wood, how much work does she do?

13. A boy is giving his baby sister a ride on a wagon. He exerts a constant horizontal force of 150 N to move the wagon. If 364 J of work are done, how far does he move it?

14. A librarian does 8.0 J of work to stack five identical books on top of each other. If each book has a thickness of 4.0 cm, what is the mass of a book?

15. You have two elastic springs. Spring A is stiffer than spring B. Compare the work,
a) if both springs are stretched the same amount
b) if both springs are stretched by the same force

16. A child is jumping on a pogo stick. Why does she have to do work continually? Explain your answer by referring to the energy changes taking place.

17. Three students of equal mass on the same hike encounter a log across their path. Student A walks around it, student B steps over it, and student C steps up on it and down on the other side. Compare the work done by each student.

18. Which of the following factors affect the work needed to lift a heavy suitcase onto a high bed? Explain each answer.
a) the height of the bed
b) the mass of the suitcase
c) whether the room is on Earth or on the Moon
d) whether the suitcase is lifted straight up or on a diagonal

19. A 75-kg passenger in a van is wearing a seat belt when the van, moving at 15 m/s, collides with a concrete wall. The front end of the van collapses 0.50 m as it comes to rest.
a) What was the passenger's kinetic energy before the crash?
b) What average force did the seat belt exert on the passenger during the crash?

20. Uranium is used in a nuclear-fission power plant to make steam to run a turbine that turns a generator. You use this electric supply to run an electric hair dryer. List, in order, all of the energy transformations that take place.

21. The Horseshoe Falls on the Niagara River in Ontario are about 48 m high and 780 m wide. The water at the top of the falls is moving at 9.0 m/s and has a depth of about 0.80 m as it goes over the falls.
   a) If the density of the water is 1000 kg/m^3, what mass of water goes over the falls every second?
   b) What is the change in gravitational energy of this mass of water?

22. A beach ball is thrown straight up with a speed of 10 m/s from a point 2 m above the ground.
   a) Assuming no air resistance, calculate how far up the ball will go.
   b) At what speed will the ball eventually hit the ground?
   c) Predict the effect that air resistance will have on your answers to a) and b).

23. Look at Figure 4.39. Predict what will happen when the string is cut. Is any work being done before the string is cut? Is any work being done before the string is cut? What energy does the paper clip have while it is suspended? What energy transformations take place when the string is cut?

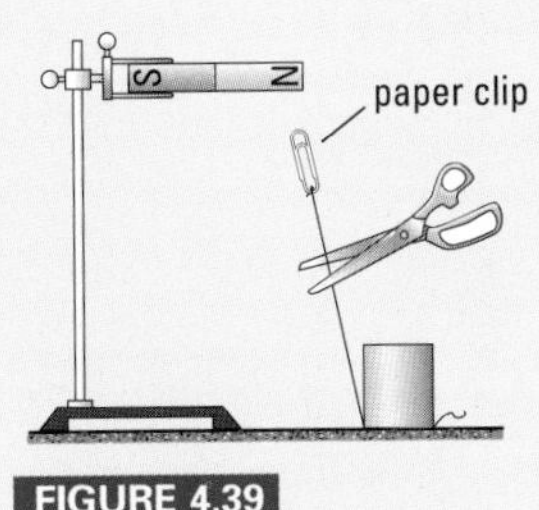

FIGURE 4.39

Applying Inquiry/Communication Skills

24. If your school has an air table with a spark timer, design and perform an experiment to compare the kinetic energy before and after a soft off-centred collision between two magnetic pucks. In a soft collision the pucks do not touch each other.

25. Use your knowledge of kinematics and dynamics to determine the energy needed to operate one flush toilet for a year in an average household.

26. Estimate the kinetic energy of your pen as you write words on paper and explain your estimate.

27. If a coil spring is placed on the top step of a flight of stairs, it will "walk" down the stairs to the bottom. Outline the types of energy involved in this activity and describe the order of the energy conversions involved.

28. A ballpoint pen can be used to test the law of conservation of energy. A pen that separates into four pieces; the ink refill, the top and bottom plastic pieces, and a small spring inside, is the kind to use. Design an experiment to investigate the law of conservation of energy when the top plastic part of the pen is launched vertically by the spring.

29. The energy consumption of a car is usually expressed in litres of fuel per hundred kilometres. For example, a typical consumption rate would be 10 L/100 km. Use unit analysis to show the strange result that car energy consumption can be expressed in the units of an area.

30. An unusual type of pendulum called a ballistic pendulum was invented in 1740. Research the structure and functions of the ballistic pendulum and write a brief report.

Making Connections

31. The construction of athletic shoes varies according to the type of motion required for different sports. Compare the motion of a tennis player and a jogger. Itemize the physics laws that apply to each sport, and describe how the shoes are designed to improve achievement.

32. Research and write a report on the roles physicists, engineers, and technicians have played in improving the pole vault record at the Olympics.

33. A 50-kg skateboarder designs a creative way to gain enough speed to coast up a ramp. By compressing a stiff spring, he finds that he can go 1.5 m up the ramp (Figure 4.40).

FIGURE 4.40

   a) List the energy conversions in this activity.
   b) How much kinetic energy does the spring give him?
   c) The energy in the spring can be calculated using the expression $\frac{1}{2}kx^2$ where k = 1470 N/m and is called the spring constant and x is the distance the spring is compressed. How much was the spring compressed in this case?

34. It is often stated that a certain person has a lot of potential. An old saying is "potential just means that you have not done it yet." Use your knowledge of the term potential and the other forms of energy to illustrate how this saying might be true.

35. On some highways near the bottom of a steep downhill portion of the road, a ramp is provided at the side of the road for trucks in case brakes fail. It is called a runway ramp. The surface is not paved and the ramp slopes steeply up. Use your knowledge of the law of conservation of energy and an estimation of the height of a steep hill to calculate a typical height for such a ramp.

CHAPTER 5

Machines, Power, and Energy

SPECIFIC EXPECTATIONS

By the end of this chapter, you will be able to:

- define and describe the concepts and units related to energy, work, and power (5.1, 5.2, 5.3)
- analyze, in qualitative and quantitative terms, simple situations involving work, gravitational potential energy, kinetic energy, and thermal energy and its transfer (heat), using the law of conservation of energy (5.3)
- apply quantitatively the relationships among power, energy, and time in a variety of contexts (5.2, 5.4)
- analyze, in quantitative terms, the relationships among percent efficiency, input energy, and useful output energy for several energy transformations (5.1)
- design and carry out experiments related to energy transformations, identifying and controlling major variables (5.1)
- analyze and interpret experimental data or computer simulations involving work, gravitational potential energy, kinetic energy, thermal energy and its transfer (heat), and the efficiency of the energy transformation
- communicate the procedures, data, and conclusions of investigations involving work, mechanical energy, power, thermal energy and its transfer (heat), and the law of conservation of energy, using appropriate means (5.3)
- analyze the economic, social, and environmental impact of various energy sources and energy-transformation technologies used around the world (5.3, 5.4)
- analyze and explain improvements in sports performance, using principles and concepts related to work, kinetic and potential energy, and the law of conservation of energy (5.1)

A mechanic needs to lift a car into the air to take a look underneath. A cyclist needs to pedal up a steep hill. A furniture mover needs to deliver a new sofa to the seventh floor of an apartment building. Accomplishing each of these tasks requires work. To make these tasks easier, we use machines. A car jack can be used to lift a car. The gears on a bike can help

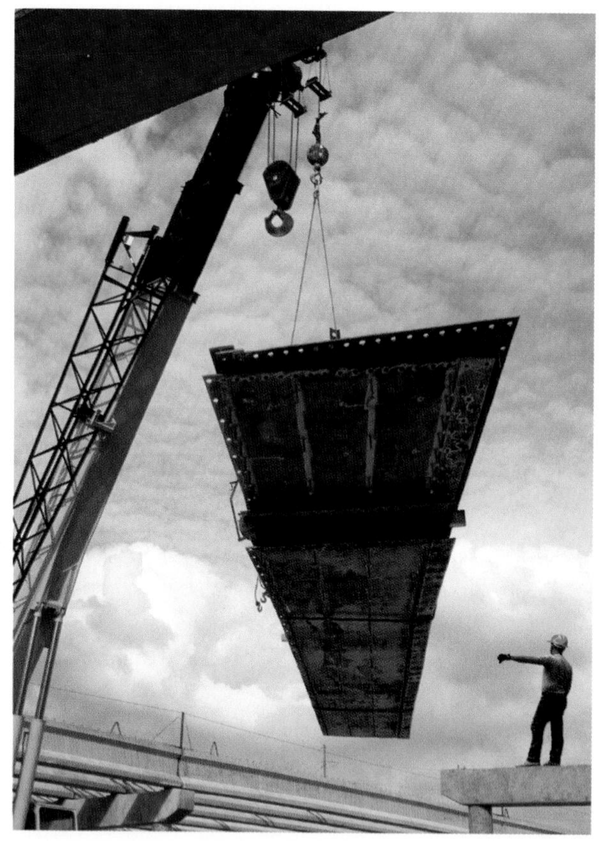

FIGURE 5.1 It would take the combined efforts of several construction workers to do the same work as this crane. Why?

to get you up a hill. An elevator can get you and your sofa up to the seventh floor. These are all examples of machines.

As consumers, we are aware that some machines do their job more efficiently than others. This is illustrated by the kinds of questions we ask the salespeople when we are shopping for a new air conditioner or lawn mower: how fast will it get the job done, how quickly will it use energy, will it waste energy? These are the very same issues that engineers deal with when designing machines. For example, some machines convert one type of energy into another, but engineers know that anytime this is done some of the energy ends up as heat. This decreases a machine's efficiency because the heat energy dissipates into the environment instead of doing work. Engineers are also concerned with machine's power output, which is a measurement of how much work it can do in a given amount of time. Without an understanding of these basic concepts, we would not have any of the machines we use today.

In this chapter, you will study the relationships between input energy, useful output energy, and efficiency as they relate to different types of machines. You will analyze the relationship between power, energy, and time. You'll examine various sources of energy such as solar, wind, and fossil fuel and investigate how each of them can be harnessed to do work. Finally, you'll take a look at the economic, social, and environmental impact of using both renewable and non-renewable energy sources. By the time you complete the chapter, you should understand the above concepts and how they can affect your life.

CHECK**POINT**

Trucker A lifts a load vertically to the flatbed of a delivery truck. Trucker B drags a load of the same mass up a rough ramp to the flatbed. How does the work done on the loads compare?

a) A does more work on the load than B.
b) B does more work on the load than A.
c) A and B do the same amount of work on the load.
d) Not enough information is given to answer the question.

Draw a sketch of each situation and explain your answer.

Discovering Physics

Make a Simple Machine

Convert ordinary broomsticks into a simple machine.

You will need: two broomsticks, some rope, and two people to help. Tie one end of the rope tightly to the middle of one broomstick. Have one person hold each broomstick, and loop the rope around the second broomstick as shown in Figure 5.2a).

The people holding the broomsticks should try to hold the sticks apart, while you pull the broomsticks closer together by pulling on the rope.

Now wrap the rope around the first stick a second time as shown in Figure 5.2b) and try again.

Continue the experiment by looping the rope around the broomsticks one additional time per try.

- As the rope is wrapped around the broomsticks does it get easier or harder to pull the sticks together?
- How many loops of the rope does it take until the sticks can be pulled together?
- Why is this arrangement of sticks and rope called a machine?

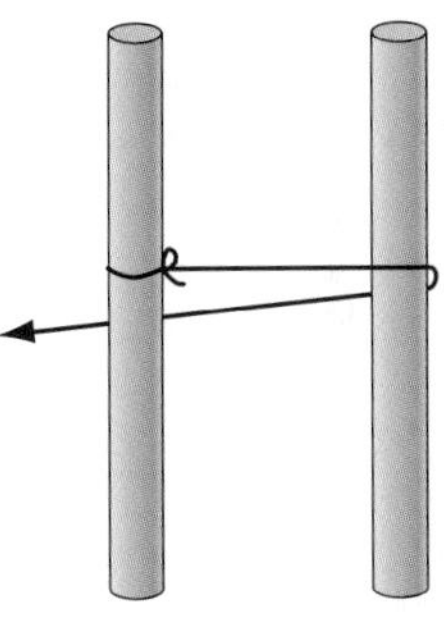

a)

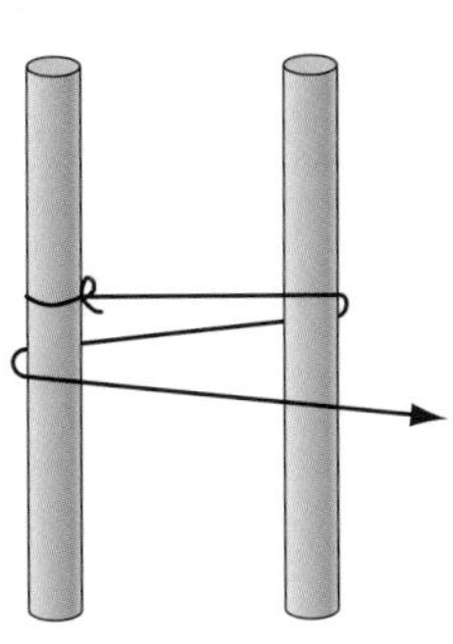

b)

FIGURE 5.2

5.1 Machines and Efficiency

Key Understandings

When you have completed this section, you will be able to:

- describe the basic kinds of simple machines
- identify the advantages of various machines
- calculate the efficiency of a machine

A **machine** is a device that enables us to do work more easily than is otherwise possible. There are two basic kinds of machines: the inclined plane, and the lever. Four other machines gradually developed from these two. The wedge and the screw are modifications of the inclined plane. The pulley, and the wheel and axle are adaptations of the lever. Figure 5.3 shows the six simple machines.

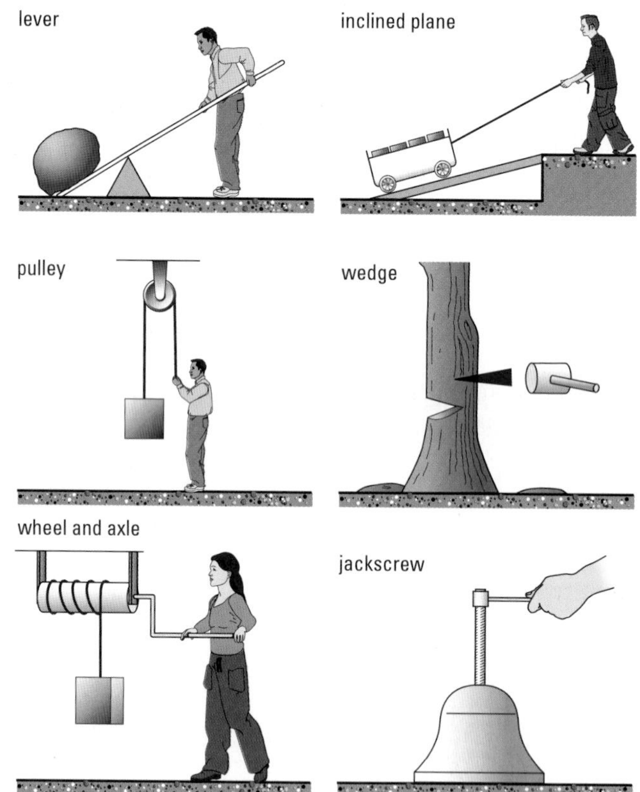

FIGURE 5.3 The six simple machines

Some machines change forces from one kind to another: a hydro-electric generator changes the force of falling water into an electric force. Other machines transfer a force from one place to another: the drive shaft of a grain combine takes the force from the engine to the wheels. Some machines increase the size of a force: a car jack amplifies a muscular force to enable us to lift a car. Other machines decrease the size of a force: the sprocket of a bicycle scales down the muscular force supplied to the pedals to a smaller force acting on the wheel in order to gain more speed. Some machines change the direction of a force: a single pulley mounted overhead changes a downward muscular force applied to a rope to an upward tensile force applied by the rope to a load.

WEBLINK

To explore the relationship between work, friction, and mass further, go to **www.pearsoned.ca/physics11.**

The Inclined Plane

The **inclined plane** is a simple machine that allows us to increase the height of an object without having to exert a force big enough to lift up its whole weight. A ramp at a parking garage or an access ramp into a buildings are examples of inclined planes. Machines like this give us an advantage. The **actual mechanical advantage** (AMA) of an inclined plane is the ratio of the magnitude of the force required to lift the load vertically (the load force) to the magnitude of the force necessary to move the object up the inclined plane (the applied force). Thus

$$\text{AMA} = \frac{\text{load force}}{\text{applied force}} = \frac{F_{\text{G}}}{F_{\text{A}}} = \frac{mg}{F_{\text{A}}}$$

For example, if an object weighing 100 N is pushed up a ramp with an applied force of 70 N, the actual mechanical advantage of this inclined plane would be 100 N/70 N = 1.4.

Access ramps enable a person to exert less force over a greater displacement but still do the same amount of work needed to climb to a certain height.

Refer to page 220, Investigation 1.

Efficiency

Scientists and engineers are interested in the **efficiency** of the energy conversions that occur in machines. They want to know how much of the energy entering the system is used to make the system work and how much is wasted as heat and undesirable by-products. The efficiency of a machine measures the useful work done (or energy output) by the machine compared with the energy put into the machine.

$$\text{percent efficiency} = \frac{\text{useful work done}}{\text{actual work done}} \times 100\%$$

$$= \frac{\text{energy output}}{\text{energy input}} \times 100\%$$

Table 5.1 shows the efficiencies of some common systems. Are you surprised at the low efficiency of the car engine and the incandescent lamp? Why do you think their efficiencies are so small?

TABLE 5.1 Efficiencies of Some Common Systems

Machine	Efficiency
Electric heater	99%
Hydro-electric generator	95%
Car generator (alternator)	93%
Electric motor, large	92%
Dry cell	90%
Home gas furnace	85%
Car battery*	73%
Home oil furnace	66%
Wind generator	60%
Diesel engine	36%
Fossil-fuelled electric generator	33%
Nuclear-fuelled electric generator	30%
Car engine	**26%**
Fluorescent lamp	20%
Silicon solar cell	12%
Steam locomotive	9%
Incandescent lamp	2%

* each charge-discharge cycle

PRACTICE PROBLEMS

1. In the pulley system shown in Figure 5.4, a 2.0-kg mass (this includes the mass of the lower pulley) is raised a vertical distance of 10 cm by a force of 11 N. The force is applied through a distance of 20 cm. Calculate the efficiency of this machine.

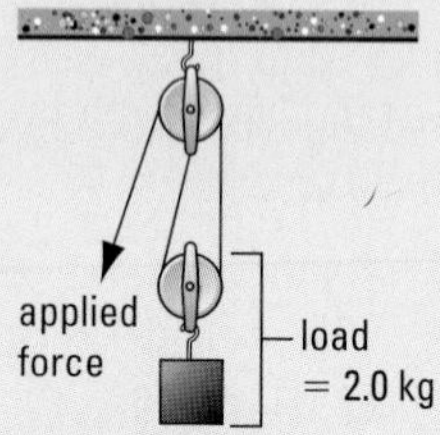

FIGURE 5.4

2. A wheel and axle are used to lift a 10-kg load a vertical distance of 30 cm. The force used to lift this load is 33 N and the force acts through a distance of 1.2 m. Calculate the efficiency of this system.

EXAMPLE 1 NUMERICAL

The work required to drag a 20-kg box to the top of a 3.0-m high ramp is 980 J. Calculate the efficiency of the ramp.

Given
$E = 980$ J
$m = 20$ kg
$\Delta h = 3.0$ m

Required
Efficiency

Analysis
- The useful work is the change in gravitational energy $mg\Delta h$.

Solution

$$\begin{aligned}\Delta E_G &= mg\Delta h \\ &= 20\text{ kg} \times 9.8\text{ N/kg} \times 3.0\text{ m} \\ &= 588\text{ J}\end{aligned}$$

$$\begin{aligned}\text{Percent efficiency} &= \frac{\text{useful work}}{\text{actual work}} \times 100\% \\ &= \frac{588\text{ J}}{980\text{ J}} \times 100\% \\ &= 60\%\end{aligned}$$

Statement
The efficiency of the ramp is 60%.

Levers

Levers can be used in a variety of ways—to increase force, vary speed, or to change direction. A **lever** consists of a rigid bar that can rotate about a fixed point called a **fulcrum**. When a load is placed at one point on a lever, a force applied at a different location can move the load. Levers are classified according to the relative locations of the fulcrum, load, and applied force. There are three classes of lever.

Figure 5.5 illustrates that a first-class lever is one in which the fulcrum is somewhere between the load and the applied force. A second-class lever has the load between the fulcrum and the applied force, while a third-class lever has the force between the fulcrum and the load.

The turning effect of a force on a lever is called **torque**.Torque is so common that it is sometimes difficult to think of situations that don't involve torque. You use torque without even thinking about it when you throw a Frisbee, turn a handle to open a window, cut paper with scissors, open a door, turn a page in a book, or simply smile.

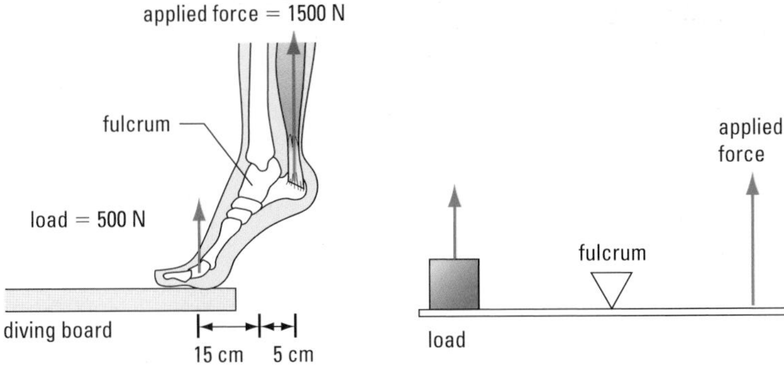

First class

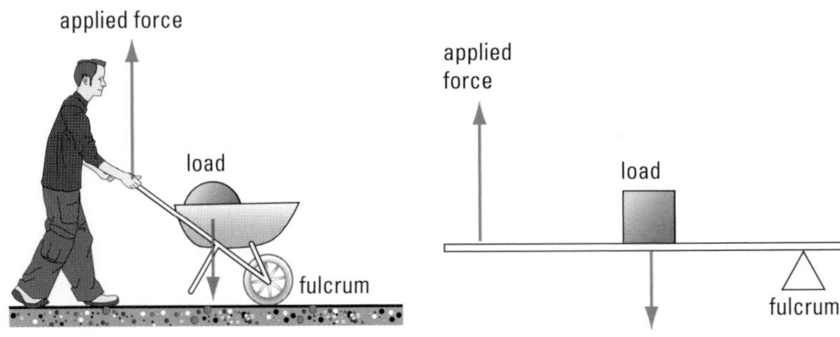

Second class

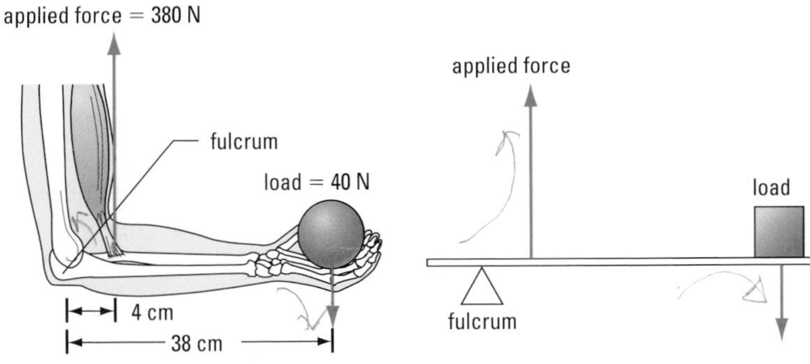

Third class

FIGURE 5.5 The three classes of lever

When there is more than one torque applied to a lever, the lever will balance if the sum of the clockwise torques is equal to the sum of the counterclockwise torques. This is called the **law of the lever**.

The magnitude of the torque τ (the Greek letter *tau*) is calculated by multiplying the force applied by the perpendicular distance of the force from the fulcrum. This perpendicular distance is called the **lever arm** ℓ. Thus

$$\tau = F\ell$$

The unit of torque is the unit of force (N) times the unit of distance (m) and is called a newton metre (N·m). This unit appears to be the same as the unit for work. But torque is not work and so we do not express this unit as a joule the way we do with work.

EXAMPLE 2 CONCEPTUAL

While entering a bank, a customer pushes on the door handle with a force of 50 N to open the door. The door handle is 90 cm from the hinges. What force would this customer have to use if, instead of pushing on the handle, she pushed near the middle of the door at a distance of 60 cm from the hinges?

Reasoning and Solution

The torque necessary to open the door is $\tau = F\ell = 50\text{ N} \times 0.90\text{ m} = 45\text{ N·m}$

It takes the same torque to open the door regardless of where the force is applied.

Thus, the force necessary to open the door at a distance of 60 cm from the hinge is

$$F = \frac{\tau}{\ell} = \frac{45\text{ N·m}}{0.60\text{ m}} = 75\text{ N}$$

It takes the larger force of 75 N to open the door when the smaller lever arm of 60 cm is used.

A father on one side of a teeter-totter can just balance his daughter who is on the other side of the teeter-totter when he sits his 75-kg body at a distance of 1.2 m from the fulcrum. How far from the fulcrum would the father have to be in order to balance his daughter and her identical twin sitting together at the same location on the teeter-totter?

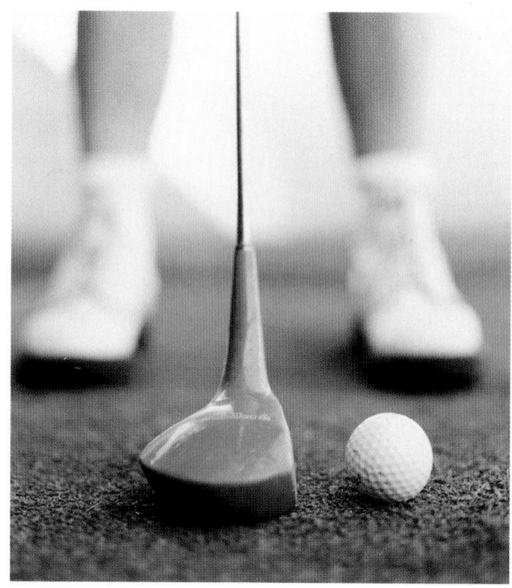

FIGURE 5.6 A poor shot could be caused by the torque in the shaft of the golf club.

In the sport of golf one common reason for a shot going in the wrong direction is the torque of the shaft during the downswing. That is, if the shaft twists on the downswing, the club head will not strike the ball squarely on impact. To minimize this twist, manufacturers now make the shafts of woods and irons thicker in diameter. These so-called "fat-shafts" make for straighter shots and a poorly struck shot will not go as far off target.

Different golfers have different performance requirements. For the casual golfer, one of the most common causes of mis-hitting with an iron, is that the club head does not strike the ball on the "sweet spot"—that small area at the middle of the club face. Manufacturers have addressed this problem by making the club face larger and changing the weight distribution on the club head (Figure 5.6). Perimeter weighting of the club face puts most of the weight around the perimeter of the club head so that the chances of striking the ball solidly on the sweet spot are greatly increased.

Pulleys and Pulley Systems

A **pulley** is a modified lever. It consists of a grooved wheel that is free to turn in a frame called a block. A combination of several pulleys is called a tackle. (This is where the term "block and tackle" came from.) Pulleys have a variety of uses from machines used in physiotherapy (Figure 5.7) to industrial applications and body-building machines.

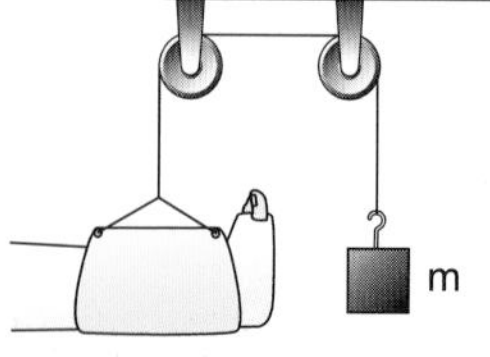

FIGURE 5.7 Pulleys and a counterweight help support a person's leg and plaster cast.

Pulley systems can be designed to perform certain tasks. The **ideal mechanical advantage** (IMA) of a pulley system is the

Discovering Physics — A First Class Lever

A metre-stick can be used as a first class lever. Try this experiment and see how you can use a lever to gain force. Suspend the metre-stick by a string so that the metre-stick is balanced (Figure 5.8).

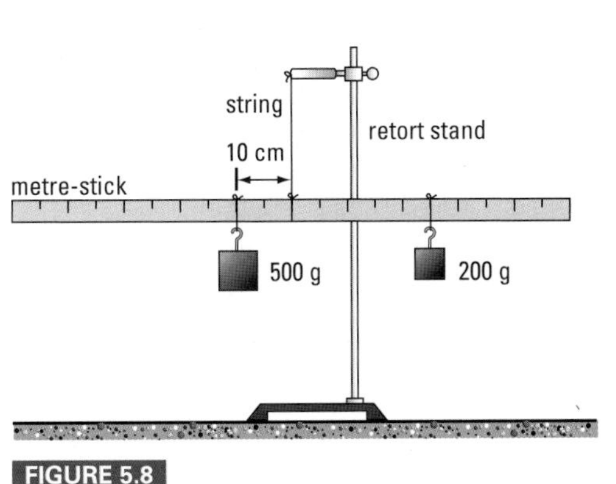

FIGURE 5.8

Place a loop of string on each side of the fulcrum. Use a 500-g mass as the load and suspend it from one of the string loops so that it is 10 cm from the fulcrum. On the other side of the fulcrum, find out at what distance from the fulcrum a 200-g mass must be placed to supply enough torque to just balance the lever. Make a chart to record the load, the distance of the load from the fulcrum, the torque produced by this load, the force, the distance of the force from the fulcrum, the torque produced by this force, and the actual mechanical advantage of the system (AMA = load/force). Now repeat the experiment three more times by slightly moving the load and measuring the new position of the force necessary to provide enough torque to just balance this load. How are the load and force torques related? Calculate the ratio of the force arm to the load arm in each case. How is this ratio related to the AMA of the system?

mechanical advantage of the system neglecting friction. Of course friction exists, so the **actual mechanical advantage** (AMA) of the pulley system is always less than the IMA. To predict the IMA of a pulley system, you simply count the number of strands of string or rope that are pulling the load up. In Figure 5.9a) the IMA is one because only one strand is pulling the load up. The other strand is pulling down. In Figure 5.9b), both strands are pulling up, so the IMA is two. Similarly the IMAs in Figures 5.9c), d), and e) are two, three, and three, respectively.

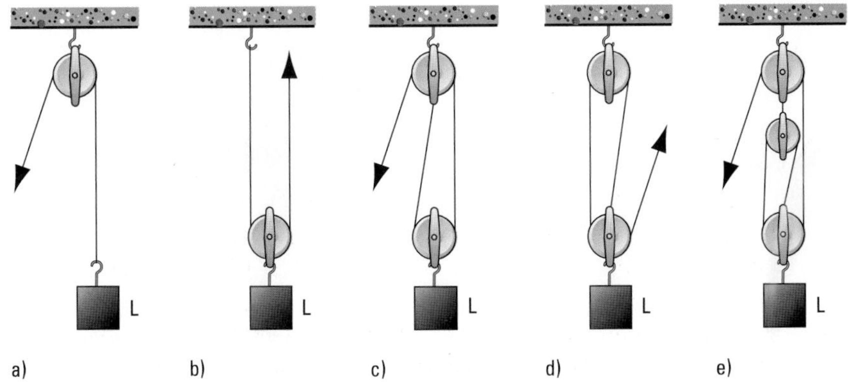

FIGURE 5.9 Pulley systems

Discovering Physics — *Pulleys and Efficiency*

Set up a pulley system (block and tackle) and use a spring scale to measure the force necessary to lift the load at a constant speed. Then use a formula to calculate the percent efficiency of the system.

1. Set up a pulley system (block and tackle) consisting of a single fixed and a single movable pulley as shown in Figure 5.9c).
2. Use a 500-g mass as a load.
3. The total load, however, consists of the 500-g mass and the movable pulley, so you will need to measure the mass of the pulley.
4. Use a spring scale to measure the force necessary to lift the load at constant speed. Remember to hold the scale upside down when you set the zero on the scale.
5. Set up a chart to record the total load, the applied force, the AMA, the IMA, and the efficiency.
6. Repeat the experiment for three more loads different from the first one and record your results.

The percent efficiency of a pulley system is the ratio of the actual mechanical advantage to the ideal mechanical advantage. Thus

$$\text{percent efficiency} = \frac{\text{actual mechanical advantage}}{\text{ideal mechanical advantage}} \times 100\%$$

$$= \frac{\text{AMA}}{\text{IMA}} \times 100\%$$

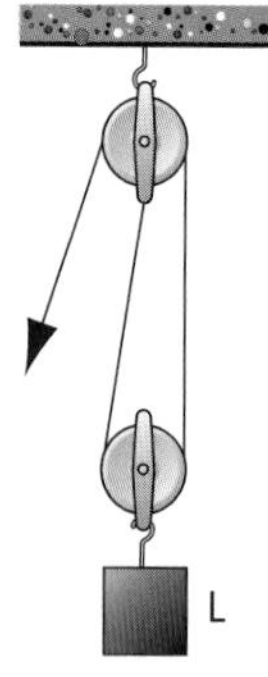

- How efficient is this system on average?
- Why is the actual mechanical advantage somewhat less than two?

Section 5.1 Review

Understanding Concepts

1. How is the actual mechanical advantage of a simple machine calculated?
2. A force of 300 N is necessary to slide a 50-kg mass up an inclined plane.
   a) Calculate the actual mechanical advantage of this inclined plane.
   b) If the ramp is 2.0 m long and 1.0 m high, calculate the efficiency of this machine.
3. Classify each of the following as either a first-, second-, or third-class lever:
   a) a broom used for sweeping the floor
   b) a screwdriver used to pry the lid from a paint can
   c) an oar used to row a boat
   d) a nutcracker used to crack open a cooked lobster claw

Applying Inquiry/ Communication Skills

4. a) What causes the efficiency of a machine to be less than 100%?
   b) Predict what would happen to the (i) ideal mechanical advantage and (ii) the efficiency of a pulley system as more pulleys are added to the system.
5. The pulley system shown in Figure 5.10 consists of a 19.5-kg load attached to a 0.50-kg pulley. A force of 123 N is necessary to lift the total load.

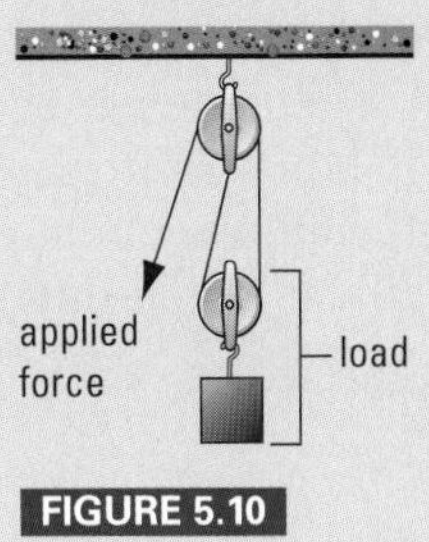

FIGURE 5.10

   a) What is the ideal mechanical advantage of this system?
   b) Calculate the actual mechanical advantage of this system.
   c) What is the efficiency of this system?
   d) How would you redesign this system so that a force of only 100 N was necessary to lift the load?

Making Connections

6. Research ways in which torque is used in sports such as hockey, figure skating, judo, and tennis. Write a paragraph explaining how a knowledge of torque could help an athlete reduce the amount of force needed to perform a specific task.

5.2 Power

Key Understandings

When you have completed this section, you will be able to:

- describe the two factors affecting power
- solve problems involving time, power, and work or energy
- solve problems involving applied force, average speed, and power

You can dig a hole with a shovel, or you can rent a machine to help do the job. If you dig the same size hole by yourself or with a shovel or a larger machine, you will still do the same amount of work. But the machine has more of something than you do. What is this "something"? How can it be calculated?

FIGURE 5.11 An excavator

Power

Power is the rate at which work is done. Since energy is consumed when work is done, power is also the rate at which energy is used. Two factors determine power: the amount of work done or energy consumed, and the time taken. Power is calculated by dividing the work done, or the energy consumed, by the elapsed time.

Investigation Refer to page 221, Investigation 2.

$$\text{Power} = \frac{\text{work}}{\text{elapsed time}} = \frac{\text{energy}}{\text{elapsed time}}$$

If P is the symbol for power, W for work, E for energy, and Δt for elapsed time, the equations for power are:

$$P = \frac{W}{\Delta t} = \frac{E}{\Delta t}$$

Note that since energy and time are both scalar quantities, power is also a scalar quantity.

The SI unit for power is the joule per second (J/s). The joule per second has been given the special name, watt, in honour of James Watt. He was the Scottish engineer who in 1769 devised a more efficient way to harness the energy in steam. One watt (W) is the power available when one joule (J) of work is done in one second.

$$1 \text{ W} = 1 \text{ J/s}$$

WEBLINK

To explore the factors affecting power, work done, and time taken to do the work, go to **www.pearsoned.ca/physics11.**

EXAMPLE 3 NUMERICAL

Some people are capable of doing large amounts of work for very brief periods of time. Chen Xiaomin of China participated in the first women's weightlifting event ever in the Olympics at the 2000 Sydney Games. She set a world record of 112.5 kg in the "snatch" where the barbell must be raised over the head in one continuous motion. If she lifted this mass through a vertical distance of 2.0 m in 2.1 s, what was her power output?

Given

$m = 112.5$ kg
$\Delta d = 2.0$ m
$\Delta t = 2.1$ s

Required

P

Analysis

- The weightlifter must exert an average force [up] equal to the force of gravity on the mass.
- Calculate the force using $F_G = mg$.
- Then calculate the work using $W = F\Delta d$ and the power using $P = \dfrac{W}{\Delta t}$.

Solution

$$\begin{aligned} F_G &= mg \\ &= 112.5 \text{ kg} \times 9.8 \text{ N/kg} \\ &= 1.1 \times 10^3 \text{ N} \end{aligned}$$

$$W = F\Delta d$$
$$= 1.1 \times 10^3 \text{ N} \times 2.0 \text{ m}$$
$$= 2.2 \times 10^3 \text{ N·m}$$
$$= 2.2 \times 10^3 \text{ J}$$

$$P = \frac{W}{\Delta t}$$
$$= \frac{2.2 \times 10^3 \text{ J}}{2.1 \text{ s}}$$
$$= 1.0 \times 10^3 \text{ W}$$

Statement

The power of the weightlifter was 1.0×10^3 W = 1.0 kW. Actually the weightlifter's power was larger since she raised her centre of mass as well as the mass of the barbell. People are not capable of such a high power output for long. The sustained power output of the average person is about 75 W. It is worth noting that, as the weightlifter holds the barbell above her head sweating and straining, she is not doing any physical work. Why? Because the barbell is stationary.

PRACTICE PROBLEMS

1. A car jack is used to lift up a quarter of the weight of a 1200-kg car 20 cm in 20 s. Calculate the power of the car jack.
2. A 250-W hydraulic car jack is used to do the same work on the same car as in the previous problem. How long will it take to lift the car this time?

Table 5.2 shows how powerful some biological systems are.

TABLE 5.2 Sample Powers of Biological Systems

System	Power (P [W])
Left ventricle of human heart	3
Human reclining	17
Human walking at 3.2 km/h	230
Horse working steadily	750
Average human sprinting	1 000
Top athlete sprinting	1 700

Power and Speed

Transportation vehicles, such as cars, buses, and trains, do work to accelerate and to climb hills. They also work to overcome air resistance and rolling friction. The total frictional force on a car varies, but is usually in the range of 400 N to 1000 N.

We can develop an expression that will help us calculate the power of a moving vehicle. Consider a force F applied by the engine on a vehicle moving with an average speed, v_{av}

Since $P = \frac{W}{\Delta t}$ and $W = F\Delta d$

then $P = \frac{F\Delta d}{\Delta t}$

but average speed $v_{av} = \frac{\Delta d}{\Delta t}$

therefore $P = Fv_{av}$

Where P is the power, in watts
F is the magnitude of the applied force, in newtons
v_{av} is the average speed, in metres per second

EXAMPLE 4 NUMERICAL

A car on a level road accelerates from 0 to 28 m/s with an average acceleration of 5.0 m/s². The total friction on the car is 600 N. Calculate the power of the engine if the car has a mass of 1400 kg.

Given

$v_1 = 0$
$v_2 = 28$ m/s
$a = 5.0$ m/s²
$m = 1400$ kg
$F_f = 600$ N

Required

P

Analysis

- Power is required to overcome friction and for acceleration.
- Use $F_{net} = ma$ to find the force to accelerate the car.
- Add the force of friction to find the applied force.
- Then use $P = Fv_{av}$, where v_{av} is the average speed, to find the power.

Solution

Net force $F_{net} = ma$
$= 1400 \text{ kg} \times 5.0 \text{ m/s}^2$
$= 7000 \text{ N}$

Applied force $= F_{net} - F_f$
$= 7000 \text{ N} - (-600 \text{ N})$
$= 7600 \text{ N}$

Average speed $= \dfrac{v_1 + v_2}{2}$
$= \dfrac{0 + 28 \text{ m/s}}{2}$
$= 14 \text{ m/s}$

Power $P = Fv_{av}$
$= 7600 \text{ N} \times 14 \text{ m/s}$
$= 1.1 \times 10^5 \text{ W}$
$= 1.1 \times 10^2 \text{ kW}$

Statement

The engine has a power of 1.1×10^2 kW.

PRACTICE PROBLEMS

1. A crane lifts a 1000-kg load at a constant speed through a distance of 30 m in 40 s. Calculate:
   a) the work done by the crane
   b) the power of the crane in watts and kilowatts
2. A car engine exerts a force of 4000 N [E] to accelerate a car over a displacement of 100 m [E] in 8.0 s. Calculate the power of the engine in watts and kilowatts.

TABLE 5.3 Sample Powers of Transportation Systems

System	Power (P [kW])
Automobile (speed 100 km/h)	29
Automobile (top acceleration)	100
Bus	150
Commuter train	3 000
Ocean liner	21 000
Boeing 707 Jet aircraft	21 000

Table 5.3 shows some sample powers of transportation systems.

Section 5.2 Review

Understanding Concepts

1. Define power.
2. What two factors determine the power of a machine or person?
3. Calculate the work done in joules by a combine harvester that has a power of 4.0 kW working for 8.0 h.
4. Calculate the time to do 4.0×10^5 J of work by an intercity bus that has a power of 1.5×10^2 kW.
5. Calculate the power of a truck that travels at a constant speed of 100 km/h up a hill if the engine exerts a force of 2500 N on the truck.
6. An electric drill is rated at 260 W. What energy is consumed by the drill if it is used steadily for 4.0 h?
7. A food processor is rated at 750 W. How much energy in kilojoules is consumed by the food processor in 10 min?

Applying Inquiry/ Communication Skills

8. Although the SI unit of power is the watt, there is an old-fashioned unit called the horsepower. Research to find out what one horsepower is and how this unusual unit was originally defined.

Making Connections

9. The Canadian Standards Association tests all models of common appliances, and places an "Energuide" sticker on any new appliance. Find out what information is on an Energuide sticker and evaluate its usefulness. Suggest any changes to the sticker that you think would make it even more useful.

5.3 Thermal Energy and Heat

Key Understandings

When you have completed this section, you will be able to:

- describe the differences between thermal energy and heat
- solve problems involving specific heat capacity, mass, temperature change, and quantity of heat
- apply the principle of heat exchange
- solve problems involving specific latent heat, mass, and quantity of heat
- identify some applications of the latent heat of water

The boiling water from a kettle sculpts a hole in a block of ice, changing it from a solid to a liquid. Some of the liquid molecules turn into an invisible gas, rise above the ice where they cool, and condense to form a fragile cloud of mist. Water seems to change temperature and state with miraculous ease. However, it requires tremendous amounts of energy to produce these changes in state. In fact, the energy required to melt a small iceberg could drive a train across Canada several times. What is the difference between thermal energy and heat? How is the heat capacity of water used to cool nuclear power stations and to drive steam turbines?

Thermal Energy

WEBLINK

SIMULATION

To explore heat transfer, temperature change, and specific heat capacity, go to **www.pearsoned.ca/physics11.**

Thermal energy is the sum of the potential energy and the kinetic energy possessed by the molecules of an object. A hot object has more thermal energy than a cold object because the molecules are moving faster. A substance in the liquid state at its boiling point has less thermal energy per kilogram than when it is a gas at the same temperature. This is because the molecules of a liquid are closer together, and so have less potential energy.

For example, water at a temperature of 100°C has less thermal energy than steam (water vapour) at 100°C (Figure 5.13). A unit volume of water expands in volume by about 1700 times in changing state to steam at the same temperature. The molecules in the liquid and gas have the same average speed and, as a result, the same average kinetic energy, but the thermal energy is greater because of the larger potential energy. The thermal energy stored in a substance depends on only two factors, the kinetic and the potential energy of the molecules. The greater the kinetic energy, and/or the larger the potential energy, the larger the thermal energy.

Heat

Some people use the terms **heat** and thermal energy to mean the same thing. However, thermal energy and heat are two different concepts. Heat is thermal energy being absorbed, released, or transferred from one object to another. Suppose we increase the thermal energy of the molecules in a cube of iron by heating the iron with a flame. The molecules of the hot gas from the flame are moving randomly at high speed. Thus, they possess a lot of kinetic energy. As they strike the cube they transfer some of this kinetic energy to the molecules making up the cube. This causes the iron molecules to vibrate faster and moves them farther apart (Figure 5.12). As a result, the cube has more thermal energy. Heat has been added to the cube because thermal energy has been transferred.

steam at 100 °C

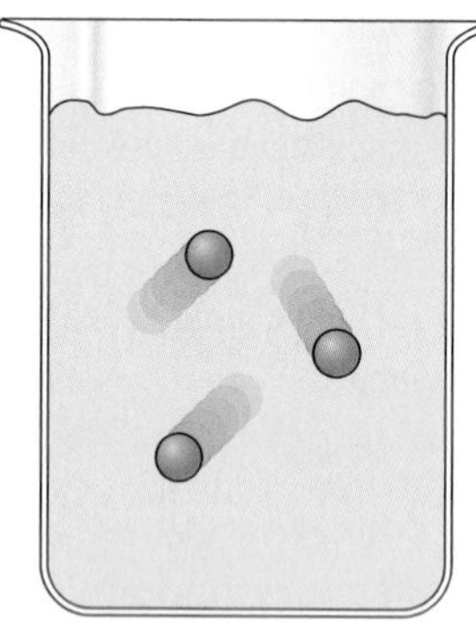

water at 100 °C

FIGURE 5.12 Molecules of steam and water at 100°C have the same kinetic energy. However, molecules of steam are farther apart and have more potential energy and therefore more thermal energy than molecules of water (not to scale).

$$E_{Thermal} = E_{Kinetic} + E_{Potential}$$

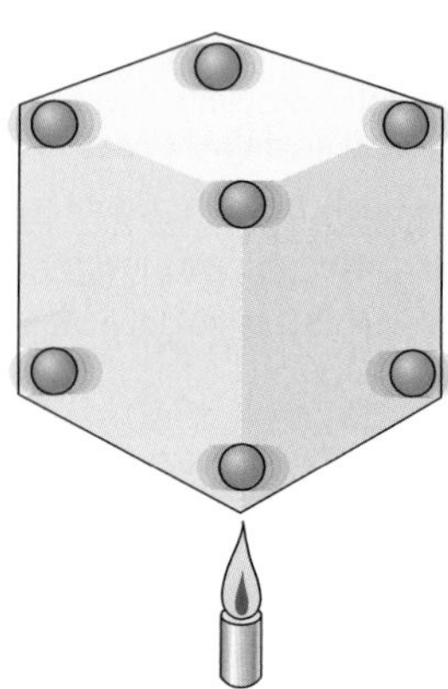

FIGURE 5.13 When heat is added to a solid, the molecules vibrate faster and move farther apart. This is observed as an expansion of the solid.

$$Q_{Heat} = \Delta E_{Thermal}$$

Measuring Heat

You can measure temperature with a thermometer, but there is no instrument for directly measuring the quantity of heat. During a temperature change, three factors affect the amount of heat transferred: the mass of the substance, the temperature change produced, and the type of material.

Mass The quantity of heat needed to raise the temperature of a substance by a set amount is directly proportional to its mass. It takes twice as much heat to increase the temperature of 2 kg of water by 1 K as it does to increase the temperature of 1 kg of water by 1 K (Figure 5.14).

Temperature Change The quantity of heat needed to raise the temperature of a constant mass of a substance is directly proportional to the temperature change produced. It takes twice as much heat to increase the temperature of 1 kg of water by 2 K as it does to increase its temperature by 1 K (Figure 5.15).

Type of Material A car radiator filled with water stores more heat than the same radiator filled with ethylene glycol. This is a property of the material itself. We say that substances with a different ability to store heat have a different specific heat capacity.

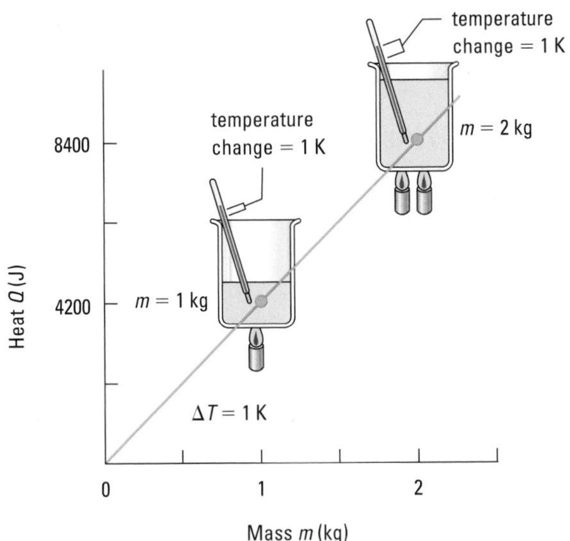

FIGURE 5.14 It takes twice as much heat to warm double the mass of a substance through the same temperature change.

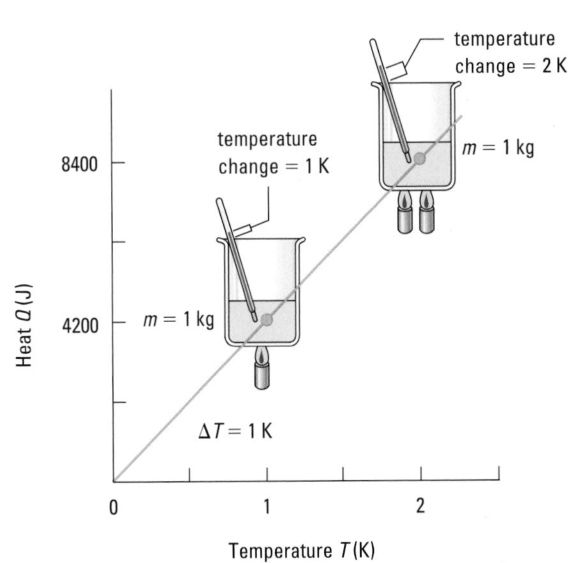

FIGURE 5.15 It takes twice as much heat to produce twice the temperature change with the same mass of a substance.

Specific Heat Capacity

Specific heat capacity is the quantity of heat needed to change the temperature of a unit mass of a substance through a unit change in temperature. Substances with a small specific heat capacity warm rapidly because they absorb less heat energy for a given temperature change. They also cool rapidly because they have less heat to give up.

$$\text{specific heat capacity} = \frac{\text{quantity of heat}}{\text{mass} \times \text{temperature change}}$$

Specific heat capacity is given the symbol small c, quantity of heat the symbol Q, mass the symbol m, and temperature change the symbol ΔT. Thus

$$c = \frac{Q}{m\Delta T}$$

INSIGHT

The specific heat capacity of the human body is very close to the specific heat capacity of water, because the body consists mostly of water.

The units for specific heat capacity are joules per kilogram kelvin (J/(kg·K)), or joules per kilogram degree Celsius (J/(kg·°C)). We can rearrange this equation as follows:

$$Q = m \cdot \Delta T \cdot c$$

This shows that the heat transferred is indeed directly proportional to mass, temperature change, and specific heat capacity of a substance. The specific heat capacities of some common substances are listed in Table 5.4. Note that there is a different specific heat capacity for ice, water, and water vapour.

EXAMPLE 5 NUMERICAL

An 80-kg patient has the flu and his temperature increases from 37°C to 39°C. How much extra heat do the chemical reactions in his cells have to generate to cause this temperature change?

Given

$m = 80$ kg

$T_i = 37°C$

$T_f = 39°C$

$c = 3\,470$ J/(kg·K) (from Table 5.4)

Required

Q

Analysis

- Find ΔT
- Use the equation $Q = m \cdot \Delta T \cdot c$

Solution

$$\begin{aligned}\Delta T &= T_f - T_i \\ &= 2°C = 2\text{ K} \\ Q &= m \cdot \Delta T \cdot c \\ &= 80\text{ kg} \times 2\text{ K} \times 3470\text{ J/(kg·K)} \\ &= 6 \times 10^5\text{ J}\end{aligned}$$

Statement

The patient's cells had to generate 6×10^5 J to cause the temperature change.

PRACTICE PROBLEMS

1. The temperature outside on a cold winter night is −25°C. How much heat energy is needed to warm a block of ice of mass 30 kg to its melting point of 0°C?
2. It takes 1.5×10^5 J of energy to raise the temperature of 2.0 kg of an unknown liquid from 20°C to 54°C. What is the specific heat capacity of the substance? What liquid might it be?

Effects of Different Specific Heat Capacities

Beach Breezes Look closely at Table 5.4. Water has a specific heat capacity over five times that of sand. Thus, it takes more energy to heat up water than sand. As a result, sand on a beach gets much hotter than water on a sunny day. The air above the sand heats up and rises as a result of convection. Cold air moves in from over the water to take its place. That is why the breeze often travels toward the beach from the water on a hot day. Can you explain why the breezes reverse direction in the evening?

Climate Table 5.5 shows the mean January and July temperatures for several cities across Canada.

TABLE 5.5 Mean January and July Temperatures

Province	City	Temperatures (°C)	
		January Average	July Average
British Columbia	Victoria	3	16
Alberta	Calgary	−11	17
Saskatchewan	Regina	−17	19
Manitoba	Winnipeg	−18	20
Ontario	Toronto	−4	22
Quebec	Quebec City	−12	19
New Brunswick	Saint John	−7	17
Nova Scotia	Halifax	−4	18
Prince Edward Island	Charlottetown	−7	18
Newfoundland	St. John's	−4	15

Compare the average January and July temperatures in Victoria, Halifax, and Winnipeg. Look at their positions on a map. What causes the differences? Other than latitude, two key factors affect the temperature of a region: proximity to a large body of water, and wind direction.

The winds in Canada are mainly westerly. As a result, on the west coast the winds blow off the Pacific Ocean onto the land. Because of its high specific heat capacity, the temperature of the ocean stays fairly constant all year round. During winter, some of the moving air mass picks up heat from the ocean and carries it inland. This means that west coast cities are generally fairly warm during the winter.

On the east coast of Canada the winds are moving from the land to the Atlantic Ocean. Soil and rock, because of their lower specific heat capacities, change temperature faster. Since the wind reaches Halifax from over the land, this city is cooler than Vancouver in the winter. Fortunately, the nearby Atlantic has some moderating effect. But Winnipeg is too far inland to benefit from the high specific heat capacity of water. That is why Winnipeg gets much hotter in the summer and much colder in the winter than coastal cities.

TABLE 5.4 Specific Heat Capacities

Substance	Specific heat capacity, J/(kg·K)
Aluminum	900
Copper	390
Concrete	2900
Glass	600
Gold	130
Human body	3470
Ice	2100
Iron	450
Lead	130
Magnesium	980
Nickel	444
Sand	800
Silver	240
Wood	1760
Zinc	390
Ethylene glycol	2200
Glycerin	2430
Mercury	140
Methanol	2500
Paraffin oil	2100
Water	4200
Air	990
Argon	512
Hydrogen	14 320
Oxygen	920
Water vapour	2000

INFOBIT

A west wind travels from west to east.

INFOBIT

The use of the wind chill factor originated about 60 years ago and it is based on the rate at which heat is lost by a bottle of water exposed to winds of various speeds and temperatures.

The Principle of Heat Exchange

A transfer of heat occurs when substances at different temperatures are mixed. The warmer substance loses heat in cooling, the cooler substance gains heat in warming, and energy is conserved in the process. This special case of the law of conservation of energy is called the **principle of heat exchange**. It states:

Whenever two substances at different temperatures are mixed, the amount of heat lost by the hotter substance in cooling is equal to the amount of heat gained by the colder substance in warming.

Thus, thermal energy is conserved when two substances at different temperatures are mixed. The calculation of the heat exchanged when substances are mixed is called the **method of mixtures**.

In the method of mixtures, the heat lost or gained by each component of the mixture must be taken into consideration. Also, any heat transferred between the mixture and the surroundings must be minimized. Containers used for this purpose are called **calorimeters**. The name comes from the old unit of energy, the calorie. In its simplest form, a calorimeter consists of an insulated vessel of a known heat capacity, as shown in Figure 5.16.

WEBLINK

Canadian scientist Randall Osczeoski proposed a new way of meaning wind chill. Research to find out how he adapted the old method to apply better to humans. Write a short report. Begin your research at **www.pearsoned.ca/physics11.**

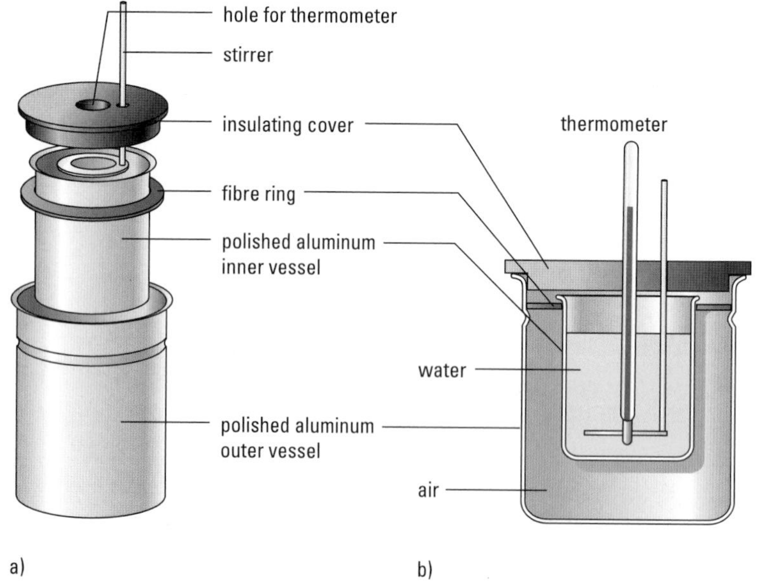

FIGURE 5.16 An aluminum calorimeter

Discovering Physics — *Principle of Heat Exchange*

The principle of heat exchange is a special case of the law of conservation of energy. Design and implement a procedure to verify this principle, using the ideas presented below.

Design and implement a procedure to verify the principle of heat exchange. Try to minimize heat transfer between the samples and the surroundings. You will need styrofoam cups, a source of hot water, a source of cold water, two thermometers, a 100-mL graduated cylinder, and a balance. Try mixing different masses of hot and cold water. Measure the temperature of the hot and cold water and the mixture. Use the heat transfer equation and compare the heat gained by the cold water with the heat lost by the warm water. Account for any consistent differences.

Finding the Specific Heat Capacity of a Solid

Suppose someone sells you a gold-coloured bar at a discount price, claiming it to be gold. You decide to check whether it is pure gold or a combination of gold and copper. You can do this by measuring the specific heat capacity of the bar and comparing it with the published value.

It is difficult to measure the specific heat capacity of a solid directly. The heat source and the thermometer cannot be easily immersed in the solid! However, we can use the principle of heat exchange and the method of mixtures. The bar is first heated to a known temperature in a liquid bath (Figure 5.17). Then the hot solid is immersed in cold water. To compensate for heat transferred to the surroundings, the cold water must be below room temperature if the solid is above room temperature. Can you explain why? Heat is transferred until both components of the mixture reach the same final temperature. Look at the following problem to see how the method of mixtures is used.

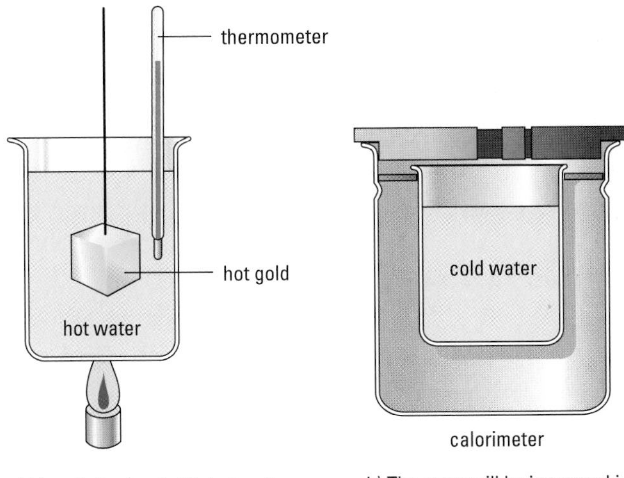

FIGURE 5.17 Using the method of mixtures to find the specific heat capacity of a metal

EXAMPLE 6 NUMERICAL

A gold-coloured bar of mass 4.0 kg is placed in boiling water until its temperature stabilizes at 100°C. It is then immersed in 0.50 kg of water in an aluminum calorimeter, both at a temperature of 20°C. The calorimeter has a mass of 0.10 kg. The mixture reaches a final temperature of 35°C. Refer to Table 5.4 and calculate the specific heat capacity of the golden bar.

Given

Golden Bar

$m_{\text{bar}} = 4.0 \text{ kg}$

$T_{\text{i bar}} = 373 \text{ K}$

Calorimeter

$m_{\text{cal}} = 0.10 \text{ kg}$

$c_{\text{cal}} = 900 \text{ J/(kg·K)}$

$T_{\text{i cal}} = 293 \text{ K}$

Cold Water

$T_{i\,w} = 293\ K$

$m_w = 0.50\ kg$

$c_w = 4200\ J/(kg{\cdot}K)$

Mixture

$T_{f\,mix} = 308\ K$

Required

Specific heat capacity of the bar, c_{bar}

Analysis

- Calculate the heat gained by the cold water in warming.
- Calculate the heat gained by the cold calorimeter in warming.
- Calculate the heat lost by the hot bar in terms of the unknown, c_{bar}.
- Equate the heat gained by the cold water and calorimeter to the heat lost by the hot bar.
- Solve for the unknown, c_{bar}.

Solution

$$\begin{aligned}\Delta T_w &= T_{f\,mix} - T_{i\,w}\\ &= 308\ K - 293\ K\\ &= 15\ K\end{aligned}$$

Heat gained by cold water

$$\begin{aligned}Q_w &= m_w \times \Delta T_w \times c_w\\ &= 0.50\ kg \times 15\ K \times 4200\ J/(kg{\cdot}K)\\ &= 31.5 \times 10^3\ J\end{aligned}$$

Heat gained by cold calorimeter

$$\begin{aligned}Q_{cal} &= m_{cal} \times \Delta T_{cal} \times c_{cal}\\ &= 0.10\ kg \times 15\ K \times 900\ J/(kg{\cdot}K)\\ &= 1.35 \times 10^3\ J\end{aligned}$$

$$\begin{aligned}\Delta T_{bar} &= T_{i\,bar} - T_{f\,mix}\\ &= 373\ K - 308\ K\\ &= 65\ K\end{aligned}$$

Heat lost by hot bar

$$\begin{aligned}Q_{bar} &= m_{bar} \times \Delta T_{bar} \times c_{bar}\\ &= 4.00\ kg \times 65\ K \times c_{bar}\\ &= (260\ kg{\cdot}k)c_{bar}\end{aligned}$$

By the principle of heat exchange,

heat lost by bar = heat gained by water + heat gained by calorimeter

$$\begin{aligned}(260\ kg{\cdot}k)c_{bar} &= 31.5 \times 10^3\ J + 1.35 \times 10^3\ J\\ c_{bar} &= \frac{32.85\ J}{260\ kg{\cdot}°C} \times 10^3\\ &= 126\ J/(kg{\cdot}K)\end{aligned}$$

Statement

The specific heat capacity of the gold-coloured bar is 1.3×10^2 J/(kg·K). By referring to Table 5.4, it appears that the bar is pure gold. This could be verified by measuring another characteristic property such as density.

PRACTICE PROBLEMS

1. When 1.5 kg of a cold metal at a temperature of 258 K is immersed in 2.5 kg of water at a temperature of 343 K, the final temperature of the mixture was 333 K. What is the specific heat capacity of the metal?
2. When an unknown mass of nickel at a temperature of 240 K is immersed in 2.0 kg of water at a temperature of 355 K the final temperature became 345 K. What mass of nickel was immersed in the water?

Specific Latent Heat

A definite amount of heat is required to change the state of a substance. Heat that causes a change in state is called **latent heat** because no change in temperature occurs. "Latent" means hidden. The quantity of heat required to change the state of a unit mass of a substance is called the **specific latent heat**. Specific latent heat has units of energy per unit mass. If heat energy is represented by Q, mass by m, and specific latent heat by l, the equation for specific latent heat is

$$l = Q/m$$

Rearranging, this becomes

$$Q = m \cdot l$$

The SI derived unit for specific latent heat is the joule per kilogram (J/kg).

WEBLINK

A knowledge of friction is important in the physics of curling. Sweeping allows the stone to curve less and travel farther. But the path of the curling stone depends on the melting and freezing of the ice below the concave stone. Search the Internet to find out how this works and write a paragraph for an instruction manual for beginners to the sport. Begin your search at: **www.pearsoned.ca/physics11.**

Specific Latent Heat of Fusion

The **specific latent heat of fusion** l_f is the quantity of heat required to melt 1 kg of a substance without changing its temperature (Figure 5.18).

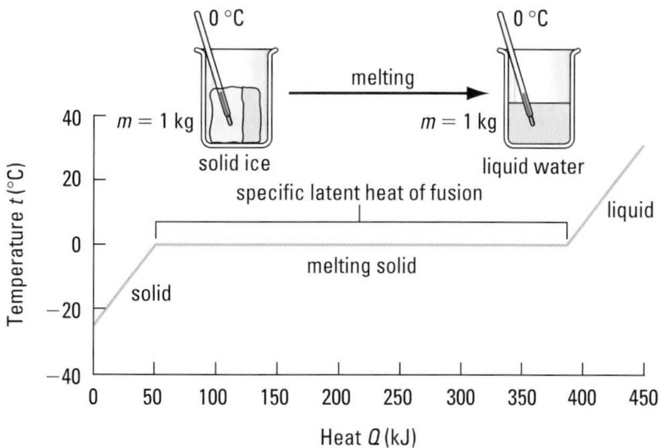

FIGURE 5.18 The specific latent heat of fusion changes a solid to a liquid without changing its temperature.

EXAMPLE 7 CONCEPTUAL

Heat energy is necessary to melt a substance even though the temperature of the substance does not change during the melting. The heat is used to change the structure of the substance from a solid to a liquid.

Gallium is one of the few metals that melts near body temperature; its melting point is about 30°C. The latent heat of fusion of gallium is 80.4 kJ/kg. Calculate how much heat is required to melt 150 g of gallium.

Reasoning and Solution

The quantity of heat necessary to melt the gallium is

$$\begin{aligned} Q &= ml_f \\ &= (0.150\ \text{kg})(80.4\ \text{kJ/kg}) \\ &= 12.1\ \text{kJ} \end{aligned}$$

The heat required to melt 150 g of gallium is 12.1 kJ.

CHALLENGE

The latent heat of fusion of copper is 134 kJ/kg. How much heat does it take to melt 10.0 kg of copper at its melting point of 1083°C?

Specific Latent Heat of Vaporization

The quantity of heat needed to vaporize 1 kg of a substance without changing its temperature is called the **specific latent heat of vaporization** l_v (Figure 5.19).

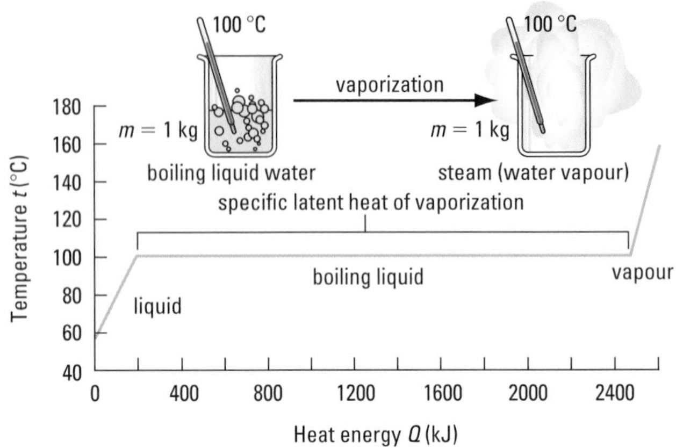

FIGURE 5.19 The specific latent heat of vaporization changes a liquid to a gas without changing its temperature.

EXAMPLE 8 NUMERICAL

The specific latent heat of vaporization of ethanol is 854 kJ/kg.

What mass of liquid ethanol, at its boiling point of 78°C, can be changed into vapour at 78°C by the addition of 2.40×10^6 J of heat?

Given

$l_v = 854$ kJ/kg

$Q = 2.40 \times 10^6$ J

Required

m

Analysis

Rearrange the formula $Q = ml_v$ to solve for m

Solution

$$m = \frac{Q}{l_v}$$

$$= \frac{2.40 \times 10^6 \text{ J}}{854 \times 10^3 \text{ J/kg}}$$

$$= 2.81 \text{ kg}$$

Statement

The heat can vaporize 2.81 kg of ethanol.

PRACTICE PROBLEMS

1. How much heat does it take to vaporize 400 g of ethanol at its boiling point of 78°C?
2. Helium boils at −269°C. How much helium could be vaporized when at its boiling point by 100 kJ of heat energy? (See Table 5.6.)

Table 5.6 shows the melting point, boiling point, and specific latent heats for several substances.

TABLE 5.6 Melting Point, Boiling Point, and Specific Latent Heats of Substances

Substance	Melting point (°C)	Boiling point (°C)	Specific Latent Heat l (kJ/kg) Fusion l_f	Vaporization l_v
Ammonia	−78	−33	352	1370
Copper	1083	1187	134	5069
Ethanol	−114	78	104	854
Freon-12	−158	−30	*	168
Freon-14	−184	−128	*	143
Glauber's salt	32	100	241	*
Gold	1063	2660	65	1578
Helium	−270	−269	5	21
Hydrogen	−259	−253	56	452
Lead	327	1750	25	871
Mercury	−39	357	12	272
Nitrogen	−210	−196	26	201
Oxygen	−219	−183	14	213
Silver	961	2193	88	2336
Tungsten	3410	5660	184	4813
Water	0	100	333	2255

* unavailable

Applications of the Latent Heat of Water

Water has one of the largest specific latent heats of fusion of all substances. The specific latent heat of fusion of ice is 333 kJ/kg. In other words, 333 kJ of heat are absorbed every time 1 kg of ice melts. This is about 80 times as much heat as is needed to change the temperature of water by 1°C. For this reason ice is an excellent refrigerant to use in picnic coolers.

Conversely, when water freezes it gives heat to its surroundings. In fact, when 1 kg of water freezes, it releases 333 kJ of heat into its surroundings. Farmers often use this heat to protect crops from frost damage. When they expect a frost, they turn on the irrigation (sprinkler) system. The water from the irrigation system falls on the plants and freezes, releasing heat to the plants. This heat helps prevent damage to the cells of the plants (Figure 5.20).

When water vaporizes it takes heat from its surroundings. The specific latent heat of vaporization of water is 2255 kJ/kg. In other words, 2255 kJ of heat are needed to vaporize 1 kg of water. This is about 540 times as much heat as that needed to raise the temperature of water by 1°C.

FIGURE 5.20 A water sprinkling system can prevent frost damage.

Storing Heat through Phase Changes

Decision-Making Skills

- ▶ Defining the Issue
- Developing Assessment Criteria
- ▶ Researching the Issue
- ▶ Analyzing Data and Information
- Proposing a Course of Action
- Justifying the Course of Action
- ▶ Communicating Your Proposal

BACKGROUND INFORMATION

Have you ever wished that you could flip a switch in January and bask in the warmth of July? Scientists are researching ways to do exactly that.

Scientists and engineers are experimenting with phase changes as a way to store large quantities of heat. A material that undergoes a phase change at a desirable temperature is placed in walls, floors, ceilings, and 2000-L underground tanks. The amount of thermal energy stored depends on the mass of the material and on its specific latent heat of fusion. A material with a high specific latent heat of fusion and a melting point between 20°C and 25°C is ideal. On sunny days, the material absorbs heat from the sun and melts (Figure 5.21). When the surroundings become cooler than the freezing point of the material it refreezes and heat is released (Figure 5.22). As long as there is enough of the substance that it never completely melts or freezes, the building remains close to the freezing temperature of the substance.

Materials that store heat as a result of a phase change have other uses as well. They can be stitched into clothing to improve their insulating ability, and they can be mixed with the asphalt and concrete used on overpasses to prevent the build-up of dangerous ice. It is impossible to predict all the future uses of materials that store heat by a phase change. They will certainly be used for seasonal and daily storage; saving up heat at one time for use at another.

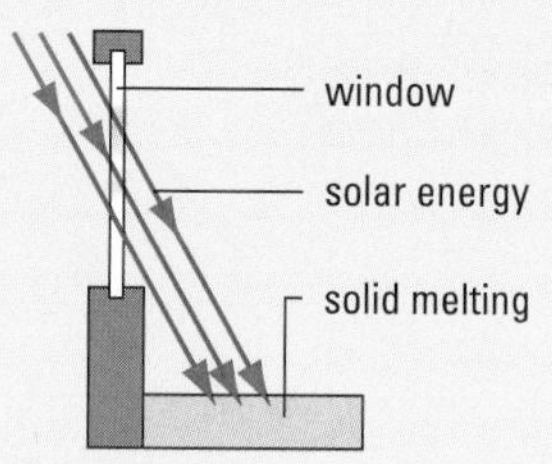

FIGURE 5.21 During the day, the solid absorbs heat and melts.

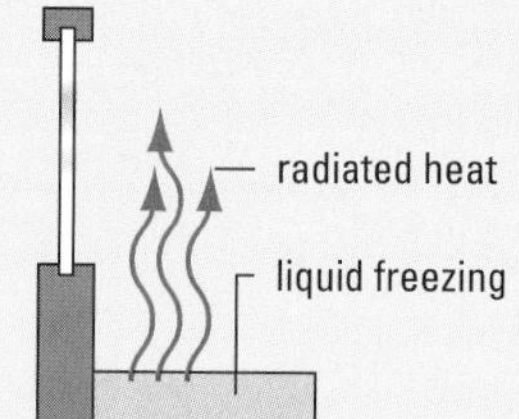

FIGURE 5.22 At night the liquid gives off heat to the room and freezes.

Analyzing the Issue

1. Research applications of heat storage through phase changes using journals, magazine articles, the Internet, and other electronic resources. Make a chart to summarize the advantages and disadvantages of each application.
2. Analyze your research, and predict two future uses of storing heat through phase changes. Explain your prediction.
3. Evaluate the environmental impact of storing heat through phase changes. What effects might this have on society and the economy?
4. Select one of the applications you researched and prepare a one-page description of a marketing strategy to educate the public about the benefits of this application. Consider use of the media and advertising as you plan your strategy.

Swimmers usually feel cool when they step out of the water, particularly when it is windy. This is because water evaporates from the skin, even when the water is below the boiling point. If only 10 mL of water evaporates, 22680 J of heat are required. Much of this heat comes from the swimmer's body. As a result, the skin cools down.

When steam condenses it gives heat to its surroundings. This explains why a burn from steam is much worse than a burn from boiling water. When the steam condenses on a person's skin, it gives off heat. If only 1 mL of water condenses, 2268 J of energy are transferred to the skin. That alone is enough to cause a severe burn. The condensed steam also cools from 100°C to a body temperature of 37°C. This transfers another 265 J to the skin. So don't pass your arm across the spout of a boiling kettle!

Section 5.3 Review

Understanding Concepts

1. Refer to Table 5.4 and calculate
   a) the amount of heat when 3.8 kg of ethylene glycol cools from 35°C to 20°C
   b) the temperature change when 15 kg of mercury loses 25 kJ of heat
   c) The mass of copper if 7.8 kJ of heat changes its temperature from 20°C to 298 K
2. Determine the specific heat capacity of aluminum if 715 J of heat warms 40.0 g of aluminum from 20.0°C to 40.0°C.
3. When 2.0 kg of a cold metal at a temperature of 248 K is immersed in 3.0 kg of water at a temperature of 313 K, the final temperature of the mixture is 309 K. What is the specific heat capacity of the metal?
4. Refer to Table 5.6 and calculate the following:
   a) the heat given off when 3.2 kg of water at the freezing point freezes
   b) the mass of solid lead at the freezing point that requires 5000 J of heat to melt
5. When doing an experiment to find the specific latent heat of fusion of liquid nitrogen, you find that 100 kJ of heat must be removed to freeze 3.8 kg of nitrogen at its freezing point. What value will you get for the specific latent heat of fusion of nitrogen?
6. Calculate the amount of heat needed to vaporize 2.50 kg of freon 14 at its boiling point.

Applying Inquiry/ Communication Skills

7. If you do work on a rubber band by stretching and releasing it several times, the rubber band will heat up. Design an experiment to measure the relationship between the number of times you stretch and release the rubber band and the heat gained by the rubber band.
8. Design a procedure using the principle of heat exchange and the method of mixtures to determine the specific latent heat of fusion of ice. Compare your value with the accepted value and quote the percentage error. Outline procedures you could use to minimize the errors.

Making Connections

9. The engineer in charge of designing a solar-heated home is planning to include a tank containing paraffin wax in the basement to store heat during the day and to release it at night. Write a one-page report outlining what the engineer will need to research before choosing the paraffin wax and constructing the tank.

5.4 Harnessing Energy Sources

Key Understandings

When you have completed this section, you will be able to:

- distinguish between nonrenewable and renewable energy sources
- describe ways of harnessing nonrenewable energy
- describe ways of harnessing renewable energy
- analyze the economic, social, and environmental impacts of various energy sources

FIGURE 5.23 Nuclear energy using fission is an example of nonrenewable energy.

Many North Americans enjoy a high standard of living. At present this is achieved by using huge amounts of energy. Ontario's use of electricity is increasing at a rate of 1.4% per year. That means that we will need twice as much generation capacity in 50 years. Although North Americans consume about 40% of the world's energy, we make up only about 7% of the world's population. Over 90% of the energy we use today is nonrenewable. **Nonrenewable energy** is energy that is used up faster than it is replaced. There are two kinds of nonrenewable energy: fossil fuels and nuclear fuels (Figure 5.23).

Before this nonrenewable energy runs out, we must learn to use **renewable energy** sources. Renewable energy is energy that is replaced as fast or faster than it is used up. Examples of renewable energy include moving water (Figure 5.24), sunlight, wind, and **geothermal energy** (heat energy from deep in Earth's crust).

How is thermal energy used to produce electricity? How can renewable energy sources be harnessed?

FIGURE 5.24 Moving water is an example of renewable energy.

Generating Electricity Using Heat Energy

Conventional nonrenewable fossil fuels, including coal, petroleum, and natural gas are used to produce electricity. The parts of a fossil-fuelled power station are shown in Figure 5.25. Heat produced by burning the fossil fuel changes water into steam. This steam is passed through a steam turbine consisting of many wheels with paddle-like blades. The high-speed molecules of water cause the turbine to rotate. The turbine turns the generator, which converts kinetic energy into electrical energy.

INFOBIT

Ontario's fossil-fuelled power plants produce as much electricity as they did in the early 1980s, but they have achieved a 60% reduction in both their emission rate and in the total amount of nitrous and sulfur oxides produced. In 1900 Svante Arrenius, of Sweden, predicted that if we burned fossil fuels, the temperature of the earth could increase by 6°C. We are now running 1.5–4.5°C above the value in 1900.

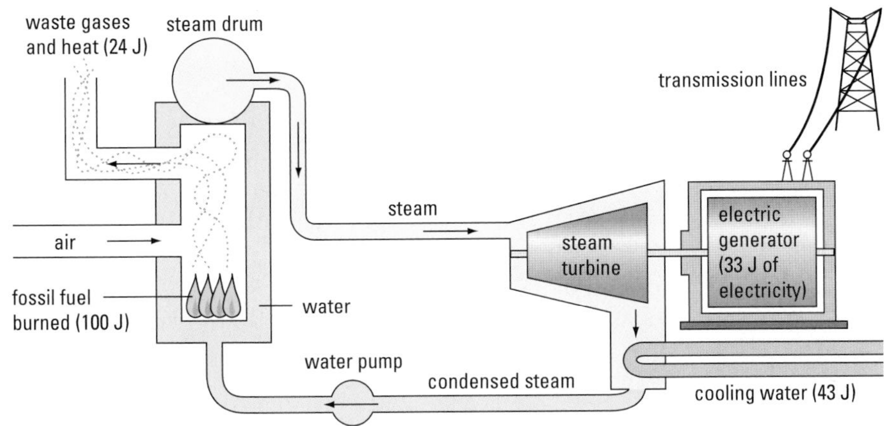

FIGURE 5.25 Elements of a thermal power system that is only 33% efficient

Generating electricity in a fossil-fuelled power plant has disadvantages. Two forms of energy leave the plant. One is electricity from the generator and the other is waste heat from the steam turbine and hot gases. The waste heat causes the fossil-fuelled generator plant to be only 33% efficient. When fossil fuels are burned they release oxides of sulfur, nitrogen, and carbon. These contribute to smog. Just look to the horizon on a clear, sunny day in a large city and you will see a greenish-yellow layer above the earth. Unfortunately, the layer is not only above the horizon but is all around us too. We inhale these pollutants every day.

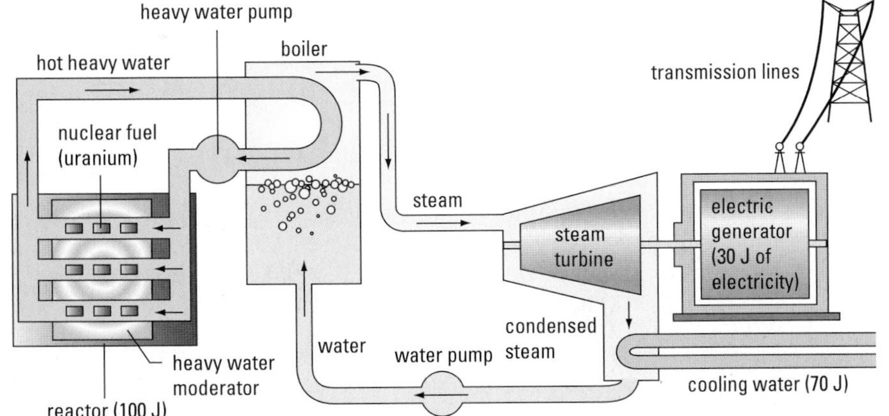

INFOBIT

Producing 10 billion kW·h of electricity per year requires one nuclear power plant of 1300 MW capacity occupying an area of 0.2 km².

FIGURE 5.26 The CANDU nuclear power generating system (simplified). It is only 30% efficient.

Nuclear-fission power plants also use heat to generate electricity. Figure 5.26 is a diagram of a CANDU nuclear-fission generating station. Heat is produced when uranium atoms are split in the fuel rods. This heats the heavy-water moderator. Heat is transferred to ordinary water and used to produce steam and then electricity. At present, nuclear stations emit more heat to the water used for cooling than the total from fossil-fuelled plants. A lot could be done to harness this heat. It could be used to heat nearby greenhouses and homes. Nuclear plants are about 30% efficient. But nuclear plants pollute less than fossil-fuelled plants do.

INFOBIT

Nuclear energy accounts for half of Ontario's electrical energy production. As a by-product Ontario produces about 600 m^3 of used fuel rods each year—enough to fill three two-car garages.

EXAMPLE 9 NUMERICAL

A CANDU nuclear reactor produces steam at 350°C to drive a steam-electric turbine. The temperature of the condensed steam when it returns to the boiler is 30.0°C. Calculate the heat extracted from each 100 kg of the steam.

Given

Initial temperature = 350°C

Final temperature = 30°C

Required

The total heat available from each 100 kg of steam

Analysis

- assume a boiling point of 100°C
- find the heat lost by 100 kg of steam in cooling
- find the heat lost by 100 kg of steam in condensing
- find the heat lost by 100 kg of condensed steam in cooling

Solution

The specific heat capacity of water vapour is 2000 J/(kg·°C)(Table 5.4). The heat lost by 100 kg of steam in cooling from 350°C to 100°C (the boiling point) is

$$\begin{aligned} Q &= m \cdot \Delta T \cdot c \\ &= 100 \text{ kg} \times 50°\text{C} \times 2000 \text{ J/(kg·°C)} \\ &= 1.00 \times 10^7 \text{ J} \\ &= 1.00 \times 10^4 \text{ kJ} \end{aligned}$$

The specific latent heat of vaporization of water is 2255 kJ/kg (Table 5.6). The heat lost by 100 kg of steam at 100°C condensing to water at 100°C is

$$\begin{aligned} Q &= m\, l_v \\ &= 100 \text{ kg} \times 2255 \text{ kJ/kg} \\ &= 22.6 \times 10^4 \text{ kJ} \end{aligned}$$

The specific heat capacity of water is 4200 J/(kg·°C) (Table 5.4). The heat lost by the 100 kg of water at 100°C cooling from 100°C to 30.0°C is

$$\begin{aligned} Q &= m \cdot \Delta T \cdot c \\ &= 100 \text{ kg} \times 70°\text{C} \times 4200 \text{ J/(kg·°C)} \\ &= 2.94 \times 10^7 \text{ J} \\ &= 2.94 \times 10^4 \text{ kJ} \end{aligned}$$

WEBLINK

One safety issue in nuclear power generation involves a substance called tritium. What is tritium? Search the Internet to find out about the properties of tritium and the role it plays in safety and environmental issues. Use your information to design a brochure that could be distributed to neighbourhoods close to a nuclear power station. Begin your research at **www.pearsoned.ca/physics11.**

Total heat energy extracted from the water is

heat lost by steam in cooling from 135°C to 100°C, plus heat lost by steam in condensing plus heat lost by water in cooling from 100°C to 30°C.

$= (1.00 \times 10^4 \text{ kJ}) + (22.6 \times 10^4 \text{ kJ}) + (2.94 \times 10^4 \text{ kJ})$

$= 26.5 \times 10^4 \text{ kJ}$

Statement

The heat extracted from each 100 kg of water is 2.65×10^5 kJ. Notice that most of this heat comes from the condensation of the steam.

PRACTICE PROBLEMS

1. What percentage of the 2.65×10^5 kJ extracted from the 100 kg of water comes from the condensation of the steam?
2. How much heat would it take to change 1.0 kg of water at 20°C to steam at 110°C?

Generating Electricity Using Moving Water

Energy from Rivers A hydro-electric power plant changes the gravitational potential energy of dammed water to electric energy. Figure 5.27 shows how this is done. The potential energy in the dammed water is changed to kinetic energy as the water flows down through large tubes. Turbines at the bottom are turned by the moving water and gain kinetic energy. The turbines turn electric generators, which convert this kinetic energy into electrical energy with an efficiency of about 85%.

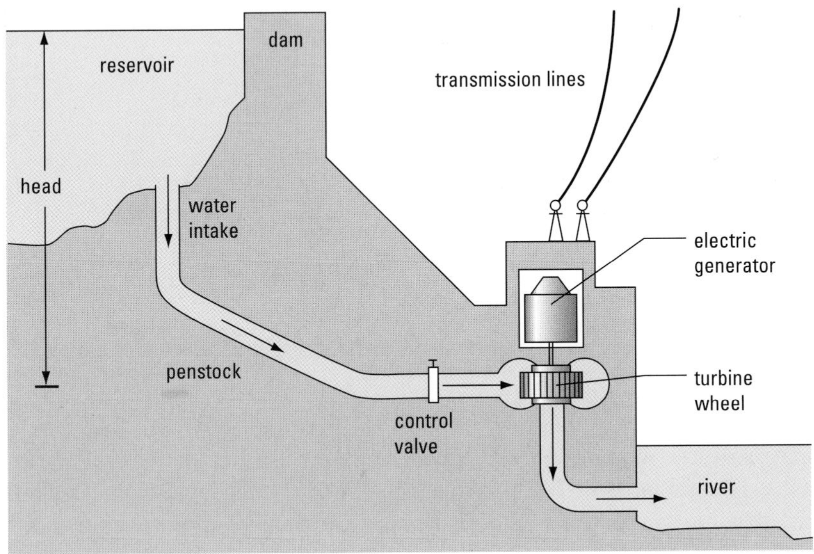

FIGURE 5.27 A hydro-electric power system. A system like this is 85% efficient.

Only one-third of North America's hydro-electric potential is currently being used, and there are problems in harnessing the rest. Small projects are not economical, and major projects such as the James Bay project in Quebec cost billions of dollars. There are also environmental concerns. Large reservoirs flood river valleys destroying native settlements, plants, and animals. In addition, decaying matter from flooded vegetation interferes with the hatching of fish eggs.

INFOBIT

Hydro-electric generation in Ontario represents about 25% of the power provided to customers. It is emission-free, very low cost, safe, and reliable, but may have environmental impacts.

EXAMPLE 10 — CONCEPTUAL

How much electrical power can be generated by each tonne of water that flows through a gate 100 m above a water-powered turbine every second? Assume an efficiency of 85%.

Reasoning and Solution

A percentage (in this case 85%) of the gravitational potential energy lost by falling water is converted into the kinetic energy of a turbine, which in turn produces electrical energy. The rate of production of this electrical energy is called power generation.

A tonne of water has a mass of 1000 kg. The gravitational energy of the water is:

$$\begin{aligned} E_G &= mg\Delta h \\ &= 1000\text{ kg} \times 9.8\text{ N/kg} \times 100\text{ m} \\ &= 9.8 \times 10^5\text{ J} \end{aligned}$$

Since the conversion of kinetic energy to electrical energy is 85% efficient, the amount of electrical energy generated is

$$\begin{aligned} E_E &= 9.8 \times 10^5\text{ J} \times 0.85 \\ &= 8.3 \times 10^5\text{ J} \end{aligned}$$

The electrical power generated each second is

$$\begin{aligned} P &= \frac{E_K}{\Delta t} \\ &= \frac{8.3 \times 10^5\text{ J}}{1.0\text{ s}} \\ &= 8.3 \times 10^5\text{ J/s} \\ &= 8.3 \times 10^5\text{ W} \\ &= 8.3 \times 10^2\text{ kW} \end{aligned}$$

At an efficiency of 85% each tonne of water falling through 100 m each second generates 8.3×10^2 kW of electricity.

CHALLENGE

Smaller hydro-electric power generators are sometimes called "run-of-the-river" generators. There are many of these smaller power generators in Ontario. How much electric power can be generated if 30 t of water flow through a gate 30 m above a water-powered turbine every minute? Assume 90% efficiency.

FIGURE 5.28 The Annapolis Tidal Generating Station converts the energy in moving water to electrical energy both when the tide is coming in and when it is going out.

Energy from Tides One tidal power plant, the Annapolis Tidal Generating Station, exists at Annapolis Royal, Nova Scotia on the Bay of Fundy (Figure 5.28). It was completed in 1984. Differences in the water level between high and low tides on the Bay of Fundy can be as great as 8.3 m and occur every 12 h and 35 min. Twice a day, the tide comes in and goes out, turning the turbines, and generating electricity. The output capacity of Annapolis Tidal is 20 MW. A tidal plant with a capacity of 240 MW is located in France, in the estuary of La Rance near Malo.

There are several problems in harnessing tides. It cost millions of dollars to harness the Bay of Fundy tides. Tidal dams cause sediment to build up and this presents navigational hazards. Also, unless locks are built, ships are unable to pass through the constantly changing waters. Because tides occur at periodic intervals, electricity must be stored and/or used from other sources when tidal activity is low.

EXAMPLE 11 CONCEPTUAL

A tidal reservoir is 5.0 km by 2.0 km with a maximum tidal height of 6.0 m. Find the average power that can be produced during the time from one high tide to the next. Assume that the power plant extracts energy as the tide comes in and also as it goes out. The time between high tides is 12 h 35 min or 45300 s. Assume that the process is 84% efficient.

Reasoning and Solution

We can calculate the mass of water flowing, because we know the volume of water flowing as tides change and we know the density of water. The problem is similar to generating power from a waterfall since energy and time are known. The volume of water entering and leaving the tidal reservoir is

$$\begin{aligned} V &= Ah \\ &= lwh \\ &= 5000 \text{ m} \times 2000 \text{ m} \times 6.0 \text{ m} \\ &= 6.0 \times 10^7 \text{ m}^3 \end{aligned}$$

Since the density of water is 1000 kg/m^3, the mass of water entering and leaving the tidal reservoir is

$$\begin{aligned} m &= DV \\ &= 1000 \text{ kg/m}^3 \times 6.0 \times 10^7 \text{ m}^3 \\ &= 6.0 \times 10^{10} \text{ kg} \end{aligned}$$

The average height of the water in the reservoir is 3.0 m, half the maximum tidal height. Therefore, the average gravitational energy is

$$\begin{aligned} E_G &= mg\Delta h \\ &= 6.0 \times 10^{10} \text{ kg} \times 9.8 \text{ N/kg} \times 3.0 \text{ m} \\ &= 1.76 \times 10^{12} \text{ J} \end{aligned}$$

In the 12 h 35 min period between tides, this energy can be harnessed twice, once as the reservoir fills, and once as it empties. The total energy available during the 12 h 35 min period is

$$2 \times 1.76 \times 10^{12} \text{ J} = 3.52 \times 10^{12} \text{ J}.$$

The average power is

$$\begin{aligned} P &= E/\Delta t \\ &= 3.52 \times 10^{12} \text{ J}/45\,300 \text{ s} \\ &= 7.8 \times 10^7 \text{ W} \\ &= 78 \times 10^6 \text{ W} \\ &= 78 \text{ MW} \end{aligned}$$

But the tidal power plant is only 84% efficient. Therefore, the average power produced is 78 MW $\times$ 0.84 = 66 MW.

INSIGHT

The average height of the water is half the maximum tidal height.

CHALLENGE

A tidal reservoir has dimensions of 1.7 km $\times$ 3.2 km and a maximum tidal height of 8.0 m. Find the average power that could be produced during the time from one high tide to the next. Assume that the tidal power plant extracts energy as the tide comes in and also as it goes out. The time between high tides is 12 h 35 min or 45300 s. Assume that the process is 80% efficient.

Generating Electricity Using Wind

The Darrieus rotor (Figure 5.29) and the three-bladed wind turbine (Figure 5.30) are used to generate electricity. Any region with an average annual wind speed above 11 km/h is a good region for converting wind energy to electricity. The installed wind-generating capacity in the world is in excess of 5000 MW.

FIGURE 5.29 The Darrieus rotor wind turbine looks like a large eggbeater.

FIGURE 5.30 The three-bladed electricity generating wind turbine

INFOBIT

Producing 10 billion kW·h of electricity requires 2400 offshore wind generators of 2 MW capacity occupying an area of 380 km^2.

The power that can be produced by a wind turbine depends on the density of the air D, the cross-sectional area traced out by the blades A, and the speed of the air v. The maximum power is given by the equation

$$P = \frac{1}{2}DAv^3$$

This equation shows how crucial the wind speed is in determining how much power can be extracted from the wind. If the wind speed doubles, the available power increases by a factor of 8. Can you see why?

EXAMPLE 12 CONCEPTUAL

We have seen how the terms in physics formulas do not always carry equal weight. For example, the speed term in the kinetic energy formula $E_k = \frac{1}{2}mv^2$ is more important than the mass term because it is squared. Similarly, the wind speed is the key factor in measuring the maximum power output of a wind turbine.

A wind turbine has three blades each 30 m long. The average wind speed is 4.5 m/s (16 km/h) and the density of the air is 1.29 kg/m^3. What is the maximum power at this wind speed?

Reasoning and Solution

First calculate the area swept out by the blades. It is the area of a circle of radius 30 m. Then use this area in the formula $P = \frac{1}{2}DAv^3$ to calculate the maximum power available from this wind turbine.

The area swept out by the blades is the area of a circle of radius 30 m.

$$\begin{aligned} A &= \pi r^2 \\ &= \pi(30\text{ m})^2 \\ &= 2.83 \times 10^3\text{ m}^2 \end{aligned}$$

The maximum power of the wind generator is

$$\begin{aligned} P &= \frac{1}{2}DAv^3 \\ &= \frac{1}{2} \times 1.29\,\frac{\text{kg}}{\text{m}^3} \times 2.83 \times 10^3\text{ m}^3 \times \left(4.5\,\frac{\text{m}}{\text{s}}\right)^3 \\ &= 1.7 \times 10^5\text{ W} \\ &= 1.7 \times 10^2\text{ kW} \end{aligned}$$

The maximum power available from this wind turbine is 1.7×10^2 kW.

CHALLENGE

Calculate the maximum power output of a wind turbine consisting of three blades, each 35 m long, if the average wind speed is 4.2 m/s and the density of air is 1.29 kg/m^3.

Exploration Using a Graphing Calculator

Wind Power and Wind Speed

The performance of wind turbines depends on the power curve, the relationship between the turbine's electrical power output and the wind speed (Figure 5.31). Assume that the air density is 1.25 kg/m^3 and that you are plotting the power curve for a wind turbine whose blades have a radius of 25 m. The equation for calculating the maximum wind power is $P = \frac{1}{2}DAv^3$. Graph this equation on a graphing calculator. Plot wind power on the vertical axis (with a range of 3.3×10^4 W to 4.3×10^5 W) and wind speed on the horizontal axis (with a range of 3.0 m/s to 7.0 m/s). Sketch the graph. Use the calculator to read the coordinates of the curve and answer the questions below.

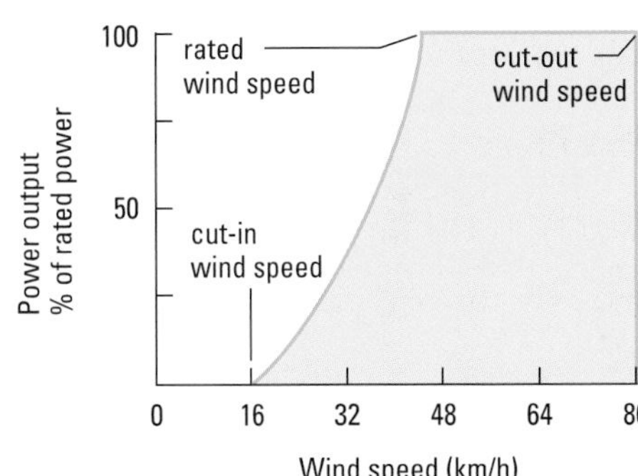

FIGURE 5.31 Idealized power curve for wind generation. Why do you think there is a cut-out wind speed?

Discussion

1. Describe the graph.
2. As the wind speed doubles, what happens to the wind power?
3. What does the wind speed have to be to double the wind power from that at 5.0 m/s?
4. What is the most important factor in the wind power equation, air density, cross-sectional area, or wind speed? Why?

INFOBIT

Equally important to the power curve is the wind speed frequency distribution. This is the number of hours per year that the wind speed lies within a narrow speed interval best matched to the wind turbine. Why do you think this is important?

INFOBIT

Wind farms are comprised of arrays of wind turbines interconnected electrically so as to deliver their power to the utility grid. Currently the power ratings of wind turbines used on wind farms range from about 300 kW to 750 kW, with rotor diameters ranging from 35 m to 50 m.

Because wind is irregular, some means of storing the electrical energy generated is needed. Storage batteries can be charged, or excess electricity can be used to pump water to a higher level which can be used later to produce electricity. The electricity can also be used to split water into hydrogen and oxygen gas and the gases burned later to produce electricity. Another problem is the noise and sight pollution. Imagine thousands of windmills dotting the landscape. Finally, not all the energy available in the wind is converted to kinetic energy in the rotating blades. In fact, the efficiency is less than 40%.

Energy from the Sun

Except for nuclear energy, sunlight is the primary source of all our energy. Radiant energy from the Sun is called solar energy.

Passive Solar Systems This is the simplest and least expensive way to use solar energy for heating buildings. The building itself is designed to collect solar energy. Most of its windows face south. They permit solar energy to enter the building in winter when the Sun is low in the sky. Heavy stone or brick walls inside store the heat in the daytime. Brick has a specific heat capacity of about 850 J/(kg·°C). The bricks cool and radiate heat to the inside at night. Insulating blinds pulled down at night decrease heat loss to the outside.

Active Solar Systems Buildings with active solar systems have special features to collect, store, and circulate energy from the Sun (Figure 5.32). These include flat-plate collectors, storage tanks, pumps, and fans. A flat-plate collector is shown in Figure 5.33. Flat-plate collectors are placed on a roof with a southern exposure. The flat-plate collector changes solar energy directly to heat energy.

FIGURE 5.32 A solar-heated home. The roof contains solar collectors to trap heat energy from the Sun.

It is covered by a transparent surface and has one or more air chambers, a coated plate, tubes, and insulation. The flat-plate collector makes use of the greenhouse effect. The glass surface lets in the sun's short-wavelength radiant energy. The coated plate absorbs the short-wavelength radiant energy and increases in temperature. At the higher temperature it gives off long-wavelength radiant energy that cannot pass through the glass. Thus the energy is trapped in an air chamber under the glass. The chamber and the coated collector plate heat up. The pipes under the coated metal plate carry a fluid such as water. Recall that water has a high specific heat capacity, 4200 J/(kg·°C). This fluid absorbs and conducts the heat to a storage area. Heat from the storage area is used when needed to heat the home.

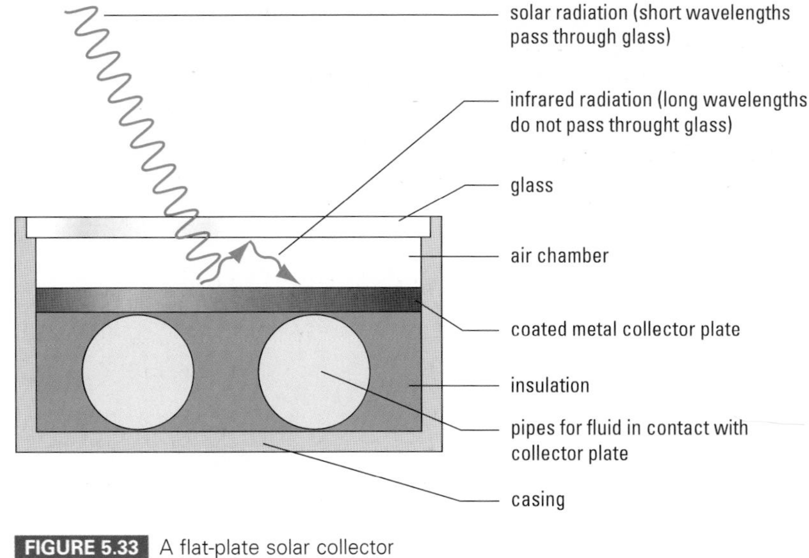

FIGURE 5.33 A flat-plate solar collector

Discovering Physics — A Flat-plate Collector

Build a simple flat-plate collector like the one shown in Figure 5.34. Investigate some factors that affect its operation. Is a transparent cover needed? Does it matter whether the cover is made of glass or plastic? What effect does the colour of the absorbing surface have? Which works better, a white absorbing surface or a black absorbing surface? What effect does the angle the light makes with the surface have? Use the temperature change inside the box as a measure of its ability to collect light.

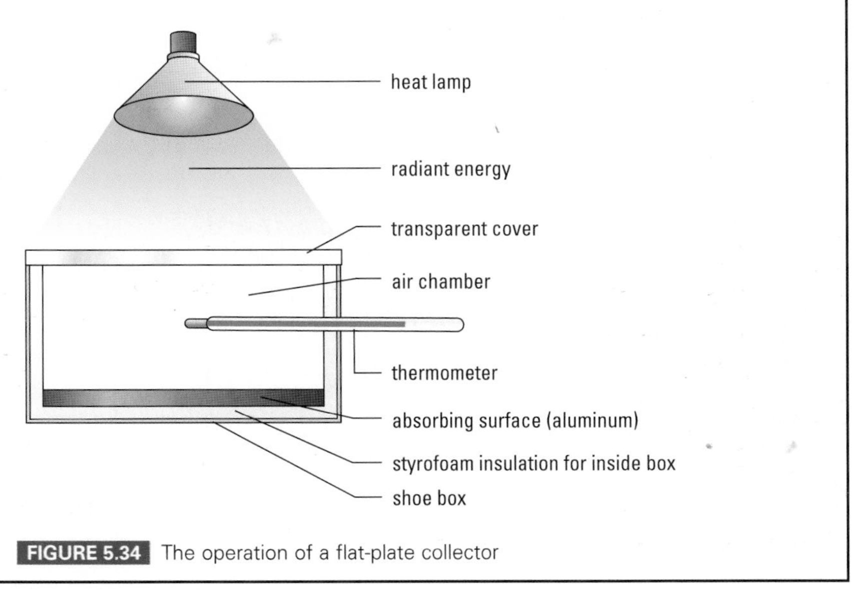

FIGURE 5.34 The operation of a flat-plate collector

FIGURE 5.35 Parabolic solar reflectors located in a desert region can focus light on pipes.

FIGURE 5.36 Large curved mirrors can collect solar energy.

Solar energy can also be collected and concentrated using large curved reflectors. One example is the solar furnace at Mont-Louis in the French Pyrenees. This reflector consists of thousands of small mirrors that concentrate sunlight on a small area (Figure 5.37). Temperatures high enough to melt metals can be achieved.

Some scientists suggest locating large reflectors in desert regions (Figure 5.38). The solar energy collected by reflectors could be used to produce

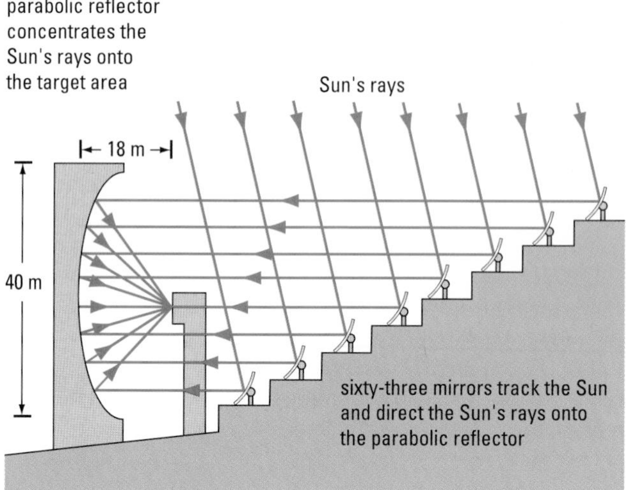

Discovering Physics — *Investigating a Solar Cell*

Investigate the factors affecting the efficiency of a solar cell.

Connect a small solar cell to a voltmeter as shown in Figure 5.37. Use different power light bulbs, a converging Fresnel lens, and a mask to study the affects on the potential difference produced by i) the brightness of the incident light, ii) the concentration of the light, iii) the cross-sectional area of the cell exposed, and iv) the angle the solar cell makes with the incident light. Also, research the cost of making a solar cell collector having a cross-sectional area of one square metre.

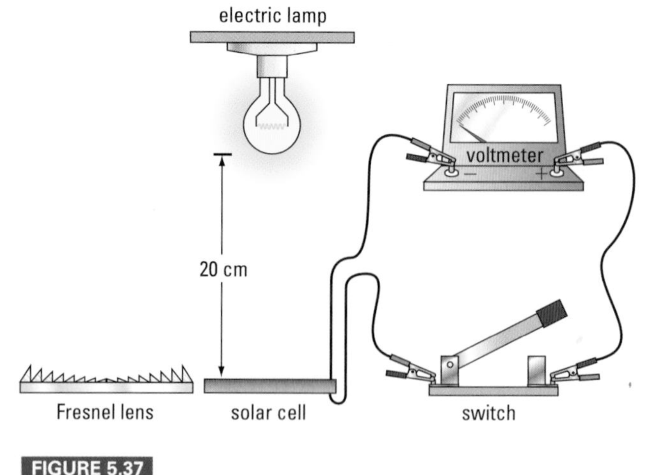

FIGURE 5.37

steam, and the steam could be used to produce electrical energy. Recall that the specific latent heat of vaporization of water is large (2255 kJ/kg). Other scientists propose a system of space mirrors. The mirrors would reflect extra solar energy to selected regions on earth. The solar energy could prevent frost damage and increase crop production.

Solar energy can be changed directly to electrical energy using solar cells. One kind of solar cell is made of silicon in two layers called n-doped and p-doped (Figure 5.38). Light shines on the silicon cells forcing some electrons from the n-doped silicon to the p-doped silicon. These moving electrons constitute an electric current. The greater the number of silicon cells connected together, the greater the electric current and the greater the energy harnessed from sunlight.

There are several problems with using solar cells today to power our appliances. The average efficiency of modern commercial solar cells is about 15%. Also they are very costly to produce.

INFOBIT

Innovative solar cell technology using combinations of new materials and ways of concentrating the sunlight onto the cells has achieved efficiencies in the range of 25–32%. The challenge will be for industry and government to work together to get these cells into power-generating systems once their reliability has been demonstrated.

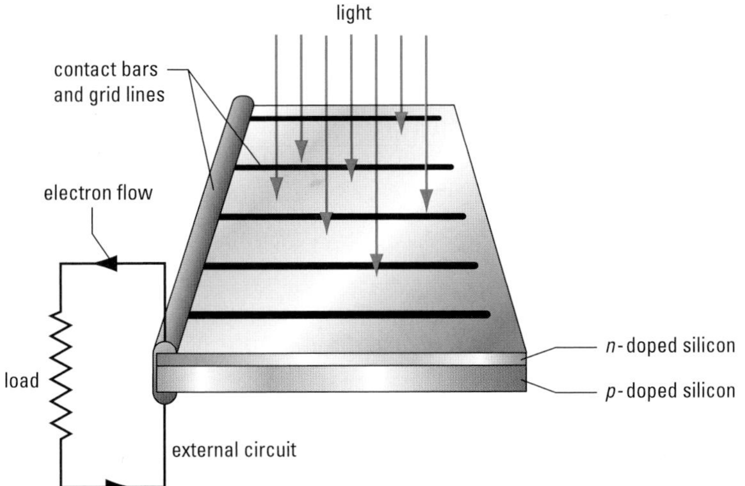

FIGURE 5.38 Light energy incident on the silicon solar cell causes a surplus of electrons to build up on the n-doped silicon and a deficiency on the p-doped silicon This causes a current to flow through the load (such as a light bulb or motor) in the external circuit.

EXAMPLE 13 CONCEPTUAL

Assume that the average rate at which solar energy falls on a desert region is 200 W/m^2 and that the efficiency of silicon solar cells is 15%. What ground area must be covered with solar cells if one kilowatt of electrical power is to be generated?

Reasoning and Solution

Since the efficiency is only 15%, $0.15 \times 200\ \text{W/m}^2 = 30\ \text{W/m}^2$ is converted to electricity. To produce one kilowatt of electricity, the area needed is

$$A = \frac{1000\ \text{W}}{30\ \dfrac{\text{W}}{\text{m}^2}} = 33\ \text{m}^2$$

An area of 33 m^2 is needed to provide 1000 W of electricity at an efficiency of 15%. Note that if the efficiency doubled, the area required and the cost would halve.

CHALLENGE

Solar cells occupying an area of 50 m^2 receive 150 W/m^2 of power from the sun. If the cells are 20% efficient, how much electrical power do they generate?

INFO BIT

Ontario now generates 125 MW from green power sources—small hydro plants, a wind turbine, and the power from landfill gas-powered stations. This represents half of one percent of the total generation. By 2003 it is planned to double the green power capacity and double it again by 2005 by using power wind farms, plants that burn biomass, and solar cells.

Photosynthesis Plants grow by absorbing light energy. Light (photo) energy is converted to chemical energy by a process called photosynthesis. One key product of the chemical reaction is sugar. The sugar is converted into plant-building material that together with water and minerals from the soil becomes a plant. Plant matter, or biomass, can be used for food, fuel, shelter and even medicine.

Wood could be used to power electricity generating stations or to produce methanol. Methanol can run engines at a cost comparable to gasoline. Methane can be made from plant and animal waste. It is produced when organic material contained in manure decays in the absence of oxygen. Methane is natural gas and can be burned to heat homes. Methane can also be changed to methanol to run engines.

Energy from the Oceans

The oceans receive and store much of the solar energy reaching Earth. Solar energy heats up the upper surface of the tropical oceans, leaving the deep water cold, and creating a temperature difference between the top and bottom water. Scientists are looking for an economical way to extract the heat from the warmer water. But removing the heat is difficult and expensive. The heat must be removed from huge volumes of water and transporting the energy to distant markets is costly.

Energy from Earth's Crust

The core of Earth is molten rock at a temperature over 1000°C. The temperature of Earth increases between 10°C and 30°C for each one kilometre depth from the surface. The heat inside Earth is called **geothermal energy**. Some of this heat is in the form of pockets of steam. Steam can be used to heat buildings, as is already being done in Iceland. Steam can also turn

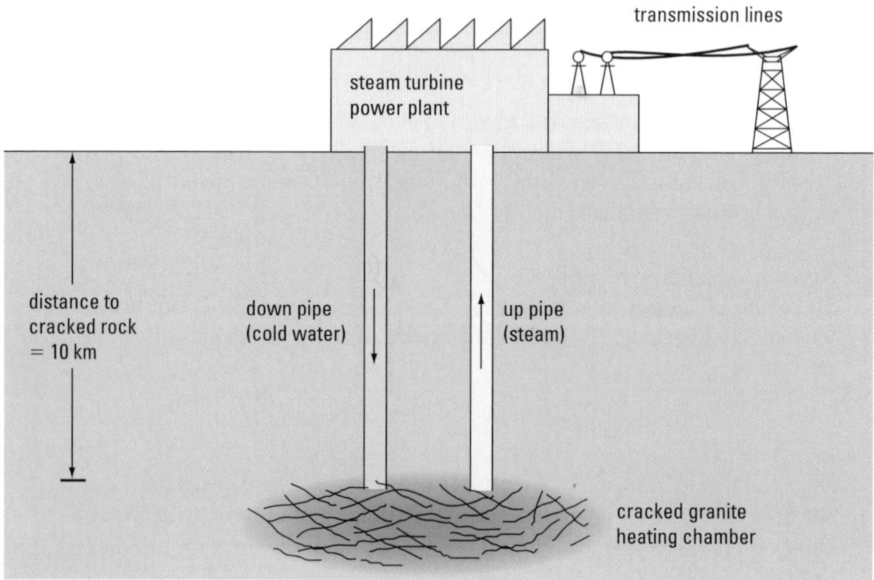

FIGURE 5.39 A geothermal power system

steam turbines to generate electricity. This is being done in San Francisco, U.S.A. Scientists also hope to harness the heat in the dry rock beneath the surface. To do this, Earth's crust must be drilled to great depths as shown in Figure 5.39. Water is circulated through the hot rock and returns as steam. The steam is used to generate electricity. But there are problems. The hot water brings salts to the surface and conventional drill bits overheat and break.

Energy from Hydrogen

Although it is not a primary energy source hydrogen is one fuel that may replace fossil fuels. Although hydrogen can be obtained from coal, water is the cheapest source. When an electric current is passed through water, the water breaks apart and two gases, hydrogen and oxygen, are formed.

Fuel cells are devices that convert a fuel's energy directly to electrical energy. They operate much like a continuous battery when supplied with fuel (e.g. hydrogen) to the anode (negative electrode) and oxidant (e.g. air) to the cathode (positive electrode). Fuel cells in a vehicle can convert natural gas, methanol, or hydrogen into zero-emissions power; the exhaust is water (Figure 5.40). Although in the development stage, fuel cells with a power of 250 kW have been developed.

Hydrogen has several advantages as a fuel. Hydrogen does not pollute when it burns, and the end product is water. Thus, hydrogen is a renewable source of energy. Hydrogen releases large amounts of energy during burning; a kilogram of hydrogen releases more than three times the energy released by a kilogram of gasoline. Hydrogen can be transported easily and stored for long periods of time. Hydrogen, however, has several disadvantages. It is costly to produce hydrogen from water using electricity, stored hydrogen can explode, and the material for storing hydrogen in transportation vehicles is costly.

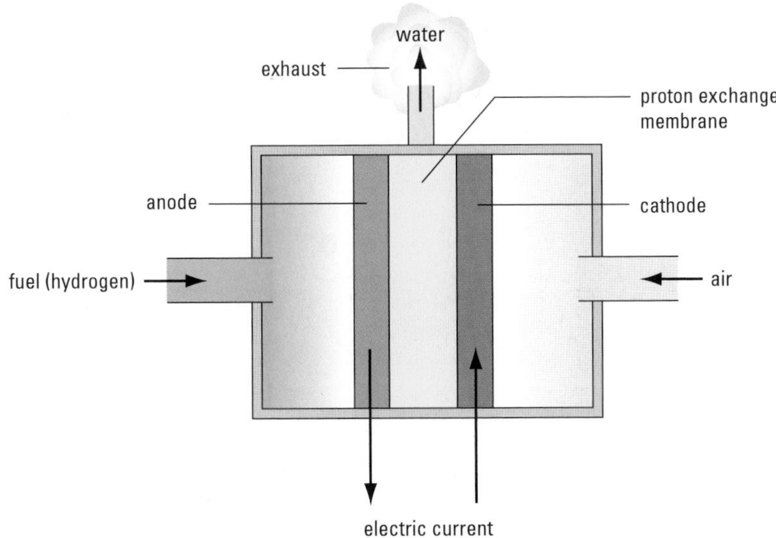

FIGURE 5.40 A hydrogen fuel cell uses hydrogen and oxygen from the air as the reactants and produces water and generates electricity.

Conserving Energy in Transportation

Decision-Making Skills

- ▶ Defining the Issue
- Developing Assessment Criteria
- ▶ Researching the Issue
- ▶ Analyzing Data and Information
- Proposing a Course of Action
- Justifying the Course of Action
- Communicating Your Proposal

BACKGROUND INFORMATION

Fossil-fuelled power plants in Ontario emit about 12% of the nitrogen oxide, smog-causing emissions produced in Ontario. Other large industries such as primary metals, mining, smelting, and refineries emit 25%. Cars, trucks, and other forms of transportation emit 63%. How can we improve the efficiency of transportation and hence reduce smog and pollution? There are at least two approaches we can take to decrease fuel consumption.

Drive a smaller car. Engines can be made more efficient. This will decrease fuel consumption. But the basic problem is one of mass. For each 100 kg of additional mass, fuel consumption increases by 6%. Figure 5.41 shows a graph of gasoline consumption plotted against mass. Note how much more gasoline it takes to go 100 km in a large car or an SUV than a sub-compact.

Use other means of transportation. Energy is saved by leaving the car at home. If you drive, don't travel alone; use car pools. For travel between cities, use a passenger train or a bus. A passenger train uses one-sixth as much energy per person as a car carrying one person. A bus uses half the energy. For travel within the city use buses and subways; they are three and a half times as efficient as a car. A bus is twice as efficient. Better still, use a bicycle. It carries a passenger over forty times as far as a car for the same energy, and it enables you to keep fit.

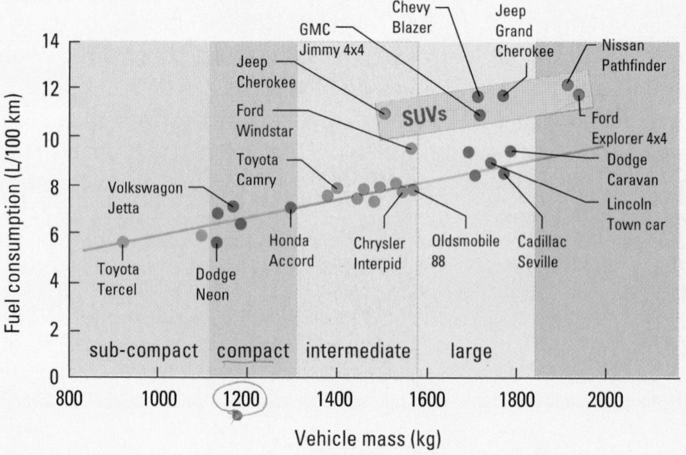

FIGURE 5.41 Gasoline consumption against mass. SUVs are gas guzzlers.

Analyzing the Issue

1. Draw a consequence map to show the social, political, economic, and environmental impacts of developing technologies to increase fuel efficiency.
2. Research fuel efficiency in cars. Identify the environmental factors that make the issue of fuel efficiency so significant.
3. Analyze the graph in Figure 5.41. Determine the placement of your family car on this graph. Explain the relationship of the mass of your family car to the fuel it consumes.
4. Propose additional ways to conserve energy (and reduce exhaust emissions) by the mode of transportation chosen.
5. In groups, develop future city planning guidelines for lobbying a city government to address the issue of transportation and fuel emissions. Justify your guidelines by providing examples of the benefits associated with what you propose.
6. With what criteria will the city government evaluate your guidelines?

Section 5.4 Review

Understanding Concepts

1. What sources of energy are used to generate electricity in
   a) a fossil-fuelled power plant
   b) a nuclear power plant
2. What energy conversions take place in a hydro-electric power plant?
3. How efficient are hydro-electric power plants and why are they more efficient than fossil-fuelled or nuclear plants?
4. A tidal power plant generates 10 MW of electricity during a period of 12.5 h. Assume that the water is collected behind a dam 6.0 m high and is allowed to pass through a turbine twice to generate this electricity, once as the tide comes in and once as it goes out. What mass of water flows through the turbine if the efficiency is 85%?
5. What is the pollution problem in capturing energy in wind?
6. A wind turbine has three blades each 20 m long. The average wind speed is 5.5 m/s and the density of the air is 1.3 kg/m^3.
   a) What is the maximum power at this wind speed?
   b) If the efficiency of the wind turbine is 30%, how much usable electrical power is generated?
7. Describe how the greenhouse effect is used in a flat-plate collector.
8. Describe the advantages and disadvantages of using hydrogen as a fuel.

Applying Inquiry/ Communication Skills

9. Compare renewable energy sources with nonrenewable energy sources and determine which are more dependable in the long run.

Making Connections

10. Lighting consumes 25% of all power used in Ontario. Less than 5% of the energy from a light bulb produces light. Propose courses of practical action that would help stop this waste of energy.
11. When excess electricity is generated at a hydro power plant, what methods can be used to store the energy and what are benefits and drawbacks to each?
12. Storage of the nuclear waste from the CANDU nuclear reactors is a significant environmental issue. Prepare a risk–benefit analysis to demonstrate the potential impact this can have on the environment and society.
13. Suppose your home is equipped with a wind turbine that provides 2 kW·h of usable energy each day, which can be stored in a storage battery. The battery can provide energy for up to three "wind-less" days with a maximum power output of 2000 W. How would you allocate this electrical energy over the three days? Which appliances, lightbulbs, heaters, etc. would you use and for how long would you operate each item in order to provide for the needs of your home over the three-day period. Would your plan differ at different times of the year?

Investigation 1 (Section 5.1)

Inquiry Skills

- Initiating and Planning
- Applying Technical Skills
- Using Tools, Materials, Equipment
- Conducting and Recording
- Analyzing and Interpreting
- Concluding and Communicating

The Inclined Plane

Machines allow us to do work easier or faster. Thus, they give us an advantage—a mechanical advantage—when we use them to help us do work. Friction, however, reduces a machine's efficiency to something less than 100%. One kind of simple machine, called an inclined plane, is used to increase the height of an object without having to exert a force big enough to lift up its whole weight.

Problem

To measure the efficiency of an inclined plane tipped at various angles.

Materials

- wooden plank
- wood block
- spring scale
- protractor
- metre stick
- four text books

Procedure

1. Set one end of the wooden plank on a block as shown in Figure 5.42.

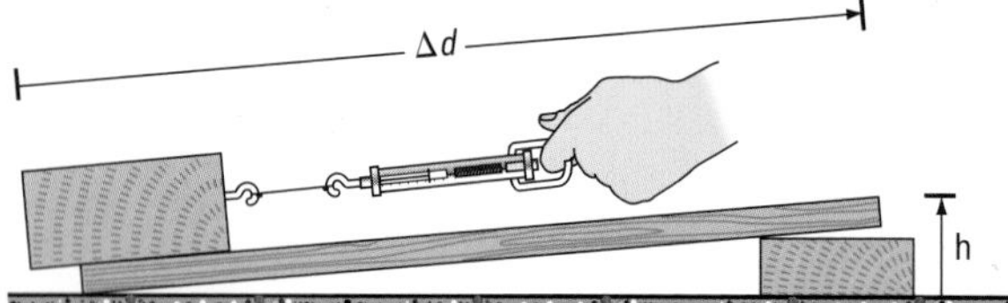

FIGURE 5.42

2. Construct an observation table in your notebook consisting of eight columns and four rows. The headings for the columns are: weight of block (N), height of incline (m), length of incline (m), angle of incline (degrees), force needed to slide the block up the incline (N), useful work done $mg\Delta h$ (J), actual work done $F\Delta d$ (J), and efficiency (%).
3. After setting the zero on the spring scale, measure and record the weight of the wood block.
4. Measure and record the height, length, and angle of the incline. To measure the angle you can either use a protractor or you can use your knowledge of trigonometry.
5. Hold the spring scale parallel to the incline and reset its zero.
6. Measure and record the force necessary to pull the block up the ramp at constant speed.
7. Repeat procedures 4–6 with three more different ramp angles by using the remaining three textbooks to raise the incline higher.

Analyzing and Interpreting

1. As the angle of the incline increases, what happens to the value of the force necessary to slide the block up the ramp?
2. How do the values of useful work and actual work done compare at each new angle?
3. Why is the efficiency less than 100% in each case?

Concluding and Communicating

4. Why does the force necessary to pull the block up the ramp increase as the angle increases?
5. The force of kinetic friction is $F_k = \mu_K F_N$. Why does this force of friction decrease as the angle of the ramp increases?
6. As the ramp angle increases and the force of kinetic friction decreases, what happens to the efficiency of the system?
7. What is the maximum theoretical value for the efficiency of a simple machine? Why?
8. A road that leads up a hill or a mountain is really an inclined plane. The road can't be too steep or cars won't be able to make the grade! Do some research to find out how the grade of a road is measured and what would be the maximum grade for a good road.
9. What could you do to increase the efficiency of an inclined plane that is fixed at a certain angle?

Extending

10. Figure 5.43 shows a pulley system that can be used to lift an object. Note that part of the load being lifted is the lower pulley. Design and perform an experiment to measure the efficiency of this kind of simple machine.

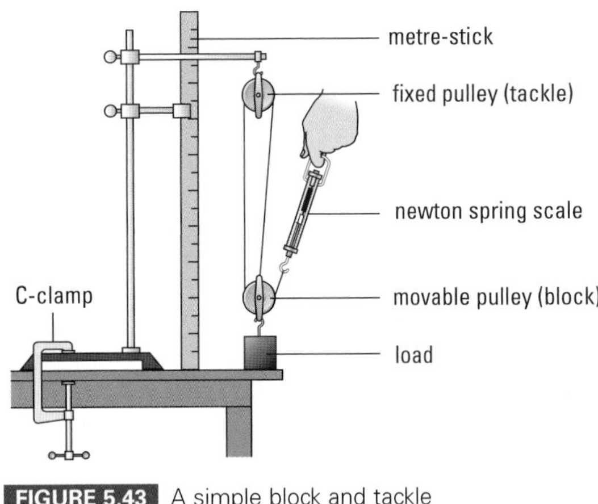

FIGURE 5.43 A simple block and tackle

Investigation 2 (Section 5.2)

Inquiry Skills

- Initiating and Planning
- Applying Technical Skills
- Using Tools, Materials, Equipment
- Conducting and Recording
- Analyzing and Interpreting
- Concluding and Communicating

Measuring the Power of Your Body

A top athlete sprinting has a power of about 1700 W. The average person running has a power of about 1000 W. How powerful do you think you are? Write a prediction in your notebook. When you walk or run up a flight of stairs, you increase your gravitational potential energy. If you start from rest and finish at rest, your change in kinetic energy is negligible.

Problem

How much power do you generate when walking up a flight of stairs?

Materials

- roll of string and a bob
- kilogram bathroom scale
- metre-stick
- stopwatch

CAUTION: Students with health problems should not do this experiment.

Experimental Design

1. Review the definition of power and decide what measurements must be made.
2. Write out a list of procedures you will use to obtain the required measurements.
3. Design a data table to record your measurements.
4. When your teacher approves your procedure, carry out the experiment.

Analyzing and Interpreting

1. How much power did you develop when running up the stairs?

Concluding and Communicating

2. Do you think this activity is a true measure of your body power? Discuss.
3. How is it possible for you to run up the same flight of stairs quicker than your friend does, and yet you might have generated the same power?
4. A 200-g bag of potato chips contains 4.8 MJ of energy. How long would it take you working at your maximum body power to consume this energy?

Extending

5. Do you think the number of steps you take at a time in climbing the stairs makes any difference to your power? Make an hypothesis. Then climb the stairs, one step at a time, and then two steps at a time, and compare the results. Be careful!

Design & Build

A Tomato Tester

BACKGROUND INFORMATION

When harvesting tomatoes, if the tomatoes are physically strong enough, they can be subjected to the forces exerted by machines during mechanical harvest as opposed to being picked and processed one-by-one by people.

Proposal

A company is hiring your team to design a device that tests the strength of various types of tomato to determine which ones are candidates for mechanical harvesting. Tomatoes are to be dropped and then examined for damage.

Materials

Construction materials (likely made of wood but not necessarily). At least three varieties of tomatoes including cherry tomatoes, plum tomatoes, and a typical garden variety of tomato.

Specifications

Your tomato dropper needs to accommodate tomatoes of various sizes and shapes. It needs to be adjustable in height so that tomatoes can be dropped from various heights and then examined for damage to the skin or the pulp. Some way of controlling the splashes when tomatoes smash to bits would be desirable. Composting the remains would also be a good feature of your project.

Plan

Draw up your plans for the design of the system and discuss the features of your plan with classmates. They should provide input and ask you specific questions about your design. Be sure to use proper drafting procedures including the dimensions of your apparatus.

Construction

a) Construct your model according to the plan.
b) Test the model using various release heights and types of tomato.
c) Record your results specifying the heights of release, the types of tomato used, and the damage sustained by each tomato.

Evaluation

Provide a written summary of your results including your recommendations as to which type(s) of tomato would be good candidates for mechanical harvesting and which one(s) would not.

Evaluate the design of your tomato tester and explain how the design could be improved.

CHAPTER SUMMARY

Key Terms

actual mechanical advantage
calorimeter
efficiency
fossil fuel
fulcrum
geothermal energy
ideal mechanical advantage
inclined plane
latent heat
law of the lever
lever
lever arm
machine
method of mixtures
non-renewable energy
nuclear fuel
photosynthesis
power
principle of heat exchange
pulley
renewable energy
specific heat capacity
specific latent heat
specific latent heat of fusion
specific latent heat of vaporization
torque
watt

Key Understandings

- Machines are used to alter force or speed.
- The actual mechanical advantage of a machine is the ratio of the load to the applied force.
- Efficiency is the ratio of the work done to the energy consumed.
- Power is the rate of doing work.
- 1 W = 1 J/s
- Thermal energy is the total energy an object has as a result of the random motion of its molecules.
- Heat energy is thermal energy being transferred from one material substance to another.
- Specific heat capacity is the quantity of heat transferred, in joules, to change the temperature of a kilogram of material by one degree Celsius.
- Thermal energy is conserved when substances are mixed in a closed system.
- Specific latent heat is the quantity of heat transferred when a kilogram of a substance changes state without a change in temperature.
- Specific latent heat of fusion is the quantity of heat required to melt 1 kg of a substance without changing its temperature.
- Specific latent heat of vaporization is the quantity of heat needed to vaporize 1 kg of a substance without changing its temperature.

Key Equations

$$\text{AMA} = \frac{F_G}{F_A} = \frac{mg}{F_A}$$

$$\text{percent efficiency} = \frac{\text{useful work done}}{\text{actual work done}} \times 100\ \%$$

$$= \frac{\text{energy output}}{\text{energy input}} \times 100\ \%$$

$$\tau = Fl$$

$$P = \frac{W}{\Delta t} = \frac{E}{\Delta t}$$

$$P = Fv_{av}$$

$$Q = m{\cdot}\Delta t{\cdot}c$$

$$Q = m{\cdot}l_f$$

$$Q = ml_v$$

$$P = \frac{1}{2}DAv^3$$

Consolidate Your Understanding

1. Look back to your answer for the Checkpoint on p. 179. What answer would you give now? Explain why each of the other answers is incorrect.
   A trucking company has purchased a "smooth" ramp which they intend to use along with a rope to drag heavy loads to the flatbed of a truck. The manufacturer claims that both the energy used and the force applied are the same, whether the load is lifted straight up or dragged along the ramp. Write a one-paragraph answer to their claim.

2. Create a concept map to be used as a study map for machines, power, and energy. Consult the Key Terms above and include as many terms as possible in your concept map. Include two Key Equations and an example problem involving both. Show a model solution using the GRASS strategy.

3. Write a paragraph explaining how a knowledge of the law of conservation of energy, and of heat transfer is necessary to an understanding of the operation of thermal power plants. Use an example to explain to another student why a thermal power plant is so inefficient. In your explanation suggest ways to use the waste heat.

CHAPTER 5 REVIEW

Understanding Concepts

1. One megawatt is equivalent to
   a) 10^{-6} W b) 10^{-3} W c) 1 W
   d) 10^{3} W e) 10^{6} W

2. What force does the engine of a car apply if its power output is 30 kW and the car is travelling at a steady speed of 28 m/s?
   a) 9.3×10^{-4} N b) 9.3×10^{-1} N
   c) 1.1 N d) 9.3×10^{2} N
   e) 1.1×10^{3} N

3. A force F acting on a stationary block on a smooth level surface moves the block a horizontal displacement Δd in a time Δt. The power is
   a) zero. b) $\frac{F\Delta d}{\Delta t}$ c) $F\Delta d$
   d) $F\Delta d\Delta t$ e) $\frac{F\Delta t}{\Delta d}$

4. Identical masses of three different liquids x, y, and z are heated with identical immersion heaters. The heat energy against temperature graph for all three liquids is shown in Figure 5.44. Which one of the following statements is correct for the liquids?
   a) The specific heat capacity of x, y, and z are the same.
   b) The specific heat capacity of y and z are the same and larger than x.
   c) The specific heat capacity of x and y are the same and larger than z.
   d) The specific heat capacity of y and z are the same and smaller than x.
   e) The specific heat capacity sequenced from largest to smallest is x, y, z.

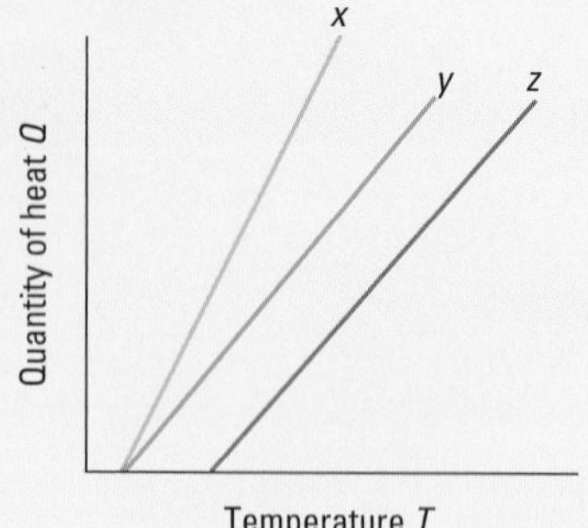

FIGURE 5.44 Heat-temperature graph for three liquids

5. Which of the following is NOT a way to store the energy from wind?
   a) as chemical energy in storage batteries
   b) as gravitational energy in raised water
   c) as chemical energy in the form of hydrogen
   d) as nuclear energy in the form of uranium
   e) as sound energy in turning wind turbines

6. Archimedes (287–212 B.C.), arguably one of the three best mathematicians of all time, said "Give me a place to stand and I will move the Earth." Which class of lever would be best for this purpose? Why?

7. Explain why a 0.1-kg aluminum pan cools faster than 0.1 kg of cooked apples when both are removed from the same oven at the same time. (See Table 5.4)

8. The temperature variations in Newfoundland from winter to summer are less extreme than in Saskatchewan. Explain why.

9. City streets are sometimes designed so that, when it rains, the water drains away quickly. How does this affect the air temperature in summer? Why?

10. Distinguish between renewable energy and nonrenewable energy and give an example of each to support your answer.

11. Name three fossil fuels and explain why they are considered non-renewable energy sources.

12. Why is uranium considered a nonrenewable energy source?

13. Where does the energy come from during nuclear fission?

14. Describe one advantage and one disadvantage of using nuclear fission to generate electricity.

Applying Inquiry/ Communication Skills

15. With the aid of diagrams, distinguish between using a shovel to lift and throw sand and using a shovel to pry a rock from the ground. What class of lever is illustrated in each case?

16. Draw a pulley system that would be just good enough to lift up a 50-N load with a force of 12 N. Explain why your pulley system should work.

17. The magnitude of the torque on a lever is calculated by multiplying the force applied by the perpendicular distance of the force from the fulcrum. Make a scale diagram (or use your knowledge of trigonometry) to calculate the torque when a force of 25 N is applied at an angle of 40° to a lever when the lever arm is 60 cm long.

18. One of the simple machines is a wheel and axle. It is comprised of a large-diameter wheel connected to a smaller-diameter axle (Figure 5.45).

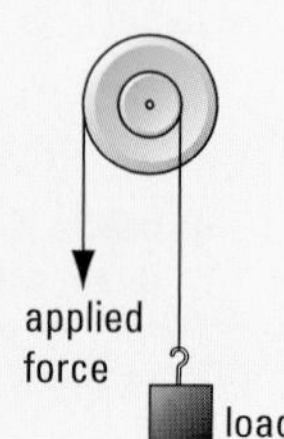

FIGURE 5.45 This wheel and axle is used to gain force.

It can be used to gain force or speed. A force applied to the wheel can be used to exert a larger force at the axle. If a force is applied to the axle, then the speed of an object attached to the wheel is greater than the speed at which the force moves. Classify each of the following wheels and axles according to what it is used for (multiplying force or speed) and make a sketch of each one showing the point of application of the force and the location of the load being moved.

a) a doorknob
b) a screwdriver
c) the axle and wheel of a car
d) an automobile steering wheel
e) water faucet handles

19. The rate of energy consumption (power) of an adult walking at a steady speed of 1.5 m/s can be expressed by the formula $P_W = 5.065m$ where P_W is the power in watts and m is the mass of the person in kilograms.

a) Use your graphing calculator to draw a graph of P_W against m for masses ranging from 50 kg to 80 kg.
b) How much more power is needed to walk at this speed for every 5-kg gain in weight?

20. Figure 5.46 shows a heat energy against temperature graph for 50 g and 100 g of water and 100 g of ethylene glycol. Determine the specific heat capacities of water and ethylene glycol.

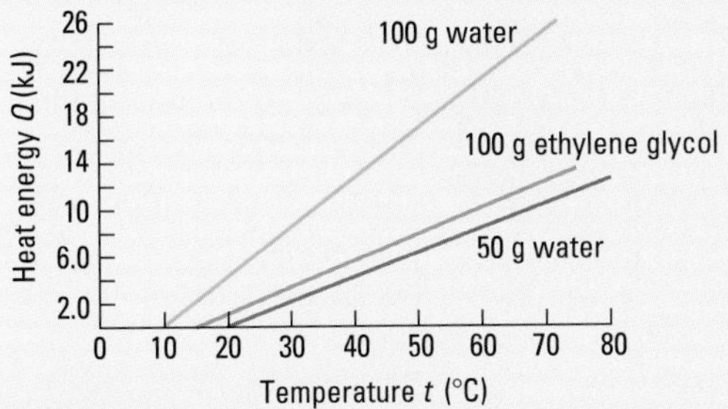

FIGURE 5.46 Graph of heat against temperature for water and ethylene glycol

21. In a physics experiment, a copper cube of mass 300 g is immersed in 100°C boiling water and left there for several minutes. The cube is then transferred to 0.200 kg of water at 10.0°C. The final temperature of the mixture is 21.0°C. What is the specific heat capacity of copper? Identify possible sources of experimental error.

22. Design and carry out an experiment to compare the specific heat capacity of dry and wet sand. Would crops in dry or wet lands be hurt more by frost? Why?

23. The power output of a Darrieus rotor windmill changes with speed as shown in Figure 5.47 in an ideal situation.

a) Find the power output in kilowatts (kW) at a speed of 40 km/h.
b) Find the wind speed needed for a power output of 3 kW.
c) Explain why the power output shown by the graph is larger than the electric power actually captured by the windmill in real life.

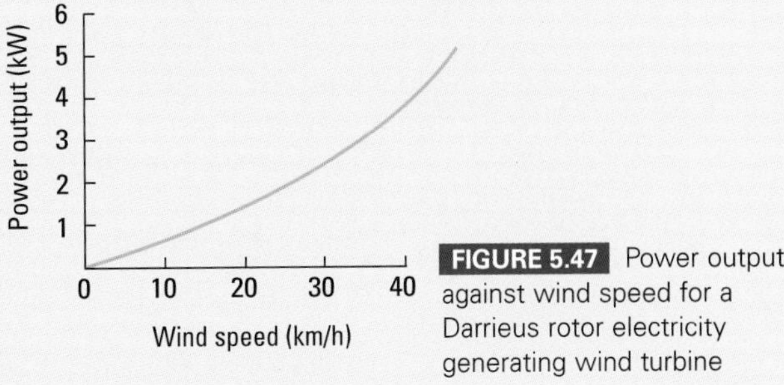

FIGURE 5.47 Power output against wind speed for a Darrieus rotor electricity generating wind turbine

Making Connections

24. The next time you enter your kitchen for something, keep track of the first five things you do. Note how many involve the use of simple machines and describe, including diagrams, how these machines work.

25. A cyclist wraps her water bottle in a wet towel. Explain how this helps keep the bottled water cool during a summer bike ride.

26. A technician makes a 5.0-kg metal object containing two parts, one of iron and the other of aluminum. If it takes 504 kJ to change the object's temperature from 25°C to 165°C, what is the mass of each part (see Table 5.4)?

27. A solar-heated home has a tank containing Glauber's salt in the basement. Its purpose is to store 2.8×10^9 J of heat energy, and it can be heated from 22°C to 50°C. The melting point of Glauber's salt is 32°C and it has a specific latent heat of fusion of 241 kJ/kg. Its specific heat capacities in the solid and liquid states are 1066 J/(kg·°C) and 1576 J/(kg·°C) respectively. Calculate the mass of Glauber's salt required to store the heat.

28. When excess electricity is generated at a hydro power plant, it is used to pump water to a 1000 m^2 storage reservoir. At peak electricity demand periods the energy in the raised water powers the generator to produce electricity. If a reservoir is located 250 m above the electric generator, what depth of water must be stored to produce 9.0×10^{12} J of energy during a peak demand period? Assume an efficiency of 85% and a water density of 1000 kg/m^3.

Skills: Discovering Yours

You've used and developed a variety of skills in physics, many of which will be of value to you in any career. But there's another way to look at those skills. They can help you choose a career that might be just right for you. How? You've probably heard that people tend to do better at things they enjoy. By discovering which of your own skills are your best, you may find useful clues as to what you might enjoy doing, in physics or elsewhere.

Assessing Skills by Likes and Dislikes

1. Make a two-column chart like the one shown at the bottom of this page. Write down the skills you like using in physics class.
   - Think about what you have enjoyed doing and learning. Where have you been most successful?
   - Which topics and experiments seemed to go quickly? Which made you curious to know more? Which skills did you use for these?

2. Do the same thing for skills you may have disliked using, or not liked as well, in physics.
   - Think about what you didn't enjoy—or enjoyed least. What, if anything, did you find frustrating or difficult?
   - Where did you have to work hardest or need help? Which skills gave you problems?

3. Compare your likes and dislikes.
   - Why did you enjoy or not enjoy using that skill?
   - How would your attitude change if you knew or understood more about that skill?
   - Would it make a difference if you were to use that skill in a different setting or with different people? Is your attitude a result of external factors, or something inside yourself?

The Connection between Skills and Career Choices

You can and will learn new skills all the time. But you can take what you've discovered about your skills and your attitude toward them, and use this information to help focus your career investigation.

The chart on the next page matches some types of careers found in physics with the skills that are particularly important for them. Keep in mind that these skills are useful in all career types. For example, communication skills are useful in any career, but are particularly important for an educator such as a teacher.

Skills I enjoy using ...	Skills I don't enjoy using or enjoy least ...
recording results for experiments	remembering to use the right units
building apparatus	communicating in a group

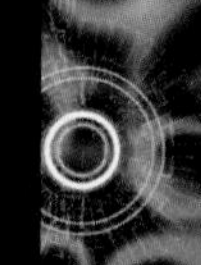

4. Think about your favourite skills. See if you can match any of your favourite skills to a type of career. Which other skills do you think would be important for that career?

Looking Outward

5. Return to Exploring Careers in Unit 1, which lists the variety of fields in physics. Choose a field of interest to you. Now choose a career type and research a specific career you might enjoy in your chosen field. For example, if geophysics interests you and consultant is the type of career you might enjoy, find out what geophysical consultants do, where they work, what education they need, and so on. Repeat for other combinations of field and career type.

List of Skills

- assembling apparatus
- communicating with others
- coordinating tasks
- decision-making
- designing procedure
- identifying variables
- interpreting patterns and trends in data
- problem-solving
- recording observations
- selecting the appropriate graphing technique
- time management
- understanding and applying equations
- using vector diagrams

Skill *This skill ...*	**Career Type** *is particularly important for this type of career.*
• communicating information	educator (such as: teacher, teaching assistant, professor)
• identifying variables • interpreting patterns and trends • designing procedure	researcher (such as: industrial and applied physicist, academic researcher)
• recording observations • assembling apparatus	technician, technologist (such as: equipment specialists or operators, research assistants)
• coordinating tasks • time management • decision-making	management (such as: senior administrators, business owners, planners)
• understanding and applying equations	analyst, consultant (such as: industrial and applied physicist, designer, accident reconstruction specialist)
• using vector diagrams • selecting the appropriate graphing technique • problem-solving	engineer, designer (such as: industrial and applied physicist, academic researcher, product developer)

FIGURE 1 Look at the list of skills provided above. Which of them would be important in doing this activity? Rate yourself on these skills. Which do you consider your strongest? Which do you still need to develop? What could you do about these skills?

The Global Energy Community

Background Information

Canadians have one of the highest standards of living in the world, but we seldom analyze the economic, social, and environmental impacts of the various energy sources we use to achieve this. We heat our homes using electricity, oil, or natural gas; we power motor vehicles mainly using petroleum products; we energize television sets, radios, and CD players using electricity generated from hydro-electric sources, nuclear, coal, natural gas and oil; and we cook meals using electric stoves or gas ranges. Where does this energy come from and what global impact does it have on the environment?

Over the past ten years, the world's output of primary energy (petroleum, natural gas, coal) and electric power (hydro, nuclear, solar, wind, and wood and waste) increased at an annual rate of 0.9%. Figure 1 shows the percentage of each primary energy source in the mix in 1999. Petroleum, (crude oil and natural gas plant liquids) was the world's most important primary energy source, accounting for about 39%. Natural gas and coal followed each with 23.0%. Hydro-electric and nuclear electric sources together made up 14%. Energy sources such as geothermal, solar, wind, wood and waste, made up a very small but increasing part of the mix at less than 1%.

SCENARIO

You are a member of a Canadian Energy Impact Committee, which has been asked to develop a plan for increasing the percentage of renewable energy in the primary energy mix. You are to review the current production of primary energy in Canada and compare this to global energy production, then evaluate the effects various energy sources are having on the Canadian and global environment.

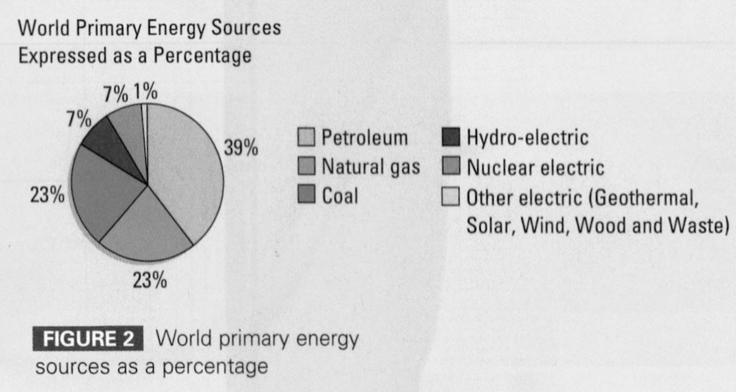

FIGURE 2 World primary energy sources as a percentage

Part A: Primary Energy Sources

1. a) How does a primary energy source differ from a secondary energy source?
   b) State the law of conservation of energy and explain why this law is so important in harnessing primary sources of energy?

2. Distinguish between gravitational potential energy and kinetic energy and give a primary energy source example for each.

3. Use an example to explain the difference between heat and thermal energy.

4. a) What is the difference between renewable and non-renewable energy sources?
   b) Why do you think renewable energy sources make up such a small portion of our energy mix and why is it necessary that they play a larger role?

5. Prepare a chart summarizing the efficiencies of the following power plants for producing electricity: fossil fuelled; nuclear fuelled, hydro-electric, tidal turbines and wind turbines.

Part B: World Energy Resources

6. Who are the producers and the consumers of this energy? Research publications and search the Internet, to determine Canada's production and consumption of the primary energy sources in relation to other countries around the world, including: petroleum, natural gas, coal, hydroelectric, nuclear electric, and other electric. Summarize your results in graphical form.

7. Research the mix of renewable energy sources in Canada and the world, including rivers, tides and waves, geothermal, wind, solar and photosynthesis. Summarize your findings in a table and in a graph.

8. Identify how these renewable energy sources are presently being harnessed, their efficiencies, and the potential for increasing their contribution to the global energy mix.

Part C: Looking to the Future

9. Identify primary energy sources we export and those we import and identify the net cost/profit for Canada. Analyze your research and predict how exports and imports could change without global planning for the future.

10. Propose a plan to assign roles in a global committee that will set policy for future use of energy resources. Develop your plan using social, economic, and technological considerations to determine who will participate from each country (i.e. what background, skills each member should possess), as well as the countries that will be represented.

Part D: Communicating Your Plan

11. Prepare your plan for increasing the percentage of renewable energy. Your plan should incoude a comparison of Canadian energy production to world energy production and the effects various energy sources have on Canada and the world.

UNIT 2 REVIEW

Understanding Concepts

1. A worker applies a force of 220 N horizontally to the right to move a 50-kg crate. The force of friction between the crate and the floor is 200 N. If the crate is pushed 2.0 m, the work done against friction is
   a) 840 J b) 440 J c) 400 J
   d) 200 J e) 40 J

2. A mass of 2.0 kg is hurled upward from a point situated 20 m above Earth's surface. What will be the height of the mass above Earth's surface when its gravitational energy has increased by 500 J?
   a) 5.0 m b) 25 m c) 45 m
   d) 70 m e) 2.7×10^2 m

3. The kinetic energy of a 0.900-kg football traveling through the air at 15 m/s would be
   a) 202 J b) 101 N c) 101 J
   d) 68.0 J e) 68.0 N

4. When a brick is dropped from the roof of a house, it lands on the ground with a speed v. What will the speed at ground level be for an identical brick dropped from a roof twice as high as the first one?
   a) 0.5 v b) v c) 1.4 v
   d) 2 v e) 4 v

5. A tin can topples from a balcony ledge that is at height h above the ground and it hits the sidewalk with velocity v. How high would the balcony have to be in order for the can to hit ground with velocity $2v$?
   a) $2h$ b) $3h$ c) $4h$
   d) $5h$ e) $6h$

6. Which one of the following units is NOT an energy unit?
   a) J b) MW c) kW·h
   d) W·s e) MJ

7. "The time rate at which energy is used" is a definition of
   a) force b) work c) energy
   d) change in energy e) power

8. Which of the following is NOT an expression for energy?
   a) $\frac{1}{2}mv^2$ b) $F\Delta d$ c) $mg\Delta h$
   d) $ma\Delta d$ e) $\frac{P}{\Delta t}$

9. Two samples of the same liquid are heated using identical immersion heaters. Sample x has half the mass and is heated for twice as long as sample y. The ratio of the temperature change of x to the temperature change of y is
   a) 1:1 b) 2:1 c) 1:2
   d) 4:1 e) 1:4

10. Equal masses of hot water and cold iron are mixed. Which of the following statements apply when the mixture reaches its final temperature?
    I The heat lost by the water equals the heat gained by the iron.
    II The temperature change of the water and the iron are equal.
    III The thermal energy of the water and the iron are equal.
    IV The average kinetic energy of the molecules of water and iron are equal.
    Choose your answer from the following:
    a) I and II only b) I and III only
    c) I and IV only d) III and IV only
    e) II and IV only

11. Which of the following energy sources is not renewable?
    a) geothermal b) nuclear
    c) solar d) tidal
    e) water

12. Using an example, distinguish between positive work and negative work.

13. Use Einstein's famous equation to explain why a very small amount of mass is equivalent to a very large amount of energy.

14. Use an example to distinguish between gravitational potential energy and relative gravitational potential energy.

15. Identify the two factors that affect kinetic energy, state which is the more important factor and explain why it is the more important factor.

16. Use units analysis to express the watt in SI base units.

17. a) State the principle of heat exchange and explain how it is a special case of the law of conservation of energy.
    b) Describe the method of mixtures.

18. Why is a steam burn so severe?

Applying Inquiry/ Communication Skills

19. A physics teacher pushes a lab cart with a steady force of 50 N for a displacement of 3.0 m [forward] and then decreases the force steadily to zero over the next 3.0 m [forward]. Draw a force against displacement graph of this motion and use the graph to calculate the total work done by the physics teacher.

20. Design and perform an experiment to study the efficiency of the conversion of gravitational energy to kinetic energy for a toy car as it coasts from one level to another down a track. One way is to take a videotape of the car's motion to help analyze the motion.

21. Suppose that your task as an engineer is to design a pulley system that can lift a 50-kg load with a force of 100 N. Make a diagram of the pulley system you design and include a 20% efficiency loss due to friction.

22. A force of 1000 N is necessary to pry a rock out of the ground. With the aid of a diagram and some calculations, show how a 2.0-m long bar could be used to move the rock with a force of only 200 N.

23. The waste heat from manufacturing processes causes thermal pollution. Electrical energy generation using fossil and nuclear fuels also causes thermal pollution. Much of this heat enters our waterways. Do a library search to identify ways that this waste heat is being used.

24. Design and perform an experiment using a CSA approved immersion heater to measure the specific heat capacity of water and ethylene glycol. (Hint: Plot a heat energy against time graph for a 100-g sample of each substance)

25. Search the Internet to find ways that solar cells are being made more efficient. Calculate the cost of using solar cells to meet the electrical needs of the average home. Remember that a way will be needed to store energy for use when there is no sunlight.

Making Connections

26. The energy it takes to heat water can be calculated using the formula $Q_H = mc\Delta T$ where m is the mass of the water in kg, c is the specific heat capacity of water which equals 4.2×10^3 J/kg·°C, and ΔT is the temperature change of the water in °C. If the energy used to heat 1.0 kg of water from 20°C to 100°C were used instead to lift the water up vertically, how high could it be lifted? Comment on your answer.

27. Estimates suggest that the human body is about 25% efficient as a machine that converts metabolic energy (chemical energy) into mechanical energy in a wide range of activities including walking. One way to express how much energy is needed for walking is by using the formula $P_W = (2.23 + 1.26v^2)m$ where P_W is the power in watts, v is the walking speed in m/s, and m is the mass of the person in kilograms

a) Calculate the power developed by a 70-kg adult walking at 1.4 m/s

b) How long could this 70-kg adult walk at this speed on the 1000 kJ of energy from a candy bar?

28. The owners of a home 8.0 m × 21 m × 5.0 m turn the thermostat down to 14°C when they go on vacation. On their return, how much heat is needed to raise the temperature of the air inside the home to 21°C? Ignore the heat needed to warm the walls and the contents of the house. The density of air is 1.3 kg/m^3. (See Table 5.1, page 181)

29. At a nuclear power plant, water at 8°C from a nearby lake is used in a heat exchanger to condense spent steam, at a temperature of 120°C, to water, at 85°C, before it is recycled to the reactor. If the cooling water returns to the lake at a temperature of 19°C, how many kilograms of water are needed per kilogram of steam? Ignore the pressure changes in the steam. (See Tables 5.4 and 5.6 on pages 195 and 201)

30. The equation for determining the power produced by a tide is $P = \frac{ADg\Delta h^2}{2\Delta t}$. Consider a tidal reservoir with a surface area of 16 km^2, a tidal height of 8.0 m, and a tidal period of 12.3 h. If energy is captured twice during the tidal period with an efficiency of 82%, calculate the average power generated.

31. Scientists often use models to solve problems. To simulate the effect of an object from space striking the Earth, marbles were dropped into large containers of sand. How does the energy of the marble affect the diameter of the crater it produced? Design and perform an experiment and use graphical analysis techniques to analyze your results.

32. Fitness machines are designed to allow people to exercise specific muscles or muscle groups. Levers and pulleys are common elements in these machines. Visit a local fitness gym and survey the machines available. Select one machine and outline the various ways that the machine can be used to exercise different muscles. In your report, include diagrams to show the pulley or lever action(s) of the machine(s).

33. Compound machines consist of two or more different machines connected together to accomplish some work. For example, a wheel and axle might be connected to a pulley system, or a lever might be connected to a wheel and axle. It is said that the efficiency of a compound machine is the product of the individual efficiencies. That means if two machines are connected together and one is 70% efficient while the other is 80% efficient, the compound machine will be 0.70 × 0.80 = 0.56 or 56% efficient. Design and perform an experiment to test the efficiency of a compound machine.

34. Use your knowledge of levers to design and build a mobile that will fit into a 1-m^3 space. The mobile should have at least four components. Include a lever diagram with calculations along with your mobile when you submit this project.

35. Design and build a model of a flat-plate collector. Investigate the factors affecting its operation. Determine how much heat energy can be collected on a hot day and how this energy can be stored and re-used.

36. People are becoming increasingly concerned about the amount of radiation they are receiving from various sources. The measurement of radiation and its effects on organisms is called "dosimetry." To measure how much biological damage is done by radiation, a quantity called the "dose equivalent" is used. Do a research report to find out how the dose equivalent is measured, how it accounts for the fact that some organs are more sensitive to certain kinds of radiation than others, and the significance of the "quality factor" in measuring the energy deposited in each kilogram of human tissue.

37. Although the joule is the SI unit for energy, a useful non-SI unit of energy is the electron-volt and its multiples, the MeV and the GeV. Write a report on the meaning and the uses of these units.

38. Research and write a report on the work being done to harness wind energy in Ontario. How many wind turbines have been built and how successful is the project?

39. In 1483, Leonardo da Vinci proposed the idea of the helicopter. The horizontal blades of the rotor provide lift, but they also provide torque. The torque of the blades rotating in one direction tends to make the body of the helicopter rotate in the other direction. Research the design of modern-day helicopters to find out how the torque on the fuselage is controlled.

40. The pedals on a bicycle act as a wheel and axle. The pedals are connected to a toothed gear wheel (called a sprocket) which by means of a chain is in turn connected to a rear axle toothed gear wheel. Using a three-, five-, or ten-speed bicycle, design and perform an experiment to find out what relationship exists between the number of teeth on the pedal sprocket, the number of teeth on the axle sprocket, the diameters of these sprockets, and the distance the bicycle will travel during ten revolutions of the pedals.

41. Research how the waste heat from nuclear power generators in Ontario is being used. Make a list of other ways it could be put to good use.

42. One of the problems with nuclear power reactors is that of disposing of the spent nuclear fuel. Research the literature to find out about the different disposal systems that exist and outline in point form the positive and negative features of each system. How does the spent fuel from CANDU reactors differ from that of other reactors?

Problem Solving

43. A car comes to a skidding stop in 5.0 m. While stopping, the road exerts a force of 600 N opposite to the motion.
a) How much work does the road do on the car?
b) How much work does the car do on the road?

44. A labourer working for a construction company does 220 J of work in lifting a 15-kg cement block at a constant speed. How high does he lift it?

45. Yelena Yelesina of Russia won the women's high jump at the 2000 Sydney Olympics with a jump of 2.01 m. If Yelena had a mass of 55 kg, and her centre of mass was 0.70 m above the ground just before the jump, what was her minimum gravitational energy increase just as she cleared the bar?

46. A snowball with a mass of 500 g has a kinetic energy of 2.5×10^2 J. How fast is the snowball moving?

47. In the absence of friction, what stationary mass can be given a speed of 40 m/s by 2.4 kJ of work?

48. The 7.26-kg men's hammer throw at the 2000 Sydney Olympics was won by Szynon Ziolkowski of Poland with a throw of 80.02 m. If the hammer reached a maximum height of 21.7 m and was travelling horizontally at a speed of 20.6 m/s at this height, calculate the work done on the hammer.

49. A technician working for a farm machinery company pushes a box of pulleys, weighing 500 N, 12 m across a floor at constant speed. How much work does he do as he moves the pulleys, if the coefficient of sliding friction is 0.38?

50. One kilogram of fat is equivalent to about 30 MJ of energy. The efficiency of converting fat to mechanical energy is about 20%.
a) Suppose you lift a mass of 12 kg 2.0 m vertically, 500 times, how much work do you do? (Assume that the work done by the mass on you is dissipated as heat to the surroundings).
b) If all the energy used to do the work comes from "burning" fat, how much fat is used up by the exercise?

51. When a 0.50-kg toy is hung from an elastic spring it stretches the spring 0.20 m.
a) How much work is done to stretch the spring 0.20 m?
b) How much elastic energy is stored in the spring at this stretch?

52. At the 2000 Sydney Olympics, Canadian high jumper Mark Boswell finished sixth with a height of 2.32 m (only 3 cm lower than the gold medal winner). What was his kinetic energy when he left the ground if his mass was 60.0 kg and he crossed the bar with a speed of 1.24 m/s?

53. A pitcher throws a fastball, off target, at a speed of 90 km/h and hits home plate. The ball, of mass 0.14 kg, is 2.2 m above the ground when it leaves the pitcher's hand.
a) What is the total gravitational and kinetic energy of the ball at the time of release?
b) What is the ball's kinetic energy when it reaches home plate?
c) How fast is the ball moving when it collides with home plate? (Assume no air resistance).

54. A 1400-kg car is accelerating up a hill. The hill is 150 m long and the total rise of the hill is 6.0 m. The car accelerates from a speed of 7.0 m/s at the bottom to 15 m/s at the top. If the average retarding force of friction is 700 N, find the change in potential energy of the car, and the change in kinetic energy of the car.

55. A single movable pulley is used to lift a 12-N load (this includes the weight of the pulley itself) with a force of 8.0 N. What is the actual mechanical advantage of this system and why is it less than 2.0?

56. The engine of a hay baler exerts an average force of 30 kN to move the baler at a constant speed of 5.4 km/h. What is the power of the engine?

57. A 90-kW motor exerts an average force of 4.0 kN to move a speedboat at constant speed through the water. How fast, in km/h, is the boat moving?

58. A swimming pool contains 24 t of water at a temperature of 15°C. What is the final temperature if 30 t of water at a temperature of 35°C are added to the pool?

59. What mass of steam is produced when 2.0 MJ of heat is supplied to 5.0 kg of water at 20°C (see Table 5.4)?

60. Assume that the average rate that solar energy falls on the roof of a house is 200 W/m^2. The roof has a useful surface area of 150 m^2. The maximum efficiency of a solar cell is 15%.
a) What is the rate in watts that solar energy strikes the roof?
b) How much electric power can be generated by solar cells on this roof?
c) If solar cells cost \$500/m^2, what will it cost to cover the roof with solar cells?

61. Figure 1 represents a human forearm balancing a weight *W*. If $W = 120$ N, what force must the biceps muscle exert to hold the weight in equilibrium?

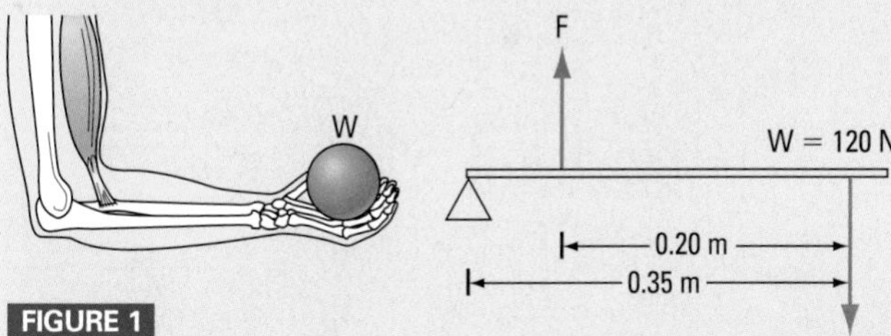

FIGURE 1

62. A man with a mass of 70 kg walks up a flight of stairs 5.0 m high in 15.0 s. What average power is he using?

63. Kanellos Kanellopoulos, a Greek cycling champion, crossed the Cretan Sea in a self-powered flying machine in 1988. The flight was 20 km long and took 3 h 55 min. If he exerted an average force of 63 N on the pedals of the flying machine, what was his average power?

64. An ice cube tray contains 1.2 kg of water at 18°C. How much heat must be removed to cool the water to 0°C and then freeze it (see Tables 5.4 and 5.6)?

65. A large wind turbine has two blades each with a diameter of 50 m. It is operating in an area where the average wind speed is 19 km/h. The density of the air is 1.32 kg/m^3.

Calculate:
a) the average wind power available from this wind turbine at this wind speed
b) the wind speed needed to double the power at a speed of 19 km/h

66. A ramp is used to load crates onto a railway car. The length of the ramp is 6.0 m. The platform of the railway car is 1.5 m above the ground. Each crate has a mass of 450 kg. A force of 2025 N applied parallel to the ramp moves the crate at constant speed up the ramp.

Calculate:
a) the useful work accomplished in moving a crate up the ramp
b) the actual work done in moving a crate up the ramp
c) the actual mechanical advantage of this machine
d) the efficiency of this inclined plane

67. The machine shown in Figure 2 consists of a pulley and a lever connected together. Two boxes of masses 10 kg and 20 kg are supported by a mass *m* suspended from the pulley. Use the information given in the figure to calculate the value of the mass *m*.

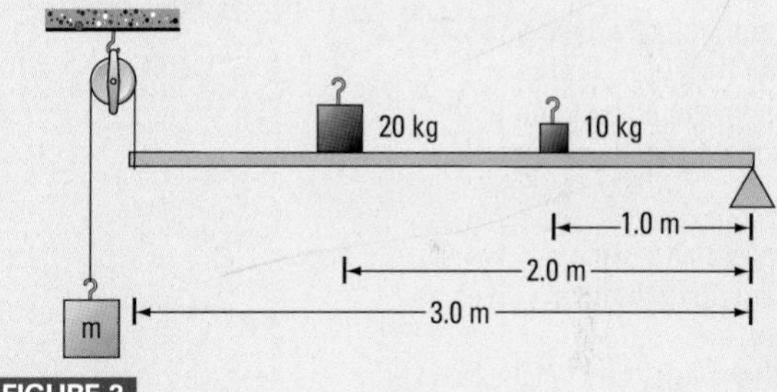

FIGURE 2

68. An aluminum calorimeter of mass 400 g contains 200 g of water at a temperature of 18°C. When a block of nickel at a temperature of 80°C is dropped into the water, the final temperature of the mixture becomes 28°C. Find the mass of the nickel assuming that there is no loss of heat to the surroundings.

69. The head of water behind a large power dam is 180 m and the average rate of flow is 6.6×10^2 m^3/s. If a hydro plant harnesses the gravitational energy in the water with an efficiency of 86%, what is the power of the hydro power plant? The density of water is 1000 kg/m^3.

UNIT

3 Waves and Sound

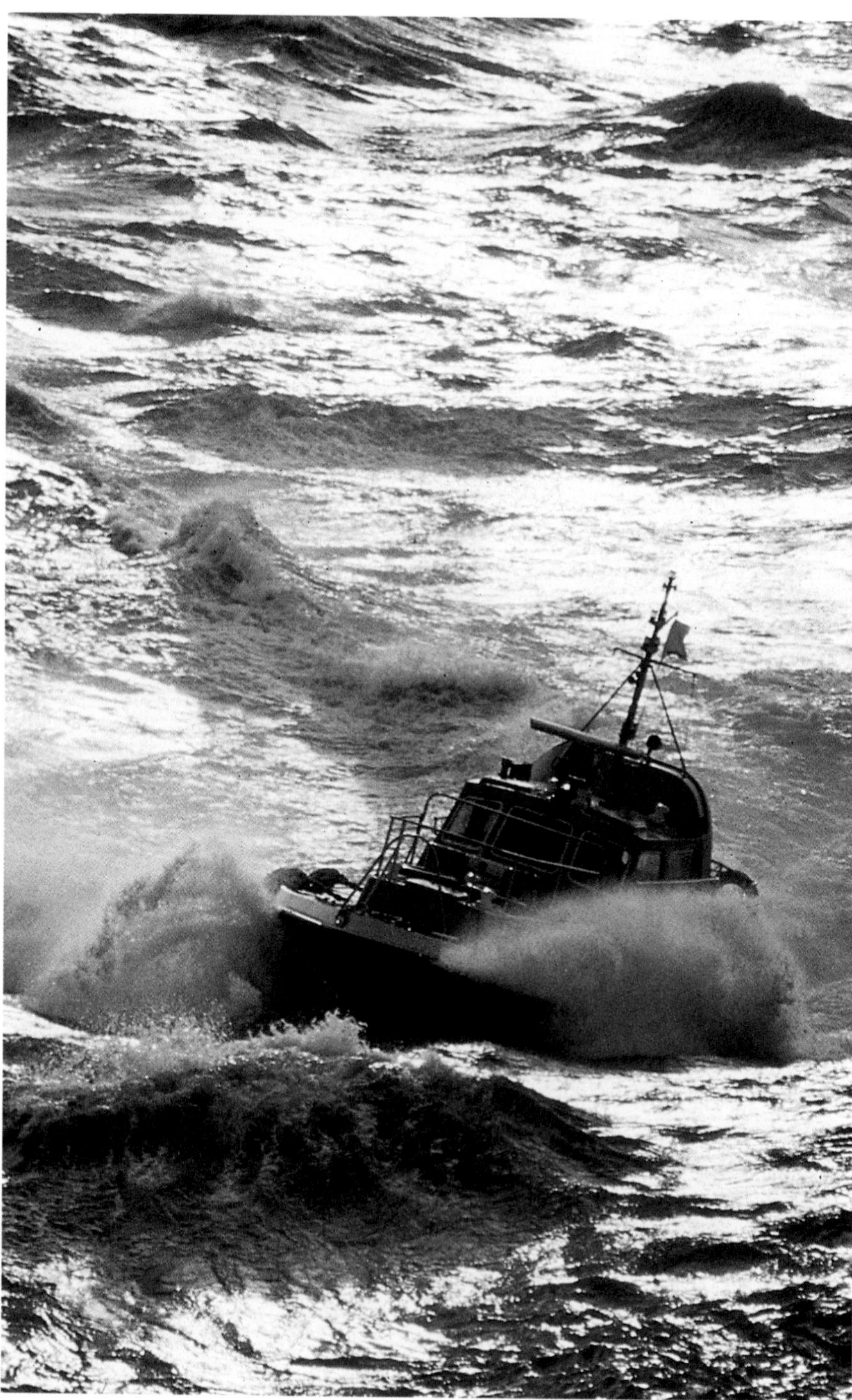

OVERALL EXPECTATIONS

By the end of this unit, you will be able to:

- demonstrate an understanding of the properties of mechanical waves and sound and the principles underlying the production, transmission, interaction, and reception of mechanical waves and sound
- investigate the properties of mechanical waves and sound through experiments or simulations, and compare predicted results with actual results
- describe and explain ways in which mechanical waves and sound are produced in nature, and evaluate the contributions to entertainment, health, and safety of technologies that make use of mechanical waves and sound

A cruise ship rolls gently in the ocean swells. Passengers talk excitedly while dancing to a band. Several sunbathers move inside as the wind picks up and clouds spread across the sky. On the bridge, officers scan the radar, alert for the presence of other ships and watching the progress of the oncoming storm. They also check their Global Positioning System (GPS) unit, which tells them exactly where they are on the surface of the ocean while sonar keeps track of the depth of water beneath the hull.

The radio crackles with an emergency call. Far to the south, a fishing boat had been riding out the storm when a towering wave, much larger than the others, smashed over the boat, causing heavy damage. It needs help right away. Fortunately, a Coast Guard ship has heard the message and is already heading toward the floundering boat.

Vibrations and waves are involved throughout this scenario—the churning of the ocean, the radio waves of the GPS, radar, and radio communications systems, the voices of the passengers, the music of the band, and the tanning of the sunbathers. Even the sudden appearance of an unusually large wave is a common wave effect. To understand much of the world around us, we need to understand waves and vibrations.

PHYSICS HEADLINES

- **Headphones Can Cause Permanent Hearing Damage**

  The *Journal of the American Medical Association* reported in 1999 that almost 15% of people aged 6 to 19 showed signs of hearing loss. Much of this is due to headphone use. Researchers pointed out that rock music at full volume is at the same decibel level as a chainsaw, or a jet plane taking off.

- **Beyond Cochlear Implants**

  A new auditory prosthesis now exists to allow hearing-impaired individuals to hear. Unlike a cochlear implant, this device has electrodes implanted directly in the brain stem. Normal speech comprehension requires four frequency channels. The device's microelectrodes penetrate and stimulate these frequency bands. Animal tests have proven that it works. Humans are next.

- **Finding Landmines with Sound**

  A Newfoundland company, Guigné International, is developing sonar technology to find landmines under water. This sonar can detect the difference between metal, glass, or plastic. Because of this, the sonar can limit false alarms, speeding up clearing operations. There are approximately 110 million landmines in 64 countries, and most of their exact locations are unknown.

ACHIEVEMENT TASK PREVIEW

Once you have completed the study of waves and sound, you will put your knowledge to use in the study of wind chimes and how they produce their musical tones. See page 322.

CHAPTER 6

Vibrations and Waves

SPECIFIC EXPECTATIONS

By the end of this chapter, you will be able to:

- define and describe the concepts and units related to mechanical waves (6.1, 6.2, 6.3, 6.4, 6.5)
- describe and illustrate the properties of transverse and longitudinal waves in different media, and analyze the velocity of waves travelling in those media in quantitative terms (6.3, 6.4, 6.5, Investigation 2)
- explain and graphically illustrate the principle of superposition, and identify examples of constructive and destructive interference (6.5)
- analyze the components of resonance and identify the conditions required for resonance to occur in vibrating objects and in various media (6.2)
- explain the Doppler effect, and predict in qualitative terms the frequency change that will occur in a variety of conditions (6.4)
- draw, measure, analyze, and interpret the properties of waves during their transmission in a medium and from one medium to another, and during their interaction with matter (6.5, Investigation 2)

When you were younger, did you ever try to see how high you could get on a swing? Do you remember pumping your legs at just the right moment to gain elevation? If you timed it just as you were beginning your downward arc, you would increase your height. But if you got the timing wrong, even slightly, you would quickly lose elevation. The swing seemed to have its own natural rhythm. If you wanted to go higher, you had to match this rhythm.

FIGURE 6.1 A construction drill creates vibrations.

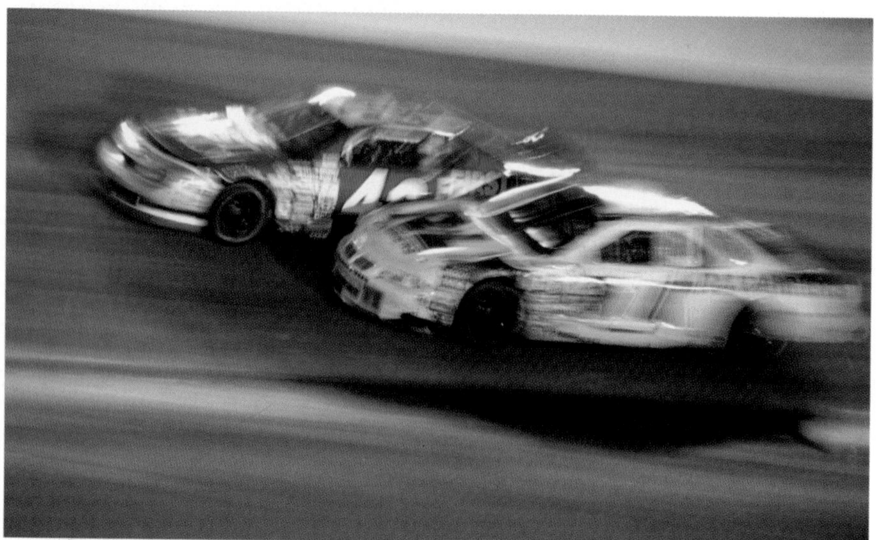

FIGURE 6.2 Waves, including sound, change as the source moves toward you or away from you.

All objects, including swings, vibrate back and forth at their own natural frequency. As you learned on the swing, it takes much less energy to make an object vibrate at its own frequency than to try to force it to vibrate at another frequency. This basic principle is extremely important when it comes to understanding how vibrating objects affect waves and how waves affect vibrating objects. It can explain that annoying rattle in a car and why certain structures collapse during an earthquake while others remain standing.

The introduction to this unit contains several examples of waves and the vibrations that make up the waves. These fundamental concepts find great use in our daily lives. The whole electromagnetic spectrum from radio waves to the energetic gamma rays consists of waves. So too does sound. A quartz watch employs a precisely vibrating crystal. Even the atoms in the book you are reading right now are undergoing different types of vibrations. The study of vibrations and waves is basic, not only to physics, but to all sciences.

Discovering Physics

Interacting Pendulums

If a swinging pendulum hangs from a horizontal string, it will cause the string to vibrate along with it. Find out whether these vibrations can be used to make a second pendulum begin to vibrate. You will need: 2 ring stands, 2 iron rings, string (1 50-cm piece and 2 20-cm pieces), 4 clips, and 2 rubber stoppers.

1. Use Figure 6.3 as a guide to set up your materials.
2. Attach an iron ring near the top of each of two ring stands.
3. Connect a 50-cm long string between the iron rings and move the stands apart until the horizontal string is taut.
4. Attach a clip to one end of a 20-cm string and hang it from the horizontal string. Push the base of a second clip into one of the rubber stoppers. Use this clip to attach the stopper to the hanging string. The stopper is now the bob on a pendulum.
5. Make a second pendulum with the remaining string, clips, and stopper. You can change the length of the pendulum by attaching the stopper at different points on the short string. Hang the second pendulum beside the first one.
6. Experiment with the set up until one pendulum is able to set the other one vibrating. Then answer the following questions.

- Can vibrations from one pendulum make another pendulum vibrate? Use your observations to explain your answer.
- Under what conditions can one pendulum set another vibrating consistently? Explain why these conditions are necessary?

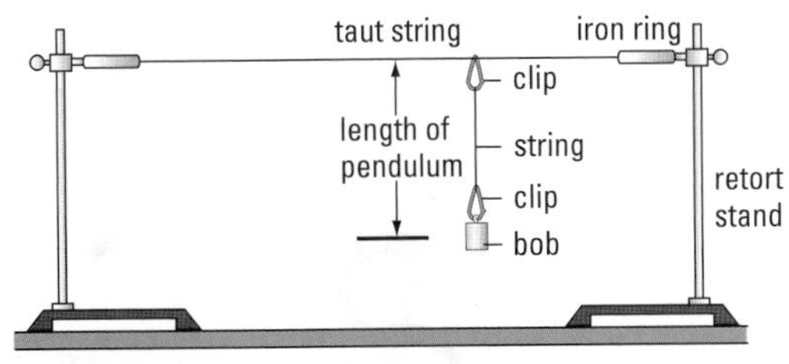

FIGURE 6.3 A pendulum set-up

CHECKPOINT

Tidal waves (tsunami) are caused by

a) storms over the ocean
b) Earth movements under the ocean
c) the moon's gravitational field only
d) the sun's gravitational field only
e) gravitational fields of both the moon and sun

6.1 Characteristics of Vibrations

Key Understandings

When you have completed this section, you will be able to:

- define cycle, period, frequency, amplitude, and phase as related to vibrations
- describe the relationships among cycle, period, and frequency
- distinguish between vibrations that are in the same phase and vibrations that are in opposite phase

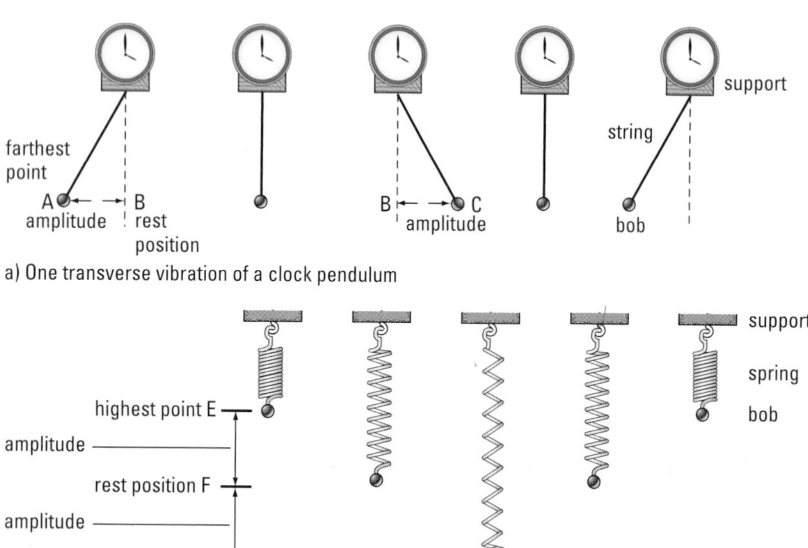

FIGURE 6.4 Examples of vibrations or cycles

A hawk beats its wings at a constant rate. A yo-yo rises and falls steadily. If these patterns repeat themselves at regular intervals, they are called **periodic motion**. The repeated pattern is called a **cycle** or a **vibration**. How can one describe this motion? What terms can one use to indicate the difference between the leisurely beat of a hawk's wings and the blur of a hummingbird's wings?

If a pendulum is allowed to vibrate freely, this motion will be repeated at regular intervals. One complete cycle of a clock pendulum is shown in Figure 6.4a). Figure 6.4b) shows a bob attached to a vibrating spring as it completes one cycle.

Two different types of vibrations are shown in Figure 6.4. A vibration is called **transverse** if the motion of the vibrating object is perpendicular to its length (Figure 6.4a)). In a **longitudinal** vibration (Figure 6.4b)), the motion of the object is parallel to its length. A swing undergoes transverse vibrations and the cable of a bungee-jumper undergoes longitudinal vibrations.

Investigation
Refer to page 258, Investigation 1

One important property of a cycle is called amplitude. **Amplitude** is the maximum distance of the vibrating object from its **rest position** or **equilibrium position**. In Figure 6.4a), the rest position is B, so the amplitude is the horizontal distance between B and A or between B and C. In Figure 6.4b), the rest position is F, so the amplitude is the vertical distance between F and E or between F and G.

The time required to complete one cycle is called the **period** and is given the symbol T. Remember that T refers to the time for one cycle, while Δt represents any time interval. If 10 cycles were completed in 40 s, the time for each cycle would be $\frac{40\text{ s}}{10}$ or 4.0 s. In general, period can be calculated as

$$T = \frac{\Delta t}{N}$$

where T = period, Δt = time interval, and N = number of cycles.

Frequency f indicates the number of cycles that occur in a unit of time. If a sparrow flaps its wings 15 times in 3.0 s, then its wings are beating at the rate of 15 cycles/3.0 s or 5.0 cycles each second. This example indicates that frequency can be calculated using the equation

$$f = \frac{N}{\Delta t}$$

To measure the frequency of a golf club, it is simply clamped to a work bench and "twanged" so that it vibrates. The frequency is then measured. For the highly skilled golfer, manufacturers offer "frequency-matched" clubs. The idea is that shorter clubs vibrate with a higher frequency. When the difference between, say, a two-iron and a three-iron is the same as the difference in frequency between a three-iron and a four-iron, the irons are frequency matched. To a professional golfer, having frequency-matched clubs can mean the difference between a near-perfect shot and a perfect one.

The basic unit for frequency is simply $\frac{1}{s}$ or s^{-1}. This unit is usually written as the **hertz** (Hz) in honour of Heinrich Hertz, a pioneer in the development of the radio. Thus, 1 Hz = 1 s^{-1}. By comparing the formulas for frequency and period, you can see that frequency and period are reciprocals. This means that

$$f = \frac{1}{T} \text{ and } T = \frac{1}{f}$$

Another way to write this is $f \times T = 1$

INFOBIT

Cycles do not have to be measured in terms of seconds. It is more useful in some situations to talk of the number of cycles in one day, month, or year. For example, the lunar period (time for the moon to complete one orbit around Earth) is usually given as 27.32 d instead of 2.370×10^7 s. The orbital period of the space shuttle is about 90 min, while that of Pluto is 248 a.

EXAMPLE 1 NUMERICAL

If an electron vibrates back and forth in an electric wire with a frequency of 60 Hz, how many cycles will it make in 1.0 h?

Given

$f = 60$ Hz

$\Delta t = 1.0$ h or 3600 s

Required

N

Analysis

Use $f = \frac{N}{\Delta t}$ therefore $N = f \times \Delta t$

Solution

$$\begin{aligned} N &= f \times \Delta t \\ &= 60\ s^{-1} \times 3600\ s \\ &= 216\ 000 \\ &= 2.2 \times 10^5 \end{aligned}$$

Statement

The electron will undergo 2.2×10^5 cycles.

INSIGHT

Note that the frequency is given as 60 Hz or 60 s^{-1}. As a result, the time must be converted to seconds.

PRACTICE PROBLEMS

1. The period of the signal wave from station CSCI is 2.00×10^{-6} s. What is the frequency of that station?
2. In some regions, the frequency of the alternating current is 50 Hz. How long does it take the electrons in that alternating current to complete 10 cycles?

When objects are allowed to vibrate freely, they will generally do so at a specific frequency called the **natural frequency**. It is determined by the physical properties of the object. For example, the frequency of a playground swing depends only on its length.

It is often useful to compare different vibrations. An examination of frequency (or period) and amplitude will provide most of the information. However, two vibrating objects can have identical amplitudes and frequencies, and yet be different because they are never at the same point in their cycles at the same time. The term **phase** is used to describe this property.

Pendulums are in the **same phase** if they always are either at rest or moving in the same direction at the same time. Pendulums are in **opposite phase** if they are always moving in opposite directions at the same time or at rest and tending to move in opposite directions. Pendulums are said to be **out of phase** for any conditions between these two extremes. Figure 6.5 shows the phase relationships between two vibrating pendulums.

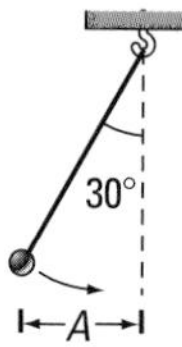

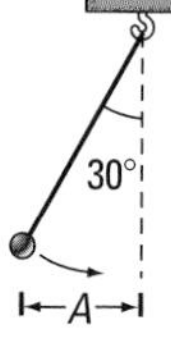

a) Pendulums in phase

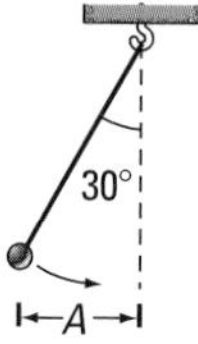

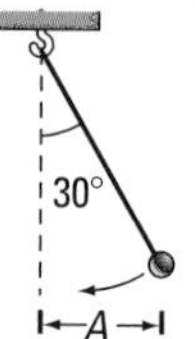

b) Pendulums in opposite phase

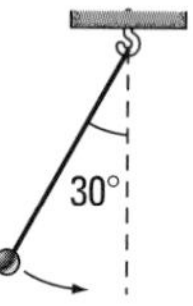

c) Pendulums out of phase

FIGURE 6.5 Phase relationships between vibrating pendulums

Section 6.1 Review

Understanding Concepts

1. Describe two examples of transverse vibrations not mentioned in the text.
2. Describe two examples of longitudinal vibrations not mentioned in the text.
3. If the bob shown in Figure 6.5b) has an amplitude of 4.0 cm, how far does it travel during 6.0 cycles?
4. A hawk flaps its wings 10 times in 15 s. Calculate
   a) the period of the wing beat
   b) the frequency of the wing beat
5. The electrons in an alternating current vibrate with a frequency of 60 Hz.
   a) What is the period of that vibration?
   b) How many times do these electrons reverse their direction each second?

Applying Inquiry/ Communication Skills

6. A rotating fan with two oppositely mounted blades, one of which is marked, is illuminated by a flashing strobe light. When the light flashes at 10 Hz, the fan appears to be stopped. When the light flashes at 20 Hz, the fan also appears to be stopped. At 40 Hz, it appears stopped, but with two marked blades.
   a) Explain why the fan might appear to have two marked blades.
   b) What is the rotation rate of the fan? Explain your reasoning.
7. The word *transverse* comes from the Latin word, *trans*, which means "across." Give three more examples of words which also use "trans" in this way.

WEBLINK

To view an animation of a transverse pendulum and a longitudinal pendulum, go to **www.pearsoned.ca/physics11.**

6.2 Mechanical Resonance

FIGURE 6.6 A tuba player

Key Understandings

When you have completed this section, you will be able to:

- define resonance
- describe mechanical resonance and state common examples of resonance
- analyze the components of resonance
- identify the conditions required for resonance to occur in vibrating elastic bands

In the opening activity for this chapter, you attempted to use one vibrating pendulum to start another pendulum swinging. If you succeeded, you saw resonance in action. Examples of this effect are all around us. Vibrations in radio waves cause electrons in an antenna to vibrate, resulting in radio reception. The vibrating lips of a tuba player force the air inside the instrument to vibrate at the same frequency (Figure 6.6). This creates the notes that you hear. What conditions must be present for this effect to occur?

Anyone who has pushed a child on a swing realizes that it does not take a large force to set the child swinging with a large amplitude (Figure 6.7). Indeed, a series of small pushes works quite well, provided the pushes come at exactly the right time. If you are pushing from behind, the push must occur just as the child is beginning to swing forward. Thus, the frequency of the pushes must match the natural frequency of the swing. This is the basic idea behind resonance.

FIGURE 6.7 A child being pushed on a swing

Imagine that you have two weighted springs at rest and hanging side-by-side from the same support. They have the same natural frequency and are connected. If one of them begins to vibrate, it can exert periodic forces on

Discovering Physics *Mechanical Resonance*

Discover how changing the frequency affects mehanical resonance. Attach long elastic bands to each end of a one-hole rubber stopper. Attach one end to a rigid support such as a water tap and hold the other end in your hand as shown in Figure 6.8. Give the elastic bands some stretch. Apply a periodic force back and forth along the axis of the system by vibrating your arm. Gradually increase the frequency, keeping the amplitude the same, until mechanical resonance occurs. Increase the frequency.

- What do you see when mechanical resonance occurs?
- Where is the energy that the system picks up coming from?
- What happened as you changed the frequency above and below the resonant frequency?

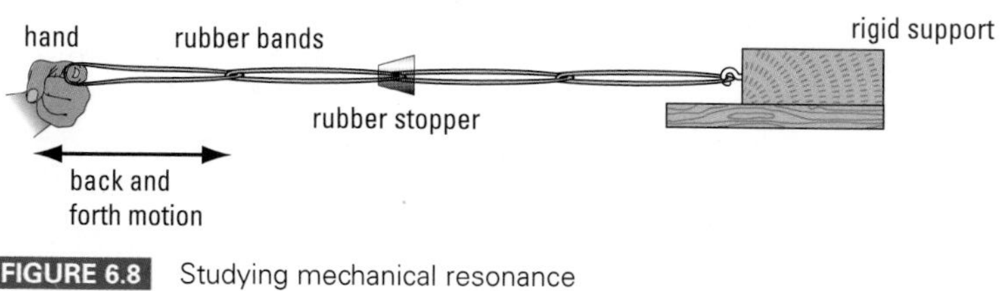

FIGURE 6.8 Studying mechanical resonance

the other. This is similar to the pushes given to the child on the swing. These forces will occur at just the right frequency to start the second spring vibrating with increasing amplitude. This transfer of the energy of vibration from one object to a second object having the same natural frequency is called **resonance**. When the resonance involves mechanical systems such as pendulums and springs, it is known as **mechanical resonance**.

Components of Resonance

Resonance is a common effect. If a glass ornament on the top of a piano buzzes whenever a certain note is played, resonance is involved. The note has the same frequency as the natural frequency of the ornament. As a result, the ornament begins to vibrate when the note is struck. The annoying rattle heard whenever a car reaches a certain speed is the result of resonance between the engine and the vibrating part.

FIGURE 6.9 Tacoma Narrows bridge collapse

Engineers have come to realize that resonance can be quite destructive. A famous case of this occurred in the suspension bridge over the Tacoma Narrows in the State of Washington (Figure 6.9). On November 7, 1940, the bridge began an hour-long wild vibration due to resonance triggered by the wind. The speed of the wind was not that great—only about 60 km/h. However, the bridge eventually tore itself apart and much of the centre span tumbled into the river.

In June 2000, a new pedestrian bridge in London, England, was shut down for modification because it was resonating with the walking frequency of the pedestrians.

It is now common for wind tunnel studies to be done on scale models of large structures or even bicycles (Figure 6.10). Tests are done to determine how the structure will behave in winds, or will affect the surrounding wind patterns. Computer simulations are also used in these predictions.

FIGURE 6.10 Testing a bicycle for wind resistance in a tunnel

At the heart of a quartz watch is a tiny quartz crystal, less than a millimetre in size. To provide the necessary precision, the crystal is cut by means of a laser until its natural frequency matches the required frequency of 32 768 Hz (or 2^{15} Hz). When the watch is operating, an electric circuit forces the crystal to resonate at its natural frequency. Computer chips then reduce the frequency by dividing repeatedly by two until the pulses are correct for driving the hour and minute displays.

Section 6.2 Review

Understanding Concepts

1. Express in your own words what resonance means.
2. When crossing a bridge, a troop of soldiers is ordered to march out of step. Why?
3. Explain why it could be dangerous for spectators in bleachers to stamp their feet in unison (all at the same time).
4. A cup of water was placed on top of a washing machine. When the machine was running, circular ripples appeared on the surface of the water. Explain this effect.
5. Describe one example of resonance not already mentioned in this section.

Applying Inquiry/ Communication Skills

6. Sometimes a moving school bus is seen rocking from side to side.
   a) What is likely happening?
   b) Should the rocking be allowed to continue? Give reasons for your answer.

WEBLINK

There is still much discussion about what happened during the collapse of the bridge over the Tacoma Narrows. Find out more about this amazing event, and explore the possibilities that it could happen elsewhere. Write a one-page newspaper story about the event and its probable causes. Begin your research at **www.pearsoned.ca/physics11.**

6.3 Transverse and Longitudinal Waves

Key Understandings

When you have completed this section, you will be able to:

- define longitudinal wave, transverse wave, and wavelength
- distinguish between transverse and longitudinal waves using labelled diagrams
- describe and illustrate the properties of transverse and longitudinal waves in water, in an elastic spring, and on the surface of Earth

Imagine that you are standing beside a swimming pool. The water is calm. Suddenly a diver slashes through the surface of the water (Figure 6.11). Ripples move out from that point and a nearby buoy, which had been motionless, begins to bob up and down. By what means is the energy transmitted to the buoy? Does water actually move over and move it aside?

Obviously the buoy gained energy, which came from the diver by means of the ripples or waves. A **wave** is a disturbance that transfers energy through a **medium** by means of a series of vibrations. Energy is transmitted by means of a wave, but the medium through which the wave is travelling does not move along with the wave.

John Milne, who invented an accurate seismograph while working as a professor of geology and mining in Tokyo between 1875 and 1895, discovered that earthquake shocks actually consisted of waves. Earthquakes occur when Earth's crust, under intense local stress, snaps. The elastic rock then propagates the waves outward from the epicentre.

FIGURE 6.11 A diver smoothly entering water

Throughout history, cities have been wrecked, landscapes have been reshaped, and *tidal waves* or *tsunamis* have flooded coastlines. And throughout history people have tried to understand earthquakes. It is profoundly disturbing to know that the usually solid ground could writhe and twist, and to have no idea as to when or where this would next occur. Seismology, the study of earthquakes, is a relatively new science. Today we have a great deal of accurate knowledge about earthquakes. We can hope that this knowledge will be used to forecast earthquakes accurately and to design structures that can better withstand these violent events.

The Richter Scale

In 1935, Dr. Charles Richter devised a scale to register the intensity of an earthquake. The present version, although slightly modified in 1977, still bears his name. The scale is constructed so that each increase of one unit in the scale indicates a ten-fold increase in the intensity of the earthquake. Although there is no theoretical upper limit to the scale, it is expected that no earthquake will exceed 10 on the Richter scale.

FIGURE 6.12 Dr. Charles Richter

Transverse Waves

A **transverse wave** is one in which the medium vibrates at right angles to the direction of travel of the wave. One example is provided by the waves that travel along the surface of water. A transverse wave along a rope is illustrated in Figure 6.13. The source of this wave is a hand.

Figure 6.13c) shows the rope when the source has completed one-quarter of a cycle. In Figure 6.13e), the source has completed exactly one-half of a cycle. By Figure 6.13i), the source has completed exactly one cycle. Notice the shape of the wave after one complete cycle. If you look closely at Figure 6.13, you will see that if the hand only goes through one cycle, then each point along the rope will also complete only one cycle as the wave travels down the medium. Consequently, the frequency of the source matches the frequency of the wave.

Figure 6.13 also shows that points such as A and B are vibrating in phase with each other. The distance between adjacent points, which are vibrating in phase with each other, is called the **wavelength** and is symbolized by the Greek letter lambda (λ).

If one could freeze a transverse wave in time, it would appear as shown in Figure 6.14a).

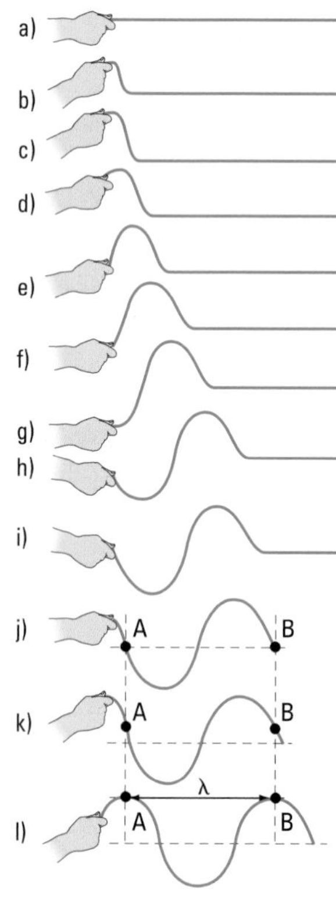

FIGURE 6.13 A transverse wave along a rope

WEBLINK

From time to time we hear of earthquakes measuring between six and seven on the Richter scale. What does this mean? How dangerous was the earthquake? Prepare a table showing the Richter scale and the likely outcomes at each level. Begin your research at **www.pearsoned.ca/physics11.**

Investigation
Refer to page 259, Investigation 2

Each of the points along the wave is vibrating up and down, but not moving along the axis at all. As a result of these vibrations, the wave consists of regions that are above and others that are below the equilibrium or rest position. Regions above the rest position are called **crests** while those below are called **troughs**. An easy way to identify one wavelength in a transverse wave is to realize that one wavelength contains one complete crest plus one complete trough.

Since a wave actually consists of vibrating particles, the amplitude of a wave has the same meaning as it does for simple vibrations. The amplitude of a transverse wave is therefore the perpendicular distance from the rest position to the top of a crest, or to the bottom of a trough. We will use A to represent amplitude. Wavelength and amplitude are indicated in Figure 6.14.

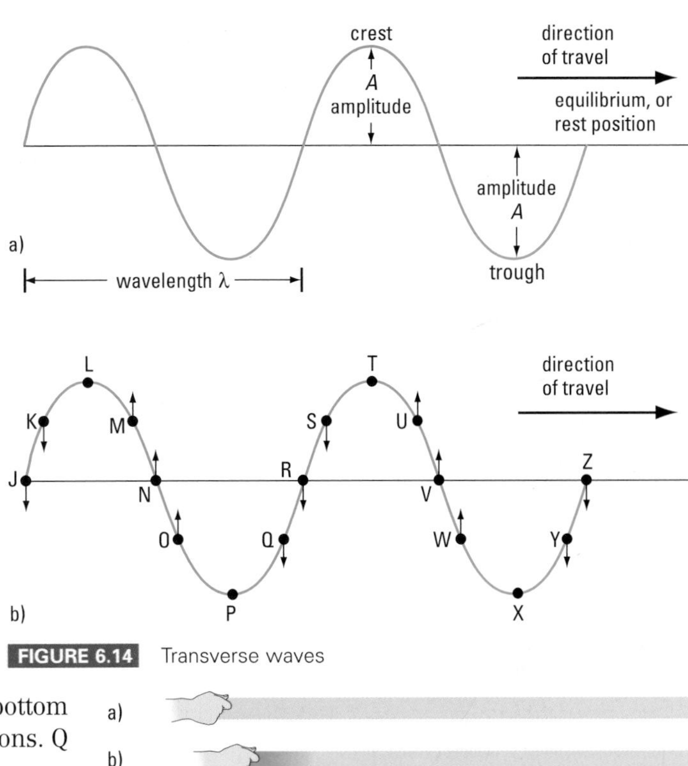

FIGURE 6.14 Transverse waves

The crests of the wave in Figure 6.14b) will soon be moving through points M and U. As a result, M and U must be rising at this instant. Likewise, points such as Q and Y will soon form the bottom of a trough as the wave passes through their locations. Q and Y must be moving downward at this instant.

It is apparent, then, that any point on the leading side of a crest moves upward, while any point on the trailing side of a crest moves downward. But what about points that are located at the top of a crest or at the bottom of a trough? Point T had been rising while the crest moved to the right. However, as the top of the crest passes by, the point will begin to drop. At the top of the crest then, point T is neither moving upward nor downward. It is motionless for an instant. Similarly, a point at the bottom of a trough, such as X, is motionless for a brief instant of time.

Longitudinal Waves

In the case of a **longitudinal wave**, the particles of the medium vibrate back and forth parallel to the direction in which the wave is travelling. Figure 6.15 portrays a longitudinal wave. In this diagram, the vertical lines represent the coils in a long coil spring. As before, the source of the wave is a hand. Figure 6.15c) shows the positions of points in the medium after the source of the wave has completed one-quarter of a cycle. In Figure 6.15e) you see the position of the points on the spring after the source has completed one-half of a cycle.

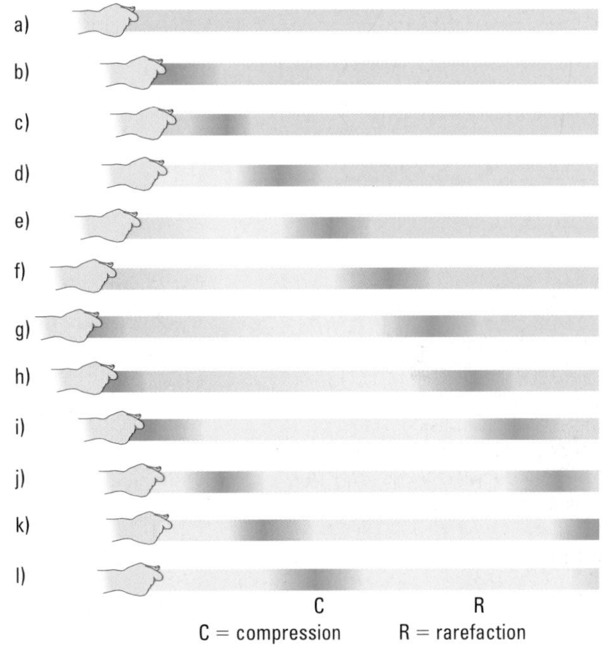

FIGURE 6.15 The propagation of a longitudinal wave

Because the coils are vibrating parallel to the direction of travel, from time to time they move closer to each other than normal. This creates a region called a **compression** (C) shown in Figure 6.16. At other times they move farther from each other, forming a **rarefaction** (R). Figure 6.16 shows compressions and rarefactions labelled on a frozen view of a longitudinal wave.

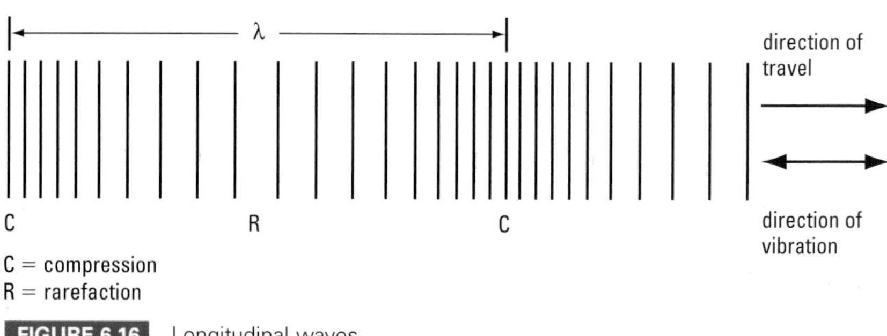

FIGURE 6.16 Longitudinal waves

INFOBIT

Waves that travel across the surface of water are not perfectly transverse. If you watch a floating duck as a crest passes by, you will see it move forward a bit at the top of the crest and backward a bit at the bottom of the trough. However, at the end of one cycle, the duck is back where it started. The molecules of water are vibrating horizontally as well as vertically. In other words, the molecules are undergoing both transverse and longitudinal vibrations at the same time. If the amplitudes of both vibrations are equal, then the molecule goes around in a circle (Figure 6.17).

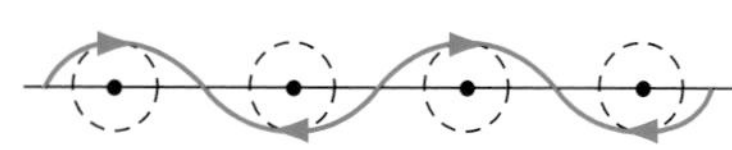

FIGURE 6.17 Circular motion in a water wave

You will notice that the amplitude of the longitudinal wave has not been marked. Although you can deduce the amplitude from this diagram, it is not a measurement that can be easily indicated since the rest position is difficult to label on the diagram.

One event that consists of both longitudinal and transverse waves is an earthquake. The destruction at the surface is caused mainly by transverse waves which travel along the surface, vibrating up and down as well as sideways, parallel to the surface. Fortunately, these waves do not travel far from the epicentre.

Other less destructive waves travel below Earth's surface. They consist of two types called primary (P) waves and secondary (S) waves. The P waves are longitudinal and travel at about 8 km/s. The S waves are transverse and travel slower, at about 4.5 km/s.

WEBLINK

To view the motion of particles in a transverse wave and a longitudinal wave, look at **www.pearsoned.ca/physics11.** Draw a series of diagrams to illustrate part of the animations.

Section 6.3 Review

Understanding Concepts

1. State the essential difference between a transverse wave and a longitudinal wave.
2. In Figure 6-14b), identify a point which is vibrating
   a) in phase with point K
   b) in phase with point N
   c) in opposite phase to point W
   d) out of phase with point T
3. A transverse water wave has a wavelength of 16 m and an amplitude of 3.0 m. If a duck is floating at the top of one crest while a swan is floating at the bottom of the adjacent trough, what is the straight-line distance between them?

Making Connections

4. Wave height on the seas is defined as the difference in height between the bottom of a trough and the top of a crest.
   a) If the wave height on a particular day is 12 m, what is the amplitude of the wave?
   b) Wave height may sometimes be a dangerous factor to boats on lakes or seas. Predict which other properties of waves may pose potential risk to boats.

6.4 The Speed of Waves

Key Understandings

When you have completed this section, you will be able to:

- describe the relationship among velocity, frequency, and wavelength
- analyze the velocity of waves in quantitative terms
- explain the Doppler effect
- predict in qualitative terms the frequency change that will occur in water as a result of the Doppler effect

Knowledge of the speed of waves is extremely important, especially to countries with coasts on the Pacific Ocean. Underwater earthquakes may trigger a colossal wave known as a tsunami. Such a wave can speed across the ocean at over 100 m/s. Ships may not notice its passage since the amplitude is slight in deep water. But by the time it smashes into shallow coastal waters, the wave can be as high as a four-storey building. What factors affect the speed of such a wave? How can seismic observatories predict the time to impact?

FIGURE 6.18 Tsunami smashing into a coast

INFOBIT

The damage caused by a tsunami occurs when the huge crest breaks over the coast. Since a lot of water must be pulled up to form that crest, it is often preceded by a deep trough. If you happen to be on shore and notice that the level of the ocean suddenly goes down, you had better get inland as fast as you can. The trough that you are observing will be followed by a massive crest. Many people have perished by going down to the harbour to watch the strange behaviour of the sea as its level drops rapidly.

The Universal Wave Equation

Speed is defined in terms of distance and time. It would be reasonable that wavelength (a distance) and period (a time) would be involved in the speed of a wave. By referring to the formation of a transverse wave as shown in Figure 6.19, you will see that while the leading edge of the wave has moved one wavelength, the hand creating the wave has completed one cycle.

The wave has travelled a distance of one wavelength (λ) in a time equal to the period of vibration (T). Speed is equal to distance travelled divided by the time taken. This can be written as

$$v = \frac{\Delta d}{\Delta t}$$

Substituting the wavelength (λ) for Δd and the period (T) for Δt gives

$$v = \frac{\lambda}{T}$$

One can use this formula to determine the speed of a wave. Alternatively, one can use the frequency of a wave rather than its period. To determine an equation in terms of the frequency f, use the fact that

$$f = \frac{1}{T}$$

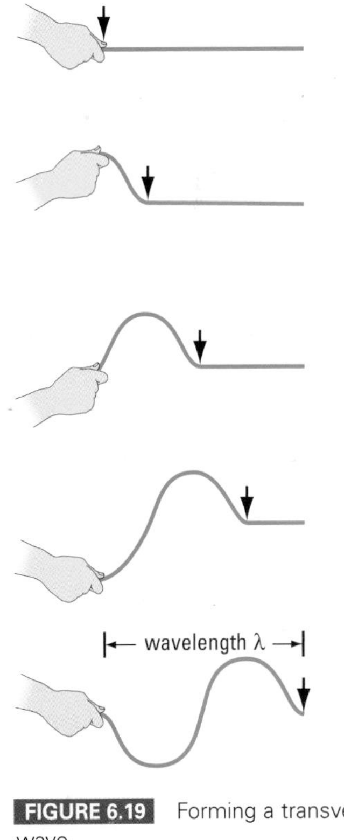

FIGURE 6.19 Forming a transverse wave

Beginning with

$$v = \frac{\lambda}{T}$$

one can rewrite it as

$$v = \frac{1}{T} \times \lambda$$

Substituting f for $\frac{1}{T}$ the resulting equation becomes:

$$v = f\lambda$$

In general, the speed of a wave is given by multiplying its frequency by its wavelength. This equation is known as the **universal wave equation**. It is universal in that it applies to all types of waves—from water waves to seismic waves, and from radio waves to gamma rays.

WEBLINK

The threat of a tsunami is frightening. They have ravaged coastal regions and killed thousands. Write a newspaper-style account of the history of tsunamis. Begin your research at **www.pearsoned.ca/physics11.**

EXAMPLE 2 NUMERICAL

A longitudinal wave with a frequency of 2000 Hz and a wavelength of 3.00 m travels along a steel rail. How long will it take the wave to travel 100 km?

Given

$f = 2000\text{ Hz}$

$\lambda = 3.00\text{ m}$

$\Delta d = 100\text{ km}$

$= 1.00 \times 10^5\text{ m}$

Required

Δt

Analysis

- To calculate the time required to travel a distance, you need to know the speed.
- The speed of a wave can be found from $v = f\lambda$
- Then use $\Delta t = \frac{\Delta d}{v}$

Solution

$$v = f\lambda$$
$$= 2000\text{ Hz} \times 3.00\text{ m}$$
$$= 6.00 \times 10^3\text{ m/s}$$

$$\Delta t = \frac{\Delta d}{v}$$
$$= \frac{1.0 \times 10^5\text{ m}}{6.00 \times 10^3\text{ m/s}}$$
$$= 16.7\text{ s}$$

Statement

The time taken for the wave to travel 100 km would be 16.7 s.

INSIGHT

It is important to make sure that the units agree with each other. In this case, the wavelength is given in metres but the overall distance is in kilometres. The kilometres should be converted to metres.

PRACTICE PROBLEMS

1. A tsunami covers a distance of 500 km in 83.3 min. If the period of vibration of the molecules in the wave is 35.0 min, what is the wavelength of the wave?
2. As red light passes through a glass block, the frequency of the light wave is 4.6×10^{14} Hz and its wavelength is 4.3×10^{-7} m. If the light takes 4.0×10^{-10} s to cross the block, how thick is the block?

Discovering Physics — Water Waves From a Moving Source

If a source of waves is moving, how will that affect the wave pattern? To find out add water to a transparent glass pie plate to a depth of about one centimetre. Place the plate on the stage of a level overhead projector and turn it on. Dip the blunt end of a pencil at regular time intervals into the water at the centre of the dish. Observe and sketch the resulting pattern of ripples. Let the ripples die away. Now begin again to dip the pencil at regular time intervals, but this time gradually dip the pencil farther away from the centre. Observe and sketch the ripple pattern.

- What happens to the wavelength of the waves in front of and behind the moving pencil? Are they the same or different? Can you explain why?

The Doppler Effect

Up until now, waves have been described as coming from sources that were vibrating at a single location. But what would happen if the source moved through the medium at the same time as it was generating waves? The result should look much like Figure 6.20.

In Figure 6.21a), the source has just produced a crest which will spread out in all directions from point A. The next diagram shows that the first crest has moved outward while the source moved to the right. Point B is located where the source has gone through one cycle and is ready to give off a second crest.

One cycle later the source is at point C (Figure 6.21c)) and is just producing the third crest.

Since the distance between adjacent crests equals the wavelength, you can see that the wavelength in front of the moving source is shorter than the wavelength behind the moving source. This effect known as the Doppler effect can easily be shown in water waves as in Figure 6.20b).

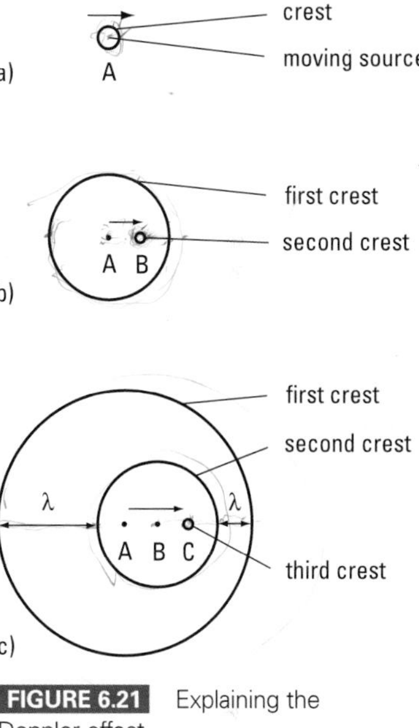

FIGURE 6.21 Explaining the Doppler effect

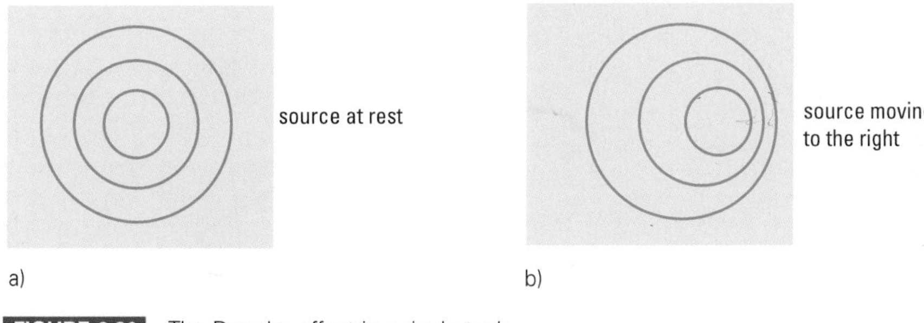

FIGURE 6.20 The Doppler effect in a ripple tank

The universal wave equation may be rearranged as:

$$f = \frac{v}{\lambda}$$

Since the speed of the waves is constant, the equation indicates that

- as the wavelength decreases, the frequency increases, and
- as the wavelength increases, the frequency decreases.

FIGURE 6.22 Police radar

As a result, the waves in front of the moving source have a higher frequency and shorter wavelength than if the source were at rest. The waves behind the moving source have a lower frequency and longer wavelength than if the source were at rest. This is the essence of the **Doppler effect**.

The Doppler effect is often used to determine the speed of an object. In many police speed traps (Figure 6.22), radio waves are aimed at a car. The moving car then acts as a source of the reflected waves. By comparing the frequency of the original wave with that of the reflected wave, the speed of the car can be determined.

Hubble's Major Discoveries

While working at the Mount Wilson Observatory, Edwin Hubble made two astounding discoveries. The first, announced in 1924, was that many of the clouds of stars that had been thought to be in our own Milky Way galaxy, were really several hundred thousand light years farther away. They were, in fact, other galaxies. The second discovery, made in 1927, was that most galaxies are moving away from us. Hubble found this out by looking at the wavelengths of light coming from the stars in those galaxies. In almost all cases, the wavelengths had been lengthened by means of the Doppler effect.

FIGURE 6.23 Edwin Hubble

WEBLINK

The Doppler effect can be easily heard any time a car or truck speeds past you. To view a simulation of this wave effect, Look at **www.pearsoned.ca/physics11.** Draw a diagram to summarize how wavelength and frequency are involved in the Doppler effect.

FIGURE 6.24 Tornado

The latest weather radar uses the Doppler effect to measure the wind velocities during storms. Radio waves reflected from raindrops that are moving toward the radar weather station will have their frequencies increased. The waves reflected from drops that are moving away from the station will have their frequencies decreased. In either case, the amount of the change in frequency depends on the horizontal speed of the drops, which in turn depends on the speed of the winds. Whenever the meteorologists see a reversal of wind direction over a short distance, that indicates a whirling pattern, which could become a tornado.

Section 6.4 Review

Understanding Concepts

1. Calculate the speed of a wave that has a wavelength of 34 m and a frequency of 2.5 Hz.
2. A light wave has a frequency of 5.0×10^{14} Hz and a speed of 3.00×10^{8} m/s. Calculate its wavelength.
3. A tsunami travels with a speed of 150 m/s and a wavelength of 300 km. Determine the frequency and period of that wave.
4. An earthquake wave travels at 4.0 km/s. If its wavelength is 500 m, what is its frequency?
5. A longitudinal wave in iron has a frequency of 10.0 kHz and a wavelength of 50.0 cm. How long will it take that wave to travel 15.0 m?
6. When radar (radio) waves were reflected from a cloud of insects, the reflected waves had a lower frequency than the original waves. What can you conclude about the motion of the insects from that information?
7. The human eye is most sensitive to yellow-green light with a frequency of 5.5×10^{14} Hz.
   a) What is the corresponding wavelength of this light inside the eye if the speed of light inside the eye (in the vitreous humour) is 2.3×10^{8} m/s?
   b) If the cells in the retina are about 20 μm across, how many times larger are they than the wavelength of the light?

Applying Inquiry/ Communication Skills

8. Design an experiment to show that when sound reflects, it makes equal angles of incidence and reflection.

Making Connections

9. Radar has changed from a secret invention, which was very important to the outcome of World War II, to one of the most widely used technologies saving lives every day.
   a) How many different applications can you identify?
   b) Though radar has the potential to virtually eliminate speeding on major highways, its use is very unpopular. What kind of evidence should be found and publicized to educate the public on this issue?

WEBLINK

Radar and laser pointers are among the most recent weapons in the war on speeding. How do they work? How accurate are they. Use a Venn diagram to compare and contrast the two common methods of measurement: the Doppler frequency shift and pulse timing. Begin your research at **www.pearsoned.ca/physics11.**

WEBLINK

Tornados are a source of both terror and fascination for many people. Find out more about tornados, see photos of them, and learn how we predict their possible arrival. Write a report in the form of questions and answers as if you were interviewing a tornado expert. Begin your research at **www.pearsoned.ca/physics11.**

6.5 Wave Behaviour

Key Understandings

When you have completed this section, you will be able to:

- define superposition, and constructive and destructive interference
- describe and illustrate the properties of transverse waves in water and in a spring
- analyze the velocity of waves in quantitative terms
- explain and graphically illustrate the principle of superposition
- identify examples of constructive and destructive interference
- draw, measure, analyze, and interpret the diffraction and interference of waves during their transmission in a medium and during their interaction with matter
- draw, measure, analyze, and interpret the refraction of waves during their transmission from one medium to another

Ships sometimes suffer major damage when struck by a rogue wave that towers over the other waves. Why should such a wave occur? Can regions in our seas and oceans be identified where these waves are most likely to occur?

FIGURE 6.25 Colossal waves

FIGURE 6.26 A smooth lake

So far you have been studying single waves. Now you will consider what happens when two or more transverse waves pass through each other. This effect is known as **interference**.

FIGURE 6.27 Overlapping bow waves

Imagine yourself beside a smooth lake (Figure 6.26). The air is still, there are no waves, and the water reflects the surrounding shoreline like a mirror. Suddenly, across the lake speed two boats, each pushing out a crest of water from its bow (Figure 6.27). The crest from one boat has an amplitude of 30 cm, while the crest from the other boat has an amplitude of 40 cm. Eventually the two crests meet. What will happen at the centre point when the two crests completely overlap?

If there had been only the 30-cm crest, the water molecules at that point would have been lifted by 30 cm. However, in addition to that effect, the 40-cm crest is in the process of lifting the same molecules by 40 cm. The net effect is that the molecules are lifted through a total of 70 cm (Figure 6.28).

These two crests pass through each other and soon encounter troughs. When a 30-cm crest meets a 40-cm trough, the result is a 10-cm trough as shown in Figure 6.29. This addition of the displacements of waves is known as **superposition**.

These examples illustrate the **principle of superposition**: Whenever two or more waves pass through each other, the resultant displacement at each point is the sum of all the individual displacements occurring at that point.

before
a)
30 cm
40 cm

during
b)
70 cm

after
c)
40 cm
30 cm

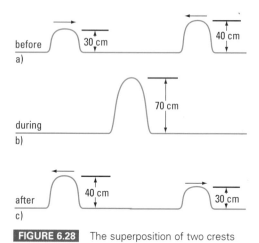

FIGURE 6.28 The superposition of two crests

Constructive Interference

Constructive interference occurs if both waves push the medium in the same direction. A crest meeting a crest produces a resultant crest that is larger than either individual crest. This crest is called a **supercrest**. Likewise, a trough meeting a trough yields a **supertrough**.

Constructive interference can be a hazard on the seas. In the introduction to this unit, you considered a sailing boat sailing through rough seas and suddenly encountering a huge trough. While it slid down into that trough, an equally huge crest appeared, submerging the boat. Such incidents do occur. There are regions where waves moving past each side of a large island overlap once they have cleared the island. This creates areas in which constructive interference can occur leading to supercrests and supertroughs. Many ships, including large tankers, have been lost or seriously damaged due to these "killer waves."

Destructive Interference

Interference of waves does not necessarily produce larger amplitudes. When a 30-cm crest meets a 40-cm trough, the resultant displacement is given by:

$$\Delta d_R = (+30 \text{ cm}) + (-40 \text{ cm})$$
$$= -10 \text{ cm (a 10-cm trough)}$$

In this case, both waves push the medium in opposite directions as shown in Figure 6.29. The effect is known as destructive interference. The net effect of a crest meeting a trough of different amplitude is a shallower crest or trough. No special name is given to these resultant waves.

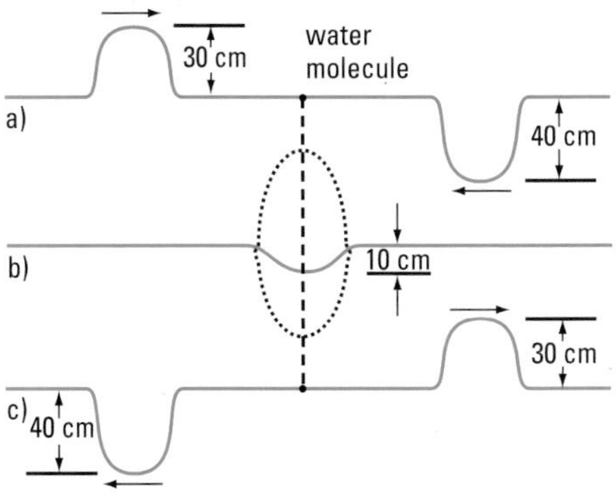

FIGURE 6.29 The superposition of a crest and a trough with different amplitudes

The Formation of Nodal Points

What happens at the centre point if a crest meets a trough of equal amplitude? Let's look at this case carefully.

Figure 6.30 shows a crest and a trough of the same amplitude approaching and meeting each other. The dotted lines represent the crest or trough by itself. The solid coloured line represents the pulse resulting from their interference. In Figures 6.30c), d), and e), the crest and trough are shown progressing farther through each other.

The important point to observe is the centre point. Notice that the individual upward and downward displacements are always equal in magnitude at that point. As a result, this centre point always stays at the equilibrium or rest position. It never vibrates. When a crest and a trough of equal magnitude interfere, the point that remains at rest throughout the interference is called a **nodal point**, or more simply, a **node**. Notice that when opposite pulses of the same amplitudes completely overlap, as in Figure 6.30d), the pulses seem to disappear. However, even though the points form a horizontal line at that instant, the pulses are still moving.

Interference produces lively effects when water waves crash into the base of a steep cliff. The waves, which reflect back from the cliff, interfere with the incoming or incident waves. Supercrests and supertroughs alternate with nodal points to create a chaotic, churning stretch of water.

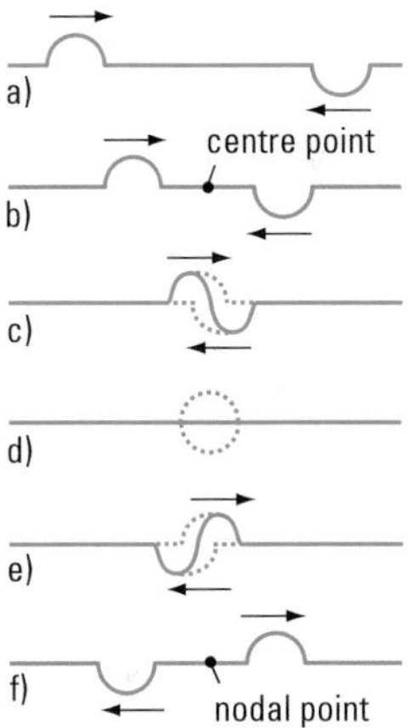

FIGURE 6.30 The superposition of opposite waves

Discovering Physics — *Comparing Amplitudes of Transverse Waves*

Work with a partner to see if you can create supercrests or supertroughs using a coiled spring.

1. With a partner, stretch a long, flexible coiled spring across an open area on the floor. (Note: Overstretching the spring will deform it and ruin your experiment!)
2. Observe what happens when you send identical pulses from opposite ends. Now observe what happens if you send *opposite* pulses from each end. (You might need to look carefully to see if there is a point that barely moves as the waves pass through.)
   - How do the amplitudes of the two pulses compare when a nodal point is produced?

WEBLINK

SIMULATION

For a simulation to show constructive and destructive interference in transverse waves, go to **www.pearsoned.ca/physics11.**

Exploration Using a Graphing Calculator

The graphing calculator is very useful in the study of waves. Transverse waves can be represented by a sine function. Graph the equation $y = 4\sin(2\pi x \div 10)$ on the graphing calculator, with a range 0 to 20 on the x-axis and -5 to $+5$ on the y-axis.

Discussion

1. From comparing the graph with the equation decide
   a) what property of the wave is represented by x
   b) what property of the wave is represented by y
   c) what property of the wave is represented by the number 4
   d) what property of the wave is represented by the number 10
2. Rewrite the function (equation) by substituting A for the amplitude and λ for the wavelength.
3. How do you think the wave given by the function $y = 2\sin(2\pi x \div 20)$ would compare with the original function? Make your prediction, then try it.
4. Predict what the result would be if both waves actually overlapped. Now, try it.
   a) At each point, how do y_1 and y_2 compare with y_3?
   b) How well do these results agree with the Principle of Superposition?

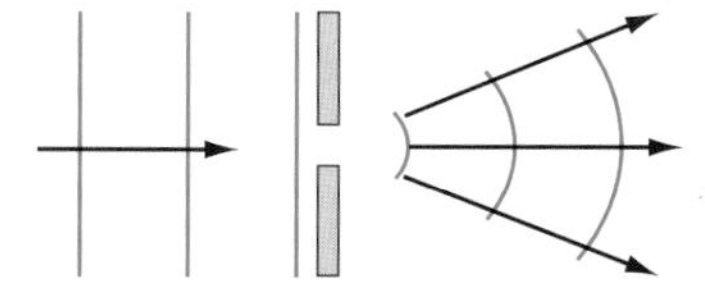

a) Waves pass through an opening smaller than the wavelength

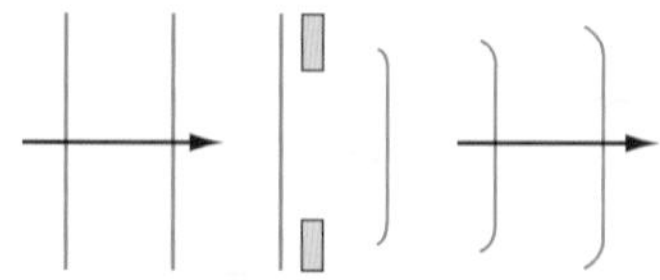

b) Waves pass through an opening larger than the wavelength

FIGURE 6.31 Diffraction of waves

Diffraction of Waves

Predict and discuss what might happen when a wave is allowed to pass through an opening. The resulting effect will likely surprise you. After the wave clears the opening, it tends to spread out. This effect is shown in Figure 6.31. The spreading out is known as **diffraction**. Waves experience a large amount of diffraction when they pass through an opening which is smaller than the wavelength. Very little diffraction occurs when waves pass through an opening which is larger than the wavelength. Diffraction can also occur when a wave passes by an edge or around an object. Although

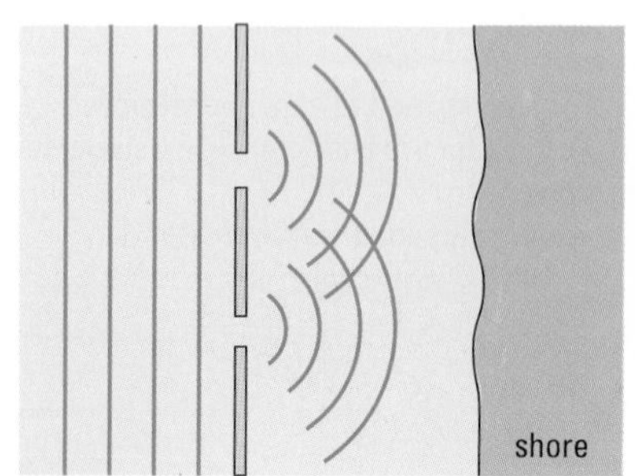

FIGURE 6.32 Waves passing through a breakwater (aerial view)

there is a change in direction during diffraction, there is no change in frequency or wavelength.

Diffraction is responsible for the beauty of sunsets. As light waves encounter small particles suspended in air, the longer wavelengths of red and orange allow these waves to diffract around the particles and keep on going. The shorter wavelengths corresponding to blue light tend to reflect off these particles. Since the sunlight that we observe at sunsets has travelled a long distance through air, we see the reds and oranges (Figure 6.34).

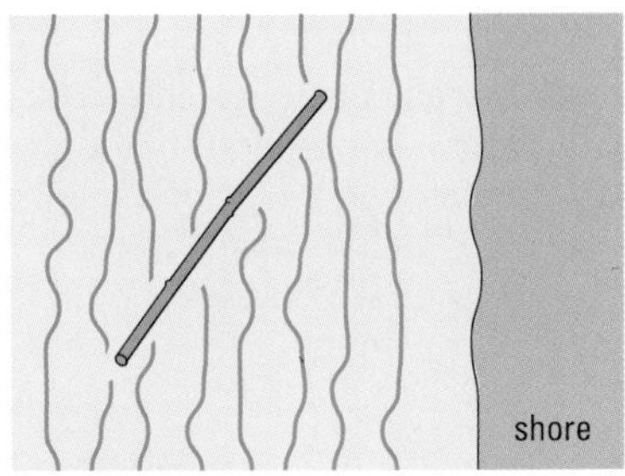

FIGURE 6.33 Waves diffracting around an object such as a tree limb in water

Refraction of Waves

In general, a wave will change its speed when it enters a new medium. However, its frequency remains the same. After all, if nine crests are approaching the boundary between the media each second, then nine crests should pass into the new medium each second.

The change in speed will result in a change of wavelength. If the wave slows down as it enters the new medium, the crests will tend to bunch up and so the wavelength will become shorter.

FIGURE 6.34 Sunset

EXAMPLE 3 NUMERICAL

A wave with a speed of 60 cm/s and a wavelength of 10 cm passes into a second medium in which its speed becomes 40 cm/s. What will be the wavelength in the second medium?

Given

$v_1 = 60$ cm/s

$\lambda_1 = 10$ cm

$v_2 = 40$ cm/s

Required

λ_2

Analysis

- Calculate f_1 using the universal wave equation.
- f_2 is the same as f_1. (A wave does not change frequency when it passes into a second medium.)
- Use v_2 and f_2 to calculate λ_2

Solution

$$v_1 = f_1 \times \lambda_1$$

$$f_1 = \frac{v_1}{\lambda_1} = \frac{60 \text{ cm/s}}{10 \text{ cm}} = 6.0 \text{ Hz}$$

PRACTICE PROBLEMS

1. A wave has a speed of 100 m/s and a wavelength of 4.0 m. It then enters a second medium in which its speed becomes 150 m/s. What will be the new wavelength?
2. A wave has a speed of 20 m/s and a wavelength of 50 m. After it passes into a second medium, its wavelength is observed to be 30 m. What is the speed in the second medium?

$$f_2 = f_1$$
$$= 6.0 \text{ Hz}$$
$$\lambda_2 = \frac{v_2}{f_2}$$
$$= \frac{40 \text{ cm/s}}{6.0 \text{ Hz}}$$
$$= 6.7 \text{ cm}$$

Statement

The wavelength in the second medium will be 6.7 cm.

The change in speed may have a second effect as well. If the wave does not strike the second medium head on, then one part of the wave will slow down sooner than the rest. This causes the wave to change direction as it enters the new medium. This effect is known as **refraction**. Figure 6.35 shows what happens when a wave slows down.

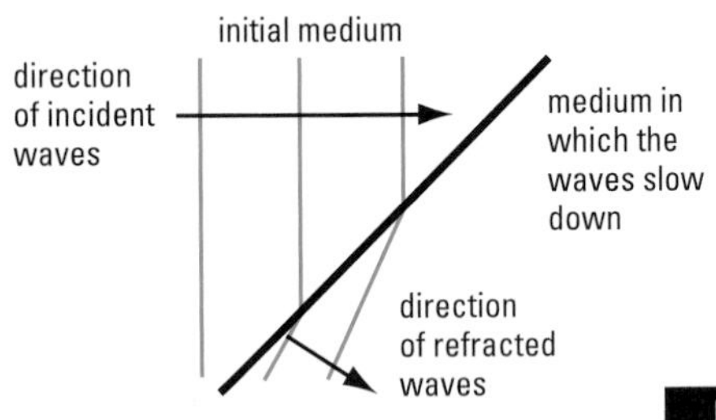

FIGURE 6.35 Refraction at a boundary between two media

WEBLINK

Diffraction and refraction are important concepts that apply to both sound and light. Compare and contrast these two effects by means of a graphic organizer such as a Venn diagram. Begin your research at **www.pearsoned.ca/physics11.**

Discovering Physics — *Analyzing the Properties of Waves*

Observe the change in direction of waves due to a change in speed. You will need a ripple tank, pane of flat transparent glass or plastic, a ruler, and water.

To see the change in direction of waves due to a change in speed,

1. Obtain a ripple tank. Lay a flat pane of glass or clear plastic in the bottom so that it covers less than half of the tank.
2. Now add water to the tank until the water is about 2–3 mm deep over the pane.
3. Dip the edge of a ruler repeatedly into the deep section of the tank.
4. Observe the plane waves as they pass from the deep water into the shallow water. What happens to the speed and wavelength in the shallow water? If the waves are not striking the edge of the shallow region head on, what happens to the direction of the waves?
5. Draw a series of diagrams to illustrate your observations, then answer the following questions.
   - Did the waves strike the edges of the shallow region head on? What effect did that have on the direction of the waves?
   - Draw a diagram showing the pattern of incident and refracted waves.
   - Did you observe any evidence of reflected waves? If so, make a diagram showing several incident waves and several reflected waves.
   - How does the angle at which the waves approach the boundary compare with the angle at which the waves reflect from the boundary?

Section 6.5 Review

Understanding Concepts

1. When water waves crash against a cliff, the incoming waves interfere with the reflected waves. This causes both constructive and destructive interference to occur. How could you identify each in the resulting wave pattern?
2. Predict the result when waves with the following amplitudes overlap:
   a) a 10-cm crest meets a 15-cm trough
   b) a 10-cm trough meets a 15-cm trough
   c) a 15-cm crest meets a 15-cm trough
3. Name the type of interference involved in 2.a), 2.b), and 2.c).
4. A wave with a speed of 300 m/s and a frequency of 100 Hz passes into a second medium in which the wavelength is 2.0 m.
   a) What is the wavelength of the wave in the first medium?
   b) What is the speed of the wave in the second medium?

Applying Inquiry/ Communication Skills

5. Figure 6.36 shows rectangular pulses as they approach each other. The divisions on the axes represent 1 cm. Pulses A and B are moving to the right at 1.0 cm/s. Pulse C is moving to the left at 1.0 cm/s. The position of the pulses is indicated at time $t = 0$ s. Determine the shape of the superimposed pulses at:
   a) $t = 2.0$ s   b) $t = 3.0$ s
   c) $t = 5.0$ s   d) $t = 6.0$ s

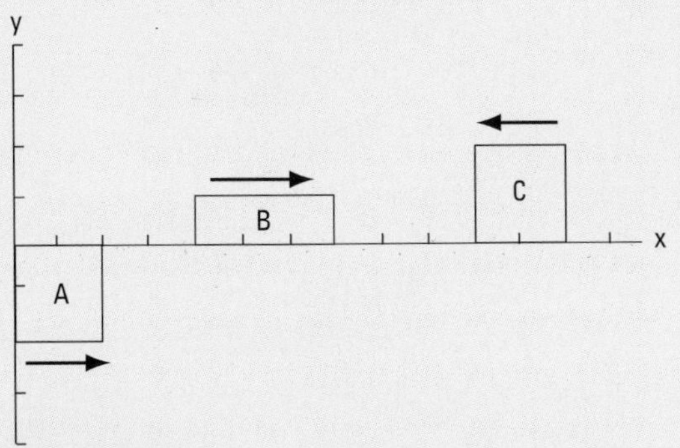

FIGURE 6.36 Superposition of rectangular pulses

6. Draw a diagram similar to Figure 6.35 to show how water waves would bend if they passed into a medium in which they speeded up.
7. In one medium, a wave has a speed of v_1 and a wavelength of λ_1. When it passes into a second medium, its speed is v_2 and its wavelength is λ_2. Prove that $\frac{\lambda_2}{\lambda_1} = \frac{v_2}{v_1}$. [**Hint:** Remember that the frequency is the same in both media.]

Making Connections

8. X-rays seem to pass in a straight line through a slit that is 1.0 μm wide (1.0×10^{-6} m). However, diffraction is seen when the X-rays pass between the atoms in a crystal where the spacing is about 1.0×10^{-10} m.
   a) What does that information tell you about the X-rays?
   b) What can you find out about how X-rays have been used to determine the structure of crystalline solids?

Investigation 1 (Section 6.1)

Inquiry Skills

- Initiating and Planning
- Applying Technical Skills
- Using Tools, Materials, Equipment
- Conducting and Recording
- Analyzing and Interpreting
- Concluding and Communicating

Longitudinal Vibrations

Problem

An object hanging on a spring can vibrate longitudinally if pulled down and released. The purpose of this activity is to examine the effect of a change in mass of the hanging object on the frequency of a spring undergoing longitudinal vibrations. State a hypothesis about the effect of an increase in mass on the frequency.

Materials

- ring stand
- iron ring
- short spring
- metre-stick
- timer such as a stopwatch
- selection of masses
- C-clamp

Procedure

1. Set up a table with the following headings:
   Mass *m* (g), Time for 10 cycles *t* (s), Frequency *f* (Hz)
2. Attach the iron ring near the top of the stand so that it overhangs the base.
3. Hang the spring from the ring so that it is suspended as shown in Figure 6.37.

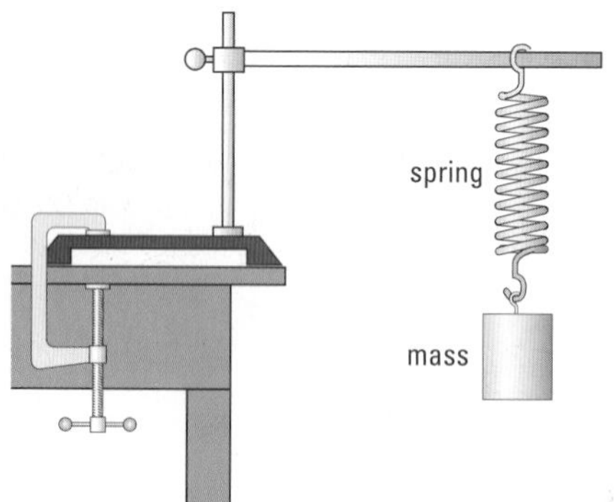

FIGURE 6.37 Longitudinal vibrations, mass, and frequency

4. Attach the largest mass to the lower end of the spring. Make sure that the spring is not stretched too far.
5. Pull the mass downward by one centimetre and release it. Measure the time taken for 10 cycles. Record your time in the table.
6. Repeat the last two steps for several other masses.

Analyzing and Interpreting

1. Calculate the frequency for each mass.
2. Plot a graph of frequency against mass.
3. Describe the shape of the graph.
4. Which is the dependent variable, and which is the independent variable?

Concluding and Communicating

5. What happens to the frequency of the vibrating spring when the mass increases? Did the results of this investigation support your hypothesis?
6. Predict the shape of the graph of period against mass.

Extending

7. If a graphing calculator is available, enter the data for frequency and mass into the calculator and plot a graph. Use the calculator to find the equation that best relates frequency and mass.

Investigation 2 (Section 6.3)

Inquiry Skills

- Initiating and Planning
- Applying Technical Skills
- Using Tools, Materials, Equipment
- Conducting and Recording
- Analyzing and Interpreting
- Concluding and Communicating

Transverse and Longitudinal Pulses

One of the major topics in physics is that of how a wave is transmitted through a medium. Many questions arise. What happens to the medium as the wave passes through it? What changes occur in the wave due to its interaction with the medium? How fast does the wave travel and does the medium have any effect on this speed? In this activity you will attempt to answer these questions.

Problem

What changes occur as a transverse or a longitudinal pulse travels along a spring?

Materials

- masking tape
- metre-stick
- stopwatch
- Slinky spring (at least 5 m long when moderately stretched)

Caution: Do not overstretch the spring. Do not let it become tangled.

Experimental Design

Part A: Observing Transverse Pulses

Transverse pulses can be created in a spring by laying it on the floor, stretching it slightly, then flicking one end of the spring sideways and back.

1. As a small group, decide on a procedure for studying the changes that occur as a transverse pulse travels along a spring. Consider the following questions:
   - How could you tell how the medium (the spring) is moving as the pulse travels through it?
   - How could you determine if there is any change in amplitude of the pulse as it travels along the spring?
   - How could you measure the speed of the pulse along the spring? What quantities would you have to measure?
   - How many trials do you intend to run in order to find an average speed?
2. Write an outline of your procedure. Once your teacher has approved your outline, carry out the investigation. Carefully record all observations.

Part B: Factors Affecting the Speed of the Transverse Pulse

3. As a small group, decide on a procedure for investigating the factors that affect the speed of the transverse wave through the spring. State your prediction as to how each factor might affect the speed. Give reasons for your predictions or hypotheses. Consider the following questions:
   - How could you determine if the speed of the wave is affected by changes in the wave itself? For example, would the speed be different for a higher frequency or for a larger amplitude?
   - How could you determine if the speed of the wave is affected by changes in the medium? For example, would the speed be different if the spring were under greater tension (stretched tighter)?
   - What steps should you consider to make sure that this is a controlled experiment?
   - How many trials do you intend to run in order to find an average for each condition?
4. Outline your procedure to answer these questions and any others that you may have posed. Once your teacher has approved your outline, carry out the investigation. Carefully record all observations.

Part C: Observing a Longitudinal Pulse

A longitudinal pulse can be created in a spring by placing the spring on the floor, stretching it slightly, compressing a few coils at one end of the spring, and then releasing them.

5. As a group, decide on a procedure to investigate the motion of a longitudinal pulse through the spring. Consider the following questions:
   - How could you determine the movement of coils in the spring as the longitudinal pulse travels through it?
   - How could you measure the speed of the longitudinal pulse?

- How could you determine the effect of an increase in amplitude on the speed of the pulse?
- How could you determine the effect of increased tension on the speed of the pulse?
- How will you ensure that this is a controlled experiment?

6. Outline your procedure to answer these questions and any others that you may have posed. Once your teacher has approved your outline, carry out the investigation. Carefully record all observations.

Analyzing and Interpreting

1. Does the motion of the coils agree with your expectations for transverse and longitudinal pulses (or waves)?
2. Were your speed results fairly consistent or did they show a wide range for each of the different conditions investigated?
3. What was the initial speed of the transverse pulse?
4. What happened to the speed of the transverse pulse when
   a) the frequency was increased?
   b) the amplitude was increased?
   c) the tension in the spring was increased?
   d) any other factor that you investigated was changed?
5. What was the initial speed of the longitudinal pulse?
6. What happened to the speed of the longitudinal pulse when
   a) the amplitude was increased?
   b) the tension in the spring was increased?
   c) any other factor that you investigated was changed?

Concluding and Communicating

7. As a transverse pulse (wave) travels along the spring, how do the coils move relative to the long axis of the spring?
8. As a longitudinal pulse (wave) travels along the spring, how do the coils move relative to the long axis of the spring?
9. Which factors influence the speed of a transverse pulse, and what effect does each one have?
10. Which factors influence the speed of a longitudinal pulse, and what effect does each one have?
11. Which factors do not noticeably influence the speed of the transverse pulse (wave) through the spring?
12. Which factors do not noticeably influence the speed of the longitudinal pulse (wave) through the spring?

Extending

13. If the transverse wave is allowed to reflect at an end held firmly in place, what changes occur in the wave? Does its speed change after reflection? If a crest is sent down on one side, does a crest or a trough reflect back?

CHAPTER SUMMARY

Key Terms

amplitude
compression
constructive interference
crest
cycle
destructive interference
diffraction
Doppler effect
equilibrium position
frequency
hertz
interference
longitudinal vibration
longitudinal wave
mechanical resonance
natural frequency
nodal point
period
periodic motion
phase
principle of superposition
rarefaction
refraction
resonance
transverse vibration
transverse wave
trough
universal wave equation
vibration
wave
wavelength

Key Equations

$T = \frac{\Delta t}{N}$

$f \times T = 1$

$v = f\lambda$

$f = \frac{N}{\Delta t}$

Essential Understandings

- All waves of a specific type behave predictably in various media.
- Periodic motion is motion that repeats itself at regular intervals.
- Periodic motion is measured in terms of frequency (or period) and amplitude.
- Resonance is the transfer of energy of vibration from one object to a second object having the same natural or resonant frequency.
- A wave is a disturbance in a medium that transfers energy by means of a series of vibrations.
- The two main types of waves are transverse and longitudinal.
- The wavelength of a wave is the shortest distance between successive points vibrating in the same phase.
- The universal wave equation states that the speed of a wave equals its frequency multiplied by its wavelength.
- The Doppler effect is the change in the frequency and wavelength of a wave due to the motion of the source of the wave.
- The principle of superposition states that when two waves intersect, the resulting displacement is the sum of the individual displacements of the waves.
- Waves produce constructive and destructive interference when they pass through each other.
- Diffraction is the spreading of a wave as it passes through an opening or by an edge.
- Refraction refers to the change in direction of a wave as it travels from one medium to another.

Consolidate Your Understanding

1. Look back to your answer for the Checkpoint on page 237. Would you still give the same answer? Why do you think that such waves were called "tidal waves"?
2. While standing on the pier by the ocean, you notice that the level of the water in the harbour is decreasing fairly quickly.
   a) What is likely happening? Explain in terms of the properties of waves.
   b) What should you do? Why?
3. Create a concept map to illustrate the ideas and quantities involved in wave motion. Try to include as many of the Key Terms listed above as possible.
4. If you discovered a new type of radiation, what evidence might you look for in order to decide if it travels as a wave? If it does travel as a wave, which wave properties might you be particularly interested in? Give reasons for your selection.
5. How would you describe resonance to a friend who has not studied waves and vibrations? What examples would you choose to emphasize the importance of the concept?

CHAPTER 6 REVIEW

Understanding Concepts

1. A wave has a speed of 300 m/s and a frequency of 10 Hz. What is its wavelength?
   a) 0.033 m b) 3.0 m c) 30 m
   d) 3.0×10^2 m e) 3.0 km

Figure 6.38 applies to questions 2 to 4.

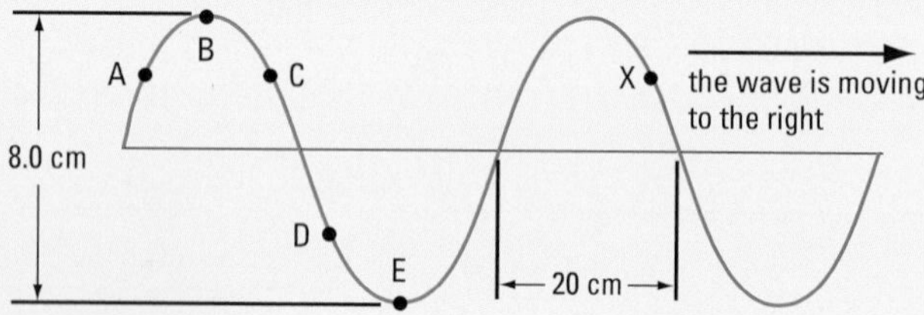

FIGURE 6.38 A transverse wave

2. What is the amplitude of the illustrated wave?
   a) 4.0 cm b) 8.0 cm c) 10 cm
   d) 20 cm e) 40 cm
3. Which point is vibrating in phase with point X?
   a) A b) B c) C
   d) D e) E
4. Which way is point C moving?
   a) vertically upward
   b) vertically downward
   c) diagonally downward toward the right
   d) diagonally upward toward the left
   e) horizontally to the right
5. A crest with an amplitude of 15 cm meets a trough with an amplitude of 18 cm. The result will be a
   a) crest with a 33-cm amplitude
   b) trough with a 33-cm amplitude
   c) crest with a 3-cm amplitude
   d) trough with a 3-cm amplitude
   e) crest with a 1.2-cm amplitude
6. As water waves approach a beach, their wavelength decreases. If the frequency of the waves does not change, what must be happening to their speed? Explain.
7. Water waves near the base of a cliff often possess greater amplitude than those out a bit farther from the base. Explain why.
8. As a crest moves through a point, in what ways is the motion of that point like the motion of a ball thrown straight upward?
9. As a transverse wave travels along a spring, where is the speed of the spring
   a) greatest?
   b) least?
   Give reasons for your answer.
10. When the spectators at an event do "the wave," one person stands up and sits down. The next person does the same, starting a little later. The process continues and a crest seems to run along the crowd.
    a) In what way does this resemble a transverse wave?
    b) How is it different from a transverse wave?
    c) How could you get the impression of a trough travelling through the crowd?
11. Calculate the frequency of a tuning fork which has a period of 1.0×10^{-3} s.
12. A child on a swing completes 18 cycles in 70 s. What is the
    a) period of the swing?
    b) frequency of the swing?
13. A duck is floating on water waves that have a frequency of 0.25 Hz. How long does it take the duck to complete 5.0 cycles?
14. Radio station CPHY broadcasts at 80 kHz. What is the period of the radio waves?
15. The quartz crystal in a watch vibrates at 32 768 Hz. How many cycles will it complete in one day?
16. A sound wave travels with a frequency of 2000 Hz and a wavelength of 0.180 m. Calculate its speed.
17. An X-ray travels at 3.0×10^8 m/s. If its wavelength is 6.0×10^{-10} m, what is its frequency?
18. In 1958, J. Weber searched for gravity waves having a frequency of 1660 Hz. Since these waves are expected to travel at 2.998×10^8 m/s, what is their expected wavelength?
19. X-rays travel at 3.00×10^8 m/s. If the frequency of X-rays is 5.0×10^{18} Hz, what is the wavelength?
20. Red light with a wavelength of 7.0×10^{-7} m travels at a speed of 3.0×10^8 m/s through air. When it enters glass, its speed is reduced to 2.0×10^8 m/s. Calculate the new wavelength in glass. Assume that the frequency has not changed.
21. Two sunbathers were sitting on a raft. One noted that the raft bobbed up and down at a frequency of 0.20 Hz. The other observed that a crest took 5.0 s to cover the 15 m to shore. How far apart were the crests?
22. Two ducks, floating on the water, bob up and down with the waves (Figure 6.39). If they are 1.5 m apart and are in opposite phase, what is the longest possible wavelength of the water wave?

FIGURE 6.39

Applying Inquiry/ Communication Skills

23. Draw an accurate, scaled diagram of a transverse wave with an amplitude of 4.0 m and a wavelength of 20 m.

24. Suggest a way for determining the pattern of vibration of water molecules 2.0 m below the surface of a lake.

25. a) Use a graphing calculator to illustrate the appearance of two waves. They must both have the same amplitude, but the wavelength of one must be twice the wavelength of the other.
    b) Use the graphing calculator to show the superposition of the waves from part a).

26. In Figure 6.40, pulses A and B are moving toward the right at 1.0 cm/s. Pulses C and D are moving toward the left at 1.0 cm/s. Their position is shown for $t = 0$ s. Determine the resulting shape of the waves after
    a) 3.0 s
    b) 5.0 s

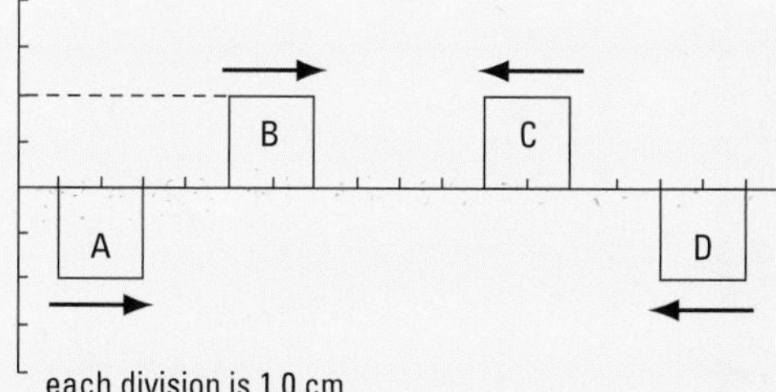

FIGURE 6.40 Superposition of pulses

27. When a ball is allowed to bounce, the period of the bounce decreases as the height of the bounce decreases. A student made the following measurements of the ball and the period between bounces.

Height of ball, h (m)	Period of bounce, T (s)
1.00	0.90
0.90	0.85
0.80	0.81
0.70	0.75
0.60	0.70
0.50	0.64
0.40	0.58
0.30	0.49
0.20	0.40
0.10	0.29

   a) Store the data as lists in a graphing calculator.
   b) Graph the scatter plot with period on the y-axis.
   c) Determine the equation for the relation between period and height.
   d) Describe in your own words the sound you hear while the ball is bouncing.
   e) Is a wave pattern created moving away from the point of impact? How is the wave character different from that of normal waves?

28. The water molecules at the surface of a lake undergo both transverse (up and down) and longitudinal (parallel to the surface) vibrations as a surface wave passes by. What would be the shape of the path followed by a molecule if
    a) both types of vibrations have equal amplitudes?
    b) the longitudinal vibration has a larger amplitude than the transverse vibration?
    c) the transverse vibration has a larger amplitude than the longitudinal vibration?

29. Imagine that a source of transverse waves is moving to the right as shown in Figure 6.21. It has a frequency of 2.0 Hz and is traveling at 2.0 cm/s. The speed of the waves is 4.0 cm/s.
    a) Construct a full-scale diagram such as in Figure 6.21c).
    b) Determine the wavelength in front of the source and behind the source.
    c) Calculate the frequency of the wave in front of and behind the source.

30. The S waves (transverse) from an earthquake arrive at a monitoring station 22.0 s later than the longitudinal P waves. If the S waves travel at 4.50 km/s and the P waves at 8.00 km/s, how far away was the epicentre (source) of the earthquake? Assume that the waves have travelled in a straight line.

Making Connections

31. Station CPHY AM broadcasts at 720 kHz while station CPHY FM broadcasts at 92 MHz. Which signal will bend better around obstacles? Explain your answer. What difference could that make to radio reception?

32. Ultraviolet waves travel at 3.00×10^8 m/s. If ultraviolet diffracts strongly through a slit 2.0×10^{-7} m wide, estimate its frequency.

33. A tsunami has a period of 30 min and a wavelength of 270 km. How long will it take the wave to travel 200 km?

34. During refraction, light waves with a wavelength of 6.00×10^{-7} m enter diamond where their speed decreases from 3.00×10^8 m/s to 1.25×10^8 m/s. If their frequency stays the same during refraction, what will be the wavelength of the light inside the diamond?

CHAPTER 7

Production, Transmission, and Reception of Sound

SPECIFIC EXPECTATIONS

By the end of this chapter, you will be able to:

- define and describe the concepts and units related to energy, and work (7.1, 7.2)
- describe and illustrate the properties of transverse and longitudinal waves in different media, and analyze the velocity of waves travelling in those media in quantitative terms (7.3)
- compare the speed of sound in different media, and describe the effect of temperature on the speed of sound (7.3)
- explain and graphically illustrate the principle of superposition, and identify examples of constructive and destructive interference (7.4)
- draw, measure, analyze, and interpret the properties of waves during their transmission in a medium and from one medium to another, and during their interaction with matter (Investigation 2)
- design and conduct an experiment to determine the speed of waves in a medium, compare theoretical and empirical values, and account for discrepancies (Investigation 1)
- describe how knowledge of the properties of waves is applied in the design of buildings and of various technological devices, as well as in explanations of how sounds are produced and transmitted in nature, and how they interact with matter in nature (7.1, 7.2, 7.3)
- identify sources of noise in different environments, and explain how such noise can be reduced to acceptable levels (7.2)

Stop what you're doing for a moment, close your eyes, and just listen. Identify the different sounds you can hear—the hum of a ceiling fan, an airplane overhead, a dog barking, your stomach growling. Your world involves a multitude of sounds. We tend to take sound for granted, but what exactly is sound? How are sounds produced? How do they travel from a source to your ears? How do your ears detect them?

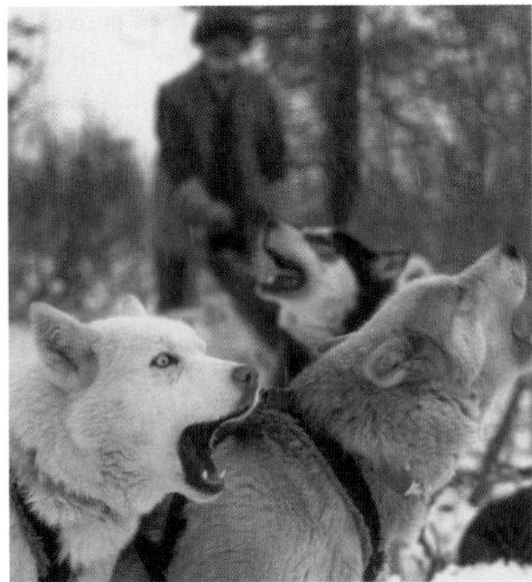

a) Barking dogs

FIGURE 7.1 Our ears detect a multitude of sounds.

b) An airplane

Notice that a rise in pitch of one octave on either scale is produced by a doubling of the frequency.

As the music becomes louder, the frequency does not necessarily change, but the amplitude increases. This is not surprising. Anyone who has stood on the shore of a large lake or ocean knows that large-amplitude waves have more energy than small-amplitude ripples. As long as the wave is in the audible range, loudness depends on the amplitude of the wave. In Figure 7.8 you can see that a larger amplitude produces a louder sound.

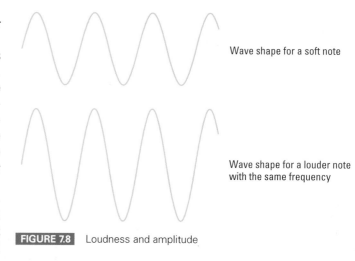

Wave shape for a soft note

Wave shape for a louder note with the same frequency

FIGURE 7.8 Loudness and amplitude

When the vocalist sings (Figure 7.9), you suddenly see a major change in the wave displayed on the oscilloscope. Even though the vocalist sings as loudly as the flute or guitar is played, and sounds the same note (the same pitch), the shape of the wave is different. Peaks and valleys are added to the basic wave. This complexity is caused by the existence of higher frequencies that are produced at the same time as the basic or fundamental frequency. These additional frequencies are called **overtones**, and will be discussed more in the next chapter. Although our ear does not usually hear these higher frequencies as separate notes, they do change the quality of the note. A **pure note** has no overtones and takes the basic wave shape. A **rich note** contains several overtones in addition to the fundamental frequency and so produces a more complex wave pattern.

FIGURE 7.9 A singer's voice has many overtones.

The quality of a note is determined by the presence of overtones in addition to the fundamental frequency. This produces a complex and distinctive wave pattern.

Noise

If the singer suddenly coughs, the wave pattern changes drastically (unless the singer was really terrible in the first place). Instead of regular waves with added peaks and valleys to give richness, the pattern looks like a jumble of vibrations (Figure 7.10). **Noise** is a result of an irregular mixture of frequencies. Distortion refers to how much the actual shape of a recorded wave differs from the shape formed by the original source.

The ability to imitate or create sounds has many applications. How many can you think of? The synthesizer is one device used by musicians to reproduce the sounds of different instruments. The function of the synthesizer is to produce a wave shape that matches the shape of the desired sound wave. The required wave can be synthesized in several ways.

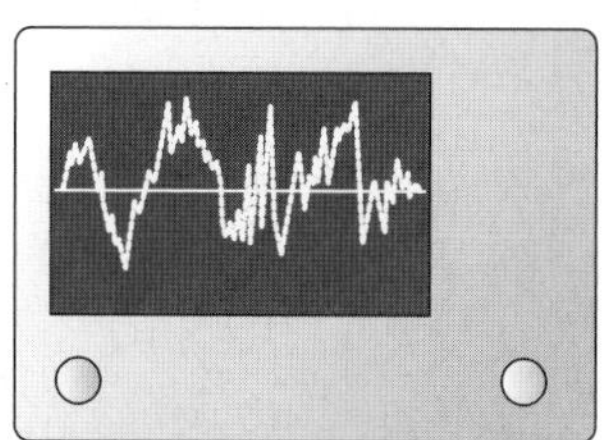

FIGURE 7.10 Appearance of noise on an oscilloscope

WEBLINK

We now have the ability to reproduce sounds and create completely new sounds through electronic synthesis. Write a couple of paragraphs describing a technique that you find interesting. Begin your research at **www.pearsoned.ca/physics11.**

Additive Synthesis In this technique, the wave is produced by adding together waves of many different frequencies called harmonics. The wave is further shaped to give the desired sound.

Subtractive Synthesis The synthesizer begins with a wave that contains many harmonics (different frequencies). The required wave shape is formed by selectively filtering out some of the harmonics.

FM Synthesis This technology is quite similar to that of the FM radio. The wave shape is created by frequency modulation of a basic wave.

Sampling This method begins by actually sampling at regular intervals the longitudinal wave produced by an instrument whose sound is to be imitated. In order to reproduce the sound as closely as possible, $2R$ samples should be taken per second, where R is the highest frequency to be reproduced. Since humans can hear up to 20 kHz, samples should be taken at the rate of 40 000 per second. The positive or negative value representing the relative pressure of the wave at each sampling time is then recorded as a binary number. As a result, this is known as digitization. A microprocessor in the synthesizer can then recreate the shape of the wave from this information.

In all of the above methods, the frequency and amplitude variations are mimicked by variations in an electric current. The current is then used to drive a piezoelectric crystal or a speaker in order to produce the actual sound.

Section 7.1 Review

Understanding Concepts

1. What is the source of sound in
   a) a drum?
   b) a clarinet?
   c) a violin?
   d) a bell?
2. In space, and on the Moon, there is no air. Communication is therefore achieved by the use of radio waves. If the radio link between the two astronauts shown in Figure 7.4 were broken, what could they do to "hear" each other?
3. Which wave property determines a note's:
   a) loudness?
   b) pitch?
   c) quality?
4. Calculate the frequency of the note:
   a) one octave below 440 Hz
   b) two octaves below 440 Hz
   c) one octave above 512 Hz
   d) three octaves above 512 Hz

Applying Inquiry/Communication Skills

5. If sound travels as a wave, it should diffract (or spread out). Suggest a way of demonstrating the diffraction of sound.

7.2 Hearing Sound

Key Understandings

When you have completed this section, you will be able to:

- describe how knowledge of waves explains how organisms produce and receive ultrasonic sounds
- identify sources of noise in different environments, and explain how such noise can be reduced to acceptable levels

FIGURE 7.11 Bats use ultrasound to locate insects for food.

A bridge in Austin, Texas, is home to thousands of bats. Each evening, as dusk falls, these bats emerge from the girders and swirl like smoke up and down the river in search of flying insects. Dim light or darkness does not hinder them. As they fly they emit squeaks of ultrasound. The returning echoes paint the picture of their surroundings and the location of their evening meal. Why do we not hear these squeaks? Why is ultrasound more useful to the bats than normal sound?

Textbooks often define **sound** as that form of energy that can be detected by the human ear. This definition is restrictive because many animals sense frequencies that humans cannot hear. We will instead consider sound as energy that travels as longitudinal waves containing regions of high and low pressure. The **audible region** of the sound spectrum for humans extends from about 16 Hz at the low-frequency end to about 20 kHz at the high-frequency end.

Audio engineering strives to reproduce sound in such a way that the listener cannot tell the difference between the original sound and the recording. In the 1930s recordings had a frequency range of only 3 kHz. This was good enough to understand speech, but music was muffled. The frequency range had to improve. By the 1960s it was 15 kHz. Finally, in the 1980s, frequencies were reproduced from 20 Hz to 20 kHz. Today, frequencies up to 25 kHz can be provided. However, only children under the age of five and some animals, such as dogs, can actually hear up to 25 kHz. Due to the limitations of the human ear, reproduction beyond 25 kHz is unnecessary.

Frequencies below 16 Hz are called **infrasonic**. If we could hear infrasound, we would hear the waves on a lake before they break against the shore. We would hear the vibration of a pendulum, just as we can hear the vibrations of the wings of a bee. Recent studies suggest that many birds and animals can detect these frequencies. Birds many kilometres inland may hear the lake and know how to find it. Although most animals communicate in the audible or ultrasound range, rhinoceroses use infrasound. They communicate with each other using frequencies as low as 5 Hz. There are so many accounts of animals being disturbed before earthquakes that some scientists are considering the possibility that earthquakes produce low-frequency infrasound before the main shock waves begin. Possibly these waves alert the animals.

Frequencies higher than 20 000 Hz are known as **ultrasonic**. There are many applications of **ultrasound**. It is used by jewellers to clean jewellery and can be used to find internal flaws in castings. Doctors use ultrasound to break up gallstones. Because ultrasound is reflected at the boundary between different types of tissue, it can be used to form internal images of the body that are in many ways more useful than those from X-rays. It is also used in therapy to accelerate the healing of damaged tissues such as muscles.

INFOBIT

Arrays of transducers can re-create a sound and send it back exactly to its source as if time has been reversed. For example if you say "TV" it would echo back to your mouth as "eeveet." The process can be used to locate and destroy tumours and kidney stones, detect defects in materials, and detect a mine in the ocean.

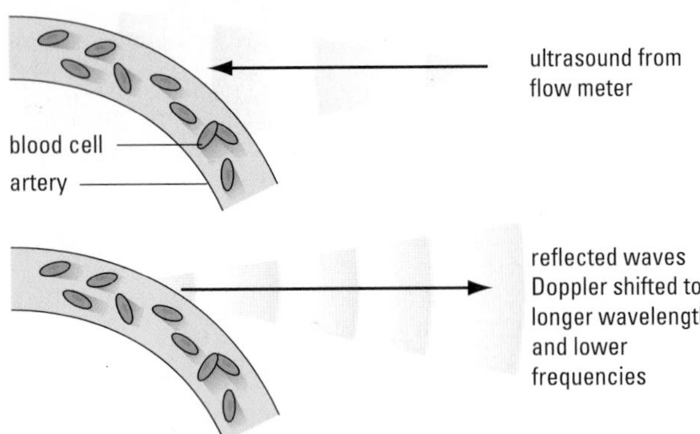

FIGURE 7.12 Doppler shift from blood cells

The flow meter is an ultrasound device that can measure the rate of blood flow through blood vessels using the Doppler effect. The meter emits ultrasound pulses and then examines the returning echoes. Any blood cells that are moving toward the meter shift the reflected waves to higher frequencies. Those moving away from the meter shift the reflected waves to lower frequencies (Figure 7.12). The speed of the cells can be determined from the change in frequency.

Ultrasound is used extensively by several animals. Bats locate objects in the dark by emitting ultrasonic squeaks and then listening for the returning echoes. Because of the short wavelength of ultrasound, the waves do not simply diffract around small objects such as insects. Instead, the waves reflect strongly back to the bats. Dolphins and porpoises use ultrasound for navigation and communication too (Figure 7.13).

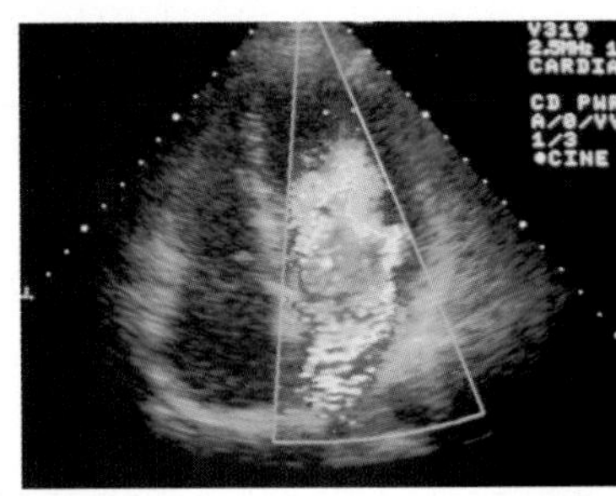

FIGURE 7.13 What use is being made of ultrasound in each of these situations?

FIGURE 7.14 Worker with ear protection

Intensity of Sound

When feeding branches into a chipper a worker must wear ear protection (Figure 7.14). Without it, the intense noise of the machine could rupture the eardrum.

The amount of sound energy passing each second through a unit area is called the **intensity** of the sound. If one joule of sound energy per second passes through an area of one square metre, then the intensity is one joule per second per square metre, or one watt per square metre.

Our ears are so sensitive that an intensity of one watt per square metre is too large a sound level for us to cope with. To accommodate smaller values, a unit called the **bel (B)**, named in honour of Alexander Graham Bell, has been defined. One bel is equal to ten pico-watts per square metre ($1\ B = 10\ pW/m^2$). (Remember that pico is the SI prefix meaning 10^{-12}.) A smaller unit, the **decibel (dB)** is also used ($1\ dB = 0.1\ B$). Table 7.2 shows the relationship between the three units.

TABLE 7.2 Sound Intensity Conversions

dB	B	pW/m²
0	0	1.0×10^0 or 1.0
10	1	1.0×10^1
20	2	1.0×10^2
30	3	1.0×10^3
100	10	1.0×10^{10}

The table shows that the sound intensity in bels corresponds to the exponent of the power of 10 when the intensity is expressed in pW/m^2. The

WEBLINK

Bats and dolphins both use ultrasound for navigating. Are there any other creatures that use ultrasound this way? Could a dolphin hear a bat flying overhead? Prepare a table showing the frequency ranges that various animals can detect. Begin your research at **www.pearsoned.ca/physics11.**

faintest sound that most of us can hear (when young) is close to 0.0 dB. This is often referred to as the threshold of hearing and leads to an alternate method for calculating or comparing sound intensities.

Table 7.3 gives the sound intensity from various sources. The intensity close to a pneumatic drill used to smash concrete is 110 dB. This converts to 11 B, 1.0×10^{11} pW/m^2, or 0.10 W/m^2.

A weak light bulb radiates energy at the rate of 40 W. We experience difficulty reading beside such a lamp. It is hard to believe that the sound energy flow from a pneumatic drill, for which workers must wear ear protection, is the same as the amount of radiant energy received from a 40-W light bulb at a distance of about 6.0 m. This indicates how sensitive the human ear is.

Sound intensity depends on several factors. First, it depends on the strength of the source of sound. Second, it depends on how far away the listener is from that source. And third, it depends on the ability of the medium between the listener and the source to transmit sound energy.

Although many people use the terms "loudness" and "intensity" interchangeably, they are not the same. **Loudness** is a measure of the response of the ear to sound. Even though two sounds are of equal intensity, you can hear one as louder than the other simply because your ear can detect it better.

TABLE 7.3 Sound Intensities from Various Sources

Source	Intensity (dB)
threshold of hearing	0.0
quiet recording studio	10
quiet living room	20
quiet office	30
quiet street, subdued conversation	40
class working on assignment	50
average conversation	60
busy street, class entering room	70
school cafeteria at lunch	80
subway	90
thunder (close)	100
pneumatic drill (close)	110
threshold of pain	120
jet engine (close)	150

Figure 7.15 shows the frequency response of the human ear. One curve represents the minimum intensity required for very acute ears to detect the different frequencies. A second curve represents the ability of the average person to detect the different frequencies. For example, a person with acute hearing can detect a frequency of 1000 Hz at a minimum intensity of 0 dB. An average person must receive 12 dB to be able to hear that same frequency. This means that the average person requires slightly more than 10 times the intensity to hear what those with excellent hearing can detect. The third curve represents the sensitivity of an average dog.

Investigation

Refer to page 285, Investigation 2

Because 20 000 Hz is the upper limit of the audible range for humans, a frequency of 25 000 Hz would sound silent to the human ear. To humans, this sound has a loudness of zero even though its intensity might be 100 dB.

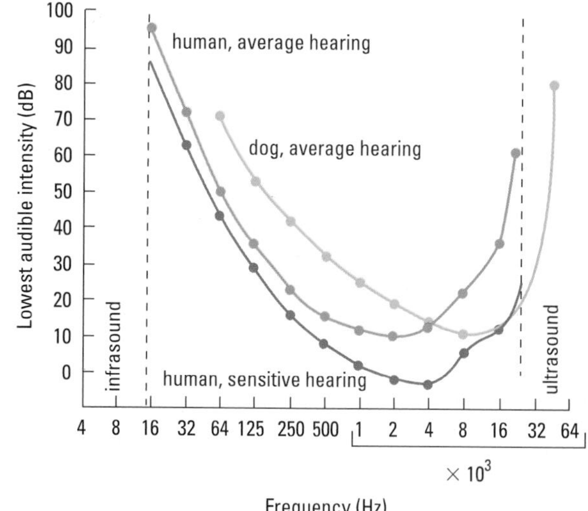

FIGURE 7.15 Frequency response of human and canine ears

Structure and Function of the Human Ear

The human ear is an extremely sensitive device. It allows us to convert pressure variations in the air, with frequencies between 16 Hz and 20 kHz, into electric impulses that travel to the brain. A full treatment of the physical, biological, and chemical factors that play a part in this process is quite complicated. Therefore, only the basic physical factors involved will be examined here.

The process of hearing begins with the passage of a sound wave down the **auditory canal** (Figure 7.16). When a compression reaches the **tympanic membrane**, commonly called the eardrum, the pressure on the outside of the eardrum increases. Since the **Eustachian tube** keeps the air in the middle ear at atmospheric pres-

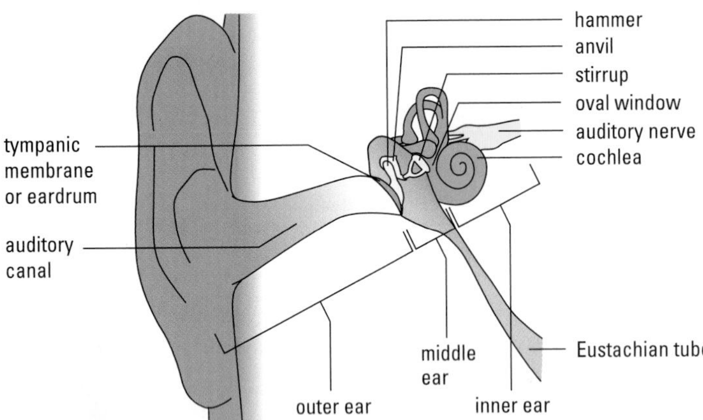

FIGURE 7.16 Auditory parts of the human ear

sure, the compression forces the eardrum inward. Similarly, the eardrum moves outward when a rarefaction (a low-pressure region) passes down the canal. In this way, the eardrum vibrates in phase with the incoming sound wave.

If the Eustachian tube is blocked, which can occur with allergies or colds, then the pressure inside the ear cannot adjust quickly to changes in atmospheric pressure. This can lead to severe earaches when rapid changes in elevation occur in, for example, a high-speed elevator or an airplane.

Within the middle ear, three tiny, linked bones transmit vibrations from the eardrum to the **oval window** of the **cochlea**. The vibrations travel from the eardrum to the **hammer**, then to the **anvil**, and finally to the **stirrup** which is attached to the oval window. Together these bones act as interlocking levers that cause the force exerted by the stirrup on the oval window to be about double the force exerted by the eardrum on the hammer.

Since the oval window possesses about 1/20 of the area of the eardrum, the pressure variation is magnified about 20 times. Taken together, these two factors magnify the pressure about 40 times. The middle ear transmits and amplifies the pressure variations received from the sound wave.

From the middle ear, the vibrations are passed to the fluid inside the snail-shaped cochlea. Within the cochlea are roughly 23 000 specialized hair-like cells that respond to different frequencies. Their vibrations stimulate nerve cells to emit electric impulses that are carried along the **auditory nerve** to the brain. And, because these cells only respond to specific frequencies, their electric impulses carry the frequency information to the brain. In this respect, the auditory nerve and the optic nerve behave very much alike.

Although the ear can detect an enormous range of frequencies, it is most sensitive to frequencies lying between 1 kHz and 5 kHz. The ability of the human ear to detect sound decreases as we move away from this region toward the audible limits of 16 Hz and 20 kHz (Figure 7.15).

Care must be taken to prevent damage to the hearing mechanism of the ear. Unfortunately, some people who work in areas of intense noise suffer loss of hearing. This loss often occurs in the sensitive region between 1 kHz and 5 kHz. Many of the frequencies found in normal conversation occur in this region. As a result, such hearing-impaired people believe that they can hear well, and yet find it difficult to understand conversation, or to distinguish between the sound of normal conversation and background noise. Laws and standards are now in place to control the exposure of workers on the job. However, scientists and doctors are also concerned about the sound levels that many young people are exposing themselves to while listening to their audio systems. The damage to the cells in the cochlea may not show up for several years.

Even if we have not damaged our hearing when young, as we get older, the upper limit of hearing drops below 20 kHz. As a result, students in a physics class can generally detect higher frequencies than their teacher can.

WEBLINK

Because of the possibility of damage to their hearing, workers in industry are protected against loud noise. Prepare a poster on industry and government standards as if you were the health and safety officer for your company or union. Begin your research at **www.pearsoned.ca/physics11.**

WEBLINK

Can you hear colours sing? Some people can. They might even sense a particular odour when they feel a certain shape. This mixing of sensory data is known as synethesia. Write a descriptive paragraph on what it would be like for a person with synethesia to walk down a busy street. Begin your research at **www.pearsoned.ca/physics11.**

Dealing with Noise Pollution

Decision-Making Skills

- Defining the Issue
- Developing Assessment Criteria
- Researching the Issue
- Analyzing Data and Information
- Proposing a Course of Action
- Justifying the Course of Action
- Communicating Your Proposal

BACKGROUND INFORMATION

Have you ever come back from a concert and found that you cannot hear properly for a few hours? Whether we are talking about music or noise, we are bathed in a sea of sound. It surrounds us in our cities and towns, in our homes, and our workplaces. Traffic and industrial noise compete with the sound of home appliances, radios, television, and people. The level of noise in some restaurants exceeds the noise levels permitted for workers in industry.

Audiologists are finding increasing numbers of people who are experiencing hearing loss. A study of hearing loss was done with 60 students at Queen's University in Ontario. The hearing of over one-third of the participants who listened regularly to loud music and played video games had already been affected. Exposure to high noise levels can have other effects as well, including high blood pressure and sleep disturbance.

This is not an easy issue to resolve. People often define "noise pollution" in different ways. Animated conversation at one table in a restaurant can be an irritation at another table. Since issues of personal freedom are involved, it is likely there will always be different perspectives on noise pollution and the dangers it poses.

FIGURE 7.17 Traffic causes a lot of noise.

Analyzing the Issue

1. As a class, identify the principle stakeholders who could be affected by this issue. Consider the social, economic, and health impacts that noise pollution may cause.
2. Research the different sources of noise pollution in the workplace and the community, and the level of hearing loss that can result. Prepare a chart to summarize your research.
3. Reducing noise levels is often a matter of personal choice. In your opinion, are there circumstances when a person has a right to ask others to "turn down the volume"? Explain.
4. A community benefit rock concert is planned. The concert will be held in an outdoor park, which borders both a residential area as well as a group of commercial businesses. In a town hall meeting, develop a course of action regarding noise regulation for the concert. Representatives from the local community, business owners, and concert promoters will attend the meeting.
5. Summarize the regulations resulting from the town hall meeting in a one-page report to be distributed to the community. Each regulation should include a brief description of why that regulation has been put in place.

Section 7.2 Review

Understanding Concepts

1. What is the audible range of the average human ear?
2. Approximately how many octaves fit into the audible region of the human ear?
3. What frequencies are associated with
   a) infrasound?
   b) ultrasound?
4. Briefly describe three uses of ultrasound by humans.
5. Briefly describe two uses of ultrasound by animals.
6. Distinguish between sound intensity and loudness. How do they relate to amplitude and pressure variation in sound waves?
7. What are the base units for sound intensity?
8. Convert the following sound intensities to pW/m^2:
   a) 80 dB
   b) 9.0 B
   c) 130 dB
   d) 20 B
9. What role do levers play in hearing?
10. How is the pressure variation in a sound wave amplified in the human ear?
11. How is pitch information transmitted to the brain?

Applying Inquiry/ Communication Skills

12. Outline an experiment to determine the presence of ultrasound in an apparently silent room.

Making Connections

13. Test the sound intensity of various children's toys and compare them with the sound levels permitted in industry. Find out whether any agency tests toys for sound levels.

7.3 The Speed of Sound

FIGURE 7.18 The sound of fireworks doesn't reach us as quickly as the light-explosion.

Key Understandings

When you have completed this section, you will be able to:

- analyze the velocity of waves travelling in different media in quantitative terms
- compare the speed of sound in different media
- describe the effect of temperature on the speed of sound
- describe how knowledge of acoustics is applied in the design of concert halls and theatres

Sound travels much more slowly than light. We see the flash of lightning before we hear the crack of thunder. The burst of fireworks appears before the sound of the explosion reaches us. But how much slower is sound? Does it always travel at the same speed through air? Is it possible that sound could reach us faster through water than through air?

Temperature and the Speed of Sound

Investigation
Refer to page 285, Investigation 1

Sound travels through air by means of moving molecules. So, the speed at which a compression or a rarefaction can spread through a gas cannot be faster than the normal molecular speeds. Since these speeds increase with a rise in temperature, the speed of sound should increase as well. At a temperature of 0°C and a pressure of 101 kPa (one standard atmosphere of pressure), the speed of sound in air is 331 m/s. For each rise in temperature of 1°C, the speed increases by 0.59 m/s. This is expressed by

$$v = 331 \text{ m/s} + 0.59 \text{ m/s·°C} \times T$$

where v is the speed of sound in air in m/s, T is the air temperature in °C, and 0.59 is a constant that has units of m/(s·°C)

For all problems that follow we will assume that the air pressure is one atmosphere.

EXAMPLE 1 NUMERICAL

Two mountain-climbers, part way up a mountain, clapped their hands and heard the echoes return from the mountain face opposite them in 6.0 s. If the air temperature was −5.0°C, how far away was the mountain face?

Given
$\Delta t = 6.0 \text{ s}$
$T = -5.0°\text{C}$

Required
Δd

Analysis
- From the temperature, calculate the speed of sound.
- From speed and time, calculate the distance.
- Divide this total distance by two.

Solution

$$v = 331 \frac{\text{m}}{\text{s}} + 0.59 \frac{\text{m}}{\text{s·°C}} \times T$$

$$v = 331 \frac{\text{m}}{\text{s}} + 0.59 \frac{\text{m}}{\text{s·°C}}(-5°\text{C})$$

$$v = 331 \frac{\text{m}}{\text{s}} + (-3) \frac{\text{m}}{\text{s}}$$

$$v = 328 \frac{\text{m}}{\text{s}}$$

$$\Delta d = v \times \Delta t$$

$$\Delta d = 328 \frac{\text{m}}{\text{s}} \times 6.0 \text{ s}$$

$$\Delta d = 1968 \text{ m}$$

distance one way = 1968 m ÷ 2
= 984 m

Statement
The distance to the mountain face was 9.8×10^2 m.

INSIGHT

Although the temperature is given to only one significant digit, the resulting speed of sound is good to three figures. This is a result of the rule for adding and subtracting measured digits.

PRACTICE PROBLEMS

1. On a chilly winter's day (−20°C), an echo returned in 3.00 s. How far away was the reflecting surface?
2. A cliff is located 100 m away from a climber. If the climber shouts, how long will it take the echo to return if air temperature is 30°C?

TABLE 7.4 Speed of Sound in Various Media at 25°C

State	Substance	Speed v (m/s)
solids	aluminum	6420
	nickel	6040
	steel	5960
	iron	5950
	glass (crown)	5100
	brass	4700
	glass (flint)	3980
liquids	water (sea)	1531
	water (distilled)	1498
	mercury	1450
	ethanol	1207
	methanol	1103
	carbon tetrachloride	926
gases	hydrogen	1339
	helium	985
	carbon monoxide	353
	air	346
	oxygen	330
	carbon dioxide	269
	sulfur dioxide	225

The speed of sound depends on the ability of the medium to transmit a longitudinal wave. How do you think the mass of the molecules would affect this speed? You might expect that hydrogen gas, which possesses the lightest molecule, would have the highest speed. Helium should be close behind since the mass of a helium atom is twice that of the hydrogen molecule. Sulfur dioxide, a molecule with 16 times the mass of the hydrogen molecule, should transmit sound much more slowly. The data in Table 7.4 will verify this prediction.

Echoes and Reverberations

The reflection of sound is a common occurrence in the world around us. **Echoes** are a source of amusement for children in underpasses and tourists on mountain slopes. In large cathedrals, echoes cause notes to gradually fade away as they reflect back and forth from wall to wall in the process called **reverberation**. In concert halls (Figure 7.19), echoes can severely interfere with the quality of sound from the stage. Strong reverberation must be prevented through the design of the walls, ceiling, and seats. A long reverberation time is generally not desirable, because if the sound waves from the performer reflect several times before reaching a listener, the spoken words will become blurred and distorted. One method of absorbing sound in a theatre is by selecting seat material that has the same sound absorption qualities as an average member of the audience. This enables the hall to sound the same regardless of the size of the audience. Many other acoustical properties can now be designed directly into halls during their construction. Echoes, however, should not be totally omitted. If too much of the sound is absorbed, the theatre will sound "dead."

WEBLINK

Many sonar devices have come on the market. Explore the range of styles and applications of these devices. Prepare a poster that could act as an advertisement for a company which produces sonar devices. Begin your research at **www.pearsoned.ca/physics11.**

Sonar is an acronym for sound navigation and ranging. Echoes have an important use in sonar. A short pulse of sound is emitted under water, and the time measured until the return of the echo. The distance to the object that reflected the sound waves can then be calculated by knowing the speed of sound through the water (Figure 7.20).

The hand-held ultrasonic ruler emits brief pulses of ultrasound. The ruler then measures the time required for the echo to return in order to calculate the distance to the remote object. If you had one that was meant to be operated in air and tried to use it under water, would the distance measurements be too large or too small?

FIGURE 7.19 The interior of a large concert hall

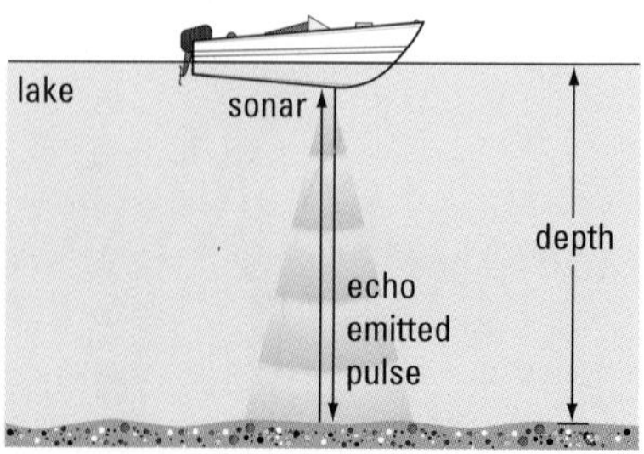

FIGURE 7.20 Depth determination with sonar

EXAMPLE 2 NUMERICAL

A ship sends out a pulse that returns from the floor of the sea in 3.42 s. If the speed of sound through salt water is 1531 m/s, what is the distance to the bottom of the sea?

Given

$\Delta t = 3.42$ s

$v = 1531$ m/s

Required

depth

Analysis

- From speed and time, calculate the distance Δd.
- The depth will be half of the total distance travelled by the sound.

Solution

$$\begin{aligned}\Delta d &= v \times \Delta t\\ &= 1531 \text{ m/s} \times 3.42 \text{ s}\\ &= 5236 \text{ m}\\ \text{depth} &= 5236 \text{ m} \div 2\\ &= 2618 \text{ m}\end{aligned}$$

Statement

The distance to the bottom of the sea is 2.62×10^3 m or 2.62 km.

PRACTICE PROBLEMS

1. The speed of light through air is 3.00×10^8 m/s. At a temperature of -52.5 °C, how many times faster does light travel through air than does sound?
2. A submarine emits a sonar pulse, which returns from an underwater cliff in 1.02 s. If the speed of sound in salt water is 1531 m/s, how far away is the cliff?
3. A dolphin squeals when a shark is 42.0 m away from it. How long will it take the echo to return from the shark if the speed of sound through sea water is 1531 m/s?

If you have ever watched a car race, you may have noticed the sudden drop in pitch of the motor as each car speeds past. Some observers incorrectly believe that the driver has shifted gears at that instant. In fact, you are observing the **Doppler effect** with sound waves. As the source of sound roars toward you, the wavelengths in front are shortened, resulting in higher frequencies and a higher pitch. Once the source has gone by, the wavelengths behind it are stretched out and you hear a lower frequency and lower pitch. These wavelength relations are shown in Figure 7.21.

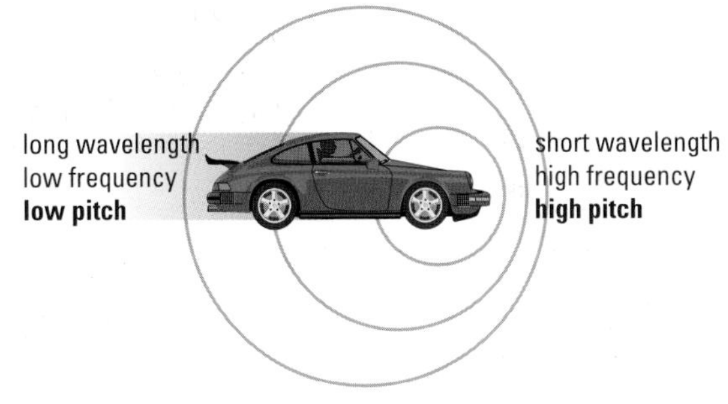

FIGURE 7.21 Doppler effect from a race car

Breaking the Sound Barrier

Prior to 1948, many people believed that it would be impossible to fly faster than the speed of sound. They had good reason. When an airplane is travelling at **subsonic** speeds (slower than the speed of sound), the air molecules in front of the wing are pushed forward by the leading edge of the wing. As a result, a compression travels forward faster than the wing. The compression pushes other air molecules out of the way. Consequently, most of the air molecules are above or below the wing as it passes by, as Figure 7.22 shows.

When the wing reaches the speed of sound, the compression cannot move faster than the wing. Air molecules start

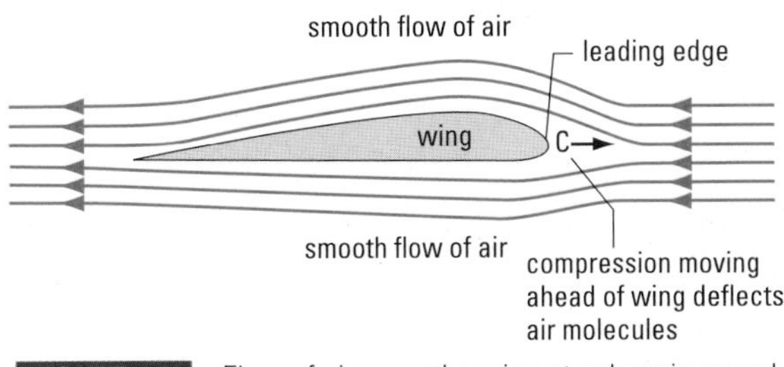

FIGURE 7.22 Flow of air around a wing at subsonic speed

Discovering Physics — Detecting Changes in Pitch

When you blow a whistle by blowing on a tube attached to the whistle, you can hear changes in pitch. Insert the mouthpiece of a whistle firmly into one end of a 60-cm length of tubing. Tape the whistle in place. Roll up some clean paper into a cylinder and insert it into the other end of the tubing to act as a sterile mouthpiece. Have one person blow the whistle through the tubing while whirling it horizontally around her head. The rest of the class should stand well back and listen.

- Can you detect the flutter in the pitch of the whistle as the pitch rises when the whistle moves toward you and then drops as it moves away?

to pile up in front of the wing. From time to time, this pile-up of air molecules spills across the wing causing buffeting. This instability was the cause of many jet crashes as test pilots strove to "break the sound barrier."

In 1948, the sound barrier was broken and a **sonic boom** was heard for the first time from an airplane. When a plane reaches or exceeds the speed of sound, the leading edge of the wing rams constantly into air molecules that have not been deflected. A region of intense pressure builds up in front of the wing. The continual spillage of this compression above and below the wing forms a **shock wave** (Figure 7.23).

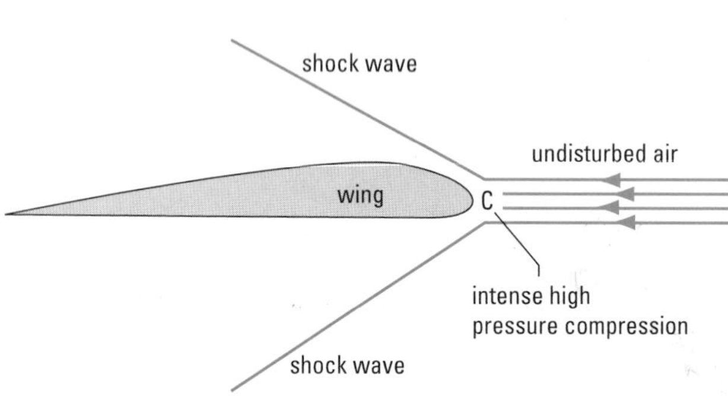

FIGURE 7.23 Shock wave at supersonic speeds

As long as the plane is flying at **sonic** or **supersonic** speeds (at the speed of sound or greater), this shock wave continuously spreads out from the plane. The sonic boom that breaks windows is the arrival of this shock wave at the ground. The sonic boom does not signal that the jet has just exceeded the speed of sound. It merely indicates that a plane flying at or faster than the speed of sound is in the vicinity. The jet could have passed through the sound barrier hours earlier or at another location.

The sonic boom is not restricted to aircraft. The next time you observe a flag on a windy day, listen for the snapping sound. It indicates that the edge of the flag has surpassed the speed of sound. The crack from a flicked, wet towel indicates that the tip of the towel has in fact exceeded the speed of sound, producing a shock wave.

WEBLINK

Because of sonic booms, supersonic transport (SST) aircraft are not permitted to travel faster than the speed of sound over any urban area. Find out more about these aircraft and the problems associated with them. Construct a graphic organizer such as a web diagram to link the features of SSTs to their benefits and problems. Begin your research at **www.pearsoned.ca/physics11.**

Section 7.3 Review

Understanding Concepts

1. Calculate the speed of sound in air at the following temperatures:
   a) 4.0°C
   b) 35°C
   c) −30°C
   d) −15°C
2. How long will it take sound at 0.0°C to travel 100 m through air?
3. Why does air tend to flow around a wing at subsonic speeds?
4. Why does air ram into the leading edge of the wing at sonic and supersonic speeds?
5. A sailing ship is travelling in the North Atlantic at night. The captain is worried about icebergs, but has no radar. The captain sounds the ship's horn and hears the echo 2.4 s later. If the air temperature is −10°C, how far away is the iceberg?
6. How long would it take an echo to return from *The Titanic* off the coast of Newfoundland, if it is 4.0 km below the surface of the Atlantic? The speed of sound in seawater is 1531 m/s.

Applying Inquiry/Communication Skills

7. Use Table 7.4 and information on density of materials to determine whether the speed of sound in solids and liquids correlates with density. (Use a graph for your analysis.)

7.4 Interference and Diffraction

Key Understandings

When you have completed this section, you will be able to:

- explain and graphically illustrate the principle of superposition
- identify examples of constructive and destructive interference of sound
- describe and explain diffraction of sound waves

At the start of this chapter, you examined the pattern of sound intensity around a tuning fork. You probably found that it was fainter in some directions than in others. If you decided that this decrease in loudness was due to destructive interference of waves then you were on the right track. But interference requires at least two sources of waves. How is it possible to receive two sets of waves from one tuning fork?

Interference of Sound

We know that constructive interference results when two or more waves push the medium in the same direction at the same time. In sound, this occurs wherever two or more compressions or rarefactions overlap. The result is an increase in the intensity of the sound. Destructive interference occurs when two or more waves push the medium in opposite directions at the same time. In sound, this happens whenever a compression overlaps a rarefaction. Destructive interference results in a decrease in the intensity of the sound. If the compression and rarefaction have exactly the same amplitude and wavelength, the waves completely cancel each other. A nodal point or node is produced and the result is total silence.

Interference is produced in many different ways. Possibly the simplest way is with a single tuning fork, illustrated in Figure 7.24a). If you look at the tines of a vibrating tuning fork with the aid of a flashing strobe light adjusted close to the frequency of the tines, the vibration appears to be very slow. The tines are seen vibrating in opposite phase to each other. As they vibrate toward each other, they squeeze the air between them and form a compression C, as we see in Figure 7.24b). At the same time, the air expands to fill in the space left behind the tines. This creates rarefactions R at the outside edges. These compressions and rarefactions spread out from their sources. Eventually they overlap along the diagonal lines shown in Figure 7.24c), resulting in destructive interference.

Later when the tines move apart, a rarefaction forms in the region between them. At the same time, compressions form in front of the outside edges as the tines push outward into the air. Again, compressions and rarefactions meet along the same diagonal lines and produce destructive interference. Since destructive interference always occurs, these lines are called **nodal lines**. They are the reason for the **silent points** about a tuning fork.

A second method for illustrating interference in sound is to place two speakers vibrating in phase side by side. In Figure 7.25, the two speakers are connected through an amplifier to the same output from a wave generator. The compressions are shown as shaded arcs, while the rarefactions are shown as white arcs. The darkest areas indicate the overlapping of compressions, while the white areas indicate the overlapping of rarefactions. These regions of constructive interference form lines, known as **antinodal lines**, radiating outward from the midpoint between the speakers.

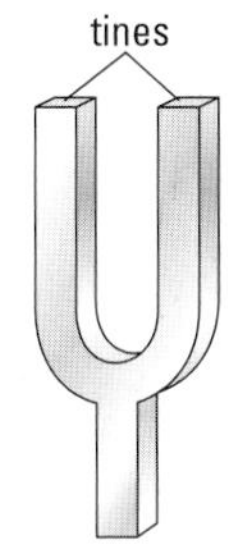

a) Side view of a tuning fork

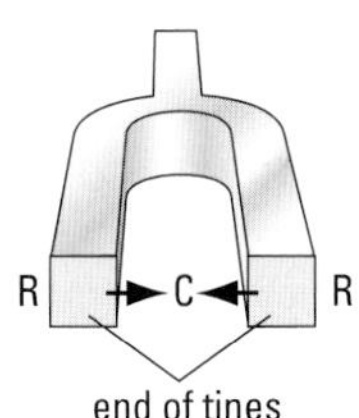

b) Top view showing the tines moving together

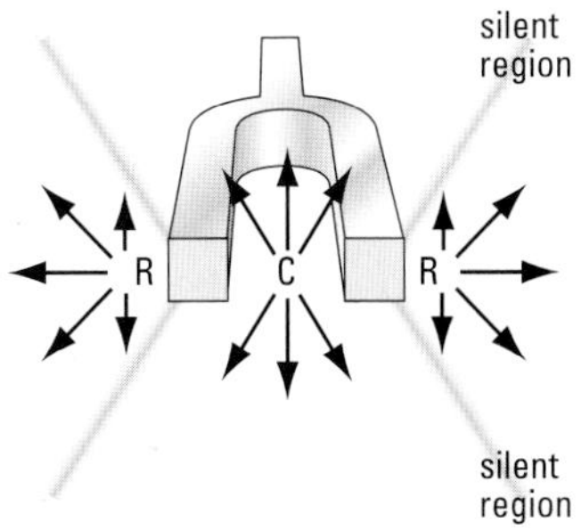

c) Compressions and rarefactions destructively interfere at the corners.

FIGURE 7.24 What causes silent points near a tuning fork?

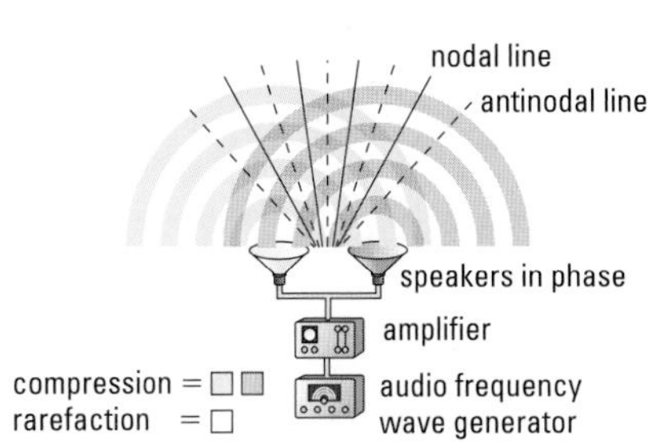

FIGURE 7.25 Interference from two speakers vibrating in phase

WEBLINK

View an animation of the production of beats. Draw a series of diagrams to illustrate beat production. Begin your research at **www.pearsoned.ca/physics11.**

Between these antinodal lines are lines along which compressions and rarefactions overlap. These lines of destructive interference, called nodal lines, likewise radiate out from the midpoint between the speakers.

The sound along a nodal line is quite faint. However, in actual demonstrations, it never becomes completely silent. People walking across the room parallel to the line joining the speakers will hear the changes in loudness as they pass through regions of constructive and destructive interference.

Interference and Beats

Consider a point that receives sound waves of different frequencies. These waves arrive alternately in phase and in opposite phase. When these waves are in phase, the sound is louder than normal. When the waves are in opposite phase they destructively interfere and the loudness decreases. These variations in the loudness are called beats. One **beat** is a full cycle of loudness variation from loud to soft and back to loud. Figure 7.26 shows the beats produced by two waves. One wave has a frequency of 10 Hz, while the other has a frequency of 15 Hz. Suppose the waves are in phase at $t = 0$ s. You can see from the diagram that the waves will be in phase five times each succeeding second, at $t = 0.2$ s, $t = 0.4$ s, $t = 0.6$ s, $t = 0.8$ s, and $t = 1.0$ s. This results in five beats each second, or a beat frequency of 5 Hz.

In general, the **beat frequency** is equal to the difference in frequency between two sources.

$$\text{beat frequency} = |f_2 - f_1|$$

The vertical lines indicate that the absolute value is required, as it is not possible to have a negative beat frequency.

This graph shows the occurrence of compressions at a point, due to two sources of different frequency.

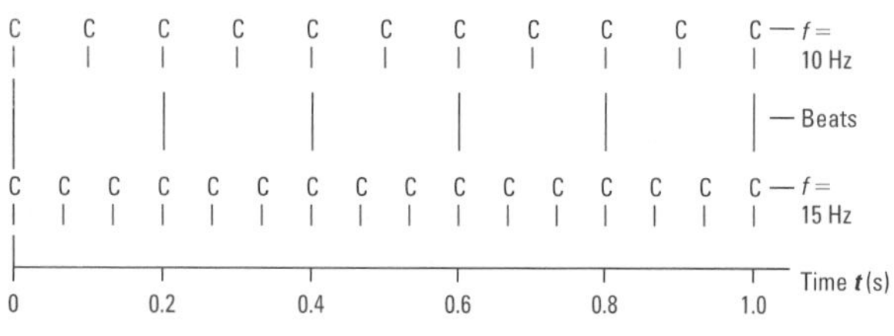

FIGURE 7.26 Production of beats

INSIGHT

If given the difference between two numbers, use the mathematical technique for solving equations involving absolute values.

CHALLENGE

1. When two trumpets were sounded together, 6 beats were heard in 2 s. If the frequency of one trumpet was 768 Hz:
   a) What were the possible frequencies of the second trumpet?
   b) How could the trumpet players have decided which frequency it actually was?
2. A person has two audio frequency generators with which to demonstrate beats. One generator is set to 1000 Hz and the other to 998 Hz. How many beats will be heard in 10 s?

EXAMPLE 3 — CONCEPTUAL

When a tuning fork of unknown frequency is sounded simultaneously with a 512-Hz tuning fork, 20 beats are heard in 4.0 s. What are the possible frequencies of the unknown tuning fork?

Reasoning and Solution

$$f_{\text{beats}} = \frac{N}{\Delta t} = \frac{20}{4.0\ \text{s}} = 5.0\ \text{Hz}$$

$$|f_2 - f_1| = 5\ \text{Hz}$$

therefore $f_2 - f_1 = 5$ Hz or $f_2 - f_1 = -5$ Hz

$$f_2 = f_1 + 5\ \text{Hz} = 512\ \text{Hz} + 5\ \text{Hz} = 517\ \text{Hz}$$

$$f_2 = f_1 - 5\ \text{Hz} = 512\ \text{Hz} - 5\ \text{Hz} = 507\ \text{Hz}$$

The two possible frequencies for the unknown tuning fork are 517 Hz and 507 Hz.

Exploration Using a Graphing Calculator

In this investigation, you will examine how the pressure changes at your eardrum during a 2-s time interval due to beats between two waves. The equation of pressure against time has the form

$$y = A \sin(2\pi f x)$$

where

y is the pressure at a given time (from -15 to $+15$)
A is the pressure amplitude of the wave
f is the frequency of the wave
x represents the time interval (from 0 to 2 s)

Show the superposition of two waves, with frequencies of 15 Hz and 18 Hz by graphing $y = 5 \sin(2\pi 15x) + 5 \sin(2\pi 18x)$. This graph will show compressions as crests (high pressure) and rarefactions as troughs (low pressure).

Discussion

1. How do beats appear on the graph?
2. When the sound is loudest, what is happening to the pressure?
3. A beat can be thought of as the cycle from loud to soft and back to loud. During the two seconds shown on the graph, how many complete beats occur? How many occur in one second? What is the beat frequency?
4. What relationship is there between the beat frequency and the individual frequencies?

Once a musical instrument has been properly tuned, it can be used as the standard to tune others. The instrument to be tuned is sounded at the same time as the standard. The player listens for beats. If beats are heard, the frequency of the instrument is then adjusted slightly. If the beat frequency increases, then the player knows that the frequency of the instrument has been tuned farther away from the frequency of the standard. The player keeps on

Discovering Physics — ***Measuring an Unknown Frequency Using Beats***

Listen for beats when you strike two turning forks.

1. Obtain two frequency-matched tuning forks that are mounted on resonance boxes.
2. Change the frequency of one tuning fork by placing clamps on its tines. If no clamps are available, attach a lump of modelling clay to the end of each tine.
3. Now strike both tuning forks with the mallet. Do you hear beats?
4. Time how long it takes for 10 beats to occur and calculate the beat frequency.
5. If the frequency of the unchanged tuning fork is known, calculate the frequency of the other one. Describe the procedure you can use to determine if the changed fork has a higher or lower frequency than the unchanged one.

adjusting the instrument until no beats are heard when the instrument and standard are played at the same time. When this occurs, the instrument and the standard have the same frequency and are in tune.

Diffraction

We may not be able to see around corners without optical aids, but we can certainly hear around corners. You hear voices out in the hall before people enter the class. Even when you are behind a building, you can hear a truck drive down the street in front of the building. You hear a car alarm sounding from blocks away. All these examples involve diffraction. Sound diffracts well in everyday situations. Since the longer wavelengths diffract more than the shorter wavelengths, we tend to hear the lower bass notes better than the higher treble notes if music has had to bend around a corner or out through a window.

INFOBIT

While the cone of a speaker pushes out a compression from its front surface, a rarefaction is forming at the back surface. If the rarefaction is allowed to diffract around, it can interfere with the compression at the front. For this reason, speakers are mounted in boxes to prevent this diffraction from occurring.

To hear this effect, connect the output of a compact disc player to an unmounted speaker and listen to the music it produces. Then, take a sheet of cardboard and cut out an opening just large enough to frame the speaker cone. Notice the improvement in sound when the opening is held right in front of the speaker cone.

Section 7.4 Review

Understanding Concepts

1. Name the effect that produces the silent points around a tuning fork.
2. Are the louder regions around a tuning fork the result of constructive interference? Explain your answer.
3. In beats, which type of interference produces
   a) the loud part of the cycle?
   b) the quiet part of the cycle?
4. When two trumpets are sounded together, 8.0 beats are counted in 2.0 s. What is the difference between the two frequencies?
5. Two tuning forks are sounded together. One has a frequency of 880.0 Hz and the other has a frequency of 886.0 Hz. How many beats will be heard in 15 s?
6. Describe two examples of diffraction of sound that were not mentioned in the text.

Applying Inquiry/ Communication Skills

7. Light will show diffraction if it passes through a very narrow slit. Describe an experiment to show which colour—red or blue—has the longer wavelength.
8. Besides diffraction, what other wave phenomenon may be involved in hearing sound "around corners"? Illustrate with a sketch.

Making Conections

9. Earphones, which can provide nearly complete silence in noisy surroundings, are now available on the market. Suggest a way in which they might work.

Investigation 1 (Section 7.3)

Inquiry Skills

- Initiating and Planning
- Applying Technical Skills
- Using Tools, Materials, Equipment
- Conducting and Recording
- Analyzing and Interpreting
- Concluding and Communicating

Speed of Sound in Air

When you watch a fireworks display you can see that sound travels much more slowly than light. The flash of each explosion is seen before the sound is heard. Also the time difference increases as the fireworks climb higher. In this activity you will measure how fast sound travels through air.

Problem

What is the speed of sound in air? Design an experiment to determine the speed of sound in air.

Materials

- stopwatch
- tape measure
- thermometer
- sound source (2 wooden blocks)
- ear protection against noise
- heavy gloves

Caution: The person who produces the noise must wear ear protection and gloves.

Procedure

1. Stand at least 50 m away from a large, long outside wall of the school.
2. Measure the distance from the wall to the observer.
3. Clap the blocks together. Measure the time interval between producing the sound and hearing the echo. (It may sound like a faint click immediately after the original noise.)
4. Measure the temperature of the air.

Analyzing and Interpreting

1. How far did sound travel from production to reception at the ear?
2. How long did this take?
3. Discuss briefly the difficulties in obtaining an accurate value for the travel time in this experiment.
4. Suggest ways to improve this experiment.

Concluding and Communicating

5. Calculate the speed of sound in the outside air.
6. Since the speed of sound depends on the speed of air molecules, what effect do you think an increase in temperature would have on the speed of sound? Explain your answer.
7. How can the distance to a lightning bolt be determined, knowing the speed of sound?

Extending

8. Express how you could use the data from this experiment to determine the distance to some large object. Design a method to evaluate the effectiveness of your procedure.

Investigation 2 (Section 7.2)

Inquiry Skills

- Initiating and Planning
- Applying Technical Skills
- Using Tools, material, Equipment
- Conducting and Recording
- Analyzing and Interpreting
- Concluding and Communicating

Sound Intensity, Distance, and Medium

It is obvious to anyone who has attended a concert or a dance club that the sound is loudest closest to the speakers. The loudness decreases as you move farther away. It will also decrease if you put some shielding material between your eardrum and the speakers. Hands held over the ears, or plugs placed into the ears, work quite effectively to reduce the loudness. In this activity you will investigate two methods for reducing the loudness of a sound.

Problem

How is the intensity of sound affected by the distance between the source and the receiver, and by the thickness of the soundproofing between the source and the receiver?

Materials

- soundproof material such as ceiling tiles or Styrofoam slabs
- metre-stick or measuring tape
- sound intensity meter or data logger sound sensor
- sound source of constant intensity such as a bell and power supply

Note: If possible, conduct this experiment in a room with a carpet and drapes. The school library may be a good location.

Experimental Design

Part A: Effect of Separation on Sound Intensity

1. In a small group, brainstorm the steps of a procedure to investigate how the intensity of the sound changes as the distance from the source of the sound increases. You should consider the following questions:
   - How could you compensate for background noise that may change during the course of the investigation?
   - What measurements will you take?
   - How many trial runs do you intend to take in order to verify the consistency of your data?
   - How will you organize and present your data?
   - How will you analyze your data in order to identify the relationship?
2. Write out the details of your procedure. When the group is satisfied, have your procedure approved by the teacher.
3. Conduct the investigation and record the data in an organized manner.

Part B: Effect of Soundproofing

4. In a small group, brainstorm the steps of a procedure to investigate how the intensity of the sound changes as the thickness of the soundproof material changes. In addition to the questions involved in Part A, you should consider the following:
   - How will you ensure that sound must travel through the soundproof material in order to reach the sensor?

Analyzing and Interpreting

1. As the distance from the source of sound increased, what happened to the intensity of the sound? If you plotted a graph of the data, what is the appearance of the graph? Identify the dependent and independent variables. Generally, the independent variable is graphed on the x-axis.
2. As the thickness of the soundproof material increased, what happened to the intensity of the sound? If you plotted a graph of the data, what is the appearance of the graph? Identify the dependent and independent variables.
3. Were the data consistent?
4. Did other factors hinder the investigation?
5. If you have access to a graphing calculator, plot the scattergraph for the data from your different investigations and try to find the curve of best fit for each.

Concluding and Communicating

6. How does the sound intensity change as the distance from the source increases?
7. How does the sound intensity change as the thickness of the soundproof material increases?
8. From your distance graph, determine:
   a) the intensity of the sound at a distance of 1.0 m from the source
   b) the distance you must be from the source to receive half the intensity of sound in dB that was received at 1.0 m
9. From your thickness graph, determine what thickness of soundproof material was required to reduce the intensity of the sound to half the original intensity.

Extending

10. Do you think there is a relationship between the ability of a substance to absorb sound and the pitch of the sound? Make a prediction. Brainstorm to determine a procedure that could be used to test your prediction. With your teacher's approval, conduct this investigation.

CHAPTER SUMMARY

Key Terms

antinodal line	infrasonic	octave	sonar
audible region	infrasound	overtone	sonic boom
beat	intensity	pitch	subsonic
beat frequency	loudness	reverberation	supersonic
bel	nodal line	shock wave	ultrasonic
decibel	noise	silent point	ultrasound

Key Equations

$v = 331 \text{ m/s} + 0.59 \text{ m/s}\cdot°\text{C} \times T$

Essential Understandings

- Sound begins as a vibration and travels as a longitudinal wave through a material medium.
- Sound properties such as pitch, loudness, and quality, are determined by the corresponding wave properties.
- The audible range of human hearing is from about 16 Hz to 20 kHz.
- Frequencies below the audible range are termed "infrasonic." Those above the audible range are termed "ultrasonic."
- Loudness is a physiological response of the ear to the intensity of the sound.
- The intensity of sound depends on the strength of the source, the type of medium between the source and the listener, and the distance between the source and the listener.
- The human ear uses physical laws involving levers and pressure.
- Echo times can be used to determine the distance to reflecting objects.
- The speed of sound depends primarily on the nature of the transmitting medium.
- The Doppler effect is the change in pitch of a sound due to the relative motion between the source of sound and the observer.
- A sonic boom is produced whenever an object travels at or greater than the speed of sound.
- Sound waves interfere both constructively and destructively.
- Silent points around a tuning fork are regions of destructive interference.
- Lines of constructive interference (antinodal lines) alternate with lines of destructive interference (nodal lines) for sound waves from two speakers vibrating in phase.
- Beats are an example of interference from two sound sources having different frequencies.
- Beat frequency equals the absolute value of the difference in frequencies between the two sources.
- Diffraction of sound is the bending of a sound wave around a corner or through an opening.

Consolidate Your Understanding

1. Look back to your answer for the Checkpoint on page 265. Would you still give the same answer? Since answer d) contains a true statement, why is it not the correct answer?
2. Sound microscopes have been developed in which the wavelength of the sound is about the same as the wavelength of light. Would this sound wave be classified as infrasound, audible sound, or ultrasound?
3. Create a concept map to illustrate the relationship between wave motion and sound. Try to include as many of the Key Terms listed above as possible.
4. As a jet plane approaches, its speed increases. Even before it reaches you, it passes through the "sound barrier." Describe how the sound that you hear would change in both pitch and intensity. Explain your answer in terms of wave properties.
5. Why might you cease to hear the sound of the jet even before it passed through the sound barrier? Explain you answer in terms of wave properties and the ability of the human ear to hear sound.

CHAPTER 7 REVIEW

Understanding Concepts

1. Which wave property causes a trumpet to sound different from a clarinet even when they are playing the same note with the same loudness?
   a) reflection
   b) complexity of wave pattern
   c) frequency
   d) amplitude
   e) speed
2. Which wave property affects the intensity of sound?
   a) reflection
   b) complexity of wave pattern
   c) frequency
   d) amplitude
   e) speed
3. At normal pressure, what is the speed of sound in air at a temperature of 40°C?
   a) 291 m/s b) 308 m/s c) 331 m/s
   d) 355 m/s e) 381 m/s
4. Which of the following frequencies is infrasonic?
   a) 12 Hz b) 60 Hz c) 200 Hz
   d) 5000 Hz e) 25 000 Hz
5. A 366-Hz note is sounded along with a 370-Hz note. What is the frequency of the beats?
   a) 1.01 Hz b) 4 Hz c) 368 Hz
   d) 736 Hz e) 1.35×10^5 Hz
6. Explain why a bass drum player seen from a distance seems to be beating out of time with the music.
7. Will an echo return fastest on a hot day or a cold day if the distance to the reflecting surface remains the same?
8. Why can you hear the bass (low) notes from the radio in the car driving behind you better than the higher-pitched notes?
9. Explain why many passengers chew gum during an airplane take-off to keep their ears from hurting.
10. Why is it never totally silent along a nodal line produced by two speakers vibrating in phase?
11. Why would "cupping your ears" by placing the curved palm of your hand behind your ears improve your ability to hear sounds coming in front of you?
12. When a frequency of 512 Hz is sounded while a trumpet plays, three beats are heard each second. Is this sufficient information to determine the frequency of the trumpet sound? Explain your answer.

Applying Inquiry/ Communication Skills

13. If the speed of sound in air is 342 m/s, what is the air temperature?
14. Consult Table 7.4 and determine how long it will take sound to travel 5.0 km through seawater.
15. A 440-Hz tuning fork is sounding along with a 443-Hz tuning fork. How many beats are heard in 2.0 s?
16. A guitar string with a frequency of 440 Hz is sounded along with one with a frequency of 438 Hz. How many beats are heard in 10 s?
17. On a certain day, the speed of sound was 333 m/s. How long would it take an echo to return from a cliff that was 200 m away?
18. Determine the wavelength in air of a 100-Hz note on a day when the temperature was 0°C.
19. When a guitar string is sounded against a 440-Hz note, 12 beats are heard in 2.0 s.
    a) What are the possible frequencies of the string?
    b) When the same string is sounded against a 435-Hz note, 33 beats are heard in 3.0 s. What is the frequency of the string?
20. A trombone is being tuned to a 233-Hz note. At first, 24 beats are heard in 3.00 s. When the pitch of the trombone is slowly raised, 5 beats are heard in 3.00 s. What was the original frequency of the trombone?
21. Calculate the wavelength of a 1000-Hz note at 25°C in
    a) hydrogen
    b) sulfur dioxide
    c) air
    d) flint glass
22. If the air temperature is 35°C, determine the wavelength range for audible sound.
23. If a sonar echo takes 2.20 s to return from a whale, how far away is the whale?
24. The bang from a fireworks explosion was heard 1.20 s after the flash. If the air temperature was 8.0°C, how far away was the explosion?
25. A physics student wanted to know the air temperature but lacked a thermometer. Being resourceful, like all physics students, she fired a cap pistol and measured the time for the echo to return to her from a cliff that was 200.0 m away. If the time interval was 1.16 s, what was the air temperature?
26. At 0°C, a cannon fires a shell at 1324 m/s.
    a) How fast is the shell travelling relative to the sound wave from the explosion?
    b) How far away from the cannon is an observer who sees the shell pass by 2.00 s before the sound of the explosion arrives?
27. A seagull drops a clam from a height of 40.0 m above the rocks. If the air temperature is 0°C, how long after the clam is dropped does the sound of it shattering on the rocks reach the seagull? Assume that it has hovered in place during the drop. Use $g = 9.80$ m/s^2.

28. Explain why there is a line of constructive interference along the centre line (or right bisector) of two speakers vibrating in phase.

29. Sound waves can diffract well around edges, while light waves show very little diffraction. What does this information tell you about sound and light waves?

30. You read in a journal that bats can hear frequencies from 1000 Hz up to 150 000 Hz. How might you design an investigation to verify this range (without hurting the bats)?

31. The gases listed in Table 7.4 have the densities listed in Table 7.5 at 25°C

TABLE 7.5 Densities of Some Gases at 25°C

Gas	Density ρ (kg/m^3)
hydrogen	0.082
helium	0.164
carbon monoxide	1.14
air	1.18
oxygen	1.31
carbon dioxide	1.81
sulfur dioxide	2.68

Using a graphing calculator,

a) plot a scatter graph of speed of sound (on the y-axis, L_2) against density (on the x-axis, L_1)

b) find the equation of the curve of best fit in the form $y = ax^b$ where y represents the speed of sound (v) in m/s and x represents the density of the gas (ρ) in kg/m^3.

Making Connections

32. Use Table 7.3 to estimate the intensity of sound in your class in pW/m^2 while working on an assignment.

33. The modern musical scale contains 12 semitones or basic steps in pitch within the octave. If each increase of one semitone increases the frequency by the same factor, prove that this factor is $\sqrt[12]{2}$.

34. If the sound intensity at a person's ear is 80 dB, and the cross-sectional area of the auditory canal is about 0.25 cm^2, at what rate is energy entering the ear?

35. An organelle in a cell can just barely be seen using white light with an average wavelength of 600 nm.
   a) What does that tell you about the size of the organelle?
   b) Explain why the image becomes clearer when viewed in blue light.

36. A microwave oven emits a microwave radiation with a frequency of 2.5 GHz. The metallic mesh in the glass at the front contains openings that are about 2 mm across. If the wavelength is much larger than the openings, the radiation cannot pass through.
   a) Compare the size of the openings with the wavelength and decide if the mesh is sufficient to block the radiation. All electromagnetic radiation travels through air at 3.00×10^8 m/s.
   b) Why can you see through the mesh?

37. Explain why thunder rumbles in hilly country but not in flat country.

38. In order to determine how far away a lightning strike is in kilometres, we are told to count the seconds between the flash and the arrival of the sound of thunder and divide by three.
   a) Explain why this works.
   b) At what temperature (to the nearest degree Celsius) would this be accurate?

39. In many science fiction movies you hear the sound of a spaceship exploding in space, or the sound of a space fighter swooshing past.
   a) What is wrong with these effects?
   b) If the effects are wrong, why are they used in the movies?

40. What changes would you notice in daily life if the speed of sound became 2.0 m/s?

41. At approximately what frequency is an average human's ear as sensitive as an average dog's ear?

42. Is it possible to have a sound intensity of -20 dB? Explain your answer.

43. Explain how the "crack" of a whip is produced.

44. a) Two cars travel around a large circular track. One completes ten laps in one hour while the other completes six laps during the same hour. Assuming that the cars were lined up at the start, how many more times during the hour are the cars lined up side by side?
   b) In what way is the previous question related to beats?

45. Small boats often have a fish finder/depth finder that shows the position of fish and of the bottom. Based on what you have learned in this chapter, predict how this device works.

46. In which part of the ear do tiny bones act as a series of levers?

47. If the intensity of sound is 1.0×10^7 pW/m^2, how many decibels does this represent?

CHAPTER 8

The Physics of Music

SPECIFIC EXPECTATIONS

By the end of this chapter, you will be able to:

- define and describe the concepts and units related to mechanical waves (8.1)
- describe and illustrate the properties of transverse and longitudinal waves in different media, and analyze the velocity of waves travelling in those media in quantitative terms (8.1)
- explain and graphically illustrate the principle of superposition, and identify examples of constructive and destructive interference (8.1)
- analyze the components of resonance and identify the conditions required for resonance to occur in vibrating objects and in various media (8.3)
- identify the properties of standing waves and, for both mechanical and sound waves, explain the conditions required for standing waves to occur (8.1, 8.3)
- analyze, in quantitative terms, the conditions needed for resonance in air columns, and explain how resonance is used in a variety of situations (8.3, 8.4)
- draw, measure, analyze, and interpret the properties of waves during their transmission in a medium and from one medium to another, and during their interaction with matter (8.1, 8.2, 8.3)
- analyze, through experimentation, the conditions required to produce resonance in vibrating objects and/or in air columns, predict the conditions required to produce resonance in specific cases, and determine whether the predictions are correct through experimentation (Investigation 1, Investigation 2)
- describe how knowledge of the properties of waves is applied in the design of buildings and of various technological devices, as well as in explanations of how sounds are produced and transmitted in nature, and how they interact with matter in nature (8.2, 8.4)

A hush falls over the audience as the performers file onto the stage. Each carries a strange-looking object in his or her hands. Some of the objects are long and cylindrical. Some are a tangle of shiny tubing. Others have taut strings stretched across their surface. Several are constructed of wood while others are made of metal. The performers seat themselves and a few of them begin to blow into their contraptions. Others pluck theirs. One even hits hers

FIGURE 8.1 A symphony orchestra

FIGURE 8.2 A jazz combo

with a stick! What reaches your ears is not the disharmony that you might have expected. Instead, you hear pleasant music.

How is this possible? How can such a diverse assortment of bizarre-looking devices combine to produce a beautiful waltz or an enchanting overture? Why are musical instruments shaped so differently? Why does a violin sound so different from a saxophone? How are the various notes produced?

To answer these questions, one must first understand how waves behave when confined to a finite space, such as that of a trombone tube or the length of a cello string. In this unit, you will study how stringed instruments such as guitars and violins make use of something called standing waves to produce rich and vibrant tones. You will also examine how wind instruments such as clarinets and tubas make use of air columns to produce sound. Understanding the principles involved in acoustics will enable you to explain other acoustical phenomena such as how the human voice works. Why does your stomach sometimes make those strange gurgling sounds? What is the source of the sound wave when a trumpet is blown? Why are female voices generally higher-pitched than male voices?

Discovering Physics

The Twirl-a-Tune

How many different notes can you make with a hose?

1. For this investigation use a "Twirl-a-Tune" or a length of ribbed flexi-hose about 50 cm to 80 cm long.
2. Whirl the tubing overhead at different rates to make different notes.
3. Connect the output of an audio frequency generator to the input of an amplifier and then connect the output of the amplifier to a speaker.
4. Turn on the amplifier and the audio frequency generator.
5. Hold one end of the hose and whirl the tubing overhead. Adjust the frequency from the generator until the pitch of the tone from the speaker matches the pitch of the lowest note that you can produce with the tubing. Repeat for a few higher frequencies produced by the tubing.
6. Calculate the ratios of the frequencies. Try to express these as ratios of small, whole numbers.

Data Logger Extension: Connect the interface to the computer. Turn on the interface, then turn on the computer. Connect the sound sensor (microphone) to the interface. Open the program that provides the sound spectrum Fast Fourier Transform (FFT) display. Hold the sound sensor close to the twirling tube and record the frequency corresponding to the main peak in the display. Also make note of the frequencies of any lesser peaks. Repeat for other tones from the tubing.

- Are there any lesser peaks present along with the lowest note? If there are, how do their frequencies compare with the higher frequencies produced when the tubing is swung faster?
- Can you recognize any pattern in the frequency ratios? If so, what is it?
- Specify what the source of the vibration is in the tubing.

CHECK**POINT**

The reason a trumpet player blows harder for louder notes is to increase

a) the speed of the air molecules coming out of the trumpet
b) the volume of air coming from the trumpet each second
c) the frequency of vibration of the air molecules
d) the amplitude of vibration of the air molecules
e) the number of air molecules coming out of the trumpet each second.

State a reason for your choice.

FIGURE 8.3 A harp

8.1 Standing Waves

Key Understandings

When you have completed this section, you will be able to:

- define and describe standing waves
- describe and illustrate the properties of transverse and longitudinal standing waves
- describe constructive and destructive interference in standing waves
- identify the properties of standing waves
- explain the conditions required for standing waves to occur
- draw, measure, analyze, and interpret the interference that results in standing waves during their transmission in a medium
- draw, measure, analyze, and interpret the reflection of transverse and longitudinal waves during their transmission in a medium

From ancient times, vibrating strings have been used to provide music. Around 550 B.C. the Greek philosopher Pythagoras discovered a relationship between the length of the vibrating string and the note it produced. Although he did not analyze the rate of vibration, his study is considered to be the foundation of **acoustics**, the study of sound. Why is it that a given length of vibrating string keeps on producing the same note? Pythagoras was unable to answer that question, but you will find out the answer in this section.

To understand why strings vibrate at specific frequencies, you have to examine a special type of interference. This is the interference that occurs when two waves with the same amplitude and wavelength pass through each other in opposite directions. This is shown in Figure 8.4. Figure 8.4a) illustrates the two waves as they approach each other.

In Figure 8.4b), the waves have advanced and completely overlap—crest on crest, and trough on trough. The resulting constructive interference produces the supercrests and supertroughs as shown on the right.

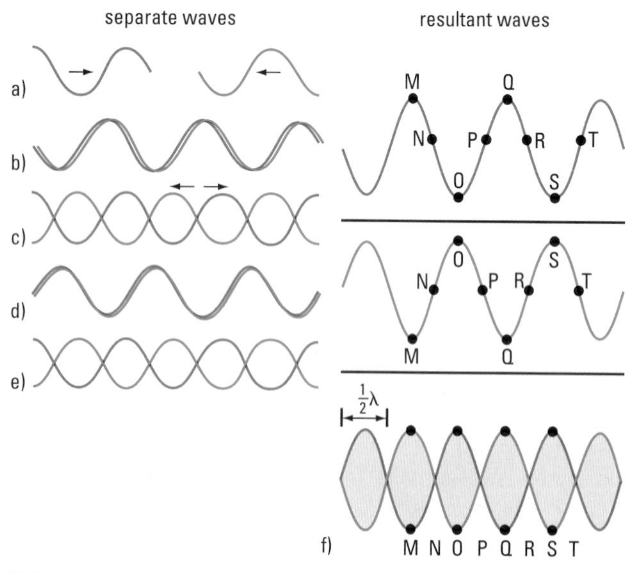

FIGURE 8.4 Formation of a standing wave

In Figure 8.4c), the advancing waves now create destructive interference since the crests of one wave overlap the troughs of the other.

In Figure 8.4d), the waves again produce constructive interference, while in Figure 8.4e) destructive interference is established once more. The overall effect is one of alternating constructive and destructive interference. Points such as M, O, Q, and S vibrate between supercrests and supertroughs, and so are called **antinodal points**, or **antinodes**. Points such as N, P, R, and T never vibrate and so are called **nodal points**, or **nodes**.

If the vibrations occur rapidly enough, a blurred pattern is seen as shown in Figure 8.4f). This pattern of vibration is called a **standing wave**. Each vibrating section is called a **loop**. Since a loop oscillates from being a supercrest to a supertrough, and cannot be both at the same time, a loop occupies half a wavelength. The distance from a node to a node in a standing wave pattern is half the wavelength of the travelling waves. It is important to remember that a standing wave pattern is produced by the interference of two identical travelling waves, moving in opposite directions in the same medium at the same time.

A standing wave can be formed in a rope or spring if one person holds one end steady while another person vibrates the other end. The waves sent down from the vibrating end are reflected by the **fixed end**, and then travel back through the incoming waves. If the frequency is just right, one loop will be formed.

What happens if shorter wavelengths are sent down the rope? Again, if the wavelength is just right, two loops will be formed. If even shorter wavelengths are used, more loops are formed.

The resulting standing wave patterns are named according to two different methods, as shown in Table 8.1.

TABLE 8.1 Standing Wave Patterns in a Rope

Number of Loops	Scientific Name	Musical Name
1	first harmonic	fundamental
2	second harmonic	first overtone
3	third harmonic	second overtone
4	fourth harmonic	third overtone

Wavelength and the Frequency of the Harmonics

If you let the length of the rope be represented by L as shown in Figure 8.5a), then the wavelength λ must be $2L$ since each loop is half a wavelength.

From the Universal Wave Equation, the frequency of a **first harmonic** or **fundamental** standing wave is given by

$$f_1 = \frac{v}{\lambda_1}$$

but

$$\lambda_1 = 2L$$

therefore

$$f_1 = \frac{v}{2L}$$

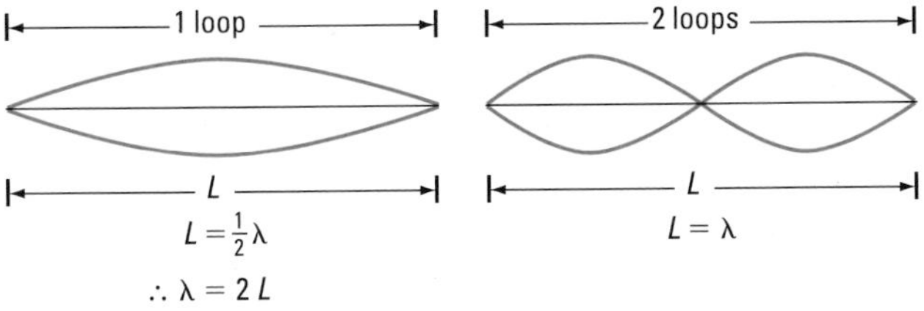

1 loop

L

$L = \frac{1}{2}\lambda$

$\therefore \lambda = 2L$

a) First harmonic (fundamental) standing wave pattern

2 loops

L

$L = \lambda$

b) Second harmonic (first overtone) standing wave pattern

FIGURE 8.5 Standing wave patterns

When two loops form in the rope, then λ_2 is equal to L, as Figure 8.5b) shows. The frequency of the second harmonic or **first overtone** is given by:

$$f_2 = \frac{v}{L}$$

therefore

$$f_2 = 2f_1$$

This means that the second harmonic has twice the frequency of the first harmonic. Similarly, the third harmonic has three times the frequency of the first harmonic.

Standing wave patterns are called harmonics if their frequencies are whole-number multiples of the first harmonic

Discovering Physics — *Creating Standing Waves with a Spring*

Observe standing waves first hand.

Caution: Do not let go of a stretched spring. When you have finished the activity move toward one another to minimize the stretch and have one partner collect both ends.

1. With a partner, stretch out a long coil spring between the two of you.
2. Have one person hold an end steady while the other person vibrates his or her end up and down. Start slowly and increase the rate of vibration until a standing wave with one loop is formed.
3. Measure the time required for 10 cycles and then calculate the frequency of the spring.
4. Increase the rate of vibration until two loops are created. Measure the time required for 10 cycles and calculate the frequency of the spring.
5. Repeat for as many loops as you can produce.
   - Is there a relationship between the frequencies and the number of loops?

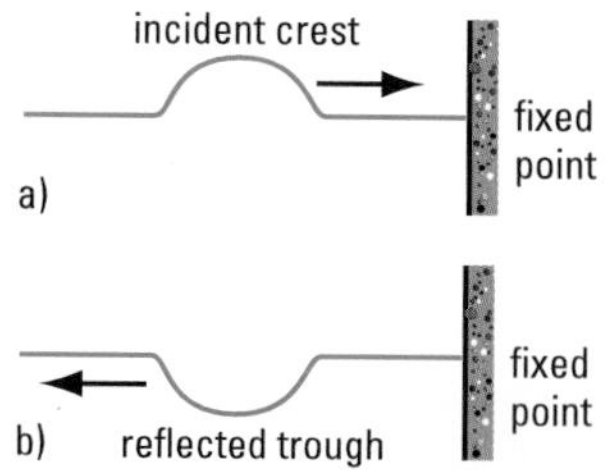

FIGURE 8.6 A transverse wave reverses phase when it reflects from a fixed point. Why?

a) Trough approaching a free point

b) Reflected trough

FIGURE 8.8 Reflection of a transverse wave at a free end

or fundamental frequency. In this way the rope can vibrate at, or resonate with, different frequencies. These special frequencies are called **resonant frequencies**.

You have examined the formation of standing waves consisting of nodes, antinodes, and loops. It is now important to understand how the loops and nodes are created. In many cases, standing waves occur when a wave is reflected back upon itself. Figure 8.6 shows that a wave that is reflected at a **fixed point** reverses phase. Crests become troughs and troughs become crests.

Phase inversion also occurs when a longitudinal wave is reflected at a fixed point. The inversion changes an incident (incoming) compression to a reflected rarefaction (Figure 8.7).

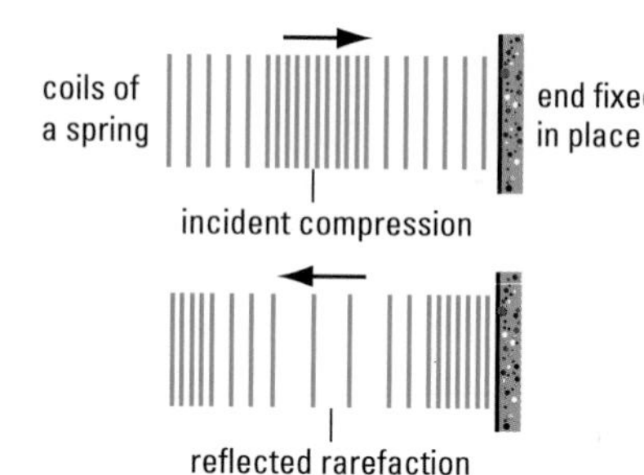

FIGURE 8.7 A longitudinal wave also reverses phase when it reflects from a fixed point.

When a crest of a transverse wave is reflected at a **free point**, there is no phase inversion of the wave (Figure 8.8). A crest remains a crest and a trough remains a trough. This is also true for a longitudinal wave. Compressions and rarefactions are not inverted when they are reflected from a free point.

In summary, a wave reverses phase when it reflects at a fixed point and keeps the same phase when it reflects at a free point.

Imagine that a transverse wave is moving along a rope toward an end that is fixed rigidly in place as shown in Figure 8.9a). Since a **fixed end** cannot vibrate, the end must be a node in the standing wave pattern. The first crest to reach the fixed end inverts into a trough. The trough then moves back through the incident waves with the same speed that it had before reflection, as seen in Figure 8.9b).

Since the reflected trough and the next incident trough are travelling with the same speed, they will meet at the midpoint between them, as in Figure 8.9c) shows. This is one-quarter of a wavelength from the fixed end. At this point, continuous constructive interference occurs, forming an antinode.

The reflected trough and next incident crest move toward each other and again meet at the midpoint between their initial positions. You can see from Figure 8.9d) that this meeting will occur half a wavelength away from the fixed end. This point represents continuous destructive interference and is thus a node.

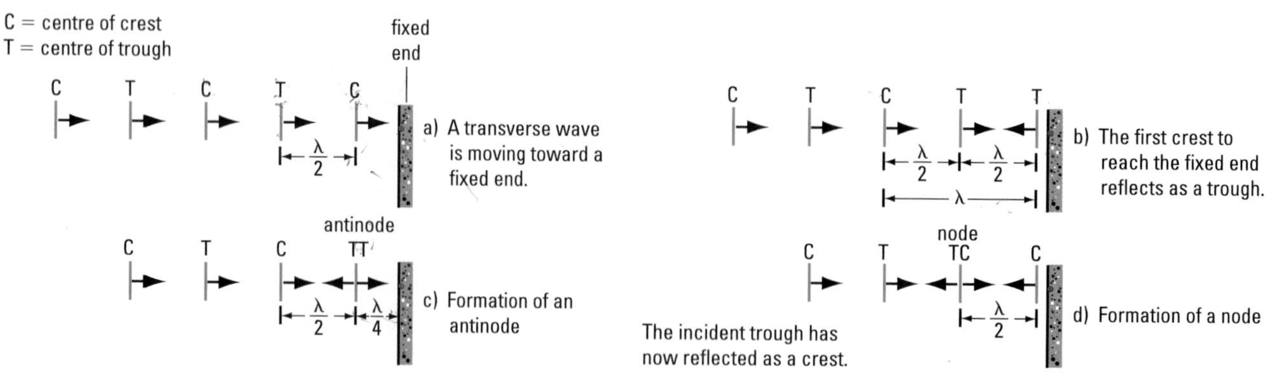

FIGURE 8.9 Standing waves being formed near a fixed end

This reasoning can be extended to prove that for a standing wave near a fixed end, nodes form at the end and every half-wavelength away from the end (Figure 8.10). The region between two adjacent nodal points is called a loop, from its appearance in a transverse standing wave. At the centre of each loop is the **antinode**.

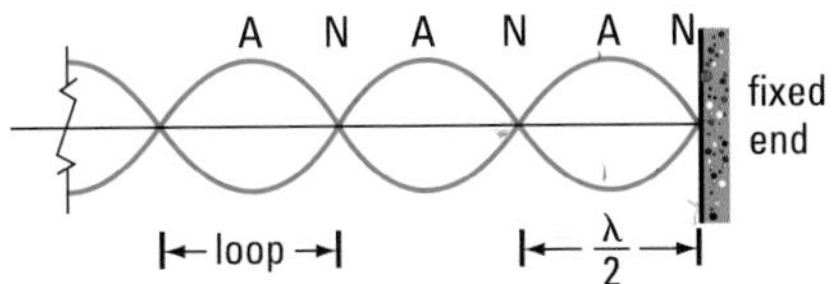

N = nodal point or node
A = antinode

FIGURE 8.10 The components of a standing wave near a fixed end

Consider a transverse wave travelling toward a **free end** as in Figure 8.11a). The first crest to reach the free end reflects as a crest (Figure 8.11 b)). Since no destructive interference occurs here, the free end becomes an antinode.

The reflected crest will meet the next incident trough at the midpoint between them. This results in a node one-quarter of a wavelength from the free end as shown in Figure 8.11c). In Figure 8.11d), the reflected crest meets the next incident crest at half a wavelength from the free end. As a result of constructive interference, this point becomes an antinode.

The reflected crest will then travel another one-quarter of a wavelength where it will meet the next incident trough and form a nodal point. This nodal point is three-quarters of a wavelength from the free end.

This reasoning applies to any type of wave. You can see that for a standing wave near a free end, an antinode is formed at the free end. The first node occurs one-quarter of a wavelength in from the end and every half-wavelength from then on. The region between nodes is called a loop and is half a wavelength long.

For *all* types of waves an antinode forms at an end that is free to vibrate while a node forms at a fixed end. Nodes and antinodes alternate every quarter wavelength. The region between adjacent nodes is called a loop and is a half wavelength long. This is summarized for both a free and a fixed end in Table 8.2.

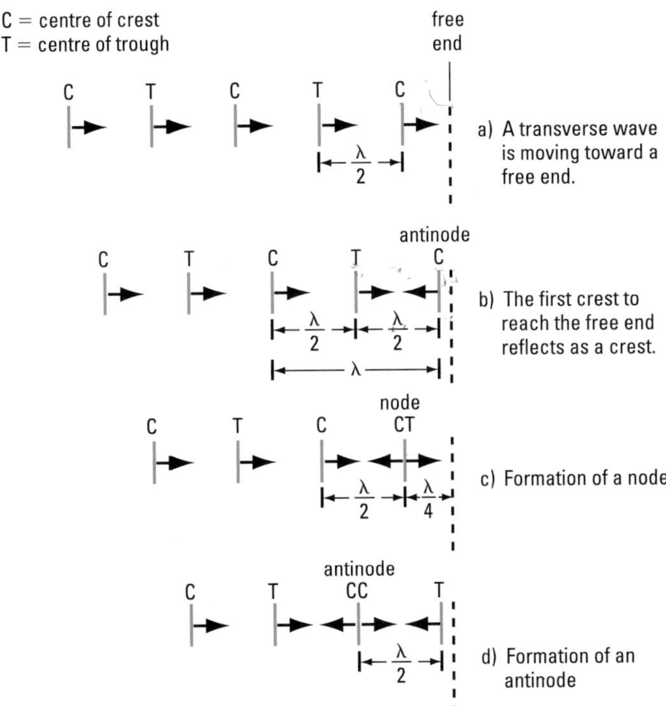

FIGURE 8.11 Standing waves formed near a free end

TABLE 8.2 Pattern of Standing Waves Formed by Reflection

Distance from End in Wavelengths (λ)	Feature of Standing Wave	
	Free End	Fixed End
0 (at end)	antinode	node
$\frac{1}{4}$	node	antinode
$\frac{1}{2}$	antinode	node
$\frac{3}{4}$	node	antinode
1	antinode	node

WEBLINK

To find a simulation, of the superposition of waves and the reflection of waves, look at **www.pearsoned.ca/physics11.** Write a critique of the simulation that you have seen and suggest improvements.

Discovering Physics — *Analyzing Sound Waves in Aluminum*

Do the following activity, and use your understanding of waves and sound to answer the questions at the end.

You will need: an aluminum rod (possibly a long, retort-stand rod), metre-stick or tape measure, a damp cloth, and a data logger with a sound sensor

1. Measure the length of an aluminum rod.
2. Hold the aluminum rod at its centre of mass.
3. Stroke one end of the rod with a slightly damp cloth, moving away from the centre and releasing near the end of the rod. Continue until the rod "sings" a loud note.
4. Measure the frequency of that note using a data logger with a sound sensor.

If an antinode occurs at each free end and the rod is vibrating in its simplest pattern.

- how long is the rod in wavelengths?
- how long is the wavelength in the rod?
- using the universal wave equation, calculate the speed of the longitudinal wave (sound) in aluminum.

Section 8.1 Review

Understanding Concepts

1. a) The standing wave pattern on a rope contains five loops. How many wavelengths is this?

b) Give two different names for this pattern.

2. A rope 16 m long vibrates with 6 loops. How long is the wavelength?

3. Explain why a node forms one wavelength in from a fixed end when a standing wave is formed by reflection.

4. A wave on a rope has a wavelength of 20 cm. If one end is fixed in place,

a) how far will the first three nodes be from the fixed end?

b) how far will the first three antinodes be from the fixed end?

5. A standing wave is formed by reflection at a free end. If the wavelength is 6.0 cm,

a) how far are the first three nodes from the free end?

b) how far are the first three antinodes from the free end?

c) would this sound be in the audible range for humans?

Applying Inquiry/ Communication Skills

6. A photograph of water waves at the base of a steep cliff shows regions of great activity separated by regions of little wave motion.

a) Why does this effect occur?

b) How could you use this effect to measure the wavelength of the water waves?

8.2 Stringed Instruments

Key Understandings

When you have completed this section, you will be able to:

- draw, measure, analyze, and interpret the properties of waves in stringed instruments
- describe how knowledge of the properties of waves is applied in the design of stringed instruments

Stringed instruments come in many different forms. The piano looks completely different from the violin. The harp and the double bass seem to have very little in common. And yet they all rely on vibrating strings as the source of their notes. In this section you will examine the guitar as an example of a stringed instrument. In what ways does it resemble other stringed instruments? Are there ways in which it is unique?

Guitar Strings

The pitch of the notes produced by a guitar is completely determined by the properties and condition of the guitar strings (Figure 8.12). Different strings are chosen for different note ranges. These strings differ in diameter and in density. Guitar strings are made of nylon, steel, or some combination of materials to produce various densities.

Once the strings are stretched across the neck and soundbox of the instrument, the guitarist tunes the strings by turning small screws called tuning heads. These alter the tension in the strings. To sound different notes, the player plucks different strings or changes the length of the vibrating segment of a string. This is done by pressing the string against one of the raised frets along the neck of the guitar. The only part of the string that vibrates is the length between the pressed fret and the saddle.

The main factors that determine the frequency of the vibrating string are length, tension, diameter, and density.

When a guitar string is plucked, it usually vibrates in its fundamental mode with a transverse standing wave. There is a node at the pressed fret and a node at the saddle. The length of the vibrating segment of the string represents one complete loop or $\frac{1}{2}\lambda$ of the standing wave.

FIGURE 8.12 An acoustic guitar

Therefore $\quad L = \frac{1}{2}\lambda$

and $\quad \lambda = 2L \qquad$ (equation 1)

The universal wave equation states

$f\lambda = v \qquad$ (equation 2)

Substituting the expression for λ from equation 1 into equation 2 and rearranging yields

$$f2L = v$$

$$fL = \frac{v}{2} \qquad \text{(equation 3)}$$

However, the speed of a wave along a string under a given tension is constant. Therefore $f \times L$ is a constant. As a result, if the tension of a given string is held constant, then the product of the frequency and length of a specific segment is constant. This relation can be written as

$$f_1L_1 = f_2L_2 \qquad \text{(equation 4)}$$

If the product is to remain constant and the length decreases, then the frequency of the note must rise. It is said that the frequency of the note varies inversely with the length of the vibrating segment.

From equation 3, you find that

$$fL = \frac{v}{2}$$

or

$$f = \frac{v}{2L}$$

Investigation
Refer to page 314, Investigation 1

The frequency of a given length of string depends on the speed of the wave along that string. You know from stretching a string that the speed of a wave in a string increases when the tension is increased. But according to equation 3, the frequency of the standing wave increases when the speed increases. Consequently, the frequency of a given length of string increases when the tension increases.

INSIGHT

As long as the units are consistent on both sides of the equation, there is no need to convert lengths from centimetres into metres.

EXAMPLE 1 NUMERICAL

A guitar string produces an A note (110 Hz) when the vibrating segment is 63.0 cm long. How long should the segment be to produce a C note (130.8 Hz)?

Given

$f_1 = 110$ Hz

$L_1 = 63.0$ cm

$f_2 = 130.8$ Hz

Required

L_2

Analysis

Use $f_2L_2 = f_1L_1$

Solution

$$L_2 = \frac{f_1L_1}{f_2} = \frac{110 \text{ Hz} \times 63.0 \text{ cm}}{130.8 \text{ Hz}} = 53.0 \text{ cm}$$

Statement

The required length of the string is 53.0 cm.

PRACTICE PROBLEMS

1. A violin string, 20.0 cm long, is emitting a G note with a frequency of 392 Hz. How long should it be to produce a C of 523 Hz?
2. If the length of the violin string in the previous question is changed to 23.8 cm with no change in tension,
   a) What frequency will be produced?
   b) Which note is this closest to?

As you have just learned, the frequency of the vibrating string depends on the speed of the wave along the string. However, the speed depends on the ability of one tiny vibrating segment of the string to force the next tiny segment to vibrate. The greater the mass of each tiny segment, the longer it takes to transfer the vibration along the string.

The mass of each segment can be increased by increasing the density or the diameter of the string. Both changes decrease the speed of the wave. This lowers the frequency or pitch of the note. In general then, if length and tension are constant, an increase in either the diameter or the density of the string results in a decrease in the frequency of the string and a lowering of the pitch of the note.

The Acoustic Guitar

Acoustic guitars come in many different forms. They differ in size and shape, and number and type of strings. Their common feature is that the amplification of the sound from the vibrating strings is accomplished by means of a **soundbox**. By contrast, an electric guitar amplifies the sound electronically (Figure 8.13).

FIGURE 8.13 An electric guitar

When a guitar string is plucked, the energy of vibration is transferred from the string to the **saddle** and **bridge**. The bridge in turn transmits the energy to the soundbox. The soundbox consists of an enclosed air space, sides, a back plate, and a top surface—called the **soundboard**. Because the soundboard has a larger vibrating surface than the string, it translates its vibrations more effectively into compressions and rarefactions of air to produce sound of a higher intensity.

Occasionally the soundbox is referred to as a resonance box, but this is a misnomer. If resonance occurs, it is very difficult to produce a uniform, controlled sound from the instrument. Care must be taken to avoid strong resonances. For example, the soundboard and back plate are designed to possess different resonant frequencies. As a result, many notes lie in a frequency range close to a resonant frequency of some part of the soundbox. These are amplified slightly by resonance. But, by making sure that there are no strong resonances, no notes will be amplified far beyond others. A skilled player automatically adjusts to the different responses that the soundbox provides for different notes.

The Violin Family

The photo of the violin in Figure 8.14 illustrates several differences between a violin and a guitar. The violin is smaller and has only 4 strings rather than 6 or 12 for the guitar. Since the violin has no frets, the player must know exactly where to press on the strings to produce each note. The physical principles on which the guitar and the violin operate, however, are the same. The energy from the vibrating string is transferred to the bridge and then to the soundbox. From there, the sound radiates into the air.

FIGURE 8.14 A violin

WEBLINK

Learn more about the construction of stringed instruments such as pianos, guitars, violins, and harps. Explore the Internet to find information that will help you prepare a sequence chart tracing the construction of a particular instrument. Begin your research at **www.pearsoned.ca/physics11.**

Section 8.2 Review

Understanding Concepts

1. On a guitar, what is the function of the
   a) tuning heads?
   b) frets?
2. a) List four factors that affect the frequency of a vibrating string.
   b) Briefly describe what effect an increase in each factor has on the frequency of the string.
3. If the string is vibrating in its fundamental mode, how long is the segment in wavelengths?
4. The vibrating segment of a string playing a B note (247 Hz) is 50.0 cm long. How long should the segment be if the same string is to produce a G note (196 Hz)?
5. Describe the path of the sound energy, as it moves from the string to the air, for an acoustic guitar.
6. a) How does the player produce different notes from the same string with a guitar?
   b) Why is this more difficult to do with a violin?

Applying Inquiry/ Communication Skills

7. Outline a controlled experiment to determine the effect of string diameter on frequency.
8. Compare the playing of a piano with the playing of a violin by means of a graphical organizer such as a Venn diagram.

FIGURE 8.15 Playing an air-column instrument

8.3 Acoustical Resonance in Air Columns

Key Understandings

When you have completed this section, you will be able to:

- analyze the components of acoustical resonance
- identify and analyze, in quantitative terms, the conditions required for acoustical resonance to occur in air columns
- explain the conditions required for standing waves to occur in air columns
- explain how different notes are produced by air columns
- draw, measure, analyze, and interpret the properties of standing waves

Many band instruments rely on air columns: the trumpet, clarinet, tuba, and oboe would sound feeble without their air columns. But air column resonances do not end with musical instruments. Our own voices require resonances. So do the embarrassing mutters and gurgles from our stomachs and intestines. How do these resonances occur? How can one use them to produce such a wide variety of musical sounds from the sweet note of a flute to the growl of a saxophone?

When you blow over the mouth of an empty bottle, a note is heard. The air molecules inside the bottle are resonating. Because this resonance involves sound waves, it is known as **acoustical resonance**.

In an air column closed at one end, such as a bottle, resonance can only occur if a standing wave is set up involving the air molecules. The open end of the air column acts as a free end. An antinode forms close to the open end. The closed end acts as a fixed end. This forces a node to form at the closed end. Figure 8.15 shows several possible patterns in columns of different lengths.

The shortest column length is known as the first **resonant length**. The next longest is called the second resonant length, and so on. Notice that once the first resonant length is determined, the others can be calculated by simply adding half the wavelength of the sound wave each time. In this way, different column lengths can resonate to the same frequency.

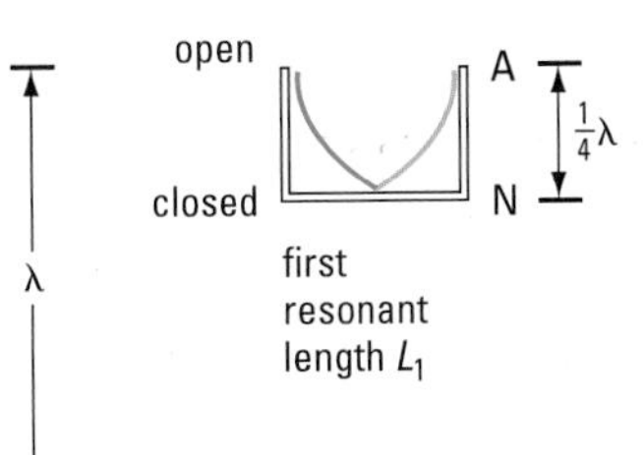

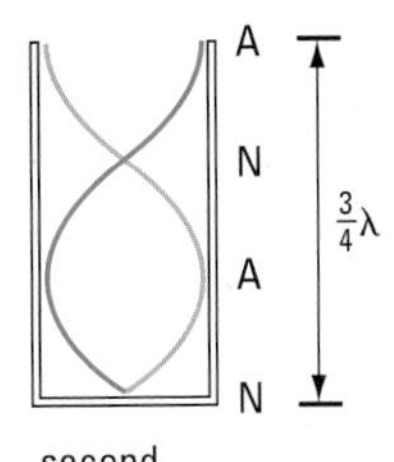

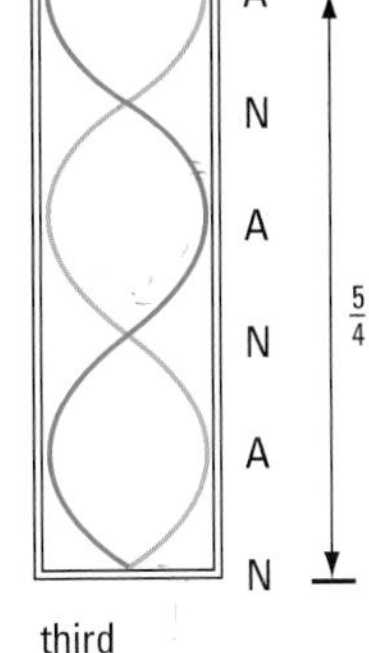

FIGURE 8.16 Resonant lengths for an air column of variable length closed at one end. The frequency and wavelength are constant.

EXAMPLE 2 NUMERICAL

A ship's whistle, 0.600 m long, is an air column closed at one end (Figure 8.17). If the speed of sound in air is 340 m/s, calculate the three lowest resonant frequencies for the ship's whistle.

Given

$L = 0.600$ m

$v = 340$ m/s

FIGURE 8.17

Required

f

Analysis

- Use L to calculate the wavelength.
- Then calculate the frequency.

Solution

a) Fundamental Mode

$$L = \frac{\lambda}{4}$$

$$\lambda = 4 \times L$$
$$= 4 \times 0.600 \text{ m}$$
$$= 2.40 \text{ m}$$

$$f = \frac{v}{\lambda} = \frac{340 \text{ m/s}}{2.40 \text{ m}} = 142 \text{ Hz}$$

b) 1st Overtone

$$L = \frac{3}{4\lambda}$$

therefore

$$\lambda = \frac{4}{3} \times L$$
$$= \frac{4}{3} \times 0.600 \text{ m}$$
$$= 0.800 \text{ m}$$

$$f = \frac{v}{\lambda} = \frac{340 \text{ m/s}}{0.800 \text{ m}} = 425 \text{ Hz}$$

INSIGHT

When dealing with air column resonances, it is often useful to sketch the arrangement of nodes and antinodes in the column.

PRACTICE PROBLEMS

1. Determine the frequencies of the lowest two notes that could be produced by an air column 0.500 m long and closed at one end. The speed of sound in air is 335 m/s.
2. How long should an air column (closed at one end) be if it is to produce a 1000-Hz note as its lowest frequency? The speed of sound in air is 335 m/s.

c) Second Overtone

$$L = \frac{5}{4}\lambda$$

$$\lambda = \frac{4}{5} \times L$$

$$= \frac{4}{5} \times 0.600 \text{ m}$$

$$= 0.480 \text{ m}$$

$$f = \frac{v}{\lambda} = \frac{340 \text{ m/s}}{0.480 \text{ m}} = 708 \text{ Hz}$$

Statement

The three lowest resonant frequencies are 142 Hz, 425 Hz, and 708 Hz.

Discovering Physics **Speed of Sound in the Classroom**

The speed of sound in air can be measured and calculated using different methods.

1. Obtain a tuning fork of known frequency and an air column closed at one end, the length of which can vary.
2. Hold the vibrating tuning fork near the open end of the air column and find the shortest length of air column that can "sing out" or resonate to the tuning fork.
3. Measure the length L_1 of the air column and then lengthen it until it resonates again.
4. Measure the new length L_2.

- How should $L_2 - L_1$ compare with the wavelength?
- How long is the wavelength of the sound?
- Use the frequency of the tuning fork to calculate the speed of sound.
- How does it compare with the value for the speed of sound obtained by measuring the air temperature?

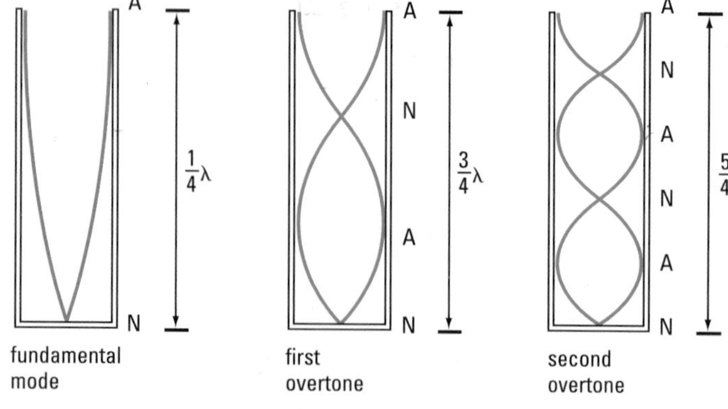

FIGURE 8.18 Standing wave pattern in an air column of constant length closed at one end. The air column can resonate at different frequencies.

Suppose that the length of the air column cannot be changed. Figure 8.18 shows possible standing wave patterns inside an air column of constant length. To produce these standing waves, the wavelength would have to become successively shorter and the frequency correspondingly higher. This means then that a given air column can resonate to a whole series of different frequencies!

The previous example indicates that if the fundamental frequency is f_0, then the overtones form the series $3f_0$, $5f_0$, $7f_0$, $9f_0$, and so on. Only odd multiples of the fundamental frequency are produced when the air column is closed at one end.

EXAMPLE 3 NUMERICAL

What length of air column, closed at one end, is required to produce a 500-Hz note as its fundamental frequency when the air temperature is 20°C?

Given

$f = 500$ Hz (fundamental frequency)

$T = 20°C$

Required

L

Analysis

- Use temperature T to calculate speed v
- Use $v = f\lambda$ to calculate λ
- Use $L = \frac{\lambda}{4}$ to calculate L

Solution

$$v = 331\ \frac{\text{m}}{\text{s}} + \left(0.59 \frac{\text{m}}{\text{s}\cdot°\text{C}}\right)T$$

$$= 331\ \frac{\text{m}}{\text{s}} + \left(0.59 \frac{\text{m}}{\text{s}\cdot°\text{C}}\right)20°\text{C}$$

$$= 343 \text{ m/s}$$

$$\lambda = \frac{v}{f}$$

$$= \frac{343 \text{ m/s}}{500 \text{ Hz}}$$

$$= 0.686 \text{ m}$$

For the fundamental,

$$L = \frac{\lambda}{4}$$

$$= \frac{0.686 \text{ m}}{4}$$

$$= 0.172 \text{ m}$$

Statement

The required length to produce a 500-Hz note is 0.172 m.

PRACTICE PROBLEMS

1. What length of air column is required to produce a 1000-Hz note as its fundamental frequency when the air temperature is 30°C?
2. What will be the frequency of the first overtone from an air column closed at one end if it is 60.0 cm long and the air temperature is 10°C?

Resonance is an effective method for amplifying the sound from a source. In the school physics laboratory you will often find tuning forks mounted on wooden resonance boxes (Figure 8.19). Generally, resonance boxes have only one open end. Since they are designed to resonate at their fundamental frequency, the length of the box is equal to one-quarter of a wavelength. Additional amplification of the sound from the tuning fork is provided by the vibrating surfaces of the box. Since the surfaces have a larger area than the tuning fork, sound energy is transferred more easily into the air than by the tuning fork alone.

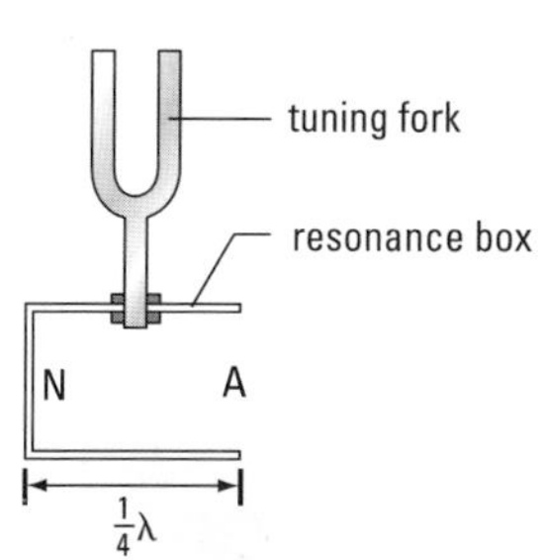

FIGURE 8.19 A resonance box amplifies the sound of a tuning fork.

FIGURE 8.20 What part of the piano amplifies the sound?

The amplification caused by the vibration of a larger area does not depend on resonance. If a tuning fork is sounded and its lower end is placed firmly against a larger, hard surface, the sound becomes louder. Because the tuning fork is held tightly against the surface, its vibrational energy is easily transmitted to the surface. The energy is more effectively transmitted into the air due to the larger vibrating area. The sounding board at the back of a piano (Figure 8.20) and the surfaces of a guitar amplify the sound in this way.

You may have seen people at fairs twirling lengths of corrugated hose to sound a series of notes. They were causing acoustical resonance in an air column open at both ends. The explanation for the process is very similar to that for air columns open at one end.

An antinode must form at the open end of an air column. The simplest pattern for a longitudinal standing wave in an air column open at both ends has an antinode at each end and a single node in the middle (Figure. 8.21). For each successive resonant length, one more node and antinode are added. Since the distance from antinode to antinode equals half a wavelength, then the resonant lengths are simple multiples of half a wavelength.

If the length of an air column is held constant, the patterns shown in Figure 8.22 can form. The wavelength becomes shorter as the number of nodes and antinodes in the column increases. This produces higher frequencies, resulting in higher-pitched sounds.

WEBLINK

All wind instruments employ the resonance properties of air columns. How could you illustrate these properties? Find animations on the Internet that illustrate these resonances. Based on the animations you find, choose a wind instrument and illustrate where the nodes and antinodes might appear. Begin your research at **www.pearsoned.ca/physics11.**

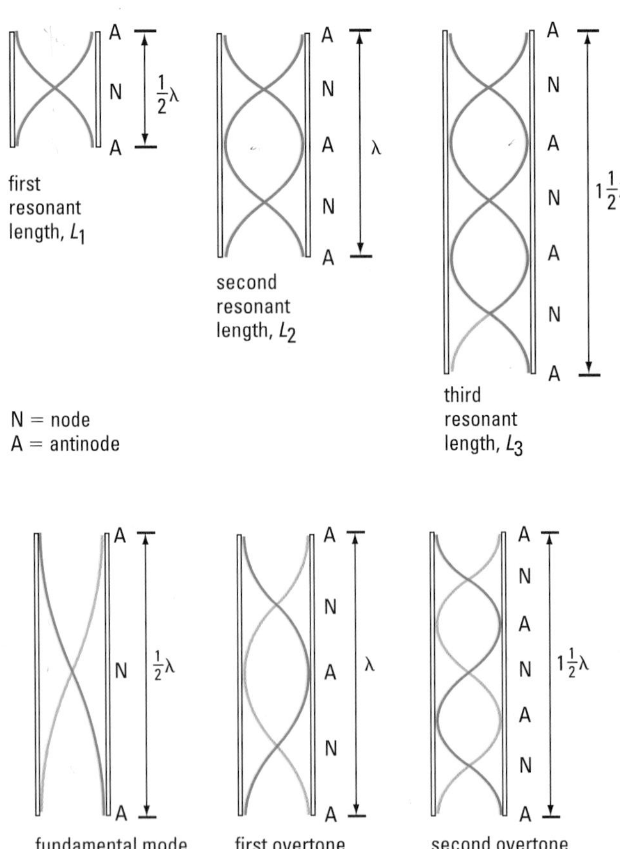

FIGURE 8.21 Resonant lengths for an air column open at both ends. The frequency is constant.

FIGURE 8.22 Standing wave pattern in an air column of constant length open at both ends. The air column can resonate at different frequencies.

EXAMPLE 4 NUMERICAL

An air column open at both ends is 1.00 m long. If the speed of sound is 340 m/s and resonance occurs, what are the two lowest resonant frequencies, and what relationship exists between these two notes?

Given

$L_1 = 1.00$ m

$v = 340$ m/s

Required

f_1

f_2

Analysis

- Use $L_1 = \frac{1}{2}\lambda_1$ to solve for λ_1
- Then use $v = f_1 \lambda_1$ to calculate f_1

Solution

$$\lambda_1 = 2L_1 = 2 \times 1.00 \text{ m} = 2.00 \text{ m}$$

$$v = f_1\lambda_1$$

$$\text{therefore } f_1 = \frac{v}{\lambda_1} = \frac{340 \text{ m/s}}{2.00 \text{ m}}$$

$$f_1 = 170 \text{ Hz}$$

$$L_2 = \lambda_2$$

$$\text{therefore } \lambda_2 = 1.00 \text{ m}$$

$$f_2 = \frac{v}{\lambda_2} = \frac{340 \text{ m/s}}{1.00 \text{ m}} = 340 \text{ Hz}$$

Statement

The frequency doubles from 170 Hz to 340 Hz. Because the frequency has doubled, the notes are separated by one octave.

INSIGHT

For air columns, the lowest frequency will always involve the longest wavelength and the simplest arrangement of nodes and antinodes. In other words, it will always involve the fundamental pattern.

PRACTICE PROBLEMS

1. An air column, open at both ends, is 0.60 m long. If the speed of sound in air is 330 m/s, what are the two lowest frequencies that could be produced from that air column?
2. How long should an air column (open at both ends) be to emit a 5000-Hz note as its lowest frequency if the speed of sound in air is 340 m/s?

For an air column open at both ends, the frequencies of the **overtones** are all whole-number multiples of the fundamental. For this reason they are known as **harmonics**. The fundamental is known as the first harmonic, the first overtone becomes the second harmonic, and so on. In this way, open air columns behave similarly to vibrating strings. (See Table 8.1 on page 293 and Table 8.3 to the right.)

It is common for a vibrating air column to form several harmonics at the same time. Because each harmonic makes up part of the total sound produced from the air column, harmonics are also known as partials. Table 8.3 compares the frequencies of the overtones produced by different types of air columns.

Investigation

Refer to page 315, Investigation 2

TABLE 8.3 Resonant Frequencies for Open and Closed Air Columns

	Frequency of Air Column	
Resonance Mode	**Open at Both Ends**	**Closed at One End**
fundamental	f_0	f_0
first overtone	$2f_0$	$3f_0$
second overtone	$3f_0$	$5f_0$
third overtone	$4f_0$	$7f_0$
fourth overtone	$5f_0$	$9f_0$

Section 8.3 Review

Understanding Concepts

1. A sound wave with a wavelength of 120 cm sets up a standing wave in an air column closed at one end. What are the first three resonant lengths?
2. An 80-cm long air column, closed at one end, contains standing sound waves. How long is the wavelength that corresponds to:
   a) the fundamental mode?
   b) the first overtone?
   c) the second overtone?
3. An air column is open at both ends. How many nodes are present in the standing wave patterns corresponding to the
   a) fundamental or first harmonic?
   b) second harmonic?
   c) second overtone?
   d) twenty-first partial?
4. If a sound wavelength is 30 cm long, how long are the first three resonant lengths for an air column open at both ends?
5. An air column open at both ends is 60 cm long. How long is the wavelength of the sound wave if the column is resonating in its
   a) fundamental mode?
   b) first overtone?
   c) fifth harmonic?

Applying Inquiry/ Communication Skills

6. Compare, by means of a graphical organizer such as a Venn diagram, air columns that are closed at one end with those that are open at both ends.
7. A wind instrument, 50.0 cm long, is closed at both ends.
   a) What would be the longest wavelength it could produce?
   b) Which type of air column—closed at one end or open at both ends—would have the same pattern of resonant frequencies as this instrument? Explain your answer.

8.4 Air Columns in Action

Key Understandings

When you have completed this section, you will be able to:

- explain how resonance is used in brass and woodwind instruments and in human vocal cords
- identify musical instruments using air columns
- explain how different notes are produced in wind instruments and in the human vocal tract
- describe how knowledge of acoustics is applied in the design of buildings
- explain how knowledge of the properties of waves is applied in the design of wind instruments
- describe how knowledge of the properties of waves explains how humans produce and transmit sounds

FIGURE 8.23 A parade

The people in a parade are marching proudly down the street. At first a bugle corps passes by. Next comes a band with trumpets, trombones, clarinets, saxophones, and tubas. And then the sound of bagpipes swirls through the air. Someone cheers from the crowd. Since air columns are involved in each of these examples, why are the sounds so different? In what way does the human voice resemble these instruments?

Wind Instruments

All of the instruments mentioned in the parade example belong to the same category—wind instruments. Wind instruments require a stream of air from the player's lungs to produce sound. Almost all wind instruments behave basically like an air column open at both ends. The player sets up vibrations at one end. These vibrations then propagate along the air column, or bore, as a longitudinal wave and are reflected at the other open end. This open end is often flared outward to form a bell (Figure 8.24).

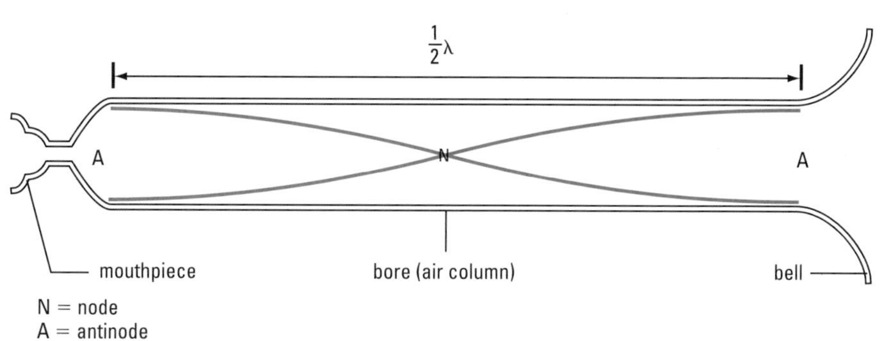

FIGURE 8.24 Fundamental standing wave in a simplified wind instrument

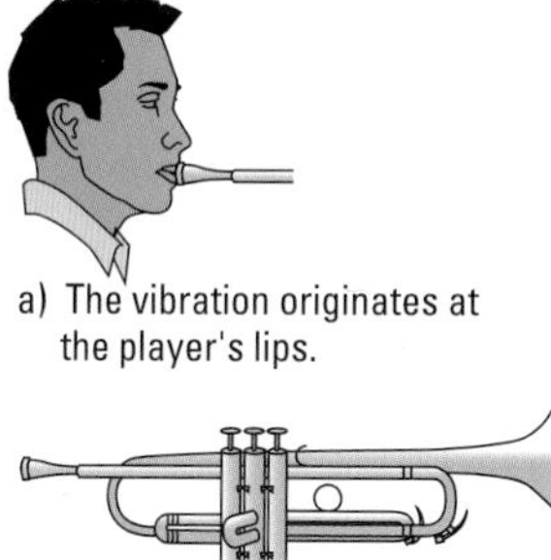

a) The vibration originates at the player's lips.
b) Trumpet with mouthpiece

FIGURE 8.25 A brass instrument has a mouthpiece.

A standing wave forms in the bore with antinodes at each end. In the fundamental mode, the length of the bore corresponds to one-half of a wavelength. The lowest note produced from such a column has a wavelength equal to twice the length of the bore. If the length of the bore is increased, then the wavelength increases. This, in turn, produces a lower-pitched note.

There are two types of wind instruments—brass and woodwind. With brass instruments, the player blows into a mouthpiece through compressed, vibrating lips (Figure 8.25b)). The more the lips are tightened, the higher the frequency of the note produced. Part of the skill of playing a brass instrument is to match the frequency of the buzzing lips to the natural frequency of the bore.

If the instrument has valves, such as a trumpet, tuba, or French horn, additional lengths of tubing can be added to the bore simply by pressing down on the valves. This increases the length of the air column and lowers the pitch.

Most trombones have no valves, but the bore can be lengthened by pushing out the slide. This decreases the frequency of the note. Such trombones are not restricted to specific lengths. As a result, all the frequencies in between the normal notes in a scale are possible (Figure 8.26)).

Some horns do not have valves and their length cannot be changed. The frequency of the note is varied by changing the tightness of the lips. A series of notes having higher frequencies than the fundamental can be produced from the same bore length. This is done by forming overtones through changing the tension in the lips. Whole fanfares have been written using only the fundamental and its overtones or partials.

FIGURE 8.26 How does this player increase the length of the bore?

Woodwind instruments differ from brass instruments in two important ways. First, the initial frequency that triggers the air column resonance is provided by the player blowing past a sliver of wood called a reed (Figure 8.27). It is the reed that vibrates instead of the player's lips. Second, the length of the bore is changed by opening and closing holes spaced along the length of the bore (Figure 8.28). When a hole is open, the pressure in the bore at that point becomes equal to atmospheric pressure. The wave is reflected at that point as it would at an open end. This means that the bore is shortened, producing a higher-pitched note.

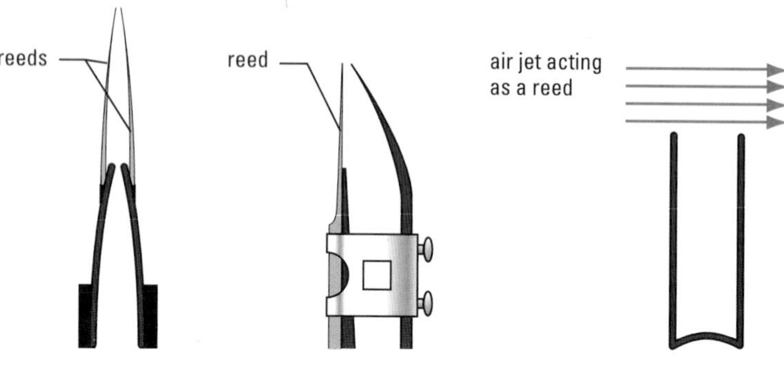

FIGURE 8.27 Woodwind reeds

FIGURE 8.28 An open hole in the side of a woodwind instrument acts as an open end.

FIGURE 8.29 An air jet can act as a reed.

The flute is unique in that the player blows over a hole. The air vibrates as the moving air stream interacts with the air in the hole. Because the air vibrates, a flute is said to use an air reed (Figure 8.29).

The clarinet is different from most other wind instruments. It behaves like an air column with an open end at the bell and a closed end at the reed. Consequently, the length of the bore represents one-quarter of a wavelength for the fundamental mode. When playing the first overtone, the bore length is three-quarters of a wavelength. You will soon see that, in this way, the clarinet resembles the human voice.

Table 8.4 compares the resonant modes for most wind instruments with those for the clarinet.

TABLE 8.4 Resonant Modes of Wind Instruments with a Bore Length of L

	Most Wind Instruments (Both Ends Open)		Clarinet (One End Closed)	
Resonant Mode	**Frequency**	**Wavelength**	**Frequency**	**Wavelength**
fundamental	f	$2L$	f	$4L$
first overtone	$2f$	L	$3f$	$\frac{4}{3}L$
second overtone	$3f$	$\frac{2}{3}L$	$5f$	$\frac{4}{5}L$
third overtone	$4f$	$\frac{1}{2}L$	$7f$	$\frac{4}{7}L$

A note rises an octave when its frequency is doubled. With brass wind instruments, musicians can obtain notes that are an octave apart without changing the bore length. They can do this by changing from the fundamental to the first overtone, or from the first overtone to the third overtone, and so on. However, with the clarinet it is impossible to produce notes one octave apart without changing the length of the bore.

The Human Voice

Sing a note to yourself. As you do, place your fingers lightly beside the thyroid cartilage (or Adam's apple) in your throat. You should be able to feel a vibration. This vibration comes from the vocal folds, or vocal cords, located in the throat at the bottom of the larynx (Figure 8.30). The larynx is the opening that leads to the trachea and eventually to the lungs.

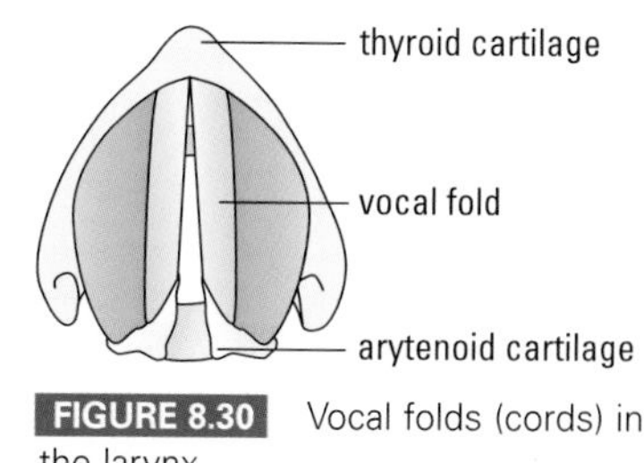

FIGURE 8.30 Vocal folds (cords) in the larynx

The lungs act as the power source for the voice. The flow of air from the lungs is modified by the vocal folds, producing a pressure wave (or longitudinal wave). The vocal folds are stretched between the cartilage at the front and back of the larynx, or voice box. The frequency of the sound is determined by the tension in the vocal folds. An increase in the tension increases the frequency. Your voice will often rise in pitch when you are frightened or angry. At such times what do you think has happened to the tension in these folds?

If the frequency of the wave imposed on the air flow by the vocal cords is close to the resonant frequency of the air column above the cords, then the note can be sung loudly. This air column is composed of the larynx, the pharynx, and the mouth. Figure 8.31 illustrates how these parts make up the vocal tract.

The vocal tract acts as an air column closed at one end. As a result, the fundamental frequency occurs when the vocal tract is one-quarter of a wavelength long. Overtones occur when the length of the vocal tract is three-quarters of a wavelength, five-quarters of a wavelength, and so on. It is the fundamental and the first two overtones that are mainly used in both speaking and singing. Figure 8.32 shows the arrangement of these waves in a straightened vocal tract.

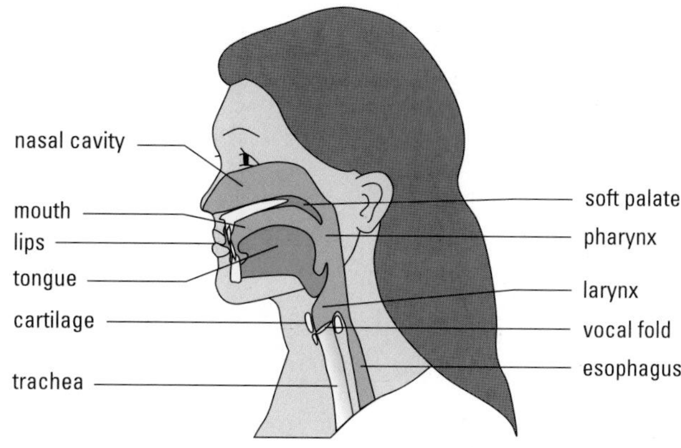

FIGURE 8.31 The vocal tract

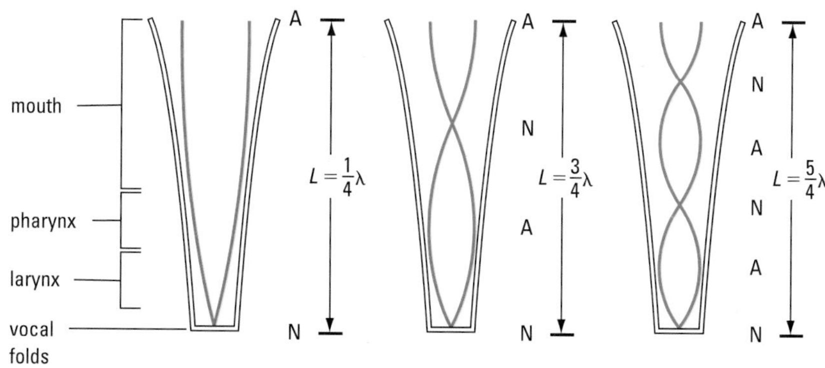

FIGURE 8.32 Resonant modes in the vocal tract

EXAMPLE 5 NUMERICAL

For a certain singer the length L of the vocal tract is about 17.5 cm (0.175 m). If the air in the tract is at a temperature of 37°C (normal body temperature), what are the frequencies of the lowest three resonant modes?

Given

$L = 0.175$ m

$T = 37°C$

Required

f

Analysis

- Use the temperature to calculate the speed of sound in air.
- Use the length of the air column to determine the wavelength.
- Combine speed and wavelength to calculate the frequency.

Solution

$$v = 331 \text{ m/s} + 0.59 \text{ m/(s·°C)} \times T$$
$$= 331 \text{ m/s} + 0.59 \text{ m/(s·°C)} \times 37°\text{C}$$
$$= 353 \text{ m/s}$$

a) For the fundamental, $L = \frac{1}{4}\lambda$

Therefore,

$$\lambda = 4L$$
$$= 4 \times 0.175 \text{ m}$$
$$= 0.70 \text{ m}$$

$$f = \frac{v}{\lambda}$$
$$= \frac{353 \text{ m/s}}{0.70 \text{ m}}$$
$$= 504 \text{ Hz}$$

b) For the first overtone, $L = \frac{3}{4}\lambda$

Therefore

$$\lambda = \frac{4}{3} \times L$$
$$= \frac{4}{3} \times 0.175$$
$$= 0.233 \text{ m}$$

$$f = \frac{353 \text{ m/s}}{0.233 \text{ m}}$$
$$= 1515 \text{ Hz or } 1.52 \text{ kHz}$$

Similarly, the second overtone occurs at 2.52 kHz.

Statement

The frequencies of the lowest three resonant modes of the vocal tract are 504 Hz, 1.52 kHz, and 2.52 kHz.

PRACTICE PROBLEMS

1. The temperature in a singer's vocal tract is 37°C. She or he is singing a 1765-Hz note as a first overtone. How long is the singer's vocal tract?
2. If your vocal tract is 18.5 cm long and is at a temperature of 37°C, what is the lowest note that you could sing?

Discovering Physics — Sound Spectrums of Instruments

Use a data logger with a sound sensor to compare the sound spectrum produced by various instruments and the human voice.

WEBLINK

The fabrication of a brass and woodwind instrument is a mixture of both science and art. What is the process? Who developed it? Has it changed over the years? Do research on the Internet to find out. Prepare a sequence chart tracing the construction of a particular instrument. Begin your research at **www.pearsoned.ca/physics11.**

If the singer in the previous question could not change the length of his vocal tract, then the only frequencies that he could sing loudly would have to be close to 500 Hz, 1500 Hz, or 2500 Hz. All other frequencies would be fainter since there would be no amplification of the vocal-fold frequency due to resonance. However, we learn early in life to adjust the length of the vocal tract by moving the larynx, tongue, jaw, and lips. For example, the larynx (voice box) lowers when you yawn, lengthening the vocal tract.

Similarly, when the mouth is opened wide, the antinode moves inward, shortening the air column, and raising the pitch of the resonance. Singers attempting a high note open their mouths very wide. This improves the match between one of the overtones and the desired frequency. In these ways, talented singers can produce a large range of frequencies.

A singer does not emit a pure tone (single frequency). In fact, the singer's vocal folds produce a whole spectrum of frequencies. The vocal folds vibrate at their fundamental frequency and many overtones at the same time. Some of these frequencies are amplified through resonance. Others are diminished. The frequency pattern of the vocal folds and the resonances of the vocal tract depend on the physical characteristics of the individual. These two factors combine to form a sound spectrum that is as individual as a fingerprint (Figure 8.33). It is now possible to identify an unknown speaker by comparing the speaker's sound spectrum with a known voiceprint for that person.

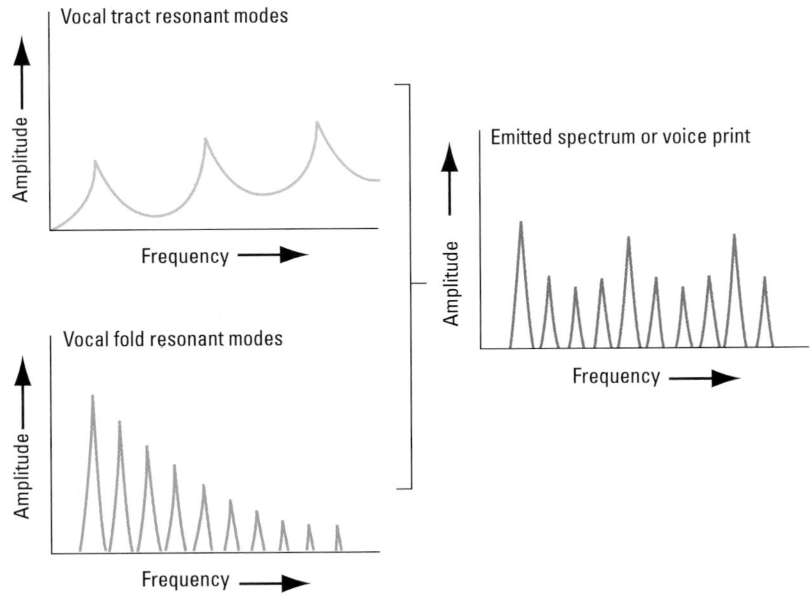

FIGURE 8.33 The interaction between the resonant modes of the vocal folds and the vocal tract produces a unique voiceprint.

Case Study

The Role of Hearing Technology

Decision-Making Skills

- Defining the Issue
- Developing Assessment Criteria
- Researching the Issue
- Analyzing Data and Information
- Proposing a Course of Action
- Justifying the Course of Action
- Communicating Your Proposal

BACKGROUND INFORMATION

Over the past 30 years, a device known as the cochlear implant has emerged to help deaf people to hear. It was originally developed in France for people in whom the cilia of the cochlea had been severely damaged. Since then, its use has spread around the world. People who are profoundly deaf and could not benefit by using a hearing aid can now hear. And people who were born deaf have the potential of being introduced to the world of sound—even at a young age.

There are risks involved in the use of a cochlear implant as well as in the operation to implant the device. Do the benefits outweigh the risks? Is the procedure safe for all patients? Under what circumstances is it not advised by a physician?

FIGURE 8.34 Using a TTY device

Several other devices have been developed to assist the hearing-impaired. There are a variety of implantable hearing aid devices, as well as telephone flashers or vibrating belt clips to signal that the telephone is ringing. Figure 8.34 shows a person using a TTY device at a public telephone. The caller types her message into the device. Then a telephone operator communicates the message to the person on the other end of the line and teletypes a message back to the caller.

Analyzing the Issue

1. Research cochlear implants and other assistive devices using the Internet and other electronic and reference resources. Compare and contrast the different features of these devices.
2. Explain how the cochlear implant affects human perception of sound. Include a diagram with your explanation.
3. Identify the impact of assistive technologies on society and the economy.
4. There are differing opinions in the deaf community about the application of cochlear implant technology. Research to find out the reasons for these different perspectives. Explain.
5. Prepare a brochure for a person requiring an assistive hearing device. Present the different options that are available, the kind of hearing impairment they are best suited for, as well as the advantages and disadvantages of each option.

Section 8.4 Review

Understanding Concepts

1. What provides the initial vibration in a
   a) trumpet?
   b) saxophone?
   c) flute?
   d) tuba?
   e) clarinet?
2. What type of air column is present in most wind instruments?
3. How is the length of the air column changed in
   a) brass instruments?
   b) woodwinds?
4. During the singing of a note, what is the function of the
   a) lungs?
   b) vocal cords?
   c) vocal tract?
5. What kind of air column does the vocal tract resemble?
6. a) How can the length of the vocal tract be changed?
   b) Why is it necessary to change the length of the vocal tract?

Applying Inquiry/ Communication Skills

7. If you were given a strange wind instrument, how could you decide whether it behaved as an open air column or a column closed at one end?
8. You have found a reed instrument and discover that the bore lengths are as follows:

Note	Frequency f (Hz)	Bore Length L (m)
C	262	0.323
D	294	0.287
E	330	0.255
F	349	0.243
G	392	0.215

   a) What kind of air column does this instrument resemble? Show your reasoning.
   b) Why might the values that you are obtaining not be working out exactly as theory would predict?
9. Explain why breathing in helium makes the pitch of your voice go higher.

WEBLINK

Find out more about how humans sing. Write a couple of paragraphs describing how a person might improve their singing voice and range. Begin your research at **www.pearsoned.ca/physics11.**

Investigation 1 (Section 8.2)

Inquiry Skills

- Initiating and Planning
- Applying Technical Skills
- Using Tools, Materials, Equipment
- Conducting and Recording
- Analyzing and Interpreting
- Concluding and Communicating

Resonance Frequencies for a Vibrating String

Vibrating strings can resonate at different frequencies by setting up standing wave patterns with different numbers of loops. The frequencies of the patterns corresponding to the overtones should be whole number multiples of the fundamental frequency. In this data logger investigation you will look for this relationship and see if the string can support several of these patterns at the same time.

Problem

Are the resonant frequencies for a vibrating string whole-number multiples of the fundamental frequency?

Materials

- computer
- interface
- detector coil with adapter plug
- voltage sensor
- sonometer with two adjustable bridges

Procedure

Part A: Preparing the Data Logger

1. Connect the interface to the computer. Turn on the interface and then the computer.
2. Connect the voltage sensor to the interface.
3. Open the computer program that displays the frequency spectrum (FFT).

Part B: Preparing the Sonometer

4. Place the bridges of the sonometer 80 cm apart. If the sonometer requires a hanging mass, use 1 kg.
5. Place the detector coil on the box of the sonometer midway between the bridges and connect the detector coil to the voltage sensor.

Part C: Detecting Resonant Frequencies

6. Pluck the string at its midpoint and observe the frequency spectrum. Locate the highest peak in the spectrum and measure its frequency with the aid of the cursor. Record this frequency. It should represent the fundamental or lowest frequency.
7. Pluck the string again at the midpoint and note the frequencies and relative heights of the other peaks (overtones).
8. Now pluck the string one-quarter of the way in from one bridge (20 cm). With the aid of the cursor, note the frequencies and relative heights of the overtones.
9. Stop the program and turn off the interface.

Analyzing and Interpreting

1. What is the fundamental frequency of the string?
2. If a node exists at each bridge and an antinode at the midpoint, determine
   a) the wavelength of the transverse wave
   b) the speed of the transverse wave (using the universal wave equation)
3. What are the frequencies of the overtones? How do they relate to the fundamental frequency? Explain why the frequencies should show that relationship.

Concluding and Communicating

4. How do the frequencies of the overtones compare with the frequency of the fundamental note?
5. Why does the sound of a plucked string change when it is plucked at different locations along its length while leaving the overall length the same?

Extending

6. Reduce the distance between the bridges to 40 cm. Predict the new frequency for the fundamental and verify your prediction using the data logger.

Investigation 2 (Section 8.3)

Inquiry Skills

- Initiating and Planning
- Applying Technical Skills
- Using Tools, Materials, Equipment
- Conducting and Recording
- Analyzing and Interpreting
- Concluding and Communicating

Resonance in an Air Column Open at Both Ends

Many wind instruments behave as if they were air columns open at both ends. Such instruments can produce a range of frequencies for the same length of column (or bore). In this activity you will investigate the frequencies produced by an open air column and compare these frequencies with those predicted by wave theory.

Problem

What are the five lowest frequencies at which a given air column open at both ends will resonate?

Materials

- amplifier
- frequency generator
- metre-stick
- microphone
- oscilloscope
- speaker
- thermometer
- tube open at both ends (such as a long mailing tube)

Experimental Design

1. Working in a small group, predict the values of the lowest five resonant frequencies for the tube. Consider the following questions:
   - What measurements will you need to take?
   - How will you calculate these values?
   - How do these predicted values compare with each other?
2. Decide how you intend to "excite" the air column (to provide frequencies to which the air column can resonate). How will you measure these frequencies?
3. Decide how you will determine when the air column is resonating.
4. Decide how many trials you intend to run to check on the consistency of your data.
5. Decide how you will organize and present your data.
6. Outline the steps for your procedure. Once your teacher has approved these steps, conduct your investigation.

Analyzing and Interpreting

1. Did you have any difficulty determining the resonant frequencies? If so, what was the problem?
2. How consistent were your data?
3. How do the measured frequencies compare with the predicted frequencies? Calculate a percent difference between the measured and predicted values for the fundamental (lowest) frequency.

$$\text{percent difference} = \frac{\text{measured value} - \text{calculated value}}{\text{calculated value}} \times 100\%$$

Concluding and Communicating

4. What are the five lowest resonant frequencies for this air column?
5. How do these frequencies compare with each other? Does this relationship agree with your prediction?

Extending

6. Your calculations of the predicted values assumed that the antinodes were located right at each end of the tube. In actual fact, these antinodes may not line up exactly with the ends. Using your data, calculate the actual location of the antinodes relative to the ends of the tube.

Design & Build

A Musical Instrument

Need

A few of you have decided to create and market a musical instrument. It is to be inexpensive and yet fun for young people to play. To be marketable, the instrument should be attractive and provide at least one full octave of notes.

Proposal

Decide on the type of instrument to be built. Will it be based on vibrating strings, air columns, or some other manner of producing notes? Consider what you can do to make it attractive. In addition, decide on presentation strategies to interest a potential manufacturer or investor.

Materials

1. Materials for the instrument are to be sturdy, low cost, and easy to work with.
2. Your presentation materials could include art materials, photographs, videotapes, or computer presentations.

Specifications

1. Design and build an instrument that is capable of
   a) producing eight notes in a musical scale (*do*, *re*, *mi*, etc.)
   b) providing different levels of loudness or volume
2. The instrument must be attractive and inexpensive.
3. Develop a presentation that includes
   a) an explanation of the physics behind the operation of the instrument
   b) instructions for playing at least two simple melodies
   c) a demonstration, either live or on videotape, of the instrument being played

Plan

As a group decide on

a) the type of instrument that you intend to create. Will it be woodwind, string, or some other possibility such as a xylophone or bell?
b) the materials you intend to use for the instrument. They should be inexpensive and easy to obtain.
c) the features that will make the instrument attractive.

Using wave principles, predict such features as the string length or tubing length. Be prepared to try these out before the final construction of the instrument.

Construction

Once you have a reasonable idea as to what you are going to do, begin construction. Remember to take precautions if you are cutting wood or metal. Wear safety goggles and use guards to protect your hands. Epoxy glue and solvents should only be used in well-ventilated areas. You might like to videotape the various stages of construction. When the instrument has been completed, develop your presentation. Make sure that you practice playing the instrument before attempting any demonstration.

Evaluation

A: The Instrument
How would you rate the instrument as to its:

- ability to produce at least eight notes of a musical scale
- range of volume of sound
- attractiveness

B: The Presentation
How would you rate the presentation with respect to:

- the clarity and accuracy of the acoustic principles behind the playing of the instrument
- the clarity and completeness of the instructions for playing two simple melodies
- the musical demonstration

CHAPTER SUMMARY

Key Terms

acoustics
antinode
fixed end
fixed point
free end
free point
fundamental
harmonic
loop
node
overtone
partials
reflection
resonant frequency
resonant length
standing wave

Key Equations

$f_1L_1 = f_2L_2$ $v = f\lambda$

Essential Understandings

- A standing wave is a stationary pattern of vibrations consisting of loops and nodes.
- A wave reverses phase when it reflects from a fixed point, but does not change phase when it reflects from a free point.
- For a standing wave formed by reflection, an antinode occurs at a free end while a node occurs at a fixed end.
- In any standing wave, the distance between successive nodes, or between successive antinodes, is half a wavelength.
- The fundamental frequency of a vibrating string depends on its length, density, diameter, and tension.
- All other factors being constant, the relationship between the length and frequency of a vibrating string is $f_1L_1 = f_2L_2$
- The different notes produced by stringed instruments can be explained in terms of the physics of vibrating strings.
- The length of an air column closed at one end that can resonate must be a member of the sequence $\frac{1}{4}\lambda$, $\frac{3}{4}\lambda$, $\frac{5}{4}\lambda$, and so on.
- The vocal tract acts as an air column closed at one end with the open end near the lips.
- The frequency of a note that is sung depends on the tension in the vocal cords.
- Amplification of the sound from the vocal cords is provided by means of resonances in the vocal tract.
- The length of an air column open at both ends that can resonate must be a member of the sequence $\frac{1}{2}\lambda$, $\frac{2}{2}\lambda$, $\frac{3}{2}\lambda$, $\frac{4}{2}\lambda$, and so on.
- Most wind instruments behave as air columns open at both ends. The clarinet is one exception.
- The initial vibration for a wind instrument occurs in the lips of a brass player and in the reed for a woodwind player.
- Different notes are produced from wind instruments by changing the length of the bore.
- With brass instruments, different notes can be played with the same bore length by forming overtones.
- The speed of sound through a gas can be accurately measured by means of resonating air columns.

Consolidate Your Understanding

1. Look back to your answer for the Checkpoint on page 291. Would you still give the same answer? Which choice of answer deals with the pitch of the sound being produced by the trumpet player?
2. Why can sound emerge from a wind instrument even if no "wind" comes out?
3. Create a concept map to illustrate the relationship between wave motion and music. Try to include as many of the Key Terms listed above as possible.
4. Longitudinal standing waves in an air column consist of nodes and antinodes. Make up a set of instructions for determining the possible resonance lengths of air columns in wavelengths. The instructions should cover air columns open at both ends and open at one end only. Make them as short and clear as possible.

CHAPTER 8 REVIEW

Understanding Concepts

1. What is the distance in wavelengths between successive nodes in a standing wave?
   a) $\frac{1}{4}\lambda$ b) $\frac{1}{2}\lambda$ c) $\frac{3}{4}\lambda$
   d) 1λ e) $\frac{5}{4}\lambda$
2. A standing wave with a wavelength of 60 cm forms in an air column open at both ends. How long is the first resonant length?
   a) 7.5 cm b) 15 cm c) 30 cm
   d) 45 cm e) 60 cm
3. When a 1024-Hz tuning fork is held over an air column closed at one end, the first two resonant lengths are 8.00 cm and 24.6 cm. What is the best value for the speed of sound in air that day?
   a) 328 m/s b) 331 m/s c) 336 m/s
   d) 340 m/s e) 343 m/s
4. A singer wishes to sing a higher note. This is done by
   a) increasing the tension in the vocal cords
   b) decreasing the tension in the vocal cords
   c) increasing the amplitude of the vocal cords
   d) decreasing the amplitude of the vocal cords
   e) decreasing the length of the vocal cords
5. A string 20.0 cm long is vibrating at 500 Hz. What would be the frequency of that string if its length became 60.0 cm?
   a) 167 Hz b) 250 Hz c) 333 Hz
   d) 375 Hz e) 1.50 kHz
6. You hear a sound while the gas tank of a car is being filled. Explain why the pitch of the sound rises as the level of the gasoline rises.
7. A tuning fork is mounted on a matched resonance box open at one end. If the apparatus is submerged in water, will the box still be matched to the tuning fork?
8. Explain why an antinode forms one half wavelength in from a free end when the standing wave is formed by reflection.
9. Would the pitch rise or fall if an open-ended resonating cylinder of air were suddenly closed at
   a) one end?
   b) both ends? (Assume that it is vibrating in its fundamental mode.)
10. Give two reasons why female vocalists tend to sing higher notes than male vocalists.
11. Why are the notes produced by a cello lower than those from a violin?
12. Describe two ways in which a brass instrument is played differently from a woodwind.
13. Which harmonics on a vibrating string have a node exactly in the middle? Explain.
14. The highest note on a piano has a fundamental frequency of 4186 Hz. If you recorded it on a system that would only respond to frequencies up to 5000 Hz, why would the notes sound poor?
15. A segment of a violin string vibrates in 1 loop with a frequency of 5000 Hz. If that loop is 10.0 cm long, what is the speed of the wave along the violin string?
16. A rope 2.4 m long vibrates with a standing wave of 3 loops and a frequency of 6.0 Hz
    a) What is the wavelength of the standing wave?
    b) What are two names for this pattern?
    c) What is the speed of the travelling waves?
    d) What would the frequency of the first overtone be?
17. A string 100 cm long is vibrating in its fifth harmonic. How far is the first node away from the end of the string? Do not count the nodes that are at each end.
18. A guitar string 63 cm long emits a 110-Hz note. How long should the string be to emit a 131-Hz note?
19. A note with a frequency of 349.2 Hz (F) is sounding from a string segment 59.5 cm long. What frequency is produced if the length of the segment is shortened to 53.1 cm?
20. A standing wave has a wavelength of 3.8 m. What is the distance between adjacent nodes?
21. If the vocal tract of a person is 17.0 cm long, how long is the wavelength of the fundamental mode?
22. If the vocalist in the previous problem forms the first overtone, what is its wavelength?
23. An air column is open at both ends. If the wavelength of the sound wave is 1.2 m, what are the first two resonant lengths of the air column?
24. An air column is open at one end. If the wavelength of the sound wave is 1.8 m, what are the first two resonant lengths for the air column?
25. The shortest resonant length of an air column closed at one end is 22 cm. What is the wavelength of the sound wave?
26. A trumpet is played in its first overtone. How long should the bore be if the wavelength is 50 cm?
27. In an experiment to determine the speed of sound, a 220-Hz tuning fork is held over the open end of an air column closed at one end. If the first resonant length is 0.380 m, what is the speed of sound?
28. The speed of sound in brass is 3500 m/s. If a brass rod 75 cm long and free at both ends is struck such that it vibrates longitudinally, what is the frequency of the fundamental mode?
29. An air column, closed at one end, has a fundamental frequency of 500.0 Hz. What are the frequencies of the first two overtones?

30. An air column, open at both ends, has a fundamental frequency of 2000 Hz.
   a) What are the frequencies of the first two overtones?
   b) Which overtone represents the highest frequency that can normally be heard by humans?

31. A trumpet is playing A (880 Hz). If it forms the first harmonic, what is the length of the tubing in the bore? The speed of sound in air is 345 m/s.

Applying Inquiry/ Communication Skills

32. A couple mounts two open metal tubes on the roof of their car for use as a roof rack. When the car reaches a speed of 60 km/h, a loud whistling noise is heard from the rack.
   a) Explain what is probably happening.
   b) Describe how they can solve the problem without throwing away the roof rack.

33. Discuss why it is important that a stringed instrument possess no strong resonances in the soundbox.

34. a) Sketch the arrangement of nodes and antinodes for the fourth resonant length of an air column closed at one end.
   b) How long in wavelengths is the fourth resonant length?

35. A guitarist measured the fundamental frequency of a guitar string as the tension was changed and obtained the following results.

Frequency f (Hz)	Tension T (N)
200	10
282	20
346	30
400	40
447	50

   a) Draw a graph of the data, placing tension on the x-axis.
   b) From the graph determine the frequency that would be produced if the tension were
      i) 33 N
      ii) 60 N
   c) By what factor must the tension be multiplied in order to double the frequency?
   d) Enter the data into a graphing calculator. Place the tension data in the L_1 list and frequency in the L_2 list. Display the scatter plot of frequency against tension. Obtain the equation of the curve in the form $y = ax^b$, where
      y represents frequency
      x represents tension
      a and b are constants

36. Design the apparatus and method that would allow you to measure the speed of sound through a gas which is less dense than air.

37. In an experiment to determine the speed of sound in air, an air column closed at one end reasonated to a 512-Hz tuning fork. The first two resonant lengths were 0.166 m and 0.498 m. Determine the speed of sound from the data.

Making Connections

38. If your vocal tract is 15.0 cm long, what would be the wavelength corresponding to:
   a) the fundamental?
   b) the first overtone?
   c) the second overtone?

39. If the air in your throat is at 36°C, what are the corresponding resonance frequencies of your vocal tract?

40. A chimney with the damper closed acts as an air column closed at one end. At a temperature of −10°C, a closed 10-m chimney is heard moaning a note that is at the very low end of the audible range.
   a) What is the frequency of the note?
   b) Which overtone does it represent?
   (See question 39.)

41. If the height of the player in Figure 8.35 is 1.8 m and the air temperature is 10°C,
   a) estimate the length of the Alpine horn
   b) estimate the lowest frequency that can be produced with this horn. Assume it behaves as an air column open at both ends.

FIGURE 8.35 An Alpine horn

42. Should the human voice be considered a wind instrument or a stringed instrument? Discuss.

Using the Internet to Research Opportunities in Physics

The Internet is an excellent resource for information about careers in physics. You may have already visited university and school Web sites. Many have lists of careers and offer guidance on undergraduate program selection. These are helpful, but what else is available to you? How can you find it?

A great place to start is to visit the Web sites of the associations of professional physicists, such as the Canadian Association of Physicists (www.cap.ca) and the American Physical Society (www.aps.org). Both list careers, scholarships, and even people to contact about different areas of physics. You can find these and other Web sites of interest by using search engines.

Search Engines

A search engine finds Web sites based on whatever criteria you supply. The key is to choose the right set of words for your search.

1. Write down several words you could use to search for information on physics careers. Use these to create a specific phrase or question. You can broaden your search if necessary.

As an example, a student using the search engine www.google.com types in: "Canadian careers in physics." She has a choice of receiving an extended list or going with the search engine's "I feel lucky" option, which gives one, hopefully the best, Web site. She chooses "lucky" and finds herself at The Department of Physics and Mathematical Physics at the University of Adelaide, Australia. Why this site? It's an excellently organized and maintained site collecting physics career Web sites from around the world, including Canada. In fact, the title of the site is: *Physics Careers: Get a Physics Degree and See the World!* Following the links from this site provides an excellent picture of the types of careers in physics as well as educational options.

Making the Most of What You Find

You will encounter a variety of information when you search the Internet. Look carefully before you dismiss anything. For example, the advertisement on the next page came from the Web site of the Canadian Association of Physicists. It isn't for a job you could apply for yet, so what use is it? It can tell you a great deal, if you look carefully.

2. Study the advertisement shown and answer the following questions.
   - What is medical physics?
   - What other specialties are included within medical physics?
   - A training position is one in which you learn while working in a particular field. What are the qualifications required for the training positions advertised?
   - What do you think of the salaries being offered for these positions entering medical physics with CancerCare Manitoba?
   - What do you think such salaries say about this field?
   - There is also an emphasis on the quality of life in this location.

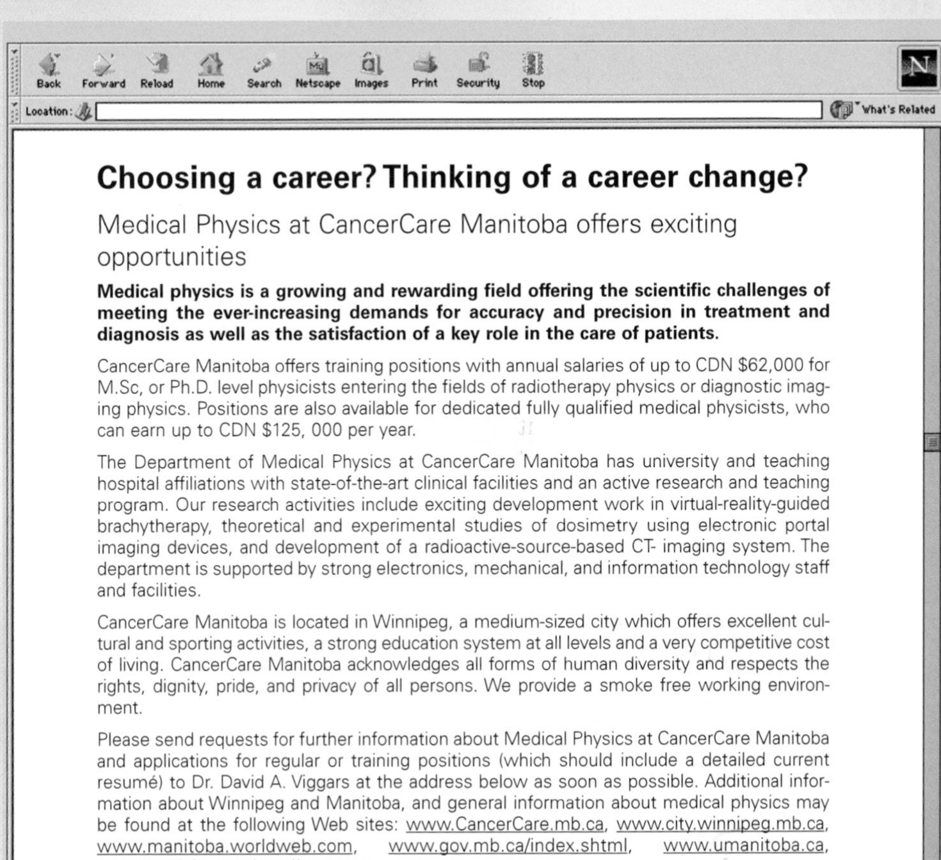

Back
Forward
Reload
Home
Search
Netscape
Images
Print
Security
Stop
Location:
What's Related
Choosing a career? Thinking of a career change?
Medical Physics at CancerCare Manitoba offers exciting opportunities
Medical physics is a growing and rewarding field offering the scientific challenges of meeting the ever-increasing demands for accuracy and precision in treatment and diagnosis as well as the satisfaction of a key role in the care of patients.
CancerCare Manitoba offers training positions with annual salaries of up to CDN $62,000 for M.Sc, or Ph.D. level physicists entering the fields of radiotherapy physics or diagnostic imaging physics. Positions are also available for dedicated fully qualified medical physicists, who can earn up to CDN $125, 000 per year.
The Department of Medical Physics at CancerCare Manitoba has university and teaching hospital affiliations with state-of-the-art clinical facilities and an active research and teaching program. Our research activities include exciting development work in virtual-reality-guided brachytherapy, theoretical and experimental studies of dosimetry using electronic portal imaging devices, and development of a radioactive-source-based CT- imaging system. The department is supported by strong electronics, mechanical, and information technology staff and facilities.
CancerCare Manitoba is located in Winnipeg, a medium-sized city which offers excellent cultural and sporting activities, a strong education system at all levels and a very competitive cost of living. CancerCare Manitoba acknowledges all forms of human diversity and respects the rights, dignity, pride, and privacy of all persons. We provide a smoke free working environment.
Please send requests for further information about Medical Physics at CancerCare Manitoba and applications for regular or training positions (which should include a detailed current resumé) to Dr. David A. Viggars at the address below as soon as possible. Additional information about Winnipeg and Manitoba, and general information about medical physics may be found at the following Web sites: www.CancerCare.mb.ca, www.city.winnipeg.mb.ca, www.manitoba.worldweb.com, www.gov.mb.ca/index.shtml, www.umanitoba.ca, www.medphys.ca, http://aapm.org
Department of Medical Physics, CancerCare Manitoba,
675 McDermot Avenue, Winnipeg, Manitoba, R3E 0V9 CANADA

What does this information suggest to you about the number of available applicants for these positions?

- What other career choices related to this field are mentioned indirectly in this advertisement?
- What satisfactions, and difficulties, might be part of the career of a medical physicist? How could you find someone to ask?

Spotting Better Web Sites

How can you tell when you've found a good source of career information? Ask yourself these questions:

- *Whose Web site is it?* Those set up by universities or professional associations are likely to be up-to-date, with links to other good resources.
- *Is the site regularly updated?* This is a sign the information is likely to be current and any emails will be active.
- *Are there contact names with email addresses listed?* Associations often list people interested in speaking to students or providing information.

Looking Outward

Make it a personal goal to become comfortable using the Internet to find information and contact people. What do you need to do? Who can help you? Become a confident "surfer" and use your skills to investigate career choices.

Wind Chimes

Background Information

Wind chimes, or wind bells, have been known since prehistoric times. Essentially they consist of a hanging cluster of objects that will chime, either when blown into each other by the wind or when struck by a wind-driven clapper. In some cases a hanging bell has a flat metal plate suspended from the clapper. When the wind blows, the swinging plate will pull the clapper over to ring the bell.

Although wind chimes are now popular in the gardens of North America, they have been used extensively in Asia for centuries. Carefully decorated chimes would be hung from sacred structures, sometimes in the hope of attracting beneficent spirits.

SCENARIO

You are on a development team that is going to manufacture wind chimes as a commercial product. You will plan a marketing strategy and advertising campaign to promote your wind chimes.

Part A: Build and Analyze a Set of Wind Chimes

1. Build a set of wind chimes. Select your own materials or use a set of hollow tubes of different lengths. The tubes could be cut from electrical conduit, about 2–3 cm in diameter. The clapper (or striker) could be a piece of wooden dowel (10 cm to 15 cm long). During this investigation you will keep a log of all procedures and record your results.

   Tube Length and Frequency
   - What relationship exists between the length of the tube and the frequency of the note it produces when struck? Describe the technique used to measure the frequency of the note produced by the vibrating tube.
   - Do you get the same frequency when the rod is struck on the side rather than at the end? Explain.

   Suspension
   - Describe the optimum place to hold the tube so that it will chime longest and clearest.
   - How critical is it to hold the tube exactly at that point? Measure the location of this point relative to the nearest end. In your log, record scale diagrams of the tubes with the "sweet spot" labelled.

   Striking Point
   - Describe the optimum place to strike the tube so that it will chime longest and clearest.
   - How critical is it to strike the tube exactly at that point? Measure the location of this point relative to the same end used for *Suspension*. Record your findings in the log.
   - What relationship exists between the length of the tube and the frequency of the note it produces when struck? Describe the technique used to measure the frequency of the note produced by the vibrating tube.

Standing Wave

- Does the tube vibrate in a standing wave pattern? Explain.
- How would you test the vibrating tube to determine whether the standing wave is transverse or longitudinal?
- If the tube does vibrate in a standing wave pattern, where are the nodes and antinodes located?

Speed of the Wave Through the Tubing

- If you have determined the location of nodes and antinodes, you can measure the wavelength of the wave in the tubing. Combining this with the frequency will allow you to calculate the speed of that wave. By checking through reference materials, find out how the speed of the wave through the tubing compares with the reported speed of longitudinal or transverse waves through the material.

2. If the tube vibrates in a standing wave pattern, is there any relationship between the location of the optimum suspension point and striking point and the location of the nodes and antinodes in the wave? Analyze and describe the vibration properties of the tubing in terms of the physical principles of wave motion.

Part B: Communicate Your Findings

3. Prepare a manual to explain the construction and operation of your wind chimes.

4. In your manual, include a glossary of the terms such as frequency, wavelength, and amplitude. Explain how each term applies to wind chimes.

Part C: Develop a Marketing Plan

5 Research the history of wind chimes and their design. Identify and describe how the design has changed over time.

6. Using your research and what you know, propose a marketing plan for your product. Consider who will potentially purchase your wind chimes and how you can make the product appealing to that market.

7. Develop an advertisement for the product (e.g. brochure, infomercial) to highlight the most important information you want to communicate to potential buyers of your product.

UNIT 3 REVIEW

Understanding Concepts

1. During a transverse vibration a particle travels 2.0 m during one cycle. What is the amplitude of that vibration?
   a) 0.50 m b) 1.0 m c) 2.0 m
   d) 4.0 m e) 8.0 m

2. A wave with a speed of 10.0 m/s has a wavelength of 20.0 m. What is its frequency?
   a) 0.500 Hz b) 2.00 Hz c) 10.0 Hz
   d) 20.0 Hz e) 200 Hz

3. A wave has a frequency of 0.400 Hz and a wavelength of 5.00 m. How far will it travel in 10.0 s?
   a) 0.800 m b) 8.00 m c) 12.5 m
   d) 20.0 m e) 125 m

4. A string, 50.0 cm long, vibrates at 1000 Hz. How long should it be to vibrate at 5000 Hz under the same tension?
   a) 250 cm b) 100 cm c) 50.0 cm
   d) 20.0 cm e) 10.0 cm

5. Which of the following combinations of changes will definitely lower the frequency of a vibrating string?
   a) decrease the length and decrease the tension
   b) decrease the length and increase the tension
   c) increase the length and increase the tension
   d) increase the length and decrease the tension
   e) none of these changes will definitely lower the frequency

6. What is the shortest resonant length of an air column closed at one end if the wavelength of the sound wave is 80.0 cm?
   a) 10.0 cm b) 20.0 cm c) 40.0 cm
   d) 80.0 cm e) 160 cm

7. What is the shortest resonant length of an air column open at both ends if the wavelength of the sound wave is 100 cm?
   a) 20.0 cm b) 25.0 cm c) 50.0 cm
   d) 100 cm e) 200 cm

8. A singer has an air tract with a length of 15.0 cm. If the speed of sound in that tract is 350 m/s, what is the frequency of the fundamental mode?
   a) 583 Hz b) 875 Hz c) 1.17 kHz
   d) 1.75 kHz e) 2.33 kHz

9. If the fundamental frequency of a standing wave in a vibrating string is 40.0 Hz, what is the frequency of the third harmonic?
   a) 40.0 Hz b) 80.0 Hz c) 120 Hz
   d) 160 Hz e) 200 Hz

10. For a longitudinal wave, in which direction is a point at the centre of a compression moving relative to the direction of travel of the wave?

11. Which property of a sound wave determines its pitch?

12. Which property of a sound wave determines its intensity?

13. Why are intensity and loudness not the same quantity?

14. State three uses that humans make of ultrasound.

15. If two astronauts are drifting close to each other in space, why do they need a radio to communicate with each other?

16. A string is vibrating in its lowest 10 harmonics at the same time. If it is touched exactly one-quarter of the distance in from one fixed end, which harmonics will be affected the least?

17. What adjustments does a bass singer make in order to reach for a lower note?

18. With respect to the human ear, state the function of:
    a) the tympanic membrane
    b) the hammer, anvil, and stirrup
    c) the cochlea

19. A longitudinal wave passing through rock has a frequency of 12 Hz and a wavelength of 700 m. How long will it take the wave to travel 50 km?

20. The tip of a tuning fork has an amplitude of 1.5 mm. If the fork has a frequency of 512 Hz, approximately how far does the tip travel in 5.0 s?

21. What is the result when a crest with an amplitude of 2.0 m completely overlaps
    a) a trough with an amplitude of 3.5 m?
    b) a trough with an amplitude of 2.0 m?
    c) a crest with an amplitude of 3.5 m?

Applying Inquiry/ Communication Skills

22. A listener finds it strange that although bass notes (low notes) travel around corners better than treble notes, the treble notes seem to be able to travel farther. How would you explain these effects to the listener?

23. What demonstrations might you provide to show that sound travels as a wave?

24. Describe how you would determine if wind chimes are vibrating
    a) longitudinally or transversely
    b) in their fundamental mode or an overtone

25. In an experiment to determine the speed of sound in air, the first two resonant lengths for an air column closed at one end were found to be 6.9 cm and 23.6 cm respectively.
    a) If the tuning fork had a frequency of 1024 Hz, what was the speed of sound according to the experiment?
    b) If the air temperature was 22°C, what was the percent error?

26. Use a graphic organizer such as a Venn diagram to describe the similarities and differences between brass and woodwind instruments.

27. Two waves are approaching each other as shown in Figure 1. All dimensions are in centimetres.
a) Determine the resulting shape of the waves due to superposition after 2.0 s.
b) Determine the resulting shape of the waves due to superposition after 3.0 s.

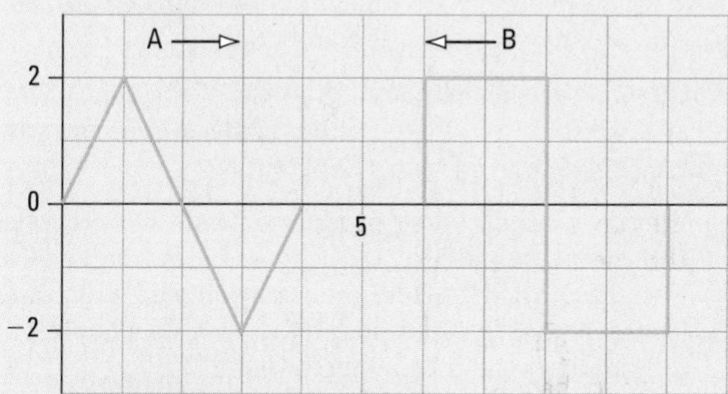

FIGURE 1

28. What is the frequency in hertz of the second hand of a clock?

29. The second harmonic on a sonometer string vibrates at 15 Hz. What is the frequency of
a) the first harmonic?
b) the second overtone?

30. Two waves are passing through each other. Wave X has an amplitude of 45 cm while wave Y has an amplitude of 32 cm. Both have the same wavelength. Determine the maximum displacement of the medium when
a) crest X overlaps crest Y
b) crest X overlaps trough Y
c) trough X overlaps crest Y
d) trough X overlaps trough Y

31. A tuning fork with a frequency of 1024 Hz is sounded at the same time as a speaker with a frequency of 1018 Hz. How many beats are heard in 4.0 s?

32. Two trumpets are being tuned using beats. One has a frequency of 440 Hz. When the second is played along with it, 15 beats are heard in 5.0 s. What are the possible frequencies of the second trumpet?

33. How long would it take a sonar pulse to return from a school of fish in Lake Ontario if the fish are 65 m away from the sonar unit?

34. A ship off the coast of Prince Edward Island sends a sonar pulse downward to determine the depth of the water. If the pulse returns 3.48 s later, how deep is the water?

35. A string is vibrating in its first harmonic. If it is 70.0 cm long, how long is the wavelength?

36. What is the intensity in pW/m^2 of sound at
a) 10 dB? b) 60 dB? c) 110 dB?

37. What is the speed of sound in air at standard pressure if the air temperature is
a) 45°C? b) −10°C?

38. Design an experiment to test the effectiveness of different materials as sound barriers used in partitions between walls.

39. A rope, 8.0 m long, contains 4 loops. If it vibrates at 3.0 Hz, determine
a) the wavelength of the wave
b) the speed of the wave

40. A guitar string, 90.0 cm long, is made to vibrate with 4 loops between the fixed ends. If the frequency of vibration is 1000 Hz, calculate the speed of the transverse wave along the string.

41. Calculate the value in W/m^2 for sound intensities of
a) 20 dB b) 120 dB
Remember that pico means X 10^{-12}.

42. A water wave has a period of 0.200 s and a wavelength of 3.50 m. How long will it take the wave to travel 7.00 km?

43. If the speed of sound in air is 352 m/s, what is the air temperature?

44. An air column is closed at one end. If the speed of sound is 330 m/s, how long must the first resonant length be to resonate at
a) 2000 Hz? b) 50 Hz?

45. A trombone is producing a fundamental note with a frequency of 110 Hz. If the speed of sound in air is 342 m/s, what length of bore is required?

46. A transverse wave has a frequency of 5.00 Hz, a wavelength of 2.00 m, and an amplitude of 0.400 m.
a) What is the speed of the wave?
b) How long would it take the wave to travel 200 m?
c) How far does each particle in the medium travel as one wavelength of the wave passes by?
d) How long does it take one wavelength of the wave to pass by a given particle?
e) What is the average speed of the particles in the wave as the wave passes by?
f) Why is the speed of the particles not the same as the speed of the wave?

47. What is the value in W/m^2 of a sound intensity of 17 dB?

48. The bore length of a trombone slide in a given position is 2.50 m. The air temperature is 20°C. What are the three lowest frequencies that can be played in that position?

49. A Twirl-a-Tune is an 80.0 cm long plastic tube open at both ends. If the Twirl-a-Tune is spun on a day when the air temperature is 30°C, what are the two lowest frequencies produced by the air column?

50. Two organ pipes—one 25 cm long and the other 27 cm long—are open at both ends. If the speed of sound is 340 m/s, what will be the beat frequency when both pipes are sounded together?

51. Imagine a medium in which the particles at rest are 2.0 cm apart. When a longitudinal wave with an amplitude of 0.5 cm passes through,
   a) what is the maximum possible distance between particles?
   b) what is the minimum possible distance between particles?
   c) which situation represents a compression and which a rarefaction?

   Explain the reasoning for your answers using a diagram.

52. Draw a diagram similar to Figure 7.25 on page 281. Show the wave sources as two points separated by 3.0 cm. Using each source as a centre, draw a series of circles with radii of 1.0 cm, 2.0 cm, 3.0 cm, 4.0 cm, 5.0 cm, and 6.0 cm. These circles represent crests. Since they are 1.0 cm apart, the wavelength is 1.0 cm.
   a) Locate all points where a crest from one source meets a crest from the second source. These points are antinodes. Determine the location of the antinodal lines.
   b) Repeat the previous diagram, but with the point sources only 2.0 cm apart. Locate the antinodal lines. How does the separation between antinodal lines change when the sources move closer together?

53. Using diagrams similar to those in the previous question, find out what happens to the antinodal line spacing when the distance between the sources stays the same, but the wavelength increases (perhaps from 1.0 cm to 1.5 cm).

54. In an experiment to determine the change in sound intensity as the distance from the source increases, a student obtained the following data:

Distance from the Source d (m)	Sound Intensity I (nW/m^2)
1.0	55
1.5	24
2.0	14
2.5	9
3.0	6

NOTE: "n" is the symbol for "nano" which means 10^{-9}.

   a) Draw an accurate graph of the data placing distance on the x-axis.
   b) From your graph determine how far away from the source you should be to receive an intensity of 20 nW/m^2.
   c) From your graph, determine the sound intensity at a distance of 2.3 m.
   d) If you have access to a graphing calculator, determine the equation which relates sound intensity to distance from the source in the form $I = ad^b$. What would be the units for "a"?

55. Explain why:
   a) high-pitched notes seem to be able to travel farther than low-pitched notes.
   b) low-pitched notes bend better around obstacles than high-pitched notes.

Making Connections

56. Why is ultrasound sometimes better than X-rays for producing images of the human body?

57. A bat sends out an ultrasonic squeak. If the echo from a car is shifted to a higher pitch, which way is the car moving relative to the bat? Explain.

58. a) Why is a shock wave produced when a jet travels faster than sound?
   b) The shock wave is continuously produced when the jet travels faster than sound, so why do people on the ground hear it as a single "bang"?

59. A clarinet is playing a fundamental frequency of 440 Hz. If the speed of sound in air is 340 m/s, what is the approximate distance from the reed to the open hole?

60. Which instrument is closest to the human voice? Give reasons for your answer.

61. A guitar is tuned in a warm room. What will happen to the pitch of the strings if it is taken outside on a cold winter's day? Explain.

62. A whistle consists of two short tubes, each open at both ends. One tube is 1.40 cm long while the other is 1.60 cm long.
   a) If they are each resonating in their second harmonic mode and the speed of sound is 355 m/s, what is the beat frequency between them?
   b) What would you hear if only one tube were sounding?

63. Early high fidelity sound systems were monaural (meaning only one source of sound both in recording and reproduction). Then the stereo was developed with sound recorded from (at least) two positions and played back from two speaker enclosures. More recent systems are "surround sound." Discuss the benefits of these developments. What advantages do stereos provide? Where should speakers be placed for best results in a room?

64. Find out what types of problems might cause people to be "sonically challenged." Would it be desirable to build any features into hearing aids for particular hearing needs? If so, which features?

65. Design a sound barrier to go alongside highways, taking cost, appearance, and effectiveness into consideration.

66. Imagine that a source of sound is at rest and you start to move away from it. What will happen to the frequency of sound you hear? Explain the reasoning behind your answer.

67. Since bats hunt their prey using ultrasound, how have insects evolved to detect this ultrasound? Search through reference material to find out the response of various insects to ultrasound.

Problem Solving

68. A moth has a body length of 1.5 cm. If the speed of sound is 340 m/s,
a) what range of sound frequencies would reflect strongly from the moth?
b) is this range audible to humans?

69. A trombone is to play an F (175 Hz) as its first overtone. If the air temperature in the bore is 30°C how long should the bore be?

70. A string 90 cm long is vibrating in its sixth harmonic mode. If the frequency of the string is 1000 Hz, what is the speed of the wave along that string?

71. a) An organ pipe, 30.0 cm long, is open at one end. If the temperature of the church is a warm 30°C, what is the fundamental frequency produced by that pipe?
b) If that pipe becomes open at both ends, what will its fundamental frequency become?
c) If the church cools to 10°C, what will be the frequency of the note from the pipe in b)?

72. An air column open at both ends has a fundamental frequency of 1000 Hz. What will that frequency become if
a) one end is closed?
b) both ends are closed?

73. An air column open at one end resonates in its second overtone at 680 Hz. If the length of the column is 64.4 cm, what is the air temperature?

74. Which harmonic on the A string (110 Hz) will be the same as the third harmonic on the D string (146.8 Hz)?

75. A singer has a vocal tract 18.0 cm long. If the note being sung has a frequency of 1046 Hz (high C), which resonant mode of the vocal tract is closest to this note? The air temperature in the vocal tract is 28°C.

76. A trumpet is tuned to 440 Hz at 30°C. If the temperature then drops to 10°C, what is the change in frequency?

77. Imagine that you are sitting in an anchored boat. You see water waves that vibrate with a frequency of 0.25 Hz. The distance from the crest to next crest is 6.0 m.
a) What is the speed of the waves?
b) With what speed and direction would you travel through the water in order to see waves that have an apparent frequency of 0 Hz? Explain.
c) With what speed and direction would you have to travel through the water in order to see waves that have an apparent frequency of 0.50 Hz? Explain.

78. Two children are swinging on swings side by side. One completes 20 cycles in 1.0 min while the other completes 26 cycles in 1.0 min. If they start out together, how many additional times will they be swinging together during that minute? Explain.

79. A bass is singing a note with a frequency of 98 Hz. A soprano is singing a note two octaves higher.
a) What is the frequency of the higher note?
b) Which note is it according to Table 7.1 on page 268?

80. How far away is an apartment building if an echo returns from it in 1.40 s? The air temperature is 22°C.

81. A sound wave travels along a steel railway track. If the frequency is 100 Hz and the wavelength is 59.6 m, how far will the wave travel in 30.0 s?

82. A sonar pulse travels through seawater at 1531 m/s. If the echo returns from a school of fish after 0.240 s, how far away are the fish?

83. Two sources of sound have frequencies of 250.0 Hz and 258.0 Hz. How many beats would you hear in 5.0 s?

84. When a flute is played at the same time as a 440-Hz note, 30 beats are heard in 5.0 s. What are the possible frequencies of the flute?

85. A standing wave is formed by reflection at a free end. If the wavelength is 20 cm, what part of the standing wave will be found:
a) 10 cm from the free end?
b) 35 cm from the free end?
Give reasons for your answers.

86. A vibrating string 60.0 cm long produces an E (330 Hz).
a) What frequency will be produced if the string is shortened to 50.5 cm with no change in tension?
b) Which note corresponds to this frequency?

87. A string 50.0 cm long vibrates at 349 Hz (middle F). How long should the string be with no change in tension to produce middle B (494 Hz)?

88. An air column, open at both ends, is 1.50 m long. If its third harmonic has a frequency of 350 Hz, what is the speed of sound in the column?

89. a) If a trumpet is sounding a high D (587 Hz) as a first overtone, what is the bore length? The speed of sound is 340 m/s.
b) How much tubing must be added to this bore length to allow the trumpet to sound a high C (523 Hz) as a first overtone?

90. a) A clarinet plays a B (494 Hz) as a fundamental frequency. How long is the bore length if the speed of sound is 344 m/s?
b) By how much must the bore length be lengthened to allow the clarinet to sound a G (392 Hz)?

91. A vocal tract is 0.150 m long. If the air temperature in the tract is 36°C, what is the frequency of the second overtone?

UNIT

4 Light and Geometric Optics

OVERALL EXPECTATIONS

By the end of this unit, you will be able to:

- demonstrate an understanding of the properties of light and the principles underlying the transmission of light through a medium and from one medium to another
- investigate the properties of light through experimentation, and illustrate and predict the behaviour of light through the use of ray diagrams and algebraic equations
- evaluate the contributions to such areas as entertainment, communications, and health made by the development of optical devices and other technologies designed to make use of light

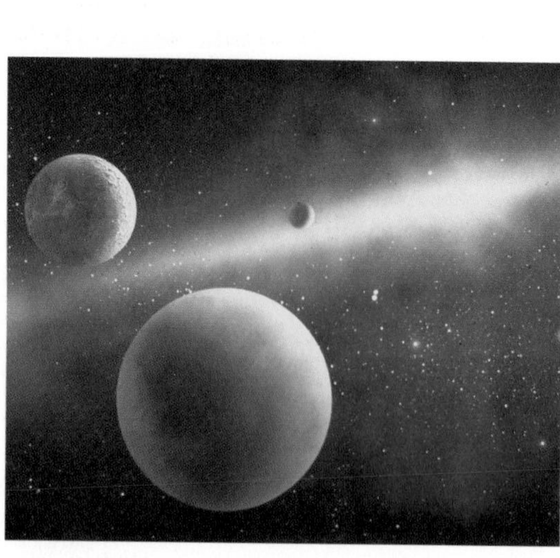

Light is a very important form of energy. It travels very fast and can be reflected, transmitted, and absorbed. Light energy can travel through the vacuum of outer space or in materials as dense as diamond. Practically everything you do in any given day, whether it's surfing the Web or driving a car depends on your ability to detect the light reflected from various objects. The light that we see is a form of radiant energy known as the visible light spectrum. Originally, this form of radiant energy was only produced by natural sources such as the Sun, stars, fire, and lightning. However, we eventually found ways to produce light ourselves. As a result, we now enjoy light produced by numerous artificial sources such as candles, light bulbs, and lasers.

Light, whether natural or artificial, interacts with different materials in different ways. Some materials reflect it, some absorb it, and others are good at transmitting it. In the past, these materials were strictly natural, like the surface of a lake that reflects the moonlight. Eventually, we learned how to design materials like mirrors, lenses, and prisms that could bend, split, reflect, absorb, and transmit light. The result has been a growing list of devices that tame light and make it do work for us. This list includes television, lasers, telescopes, fibre optics, movie projectors, cameras, eyeglasses, and microscopes (to name a few). These light-controlling devices have made huge contributions to practically every sector of society including business, industry, home comfort, entertainment, communication, and health.

The ability to control and manipulate light falls within a branch of science known as geometric optics, which deals with reflection and refraction. None of the above technological advances and their accompanying improvements to society would have been possible without it. Understanding **geometric optics** is also crucial to finding new uses for light and in creating new optical devices. In this unit, you will study the properties of light, including transmission, reflection, and refraction. You will examine the various materials used to control light such as mirrors and lenses; and you will investigate various optical devices including telescopes, lasers, and fibre optics. As you proceed through the unit, you will gain a better understanding of the countless ways you use and interact with light everyday.

PHYSICS HEADLINES

New Map of Our Cosmic Neighbourhood

Using new technology, astronomers have surveyed 141,000 galaxies within three billion light-years of Earth. A telescope using 400 tiny movable prisms, positioned by a robot, scanned the sky. The light from each galaxy passed through a pair of spectrographs, which calculated the galaxy's distance. Combined with the galaxy's position, a 3-D location in space is revealed.

Re-reading Archimedes

About A.D. 1000, a copy of the Greek mathematician, Archimedes', notes were destroyed. Someone scraped the writing off the parchment paper and reused it. Now, researchers are using satellite multispectral imaging technology to "see" the destroyed notes. By taking digital pictures under different wavelengths of light, then filtering the images through sophisticated software, Archimedes' lost notes can be read.

Better than 20/20

Earth's atmosphere distorts light travelling through it. Astronomers use lasers to measure these distortions, and flexible mirrors to compensate, making the images from space clearer. Similar technology can be used in the construction of contact lenses and in taking measurements for laser eye surgery. It can even help enhance 20/20 vision.

ACHIEVEMENT TASK — PREVIEW

At the end of this unit, you will demonstrate your learning by completing the task Presentation of Vision Corection Technology. As a member of the Health Canada executive board responsible for allocating funds to Canadian Health Care Research for the coming year, you will research the nature and cost of vision correction and the treatment of eye diseases; and make a recommendation concerning free eye care for seniors. See page 442.

CHAPTER 9

Sources, Transmission, and Reflection of Light

SPECIFIC EXPECTATIONS

By the end of this chapter, you will be able to:

- define and describe concepts and units related to light (9.1, 9.2, 9.3, 9.4)
- describe the scientific model for light and use it to explain optical effects that occur as natural phenomena (9.1)
- carry out experiments involving the transmission of light, compare theoretical predictions and empirical evidence, and account for discrepancies (Investigation 1, Investigation 2)
- describe how images are produced and reproduced for the purposes of entertainment and culture (9.1)

When you wake in the morning, one of the first things you do is look at yourself in a plane mirror. But what do you know about the reflection looking back? Why is the part in your hair on the opposite side? How does this image actually form? The answer is not in the mirror, but in an under-

FIGURE 9.1 The lion's reflection is visible in the water.

standing of the properties of light. Light is a form of radiant energy that the eye can detect. It can come directly from a source such as the sun or indirectly from an object such as the moon. It can make a piece of asphalt look like a puddle of water or allow the ghostly translucent image of an actor to walk across a stage.

Paint manufacturers are very aware of the properties of light as they label a paint finish "non-gloss" or "high-gloss." They understand what is meant by diffuse or irregular reflection. Astronomers are also aware of the properties of light as they observe the weak light from a distant star and focus it to obtain a visible image.

By understanding the characteristics of light, you will understand how light can rebound off a shiny surface, a process called reflection. You will also understand how light bends when it travels from one material into another, a process called refraction. By changing the shape of a shiny surface, you will see how an image is affected in magnification, attitude, kind, and position. Knowing these characteristics will help you to understand why the side mirrors of a car come with a warning, and why many department stores have large curved mirrors positioned up and down their aisles.

Discovering Physics

Face in a Plane Mirror

How large must a plane mirror be so that you can see the image of your entire face? Does it matter whether the mirror is close to your face or at arm's length? Write down your predictions before doing the activity.

Caution: Plane mirrors made of glass are fragile. Hold the mirror carefully.

1. Measure and record the dimensions of the plane mirror.
2. Hold the mirror vertically about 15 cm from your face.
3. Adjust the height of the mirror until you can barely see the top of your head.
4. With a piece of masking tape indicate the lowest part on your body that you can barely see using the bottom of the mirror.
5. Measure the shortest distance from the top of your head to the tape and compare the length of the mirror with the amount of your body you can see.
6. Repeat this with the mirror 30 cm from your face.

- What relationship exists between the length of the mirror and the length of an object you can see?
- Does it matter how far away the mirror is from the object?
- Compare your results with others in your class.

CHECK**POINT**

An object located at the centre of curvature of a concave mirror is brought halfway to the focal point. The image will

a) remain virtual and become larger
b) remain virtual and become smaller
c) remain real and become larger
d) remain real and become smaller
e) remain real and become the same size as the object

Use sketches to explain your answer.

9.1 Some Characteristics of Light

Key Understandings

When you have completed this section, you will be able to:

- define reflection, refraction, incident ray, reflected ray, and normal
- define point of incidence, angle of incidence, and angle of reflection
- distinguish between a parallel beam, a converging beam, and a diverging beam
- identify direct and indirect sources of light
- describe the relationship between sources of light and luminous or non-luminous objects
- describe the scientific model for light
- explain mirages based on properties of the scientific model for light
- describe how optical images are produced for the purposes of entertainment

FIGURE 9.2 The surface of a lake reflects light.

Reflecting surfaces have always been with us. Polished metals, the surface of a quiet pond, and even glass reflect light to our eyes. But it was not until Jean Bernard-Léon Foucault, the French physicist, found a way to coat a glass surface with a fine film of silver that we were able to obtain the bright images so common today. Why does a smooth surface produce a clear image and a rippled surface does not? If you turn this page upside down can you tell which scene is the object and which the reflection? What property of light accounts for the clear images in this picture?

Light is a form of radiant energy that the eye can detect. The sources of light are classified as direct (coming from luminous objects) and indirect (coming from non-luminous objects). **Luminous objects** produce light, so luminous objects are seen by their own light (Figure 9.3). Examples of luminous objects are a candle flame, the Sun, and a glowing light bulb. **Non-luminous objects** do not emit their own light, rather they reflect light from another object. Non-luminous objects are seen by the light they reflect. The Moon and Earth

FIGURE 9.3 A candle flame is a luminous source of light.

FIGURE 9.4 The Moon is a non-luminous object.

(Figure 9.4) are examples of indirect sources. They are both seen by the light they reflect. Most of the objects you see around you are non-luminous objects.

Scientific Models for Light

Light is produced by luminous bodies and comes to our eyes either directly or indirectly from its source. Once produced, light carries energy outward in straight lines at great speeds in all directions. When it encounters an object, some light energy is absorbed, some may be reflected, and some may be transmitted. These and other behaviours led early scientists to come up with two competing models for light. One, the **particle model**, described light as consisting of microscopic particles radiating away from the source. The particle model explained certain behaviours, such as propagation, reflection, and absorption, but it had difficulty explaining other behaviours, such as the fact that light slows down when it travels from air into a more optically dense material, like glass.

The second model for light, called the **wave model**, described light as consisting of transverse waves radiating away from the source. The wave model explained all of the above properties, but it could not explain the photoelectric effect—the emission of electrons from some metallic surfaces.

The currently accepted model is called the quantum model. The **quantum model** for light is a combination of the particle model and the wave model. It describes light as consisting of microscopic particles called photons, which have wave properties. The quantum model explains all properties of light discovered to date. In this section you will explore several properties of light.

WEBLINK

Light has properties of both waves and particles. Prepare a Venn diagram summarizing these properties. Include the properties that are explained by both models. Begin your research at **www.pearsoned.ca/physics11.**

Characteristics of Light

What happens to light when it leaves the source that produced it? It travels outward at great speed in all directions. **Rectilinear propagation** is the term used to describe the fact that light appears to travel in straight lines through a uniform medium. The sharp shadow of a stick cast by the Sun is evidence for this. That one cannot see around corners is further evidence. However, light can be made to change direction by bouncing it off surfaces or by passing it through different media. Light travels in a different direction when it rebounds from a shiny surface (Figure 9.5), a process called **reflection**. It also bends when it travels from one material into another at an angle other than 90°, a process called **refraction**.

Refer to page 356, Investigation 1

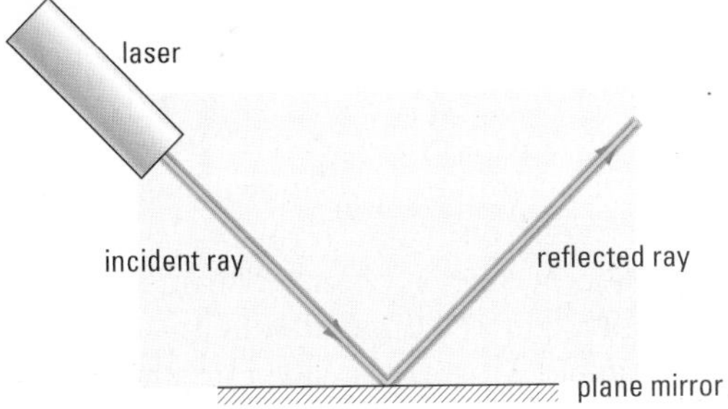

FIGURE 9.5 A ray of light from a laser reflects from a plane mirror.

WEBLINK

The quantum model of light—the presently accepted model—is able to explain all behaviours of light. Prepare a chart summarizing how this model explains luminous sources, reflection, refraction, colour, and the photoelectric effect. Begin your research at **www.pearsoned.ca/physics11.**

Reflection and refraction are evident all around you—even on the ground. On hot days black asphalt absorbs a lot of heat from the Sun and warms the layer of air immediately above it. As a result, the air close to the pavement is less dense than the air higher up. This causes light from the sky to be refracted, as shown in Figure 9.6. An image of the sky on the pavement looks like a puddle of water on the road. Watch for this phenomenon when you pass a construction crew laying hot asphalt on a sunny day.

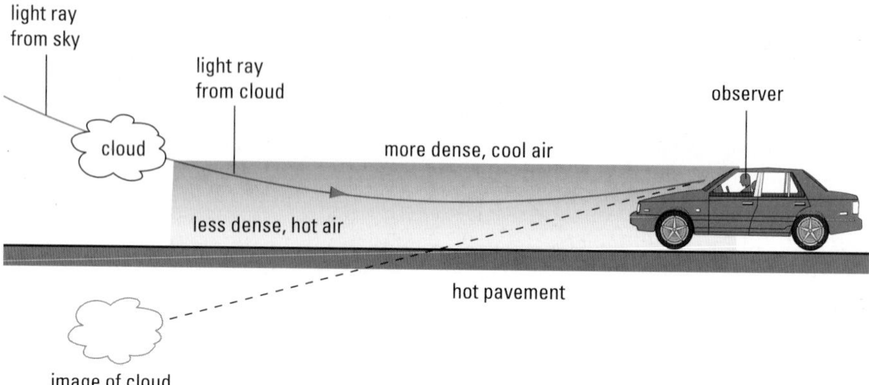

FIGURE 9.6 Light from an object in the sky is refracted due to the difference in density of the air above the pavement compared with the air higher up. Hot air is less dense than cooler air. Where is the air warmer in this case?

Sometimes the air close to the surface of Earth is cooler than the air above it. In this case light, which is reflected from an object located on Earth, gets refracted and appears to come from a location above the horizon, as shown in Figure 9.7. This is why the Rocky Mountains appear higher and closer to Calgary on some days than on others.

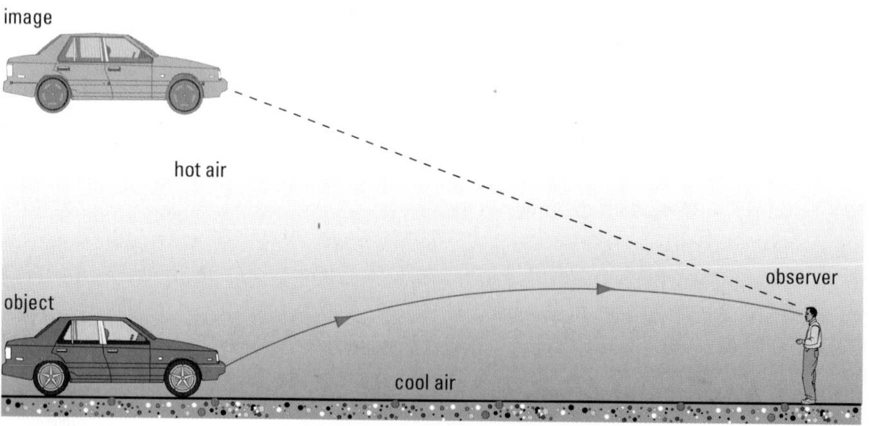

FIGURE 9.7 A layer of hot air above a layer of cooler air can cause light to refract and create a mirage.

A ray box is a device for projecting beams of light toward optical instruments such as mirrors and lenses. A directed straight line called a **ray** represents the path followed by the light. A bundle of rays is called a **beam**. A beam in which the rays are parallel to each other is referred to as a **parallel beam**. A beam in which the rays get closer together until they meet is called a **converging beam**, while one in which the rays spread out is called a **diverging beam**.

Light can travel through a vacuum and through some materials. Media are classified in terms of their ability to transmit light. **Transparent** media

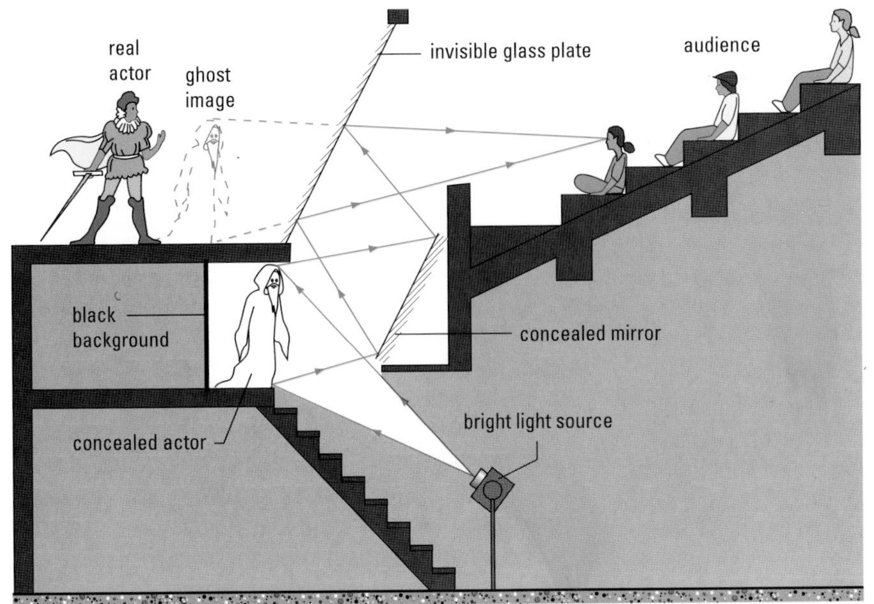

FIGURE 9.8 John Henry Pepper's ghost. In order to back away from the audience, in which direction would the concealed actor have to move?

WEBLINK

How are ghost effects produced in modern films? Is the method perfected by John Henry Pepper still used? Prepare a sequence chart showing the series of actions taken to prepare ghost images today. Begin your research at **www.pearsoned.ca/physics11.**

WEBLINK

There are several kinds of optical illusions. Some artists are very talented at creating them. Research the kinds of optical illusions, their causes, how they are created, and why they are used. Prepare a chart summarizing your findings. Begin your research at **www.pearsoned.ca/physics11.**

transmit light so well that objects are seen clearly through them. Window glass, water, and coloured plastic are transparent media. **Translucent** media also transmit light, but the light is scattered so objects cannot be seen clearly through them. Frosted glass, waxed paper, and tissue paper are translucent media. **Opaque** media, such as aluminum, wood, and asphalt, do not permit light to pass. Some of the light is reflected; the rest is absorbed.

Optical illusions can be used for the purposes of entertainment. Figure 9.8 shows how John Henry Pepper, a stage director during the Victorian era, created the illusion of a ghost on stage. The ghost appeared to walk right through the real actor. Light was reflected off the concealed actor, but not off the black background. This light underwent two reflections before reaching the audience. The audience could not see the concealed mirror or the thin glass plate in front of the stage. Why would the concealed actor appear to be headless if his head was covered with a dull, black hood? Compare that with a shiny, black hood. Differentiate between the two.

Most of us take vision for granted. Perceiving images is, however, a very complicated process because both our eyes and our minds are involved. Only in the past 100 years, and especially in the past 15 years, have scientists started to make progress in understanding vision and perception. Optical illusions are an amazing window to this process.

An **optical illusion** is a perception of a visual stimulus that represents what is perceived in a manner different from the way it is in reality. From the variety of stimuli that enter our eyes, we seek to organize and simplify this incoming information by testing it against one or more hypotheses. Psychologists now believe that there are several kinds of illusions, each requiring different explanations. Consider the famous Müller-Lyer geometric illusion shown in Figure 9.9. The distances between the two pairs of arrowheads look quite dissimilar, yet measurement with a ruler shows them to be identical. Figure 9.10

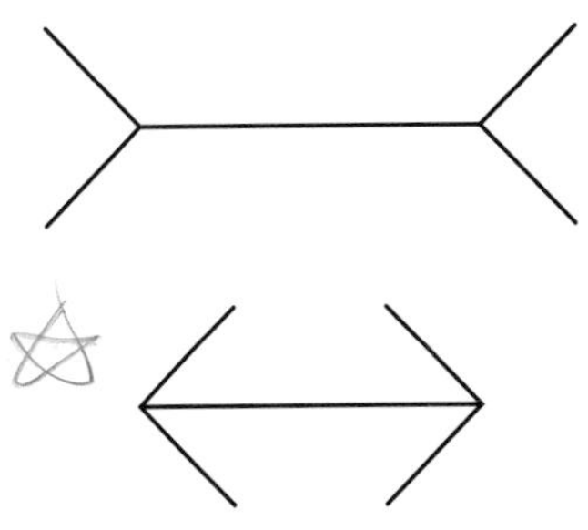

FIGURE 9.9 Müller-Lyer geometric illusion

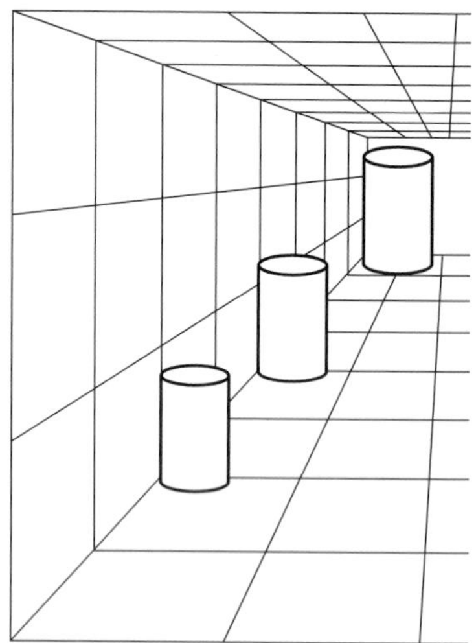

FIGURE 9.10 Why might an artist be familiar with this sort of illusion?

shows a distortion of apparent size caused by strong perspective cues. The sizes of the three cylinders are identical but when some cues are too strong, our judgment of size is distorted. Another class of illusions is called ambiguous figures. Figure 9.11 shows the "devil's tuning fork." What aspect of the drawing of the tuning fork makes it impossible?

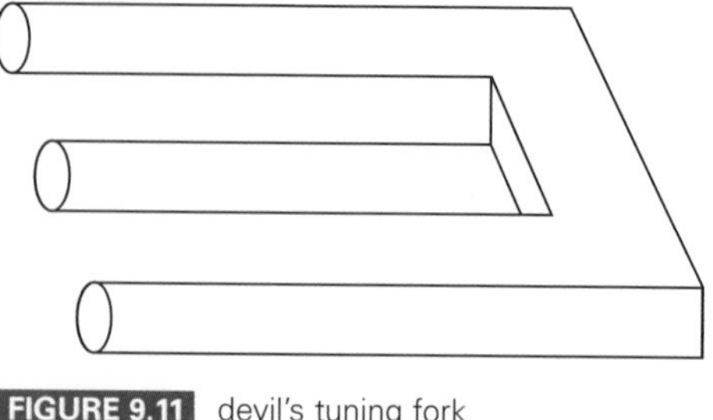

FIGURE 9.11 devil's tuning fork

These examples illustrate that optical illusions result when the visual system is overloaded, tricked, or given inadequate information. Three theories have been applied to explain different visual illusions. The illusion may be due to our interpretation of what the display represents; the illusion may be a product of a misapplied scaling mechanism; or the illusion may be due to a physiologically based coding process. Artists manipulate images into meaningful and realistic scenes, and over the centuries they have created many illusions. For scientists, optical illusions raise a lot of questions about perception. Hence, optical illusions remain an important part of the scientific study of visual perception.

When light strikes a polished surface it is reflected. The terms used to describe reflection are defined below and shown in Figure 9.12. The **incident ray** is the ray of light approaching the reflecting surface, while the **reflected ray** is the ray of light leaving the reflecting surface. The **point of incidence** is the location where the incident ray strikes the reflecting surface. The **normal** N is a line drawn perpendicular to the surface at the point of incidence. The **angle of incidence** i is the angle between the incident ray and the normal, while the **angle of reflection** r is the angle between the reflected ray and the normal.

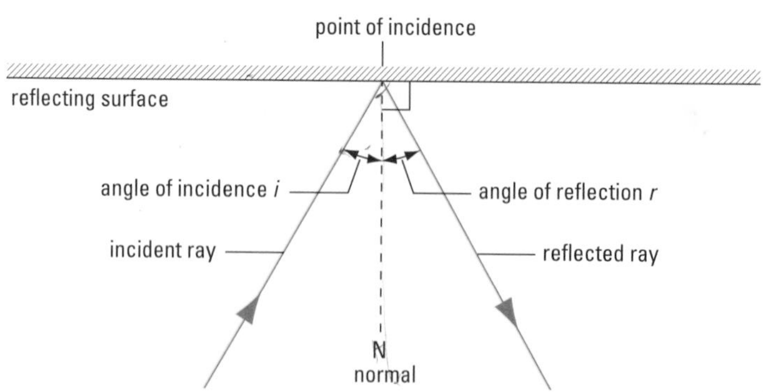

FIGURE 9.12 Ray diagram and terminology for reflection

Section 9.1 Review

Understanding Concepts

1. Distinguish between a luminous and a non-luminous source. Give an example of each, different from the ones in the text.
2. Distinguish between a ray and a beam of light.
3. Draw a parallel, a converging, and a diverging beam to illustrate the differences between them.
4. a) In a flow chart, classify the following materials as transparent, translucent, or opaque media: chocolate milk, sheer fabric, recycled paper, tinted-glass pop bottle. Add your own examples.

   b) If, instead of light being transmitted we used sound, how would your classifications differ?
5. Compare the particle and the wave models of light.

Applying Inquiry/ Communication Skills

6. Explain the propagation of light energy using

   a) the particle model

   b) the wave model.
7. a) What is meant by "rectilinear propagation of light"?

   b) What evidence do you have that light behaves in this way? Indicate specific observations you have made.
8. Look at Figure 9.13. Describe the differences between the umbra and penumbra regions.

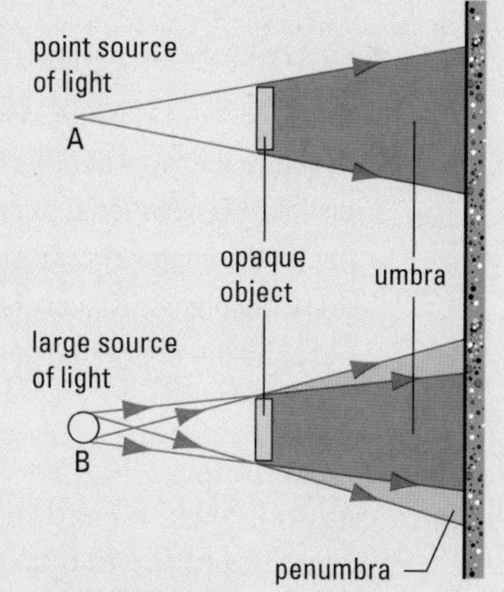

FIGURE 9.13 The shadows that form when a point source A and a large source B shine light on opaque objects of the same size

9. Design an experiment using a ray box to illustrate the role that straight-line travel of light plays in the formation of umbra and penumbra shadows.

Making Connections

10. Intensity refers to the amount of light energy that falls onto a unit area. When a piece of paper is illuminated with light from a point source, the intensity of the light decreases as the paper is moved farther from the source. In fact, the intensity is one-quarter as bright at a distance of 2 m as it is 1 m from the source. Does this support the fact that light travels in straight lines? Use ray diagrams to illustrate your answer.
11. Explain why over twice as many identical bulbs would be needed in a ceiling fixture designed to give the same illumination at floor level for a room with 3.6-m-high ceilings as for one with 2.4-m-high ceilings.

9.2 Plane Mirror Reflection and Images

Key Understandings

When you have completed this section, you will be able to:

- describe the laws of reflection
- distinguish between a real image and a virtual image
- define the image characteristics: magnification, attitude, kind, and position
- draw ray diagrams showing reflection in plane mirrors
- describe the characteristics of images produced by plane mirrors

Many electrical meters (Figure 9.14) use a plane mirror to enable the technician to obtain accurate readings. The mirror is placed directly behind the needle. Where should the eye be placed when reading such meters? Can you explain how the mirror helps you read the scale more accurately?

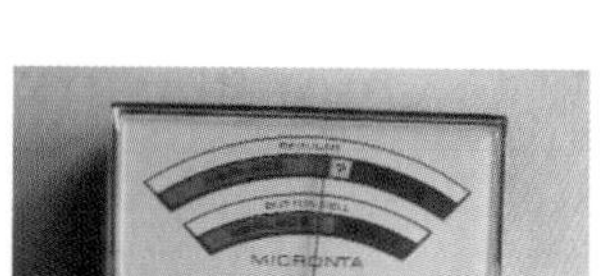

FIGURE 9.14 How can a plane mirror help you read the scale on this meter?

The Two Laws of Reflection

Light falling on the surface of a mirror is reflected. If the angle between the mirror and the incident ray is 90°, the reflected ray bounces straight back toward the source. In this case, the angle of incidence and the angle of reflection are both 0°. The angle of reflection is always equal to the angle of incidence. If the angle of incidence is 35°, the angle of reflection is also 35°. It can also be shown that the incident ray, the normal, and the reflected ray all lie on the same **plane** (the same surface—real or imagined) as shown in Figure 9.15. These statements form the basis of the two **laws of reflection**. These laws are as follows:

The angle of reflection is equal to the angle of incidence.
The incident ray, normal, and reflected ray all lie on the same plane.

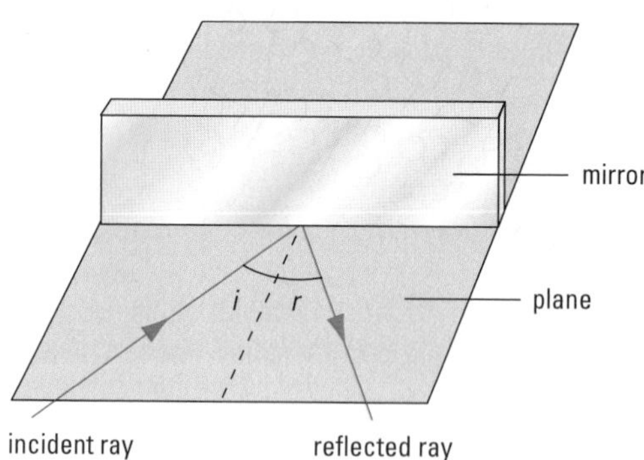

FIGURE 9.15 The laws of reflection

When parallel rays are incident on a smooth surface, like a plane mirror, the rays are reflected as a parallel beam. This behaviour, called **specular reflection** or **regular reflection**, is shown in Figure 9.16b). Figure 9.19a) illustrates specular reflection from the smooth surface of a lake.

A parallel beam that is incident on a rough surface—such as wrinkled aluminum foil, a sheet of white paper, plaster, or non-gloss paint—reflects light that is scattered in many different directions, see Figure 9.17b). This behaviour is called **diffuse reflection** or **irregular reflection**. Figure 9.17a) illustrates diffuse reflection from the surface of a windy lake. Each ray involved in diffuse reflection obeys the laws of reflection. However, the reflected rays are not parallel because the surface at each point of incidence is oriented in a different direction. Can you explain why non-gloss paint on a surface gives a softer, more pleasing effect than high-gloss paint?

WEBLINK

In astronomy, parallax is the apparent displacement of a heavenly body due to a change in position of the observer. Examples are annual, geocentric, horizontal, secular, and spectroscopic. Learn more about parallax in the field of astronomy and submit a report of your findings that includes examples.. Begin your research at **www.pearsoned.ca/physics11.**

a) Mountains and the shoreline reflected in a smooth lake

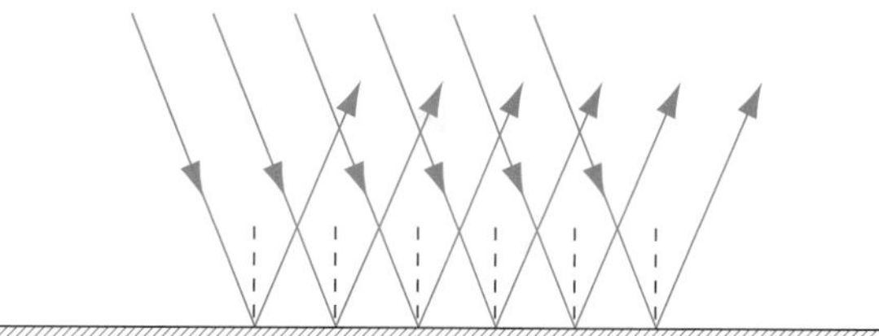

b) Specular (regular) reflection

FIGURE 9.16 Specular reflection

a) Diffuse reflection from rough water on a windy day

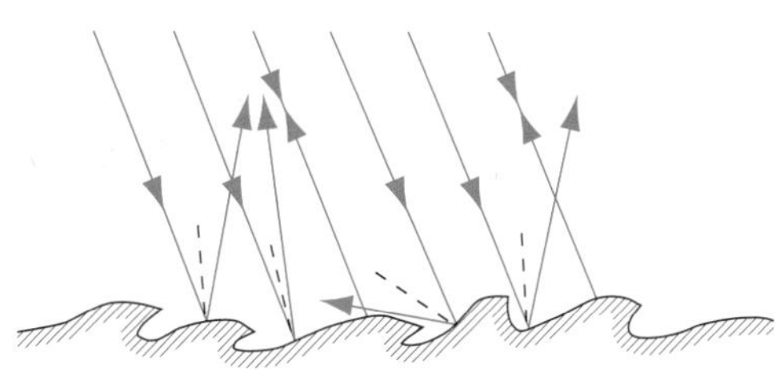

b) Diffuse (irregular) reflection

FIGURE 9.17 Diffuse reflection

Parallax

The image of a candle placed in front of a plane mirror appears to be behind the mirror. A method called **zero parallax** can be used to locate the image. **Parallax** is the apparent motion of an object or image, which is nearby, with reference to a second object, which is farther away, caused by the change in position of the observer. You may have seen parallax between two trees as you travelled along a highway. If there is no relative motion of the two objects when the observer changes position, then the two objects are at the same place. There is no parallax between the branch of a tree and a bird perched on it.

WEBLINK

Both plane and curved mirrors are used as wing mirrors on vehicles. What are the specifications for curved mirrors used as wing mirrors? What is being done to minimize the frictional drag of wing mirrors? Prepare a short report on these mirrors and include a Venn diagram summarizing the similarities and differences between the driver and the passenger wing mirror. Begin your research at **www.pearsoned.ca/physics11.**

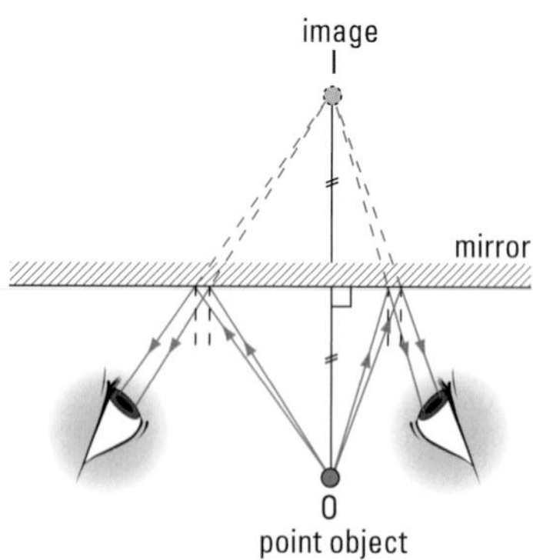

FIGURE 9.19 How the eye sees the image of a point object located in front of a mirror

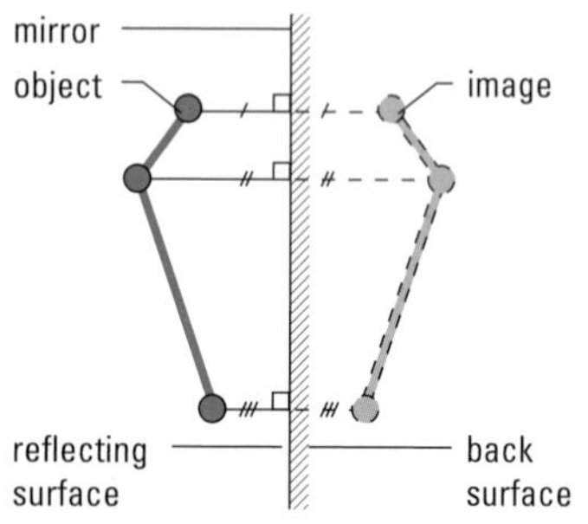

FIGURE 9.20 Locating the image of an extended object produced by a plane mirror

Discovering Physics

Locating a Plane Mirror Image

Do this activity to find out the location of an image in a plane mirror.

1. Light a candle and place it in front of an upright mirror as shown in Figure 9.18.

Caution: When using candles, tie back long hair, secure loose clothing, and avoid sudden movement.

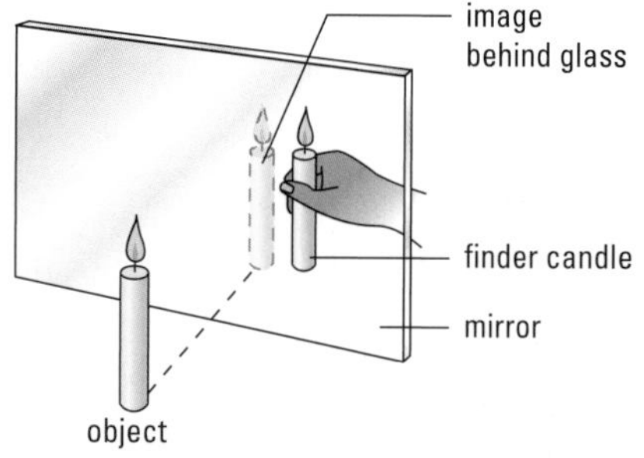

FIGURE 9.18 Locating an image in a plane mirror using the zero parallax method

2. Look into the mirror to see the image of the candle.
3. Light an identical candle and place it behind the mirror where the image appears to be.
4. While looking into the mirror, move your head from side to side, and position the finder candle until it and the image do not shift with reference to one another. When this happens there is no parallax between the finder candle and the image. The finder candle is now located at the position of the image.

- How far behind the mirror is the image?
- How does this compare with the distance the object is in front of the mirror?
- What angle does the line connecting the image and the object make with the mirror?

If you correct for parallax, you will find that the image of an object is the same distance behind the mirror as the object is in front. The line connecting the image and the object makes a 90° angle with the mirror. Figure 9.19 shows how an eye sees the image of a point object from two different locations. The rays in each diverging beam are reflected by the mirror and travel to the eye. The rays entering the eye appear to be coming from the image located behind the mirror. However, it is impossible to catch this image on a piece of paper placed behind the mirror, since no light from the object reaches this point. This shows that the light is not really coming from the image but only appears to be. An image formed in this way is called a **virtual image**. When light comes directly from the image, the image is described as a **real image**.

When drawing a ray diagram to locate the image of an object, you should follow the steps outlined below. Look at Figure 9.20. Notice that the back of the mirror is shown with hatched lines.

1. Choose several convenient points on the object (shown as solid circles).
2. Draw a perpendicular line from each point to the mirror. (If the object is not directly in front of the mirror, extend the reflecting surface of the mirror by drawing an appropriate line.)
3. Use a dotted line to extend each line the same distance behind the mirror as the point is in front.
4. Draw the image of each point (shown with broken circles).
5. Join the points with a dotted line to draw the image.

EXAMPLE 1 CONCEPTUAL

Figure 9.21 shows a woman looking at the image of her face in a plane mirror. What is the shortest mirror she can use to see her entire face?

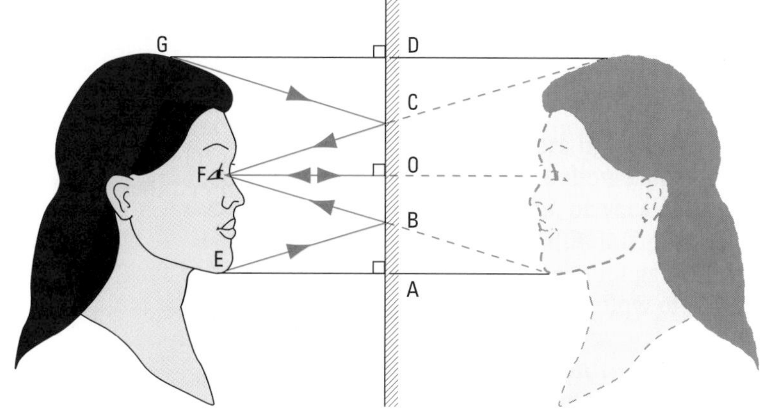

FIGURE 9.21 Minimum length mirror

The mirror surface is labelled A, B, O, C, and D. The woman's face is labelled E, F, and G. According to the laws of reflection, for a given reflection, the angle of incidence is equal to the angle of reflection. The face and its image are the same size. Also, the image is located the same distance behind the mirror as the face is in front of the mirror.

Reasoning and Solution

Light leaving the chin and incident on B is reflected and enters the eye. Light leaving the chin and incident on the mirror anywhere between A and B will be reflected, but will not enter the eye. Instead, it will strike the face someplace below the eye. Light leaving the top of the head incident on C is also reflected and enters the eye. However, light incident on the mirror between C and D does not enter the eye. Two segments of the mirror, AB and CD, can be removed without affecting the image of the face seen in the mirror. Only segments BO and CO are needed to see the full image.

Consider triangles ABE and OBF. Both contain a 90° angle, and angles ABE and OBF are equal. Can you explain why? If the distance from the eye to the mirror and from the chin to the mirror are equal, then AB = OB. Likewise, it can be shown that OC = CD. Hence, a mirror half the length of the face is needed to see the image of the full face.

CHALLENGE

Does it matter how far away the face is from the mirror? Explain and illustrate your reasoning with a diagram.

Mirror Image Characteristics

All images can be described by four characteristics: magnification, attitude, kind, and position. The **magnification** of the image, as compared with the object, may be the **same size**, **enlarged**, or **diminished**. The **attitude** may be **erect** or **inverted** compared with the object. A real image is one that can be captured on a screen. A slide projector or data projector produces a real image on a screen. A virtual image cannot be caught on a screen, but can be seen by the eye or photographed. You see a virtual image of yourself every time you look in a plane mirror. The **position** of an image created by a plane mirror is measured with reference to the reflecting surface. The above characteristics and possible descriptions are summarized in Table 9.1.

TABLE 9.1 Image Characteristics and Descriptions

Characteristic of Image	Description
magnification	enlarged, same size, diminished
attitude	erect, inverted
kind	real, virtual
position	displacement measured from reflecting surface

Rays from every point on an object in front of a mirror are reflected from the mirror and travel to the eye. These rays appear to be coming from the corresponding points on the image. Figure 9.22 shows how the eye sees the image of an extended object, such as a head, in a plane mirror.

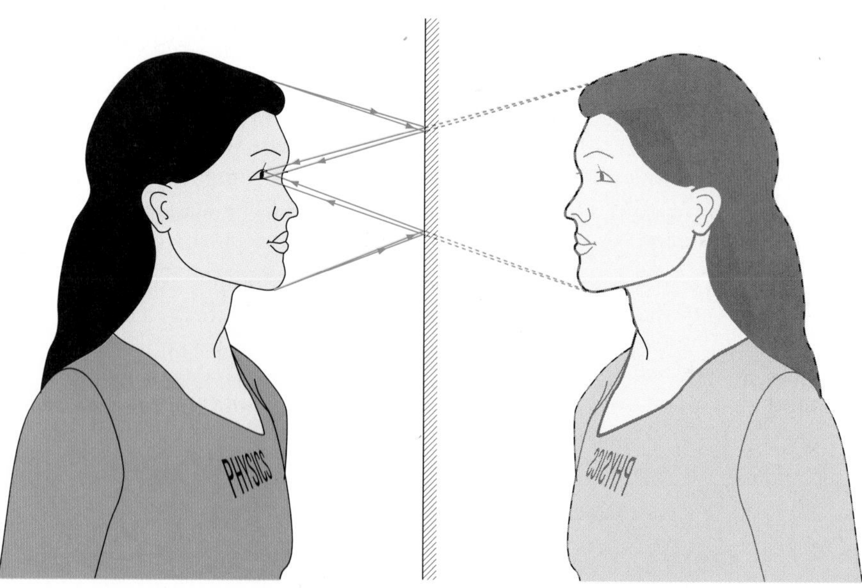

FIGURE 9.22 How the eye sees the image of an extended object produced by a plane mirror

The four characteristics of the image formed by a plane mirror are also shown. The image is the same size as the object and upright. The size is best compared by viewing the image from the same distance away from the mirror as the object. This overcomes the apparent change in size caused by the viewer being nearer or farther from the reflecting surface than the object. The image is located the same distance directly behind the mirror as the object is in front. Since the rays of light do not actually come from the image, but only appear to do so, the image is virtual. In this unit, a virtual image is drawn using dotted lines.

FIGURE 9.23 The view from the driver's-side wing mirror

Since plane mirrors do not change the size of an image, they are used as the driver's-side wing mirror of vehicles (see Figure 9.23). A plane mirror located on the driver's side enables the driver to correctly judge how far an approaching vehicle is from behind.

Figure 9.24a) illustrates the image a person sees when looking in a plane mirror. Notice that the right hand holding the toothbrush appears to be the left hand. That is why the lettering on the front of emergency vehicles is reversed (see Figure 9.24b)) so that it can be read clearly when looking in the rearview mirror.

a) The image's left hand is really the person's right hand as viewed in a plane mirror.

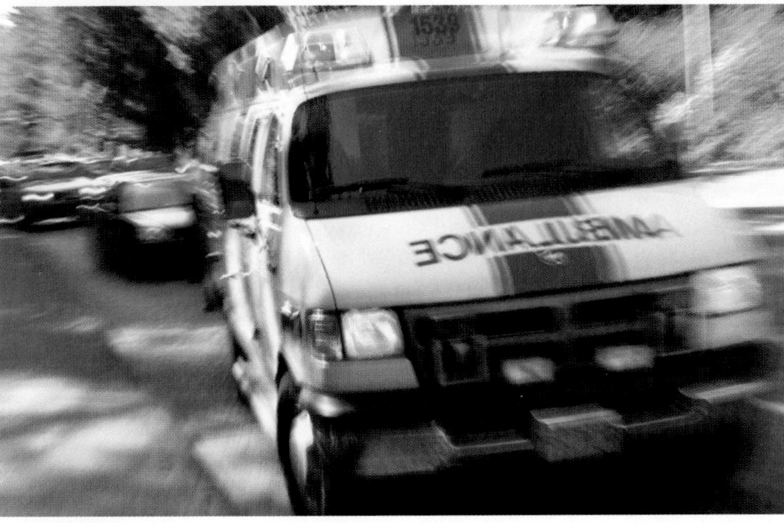

b) The reversed letters on this ambulance will appear normal when viewed using the rearview mirror of the vehicle ahead.

FIGURE 9.24 Lateral reversal

EXAMPLE 2 CONCEPTUAL

When two plane mirrors are joined at 90°, how many images are produced (Figure 9.25)? Where does each image come from? Tape two plane mirrors together and stand them on edge at an angle of 90°. Place a large-headed nail on its head between the reflecting surfaces. Look at the images in the mirrors.

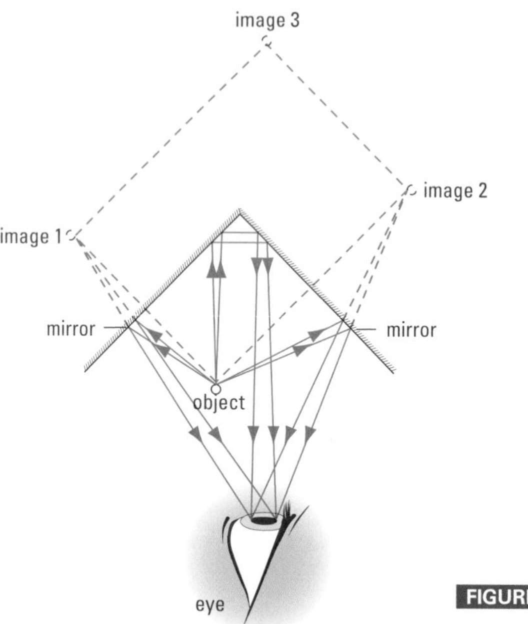

FIGURE 9.25

Reasoning and Solution

There is one image directly behind each mirror. Each image is the same distance behind the mirror as the object is in front. The light entering your eyes that appears to come from these images has undergone one reflection. This accounts for images 1 and 2.

The light that enters the eye appearing to come from the centre image has undergone two reflections, one from each mirror. One light ray from the object incident on the left mirror is reflected to the right mirror and then to the right edge of the eye. Another ray enters the left edge of the eye after two reflections. These two rays form a diverging beam. If you extend these two rays back they appear to come from image 3. Notice that image 3 is located on the extension of a line drawn from the object to the vertex of the two mirrors. Image 3 is the same distance behind the vertex as the object is in front. If you wish to see an image of yourself as others see you, look at the centre image formed by two mirrors at 90° (Figure 9.26). Can you explain why?

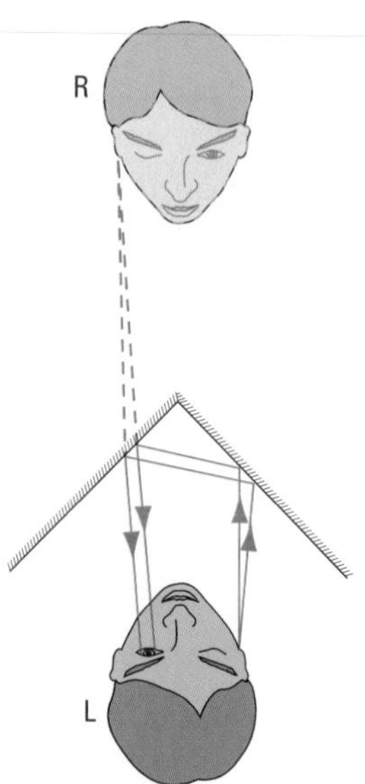

FIGURE 9.26 Two plane mirrors joined together produce an image of ourselves as others see us. Can you explain what the difference is between this image and the other two?

CHALLENGE

Analyze the extra image produced by two reflections and compare it with the images produced by single reflections.

Section 9.2 Review

Understanding Concepts

1. In your own words state the two laws of reflection.
2. Draw a diagram to distinguish between specular and diffuse reflection.
3. Describe the four characteristics of an image formed by a plane mirror.
4. Figure 9.27 shows a point object O and an eye in front of two plane mirrors joined at 90°. Trace it into your notebook.
   a) Draw a scale diagram to locate the three images of the object.
   b) Check your diagram using two plane mirrors.
   c) Draw two diverging rays to show how the eye sees the image produced by two reflections.

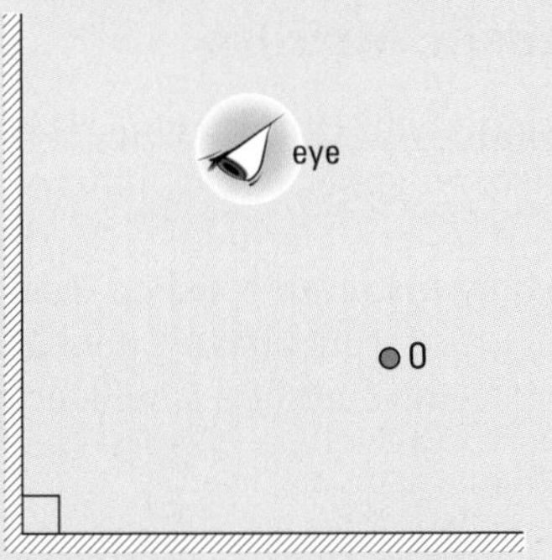

FIGURE 9.27 Trace this diagram and use it to answer question 4.

Applying Inquiry/ Communication Skills

5. An erect arrow of length 2.5 cm is located 5.0 cm from a vertical plane mirror. A person standing to one side of the mirror is viewing its image. Draw a scale diagram showing where the image is located. Draw rays to show how the eye sees the top and bottom of the image.
6. A camper viewing the reflections of a full moon in a smooth lake notices that the image is almost perfectly circular. What would happen to the image of the moon if the water became rough?
7. Many optical devices require an incident light ray to be reversed in its path regardless of the initial direction of this light ray. Using two plane mirrors, construct a type of reflector which will always produce the desired reversal of any incident light ray.

Making Connections

8. At a light target gallery in an amusement arcade, the players use a weak laser to direct light rays at a target that appears to be directly ahead. Actually, the target is below the level of the laser and positioned horizontally, as shown in Figure 9.28. A hit is recorded if the light ray, reflected by the mirror, strikes a sensitive area of the target. Explain why they use this arrangement. Construct a diagram to determine whether the location of the image in the diagram is correct.

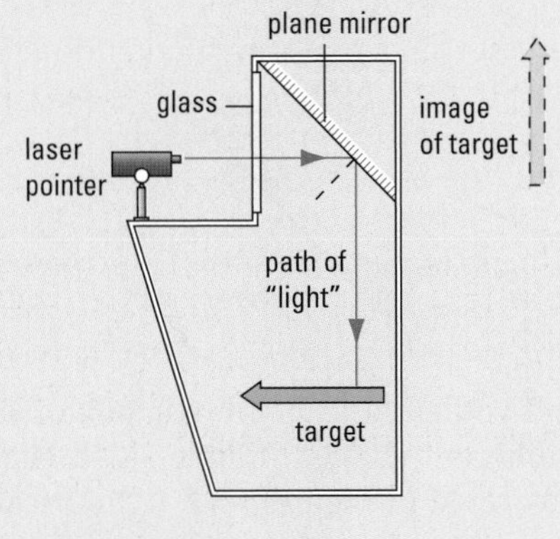

FIGURE 9.28 A "light" target gallery

9.3 Types of Curved Mirrors

Key Understandings

When you have completed this section, you will be able to:

- distinguish between cylindrical, spherical, and parabolic mirrors
- describe the effect of converging and diverging mirrors on parallel rays
- describe how parallel rays can be produced by converging and diverging mirrors
- define centre of curvature, radius of curvature, principal axis, focal point, and focal length
- define spherical aberration
- describe what causes spherical aberration and explain how to prevent it

FIGURE 9.29 Store security mirror

Diverging mirrors such as the mirror shown in Figure 9.29, are used in stores as security mirrors. The image is diminished in size, but the field of view is enlarged compared with a plane mirror. What are the benefits of diverging mirrors? What shape is this mirror? Does it matter how much it curves? Where is the focal point located? Is the image virtual or real?

Spherical, Cylindrical, and Parabolic Mirrors

Mirrors can be curved in just about any shape you can imagine. However, there are three main shapes of curved mirrors: spherical, cylindrical, and parabolic.

Imagine a hollow sphere made of some shiny material, polished inside and out. If you cut a slice off one side of the sphere, you would have a double-sided curved mirror called a **spherical mirror**, such as the one shown in Figure 9.30.

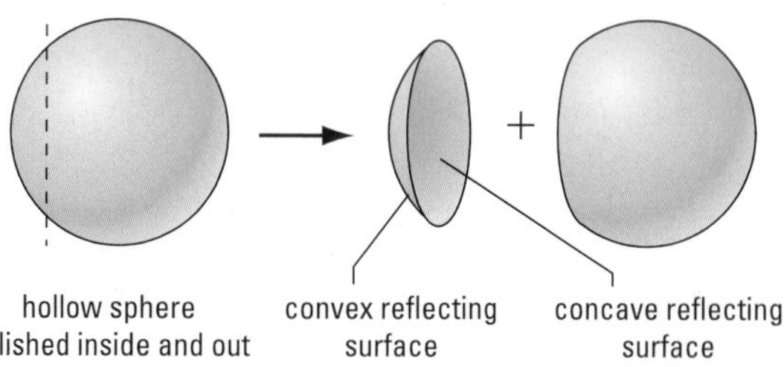

FIGURE 9.30 A spherical mirror

If you cut a slice off one side of a hollow shiny cylinder, you would have a different shaped double-sided curved mirror called a **cylindrical mirror** illustrated in Figure 9.31. Cylindrical mirrors are used in amusement parks to produce distorted images.

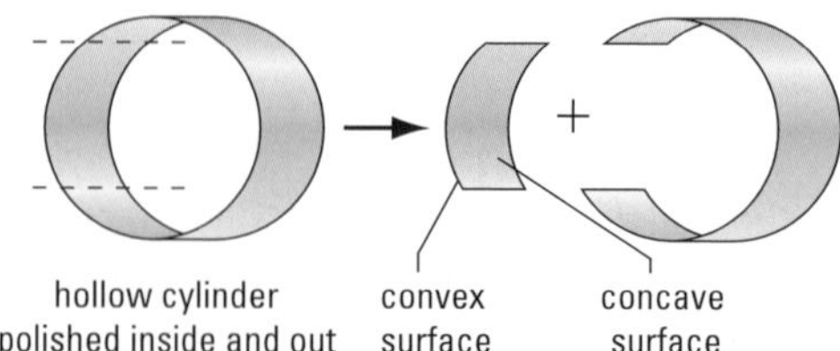

FIGURE 9.31 A cylindrical mirror

Imagine a hollow cone. If you cut a slice off one side of the cone, the slice would be a curved line in the shape of a parabola (Figure 9.32). If this parabolic line were then rotated through 180° about its axis of symmetry, the surface traced out would form a parabola. A mirror whose reflecting surface takes the shape of a parabola is called a **parabolic mirror**.

WEBLINK

Modern reflecting astronomical telescopes are very expensive and difficult to make, especially ones with large-diameter mirrors. What factors are important in the design of reflecting telescopes? How are astronomers and technologists working together to build quality telescopes? Submit a sequence chart showing the chronological order of events in building a modern telescope. Begin your research at **www.pearsoned.ca/physics11.**

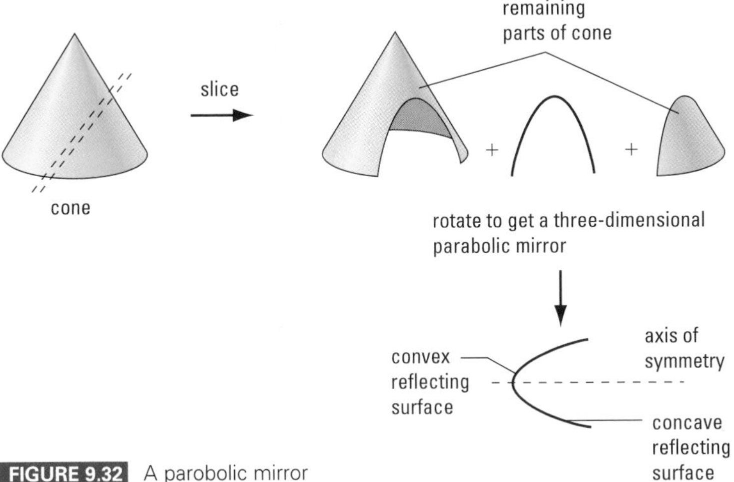

FIGURE 9.32 A parobolic mirror

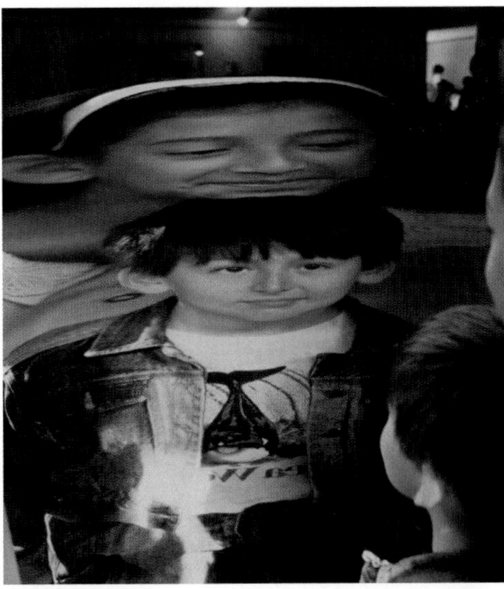

FIGURE 9.33 Have you ever seen an image like this in an amusement park?

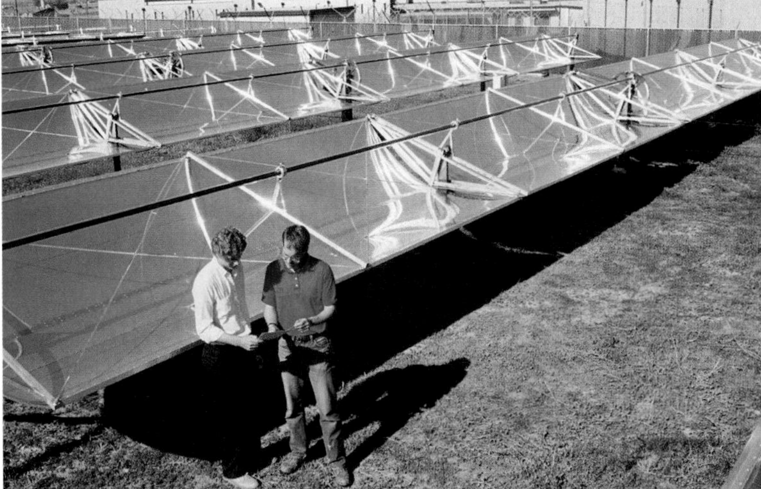

FIGURE 9.35 Parabolic mirrors being used in the Mojave Desert to capture solar energy for making electricity. Compare their size with that of the men in the front.

Parabolic mirrors are used in astronomical telescopes (Figure 9.34). They are also used in some solar collectors to concentrate the Sun's energy onto a collecting medium. A solar farm in the Mojave Desert (Figure 9.35) uses long rows of concave parabolic mirrors to direct the Sun's energy to a focal point. An oil-filled pipe located at the focal point runs the length of the mirrors. The concentrated rays of the sun heat the oil, which is then pumped to a generating station and used to produce steam to drive an electric steam turbine.

FIGURE 9.34 Astronomical parabolic telescope

Exploration Using a Graphing Calculator

In this activity you will use the graphing calculator to graph the reflecting surfaces of a spherical mirror and a parabolic mirror and compare the shapes of the two mirrors. The equations for the circle and the parabola you will generate are $y = 10 - \sqrt{100 - x^2}$ and $y = 0.05x^2$, respectively.

Record the coordinates of the circle in the positive quadrant for three points i) the vertex, ii) the point where the curves first start to separate, and iii) near the maximum visible point. Repeat this for the same x values for the parabola.

Discussion

1. Compare and contrast the shapes of the two mirrors close to the principal axis and far away.
2. Compare the x and y coordinates at the vertex, at the points where the curves visibly separate, and at the maximum points.
3. For what range of points do you expect the spherical mirror and parabolic mirror to behave in a similar fashion? Why?

INFOBIT

In the basement of the University of Arizona football stadium rests the largest telescope mirror ever made. It stretches 8.4 m from edge to edge. Normally, a mirror this big would crumble under its own weight, but this mirror benefits from a unique lightweight design that is smooth on one side and honeycombed on the other. In 2002, it will be joined by a second 8.4-m telescope on Mount Graham, Arizona, to form the large binocular telescope (LBT). Data from the two telescopes will be linked, creating an incredibly powerful instrument.

Curved Mirror Terminology

There are two classes of curved mirrors depending on their effect on light. **Converging mirrors** cause parallel rays to come to a focus. They are sometimes called **concave mirrors** because the reflecting surface is curved inward. **Diverging mirrors** cause parallel rays to spread apart from a focus. They are called **convex mirrors** because the reflecting surface is curved outward. Spherical, cylindrical, and parabolic mirrors can be either converging or diverging depending on which surface does the reflecting.

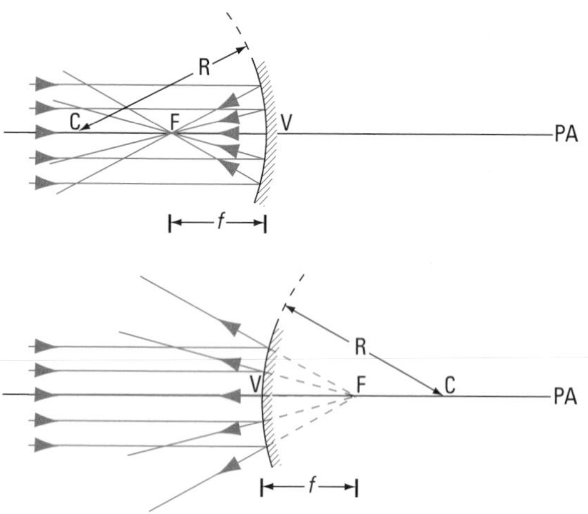

FIGURE 9.36 Terms associated with converging and diverging mirrors

Figure 9.36 shows some of the terms associated with curved mirrors. The **centre of curvature** C is the centre of the sphere or cylinder from which the mirror is made. The **radius of curvature** R is the distance from the centre of curvature to the mirror. These two terms do not apply to a parabolic mirror. Can you explain why?

The **vertex** V of any curved mirror is the geometric centre of the mirror. The **principal axis** PA is a line drawn through the vertex perpendicular to the surface. The point where light rays parallel to the principal axis either come together, or appear to diverge from, is called the **principal focus** F (or focal point). The principal focus can be either real or virtual, depending on whether the light really focusses there or only appears to do so. The **focal length** f is the distance from the vertex to the principal focus measured along the principal axis. The focal length of a mirror depends on how curved it is. The greater the curvature, the shorter the focal length of the mirror. The radius of curvature of both a spherical and a cylindrical mirror is equal to twice the focal length.

$$R = 2f$$

Parallel light rays produce focal points even if they are not parallel to the principal axis (Figure 9.37). All the focal points for a mirror fall on the **focal plane**.

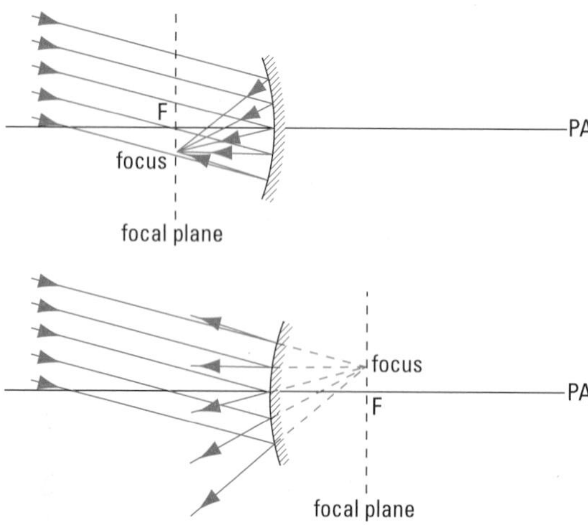

FIGURE 9.37 Focal planes of diverging and converging parabolic mirrors

Figure 9.38 shows how both converging and diverging parabolic mirrors can be used to produce parallel rays. Light rays that originate at the principal focus of a parabolic converging mirror all travel parallel to the principal axis after reflection. Light rays directed toward the principal focus of a diverging parabolic mirror travel parallel to the principal axis after reflection.

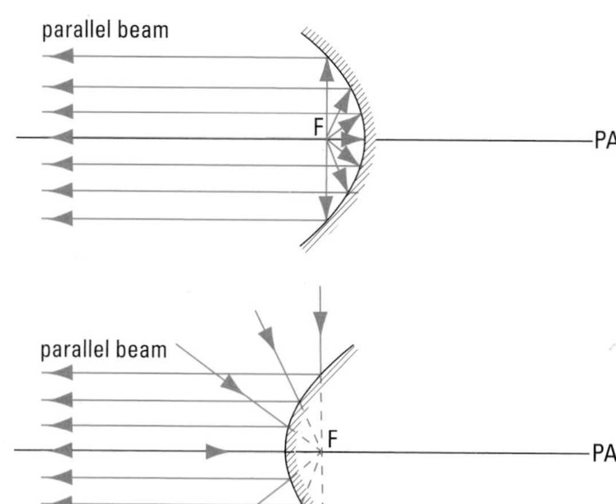

FIGURE 9.38 Producing parallel beams with converging and diverging parabolic mirrors

Avoiding Spherical Aberration

Cylindrical and spherical mirrors have a defect called spherical aberration. **Spherical aberration** is the inability of these curved mirrors to reflect all rays travelling parallel to the principal axis through a common focal point. Spherical aberration causes images to be fuzzy. Figure 9.39a) shows the fuzzy focus produced by rays distant from the principal axis of a converging cylindrical mirror. Parabolic mirrors do not have this defect, as Figure 9.39b) shows. That is why they are used in reflecting telescopes.

The first reflecting telescope was made by Sir Isaac Newton in 1668 (Figure 9.40). Newton used a converging mirror of diameter 2.5 cm to collect and focus the light. He placed a small plane mirror at a 45° angle to the path to deflect the light to the eye. An eyepiece was used to magnify and focus the final image. You will look at magnifiers in more detail in Chapter 11.

Since the intensity of the light from a distant star is very weak, a broad beam of starlight must be focussed to a point to obtain a visible image. The larger the diameter of the converging mirror and the better it focusses the light, the more

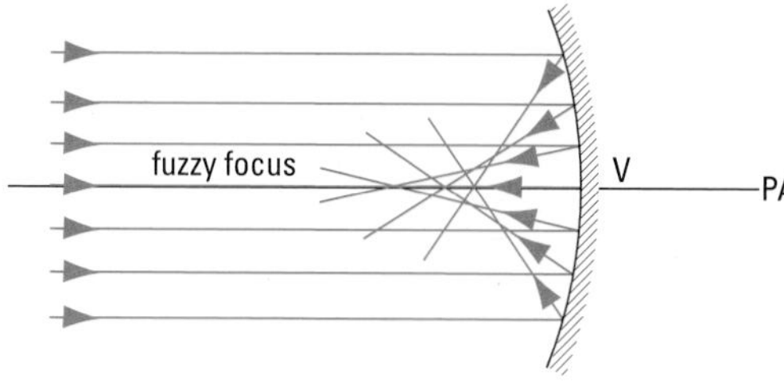

a) A cylindrical or spherical mirror has spherical aberration.

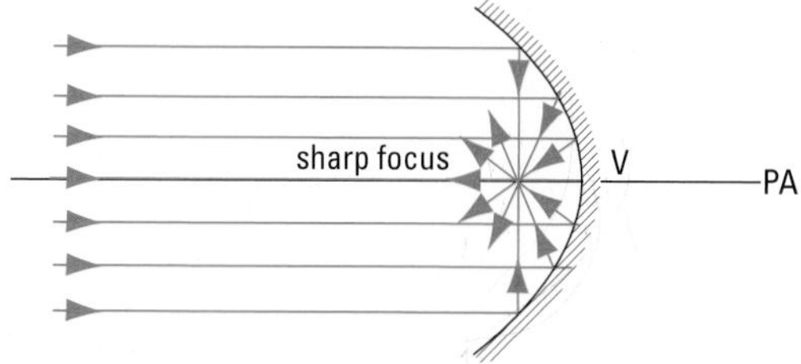

b) A parabolic mirror prevents spherical aberration.

FIGURE 9.39 Spherical aberration and its correction

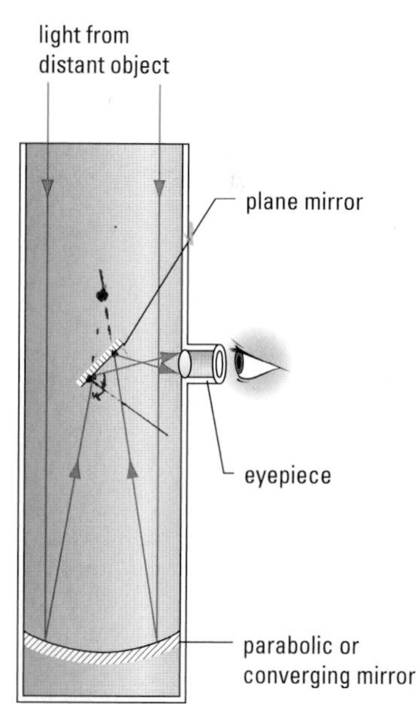

FIGURE 9.40 A Newtonian-focus reflecting telescope uses a converging mirror and a plane mirror to reflect light to the eye.

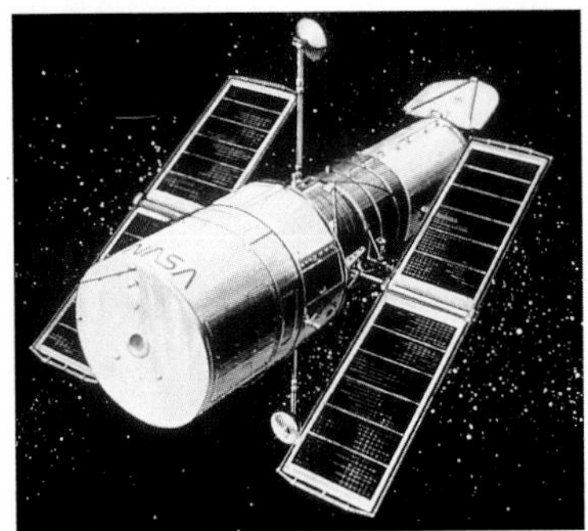

FIGURE 9.41 The Hubble Space Telescope

distant the star that can be photographed. The telescope located at the David Dunlap Observatory near Richmond Hill, Ontario, has a parabolic mirror with a diameter of about 1.9 m and a focal length of 34 m. Today, the largest reflecting telescope on Earth, at the Keck Observatory in Hawaii, has a diameter of about 10 m. The Hubble Space Telescope (Figure 9.41) has a diameter of 4 m. Why is it located in space?

INFOBIT

The Next Generation Space Telescope will be launched as early as 2008. It will have a primary mirror with 10x Hubble's light-gathering capability and will make observations in the visible to mid-infrared part of the electromagnetic spectrum. Because it is designed to operate in the infrared wavelengths, the detectors and telescope optics must be kept as cold as possible to minimize "background noise."

Section 9.3 Review

Understanding Concepts

1. What are the differences between a spherical, a cylindrical, and a parabolic mirror?
2. Draw a converging and a diverging cylindrical mirror in two dimensions. Label the following terms for each mirror: principal focus, vertex, focal plane, principal axis, focal length, and centre of curvature.
3. Use a diagram to show the difference in location between a real and a virtual principal focus.

Applying Inquiry/ Communication Skills

4. Draw a cylindrical converging mirror in the shape of a semicircle. Show its principal axis and centre of curvature. Draw two rays parallel to the principal axis: one close to the axis and one near the edge of the mirror. Use a protractor and the laws of reflection to illustrate that this shape of mirror produces spherical aberration.
5. Design an experiment using a piece of reflecting Mylar, compass, sheet of paper, and ray box with a multiple-slit aperture to demonstrate spherical aberration. Show how spherical aberration can be eliminated by bending the Mylar into the shape of a parabola.

Making Connections

6. Diverging and converging mirrors are used in "fun houses" to produce amusing images.
   a) How does the image of a person formed by a converging cylindrical mirror differ from the image formed by a plane mirror?
   b) How does the image formed by a diverging cylindrical mirror differ from the image formed by a plane mirror?

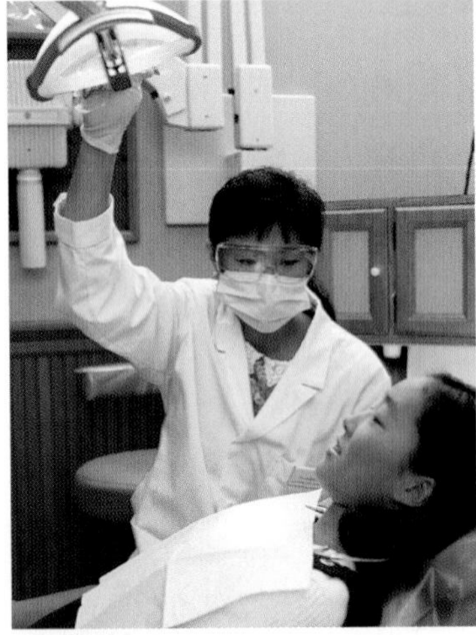

FIGURE 9.42 An examination lamp used in a dentist's office. Is the mirror cylindrical or spherical?

9.4 Ray Diagrams for Curved Mirrors

Key Understandings

When you have completed this section, you will be able to:

- draw detailed ray diagrams showing reflection of objects by converging and diverging mirrors
- use ray diagrams to predict the location and nature of images created by curved mirrors

Examination lamps such as the one shown in Figure 9.42 are used in dental offices. They employ a converging reflector to direct the light from a small source toward the patient. Does it matter where the light source is located with reference to the mirror? Is the mirror cylindrical or spherical?

Drawing Ray Diagrams

For most of the ray diagram work in this text, spherical aberration is ignored. It is also assumed that parallel light rays, incident on spherical or cylindrical mirrors, are reflected through one focal point. You can find the location and characteristics of images formed by curved mirrors using a method called **ray tracing**. This method is based on the laws of reflection and on three mirror reference points: focal point F, centre of curvature C, and vertex V. All rays diverging from a specific point on the object meet at a corresponding point on the image. All you need are three rays from each point on the object—two to locate the corresponding point on the image and one to verify its location. Figure 9.43 shows three key rays being reflected from converging and diverging mirrors. The steps for tracing their paths are outlined below.

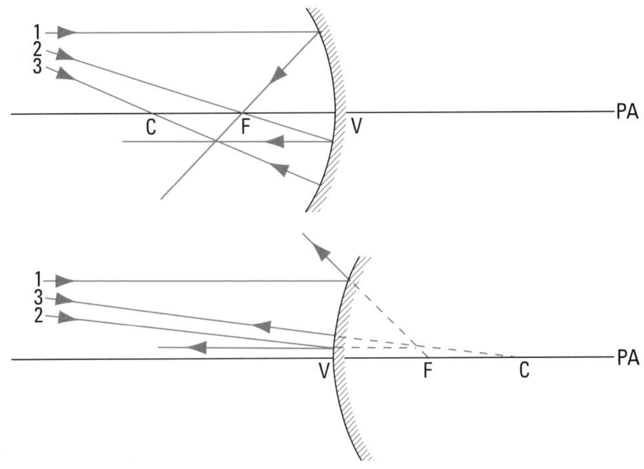

FIGURE 9.43 The reflection of three key rays from spherical mirrors

1. **Ray 1** travels parallel to the principal axis and after reflection either passes through the principal focus F of the converging mirror or appears to come from the principal focus F of the diverging mirror.
2. **Ray 2** passes through the principal focus F of the converging mirror or heads toward the principal focus F of the diverging mirror. After ray 2 is reflected, it travels parallel to the principal axis. This is to be expected because the path of ray 2 is just the reverse of ray 1.
3. **Ray 3** passes through the centre of curvature C of a converging mirror or heads toward the centre of curvature C of a diverging mirror. Because this ray hits the mirror at 90°, it reflects directly back along its path. Determine whether it is possible to draw ray 3 for a parabolic mirror. Can you explain why?

Drawing scale diagrams showing these three rays will help you predict and check the location and characteristics of an image formed by a spherical or a cylindrical mirror. As a convention, the object is always shown as a solid erect arrow. Any two of these rays are drawn from the tip of the object. The point where the rays intersect (or appear to do so) after reflection gives the location of the tip of the image. The third ray serves as a check.

Real rays are drawn as solid lines. Virtual rays, drawn behind the mirror, are shown as dotted lines. Figures 9.44a) and b) show how this is done

WEBLINK

For a simulation showing how to draw ray diagrams and how to locate images in curved mirrors, go to **www.pearsoned.ca/physics11.**

for converging and for diverging mirrors. A real image can be caught on a screen since it is formed where real rays intersect. A real image is drawn as a solid arrow as in Figure 9.44a). Notice that the base of the image is located on the principal axis directly above the tip of the image. A virtual image cannot be caught on a screen since it is formed by the intersection of virtual rays. A virtual image can, however, be seen by looking into the mirror. A virtual image is always shown using a dotted line as in Figure 9.44b).

Investigation

Refer to page 357, Investigation 2.

Images Formed by a Converging Mirror

Figure 9.45 shows the characteristics of images formed by a converging mirror for several object positions.

In Figure 9.45a), the rays reaching a converging mirror from a distant object are effectively parallel. Two parallel rays are shown coming in at an angle to the principal axis to represent rays from a point on a large distant object. The image is formed at the principal focus F. The image distance is *f*. The image is diminished, inverted, and real. As the object moves closer to the principal focus F, the real, inverted image increases in size and moves outward from the principal focus F.

When the object is at C (see Figure 9.45b)), the image is also at C. This inverted, real image is the same size as the object. When the object is between F and C, the inverted image is enlarged, real, and outside C. In Figure 9.45c), no clear image is formed when the object is precisely at the

Draw ray 1.

Add ray 2.

Draw the image.

Draw ray 3 to check the image.

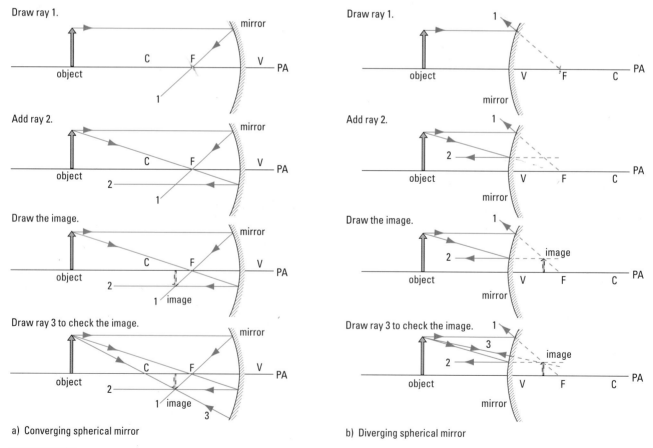

a) Converging spherical mirror

b) Diverging spherical mirror

FIGURE 9.44 The steps in drawing ray diagrams to determine the location and characteristics of images formed by spherical mirrors

principal focus because the rays leaving the mirror are parallel and never intersect. The image is said to be "undefined."

In Figure 9.45d), when the object is closer to the mirror than F, the image is erect, enlarged, and virtual. The image appears to be behind the mirror because the reflected rays leaving the mirror appear to diverge from a point behind the mirror. The imaginary rays behind the mirror are called virtual rays. Since no rays actually come from the point, a virtual image cannot be captured on a screen.

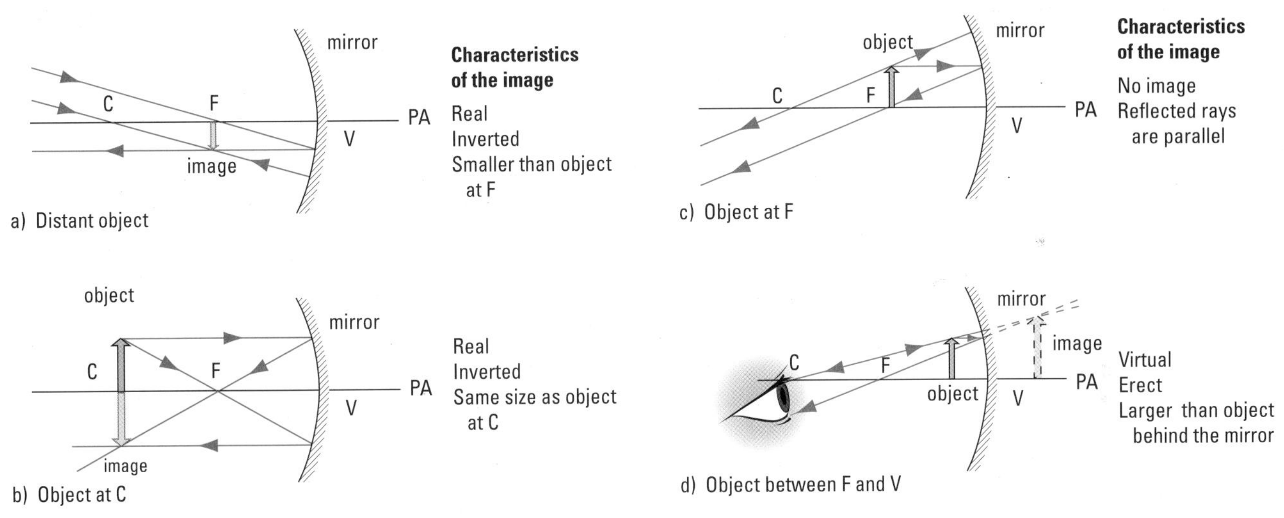

FIGURE 9.45 Images formed by a converging spherical mirror

Table 9.2 summarizes the characteristics of images for spherical and cylindrical converging mirrors.

TABLE 9.2 Image Characteristics for Converging Mirrors

	Image Characteristics			
Object Position	Position	Kind	Attitude	Magnification
distant	at F	real	inverted	diminished
outside C	between F and C	real	inverted	diminished
at C	at C	real	inverted	same size as object
between F and C	outside C	real	inverted	enlarged
at F	undefined	undefined	undefined	undefined
between F and V	behind mirror	virtual	erect	enlarged

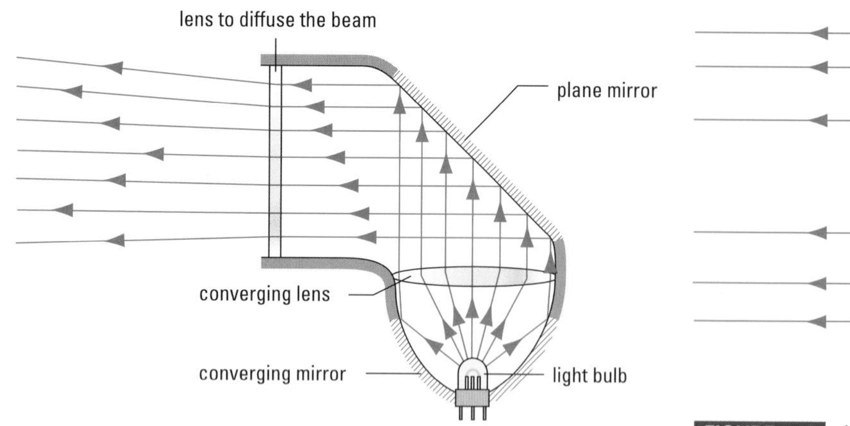

FIGURE 9.46 The parts of a modern headlight. What is the function of the converging mirror? How do the low and high beams work?

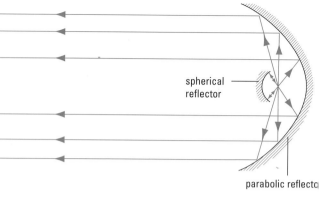

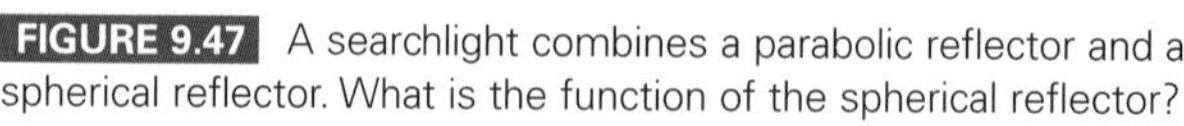

FIGURE 9.47 A searchlight combines a parabolic reflector and a spherical reflector. What is the function of the spherical reflector?

Car headlamps and searchlights use converging reflectors to direct the light from a small intense light source. The compact headlamp shown in Figure 9.46 combines a converging mirror, a lens, and a plane mirror. Can you explain the function of each mirror? The searchlight shown in Figure 9.47 uses both a parabolic and a spherical reflector. Why would a spherical rather than a parabolic mirror be used to reverse the direction of the diverging beam that is initially travelling away from the source?

FIGURE 9.49 What benefits result from using a side-view diverging mirror on the passenger side instead of a plane mirror?

Images Formed by a Diverging Mirror

Figure 9.48 shows the characteristics of an image formed by a diverging mirror. The image is behind the mirror, virtual, erect, and diminished in size. However, an image formed by a diverging mirror does not have these characteristics when the object is on the surface of the mirror. How could you check that this is true?

The passenger-side mirror in Figure 9.49 is a diverging wing mirror. What benefit comes from using the diverging mirror? What danger would result from using a diverging mirror as a rearview mirror? Have you ever seen the warning on a diverging wing mirror? Is it appropriate?

WEBLINK

Modern vehicles use halogen bulbs in headlights. What are the similarities and differences between halogen bulbs and traditional incandescent bulbs? How do their costs, life spans, and safeties compare? Submit a report of your findings, including a technical diagram of each bulb. Begin your research at **www.pearsoned.ca/physics11.**

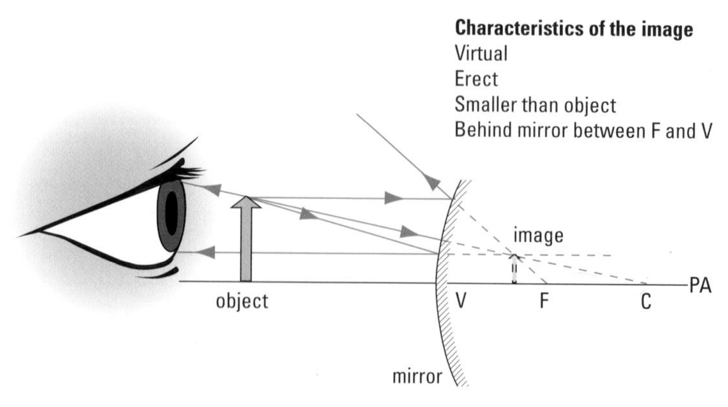

FIGURE 9.48 Images formed by a diverging spherical mirror

Section 9.4 Review

Understanding Concepts

1. Contrast a real and a virtual image, summarizing their formation and characteristics.
2. Draw ray diagrams for a converging mirror and state the characteristics of the image for the following object positions:
   a) $3.0f$
   b) $1.4f$
   c) $0.70f$
3. Draw ray diagrams for a diverging mirror, and state the characteristics of the image for the following object positions
   a) $1.0f$
   b) $0.50f$

Applying Inquiry/ Communication Skills

4. Figure 9.50 shows virtual images of the same face.
   a) What questions could you generate about these images?
   b) Make a prediction about one of the images and design an investigation to verify your predictions.

Making Connections

5. A heads-up display is now available in some cars. It presents a digital readout of the speed of the car that the driver sees as an image when looking directly through the windshield. Research how the heads-up display operates, and draw a ray diagram explaining how a converging mirror is used in its construction.

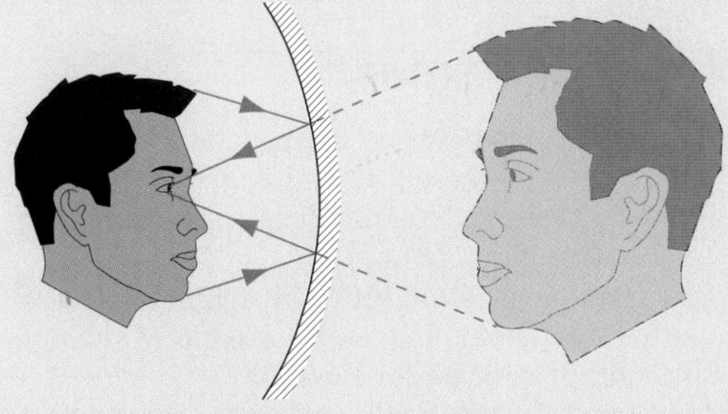

a) Converging mirror

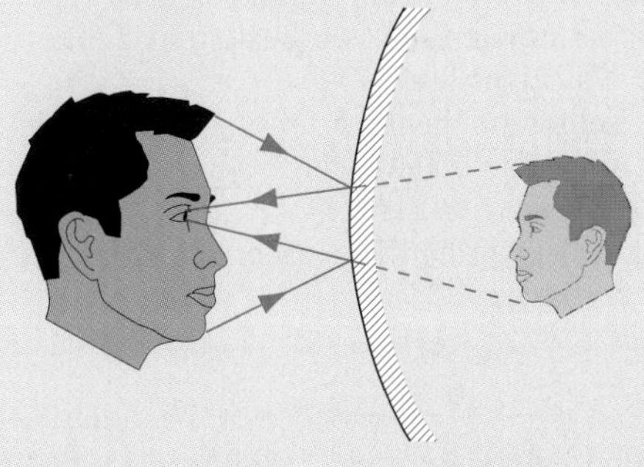

b) Diverging mirror

FIGURE 9.50 Virtual images of the same face produced by a converging and a diverging mirror

Investigation 1 (Section 9.1)

Inquiry Skills

- Initiating and Planning
- Applying Technical Skills
- Using Tools, Material, Equipment
- Conducting and Recording
- Analyzing and Interpreting
- Concluding and Communicating

Inverse Square Law for Light

If light travels in a straight line from a point source it will spread out uniformly in all directions. The farther light travels from the source, the larger the surface area it passes through and the less intense it becomes. **Intensity** is the power output of the light source divided by the area of the surface through which the light passes. Figure 9.51 shows light travelling away from a point source. Suppose at a distance of 1 m from the source the light covers an area of 1 m^2. At a distance of 2 m from the source it will cover an area of 4 m^2. Since the light spreads out to cover four times the area at twice the distance, the intensity can be only one-quarter as much.

Outline how you could test whether light travels in a straight line based on the above information about intensity. All you need to do is measure the intensity of the light at different distances from the source and see if it behaves as predicted. Express in other terms why this is true.

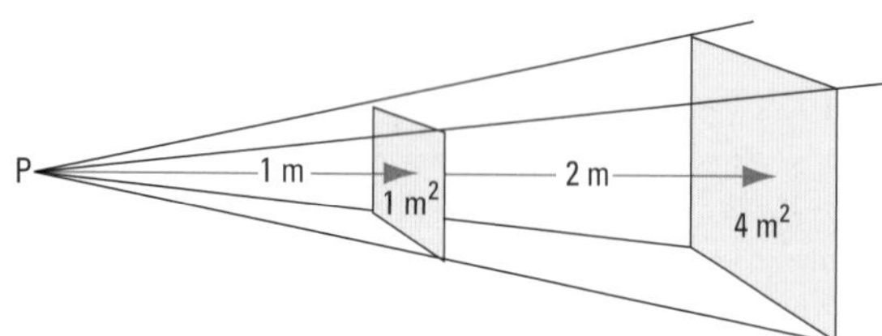

FIGURE 9.51 The inverse square law of light. What would the area be at a distance of 3 m from the source? How should the light intensity at this distance compare with the light intensity 1 m from the source?

Problem

What happens to the intensity of light as the distance from a point light source increases? Does this support the hypothesis that light travels in straight lines?

Materials

- data logger interface
- light sensor
- light bulb, 6 V DC
- metre-stick
- power source, 6 V DC

Caution: The light source may get hot.

Experimental Design

1. Connect the computer, interface, and light sensor as instructed by the manufacturer.
2. Design a procedure to collect data for the intensity of light as the light sensor is moved farther from the source.
3. Plot a graph of intensity of light against distance from the source.

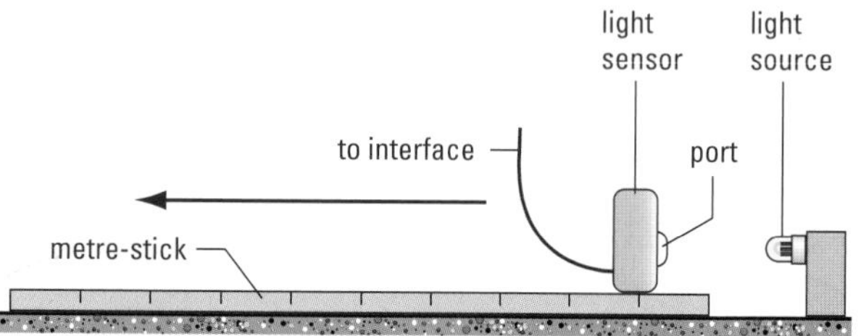

FIGURE 9.52

Analyzing and Interpreting

1. As the distance between the light source and the light sensor increased, what happened to the intensity readings? As the distance doubled, did the reading halve or quarter?
2. Describe the graph of intensity against distance plotted by the data logger. What kind of relationship does it indicate for the data?

Concluding and Communicating

3. What is the relationship between the intensity of light and the distance from a point source?
4. Do the data support the hypothesis that light travels in a straight line? Explain.
5. The light bulb is not really a point source. How does this affect the experiment? What can be done to minimize this error?
6. How does overhead lighting (other than the bulb) affect the result?

Extending

7. An extended light source will produce a shadow of an opaque object that has penumbra and umbra regions. Research the meaning of these terms. Design an experiment using the light

(continued)

sensor, an extended light source, and a small opaque object to map light intensity as a function of the distance from the centre of the shadow. Report your results including the difference between the penumbra and umbra regions. Account for your findings.

Investigation 2 (Section 9.4)

Inquiry Skills

- Initiating and Planning
- Applying Technical Skills
- Using Tools, Material, Equipment
- Conducting and Recording
- Analyzing and Interpreting
- Concluding and Communicating

Images Formed by a Converging Mirror

The focal length of a converging mirror is found by directing parallel rays toward the mirror, finding where they meet using a screen, and then measuring the distance from the vertex of the mirror to the principal focus. The rays reaching a small-diameter mirror from a distant object are considered to be parallel. The object can be either a small light source, such as a candle, or a distant object, such as a tree.

Problem

What are the characteristics and locations of the images formed by a converging mirror as the object changes position? Write down your predictions and discuss them with a partner before doing the activity.

Materials

- optical bench
- lighted candle
- converging mirror
- paper screen

Caution: When using candles, tie back long hair, secure loose clothing, and avoid sudden movement.

Procedure

1. Copy the following table into your notes.
2. Use the mirror to focus the light from a distant object onto the screen. Carefully measure the distance between the vertex of the mirror and the image. This is the focal length f of the mirror.
3. You will be placing the object (lighted candle) at the following distances from the vertex of the mirror: $2.5\,f$, $2.0\,f$, $1.5\,f$, $1.0\,f$, and $0.50\,f$. Calculate these object distances, and enter them in the table.

Object Distance d_o (cm)	Image Characteristics			
	Image Distance d_i (cm)	Kind	Attitude	Magnification
$2.5\,f =$				
$2.0\,f =$				
$1.5\,f =$				
$1.0\,f =$				
$0.50\,f =$				

4. Set up the optical bench with the converging mirror at one end (Figure 9.53).

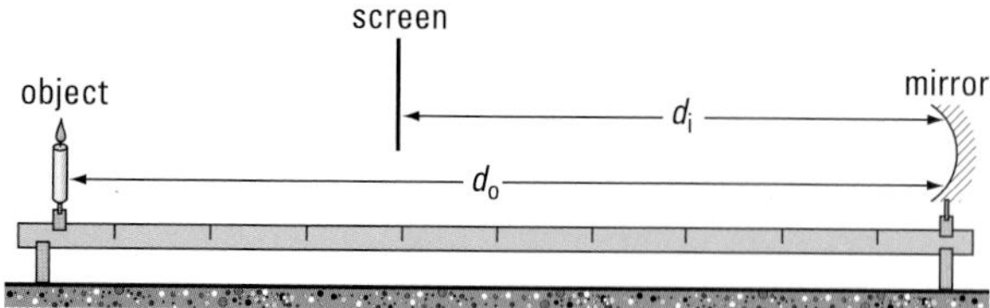

FIGURE 9.53 Images formed by a converging mirror

5. Place the object at 2.5 *f*. Move the screen until you capture a clear image on it. Record the characteristics of the image.
6. Look into the mirror and view the real image from beyond the image position.
7. Repeat step 5 for object distances of 2.0 *f* and 1.5 *f*.
8. Place the object at 1.0 *f*, and use the screen to show that the mirror produces no clear image.
9. Place the object at 0.50 *f*. Use the screen to show that the mirror produces a diverging beam of light and hence no real image. Try to capture the image on the screen. To see the image, look into the mirror from the same side as the object. Record the characteristics of the image. Your teacher will explain how to measure the image distance using the zero parallax method.

Analyzing and Interpreting

1. Why was a small distant light source used to locate the principal focus?
2. As the object moved from 2.5 *f* toward the principal focus F, what happened to
   a) the size of the image?
   b) the position of the image?
   c) the attitude of the image?
3. Why was no image formed when the object was at 1.0 *f*?
4. a) Describe the characteristics of the image when the object is between the principal focus F and the mirror.
   b) Where was this image with reference to the mirror and the object?
   c) Why was it impossible to focus the image on the screen?
5. Where must the object be placed with reference to the principal focus of a converging mirror to produce a real image? a virtual image?

Concluding and Communicating

6. For what range of positions with reference to the principal focus F does a converging mirror produce real images?
7. For what range of positions with reference to the principal focus F does a converging mirror produce virtual images?
8. In a paragraph, explain to someone who has not studied converging mirrors why a converging mirror does not produce an image when the object is placed at the principal focus F. Use a sketch in your answer.

Extending

9. Ask your teacher to show you how to use the zero parallax method to locate the position of a virtual image formed by a diverging mirror. Use the procedure to determine the focal length of a diverging mirror. Predict how you think the characteristics of the image will change as the object is brought closer to the diverging mirror. Design and perform an experiment to test your predictions.

CHAPTER SUMMARY

Key Terms

angle of incidence
angle of reflection
attitude
centre of curvature
converging beam
converging mirror
cylindrical mirror
diffuse reflection
diverging beam
diverging mirror
focal length
focal plane
focal point
incident ray
linear magnification
magnification
normal
parabolic mirror
parallax
parallel beam
plane
point of incidence
principal axis
principal focus
radius of curvature
real image
rectilinear propagation
reflected ray
reflection
refraction
specular reflection
spherical aberration
spherical mirror
vertex
virtual image
zero parallax

Essential Understandings

- When light is incident on the boundary between two media, some of the light will be reflected and some of it will be transmitted depending on the angle of incidence.
- Ray diagrams can be used to determine the location and nature of images created by mirrors.
- Reflection is the change in direction of light when it rebounds from a shiny surface.
- The four characteristics of any image are position, kind, attitude, and magnification.
- A real image can be caught on a screen while a virtual image cannot.
- Parallax is the apparent motion of one object with reference to a second object caused by a change in position of the observer.
- A single plane mirror produces an erect, virtual image, the same size as the object, and the same distance behind the mirror.
- The three shapes of converging and diverging mirrors are spherical, cylindrical, and parabolic.
- A mirror in the shape of a parabola is used to avoid spherical aberration.
- The characteristics of images formed by curved mirrors change as the position of the object changes.

Consolidate Your Understanding

1. Look back to your answer for the Checkpoint on page 331. What answer would you give now? Explain why each of the other answers is incorrect.
2. Describe the change in size, kind, and attitude of the image produced by a converging mirror as the object moves from the vertex of the mirror out to infinity.
3. Create a concept map to be used as a study map for sources, transmissions and reflection. Consult the Key Terms above, and include as many terms as possible in your concept map. Include one ray diagram and explain how a ray diagram is constructed and used to determine the characteristics of this image.
4. Write a paragraph explaining how knowledge of the laws of reflection enables us to explain the formation of images by both plane and curved mirrors. Use the laws of reflection to explain the minimum size of a plane mirror needed to see your total image.

CHAPTER 9 REVIEW

Understanding Concepts

1. The term "virtual" image means that the image
   a) is located on the surface of the mirror
   b) cannot be photographed by a camera
   c) is located in front of the mirror
   d) is the same size as the object
   e) cannot be caught directly on a screen

2. In Figure 9.54, XY is a plane mirror and O is a point object. To the eye, where will the image of O be located?
   a) A b) B c) C
   d) D e) There is no image.

O

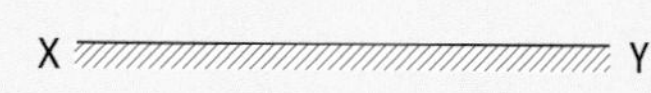

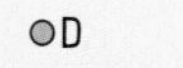

D C B A

FIGURE 9.54

3. A light ray strikes a plane mirror at an angle of 70° between its line of direction and the surface of the mirror at the point of incidence. The angle of reflection is
   a) 20° b) 40° c) 70°
   d) 90° e) 110°

4. Student A stands in front of a plane mirror and watches in the mirror as Student B comes up from behind. For the situation shown in Figure 9.55, the image of student B as seen by Student A will appear to be
   a) 1 m behind the mirror
   b) 3 m from the mirror
   c) 4 m behind the mirror
   d) 5 m behind the mirror
   e) 9 m in front of the observer

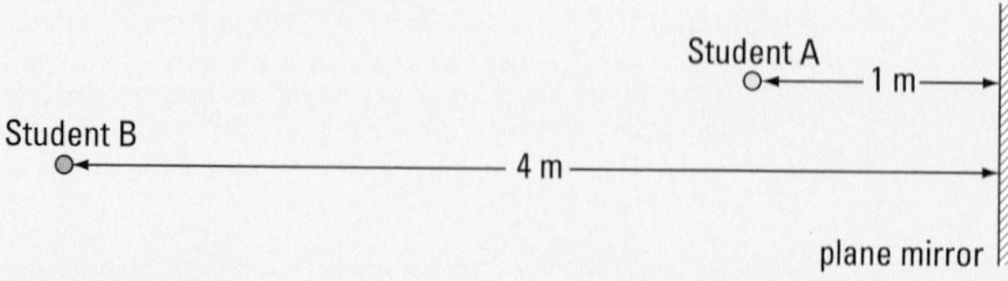

FIGURE 9.55

5. Figure 9.56 shows two rays drawn from an object O to an image I. There is also an incomplete third ray. Which of the lines correctly represents the continuation of the incomplete ray?
   a) A
   b) B
   c) C
   d) D
   e) E

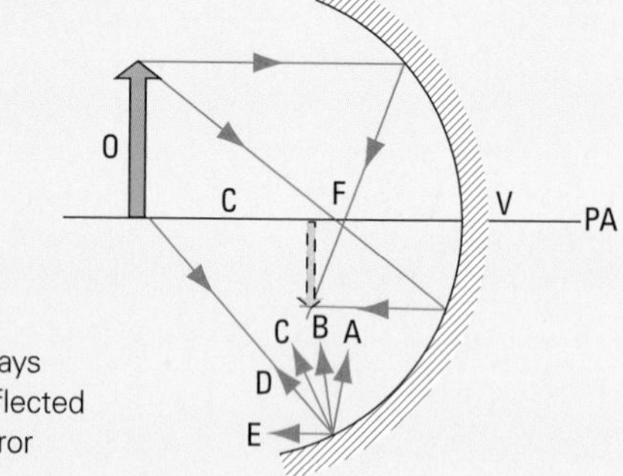

FIGURE 9.56 Rays from an object reflected by a spherical mirror

6. Draw scale diagrams to find the characteristics of the image of a 1.5-cm tall object when
   a) a converging mirror has a focal length of 5.0 cm and the object is located at
      i) 7.0 cm
      ii) 7.5 cm
      iii) 10 cm
      iv) 15 cm
   b) a diverging mirror has a focal length of 6.0 cm and the object is located at
      i) 3.0 cm
      ii) 8.0 cm

7. Why is a shaving mirror always converging rather than diverging?

8. A basketball player of height 2 m is standing in front of a vertical plane mirror.
   a) What is the minimum length of mirror needed for the player to see his or her complete image?
   b) Draw a diagram to show where the mirror should be placed.
   c) Does it matter how far the player is from the mirror? Explain.

9. For what range of object positions does a converging mirror form a virtual image?

10. What kinds of mirrors are used in a searchlight and why?

11. What advantages come from using a window shade that is translucent rather than opaque?

12. What colour are the inside surfaces of binoculars and cameras painted? Why are they painted that colour?

13. How can you tell by looking at an object and its image (formed by one reflecting surface) whether the image is real or virtual?

14. A broad parallel beam of light is directed onto a large spherical converging mirror. It is then directed onto a converging parabolic mirror. Contrast the images produced by the two mirrors and account for the difference.

15. Study the symbols shown in Figure 9.57. Sketch the images you will see when a plane mirror is placed along AB, AC, CD, and finally BD. Use a mirror to test your predictions. Explain the results.

FIGURE 9.57 Different mirror positions can give different images.

16. Imagine you are standing close to and facing a large curved mirror. Your eyes are at the level of the principal axis.
   a) Describe how the attitude, size, and kind of your image changes as you back slowly away from the mirror if the mirror is i) converging and ii) diverging.
   b) Are there any places in your journey along the principal axis where you cannot see yourself? Explain.

Applying Inquiry/ Communication Skills

17. Two vertical plane mirrors of length 4 m are connected and make an angle of 90°. They are situated along the positive x- and y-axes with the vertex of the mirrors at the origin (0,0). The coordinates, in metres, of an object placed in front of the mirror are (3, 3). Determine the coordinates of each of the three images formed by the mirrors.

18. A student is using reflective Mylar to construct a curved mirror. When five parallel rays are directed at the mirror, the rays reflect as shown in Figure 9.58. Write a paragraph explaining how the student should reshape the Mylar to obtain a sharper image. Use sketches in your answer.

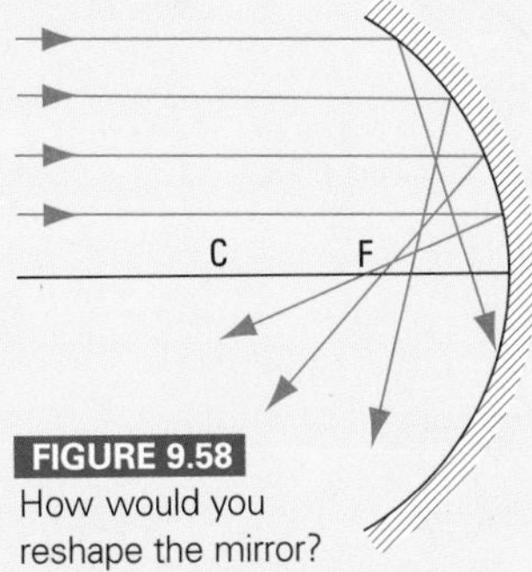

FIGURE 9.58 How would you reshape the mirror?

19. The coordinates for one-half of the surface of a parabolic mirror are shown in the table at the bottom of this page. Plot the curve representing the surface of the mirror to scale on graph paper. The principal axis is represented by the y-axis. Draw two rays parallel to the principal axis, one at $x = 4.0$ cm and one farther from it at $x = 12.0$ cm. Use a protractor and the laws of reflection to illustrate that this shape of mirror corrects for spherical aberration.

20. A wet asphalt road appears darker to a driver at night than a dry asphalt road. Explain why using what you know about diffuse and regular reflection. Include a sketch to illustrate your answer.

21. Newspaper reporters sometimes use the microphone arrangement shown in Figure 9.59 to pick up faint distant sounds. Explain how the microphone and reflecting surface work together to pick up weak sounds.

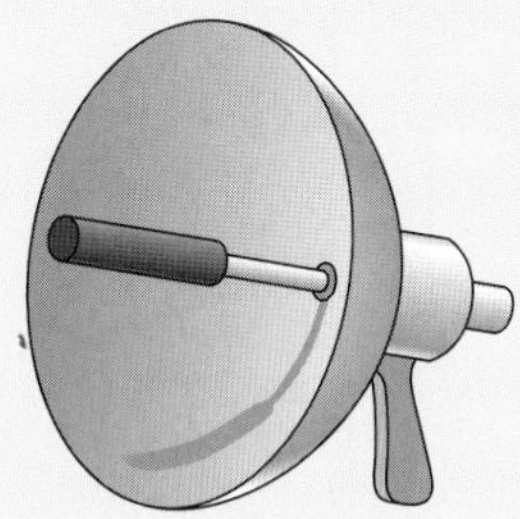

FIGURE 9.59

22. A plane mirror and a converging spherical mirror, separated by a distance of 10.0 cm, are facing each other. The converging mirror has a focal length of 4.0 cm. A 2.0-cm tall object is placed 5.0 cm in front of the plane mirror. Assume that light from the object is reflected first from the plane mirror and then from the converging mirror. Draw a ray diagram to scale to determine the position of the image that light reflected from the plane mirror to the converging mirror produces. Specify this distance relative to the centre of curvature of the converging mirror.

Making Connections

23. Write a brief report on how a television satellite (dish) antenna works.

24. Resolution is the smallest separation of two points that can be recorded separately or the smallest angular separation possible with an optical or radio telescope. Find out what factors affect the resolution of the converging mirrors used in reflecting telescopes. Why is resolution so important to astronomers and to the military?

25. The Canadian Motor Vehicle Safety Standard specifies that passenger wing mirrors on motor vehicles cannot have a radius of curvature less than 890 mm or greater than 1800 mm. Use an example to show why these safety limits have been chosen. What role do these standards play in the safety of passengers?

x (cm)	0	0.97	2.42	3.87	5.32	6.77	8.23	9.68	11.13	12.57	14.03	15.0
y (cm)	0	0.06	0.39	1.00	1.89	3.06	4.51	6.24	8.26	10.55	13.13	15.0

CHAPTER 10

Refraction and Total Internal Reflection

SPECIFIC EXPECTATIONS

By the end of this chapter, you will be able to:

- define and describe concepts and units related to light (10.1, 10.2, 10.3)
- describe the scientific model for light and use it to explain optical effects that occur as natural phenomena (10.4, 10.5)
- predict, in qualitative and quantitative terms, the refraction of light as it passes from one medium to another, using Snell's law (10.2, 10.3)
- explain the conditions required for total internal reflection, using light-ray diagrams, and analyze and describe situations in which these conditions occur (10.3, 10.4)
- demonstrate and illustrate, using light-ray diagrams, the refraction, partial refraction and reflection, critical angle, and total internal reflection of light at the interface of a variety of media (10.2, 10.3)
- carry out an experiment to verify Snell's law (Investigation 1)
- carry out experiments involving the transmission of light, compare theoretical predictions and empirical evidence, and account for discrepancies (Investigation 1, Investigation 2)
- construct, test, and refine a prototype of an optical device, and evaluate the effectiveness of a technological device or procedure related to human perception of light (10.4)
- analyze, describe, and explain optical effects that are produced by technological devices, and describe how images are produced and reproduced for the purposes of entertainment and culture (10.4)

Fibre optics is a rapidly growing branch of optics dealing with the transmission of light through transparent glass fibres. Light admitted at one end of a thin fibre, about the thickness of a human hair, can travel for many kilometres even if the fibre is curved. The simplest application of optical fibres is the transmission of light into areas that are difficult to reach such as the bore of a dentist's drill.

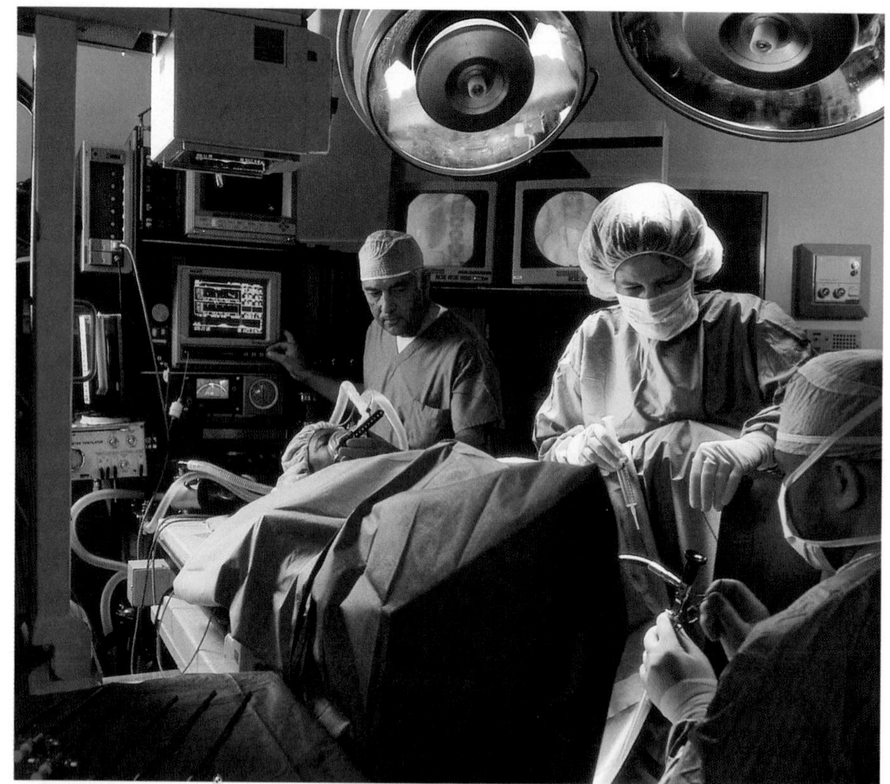

FIGURE 10.1 Colonoscopes are used to carry out non-surgical internal examinations.

Glass fibres are also used in bundles called light pipes to transmit data, voice or sound, and images over long distances. This has virtually replaced copper wire in many communications applications including long-distance telephone lines, cable television transmission, and local area computer networks. A single glass fibre can carry several thousand messages, while a pair of conventional wires can carry only 32.

Bundles of fibres are also used in medical instruments for viewing inside the human body. One bundle of fibres is used to illuminate the area being examined while another bundle transmits the image to an eyepiece or a video screen. This allows doctors to perform internal examinations of organs without surgery or to see a fetus while it is still in the uterus. Fibres have also been developed to carry high-power laser beams for performing laser surgery.

How is it possible to transmit a person's voice using light? How can light, which normally follows a straight path, travel through a curved fibre? These questions and more will be answered as you proceed through this chapter. You will study the various properties of light such as refraction and total internal reflection. Knowledge of these principles will enable you to explain many other phenomena such as the appearance of rainbows, the sparkling of diamonds, and why objects look bent when partially submerged in water.

CHECKPOINT

A ray of light travels from air toward glass at an oblique angle. At the interface, the ray

a) is totally reflected
b) is bent toward the normal
c) is bent away from the normal
d) is bent to travel along the normal
e) enters the glass without bending

Draw a sketch and explain your answer.

Discovering Physics

A Red Letter Event

How can a blue letter E be made to disappear and a red letter E be made to appear?

1. Print a large, blue E on the sticky side of a self-stick removable note.
2. Stick the note to the middle of the flat side of a semicircular glass block with the E vertical and facing inward.
3. Print a large, red E on the sticky side of another note.
4. Stick this note about a quarter of the way along the semicircular dish of the block as shown in Figure 10.2 with the E vertical and facing inward.
5. Close one eye and look at the blue E through the curved side of the dish from the location shown. While looking at the blue E, move your eye slowly along the curve away from the red E. Record what you see.
6. Move the red E to various places along the curve, and continue to record what you see each time.

- Describe the orientation of the blue E as viewed through the water.
- What happened to the blue E as your eye moved along the curve toward the corner of the dish?
- Where was your eye located when the blue E vanished?
- Where was your eye when the red E first appeared? Describe its orientation.
- What effect did changing the position of the red E have on the results? Explain your observations

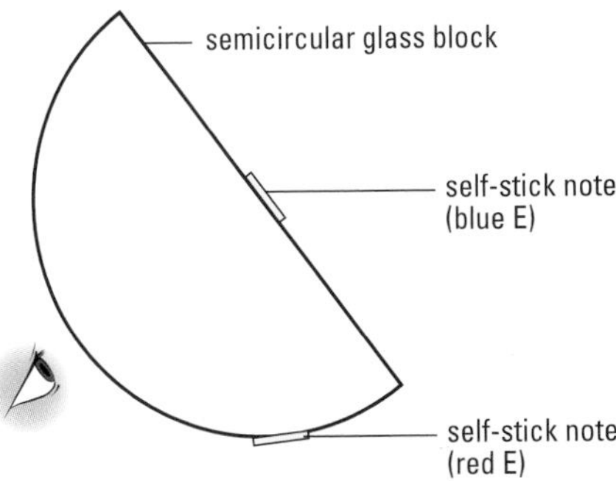

FIGURE 10.2 Can you make the red letter E appear and the blue letter E disappear?

10.1 Speed of Light and the Index of Refraction

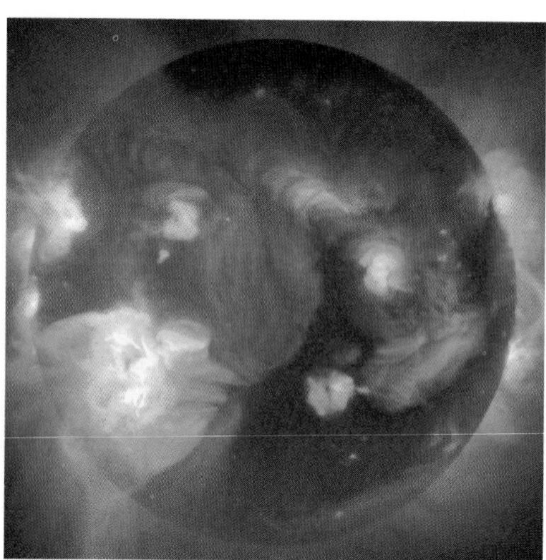

FIGURE 10.3 The Sun's coronal holes in an X-ray image

Key Understandings

When you have completed this section, you will be able to:

- describe early measurements of the speed of light
- define index of refraction and speed of light
- describe the relationship among speed of light in a vacuum, speed of light in a medium, and index of refraction of the medium

In 1989 an explosion on the Sun sent an enormous ball of searing gas hurtling toward Earth at speeds up to 1000 km/s. The gas hit Earth's magnetic field, generating a geomagnetic storm and a spectacular display of northern lights. Power systems were knocked out from James Bay to Montreal. Scientists knew it was coming because they had witnessed a tremendous solar flare two days before (Figure 10.3). Light travels much faster than the ball of gas, so it arrived first. Light takes only about eight minutes to travel from the Sun to Earth. How fast does it travel? Who first determined an accurate value for the speed of light and how was this done? Does light travel at the same speed in Earth's atmosphere as in the near vacuum of outer space?

The waves making up the electromagnetic spectrum are classified in terms of frequency and wavelength, as shown in Figure 10.4a). Examples of electromagnetic waves are: radio waves, microwaves, infrared, visible light, ultraviolet, X rays, and gamma rays.

The visible spectrum consists of the approximate wavelengths the eye can detect, and forms a very small part of the electromagnetic spectrum, as shown

WEBLINK

Ultraviolet and infrared light are similar in some respects. What uses are made of these forms of light? What dangers do they have for humans? Prepare a grid comparing these to regions of the electromagnetic spectrum. Begin your research at **www.pearsoned.ca/physics11.**

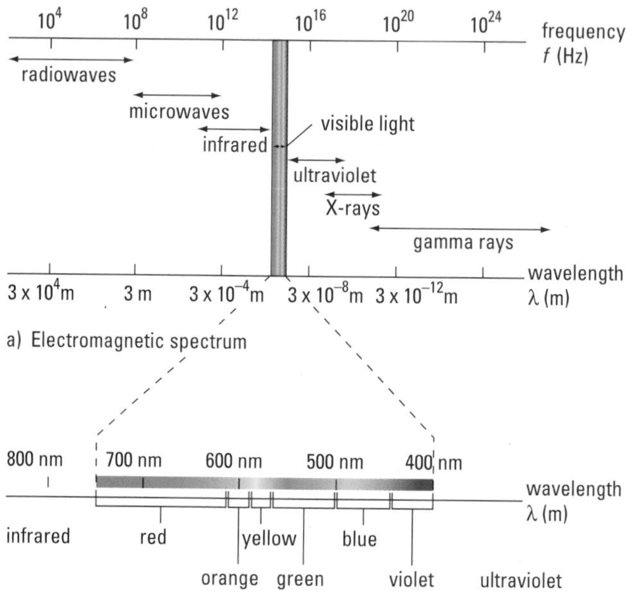

FIGURE 10.4 The electromagnetic radiation spectrum showing the visible range

in Figure 10.4b). Unlike sound and many other forms of energy, electromagnetic waves (including light) do not require a material medium for transmission. This is evident because we receive visible light and other forms of radiant energy from the sun through the near-vacuum of space.

Measuring the Speed of Light

The first recorded attempt to measure the speed of light took place in the seventeenth century. Galileo tried to measure the time it took for light to travel back and forth between two hilltops about 2 km apart. Galileo stood on one hill at night with a covered lantern while an assistant stood on the other. Galileo uncovered his lantern and as soon as his assistant saw the light he did the same. They attempted to measure the time it took the light to travel the round trip distance of 4 km, but were unable to do so. Although Galileo increased the distance in subsequent trials, he could not obtain a time measurement. He concluded that either the speed of light is infinite or it is so great that human reaction time does not permit a measurement over such a short distance.

In 1675 Olaus Roemer, a Danish astronomer, attempted to measure the speed of light, by observing the eclipse times for Jupiter's largest moons. This astronomical method gave a value of 2.27×10^8 m/s for the speed of light.

Armand Fizeau, a French physicist, was the first to successfully measure the speed of light using a terrestrial method in 1848. He used a rotating toothed disk to interrupt the incident light. The disk was placed on one hilltop and a mirror was placed on another hilltop about 3 km away. Light passed through a gap between two teeth, travelled to the mirror, and was reflected back. If the disk turned fast enough, the returning light passed through the next gap in the disk. From the rotational frequency of the disk and the number of gaps around its circumference, he was able to measure the time it took the light to travel 6 km. Fizeau measured the speed of light to be 3.15×10^8 m/s—about 5% higher than we now believe it to be. Bernard-Léon Foucault, another French physicist, replaced the rotating disk with a rotating mirror, and obtained a more accurate value.

Albert Michelson, an American scientist, perfected Foucault's method of measuring the time interval for light to travel a measured distance on Earth. Michelson replaced Foucault's single mirror with an eight-sided mirror. Figure 10.5 shows the apparatus that Michelson used. It consists of an intense light source, an eight-sided rotating mirror, a stationary mirror, and a telescope. The revolving mirror was set up on the top of Mount Wilson in southern California. The stationary mirror was placed 35 km away on the top of Mount St. Antonio. Light was directed at one face of the revolving mirror; then reflected from this face and travelled the 70-km round trip to the stationary mirror and back.

The frequency of the rotating mirror was adjusted until the next face of the mirror was in position to reflect the returning light to the observer looking through the telescope. The time for the mirror to rotate through one-eighth of a revolution was calculated from the rotation period of the mirror. The speed

WEBLINK

In 1881, Albert Michelson constructed a device called an interferometer for splitting a beam of light in two. He was able to use this interferometer to show that a light-carrying ether does not exist in space, and that in fact no material medium is necessary for the transmission of light. How does an interferometer work and what experiments did Michelson perform? Begin your research at **www.pearsoned.ca/physics11.**

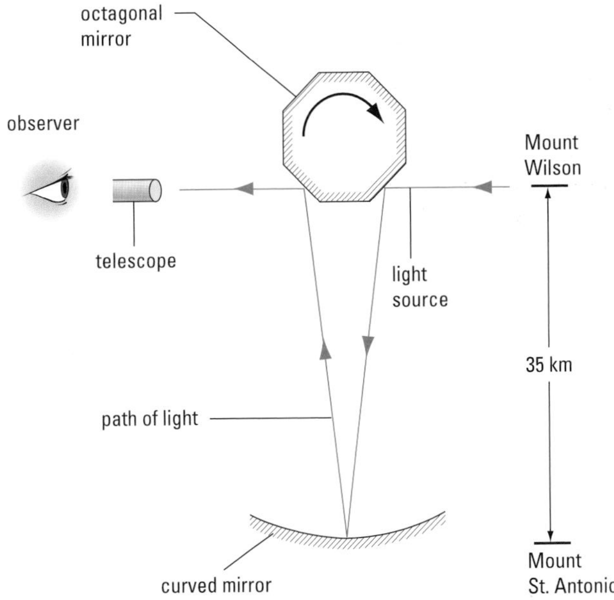

FIGURE 10.5 Michelson's method to measure the speed of light

WEBLINK

Microwave ovens are easy to use, but special kinds of ovenware must be used. A rotating platform improves the operation of microwave ovens and the door must fit tightly. What are some properties of microwaves? Prepare a web diagram summarizing the properties of microwaves and how these properties are harnessed in microwave ovens. Begin your research at **www.pearsoned.ca/physics11**

of light in air was determined using this time and the 70-km distance. It was found at that time to be 2.99798×10^8 m/s. The currently accepted value for the speed of light in air is 2.99785458×10^8 m/s.

Similar experiments were done using an evacuated chamber to measure the speed of light in a vacuum. Because the distance was less, the light was reflected between mirrors many times before returning to the rotating mirror. The accepted value for the speed of light in a vacuum is $c = 2.99792458 \times 10^8$ m/s, about 7000 m/s faster than in air. For most calculations, whether in a vacuum or in air, we use the rounded value for the speed of light c. Thus, $c = 3.00 \times 10^8$ m/s

The speed of light in other materials is significantly less as shown in Table 10.1.

TABLE 10.1 Speed of Light in Various Materials

Material	Speed c (m/s)
vacuum	3.00×10^8
air	3.00×10^8
ice	2.29×10^8
water	2.25×10^8
ethanol	2.19×10^8
glycerin	2.04×10^8
glass	
fused quartz	2.04×10^8
crown	1.97×10^8
light flint	1.89×10^8
Lucite or Plexiglas	1.97×10^8
ruby	1.95×10^8
zircon	1.56×10^8
diamond	1.24×10^8

Discovering Physics — *Using a Microwave Oven to Measure the Speed of Light*

Microwaves are part of the electromagnetic spectrum and hence travel at the speed of light. The speed of any wave can be determined using the universal wave equation $v = f\lambda$ where f is frequency and λ is wavelength. A microwave oven generates waves of known frequency. Look on the back of the oven and read the value (usually 2450 MHz or 2.450×10^9 Hz).

1. You need an oven that heats unevenly, so remove the turntable from the oven.
2. Pack the bottom of a microwave-safe casserole dish with a layer one-marshmallow thick.
3. Place the dish in the oven and heat until the marshmallows begin to melt at four or five distinct locations.
4. Remove the dish from the oven and measure the distance between adjacent melting spots. This distance is equal to the wavelength of the microwaves.
5. Take several readings and calculate the speed of the microwaves.

- What value did you get for the speed of microwaves?
- What is the percent error of your value compared with 3.0×10^8 m/s?
- What errors are there in this experiment?

EXAMPLE 1 NUMERICAL

In an experiment similar to that done by Michelson, the frequency of rotation of the eight-sided mirror is 530 Hz. Calculate the speed of light in air if the distance from the rotating mirror to the stationary mirror is 35.0 km.

Given

$f = 530$ Hz

$\Delta d = 35.0$ km (one way)

Required

c

Analysis

- The roundtrip distance is 70.0 km.
- The travel time Δt is one-eighth of the period.
- Use $c = \dfrac{\Delta d}{\Delta t}$

Solution

$$T = \frac{1}{f} = \frac{1}{530\ \text{s}^{-1}} = 1.89 \times 10^{-3}\ \text{s}$$

$$\frac{1}{8}T = \frac{1}{8}(1.89 \times 10^{-3}\ \text{s}) = 2.36 \times 10^{-4}\ \text{s}$$

$$c = \frac{\Delta d}{\Delta t} = \frac{70.0\ \text{km}}{2.36 \times 10^{-4}\ \text{s}} = 2.97 \times 10^{5}\ \text{km/s} = 2.97 \times 10^{8}\ \text{m/s}.$$

Statement

The speed of light in air is 2.97×10^{8} m/s.

PRACTICE PROBLEMS

1. In an experiment similar to Michelson's, the speed of light was found to be 2.80×10^{8} m/s using a 12-sided mirror placed 40 km from the light source. What was the frequency of rotation of the mirror?
2. In a similar experiment the speed of light was determined to be 3.0×10^{8} m/s using a mirror having a frequency of rotation of 357 Hz placed 30 km from the light source. How many sides did the mirror have?

Albert Abraham Michelson

Michelson was born in what is now Poland. He immigrated with his parents to the United States when he was two years old. During his lifetime, Michelson made two major contributions to physics. His work between 1878 and 1927 led to an accurate value for the speed of light. And his investigation with Edward William Morley showed that light travels at exactly the same speed in two mutually perpendicular directions.

Prior to 1887, it was believed that a motionless medium, called ether, existed in space. Scientists postulated the existence of ether to explain the fact that light waves travel from the sun through space. It was thought that all waves require a material medium for their travel. Michelson hypothesized, that if ether existed, then light waves sent in the same direction as Earth's motion through the ether should travel faster than light sent perpendicular to it. Michelson and Morley could find no difference in the speeds and hence no evidence for the existence of ether. In 1907, as a result of his work in light, Michelson was awarded the Nobel prize for physics.

FIGURE 10.6 Albert Abraham Michelson

WEBLINK

Astronomers must correct for the small amount of refraction that occurs when light enters Earth's atmosphere from outerspace. This process is referred to as "refraction correction." Prepare a sequence chart showing what happens to a quantum of light when it leaves the source of the light, encounters the distant planet, and travels to an Earth-based telescope. Explain what astronomers do to properly locate the planet's position. Begin your research at **www.pearsoned.ca/physics11.**

Index of Refraction for Light

Light slows down when it travels from a vacuum into any other medium. The medium in which the light travels more slowly is said to be the more refractive medium. You can see from Table 10.2, that diamond is a more refractive medium than glass. This is because light travels more slowly in diamond than in glass. Degrees of refractivity are measured by comparing the speed of monochromatic light (light of one colour) in a medium and in a vacuum. Absolute index of refraction n is defined as the ratio of the speed of monochromatic light in a vacuum c to its speed in a medium v

$$n = \frac{c}{v}.$$

Since the speed of light in air is so close to its speed in a vacuum, the indexes of refraction of air and a vacuum are considered to be equal. As a result, whenever the term **index of refraction** is used, we will be using the absolute index of refraction of the material.

TABLE 10.2 Absolute Indexes of Refraction (Sodium Yellow Light)

Substance	Index of Refraction η
vacuum	1.0000
air	1.0003
ice	1.31
water	1.33
ethanol	1.37
glycerin	1.47
glass	
fused quartz	1.47
crown	1.52
light flint	1.58
Lucite or Plexiglas	1.52
ruby	1.54
zircon	1.92
diamond	2.42

All colours of light travel at the same speed in a vacuum and more or less the same speed in air. However, different colours travel at different speeds in a material medium. For example, the speed of red light in glass is about 1% greater than the speed of violet light. The index of refraction for a specific colour is constant for a specific medium.

WEBLINK

A refractometer is a device used to measure refractive indexes vary accurately. Prepare a concept map summarizing how they work. Begin your research at **www.pearsoned.ca/physics11.**

The ratio of the two speeds has no units because it is a ratio of physical quantities both of which have the same units. The absolute index of refraction is always greater than one because light travels more slowly in any medium than in a vacuum. Table 10.2 shows some sample indexes for monochromatic sodium yellow light (yellow light with only one frequency).

Exploration Using a Graphing Calculator

Use the data from Tables 10.1 and 10.2 to plot a graph with speed of light v on the x-axis and absolute index of refraction n on the y-axis. Display a scatterplot and determine the best-fit curve and the equation. You should have found that its equation is $n = 3.0 \times 10^8\ v^{-1}$ where 3.0×10^8 is the speed of light in a vacuum c.

Discussion

1. Using the equation, estimate the refractive index for a medium where the speed of light is 1.65×10^8 m/s.
2. What is the speed of light in hydrogen (whose index of refraction is 1.000 139)?

Section 10.1 Review

Understanding Concepts

1. In an experiment similar to Michelson's, a 12-sided mirror was used. If the distance from the rotating mirror to the stationary mirror was 26 km, what was the required frequency of the mirror to enable the experiment to work?
2. Using Table 10.1, calculate the index of refraction of water.
3. What is the speed of monochromatic sodium yellow light in a material that has an index of refraction of 1.25?

Applying Inquiry/ Communication Skills

4. Identify which aspects of Galileo's experiment to measure the speed of light prevented him from succeeding.
5. Discuss how Fizeau, Foucault, and Michelson overcame Galileo's problem; and evaluate the accuracy of Michelson's value for the speed of light.
6. In an experiment using a microwave oven to measure the speed of microwaves (light), five measurements of the distance between melted marshmallow spots are: 12.1 cm, 12.1 cm, 12.2 cm, 12.3 cm, and 12.3 cm. The frequency of the microwave oven is 2450 MHz.
   a) Why should the distance measurements be averaged before calculating the speed of the microwaves?
   b) Calculate the speed of light according to the data.
   c) What is the percent error in the measurement and what might have caused the error?
   d) Why is it important to use a microwave oven without a turntable or rotating mirror?

Making Connections

7. Collect two articles (magazine, newspaper, etc.) that directly or indirectly support the statement: "It is important to both the telecommunications industry and to astronomers that the speed of light is so high."

10.2 Snell's Law of Refraction

FIGURE 10.7 An underwater diver

Key Understandings

When you have completed this section, you will be able to:

- explain partial reflection and refraction at the boundary between two materials
- define the laws of refraction
- predict, in qualitative and quantitative terms, the refraction of light as it passes from one medium to another, using Snell's law
- demonstrate and illustrate, using ray diagrams, the partial reflection and refraction of light at the interface of a variety of media

An underwater diver sees a very different world than we do (Figure 10.7). If the surface of the water is calm, there appears to be a circular window directly above. Looking toward the window, objects above the surface seem farther away and smaller than they really are. And objects off to the side seem to be even farther away. Bubbles of gas rising above the diver are clearly visible. Why do flies and birds above the surface seem smaller and farther away than they are? Why does viewing directly upward give a different perspective than viewing at an oblique angle? Why are the bubbles of transparent gas visible? The study of refraction will help us to explain these observations.

When a light ray is incident on the boundary between two materials of different refractive indexes, some of the light is reflected and some of it enters the new material. Light incident at an angle of 90° enters the new material without bending. Light incident at any other angle changes direction at the boundary as it enters. **Refraction** is the bending of light as it passes at an oblique angle from a material of one refractive index to a material of a different refractive index.

Reflection and refraction occur simultaneously at the interface between two materials. Only a small amount of light is reflected when the angle of incidence is 0° (about 2% for water). But the amount reflected increases as the angle of incidence increases. You may have experienced the glare of approaching headlights from a wet road at night. Very little of the light is refracted into the water on the road. Most of it is reflected into your eyes.

The simultaneous reflection and refraction of light has applications in a number of devices. One is the interior rearview mirror with a day/night adjustment lever. The mirror can be adjusted to reduce the glare from the headlights of cars approaching from behind at night. Rearview mirrors of this kind are constructed in the shape of a wedge as shown in Figure 10.8a).

WEBLINK

Day/night adjustment mirrors are necessary in today's vehicles. What are some of the design specifications for modren day/night mirrors? For example, what is the angle between the front and rear reflecting surfaces of the mirror? Begin your research at **www.pearsoned.ca/physics11.**

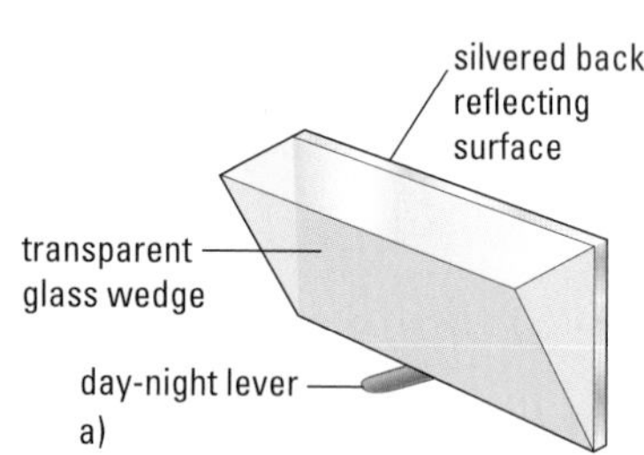

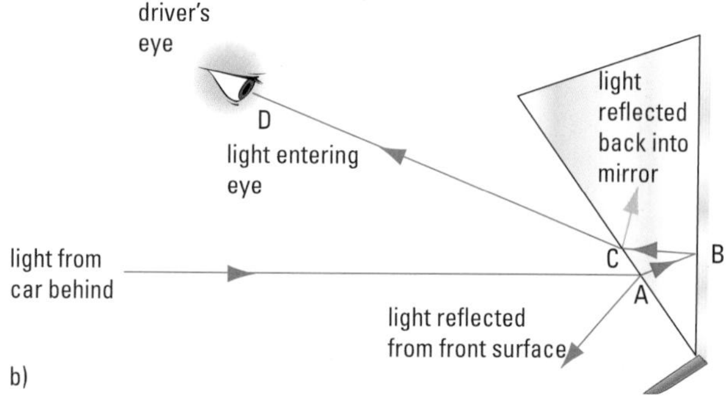

FIGURE 10.8 Reflection and refraction: the adjustable rearview mirror

The thickness of the glass making up the mirror decreases from top to bottom. The back of the wedge is silvered to produce a highly reflective surface.

Figure 10.8b) shows how the mirror is adjusted for daylight driving. Most of the light reaching the front surface enters the glass, travels to the reflecting surface, and reflects back out of the mirror (path ABCD). Refraction takes place as light enters and leaves the glass. A small amount of light is also reflected. The mirror is adjusted so that about 85% of the light incident on the mirror reaches the driver's eyes. The daylight traffic approaching from behind is highly visible in the mirror.

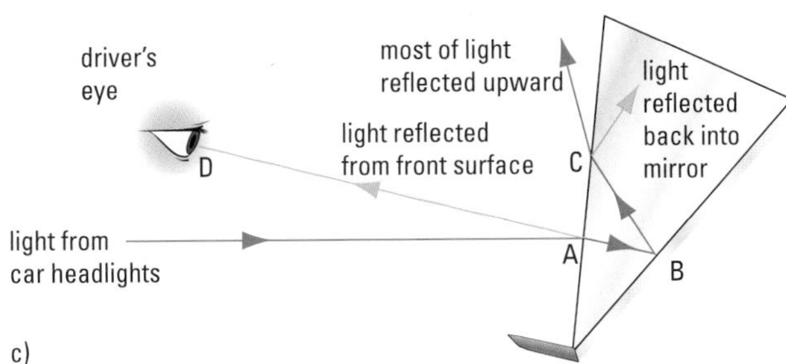

Figure 10.8c) shows how adjusting the lever swivels the mirror clockwise for night vision. Now most of the light reflecting from the silvered back surface travels upward, away from the driver. It is only the dimmer light reflected from the front surface of the glass that enters the driver's eyes (path AD). This is less than 4% of the light incident on the mirror. But because of the high intensity of the light from the approaching headlights, this small percentage is sufficient to see the approaching car. The night adjustment prevents the driver from being blinded by light reflected from the silvered surface.

Exploration Using a Graphing Calculator 

If light is incident on water at an angle of incidence 0°, only about 2% is reflected back from the surface. This rises to 4% for glass. That is why you can see your reflection when you peer through a darkened window or into a dark lake. The percentage of the incident intensity reflected I_r is given by

$$I_r = \left[\frac{n-1}{n+1}\right]^2 \times 100,$$

where n is the index of refraction of the medium.

Calculate the percent incident intensity reflected for diamond. Are you surprised by the high value?

Plot a graph of percent intensity reflected against refractive index. Look up the value for refractive index for glass and diamond and use the graph to determine the percent intensity reflected for both materials.

Discussion

1. Describe the graph. Is it a curve or a straight line?
2. What happens to the percentage of light reflected as the refractive index increases?
3. Compare the percent intensity reflected for glass and diamond.

The Two Laws of Refraction

The incident ray is the ray of light approaching the boundary between the two media, and the refracted ray is the ray of light transmitted through the boundary into the new medium. See Figure 10.9. The normal is the line drawn perpendicular to the boundary at the point of incidence. Notice that both the refracted ray and the reflected ray are on the opposite side of the normal from the incident ray. The angle of incidence i is the angle between the incident ray and the normal. The angle of refraction R is the angle between the refracted ray and the normal.

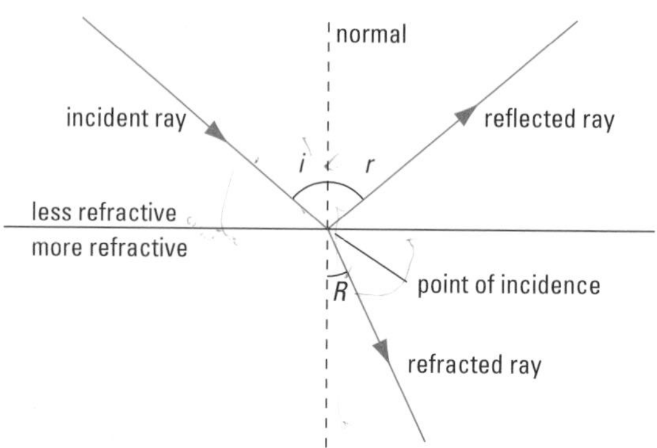

FIGURE 10.9 Both reflection and refraction occur when light is incident on a more refractive medium.

TABLE 10.3 Angles of Refraction for Water and Glass

Angle of Incidence i (°)	Angle of Refraction R (°)	
	Water	Glass
0	0	0
10	7.5	6.6
20	14.9	13.0
30	22.1	19.2
40	28.9	25.0
50	35.2	29.8
60	40.6	34.6
70	45.0	38.2
80	47.8	40.4

Table 10.3 shows angles of incidence i and corresponding angles of refraction R for light entering water and crown glass from air.

The table shows that glass bends light more than water does. Figure 10.10 shows the graph of the angle of refraction plotted against the angle of incidence for crown glass and water. At small angles of incidence, the lines appear straight. However, for angles of incidence larger than about 40°, you can see that the line curves. This means that the angle of refraction is not directly proportional to the angle of incidence.

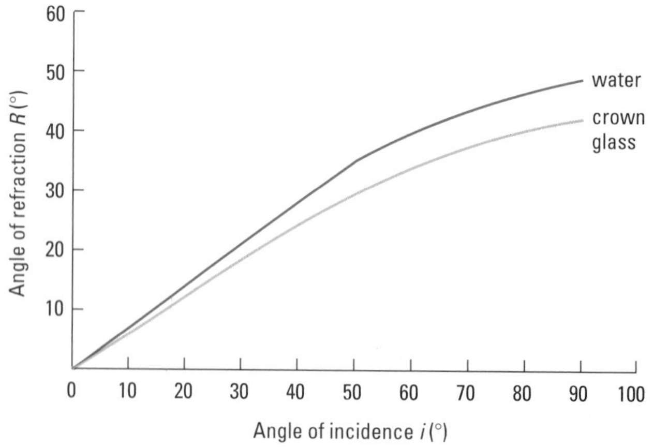

FIGURE 10.10 Graph of R against i for water and crown class. Which medium will bend light more for the same angle of incidence?

Willebrord Snell (1591–1626), a Dutch astronomer, is credited with discovering the relationship between i and R. He found that since light travels in waves, it has wave fronts. A wave front is a line joining all the points on light waves leaving the source at the same time. Lines drawn perpendicular to wave fronts represent the direction of travel of the wave fronts. These lines correspond to light rays.

Figure 10.11 shows light wave fronts incident on the boundary between air and a more refractive medium. The line AB represents a wave front at time t_1. The line CD represents where the wave front will be in the more refractive medium at time t_2. The elapsed time is Δt. Let the speed of the light wave in air be c and the speed in the medium be v. In the time interval Δt, point B of the wave front AB travels a distance $\Delta d = c\Delta t$ in air. This is represented by the length of the line BD. In the same time interval, point A of the refracted wave front travels the distance $\Delta d = v\Delta t$ in the refractive medium. This distance is represented by the line AC.

The sine of the angle of incidence is BD/AD. The sine of the angle of refraction is AC/AD. The ratio sin i / sin R simplifies to BD/AC by

$$\frac{\sin i}{\sin R} = \frac{\text{BD/AD}}{\text{AC/AD}} = \frac{\text{BD}}{\text{AD}} \times \frac{\text{AD}}{\text{AC}} = \frac{\text{BD}}{\text{AC}}$$

But BD $= c\Delta t$ and AC $= v\Delta t$

$$\text{So } \frac{\sin i}{\sin R} = \frac{c\Delta t}{v\Delta t}$$

$$\frac{\sin i}{\sin R} = \frac{c}{v}$$

The ratio of the sines of the angles of incidence and refraction is equal to the ratio of the speeds of light in the two media.

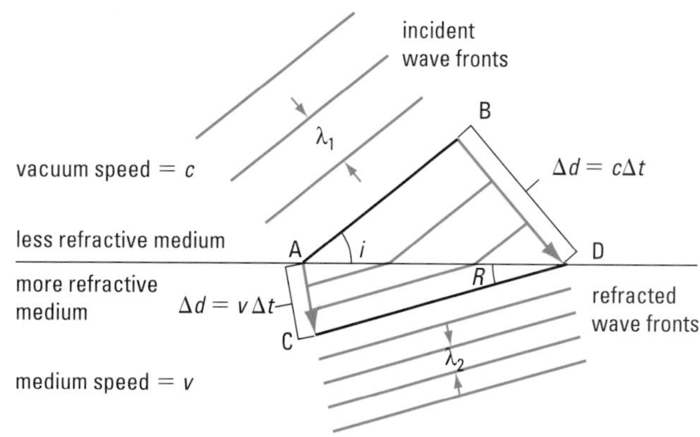

FIGURE 10.11 Wave fronts travelling at an oblique angle from a less refractive to a more refractive medium are refracted. In which medium is the wave traveling slower? How do you know?

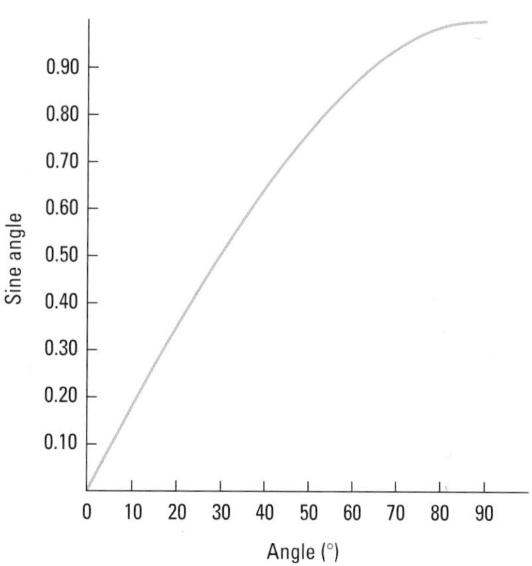

FIGURE 10.12 For small angles, the sine of the angle appears to be almost directly proportional to the angle, i.e. $\sin\theta \approx \theta$.

Exploration Using a Graphing Calculator

You may think that the data from Table 10.3 suggest a power relationship between the angle of incidence i and the angle of refraction R. Use the data from Table 10.3 to plot a graph with i on the x-axis and R^2 on the y-axis to check this hypothesis.

Discussion

How do you know that R^2/i is not a constant and that R^2 is not directly proportional to i?

EXAMPLE 2 NUMERICAL

A ray of sodium yellow light travels from air into crown glass at an angle of incidence of 25°. Use the speeds of light given in Table 10.1 to determine the angle of refraction.

Given

From Table 10.1

$c = 3.00 \times 10^8$ m/s

$v = 1.97 \times 10^8$ m/s

Required

R

Analysis

- Use the equation $\frac{\sin i}{\sin R} = \frac{c}{v}$
- Rearrange the equation to solve for the sine of the angle of refraction.
- Find the angle of refraction.

Solution

$$\frac{\sin i}{\sin R} = \frac{c}{v}$$

$$\begin{aligned} \sin R &= \frac{v}{c}\sin i \\ &= \frac{1.97 \times 10^8 \text{ m/s}}{3.00 \times 10^8 \text{ m/s}}(\sin 25^\circ) \\ &= 0.6567 \times 0.4226 \\ &= 0.2775 \\ R &= 16^\circ \end{aligned}$$

Statement

The angle of refraction is 16°.

PRACTICE PROBLEMS

1. The angle of incidence of a ray of white light on a ruby is 40°. The angle of refraction is 25°. What is the speed of light in ruby?
2. After entering zircon, a ray of light from a helium-neon laser makes an angle 32° with the normal. If the speed of light in zircon is 1.56×10^8 m/s, what was the angle of incidence?

TABLE 10.4 Refraction of Light Entering Water and Crown Glass

Air		Water		Crown Glass	
Angle of Incidence i (°)	Sin i	Angle of Refraction R (°)	Sin R	Angle of Refraction R (°)	Sin R
0	0	0	0	0	0
10	0.1736	7.5	0.1305	6.6	0.1149
20	0.3420	14.9	0.2571	13.0	0.2250
30	0.5000	22.1	0.3759	19.2	0.3289
40	0.6428	28.9	0.4833	25.0	0.4226
50	0.7660	35.2	0.5759	29.8	0.4970
60	0.8660	40.6	0.6511	34.6	0.5678
70	0.9397	45.0	0.7065	38.2	0.6184
80	0.9848	47.8	0.7406	40.4	0.6481

Table 10.4 shows angles of incidence i, angles of refraction R, and the corresponding sines for sodium yellow light entering water and crown glass.

Figure 10.13 shows the graph of sin i against sin R for water. The graph is a straight line passing through the origin. Thus

$$\frac{\sin i}{\sin R} = \text{a constant}$$

The slope is the proportionality constant between sin i and sin R. This means that

$$\text{slope} = \frac{\text{rise}}{\text{run}} = \frac{\sin i}{\sin R} = \frac{0.84}{0.63} = 1.3$$

We know that for monochromatic light, the ratio $\frac{c}{v}$ is a constant for a given medium. In section 10.1 you saw that this constant was the index of refraction n of the medium. From Table 10.2, you know that the index of refraction of water is 1.33. The ratio $\sin i / \sin R$ is also equal to 1.33. Recall that

$$\frac{\sin i}{\sin R} = \frac{c}{v}$$

Therefore $\frac{\sin i}{\sin R} = n$

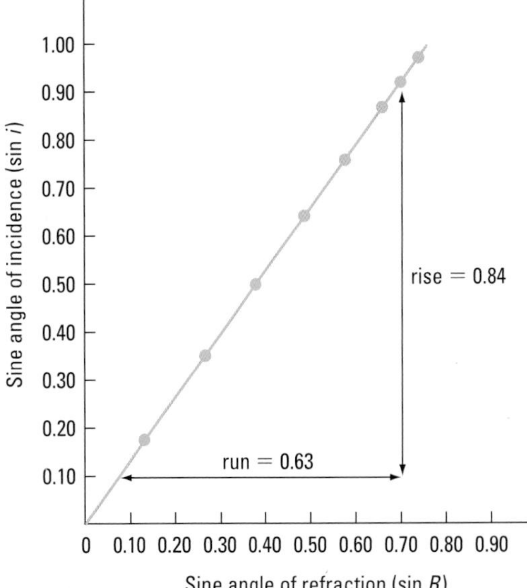

FIGURE 10.13 The graph of sin i against sin R for sodium yellow light travelling from air into water. What is the slope of this line?

This ratio is the first of the two **laws of refraction**. These laws are as follows:

The ratio sin i / sin R is a constant for a given colour of light and a given material.

The incident ray and refracted ray are on opposite sides of the normal at the point of incidence; and all three lie in the same plane.

Refer to page 395, Investigation 1

The General Equation for Snell's Law

Light bends toward the normal when it travels from a vacuum to a medium with a higher index of refraction. If the light is reflected straight back, it follows an identical path in the opposite direction (Figure 10.14). In travelling from a medium with a higher index of refraction to a medium with a lower index of refraction, light bends away from the normal. The angle of incidence in the more refractive medium is smaller than the angle of refraction in the less refractive medium. The sine ratio for light travelling from a more refractive to a less refractive medium, $\frac{\sin \theta_2}{\sin \theta_1}$ is the inverse of the sine ratio for light travelling from a less refractive to a more refractive medium, $\frac{\sin \theta_1}{\sin \theta_2}$. The equation for the index of refraction n_{m} for light travelling from a vacuum v to a more refractive material m is $\frac{\sin \theta_{\text{v}}}{\sin \theta_{\text{m}}} = n_{\text{m}}$ The equation for the index of refraction for light travelling in the opposite direction from a more refractive material to a vacuum is $\frac{\sin \theta_{\text{m}}}{\sin \theta_{\text{v}}} = \frac{1}{n_{\text{m}}}$

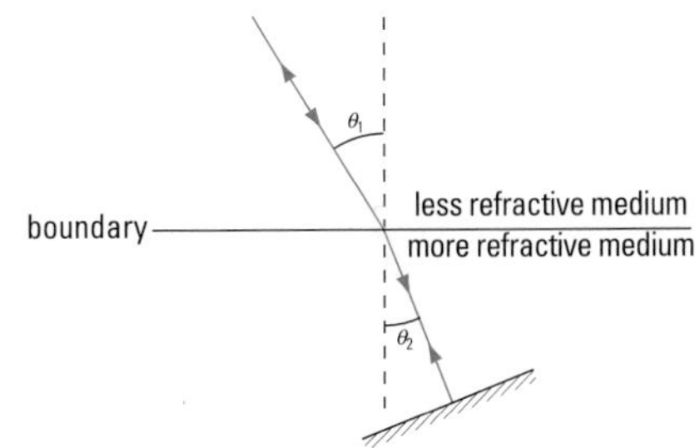

FIGURE 10.14 Light is reversible. A ray follows the same path entering a more refractive medium as leaving it. The plane mirror is used to reverse the light in this case.

WEBLINK

If you are having difficulty predicting the path of a ray going from one medium to another, viewing animations will help you. Submit a half-page report summarizing the simulations you used and what you learned. Include at least one ray diagram showing the passage of a ray through an optical medium. Begin your research at **www.pearsoned.ca/physics11.**

Since these equations are equal, we can write the equation in the form

$$\sin \theta_v = n_m \sin \theta_m$$

Suppose we compare the path of light travelling from a vacuum into medium 1 with the path of light travelling from a vacuum into medium 2. The equations would be

$$\sin \theta_v = n_1 \sin \theta_1 \quad \text{and} \quad \sin \theta_v = n_2 \sin \theta_2$$

Since the right sides of both equations are equal to sin θ_v, we can write a general equation for light travelling directly from medium 1, with an index of refraction n_1, to medium 2, with an index of refraction n_2. Hence, the general equation for **Snell's law** is

$$n_1 \sin \theta_1 = n_2 \sin \theta_2$$

This equation applies no matter which way the light is travelling between the two media.

INSIGHT

Remember that n_1 is the index of refraction for the medium in which the light is incident and n_2 is the index of refraction for the medium in which the light is refracted.

EXAMPLE 3 NUMERICAL

Light travels from ruby into water. The angle of incidence in the ruby θ_r is 35°. Calculate the angle of refraction in the water θ_w.

Given
$\theta_r = 35°$

Required
θ_w

Analysis

- From Table 10.2, $n_r = 1.54$ and $n_w = 1.33$
- From sine tables or a calculator, sin 35° = 0.5736
- Use Snell's law.

Solution

$$n_r \sin \theta_r = n_w \sin \theta_w$$

$$\sin \theta_w = \frac{n_r}{n_w} \sin \theta_r = \frac{1.54 \times 0.5736}{1.33} = 0.6642$$

$$\theta_w = 42°$$

Statement
The angle of refraction for light travelling from ruby to water is 42°, when the angle of incidence is 35°.

PRACTICE PROBLEMS

1. A sample of diamond is immersed in water. A light ray emerges from diamond with an angle of refraction of 50°. What is the angle of incidence in diamond? (See Table 10.2.)
2. The angle of incidence in a material is 40°. The corresponding angle of refraction in ethanol is 48°. Calculate the index of refraction of the material. What might the material be? (See Table 10.2.)

Ray Tracing for Air Interfaces

Light incident on the interface between air and a transparent material is refracted. A ray travelling from air into the more refractive material bends toward the normal. A ray travelling from the more refractive material into air bends away from the normal. Follow these steps when solving problems involving Snell's law.

1. Draw a diagram showing the two media. Label the media including the two indexes of refraction. Remember the index of refraction for air is one.
2. Draw a dotted line perpendicular to the boundary to represent the normal.
3. Use a protractor to measure the angle of incidence i and/or the angle of refraction R from the normal.
4. Draw the rays with a ruler. Add an arrowhead to show the direction of travel of each ray, and label the angles.
5. Use Snell's law to calculate the unknown angle or unknown index of refraction, and show this on the diagram. (If drawing a ray, be sure to measure the angle from the normal, and put an arrowhead on the ray.)
6. Verify that the refracted ray bends in the correct direction with reference to the normal and that the incident ray and the refracted ray are on opposite sides of the normal.

INSIGHT

Remember that the angle of incidence i and the angle of refraction R are measured from the normal, not from the boundary between the two media.

Exploration Using a Graphing Calculator

Use the data from Table 10.4. On the same axis, plot a graph of sin i against sin R for water and for crown glass. Find the equations for each line and compare the equations. Did you find the equations to be sin R = 0.75 sin i for water and sin R = 0.67 sin i for glass?

Discussion

1. Show that these linear regressions correspond to the equation sin i / sin R = n, where n is 1.33 and 1.5 respectively.

Section 10.2 Review

Understanding Concepts

1. In your own words, define the laws of refraction.
2. A ray of yellow light travels from air to substance X at an angle of incidence of 25°. The angle of refraction is 18°. Explain in your own words how you would go about calculating the speed of light in substance X.
3. A ray of sodium yellow light travels from air to flint glass at an angle of incidence of 30°. Refer to Table 10.2 and calculate the angle of refraction.
4. A transparent substance has an index of refraction of 1.40. What is the angle of incidence in a vacuum if the angle of refraction in the substance is 22°?
5. Calculate the index of refraction of a material if the angle of incidence is 60° and the angle of refraction is 50°.

Applying Inquiry/ Communication Skills

6. Look again at Figures 10.12 and 10.13. In your own words, describe the differences between the graph of R against i and the graph of sin i against sin R for water.
7. Consider whether it is important that the immersion oil used with glass slides and compound microscopes has a refractive index close to, or equal to, that of the glass slides. Defend your recommendation.

Making Connections

8. Three scientists independently discovered the law of refraction: Thomas Harriot in 1602, Willebrord Snell in 1626, and René Descartes in 1637. But only the last two are given credit for the law. What key steps are necessary before a scientist is given credit in the scientific community for an important discovery? Is it important to communicate a discovery as soon as possible? Can a discovery be communicated too early? Discuss.

10.3 Critical Angle and Total Internal Reflection

Key Understandings

When you have completed this section, you will be able to:

- define critical angle and total internal reflection
- predict, in qualitative and quantitative terms, the refraction of light as it passes from one medium to another, using Snell's law
- explain the conditions required for total internal reflection, using ray diagrams
- demonstrate and illustrate, using ray diagrams, the total internal reflection of light at the interface of a variety of media

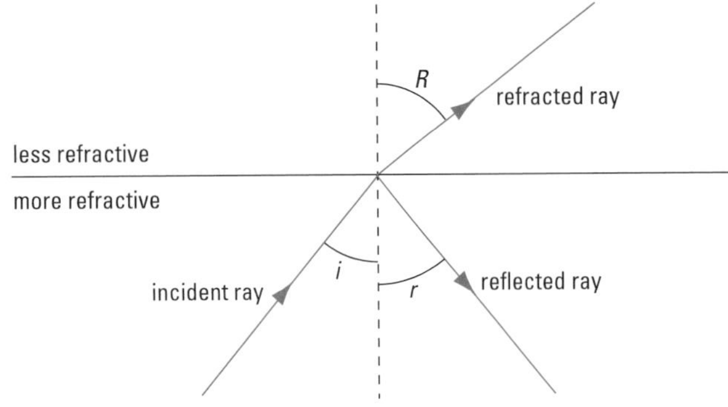

a) i smaller than the critical angle

FIGURE 10.15 In travelling from a more refractive medium to a less refractive medium, more and more light is reflected. When the angle of incidence is larger than the critical angle, all the light is internally reflected.

Diamonds form from carbon that is subjected to high temperatures and pressures deep within Earth's crust. They are the hardest natural substances on Earth and are used for cutting and polishing hard materials. The *cut* of a diamond refers not only to its shape, but also to its proportions and finish—factors that determine the sparkle. Why does a diamond exhibit such brilliance? What roles do refractive index and cut play in sparkle? And why does a diamond lose much of its shine under water?

When light travels from a more refractive to a less refractive medium, the angle of refraction is larger than the angle of incidence, as Figure 10.15a) shows. As the angle of incidence increases, the angle of refraction approaches 90°. The angle of incidence for which the angle of refraction is 90° is called the **critical angle** θ_c. At the critical angle, the refracted light grazes along the boundary between the two media, as shown in

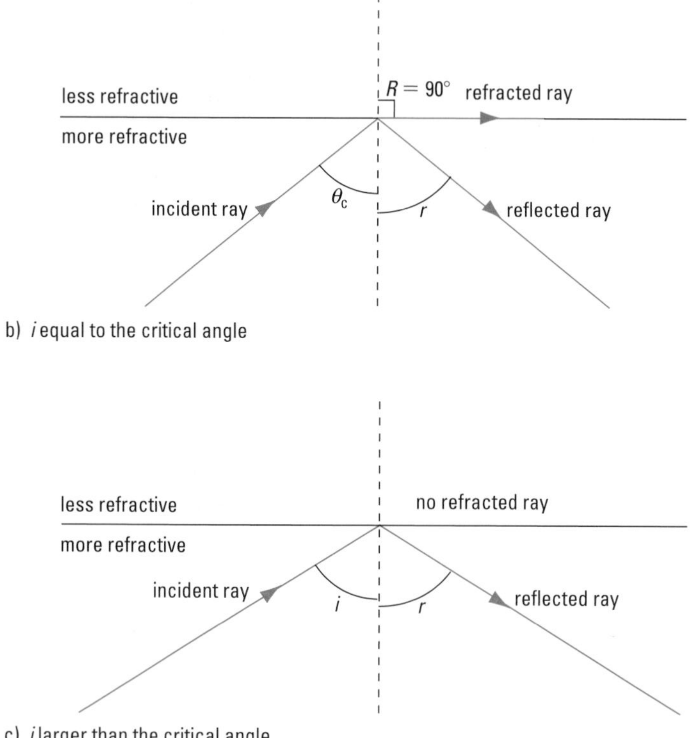

b) *i* equal to the critical angle

c) *i* larger than the critical angle

Figure 10.15b). If light is incident on the boundary at an angle greater than the critical angle, it is all reflected back into the more refractive medium. In no other situation in nature, where light is reflected, does 100% reflection occur.

The larger the index of refraction of a material, the smaller the critical angle. Diamond has a much smaller critical angle than glass. That means that a larger proportion of the light is reflected internally and then escapes from the top, which is what gives a diamond its sparkle.

The critical angle can be determined by using Snell's law and making the angle in the less refractive medium 90°. The equation becomes

$$\sin \theta_c = \frac{n_2}{n_1}$$

where medium 1 is more refractive and medium 2 is less refractive.

As the angle of incidence approaches the critical angle, a greater percentage of the light is reflected back into the more refractive medium. For angles of incidence larger than the critical angle, all the light is reflected, as shown in Figure 10.15c). This phenomenon is called **total internal reflection**. For total internal reflection to occur:

- light must be travelling in the more refractive medium.
- the angle of incidence in the more refractive medium must be larger than the critical angle.

Since the rays reflected internally obey the laws of reflection, the angle of incidence is equal to the angle of reflection.

WEBLINK

The critical angle for radio waves is the angle of incidence for which the waves will just not be reflected from the ionosphere. Research radio waves, and technologies related to their transmission. Submit a chart showing the sequence of events from when the decision is made to communicate by means of radio waves until a recipient halfway around the world receives the message. Begin your research at **www.pearsoned.ca/physics11.**

Investigation

Refer to page 396, Investigation 2

WEBLINK

SIMULATION

For simulations showing refraction, total internal reflection, and the effect of refractive index on the critical angle, go to **www.pearsoned.ca/physics11**.

Discovering Physics *Hidden Marbles*

In this activity, you will observe the effects of reflection, refraction, and total internal reflection.

1. Half fill a 250-mL Erlenmeyer flask with marbles.
2. Close the end with a rubber stopper.
3. Place the flask in a 500-mL beaker partially filled with water. Make sure the water level is above the marbles, but below the neck of the flask as shown in Figure 10.16.
4. Look down from the top of the flask beside the neck and then farther out.
5. Record your observations in a labelled sketch.
6. Add more water to the beaker and repeat your observations.
7. Remove the rubber stopper and add water to the flask until the marbles are completely covered. Look down again and record what you see.

- Explain your observations in terms of reflection, refraction, and total internal reflection.

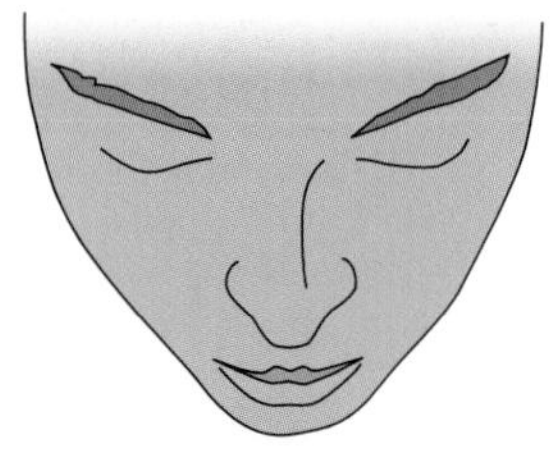

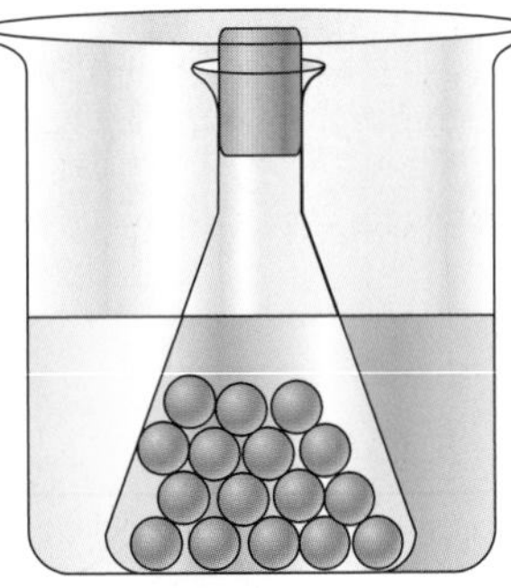

FIGURE 10.16

EXAMPLE 4 NUMERICAL

A piece of zircon is immersed in water. Find the angle above which light is totally internally reflected in zircon.

Given
Zircon and water are the media.

Required
θ_c for zircon immersed in water

Analysis

- For total internal reflection to occur, light must be travelling from zircon toward water.
- The light will be totally internally reflected if the angle of incidence i is larger than the critical angle.
- Use Snell's general equation.

Solution
From Table 10.2, $n_z = 1.92$ and $n_w = 1.33$

Snell's general equation is $n_1 \sin \theta_1 = n_2 \sin \theta_2$

Substituting for zircon and water this becomes $n_z \sin \theta_z = n_w \sin \theta_w$

Rearranging the equation yields $\sin \theta_z = \dfrac{n_w \sin \theta_w}{n_z}$

But $\theta_w = 90°$ and $\sin 90° = 1$

Substituting we get $\quad \sin \theta_z = \dfrac{1.33 \times 1}{1.92}$

$$= 0.6927$$

$$\theta_z = 44°$$

Statement

The critical angle for zircon immersed in water is 44°. All the light travelling from zircon toward water at angles of incidence larger than 44° will be totally internally reflected back into zircon.

PRACTICE PROBLEMS

1. Refer to Table 10.2 and calculate the critical angle for Lucite immersed in water.
2. Calculate the index of refraction of a material whose critical angle for air is 35°.

Section 10.3 Review

Understanding Concepts

1. Explain the conditions required for total internal relection.

2. Which model of light (particle or wave) best explains refraction?

3. How did the measurement of the speed of light affect our understanding of the nature of light?

4. A sample of Lucite is immersed in water. A light ray emerges from Lucite with an angle of refraction of 40°. What is the angle of incidence in Lucite? (See Table 10.2.)

5. The angle of incidence in a material is 45°. The corresponding angle of refraction in glycerin is 50°. Calculate the index of refraction of the material.

Applying Inquiry/ Communication Skills

6. a) Predict the path of light travelling from water to Lucite and the path of light travelling from Lucite to water.

b) Test your prediction and state your conclusions.

7. Refer to Table 10.2 and calculate the critical angle for diamond in air. Repeat for diamond immersed in water. Why do you think a diamond immersed in water sparkles less than a diamond in air?

8. Which will be larger: the critical angle at an air–glass interface or the critical angle at a water–glass interface. Explain.

Making Connections

9. When purchasing a diamond, people often use a microscope to look for tiny imperfections within the diamond called inclusions. In which case would the inclusions be more visible, with the diamond immersed in water or in air? Explain.

10.4 Examples of Refraction and Total Internal Reflection

Key Understandings

When you have completed this section, you will be able to:

- explain apparent depth based on the scientific model for light
- analyze and describe situations in which the conditions for total internal reflection occur, including reflecting prisms and fibre optics
- construct, test, and refine a prototype of an optical device producing a shimmering effect
- describe how images are reproduced using fibre optics for the purposes of entertainment and culture
- evaluate the effectiveness of fibre optics in laser surgery
- analyze, describe, and explain optical effects that are produced by optical fibres

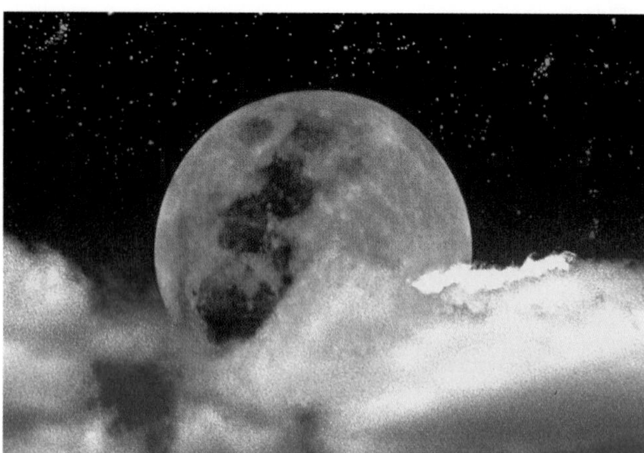

FIGURE 10.17 Magnified image of the Moon with twinkling stars in the background

While sitting on the beach watching the sunset, a student noticed that the Sun changed shape from round to oval as it neared the horizon. What caused this change? How can it be that the sunset one is observing has already set? What causes stars to twinkle (Figure 10.17)?

Apparent Depth

An oar partly under water looks bent when viewed from above. This phenomenon can be explained by the laws of refraction and the fact that the brain assumes that light travels in straight lines. Figure 10.18 shows two rays leaving point O on the blade of a paddle and travelling to the extremities of the eye of an observer. The rays are bent away from the normal as they enter the air. The brain, assuming that the light travels in straight lines, tells us that the tip of the oar is at O′. Notice that the paddle appears both shallower and displaced horizontally.

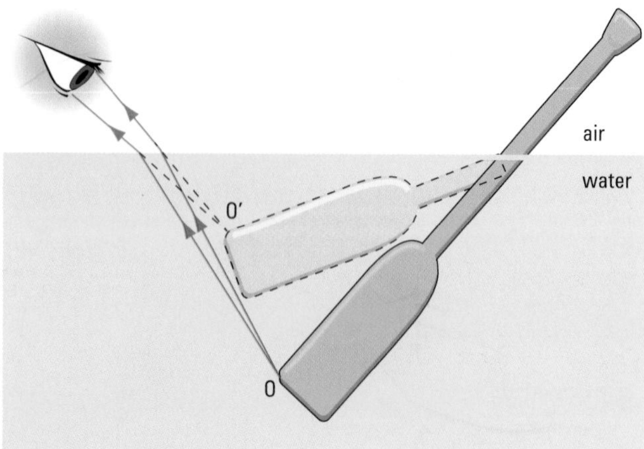

FIGURE 10.18 Refraction explains the apparent bending of a paddle partly submerged in water.

It is difficult to determine the position of the submerged tip of the paddle when viewed from the side; the mathematics is complicated. The case where the object is viewed from directly above is much simpler. When the observer is directly above the submerged object, the apparent depth d' is related to the actual depth d by the equation:

$$d' = d\,\frac{n_2}{n_1}$$

where n_1 is the refractive index of the medium in which the object is located (e.g. water), and n_2 is the refractive index of the medium in which the observer is located (e.g. air).

Exploration Using a Graphing Calculator

Graph the equation for apparent depth on the graphing calculator. Plot apparent depth d' on the y-axis (with a range 0 cm to 20 cm) and the refractive index of the medium in which the object is located n_1 on the x-axis. Assume the observer is located in air and the actual depth of the object is 10 cm.

Discussion

1. a) Describe the shape of the curve.
   b) What relationship exists between apparent depth d' and the refractive index of the material in which the object is immersed n_1?
   c) As the refractive index increases what happens to apparent depth?
2. Use the graph to determine the apparent depth for an object viewed from air that is immersed 20 cm below the surface of the following materials? Refer to Table 10.2 for refractive index values.
   a) water
   b) glycerin
   c) light flint glass
   d) zircon
   e) diamond

Discovering Physics — *Determining Refractive Index by Measuring Apparent Depth*

Try this experiment to investigate the relationship between depth and refraction.

1. Place a transparency containing the equation $n_1 = n_2 \frac{d}{d'}$ on the stage of the overhead projector.
2. Adjust the overhead to focus the image of the equation on the screen.
3. Mark the location of the head of the overhead on the vertical adjustment rod using a water-soluble pen.
4. Place two or three 1-cm thick glass plates over the transparency, as shown in Figure 10.19.
5. Refocus the image of the equation on the screen, and mark the new location of the head on the vertical adjustment arm.
6. Measure the thickness of the plates, and call this the actual depth d.
7. Measure the distance between the markings on the adjustment rod, and subtract this from the actual depth to get the apparent depth d'.
8. Determine the index of refraction of the glass making up the plates using the relationship on the transparency
   $$n_1 = n_2 \frac{d}{d'}$$

- What value did you use for n_1?
- What did you get for the refractive index of glass?
- What are some sources of error in this activity?

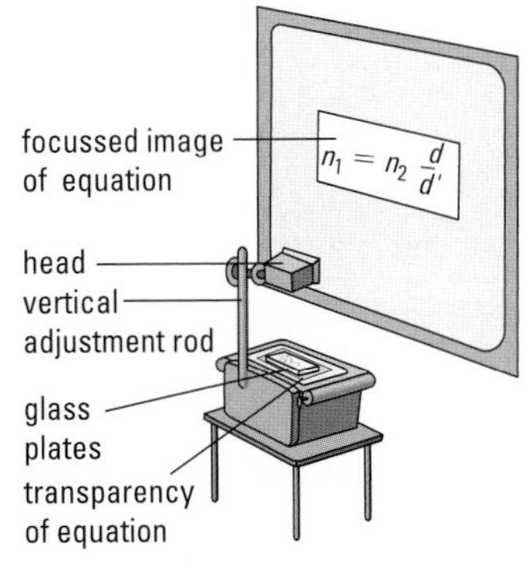

FIGURE 10.19

EXAMPLE 5 NUMERICAL

A goldfish is located 10 cm below the surface of the water in an aquarium. How deep does the goldfish appear to be when viewed from directly above?

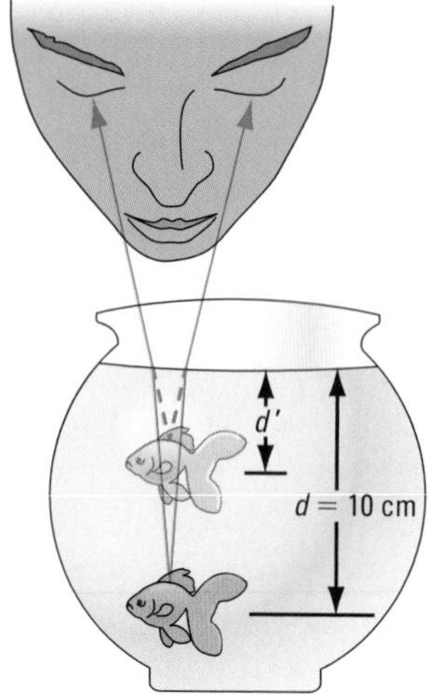

FIGURE 10.20

Given
$d = 10$ cm

Required
d'

Analysis

- Light rays are travelling from the fish to the observer.
- The incident ray is coming from the fish under water. From Table 10.2, $n_1 = 1.33$
- The refracted ray is in the air ($n_2 = 1.00$).
- Use the equation for apparent depth.

Solution

$$d' = d\frac{n_2}{n_1}$$
$$= 10 \text{ cm } \frac{1.00}{1.33}$$
$$= 7.5 \text{ cm}$$

Statement
To the observer, the goldfish appears to be 7.5 cm below the water.

INSIGHT

Remember that n_1 is the refractive index of the object's medium and n_2 is the refractive index of the observer's medium.

PRACTICE PROBLEMS

1. A small perch when viewed from directly above, appears to be 9.0 cm below the surface of a lake. What is the actual depth of the perch?
2. An object immersed in an unknown liquid to a depth of 15 cm appears to be 10 cm below the surface when viewed from directly above. What is the refractive index of the unknown liquid?

For the same reason, a person's legs beneath the surface of a lake appear shorter than they really are when viewed from the air. Also, a stone on a riverbed appears closer to the surface than it really is. When canoeing in shallow water, have you ever looked down, expecting to scrape the bottom of the canoe on a rock and glided right over it?

Apparent Height

The example that follows describes what a viewer in a higher refractive medium sees when viewing an object located in a lower refractive index medium. For example, what will the goldfish see when a person is holding a piece of fish food 10 cm above the surface of the water? Do you think the food will appear closer, at the same place, or farther away than 10 cm from the surface?

EXAMPLE 6 CONCEPTUAL

The piece of fish food is located in air 10 cm above the water. Air has a lower refractive index than water. Where will the submerged goldfish think the food is located?

Reasoning and Solution
Figure 10.21 shows the apparent height of the fish food above the surface of the water. The fish food appears to be farther above the surface than it really is. To see why, consider two diverging rays leaving the fish food incident on the surface of the water. They are travelling from a lower refractive medium, air, to a higher refractive medium, water. Both rays will bend toward the normals at the interface. By extending the two diverging refracted rays back into air (dotted lines) you can determine where they intersect. This is the location of the virtual image of the fish food. It is above the actual height. The goldfish will see the food farther above the surface than it really is.

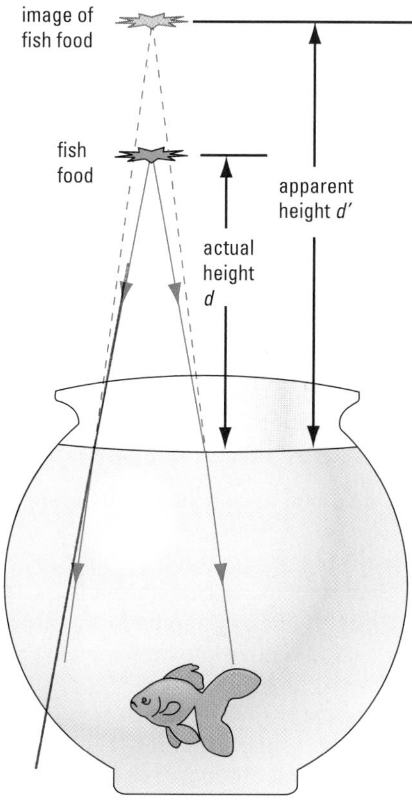

FIGURE 10.21 Where the fish sees the fish food (not to scale)

CHALLENGE

A mosquito is hovering 6.0 cm above the surface of a lake directly above a waiting perch. At what height above the surface will the submerged perch think the mosquito is located? Explain your answer.

INFOBIT

We are able to see the Sun before it rises above the horizon in the morning and after it sets at night. Light from the Sun enters Earth's atmosphere from the vacuum of outer space. The light is refracted toward Earth because of the difference in the densities of the atmosphere and the vacuum of space. The light is continually refracted and curves, as shown in Figure 10.22. Astronomers have to take refraction into account when recording sightings of stars, especially near the horizon.

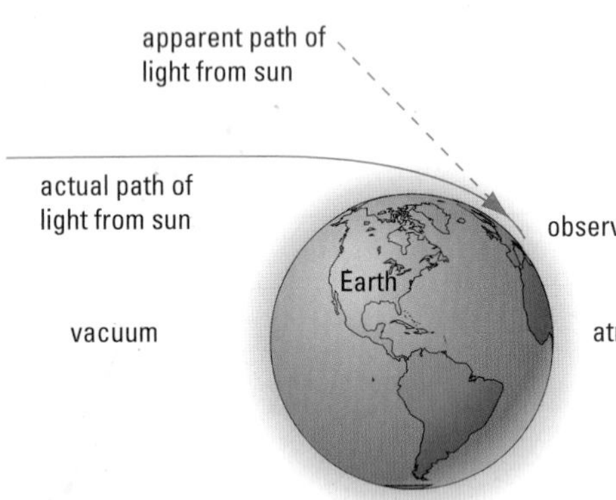

FIGURE 10.23 We can see the Sun when it is below the horizon because the atmosphere refracts the incoming light. (Bending not to scale.)

Exploration Using a Graphing Calculator

Suppose an attendant feeding goldfish lowers the fish food gradually from a height of 20 cm above the water until it touches the surface. Graph the equation for apparent height against actual height on the graphing calculator for this situation. Read from the graph apparent height values for various actual height values.

Discussion

1. a) Describe the shape of the curve.
   b) What relationship exists between apparent height h' and actual height h?
   c) If the actual height doubles, what happens to the apparent height?
2. Use the graph to determine the apparent height of the fish food located in air viewed by the goldfish for the following actual heights.
   a) 20 cm
   b) 10 cm
   c) 5.0 cm
   d) 2.5 cm
   e) 0 cm

Discovering Physics — *Simulating Twinkling Stars*

Earth's atmosphere is continuously moving. This changes the density of air and the index of refraction for air at a specific location. The random bending of the light varies the intensity of the light reaching an observer. This makes a star look as though it is twinkling.

1. Use a nail to punch several small holes in the bottom of a cereal box.
2. Turn on a flashlight and place it inside the cereal box so it lights the holes.
3. Seal the box by closing the flaps.
4. Place the box at one end of a table.
5. Position a hot plate halfway along the table and turn it on.
6. Turn off the room lights.
7. View the brightly lit holes from a distance by looking through the region of warm air rising above the hot plate (Figure 10.23).
8. Describe and explain what you see.

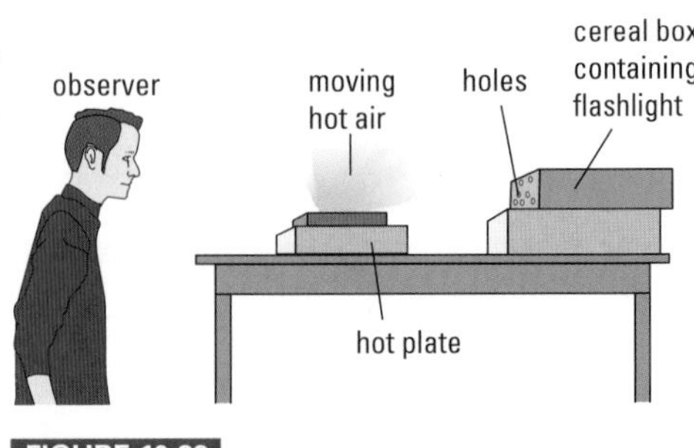

FIGURE 10.23

The Diver's Field of View

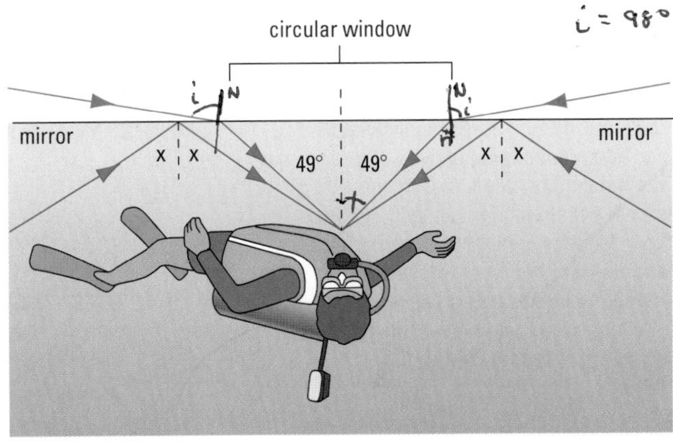

FIGURE 10.24 An underwater diver has a circular "window" to the region above the water and a "mirror" to the area beneath the water.

Figure 10.24 shows why a swimmer on her back sees the world above the water compressed into a circular "window." When the surface of the water is perfectly smooth, light that enters the water close to the horizon (at an angle of incidence of almost 90°) is then refracted through 49°. As a result, a cone of light with an angle at the apex of 98° reaches the diver. The light that enters the water with a small angle of incidence is distorted very little. However, light from the fringes produces distorted images. Remember, too, that objects in air viewed from under the water appear farther away than they really are.

Beyond the 98° cone, the surface acts like a plane mirror. The swimmer sees reflections of the bottom of the lake and immersed objects by internal reflection from the surface. Virtual images of objects under water appear suspended in space above the surface. At this location the surface is behaving exactly like a plane mirror.

Reflecting Prisms

Commercial mirrors are inefficient at reflecting light—they absorb about 10% of it. That is why the rear image you see in a clothing store mirror is dimmer than the front image. To overcome this problem, two 45° glass prisms, mounted as shown in Figure 10.26, are used to act as near-perfect reflectors in a periscope. When the periscope is being used in dim light, it is important that as much light as possible reaches the eye. Light enters and leaves each prism without being refracted. The critical angle for ordinary glass is about 42°, so all the light falling on the back of the prism at 45° is internally reflected. The image of the object seen through the prisms is clear and erect. Internally reflecting prisms are also used in binoculars to increase the

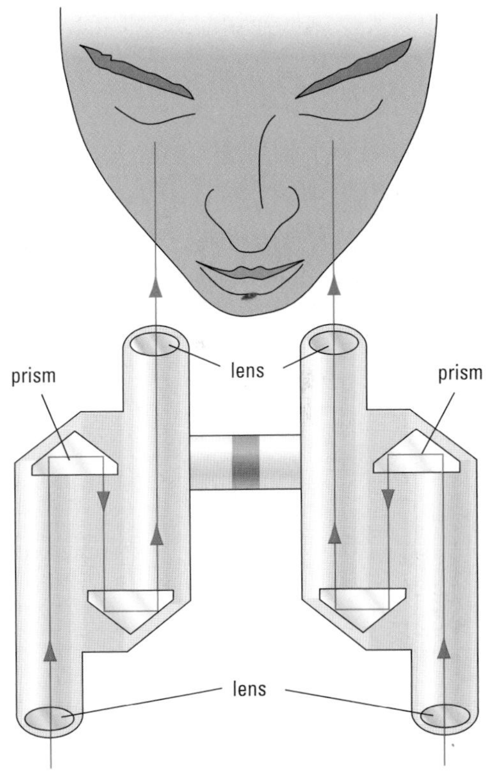

FIGURE 10.25 How light rays are reflected by prisms in binoculars. What function do the prisms serve here?

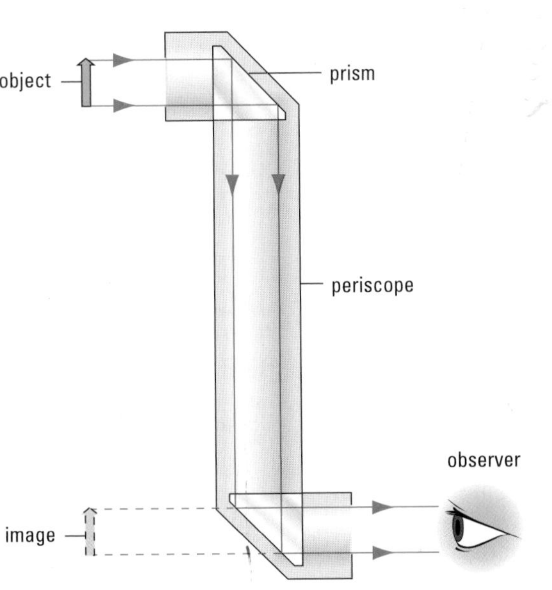

FIGURE 10.26 The 45° prisms in a periscope reflect light through 90°. The image is erect. Why?

WEBLINK

Diamonds are a valuable natural resource. They increase employment because people are involved at the mining, cutting, and sales stages. Where are diamonds found in Canada? How are they mined? Where and how are they cut and what roles does the jeweller play? Submit a sequence chart of your findings. Begin your research at **www.pearsoned.ca/physics11.**

distance light travels between lenses (Figure 10.25). As well, prisms are used in periscopes and telescopes to change the direction of light and invert images as shown in Figure 10.27.

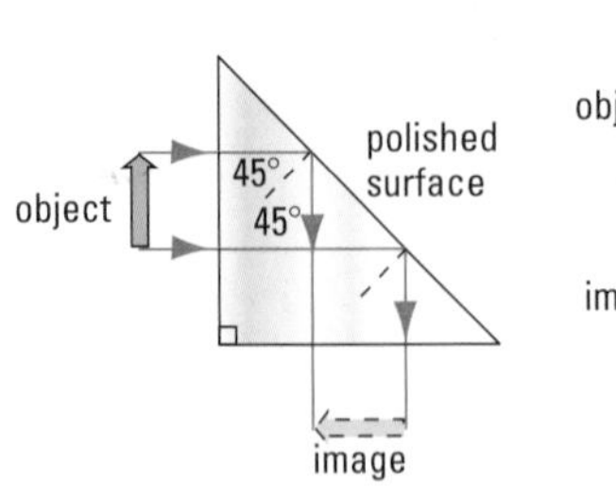

a) 90° change in direction

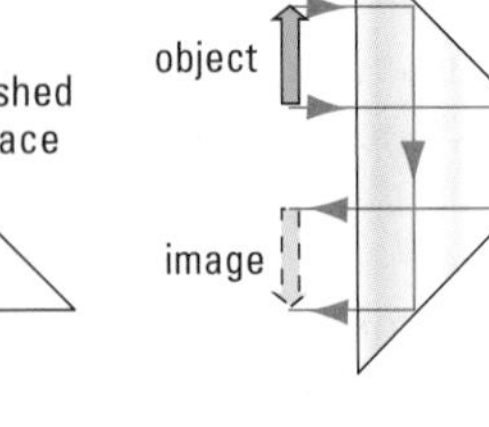

b) 180° change in direction and image inversion

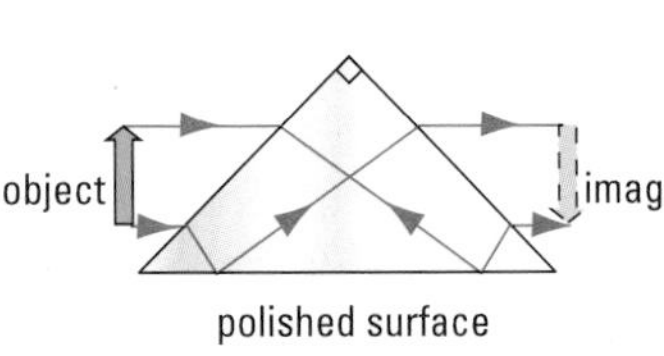

c) No change in direction, but image inversion

FIGURE 10.27 A 45°-45°-90° prism may be used to change the direction of light rays or to invert images by total internal reflection.

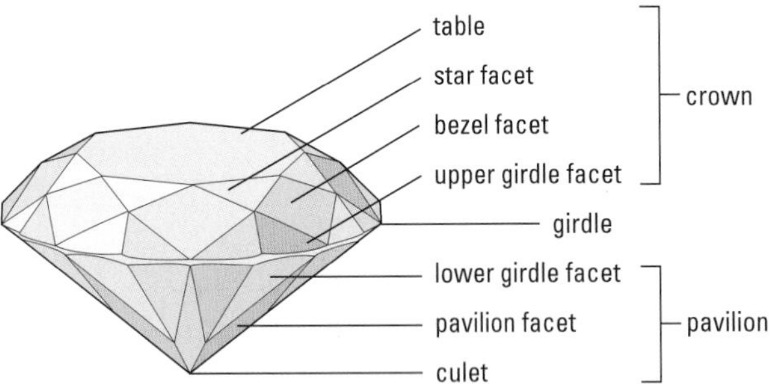

a) The different facets of a round brilliant cut diamond

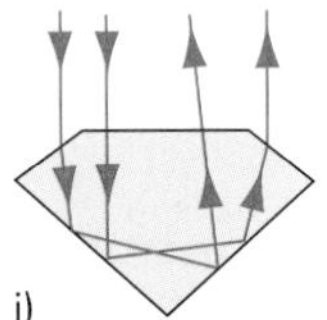

i)

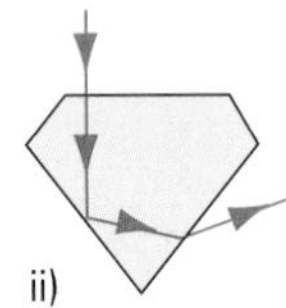

ii)

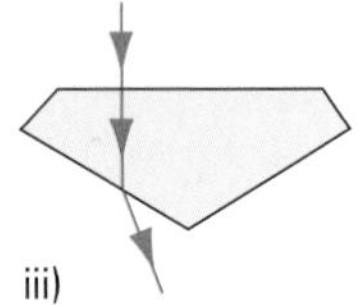

iii)

b) How the cut of a diamond affects the reflection of light

Sparkling Diamonds

A skilled diamond cutter carefully cuts the diamond to produce 58 facets, some of which are shown in Figure 10.28a). This allows the maximum number of reflections to occur before the light finally emerges through the crown. The index of refraction of diamond is large (2.42), so diamond has a small critical angle (24.5°). If a diamond is cut correctly, light that enters through the crown is either partially or totally internally reflected a number of times as Figure 10.28b)i) shows. The variation in intensity, and the dispersion of the light that eventually leaves the diamond, cause the brilliance, sparkle, and flashes of bright colours.

FIGURE 10.28 The cut is the key factor that enables one diamond to internally reflect more light than another. When the diamond is cut to good proportions, as in i), light is internally reflected from one facet to another and then is dispersed through the top. When the diamond is cut too deep or too shallow, the light escapes from the pavilion facets, as shown in ii) and iii) (Source: Gemology Institute of America)

The Invention of the "Photophone"

In 1880, Alexander Graham Bell invented the "photophone" which used a narrow sunbeam to transmit voices a short distance. The voice was projected toward a mechanism that vibrated a mirror. Sunlight was directed onto the mirror, which reflected a vibrating beam of sunlight to a nearby receiving device. A detector, then, picked up the vibrating beam and decoded it back into a voice signal. Unfavourable weather conditions would make the photophone impractical for long-distance communication. The photophone was set aside because Bell's other invention, the telephone, was considered more promising. Light signal transmission has become practical today due to advances in laser and glass-fibre technology.

Fibre Optics

Total internal reflection is the principle behind fibre optics. Figure 10.29 shows light undergoing multiple internal reflections as it travels through a curved fibre. Special plastic and glass fibres a few micrometres in diameter have been developed to transmit light from one place to another. A bundle of these fibres is called a light pipe. Light can be transmitted through a light pipe for several kilometres with little loss in intensity. Light pipes can be used to illuminate inaccessible places, to transmit telephone calls and other modulated signals, and to carry out internal examinations of the body. The finer the fibres and the greater their number, the clearer and more detailed the image being transmitted. A cable containing many small fibres is shown in Figure 10.30.

INFOBIT

Confederation Bridge is 13 km long and links New Brunswick with P.E.I. During construction, a network of fibre-optic cables and sensors was embedded in the concrete beams of a 60-m stretch at the centre of the bridge—the section subjected to the most pressure and strain. The fibre-optic sensors continuously monitor wind, ice, and traffic loads, alerting engineers to structural weaknesses before they become dangerous. Thanks to fibre-optic technology, 14 structures (including bridges, highways, and buildings) in 7 provinces now "communicate" with engineers.

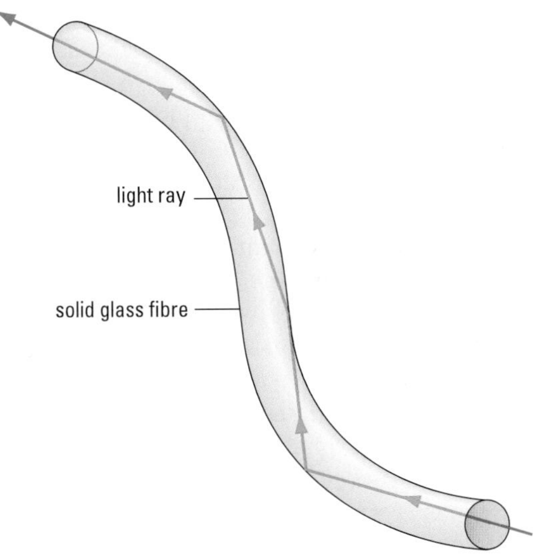

FIGURE 10.29 A light pipe can bend light around corners with little loss in energy. It is important that no scratches occur on the surface of the pipe. Why?

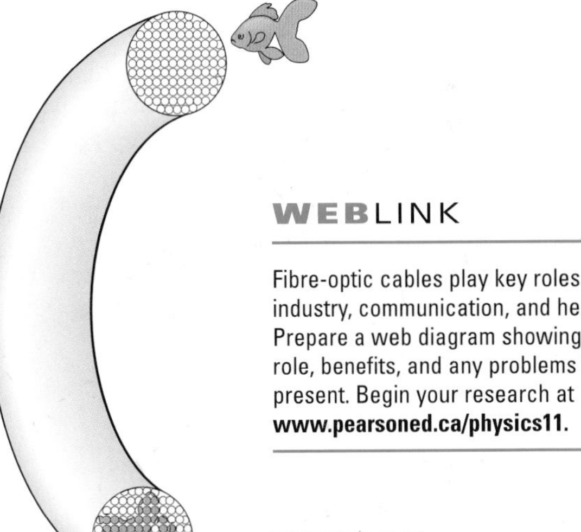

WEBLINK

Fibre-optic cables play key roles in industry, communication, and health. Prepare a web diagram showing their role, benefits, and any problems they present. Begin your research at **www.pearsoned.ca/physics11.**

FIGURE 10.30 The smaller the diameter of the fibres and the more fibres in a pipe, the clearer the image of the object at the other end of the pipe.

A glass envelope called the "cladding" raises the outside diameter of the fibre-optic cable to about two-hairs thick. The cladding keeps the value of the critical angle constant throughout the length of the fibre. Optical fibres are transparent. The glass fibre confines the light beams to a narrow core region as shown in Figure 10.31. The beams shoot down the fibre by repeatedly bouncing off the glassy walls, even when the strands bend around corners with large radii. The more the waves zigzag, the longer it takes them to travel the length of a fibre. More oblique rays travel a shorter distance and hence take a shorter time.

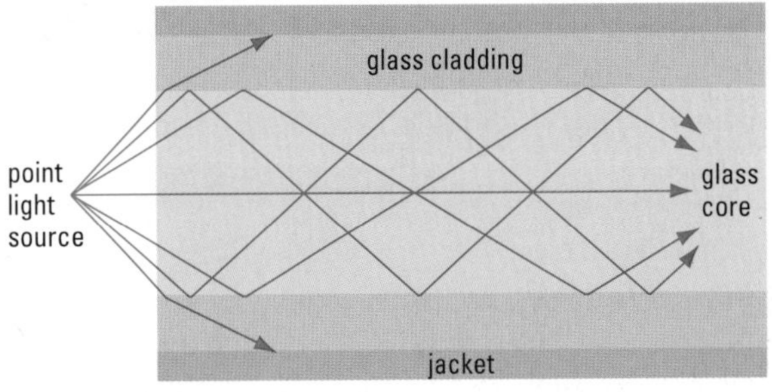

FIGURE 10.31 The basics of a fibre-optics cable. Notice that some rays zigzag more than others.

Applications of Fibre Optics

Decision-Making Skills

- Defining the Issue
- Developing Assessment Criteria
- Researching the Issue
- Analyzing Data and Information
- Proposing a Course of Action
- Justifying the Course of Action
- Communicating Your Proposal

BACKGROUND INFORMATION

Fibre Optics and Communication

Optical fibres have several advantages over traditional copper cables. The optical fibres can be routed safely through explosives or flammable atmospheres without risk of ignition. They are over 4× stronger than copper and carry signals with much less energy loss. On average a copper wire signal must be repeated every 1.5 km to keep the signal from deteriorating. Optical fibre signals can go about 100 km between repeaters. Glass fibres deliver a clean signal because they are immune to electromagnetic interference, jamming, and signal leaking. They also prevent eavesdropping.

Fibre optics integrates several separate industries: telephone, cable TV, local area networks, submarine cables, and utilities. Unlike electrical signals on a copper cable, light waves can pass right through one another without affecting each other. As a result, many kinds of information can be sent simultaneously along one fibre-optic line—even 3-D images (holograms) can be transmitted.

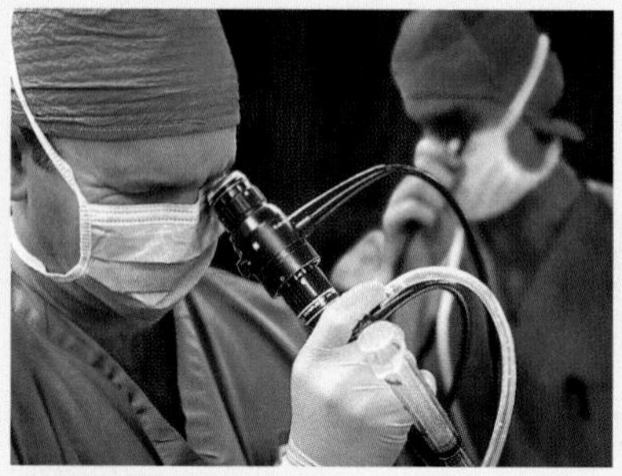

FIGURE 10.32 A fibre-optics imaging system

Fibre Optics and Medicine

Optical fibres are finding increasing use as sensors in medicine. Gas concentration, chemical concentration, pressure, and temperature can all be sensed with optical fibres. For example, they can be used to measure specific components of blood such as cholesterol, urea, and glucose. The concentrations of these chemicals are important to physicians in the diagnosis and monitoring of certain disease conditions.

Optical fibres can also be used for medical imaging. The tiny, flexible fibres can be inserted into areas of the body unreachable by other means. Figure 10.32 shows a bronchoscope being used. This kind of endoscope is inserted through the nose, down the bronchial tubes, and into the lungs.

Some of the most important applications of fibre optics are in laser surgery. Laser light transmitted through the fibres can be used to cauterize blood vessels and incisions to stop bleeding. Many applications of fibre optics do not require anesthesia. This lowers the risk of medical complications, as well as the cost.

Analyzing the Issue

1. Draw a consequence map to show the social, political, economic, and environmental impacts of fibre-optic technology.
2. Research applications of fibre optics using journals, articles, the Internet, and other electronic resources. Identify what you believe are the most significant applications. Explain.
3. Fibre optics has revolutionized the speed of communication. Evaluate how speed of communication has affected the scientific community. Identify two possible advantages and two disadvantages to this quick information access.
4. Personal information is more and more accessible as the number of individuals using the World Wide Web continues to grow. Describe the factors individuals should consider before placing any personal information on the Internet.
5. In your opinion, should the downloading of information and music from the World Wide Web be free?
6. Prepare a multimedia presentation to demonstrate how communication has changed with the development of fiber-optics. Predict how fibre optics will affect the future and what additional issues will exist relating to the applications of fibre optics

Section 10.4 Review

Understanding Concepts

1. Explain the conditions required for total internal reflection.
2. A lake trout is located 80 cm below the surface of the water. A mayfly hovers over the trout 20 cm above the surface.
   a) How deep does the trout appear to the mayfly?
   b) How far above the water does the mayfly appear to the trout?
3. A hiker sees a mirage of trees in the sky. Draw a diagram to show how this is possible. Label the different air temperature regions very carefully.

Applying Inquiry/ Communication Skills

4. Using the Internet and other electronic resources, write a paragraph explaining how total internal reflection is used in communication. List at least four advantages of fibre-optic cables over copper cables.

Making Connections

5. What impact has fibre-optic technology had on society so far? How do you think that will change in the future?

10.5 The Composition of White Light

Key Understandings

When you have completed this section, you will be able to:

- define spectrum, dispersion, and recomposition
- explain the effects of prisms on light
- describe optical effects that occur as natural phenomena, such as rainbows, based on the scientific model for light

A pendant made of diamonds produces brilliantly coloured images even though the diamond is clear. And when viewed under white light, the light that emerges from the surface of the diamond often sparkles with many different colours. Do diamonds add colour to the light, or is there something in the light that the diamond makes visible?

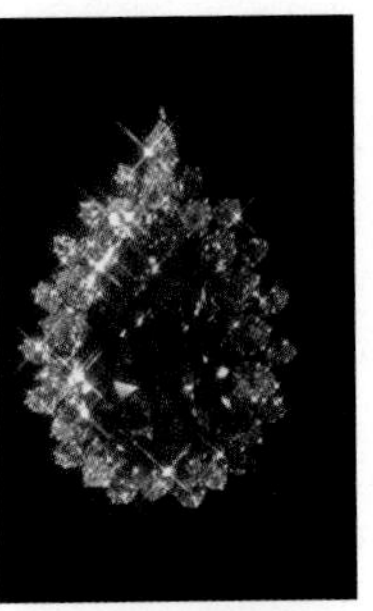

FIGURE 10.33 Cut glass can produce images with brilliant colours.

Newton's Prism Experiment

The early telescopes of the sixteenth century produced images with coloured fringes. People at the time believed that the colours were added to the white light by the telescope. However, an experiment using prisms, performed by Newton in 1666, proved otherwise.

Newton's source of white light was a beam of sunlight streaming through a circular hole in a window shutter. He put a triangular prism in the path of the light and allowed the emerging beam to fall on the wall opposite the window. The image of the hole appeared as an elongated band of colours that he called a **spectrum**. The apparatus for producing a

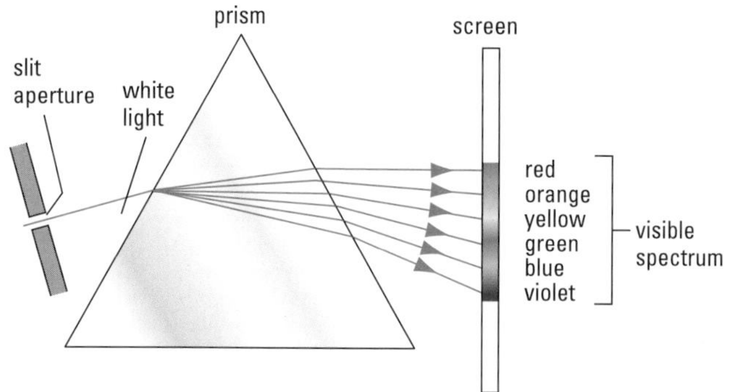

FIGURE 10.34 Dispersion of white light into a spectrum by a prism

spectrum is shown in Figure 10.34. A complete spectrum is shown in Figure 10.35. The spectrum consisted of the colours red, orange, yellow, green, blue, and violet merging into one another like the colours of the rainbow. Newton set out to determine if these colours were added to white light by the prism, or if white light was composed of these colours and the prism just separates them out. He made monochromatic light, such as red, by blocking out all other colours. The red light was then passed through another prism. The monochromatic light was farther spread out, but no new colours appeared.

FIGURE 10.35 The complete spectrum of white light

TABLE 10.5 Colours and Wavelengths of the Visible Spectrum

Colour	Wavelength λ (nm)
ultraviolet B	280–320
ultraviolet A	320–400
violet	400–450
blue	450–500
green	500–570
yellow	570–590
orange	590–610
red	610–750
infrared	> 750

Newton then reversed the second prism and allowed all of the colours from the first prism to pass through it. The spectrum, disappeared and a white image of the hole took its place. From these results, he reasoned that white light is composed of all the colours of the spectrum, and a prism just separates these colours from one another. He called the separation of white light into its composite colours **dispersion**.

The process of recombining the colours of the spectrum to form white light is called **recomposition**. Recomposition can be achieved by using a second reversed prism, a converging lens, or a converging mirror, as shown in Figure 10.36.

The wavelengths of the visible spectrum are shown in Table 10.5. The visible spectrum ranges from about 400 nm in the deep violet to about 750 nm in the deep red. Invisible ultraviolet extends from 280 nm to 400 nm, and invisible infrared has wavelengths longer than red light.

White light is refracted when it passes through a prism. As shown in Figure 10.34, the different colours making up white light are refracted by different amounts. Red is refracted the least and violet the most, with the other colours arranged in between. All colours of light travel at the same speed in a vacuum. However, violet light, because of its shorter wavelength (see Table 10.5) or higher frequency, travels more slowly in glass than red light. The shorter the wavelength or the higher the frequency of a wave, the slower it travels in a refractive medium. As a result, violet light slows down the most and is deviated the most on entering the prism. It also speeds up the most on returning to air at the second surface. Because of the shape of the prism, the different colours are farther dispersed at the second surface.

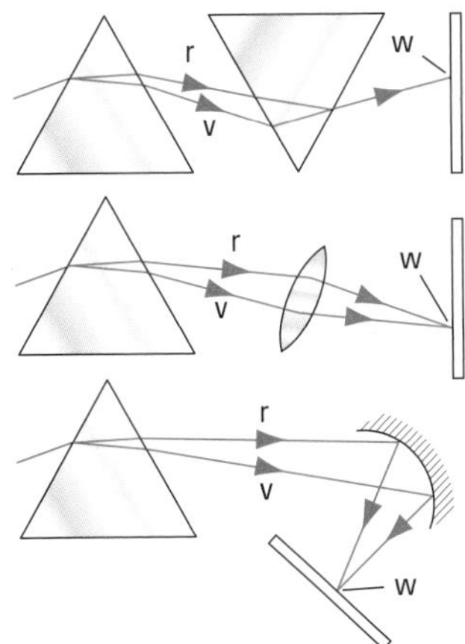

FIGURE 10.36 Three ways to recombine a complete spectrum using: i) a second reversed prism, ii) a converging lens, and iii) a converging mirror

Rainbows

A rainbow (Figure 10.37) is produced as a result of the dispersion of sunlight by tiny droplets of water in the atmosphere. The line between the observer and the top of the arc of a primary rainbow makes an angle of about 42° with the horizon, as shown in Figure 10.38. When you see a rainbow, the sunlight usually comes from behind you.

WEBLINK

Coloured transparent objects are called filters. Filters selectively absorb some wavelengths from the electromagnetic spectrum, and reflect or transmit others. Sunglasses and designed to absorb a specific range of colours and let others pass. Learn more about sunglasses and how some sunglasses are designed to protect the human eye from ultraviolet A and B radiation. Submit an agree/disagree chart concerning the need to wear sunglasses. Begin your research at **www.pearsoned.ca/physics11.**

FIGURE 10.37 A primary and a secondary rainbow

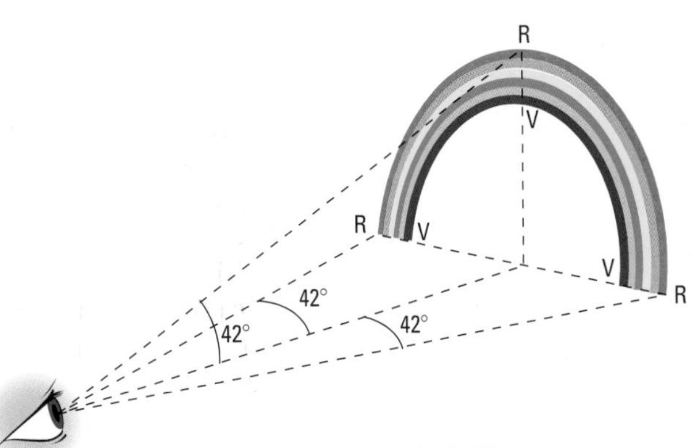

FIGURE 10.38 In the primary rainbow, red is on the outside and violet is on the inside of the rainbow. In the secondary rainbow the sequence is reversed.

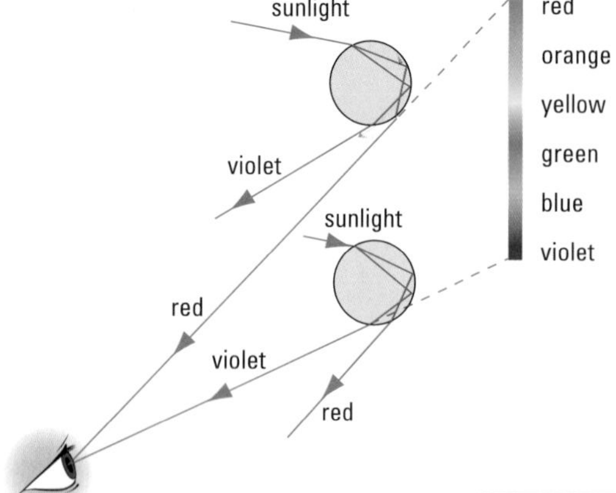

FIGURE 10.39 The red ray from the top drop and the violet ray from the bottom drop are seen by the observer. Intermediate colours from other drops are not shown. (The drops of water are not drawn to scale.)

Figure 10.39 shows how parallel rays of sunlight are refracted and dispersed at the surfaces of the water drops, and how the rays are reflected from the back surfaces to produce the different coloured bands of the primary rainbow. White light enters near the top of each drop. The red component is refracted the least and violet the most. Hence, red light reaches the observer's eye from water droplets at a greater angle above the horizon than violet light. Thus, the outside of the rainbow is red and the inside violet, with the other colours ordered in between. The secondary rainbow is formed by light that enters near the bottom of the droplets and undergoes two internal reflections before emerging.

Discovering Physics — *A Test Tube Rainbow*

Create your own indoor rainbow with water, a test tube, and a slide projector.

1. Make a slide with a vertical slit 2 mm wide from a piece of cardboard.
2. Insert the slide into a slide projector and shine light through it toward a vertical 2-cm diameter test tube filled with water as shown in Figure 10.40.
3. Adjust the position of the set-up until light is totally reflected within the water and exits out of the front surface at an angle of about 42° to the incident beam.
4. Catch the light on a white screen and tilt the screen to spread the spectrum out.
   - Compare the sequence of the colours with the sequence in a primary rainbow.
   - Which colour is nearest the incident beam and which colour is farthest away?
   - Use a protractor to measure the angle between the incident beam and the emergent coloured beam. Is it 42°?

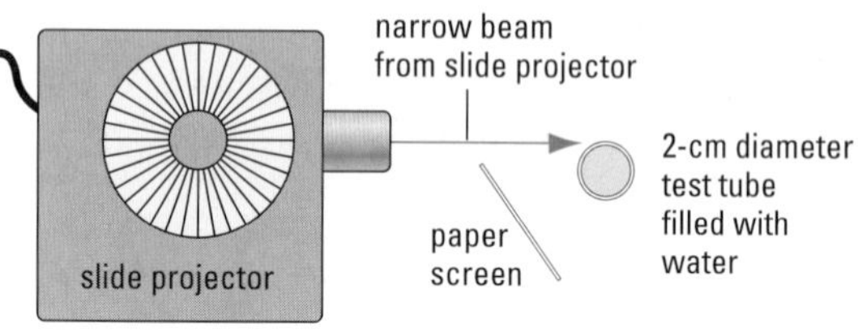

FIGURE 10.40 Set-up for demonstrating rainbow colours caused by total internal reflection

Section 10.5 Review

Understanding Concepts

1. Which colour is refracted the most and which the least when white light is incident on a triangular prism?
2. Name the six main colours of the visible spectrum in order from shortest wavelength to longest.
3. Which colour is slowed down the least when white light enters a prism?
4. Distinguish between dispersion and recomposition.
5. Explain the formation of a primary rainbow.
6. Describe three ways to recombine the visible spectrum into white light.

Investigation 1 (Section 10.2)

Inquiry Skills

- Initiating and Planning
- Applying Technical Skills
- Using Tools, Materials, Equipment
- Conducting and Recording
- Analyzing and Interpreting
- Concluding and Communicating

Refraction of Light

If the angle of incidence *i* changes from 20° to 40°, will the angle of refraction *R* double or change in some other way? Make a hypothesis, and then do the activity to test your hypothesis.

Problem

What relationship exists between *i* and *R* when light travels from a less refractive to a more refractive medium?

Materials

- polar coordinate paper
- rectangular graph paper
- liquid
- ray box (single slit)
- semicircular plastic dish

Procedure

1. Design a spreadsheet with the headings: angle of incidence *i*, angle of refraction *R*, *i*/*R*, sin *i*, sin *R*, sin *i*/sin *R*.
2. Half fill the plastic dish with a liquid. Place the dish on the polar coordinate paper so that the 0–180° line acts as the normal and passes through the centre of the flat surface, as shown in Figure 10.41.
3. Direct a single ray of light along the normal toward the flat surface. Record the angle of refraction.
4. Record the angles of refraction for angles of incidence of 10° to 70°, in steps of 10°.
5. Plot a graph of *i* against *R*.
6. Plot a graph of sin *i* against sin *R*. Calculate the slope of the graph.

Analyzing and Interpreting

1. a) Describe the graph of *i* against *R*. Is it a straight line?
   b) How did the ratio *i*/*R* change as the angle of incidence increased?
2. a) Describe the graph of sin *i* against sin *R*.
   b) What is the value of the slope?
3. What happened to the ratio sin *i*/sin *R* as *i* increased. Compare this with the slope of the sin *i* against sin *R* graph.

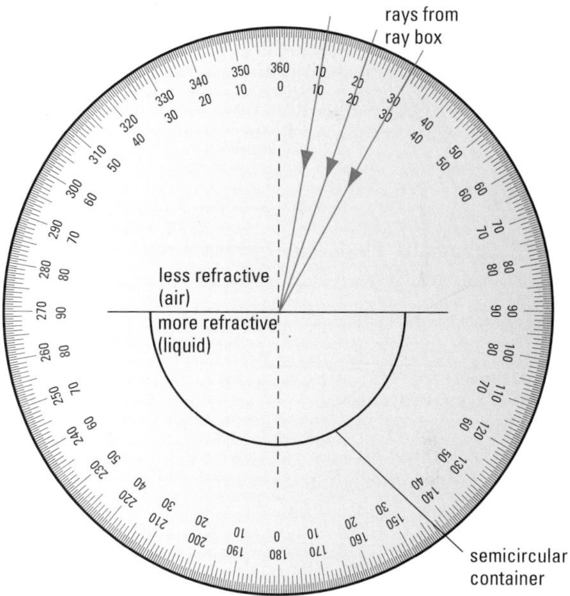

FIGURE 10.41 Refraction of light from a less refractive to a more refractive medium

Concluding and Communicating

4. Write an equation to describe the relationship between sin *i* and sin *R* for your liquid.
5. Is the bending of light as it goes from air to plastic and then from plastic to liquid a significant source of error in the experiment? Discuss.
6. Why is it important to shine the ray at the centre of the flat surface of the dish?

Extending

7. How do you think the ratio sin *i*/sin *R* will compare for different materials? Make a prediction. If you have time, repeat the whole experiment using either a different liquid in the semicircular dish or a glass block in the shape of a semicircle.

Investigation 2 (Section 10.3)

Inquiry Skills

- Initiating and Planning
- Applying Technical Skills
- Using Tools, Materials, Equipment
- Conducting and Recording
- Analyzing and Interpreting
- Concluding and Communicating

Determining Critical Angle

Light incident on a surface at a 90° angle does not bend. In this activity, you direct a ray of light at 90° to the curved surface of a more refractive medium. Then you observe the path that light takes as it travels from the more refractive to the less refractive medium through the flat surface on the other side.

Problem

What happens to the path of light when it travels from a more refractive to a less refractive medium at an oblique angle?

Materials

- liquid
- ray box (single slit)
- polar coordinate paper
- semicircular plastic dish

Experimental Design

1. Design and implement a procedure using a semicircular container to determine the angles of refraction corresponding to various angles of incidence for light travelling from a more refractive medium to a less refractive medium as shown in Figure 10.42.
2. Create a data table to record your measurements.
3. Note the angle of incidence for which the angle of refraction equals 90°
4. Find and record the sines of the angles of incidence and refraction.
5. Calculate the ratios $\sin i / \sin R$ for all angles at which refraction occurs.

Analyzing and Interpreting

1. How does the ratio $\sin i / \sin R$, travelling from a more refractive to a less refractive material, compare with the ratio $\sin i / \sin R$, travelling from a less refractive to a more refractive material? (Refer to your data from Investigation 1.)
2. What happened to the amount of incident light reflected as the angle of incidence increased?
3. Above what angle of incidence was all the light reflected? This is called the critical angle.

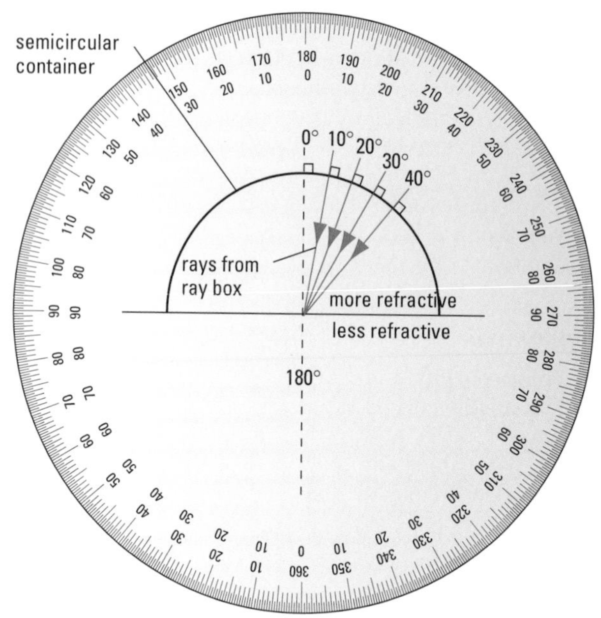

FIGURE 10.42 Refraction of light from a more refractive to a less refractive medium

Concluding and Communicating

4. Why is the light not refracted when it travels from air into the liquid at the curved surface of the dish?
5. Why is it important to shine the ray from the curved side of the dish toward the centre of the flat surface?

Extending

7. How do you think the critical angle will compare for different materials? Make a prediction. If you have time, repeat the experiment using either a different liquid in the semicircular dish, or a glass block in the shape of a semicircle.

CHAPTER SUMMARY

Key Terms

angle of incidence
angle of refraction
critical angle
dispersion
incident ray
index of refraction
laws of refraction
partial reflection
recomposition
refracted ray
refraction
Snell's law
spectrum
total internal reflection

Key Equations

$$n = \frac{c}{v}$$

$$n_1 \sin \theta_1 = n_2 \sin \theta_2$$

$$\sin \theta_c = \frac{n_2}{n_1}$$

$$d' = d \frac{n_2}{n_1}$$

Essential Understandings

- Visible light is only a small part of the electromagnetic spectrum.
- The speed of all electromagnetic waves is the same in a vacuum.
- Snell's law predicts the bending of light as it passes from one medium to another.
- Electromagnetic waves travel more slowly in a material medium than in a vacuum.
- The more refractive a medium, the slower the light travels in it.
- The index of refraction is the ratio of the speed of light in a vacuum to the speed of light in a material medium. Light of different wavelengths has different indexes of refraction in the same medium.
- Refraction is the bending of light at the boundary between two different media. Light bends toward the normal when travelling from a less refractive to a more refractive medium, and away from the normal when travelling in the opposite direction.
- The ratio of the sines of the angles of incidence and refraction is equal to the ratio of the speed of light in the two media.
- The constant is the same as the index of refraction. It is also equal to the slope of the graph of sin i against sin R.
- The second law of refraction states that the incident ray, refracted ray, and normal are all in the same plane.
- The critical angle is the angle of incidence in a more refractive medium that results in an angle of refraction of 90° in a less refractive medium.
- Light is totally internally reflected when the angle of incidence in the more refractive medium is larger than the critical angle.
- The separation of white light into its colours is called dispersion. White light is composed of the spectral colours red, orange, yellow, green, blue, and violet.
- Dispersion is caused by the different speeds of differently coloured light in a material medium.

Consolidate Your Understanding

1. Look back to your answer for the Checkpoint on page 363. What answer would you give now? Explain why each of the other answers is incorrect.
2. An experimenter directs identical rays of light from air at the same oblique angle toward identical thick glass horizontal plates. One plate is immersed in water and the other in air. How will the angle of refraction compare in the two plates? Explain your answer with the aid of a diagram and Snell's law.
3. Create a concept map to be used as a study map for refraction and total internal reflection. Consult the Key Terms above, and include as many terms as possible in your concept map. Include two key equations and an example problem involving both. Show a model solution using the GRASS strategy.
4. When looking up, a fish sees a mayfly skimming along the surface of a smooth lake as well as another fish, normally obscured from view, swimming behind a nearby boulder. Draw a diagram and use it and the concepts of refraction and reflection to explain these two observations. Share your explanations with a peer.

CHAPTER 10 REVIEW

Understanding Concepts

(Use $c = 3.0 \times 10^8$ m/s unless otherwise stated. Look up the necessary indexes of refraction in Table 10.2.)

1. A ray of sodium yellow light travelling through air enters water at an oblique angle. The light will
   a) slow down and bend toward the normal
   b) slow down and bend away from the normal
   c) speed up and bend toward the normal
   d) speed up and bend away from the normal
   e) maintain the same speed and bend toward the normal

2. The path of a light ray travelling from water to air is shown in Figure 10.43. The angle of refraction is
   a) AOE b) AOC c) AOB
   d) BOD e) BOF

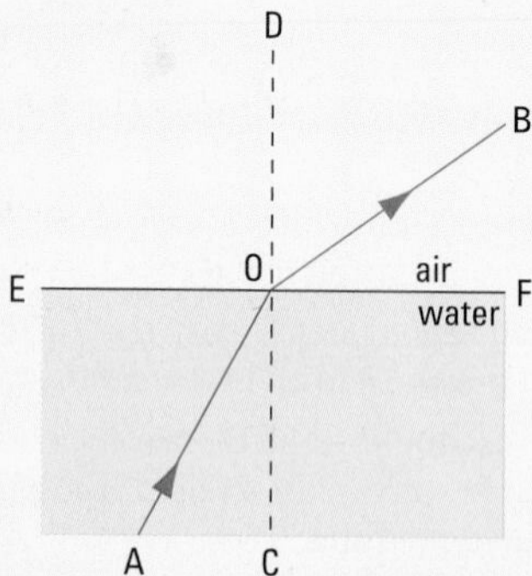

FIGURE 10.43

3. Figure 10.44 shows a ray of light travelling from a medium having an index of refraction n_1 to a medium having an index of refraction n_2.

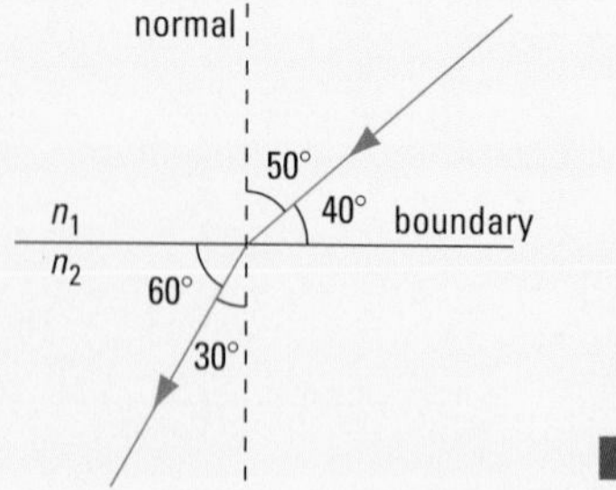

FIGURE 10.44

What is the correct expression for finding n_2?
   a) n_1 (50°/30°)
   b) n_1 (30°/50°)
   c) n_1 (sin 50°/sin 30°)
   d) n_1 sin (30°/sin 50°)
   e) n_1 sin (40°/sin 60°)

4. The critical angle for water is 49°. Total internal reflection occurs when light is incident on
   a) the air-to-water interface at an angle of incidence of 49°
   b) the air-to-water interface at an angle of incidence less than 49°
   c) the air-to-water interface at an angle of incidence greater than 49°
   d) the water-to-air interface at an angle of incidence less than 49°
   e) the water-to-air interface at an angle of incidence greater than 49°

5. In calculations involving refractive index and depth, the true depth is d, the apparent depth is d', the refractive index of the observer's medium is n_2, and the index of refraction of the object's medium is n_1. What is the correct expression for determining the refractive index of the object's medium?
   a) $n_1 = \frac{d}{d'}n_2$ b) $n_1 = \frac{d'}{dn_2}$
   c) $n_1 = \frac{d}{d'n_2}$ d) $n_1 = \frac{d'n_2}{d}$
   e) $n_1 = d'dn_2$

6. Describe the changes in the following properties of a light wave as it travels from air into glass:
   a) speed
   b) frequency
   c) wavelength

7. You observe that when a light ray enters liquid A from water it bends toward the normal. When it enters the same liquid from glycerin it bends away from the normal. What can you conclude about the refractive index of liquid A?

8. What is the angle of refraction in Lucite if the angle of incidence in air is 24° and the speed of light in Lucite is 1.97×10^8 m/s?

9. The speed of light in a material is 2.29×10^8 m/s. Calculate its index of refraction and use Table 10.2 to identify what the material might be.

10. Explain using one of the models of light, the shimmering of light above a black highway on a sunny day.

11. What is the speed of light in a medium if the angle of incidence in air is 50° and the angle of refraction is 42°?

12. The angle of incidence for light travelling from water to ice is 70°. Calculate the angle of refraction.

13. Two pulses are racing down an optical fibre. One is travelling at a speed of 1.9986×10^8 m/s and the other zigzags and travels at a speed of 1.8237×10^8 m/s. A device can determine the winner if their arrival time differs by 10 ns. How long must the optical fibre be?

14. The index of refraction of crown glass is 1.51 for red light and 1.53 for violet light. For an angle of incidence of 70.0°, calculate for crown glass:
    a) the angles of refraction for red and violet light
    b) the speeds of red and violet light

15. Prove mathematically that, for a material m in air, the sine of the critical angle is given by the expression $\sin \theta_c = 1/n_m$

16. Explain the role total internal reflection plays in the formation of a primary rainbow.

17. Medium X has a critical angle of 28° and medium Y a critical angle of 32°. In which medium does light travel faster?

18. In each of the following questions the second medium is air.
    a) Calculate the critical angle, if the index of refraction of the medium is 1.92.
    b) Calculate the index of refraction, if the critical angle of a liquid is 40.5°.

19. What is the critical angle for a diamond immersed in water?

20. A beam of light inside a diamond is incident on an air interface at an angle of incidence of 26°.
    a) Will part of the beam enter the air or will it be totally internally reflected? Show your calculations.
    b) The same diamond is immersed in water. What will happen to the beam now? Show your calculations.

21. An alligator is 1.5 m below the water. A bird is hovering 1.0 m above the water.
    a) At what depth below the water does the alligator appear to the bird?
    b) At what height above the water does the bird appear to the alligator?

22. Why are the colours reversed in a secondary rainbow from those in a primary rainbow?

Applying Inquiry/ Communication Skills

23. An experimenter claims to have discovered a liquid with a refractive index less than one. Do you think this is possible? Explain your answer.

24. Prove that $\lambda_1 \sin \theta_1 = \lambda_2 \sin \theta_2$, where λ stands for the wavelength of light in the media.

25. Figure 10.45 shows a ray of light travelling through a glass block with parallel sides. Explain why the emergent ray is displaced sideways, but parallel to the incident ray.

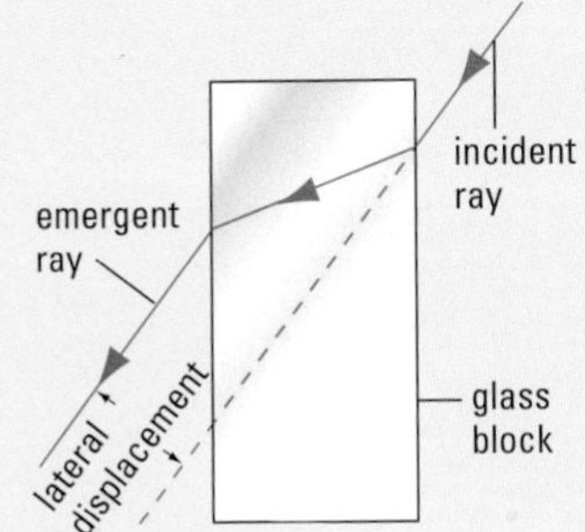

FIGURE 10.45

26. A student placed a coin on the table and put a deep empty bowl on top of it. When peering over the edge of the bowl the coin could not be seen. When water was added half of the coin could be seen. When substance X was added most of the coin was visible. Explain the results and compare the refractive index of water and substance X.

27. When walking past a row of shop windows, why can you see yourself in dark windows, but not in brightly lit windows? Which model of light explains this best?

28. A stone from the tire of a speeding gravel truck hits the windshield of a car. A silvery crack appears. The crack is visible because there is a film of air between the two pieces of glass. Draw a ray diagram to show the role total internal reflection plays in making the crack visible.

29. During a sailing trip from Iceland, Eric the Red discovered Greenland. There is a legend that he saw Greenland in a mirage. Draw a labelled sketch of the ship and Greenland, and use it to explain how a mirage might have formed.

30. A sheet of ice 0.20 m thick is floating on top of a layer of water 10 m thick. A beam of light strikes the ice at 90° and reaches the bottom in a time t. How far would the light have travelled in the same time in a vacuum?

31. Refer to Figure 10.46 and prove that for near vertical rays, $\frac{h'}{h} = \frac{n_2}{n_1}$, where h' is the apparent depth of an object beneath the surface of a liquid, h is the true depth, n_1 is the index of refraction of the liquid, and n_2 is the index of refraction of the viewer's medium (usually air).

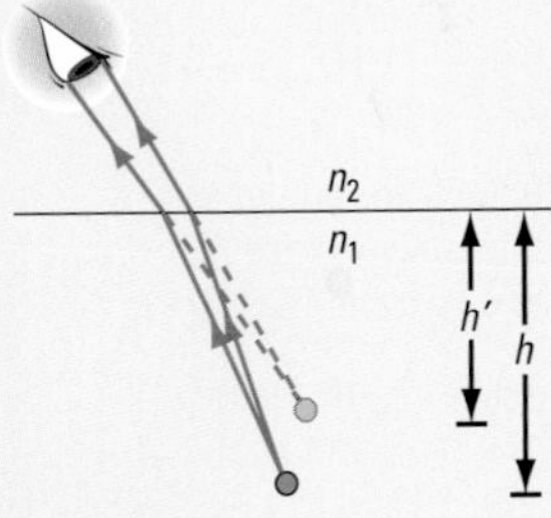

FIGURE 10.46

Making Connections

32. A golfer is trying to illuminate a golf ball in a pond using a laser pointer.
    a) Should the laser be aimed above the image, at the image, or below the image of the ball? Why?
    b) If the golfer is using a long pole with a scoop to lift the ball out, where should the pole be aimed? Why?

CHAPTER 11

Lenses and Technological Devices

SPECIFIC EXPECTATIONS

By the end of this chapter, you will be able to:

- describe and explain, with the aid of light-ray diagrams, the characteristics and positions of the images formed by lenses (11.1)
- describe the effects of converging and diverging lenses on light, and explain why each type of lens is used in specific optical devices (11.1, 11.3, 11.4, 11.5, Investigation 2)
- analyze, in quantitative terms, the characteristics and positions of images formed by lenses (11.2, Investigation 1)
- predict, using ray diagrams and algebraic equations, the image position and characteristics of a converging lens, and verify the predictions through experimentation (11.2, 11.5, Investigation 1)
- carry out experiments involving the transmission of light, compare theoretical predictions and empirical evidence, and account for discrepancies (11.1, Investigation 1)
- construct, test, and refine a prototype of an optical device (11.3, Investigation 2)
- describe how images are produced and reproduced for the purposes of entertainment and culture (11.3)
- evaluate, using given criteria, the effectiveness of a technological device or procedure related to the human perception of light (11.5)
- analyze, describe, and explain optical effects that are produced by technological devices (11.3, 11.4, Investigation 2)

Every waking second, eyes send millions of bits of visual information to the brain. Over 70% of what most people perceive and learn about the world around them comes from their eyes. For the majority of us, our eyes are the most important sense organs we have. This is clearly demonstrated by the fact that we have developed so many more technological devices to enhance and extend our visual capabilities than we have for any of our other senses.

These optical devices have dramatically altered the world. Telescopes and microscopes have given us new knowledge about the universe around us. Audiovisual devices such as cameras, movie projectors, and virtual-reality glasses have transformed how we entertain ourselves and how we spend our leisure time. Magnifying glasses, eyeglasses, and contact lenses have helped those with vision defects to see more clearly. Medical devices like endoscopes have revolutionized the diagnosis and treatment of disease. Periscopes and night-vision goggles have altered the way wars are fought. And this is just a small sampling of the vast array of optical devices being used every day.

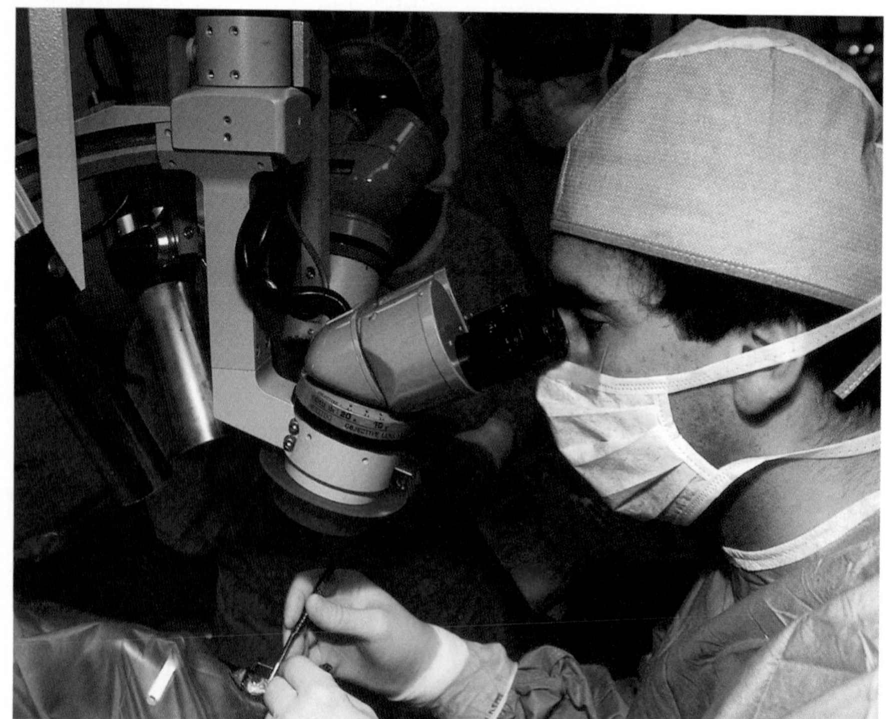

FIGURE 11.1 A patient being operated on for a cataract

All of these devices have one thing in common. They make use of lenses, mirrors, and prisms to bend and focus light. In order to understand or construct such devices, one must first understand the properties of light and how light interacts with materials. In this chapter, you will investigate how lenses, mirrors, and prisms are used in various combinations within different optical instruments. You will take a look at the insides of one of the most important optical devices ever created—the camera. Finally, you will study the human eye to see how it resembles other optical devices.

> **CHECKPOINT**
>
> A camera is used to photograph an erect burning candle. If the photographer covers the upper half of the lens and takes a picture, what will be the appearance of the image of the candle on the developed film?
>
> a) Only the upper half of the image of the candle will be visible.
> b) Only the bottom half of the image of the candle will be visible.
> c) The entire image of the candle will be unchanged and visible.
> d) The image of the candle will be reduced in size but the same shape.
> e) The image of the candle will be the same size but dimmer.
>
> Explain your answer.

Discovering Physics

Water Magnifiers

How can water be used to magnify? What factors affect the magnifying and light-gathering power of water lenses? Find out in this experiment.

1. Cut a slide, about 10 cm × 5 cm, from a plastic sheet.
2. Draw two separate circles on the slide using a wax crayon: one of diameter 1.0 cm and the other of diameter 2.0 cm. Trace each circle several times to make a continuous wax barrier.
3. Use an eyedropper to add enough water to the centre of each circle to fill it as shown in Figure 11.2.
4. Raise the slide to eye level and look at the drops from the side. Compare the curvatures of the top surfaces.
5. Keeping the slide level, carefully lower the slide toward a sheet of newsprint and observe where the lenses bring the overhead light to a sharp focus. Also compare the brightness of the images and hence the light-gathering power of the lenses.
6. Place one eye directly over the smaller drop and raise and lower the slide above the newsprint until you can clearly see a small letter through the drop.
7. Try reading a word. Note the magnification of the image produced by the lens.
8. Repeat this procedure for the larger drop.

- What kind of lens did the drop of water form?
- Which drop formed a lens with the smallest radius of curvature?
- Which lens had the shorter focal length?
- Which lens had the greatest light-gathering power?
- How is light-gathering power related to the cross-sectional area of the lens?
- Describe the characteristics of the image of the newsprint when viewed through each lens.

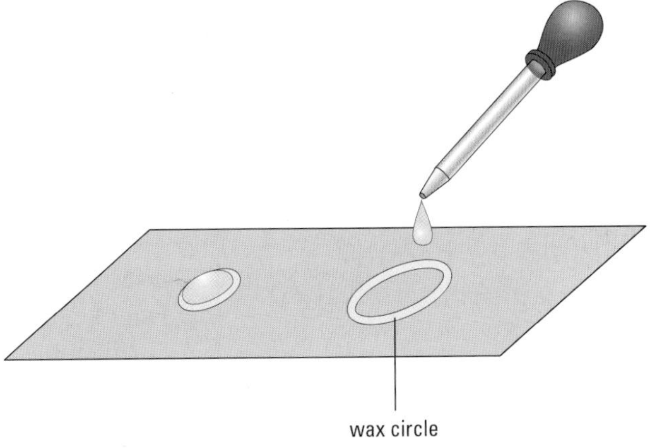

FIGURE 11.2 Making water magnifiers

11.1 Curved Lenses: Refraction and Ray Diagrams

Key Understandings

When you have completed this section, you will be able to:

- describe and explain, with the aid of ray diagrams, the characteristics and positions of images formed by lenses
- describe the effects of converging and diverging lenses on light
- predict the focal length of a plano-convex lens
- carry out an experiment to verify the focal length of a plano-convex lens

Eyeglass lenses come in many different sizes and shapes. They also have different curvatures. Some are thinner in the middle than the outside. Others thin out toward the edges. Some are made of plastic while others are made of hardened glass. A tiny diverging lens can be used as a security viewer. Inserted into a door at eye height, it lets the person inside see who is outside without opening the door. Why are lenses shaped as they are? How do they work? Why is the image erect and not inverted? Why is the field of view increased? Is the image of the person seen through the viewer real or virtual?

When light rays pass obliquely from a less refractive medium through a more refractive medium and back into the less refractive medium, they are refracted twice. Figure 11.3 shows a light ray in air passing through a rectangular glass block and back into air. The ray bends toward the normal on entering the glass block and away from the normal on leaving it. The light ray emerges from the glass block heading in the same direction, but displaced sideways. The amount of **lateral displacement** depends on the angle of incidence, the index of refraction of the medium, and the distance the light travels in the medium.

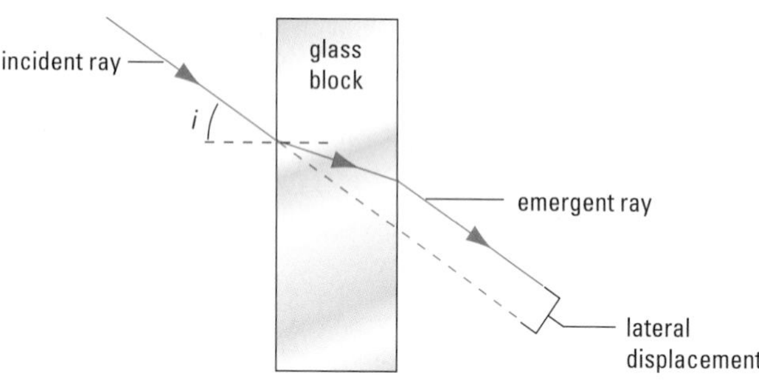

FIGURE 11.3 The lateral displacement of a light ray

Discovering Physics — *Angle of Minimum Deviation*

Observe what happens to a ray of light when it passes through a triangular prism. Then determine the angle of minimum deviation.

1. Place a triangular prism on a sheet of paper.
2. Direct a single ray of light at an oblique angle toward the prism as shown in Figure 11.4.
3. Observe the angle of deviation.
4. Repeat for several different angles of incidence until you find an angle of incidence for which the angle of deviation is a minimum. Measure this angle of minimum deviation.
5. Compare your angle of minimum deviation with the angle of minimum deviation found by other groups.

When light rays pass through a triangular glass prism they are refracted toward the normal on entering and away from the normal on leaving. Because of the shape of the prism, the rays are bent in the same direction at both surfaces, as shown in Figure 11.4. The angle between the incident ray and the emergent ray is called the **angle of deviation**. The larger the refractive index, the greater the angle of deviation. Consider how the size of the angle at the apex of the prism affects the angle of deviation.

incident ray
angle of deviation
emergent ray

FIGURE 11.4 The angle of deviation of a light ray passing through a prism

Light rays passing through a **converging lens** are shown in Figure 11.5. The lens behaves like two triangular prisms that are base-to-base. The curved sides cause the light rays to converge to a common point called the principal focus. Converging lenses are sometimes called convex lenses because they are thicker at the centre than at the edges.

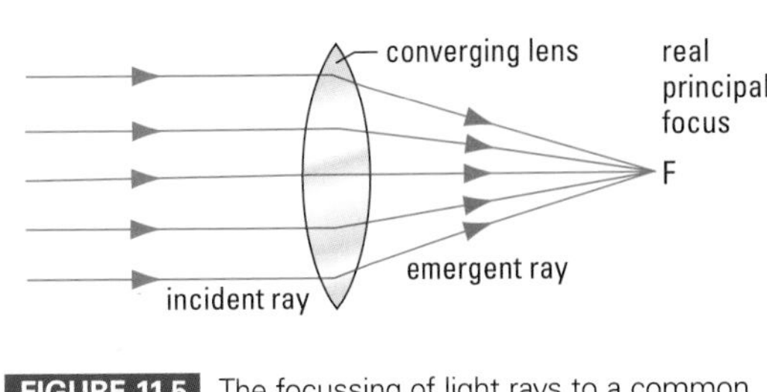

FIGURE 11.5 The focussing of light rays to a common point using a converging lens

Figure 11.6 shows light rays passing through a **diverging lens**. This lens has an effect similar to that of two triangular prisms with their tips in contact. The curved edges cause the light rays to diverge away from the principal focus. This focus is called virtual because the rays only appear to originate from this point. Diverging lenses are sometimes called concave lenses because they are thinner in the centre than at the edges.

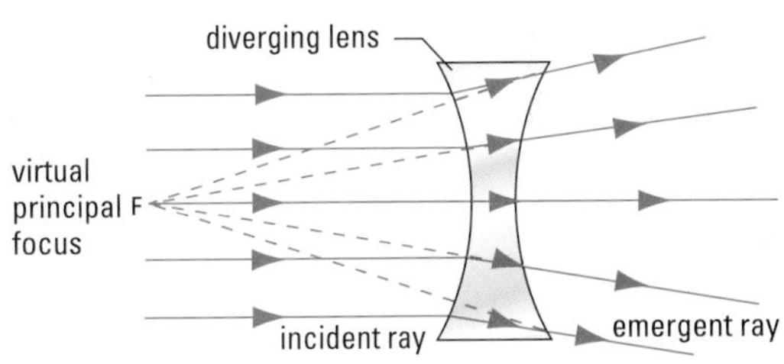

FIGURE 11.6 These light rays seem to diverge from a point behind the diverging lens.

The three common types of converging and diverging lenses are shown in Figure 11.7. Note that a meniscus lens has one concave and one convex surface. Whether the lens is converging or diverging depends on the relative thickness at the centre and the edges. Deduce what would happen if the lenses were held horizontally with the concave surface facing up and the depression was filled level with water.

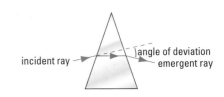

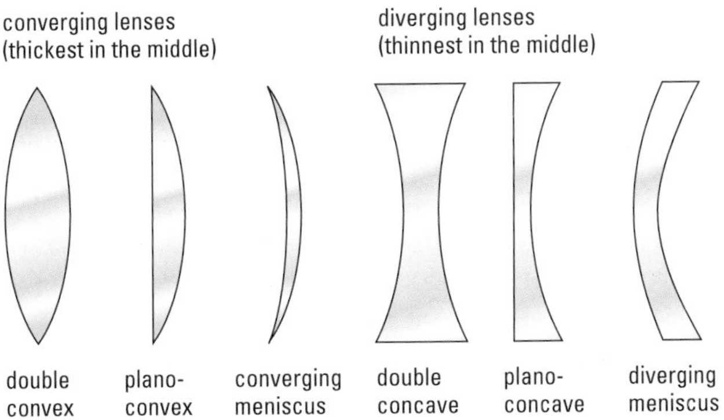

FIGURE 11.7 Various converging and diverging lenses

WEBLINK

A lens-maker is skilled at grinding lenses to correct specific eye disorders. What education must they have? How much are they paid? What are the job opportunities? Are machines replacing the need for lens? Submit a one-age report of your findings. Begin your research at **www.pearsoned.ca/physics11.**

Lens Terminology

Figure 11.8 illustrates some of the terms associated with both converging and diverging lenses. The centre of a lens is called the optical centre O. A line drawn through the optical centre perpendicular to both surfaces is called the **principal axis** PA. The plane that is perpendicular to the principal axis and

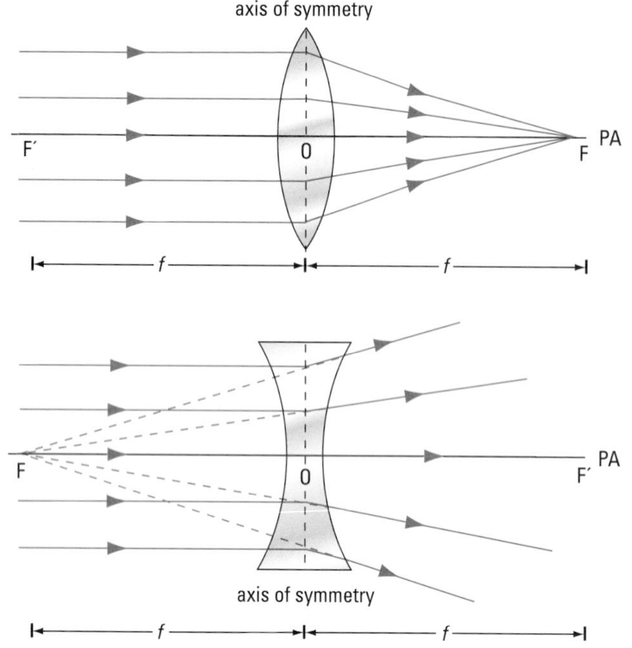

FIGURE 11.8 Terms associated with converging and diverging lenses

passes through the optical centre of a lens is called the axis of the lens. The distance from the optical centre to the principal focus F, measured along the principal axis, is called the **focal length** f. Both kinds of lenses have two principal focuses. The principal focus, where the light either comes to a focus or appears to diverge from a focus, is given the symbol F, while that on the opposite side is represented by F′. Since light behaves the same way travelling in either direction through a lens, both kinds of thin lenses have two equal focal lengths.

The focal length of a lens depends on two factors. One factor is the refractive index of the lens material compared with that of the surrounding medium. The greater the relative refractive index, the shorter the focal length. Hence, a glass lens submerged in water has a longer focal length than a glass lens in air. The other factor is the radii of curvature R_1 and R_2 of the lens (Figure 11.9). The smaller the radii of curvature, the shorter the focal length of the lens.

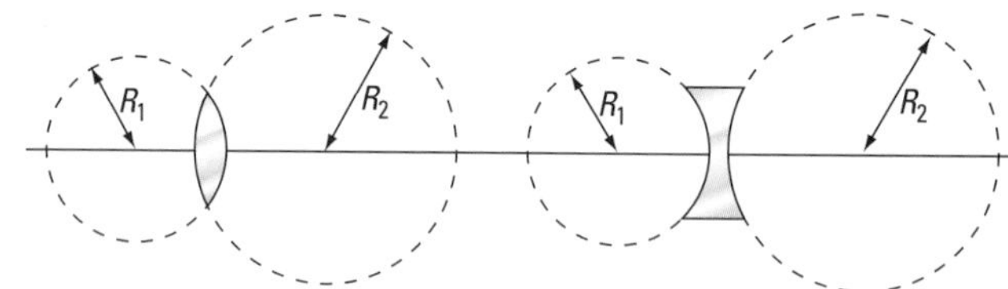

FIGURE 11.9 Any lens has two radii of curvature.

Exploration Using a Graphing Calculator

The lens-maker's equation is $\frac{1}{f} = (n - 1)\left(\frac{1}{R_1} - \frac{1}{R_2}\right)$ where f is the focal length of the lens, n is the refractive index of the material, R_1 is one radius of curvature, and R_2 is the other radius of curvature. For a plano-convex lens, which is flat on one side and curved on the other, the equation simplifies to $\frac{1}{f} = (n - 1)\left(\frac{1}{R_1}\right)$ since for an infinite radius $\frac{1}{R_2}$ becomes zero.

Use your graphing calculator to plot f on the y-axis (with a range of 6.0 cm to 22 cm) and radius of curvature R_1 on the x-axis (with a range of 2.0 cm to 7.0 cm). Assume that the lens will be made of water ($n = 1.33$). Do not erase the information from memory until you have done the Discovering Physics activity on page 405.

Discussion

1. What is the focal length of the plano-convex water lens for the following radii of curvature?
   a) 2.0 cm
   b) 5.0 cm
   c) 7.0 cm

Discovering Physics — Focal Length of a Plano-Convex Water Lens

In this experiment you will calculate the focal length of a plano-convex water lens. Refer to Figure 11.10 as a guide in setting up the apparatus.

1. Measure and record the radius of curvature of a semicircular plastic dish.
2. Estimate where the optical centre of the dish is located, and mark this location on the outside bottom of the dish.
3. Fill the dish 2/3 full of water and place it on a white sheet of paper.
4. Use your graphing calculator and the lens-maker's equation to calculate what the focal length should be for the water lens. You should be able to get this quickly by toggling through to the value of *x* on the graph plotted above, corresponding to the radius of curvature of your dish.
5. Measure and mark the location of the two focal points on the paper near the lens. These are your predictions.
6. Use a ray box with a multiple-slit aperture to direct parallel rays toward the dish from both sides, and mark the focal points.

- Compare the experimental focal points to the predicted focal points.
- Identify some sources of error in this activity.
- If you have time, repeat the activity with different liquids in the dish or with a semicircular plastic or glass lens.
- How will variations of the index of refraction affect the focal length?

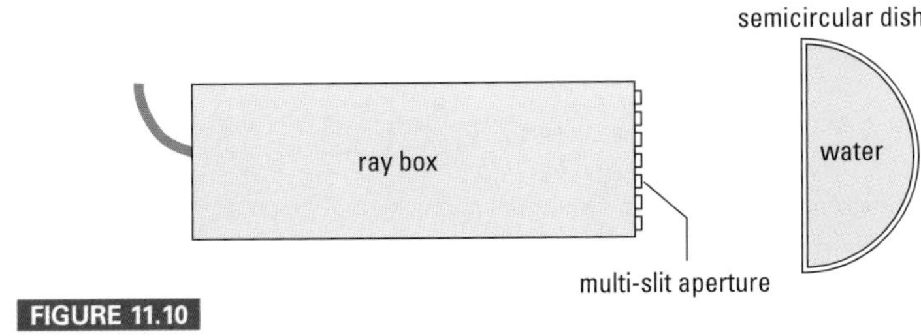

FIGURE 11.10

Parallel light rays produce focal points even if the incident rays are not parallel to the principal axis (Figure 11.11). All the focal points for a lens fall on a surface called the **focal plane**.

Since light is reversible, both converging and diverging lenses can be used to produce parallel rays (Figure 11.12). Light that comes from the principal focus F′ of a converging lens travels parallel to the principal axis after refraction. Light rays directed toward the principal focus F′ on the opposite side of a diverging lens travel parallel to the principal axis after refraction.

Images created with lenses can have the same characteristics and possible values as images created with mirrors (i.e. magnification, attitude, kind,

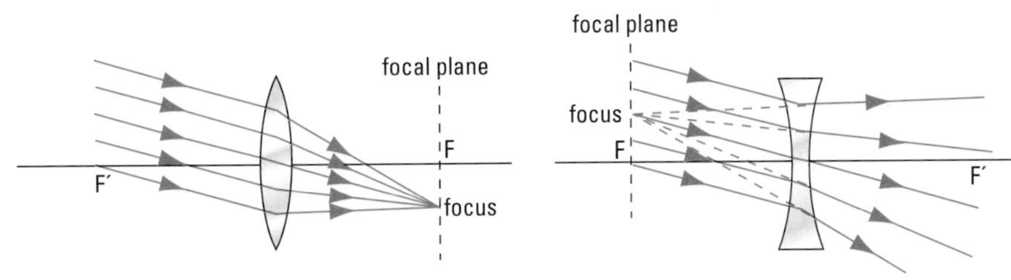

FIGURE 11.11 Focal planes for diverging and converging lenses

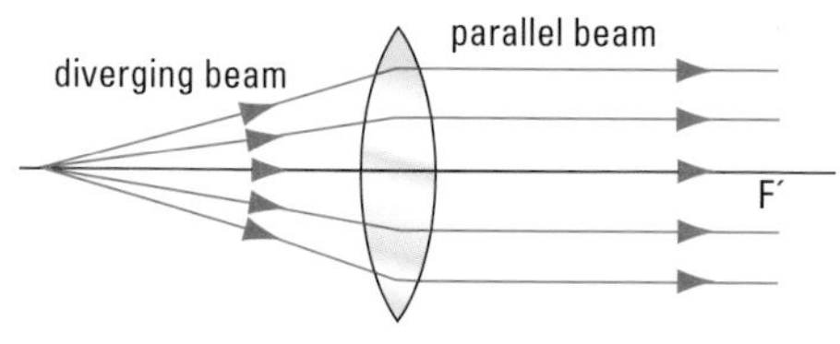

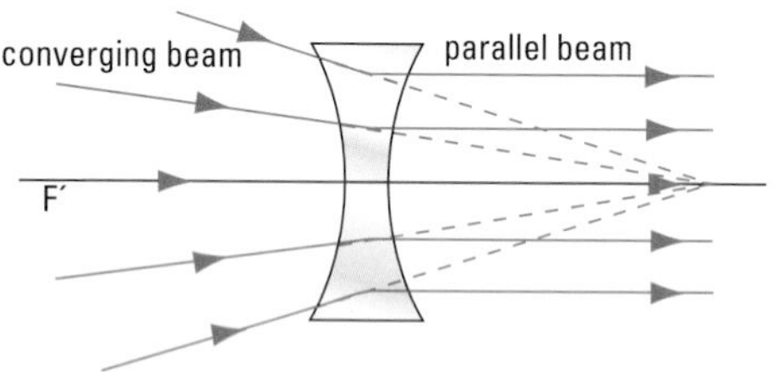

FIGURE 11.12 Producing parallel rays with converging and diverging lenses

and location). The only difference is that for lenses, the position of the image should be measured with reference to the optical centre O, which is the centre of the lens.

The ability to draw accurate ray diagrams is an important skill in optics. Figure 11.13 shows three rays passing through thin lenses. The method for tracing their paths is summarized below.

1. **Ray 1** travels parallel to the principal axis and on emerging from the lens either passes through the principal focus F of the converging lens or appears to come from the principal focus F of a diverging lens.
2. **Ray 2** passes through the optical centre. Because the sides are essentially parallel, the emerging ray is parallel to the incident ray. However, the emerging ray is slightly laterally displaced. The thinner the lens, the less the lateral displacement.
3. **Ray 3** passes through the principal focus F′ on the near side of the converging lens or aims toward F′ on the far side of the diverging lens. When ray 3 emerges, it travels parallel to the principal axis.
4. All three rays undergo two refractions, the first on entering the lens and the second on leaving it.

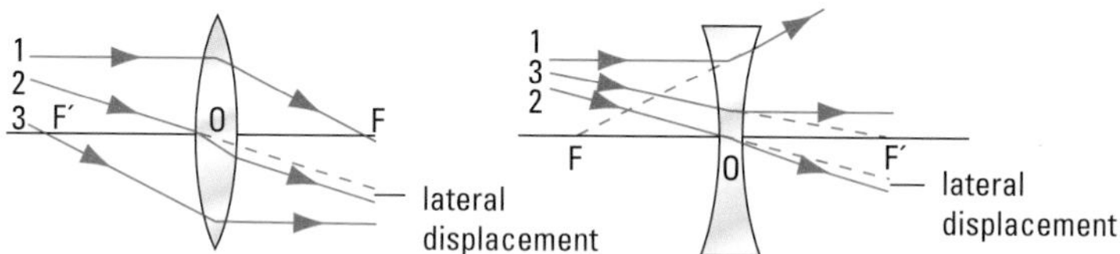

FIGURE 11.13 The passage of key rays through thin lenses showing the lateral displacement

You can simplify the drawing of the three rays for thin lenses without greatly affecting the accuracy of the drawing by making two assumptions.

1. Assume that all the refraction takes place at the axis—a vertical line drawn through the centre of the lens.
2. Since the lateral displacement of the ray that passes through the optical centre is very small for thin lenses, assume that it is negligible.

These assumptions are invalid for thick lenses. In thick lenses, the thickness is significant compared with the diameter of the lens, so lateral displacement causes errors. Figure 11.14 shows how the three rays are drawn, based on these assumptions.

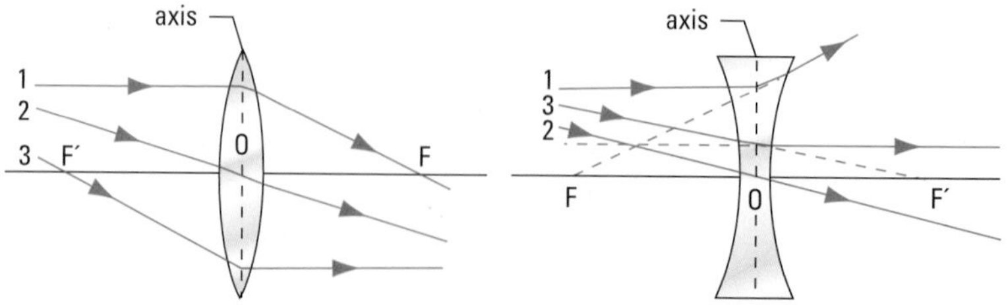

FIGURE 11.14 A simplified view of the passage of key rays through thin lenses

A scale diagram using these three rays provides a convenient way to determine and check the location and characteristics of an image formed by a thin lens. The object is always shown as a solid, erect arrow. Any two of these rays are drawn from the tip of the object. The place where the rays intersect, or appear to do so after refraction, gives the location of the tip of the image. The third ray serves as a check. Real rays are drawn as solid lines and virtual rays as dashed lines. Figure 11.15 shows how this is done for converging and diverging thin lenses. A real image can be caught on a screen since it is formed where real rays intersect. A real image is drawn as a solid arrow, as in Figure 11.15a). A virtual image cannot be caught on a screen since it is formed by the intersection of one or more virtual rays. However, a virtual image can be seen by looking into the lens. A virtual image is always shown as a dashed arrow (see Figure 11.15b)).

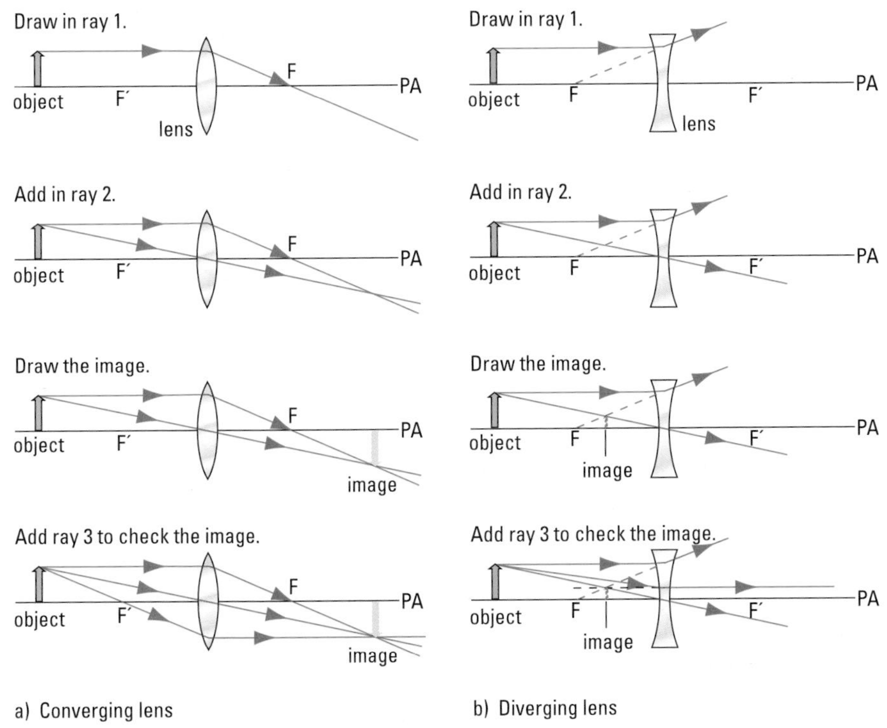

FIGURE 11.15 The steps in drawing ray diagrams to determine the location and characteristics of images formed by lenses

WEBLINK

For a simulation of the passage of rays through curved lenses, as well as spherical and chromatic aberration, go to **www.pearsoned.ca/physics11.**

Images Formed by a Converging Lens

Figure 11.16 shows the characteristics and locations of images formed by a converging lens for several object positions.

In Figure 11.16a), the rays reaching the converging lens from a distant object are effectively parallel. Two parallel rays are shown coming in at an angle to the principal axis to represent rays from a point on a large distant object. Therefore, the **object distance** is effectively infinite. The image is formed at the principal focus F. Thus, in this situation, the **image distance** is f. The image is diminished, inverted, and real.

Refer to page 434, Investigation 1

Characteristics of image

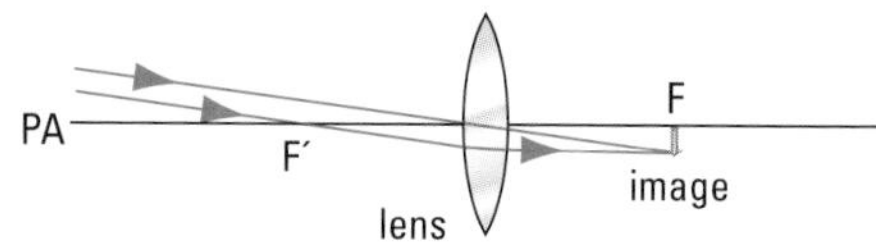

a) Distant object

Real
Inverted
Smaller than object
At F

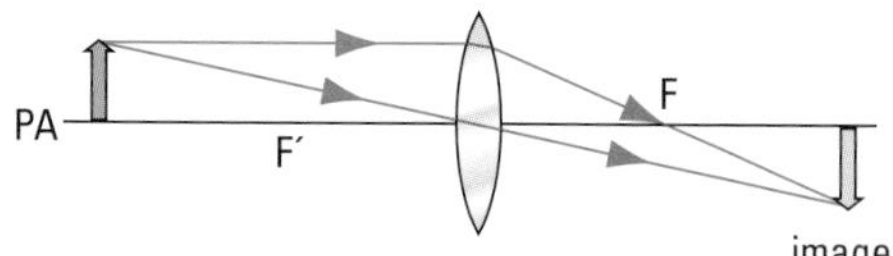

b) Object at 2F

Real
Inverted
Same size
At 2F

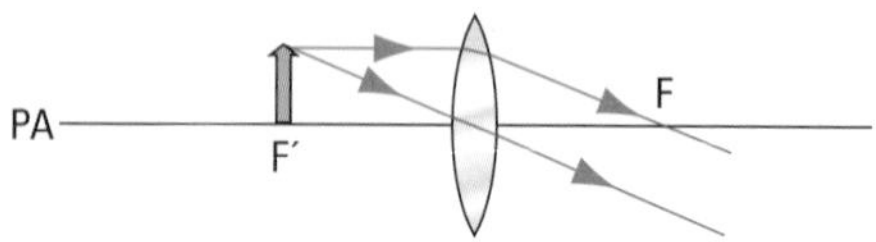

c) Object at F′

No image
Refracted rays
are parallel

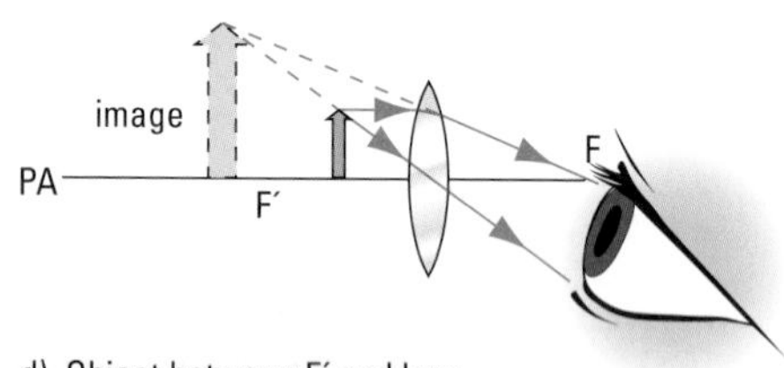

d) Object between F′ and lens

Virtual
Erect
Larger than object
Behind the object
on same side of lens

FIGURE 11.16 Images formed by a converging lens

As the object distance decreases, and the object moves closer to the principal focus F′, the real inverted image increases in size and moves outward from the principal focus F. A camera uses a converging lens in this way to create diminished images of an object. In Figure 11.16b), the object distance is $2f$ from the lens, and the image distance is $2f$ on the other side of the lens. This inverted real image is the same size as the object. Photocopiers that make identical copies place the object at this position.

When the object is between $2f$ and f from the lens, the inverted image is enlarged and real. A photocopier makes enlargements using this placement, as do photographic enlargers, slide projectors, and movie projectors. Recall that a slide must be inverted in the projector to obtain an erect image on the screen.

In Figure 11.16c), no image is formed when the object is precisely at the principal focus F′ because the rays leaving the lens are parallel and never intersect. When this happens, it is said that the image is undefined. An intense light source at the principal focus of a search-light produces the parallel beam sometimes seen sweeping the sky at an airport or shopping plaza.

In Figure 11.16d), the object is closer to the lens than F′, and the image is erect, enlarged, and virtual. The image appears to be behind the lens because the refracted rays leaving the lens appear to diverge from a point. The imaginary rays behind the lens are called virtual rays. Since no rays actually come from the point, a virtual image cannot be captured on a screen. A magnifying glass uses this property of a converging lens, as does a reading glass.

Table 11.1 summarizes the characteristics of images formed by a converging lens.

TABLE 11.1 Image Characteristics for a Converging Lens

	Image Characteristics			
Object Distance from Lens	Location of Image	Kind	Attitude	Magnification
distant	at F	real	inverted	diminished
greater than $2f$	between F and 2F	real	inverted	diminished
at $2f$	at 2F	real	inverted	unchanged
between f and $2f$	outside 2F	real	inverted	enlarged
at f	undefined	undefined	undefined	undefined
between f and 0	same side as object	virtual	erect	enlarged

Images Formed by a Diverging Lens

Figure 11.17 shows the characteristics of an image formed by a diverging lens. The virtual image is on the same side of the lense as the object, erect, and diminished in size. However, an image from a diverging lens does not have these characteristics when the object is against the lens. Can you propose an experiment to verify this?

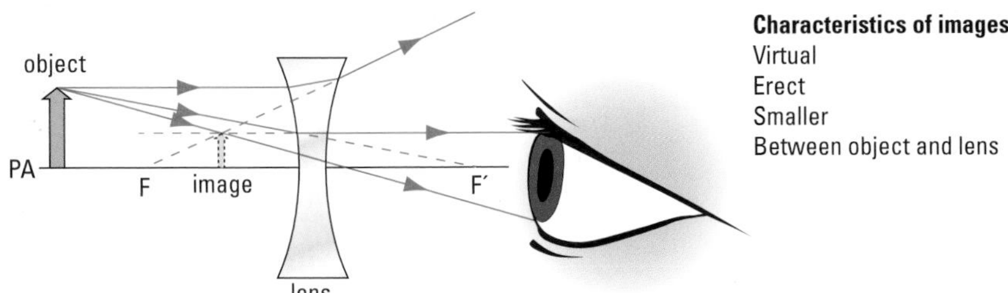

FIGURE 11.17 Image formed by a diverging lens

Chromatic Aberration

Whenever white light passes through a single lens, an image with coloured fringes is observed. This defect is called **chromatic aberration**. Chromatic aberration is due to the difference in the refractive index of the lens for different colours. Figure 11.18a) shows that the shorter-wavelength blue light is refracted more than the longer-wavelength red light. As a result, there is a slightly different focal point for each colour. Chromatic aberration can be decreased by using a combination of two lenses made of materials with different refractive indexes. A converging lens is combined with a diverging lens to produce an **achromatic lens**. An achromatic lens can be designed to eliminate chromatic aberration for two colours and to minimize it for others, as shown in Figure 11.18b).

WEBLINK

Chromatic and spherical aberration are two potential defects of both converging and diverging lenses. Lens-makers are able to correct for these defects. What is the difference between them and how are lenses constructed to prevent them? Begin your research at **www.pearsoned.ca/physics11.**

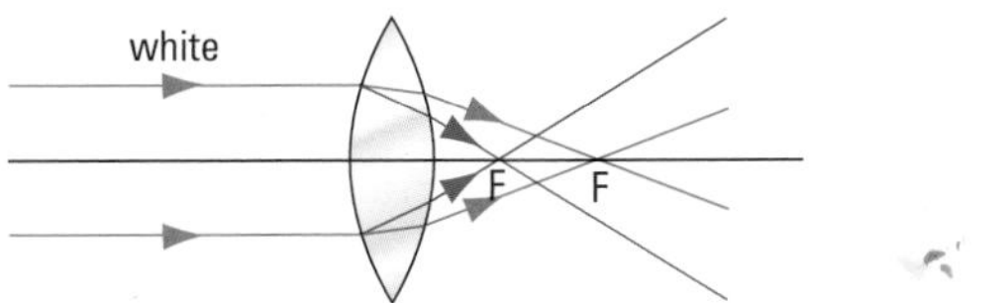

a) Ordinary lens. Different colours have different focal points.

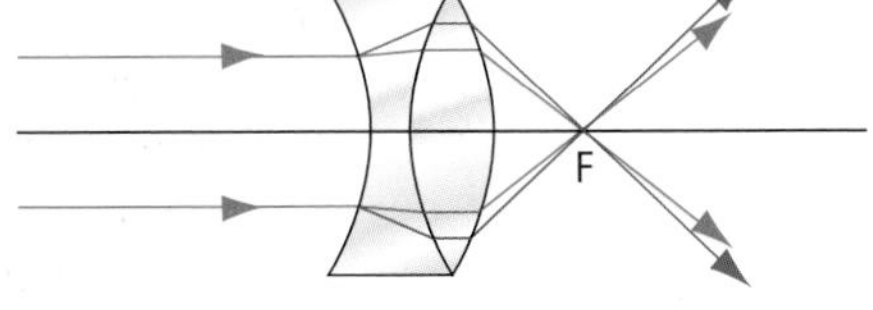

b) Achromatic lens. Different colours have the same focal point.

FIGURE 11.18 Chromatic aberration. A converging and a diverging lens made of different kinds of glass form a lens that corrects for chromatic aberration. (Bending not to scale.)

Spherical Aberration

By definition, the principal focus is the point where parallel rays meet after passing through a lens. In practice, when light of one colour passes through a single lens with spherical surfaces (Figure 11.19), the principal focus is a small circle rather than a point. This defect, called **spherical aberration**, is caused by rays at different distances from the principal axis having slightly different focal points as shown in Figure 11.20. The farther parallel rays are from the principal axis, the closer their focal points are to the lens. Spherical aberration occurs for both converging and diverging spherical lenses. It is

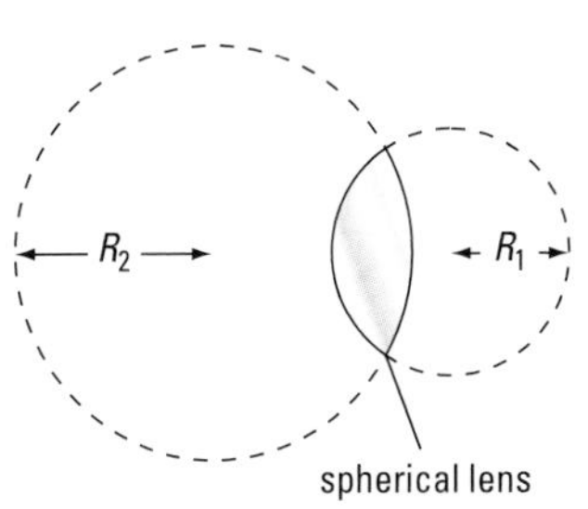

FIGURE 11.19 A lens with spherical surfaces causes spherical aberration.

corrected by grinding lenses with non-spherical lens surfaces or by using several spherical lenses in combination. Expensive cameras, microscopes, and telescopes use these combinations to correct for spherical aberration. As discussed in Chapter 9, spherical aberration also occurs in spherical and cylindrical mirrors.

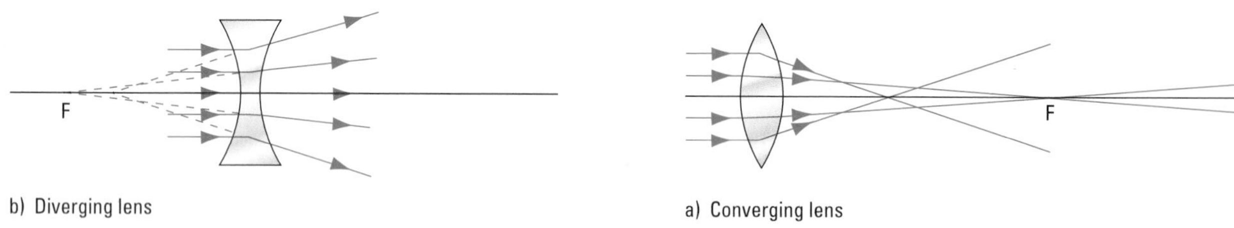

FIGURE 11.20 In spherical aberration, incident rays farther from the principal axis are focussed closer to the lens than to the principal focus.

Section 11.1 Review

Understanding Concepts

1. How would you minimize the lateral displacement of a light ray passing through a glass block with parallel sides?
2. Draw and label a diagram to show the angle of deviation for a light ray passing through a glass prism with sides of equal length.
3. Sketch a converging and a diverging lens. Label the following terms for each lens: two principal focuses, optical centre, focal plane, principal axis, and two focal lengths.

Applying Inquiry/ Communication Skills

4. a) State two assumptions made to simplify the drawing of ray diagrams for thin lenses.
   b) Explain, using a diagram, why these assumptions are invalid for thick lenses.
5. Express what is meant by: "The position of an image is undefined."
6. Compare the lateral displacements for a glass block and a water block, both with parallel sides. Explain your answer.
7. Predict how the angle of minimum deviation for a lens will change as the apex angle (the angle at the top of the lens) changes. Explain your prediction. Then design and perform an experiment to test your prediction. Pay careful attention to the control of variables.
8. a) Draw a diagram to illustrate chromatic aberration.
   b) Use a diagram to illustrate how an achromatic lens corrects the defect.
9. a) Draw a diagram to illustrate spherical aberration.
   b) Describe two ways to eliminate spherical aberration.

Making Connections

10. Some people swimming under water with their eyes open have better vision than when they are standing on the shore. Explain why.
11. Do you think the vision of an underwater diver encased in a diving suit changes as a result of refraction? Support your answer.

11.2 Thin Lens Equations

Key Understandings

When you have completed this section, you will be able to:

- analyze images formed by lenses
- predict the image position and characteristics of converging and diverging lenses
- verify through experimentation the image position and characteristics of a converging lens

Magnifying glasses are useful converging lenses. A large-diameter magnifying glass can be used to start a fire (Figure 11.21). The same lens can be used to obtain a magnified image of a small specimen. Where exactly is the image, and how much is the image magnified? Do these variables depend on where the specimen is located? How can one find answers to these questions using mathematics and physics?

FIGURE 11.21 A converging lens can be used to start a fire.

Consider the sources of error when drawing ray diagrams for lenses and mirrors. You can use geometry to derive an equation relating the position of the object, the position of the image, and the focal length of a thin lens. The equation can be derived using a ray diagram for either a converging or diverging thin lens. In Figure 11.22 you can see the triangles CDO and ABO are similar.

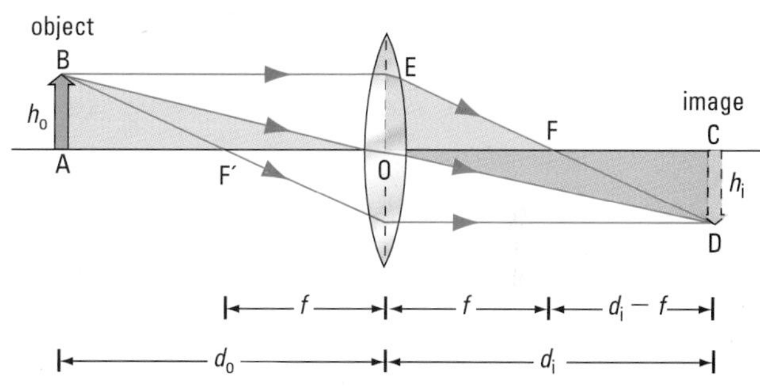

FIGURE 11.22 A ray diagram for deriving the lens equation

Therefore $\dfrac{CD}{AB} = \dfrac{CO}{AO} = \dfrac{d_i}{d_o}$ (equation 1)

Also, triangle CDF is similar to triangle OEF.

Therefore $\dfrac{CD}{OE} = \dfrac{CF}{OF} = \dfrac{d_i - f}{f} = \dfrac{d_i}{f} - 1$ (equation 2)

But $AB = OE$

Therefore $\dfrac{CD}{AB} = \dfrac{CD}{OE}$

Equating the right sides of equations 1 and 2 we obtain

$$\frac{d_i}{d_o} = \frac{d_i}{f} - 1$$

Dividing each side by d_i we obtain

$$\frac{1}{d_o} = \frac{1}{f} - \frac{1}{d_i}$$

Which re-arranges to the lens equation

$$\frac{1}{d_o} + \frac{1}{d_i} = \frac{1}{f}$$

where d_o = distance of the object from the lens

d_i = distance of the image from the lens

f = focal length of the lens

Given any two of these quantities, the lens equation can be used to solve for the third.

WEBLINK

Newton derived a different lens equation, using the focal points as references rather than the optical centre of the lens. Research Newton's lens equation. Show how it is derived and solve the same problem using both equations. Begin your research at **www.pearsoned.ca/physics11.**

INSIGHT

When using the lens equation, after combining the reciprocals do not forget to take the reciprocal of the result.

The Magnification Equation

Linear magnification m is defined as the ratio between the size of the image and the size of the object. If the magnification is 1, the image is the same size as the object. If the magnification is more than 1, the image is larger than the object. A magnification of less than 1 means the image is reduced in size compared with the object. We can write

$$\text{magnification } m = \frac{h_i}{h_o}$$

where h_i is the **image height**
and h_o is the **object height**.

From Figure 11.22, triangles CDO and ABO are similar.

Therefore $\frac{h_i}{h_o} = \frac{d_i}{d_o}$

An inverted image is considered by convention to have a negative height. We can indicate this in the equation with a negative sign. The general equation for linear magnification is

$$m = \frac{h_i}{h_o} = -\frac{d_i}{d_o}$$

Sign Conventions for Thin Lenses

The lens and magnification equations are valid for any object distance and apply to both a diverging and a converging lens provided the following sign conventions are used.

- The focal length f is positive for converging lenses and negative for diverging lenses.
- The object distance d_o is positive.
- The image distance d_i is positive for real images and negative for virtual images.
- The image height h_i and object height h_o are positive when measured upward from the principal axis and negative when measured downward.
- The magnification m is positive when the image is erect and negative when it is inverted.

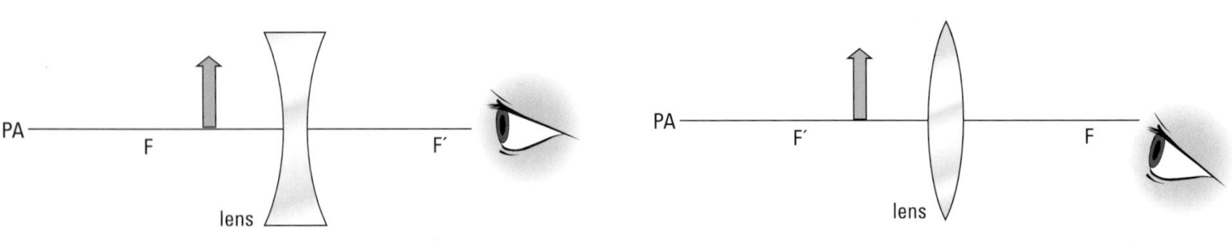

FIGURE 11.23 Applying lens conventions

Discovering Physics — *Lens Conventions*

In this activity, you will summarize the characteristics of images created using a diverging lens and a converging lens.

1. Find a diverging and a converging lens with the same focal length.
2. View the image of an object through a diverging lens for an object distance less than the focal length (see Figure 11.23a)).
3. Note the attitude, kind, and approximate location of the image.
4. Decide what signs you would give to the image distance, image height, and image magnification
5. Repeat this for a converging lens for the same object distance, (see Figure 11.23b)). Summarize the characteristics of each image.

- What signs did you assign to the image distance, image height, and image magnification when the object is inside the focal point for each lens?
- How will increasing the object distance d_o affect these signs for each lens?

Exploration Using a Graphing Calculator

A bee is hovering inside the focal point of a converging lens of focal length 15 cm. The bee is 1.0 cm in height. The equation for calculating how large the image of the bee appears when viewed through the lens is $h_i = \frac{(-h_o f)}{(d_o - f)}$.

Graph this equation on the graphing calculator. Plot h_i on the y-axis (with a range -50 cm to 50 cm) and d_o on the x-axis (with a range of 0 cm to 50 cm).

Discussion

1. How large does the bee appear for the following object distances?
   a) 5.0 cm
   b) 10 cm
   c) 13 cm
   d) 17 cm
   e) 20 cm
   f) 30 cm
   g) 50 cm
2. For which object distances is the image upright?
3. What happens at $d_o = 15$? Why is the value of h_i undefined at this value?

EXAMPLE 1 NUMERICAL

A diverging lens of focal length 25 cm is used to produce an image of a yellow dandelion 10 cm from the lens (Figure 11.24).

a) Where must the object be placed?
b) What is the magnification?

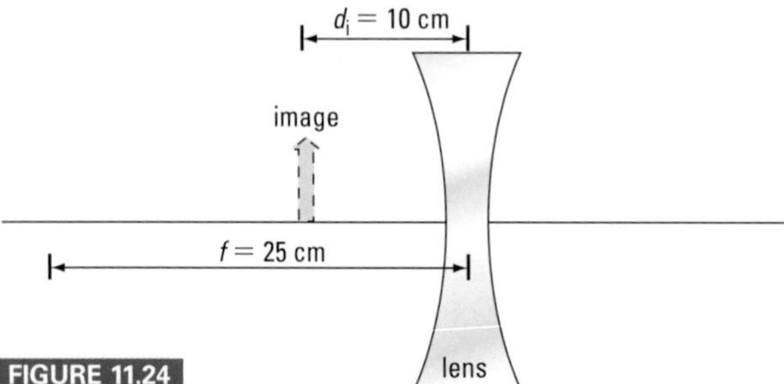

FIGURE 11.24

Given

$f = -25$ cm

$d_i = -10$ cm

Required

d_o

m

Analysis

- Using the sign conventions, a diverging lens has a negative focal length.
- The image distance is negative since a diverging lens always produces a virtual image.

Solution

a) $$\frac{1}{d_o} + \frac{1}{d_i} = \frac{1}{f}$$

$$\frac{1}{d_o} = \frac{1}{f} - \frac{1}{d_i}$$

$$= \frac{1}{-25\text{ cm}} - \frac{1}{-10\text{ cm}}$$

$$= +0.060\text{ cm}^{-1}$$

$$d_o = 17\text{ cm}$$

b) $$m = \frac{h_i}{h_o} = -\frac{d_i}{d_o}$$

$$= -\frac{-10\text{ cm}}{+17\text{ cm}}$$

$$= +0.59$$

Statement

The dandelion is 17 cm in front of the lens. Since the magnification is positive, the image is erect and is 0.59 times the size of the real dandelion.

INSIGHT

When using the lens and magnification equations, it is helpful to draw a ray diagram to direct your thinking and to verify your calculations.

PRACTICE PROBLEM

A 3.00-cm tall figurine is placed 7.10 cm to the left of a diverging lens. The focal length of the lens is 5.08 cm.

a) Calculate the image distance. Is the image real or virtual?
b) Determine the magnification.
c) What is the size of the image? Is it erect or inverted?

Section 11.2 Review

Understanding Concepts

1. A diverging lens produces an image 10 cm from the lens when the object is placed 30 cm from the lens. Calculate

a) the focal length of the lens

b) the magnification of the lens

2. a) Draw ray diagrams for a converging lens, and state the characteristics and location of the image for the following object positions:

i) $2.5f$
ii) $1.5f$
iii) $0.75f$

b) Suggest one use for each lens set-up.

3. a) Draw ray diagrams for a diverging lens and state the characteristics and location of the image for the following object positions:

i) $1.0f$
ii) $0.50f$

b) State one use for a diverging lens.

4. An object 1.2 cm high is placed 4.0 cm from a converging lens of focal length 3.0 cm.

a) Use the lens equations to find the position and size of the image.

b) Draw a scale ray diagram to verify the results.

5. A converging lens used as a reading glass is held less than its focal length from a poster. If the focal length of the lens is 15 cm, and the poster is 12 cm from the lens,

a) calculate the location of the image

b) calculate the magnification

c) use a scale ray diagram to verify your results

6. The diverging lens used in a door-security viewer has a focal length of 30 mm. The image of a 1.80-m tall technician is 2.85 cm from the lens. When the resident looks through the viewer, the technician appears to be 9.0 cm tall.

a) How far is the technician from the viewer?

b) What is the magnification?

c) Is the image real or virtual and erect or inverted? How do you know?

Applying Inquiry/ Communication Skills

7. A convention is a widely observed practice or procedure. Standard notation is a convention used to communicate sizes of physical quantities.

a) Explain the importance of sign conventions for thin lenses. What is the meaning of the negative sign in the magnification equation?

b) The lens equations only work for *thin* lenses. Outline how you would verify this using a transparent marble.

8. Suppose you are given a near object, a ruler, a screen, and a thin converging lens. Design a procedure to determine the focal length of the lens. Compare your value with the focal length provided by the manufacturer. Calculate the percent error of your value.

9. If you had constructed a "water magnifier" using a liquid other than water for the lens, would you obtain a different magnification as well? Try constructing a magnifier that uses drops of cooking oil for the lens instead of water. Compare your observations with those of the water magnifier.

11.3 Optical Instruments

Key Understandings

When you have completed this section, you will be able to:

- explain why converging lenses are used as magnifying glasses, in compound microscopes, movie projectors, and slide projectors, as well as in Keplerian, Galilean, and terrestrial telescopes
- explain why diverging lenses are also used in Galilean telescopes
- construct, test, and refine a prototype of a magnifying glass
- describe how slide and movie projectors reproduce images for the purposes of entertainment and culture
- analyze, describe, and explain optical effects that are produced by microscopes and telescopes

FIGURE 11.25 A jeweller uses a small magnifying glass called a loupe.

A jeweller uses a small magnifying glass called a loupe to examine the working parts of watches and the settings of diamond rings, including their quality (Figure 11.25). Field biologists use magnifying glasses to study specimens. Telescopes are used to magnify distant objects such as stars and planets. How does a magnifying glass work to magnify an image? Does it matter how far the magnifying glass is positioned from the object? What factor does the cross-sectional area of the lens affect? How have telescopes been improved over the years?

When you look at a moving object, its size seems to vary according to whether it is nearer or farther from you. The closer an object is to the eye, the larger the image produced on the retina. This is because the object forms a larger angle θ at the eye, as shown in Figure 11.26. An object at a distance of 40 cm from the eye appears about twice as large as an object at 80 cm because it makes an angle roughly twice as large. This explains why a small object is brought closer to the eye for examination. However, the eye cannot focus on objects closer than the **near point**. The near point for a normal eye is about 25 cm.

WEBLINK

Augustin Jean Fresnel, a French physicist (1788-1827) adopted the view that light was a transverse wave rather than a longitudinal wave, and he built up the necessary theoretical basis for it. How did Fresnel explain the double refraction produced by some crystals? Submit a concept map explaining what double refraction is. Begin your research at **www.pearsoned.ca/physics11.**

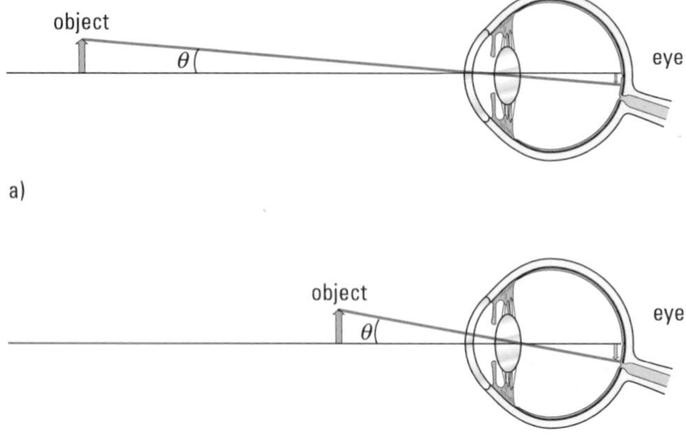

FIGURE 11.26 The closer an object is to the eye, the larger the image on the retina. The angle θ is larger in b) than in a). Therefore more detail is seen.

Discovering Physics — Converting a Diverging Meniscus Lens to a Magnifying Glass

A diverging meniscus lens, such as the one shown in Figure 11.27, is used to correct for myopia. It has one convex side and one concave side and is sometimes called a concavo-convex lens. This lens can be made into a converging lens and used by a farsighted person to read a newspaper.

1. Obtain a used diverging meniscus lens from an optometrist or borrow the glasses of a myopic person.
2. Hold the lens with the concave side up as shown. Look at some print through the lens.
3. Then use an eyedropper to fill the hollow well of the lens.
4. View the print again through the water and the lens.
   - Make a sketch of the side-view of the lens to show how you converted it from a diverging to a converging lens. Would it magnify as much as a lens made in this shape entirely of glass?
   - Can a converging meniscus lens be made to magnify more using this technique? Try it.

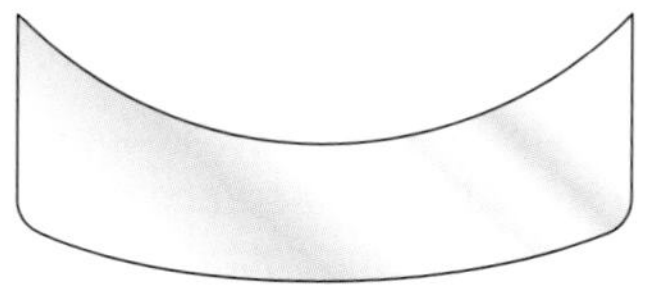

FIGURE 11.27 A concavo-convex lens used to correct for myopia.

INFOBIT

The surface of a Fresnel lens consists of a number of small narrow sections of converging lenses arranged in concentric circles on a plastic sheet (Figure 11.29). They are used where a large-diameter flat surface is desirable, as in a reading magnifier or an overhead projector. In an overhead projector, they concentrate light onto a transparency placed on the stage (Figure 11.30). They are also used in the field lens of a viewfinder, in the viewing screen of a reflex camera, in car headlights, and in searchlights. Fresnel lenses form images of lower quality than glass lenses.

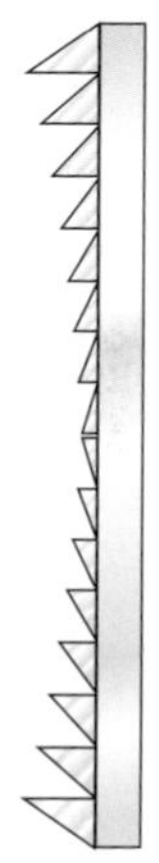

FIGURE 11.29 Cross-section of a Fresnel lens

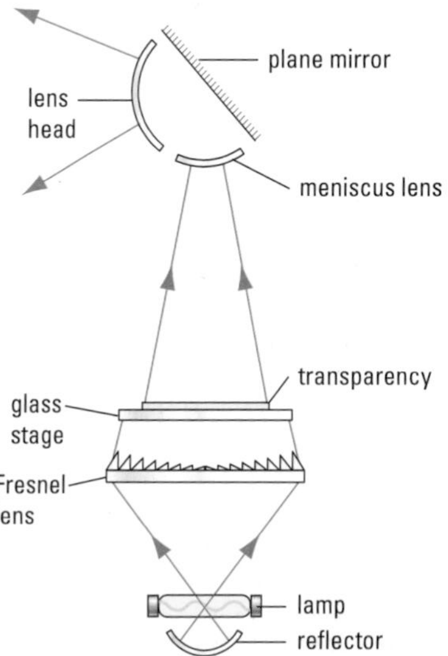

FIGURE 11.30 Optics of an overhead projector

A converging lens enables the eye to focus on objects closer than the near point, and thus allows one to see fine details better. The lens is placed next to the eye and the object is placed slightly inside the principal focus of the lens. Maximum magnification occurs when a virtual, enlarged, erect image is produced at the near point as shown in Figure 11.28. At this location, the image forms a larger angle with the lens than the object at the same location without the lens. A converging lens used in this way is called a **magnifying glass** or **hand magnifier**. A reading glass operates in the same way. So does the loupe used by jewellers. The maximum linear magnification of a hand magnifier without distortion is about 4×.

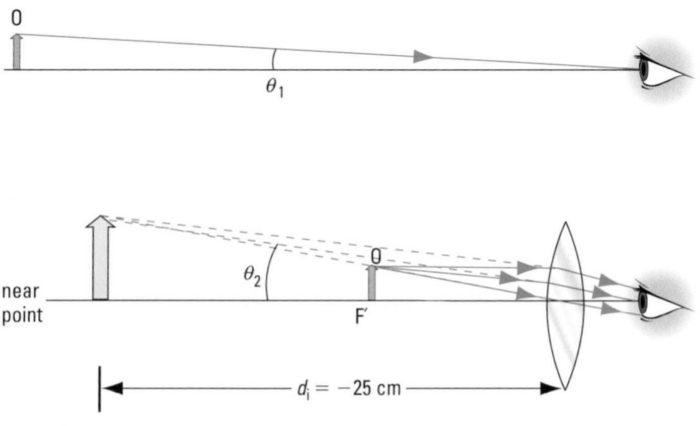

FIGURE 11.28 A simple magnifying glass enables an object to be brought closer to the eye than the near point.

EXAMPLE 2 NUMERICAL

A converging lens with a focal length of 8.0 cm is used as a magnifying glass by a person with a near point of 25 cm. The arrangement is similar to that shown in Figure 11.28. Calculate the maximum linear magnification of the magnifying glass.

Given

$d_i = -25 \text{ cm}$

$f = 8.0 \text{ cm}$

Required

m

Analysis

- The magnifying glass produces a virtual image at the near point.
- The image distance for a virtual image is negative.
- Use the lens equation and the sign conventions for thin lenses to determine the object distance.
- Apply the magnification equation.

Solution

$$\frac{1}{d_i} + \frac{1}{d_o} = \frac{1}{f}$$

$$\frac{1}{d_o} = \frac{1}{f} - \frac{1}{d_i}$$

$$= \frac{1}{8.0 \text{ cm}} - \frac{1}{-25 \text{ cm}}$$

$$= 0.17 \text{ cm}$$

$$d_o = 5.9 \text{ cm}$$

$$m = -\frac{d_i}{d_o}$$

$$= -\frac{(-25 \text{ cm})}{5.9 \text{ cm}}$$

$$= 4.2$$

Statement

The maximum magnification of the magnifying glass is 4.2×. Since the magnification is positive, the image is erect.

PRACTICE PROBLEMS

1. A converging lens with a focal length of 6.0 cm is used as a magnifying glass by a person whose near point is 24 cm. Calculate the maximum linear magnification of the magnifying glass.
2. A jeweller is using a loupe of focal length 5.0 cm to view a diamond. The jeweller's near point is 40 cm. Calculate the maximum linear magnification of the loupe.

By combining the magnification equation and the lens equation, eliminating d_o, defining N to be the absolute value of the near point of the eye, and making the image distance $d_i = N$, you obtain an equation for the magnification produced by a magnifying glass to be $m = \frac{N}{f} + 1$. Try to derive this equation.

Compound Microscopes

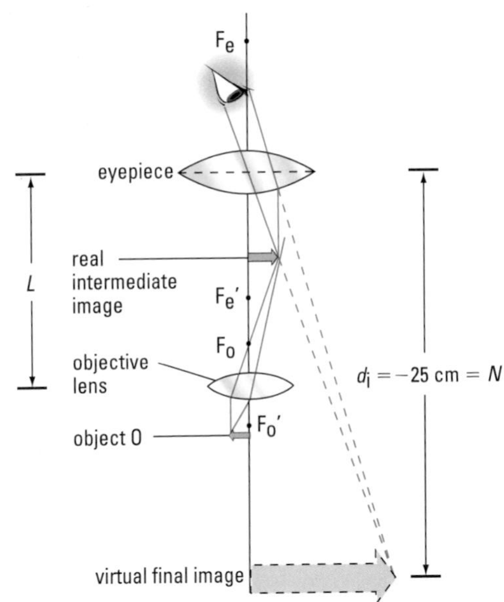

FIGURE 11.31 A compound microscope produces a final, virtual, inverted, and enlarged image of a near object.

Figure 11.31 shows how two converging lenses are arranged in a **compound microscope** to increase the linear magnification of close objects. The lens nearest the object is called the objective lens, which has many components combined to produce a short focal length lens. The object is placed slightly beyond the principal focus F_o'. The objective lens produces a real, enlarged, inverted image that serves as the object for the lens nearest the eye.

The lens closest to the eye is called the **eyepiece**. The focal length of the eyepiece is longer than the focal length of the objective lens. The intermediate image produced by the objective lens acts as the object for the eyepiece. Because it is slightly inside the principal focus of the eyepiece F_e', the eyepiece acts as a simple magnifying glass and produces a virtual, enlarged image at the near point. The final image is inverted with reference to the original object.

It can be shown that the magnification produced by a compound microscope is given by the equation $m = -\frac{N(L - f_e)}{f_o f_e}$ where N is the absolute value of the near point of the eye, L is the distance between the lenses, and f_e and f_o are the focal lengths of the eyepiece and objective lenses respectively. L must be larger than the sum of f_o and f_e. Notice that the magnification is greatest when the focal lengths of the two lenses are small, and the distance between the lenses is large. The following graphing calculator activity will allow you to analyze the relationship between the magnification m of a compound microscope and the focal length of the eyepiece f_e.

The First Compound Microscope

The first compound microscope was designed by Zacharias Janssen in 1595. He used a bi-convex lens for the eyepiece and a plano-convex lens for the objective. Three drawtubes were used as shown in Figure 11.32, with the lenses inserted in the ends. This microscope magnified between 3× and 10× depending on the extension of the drawtubes.

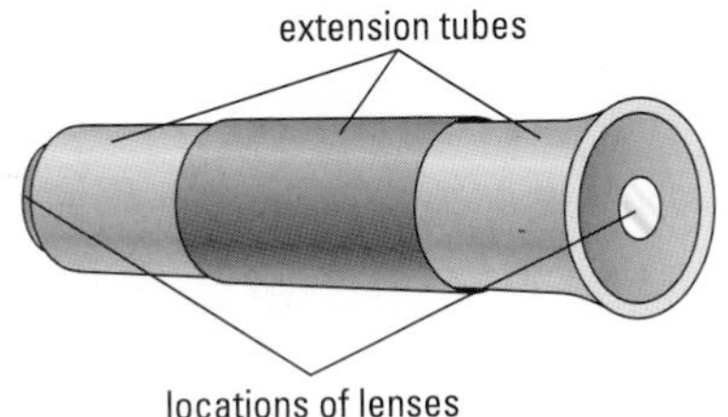

FIGURE 11.32

WEBLINK

Electron microscopes pass electrons through specimens (such as viruses) and produce vastly enlarged images on a photographic plate. Find out how they do this, and why they are more powerful than compound microscopes. Prepare a short report that includes a diagram. To view simulations of the operation of microscopes, look at **www.pearsoned.ca/physics11.**

Exploration Using a Graphing Calculator

Assume $L = 20$ cm, $f_o = 3.5$ cm, and the user has a near point N of 25 cm. The equation for the absolute value of the magnification produced by a compound microscope will simplify to $m = \frac{-25 \text{ cm } (20 \text{ cm} - f_e)}{3.5 \text{ cm} \times f_e}$. Use the calculator to plot the graph for values of f_e ranging from 0.2 cm to 1.0 cm and for magnification m from 130× to 710×. Examine the curve and study the relationship between magnification and the focal length of the eyepiece.

Discussion

1. As the focal length of the eyepiece increases, what happens to the magnification produced by the compound microscope?
2. To achieve the best magnification, what should be true about the focal length of the eyepiece?

WEBLINK

Johannes Kepler founded the science of modern optics, but was unable to deduce the general relationship describing refraction developed later by Snell. Research the contributions Kepler made to science and submit a short report. Begin your research at **www.pearsoned.ca/physics11.**

WEBLINK

Digital cameras are becoming very important because they bypass the need for photographic film. Find out how they work. Identify the strengths and weaknesses of digital cameras compared with film cameras, including cost, and submit a grid of your findings. Begin your research at **www.pearsoned.ca/physics11.**

EXAMPLE 3 NUMERICAL

The focal length of the objective lens of a compound microscope is 0.45 cm. The focal length of the eyepiece is 3.5 cm. The distance between the lenses is 18 cm. Calculate the magnification of this compound microscope if a person with a near point of 25 cm is viewing the specimen.

Given

$f_o = 0.45$ cm

$f_e = 3.5$ cm

$L = 18$ cm

$N = 25$ cm

Required

m of compound microscope

Analysis

- Use the equation to calculate the magnification.
- Remember to use the absolute value of the near point.

Solution

$$m = -\frac{N(L - f_e)}{f_o f_e}$$

$$= -\frac{25 \text{ cm } (18 \text{ cm} - 3.5 \text{ cm})}{(0.45 \text{ cm})(3.5 \text{ cm})}$$

$$= -230\times$$

Statement

The magnification produced by the compound microscope is −230×. The negative sign shows that the image is inverted with reference to the original object.

PRACTICE PROBLEMS

1. a) Determine the magnification of the objective lens in Example 3 Numerical, if the lens is used as a simple magnifying glass.
   b) By what factor does the eyepiece increase the angular magnification?
2. The lenses in a compound microscope are separated by 22 cm. The focal length of the eyepiece is 3.0 cm and of the objective lens is 0.35 cm. If a person with a near point of 30 cm uses the compound microscope, what is the angular magnification?

The total magnification of the compound microscope is the product of the magnification of the objective lens and the eyepiece as shown by the following equation:

$$m_t = m_o \times m_e$$

Common objective lenses have magnifications ranging from 10× to 100×. Common eyepiece lenses have magnifications of 5×, 10×, and 15×. The maximum magnification of a microscope with a 100× objective and 15× eyepiece is 1500×.

FIGURE 11.33 A slide projector

Slide and Movie Projectors

A slide or movie **projector** (Figure 11.33) is designed to focus an enlarged image of a scene onto a distant screen. The key components are an intense light source, a spherical converging mirror, a condensing lens system, and a projection lens.

The light source is located at the centre of curvature of the spherical converging mirror and at the principal focus of the condensing lens system. The mirror reverses light that would otherwise be lost and directs it toward the condensing lens system. The **condensing lens system** refracts the light and directs a parallel beam of light of uniform intensity toward the object.

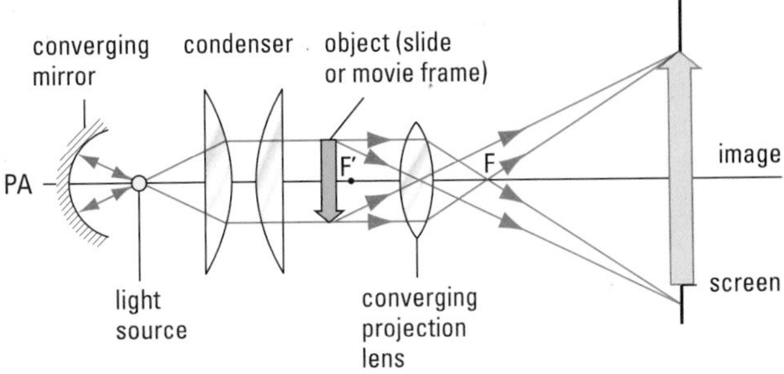

FIGURE 11.34 A slide projector produces a final, real, enlarged, and inverted image of a near object.

The object to be illuminated (slide or frame of a movie film) is placed upside down outside the principal focus of the projection lens, as shown in Figure 11.34. The position of the projection lens is adjusted until the image focussed on the screen is real, enlarged, and inverted, and thus the right way up for viewing.

FIGURE 11.35 Refracting telescope in an observatory

Telescopes

The telescope was accidentally discovered by the Dutch spectacle-maker Hans Lippershey. When one of his apprentices adjusted two lenses in front of his eyes, the apprentice was surprised to find that distant objects appeared even closer than with one lens. In 1608 Lippershey invented the first telescope, and he tried to sell it to the Dutch government. But recognizing its potential in warfare, the government decided to keep it a secret. However, Galileo, an Italian astronomer and physicist, learned of its existence from Lippershey and in 1609 built a modified version with a magnification of 32×. One of Galileo's telescopes found its way to Johannes Kepler, a German astronomer. Kepler modified it in 1611 by replacing the concave lens in Galileo's model with a convex lens.

The **Keplerian telescope** is commonly referred to as an **astronomical telescope**. It is used to view distant objects, such as planets and the Moon, and make them appear closer. As in a compound microscope, the astronomical telescope has two converging lenses—an objective lens and an eyepiece (Figure 11.36). The objective lens has a long focal length. Since the object is distant, the objective lens produces a real, diminished, inverted image at the principal focus of the objective lens. This image is positioned slightly inside the principal focus of the eyepiece. The eyepiece serves as a simple magnifying glass to produce a magnified, virtual, and inverted final image (with reference to the original

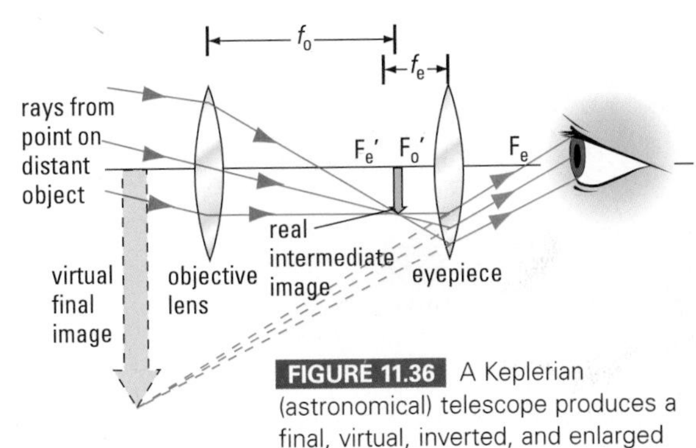

FIGURE 11.36 A Keplerian (astronomical) telescope produces a final, virtual, inverted, and enlarged image of a distant object.

WEBLINK

Laser surgery to correct eye defects is very popular today. But is it safe? How is it performed? Submit an agree/disagree chart evaluating the claim: "Laser surgery is safe for everyone." Begin your research at **www.pearsoned.ca/physics11.**

object). Since the two focal points almost overlap, the length of the Keplerian telescope is approximately equal to the algebraic sum of the focal lengths of the objective lens and the eyepiece lens.

The magnification produced by a Keplerian telescope is given by the equation $m = \frac{f_o}{f_e}$. The larger the focal length of the objective lens and the smaller the focal length of the eyepiece, the greater the magnification of the telescope.

Galilean Telescopes

Investigation
Refer to page 435. Investigation 2

In 1609 Galileo heard that Hans Lippershey, an optician in Holland, had invented a magnifying tube made using two lenses. Within six months Galileo invented his own version using a converging and a diverging lens (Figure 11.37). His telescope had a magnifying power of $+32\times$ and was useful for viewing the landscape because it produced a magnified erect image.

The **Galilean telescope** is housed in a relatively short tube and produces a magnified upright image. The length of the Galilean telescope is about equal to the algebraic sum of the focal lengths of the objective lens and the eyepiece. Because the instrument is short and lightweight, the same principle is used in making opera glasses. The Galilean telescope has two disadvantages: it has a lower magnification than the Keplerian telescope, and it diverges some of the light away from the eye, resulting in a dimmer image. Therefore, the objective lens needs to have a larger cross-sectional area.

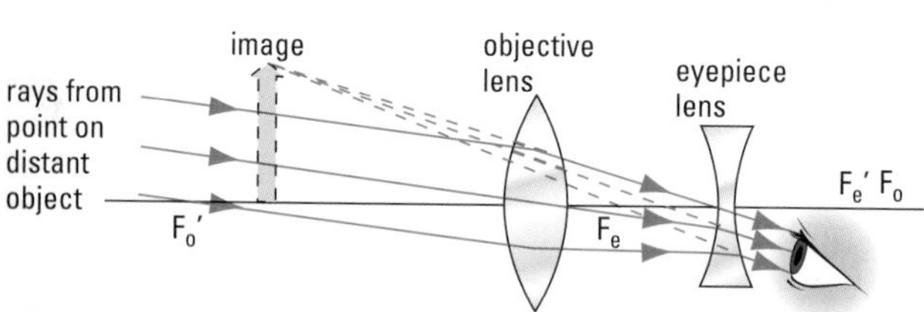

FIGURE 11.37 A Galilean telescope uses a diverging lens as the eyepiece to produce a magnified, erect, and virtual image. What would the image look like if the lenses were reversed?

EXAMPLE 4 **CONCEPTUAL**

A Galilean telescope has the following specifications: $f_o = 500$ mm and $f_e = -50$ mm. What is the magnification of the telescope? What is the approximate length of the telescope?

Reasoning and Solution

The magnification of the Galilean telescope is the ratio of the focal length of the objective lens to the focal length of the eyepiece. Since the eyepiece consists of a diverging lens, the focal length is given a negative sign.

$$m = -\frac{f_o}{f_e}$$

$$= -\frac{500 \text{ mm}}{-50 \text{ mm}}$$

$$= +10\times$$

The magnification of the telescope is about $10\times$. The final image is erect as indicated by the positive sign. The distance between the lenses is about equal to the algebraic sum of the focal lengths. Hence the length of the telescope is about 450 mm.

CHALLENGE

A Galilean telescope has the following specifications: $f_e = -40$ mm and magnification is $+12\times$. What is the focal length of the objective lens, and what is the approximate length of the telescope?

Terrestrial Telescopes

Since a **terrestrial telescope** is used to view objects on Earth, such as structures and animals, it is designed to produce an erect image. The terrestrial telescope is similar to a Keplerian telescope except for a third converging lens, called a **field lens**, located between the objective lens and the eyepiece (Figure 11.38). The field lens inverts the first image produced by the objective lens. This ensures that the magnified final image produced by the eyepiece has the same attitude as the object.

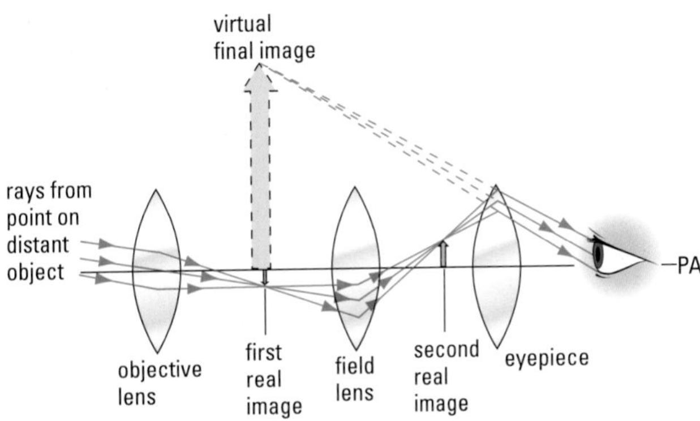

FIGURE 11.38 A terrestrial telescope uses an intermediate lens called a field lens to invert the first image to yield a final, virtual, erect, and enlarged image of a distant object.

Section 11.3 Review

Understanding Concepts

1. What are the key differences between an astronomical and a terrestrial telescope in structure and in function?
2. A hand magnifier of focal length 10 cm is used by a person with a near point of 30 cm. Calculate the object distance and the maximum magnification.
3. Where is the intermediate image of the compound microscope located with reference to the principal focus of the objective and eyepiece lenses?
4. A compound microscope is being used by a person with a near point of 22 cm. Focal lengths of the lenses are 3.2 cm and 0.40 cm. The lenses are separated by a distance of 20 cm. What is the magnification of the combination of the two lenses?
5. State the function in a movie projector of:
   a) the spherical converging mirror
   b) the condensing lens system
6. The objective lens of a Keplerian telescope has a focal length of 950 mm and the eyepiece a focal length of 45.0 mm.
   a) What is the magnification of the telescope?
   b) Approximately how long is the telescope?
7. Describe the change in the image produced by the eyepiece of a properly adjusted Keplerian telescope, if the objective lens is moved
   a) farther from the eyepiece
   b) closer to the eyepiece
8. The objective lens of a Galilean telescope has a focal length of 660 mm and the eyepiece a focal length of −60 mm.
   a) What is the magnification of the telescope?
   b) About how long is the telescope?
9. Why is a converging lens rather than a diverging lens used as a hand magnifier?
10. Why is the object not placed at the focal point of a hand magnifier?
11. State two advantages and two disadvantages of the Galilean telescope.

Applying Inquiry/ Communication Skills

12. Using a biology textbook, find the meaning of the following terms and phrases pertaining to a microscope: resolving power, field of view, ocular, and power.
13. How will the magnification produced by a hand magnifier change if it is immersed in water? Explain your prediction. Then design and perform an experiment to test your prediction.
14. A parallel beam of light is to be produced by a disc jockey. The beam will consist of an intense point light source and a lens.
    a) Recommend whether a diverging or a converging lens should be used. Why?

b) Where should the light source be placed with reference to the focal point of the lens? Why?

15. Suppose you are viewing a sample of lake water through a compound microscope. You notice that a tiny organism is moving from left to right. Which way is the organism actually moving? Explain.

Making Connections

16. Contrast the location and attitude of the specimen in a microscope with the film in a movie projector.

11.4 The Camera

Key Understandings

When you have completed this section, you will be able to:

- explain why a converging lens is used in a camera
- analyze, describe, and explain optical effects that are produced by cameras

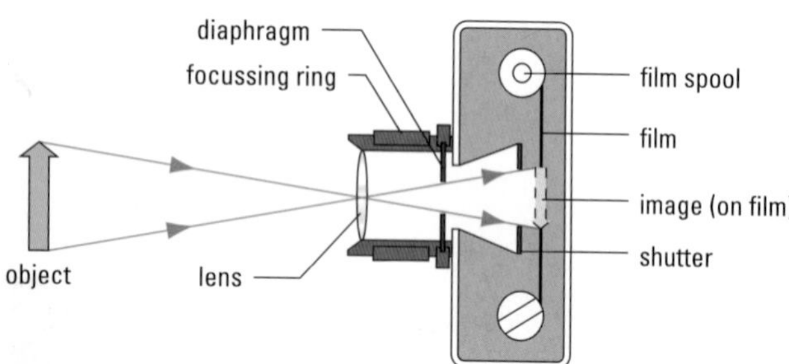

FIGURE 11.39 The parts of a simple camera

Unless you are using an automatic camera, two variables need to be adjusted to control the amount of light reaching the film: the size of the opening and how long the shutter is open (Figure 11.39). A third factor—depth of field—determines how much of the object is in focus. What is shutter speed, and why is the term a misnomer? What role does the size of the opening play in depth of field?

A camera essentially consists of a lightproof box with a lens at one end to form a real, inverted image on a light-sensitive film or plate at the other end. The converging lens in a camera focusses a real, inverted image on the film, as shown in Figure 11.39. Black-and-white film is coated with a light-sensitive chemical called silver bromide. For a distant object, the image distance d_i is equal to the focal length of the lens. For nearer objects, the focussing ring must be turned to move the lens farther from the film, so that the image is still focussed on the film.

The amount of light reaching the film is controlled in two ways:

- The shutter controls the length of time the light is let in.
- The **diaphragm** controls the size of the aperture (the hole light passes through).

The camera is designed as a lightproof box. The **shutter** can be adjusted to be open for a certain length of time, which is referred to as **shutter speed**. The term can be misleading, though, because it has nothing to do with speed. The amount of light entering the camera is directly proportional to the time the shutter is open. On high-quality cameras, the shutter speed can be adjusted from 1/1000 s to 1 s or longer. Each succeeding shutter setting increases the open time and hence the amount of light reaching the film.

EXAMPLE 5 NUMERICAL

A lens with a focal length of 50 mm is used to photograph a distant object. It is then used to photograph an object 1.0 m from the lens. How far must the focussing ring move the lens away from the film to focus the near object clearly?

Given

$f = 50 \text{ mm} = 5.0 \text{ cm}$

a) d_o = infinity when $d_i = 5.0$ cm
b) $d_o = 1.0 \text{ m} = 100 \text{ cm}$

Required

Δd_i

Analysis

- The image of a distant object is focussed at F, so the distance between the lens and the film is 5.0 cm.
- The image of a nearer object is focussed behind F. The lens must be moved away from the film until the image is captured on it.
- Both f and d_o are positive.

Solution

a) $d_i = 5.0$ cm

b) $$\frac{1}{d_o} + \frac{1}{d_i} = \frac{1}{f}$$

$$\frac{1}{d_i} = \frac{1}{f} - \frac{1}{d_o}$$

$$= \frac{1}{5.0 \text{ cm}} - \frac{1}{100 \text{ cm}}$$

$$= 0.19 \text{ cm}^{-1}$$

$$d_i = 5.26 \text{ cm}$$

$$\Delta d_i = 5.26 \text{ cm} - 5.0 \text{ cm}$$
$$= 0.26 \text{ cm}$$
$$= 2.6 \text{ mm}$$

Statement

The lens must be moved outward 2.6 mm to focus the camera on the near object.

PRACTICE PROBLEM

A lens with a focal length of 35 mm is used to photograph an object 0.50 m from the lens. It is then used to photograph a car in the distance. How far must the focussing ring be moved and in what direction?

The diameter of the aperture is controlled by the iris diaphragm. The quantity of light passing through the aperture is directly proportional to its cross-sectional area. For example, if you double the diameter, you have quadrupled the area and hence the image brightness.

Shutter speed and aperture both affect the amount of light entering the camera. Ideally, all the light should reach the film, but the more it spreads out, the less the intensity of the light falling on the film. The intensity of light reaching the film is affected by the focal length of the lens. The longer the focal length, the farther the film is from the lens, and the more the light spreads out.

INFOBIT

Miniature cameras inside capsules about 3 cm long are now being used to map the human intestine. Each pill takes about 24 h to pass through the intestine and transmits two still images per second to the outside. Doctors are using these images to diagnose the condition of the intestine in place of endoscopy—an uncomfortable invasive procedure.

Depth of Field

Depth of field is the range of object distances for which the images appear clearly focussed on the film. Figures 11.40 and 11.41 show how aperture size affects depth of field. The photographer has focussed the camera to obtain a sharp image on the film of the closer object T. The image of the more distant object S is focussed in front of the film. Ray 1 from object S is parallel to the principal axis, while ray 3 passes through the optical centre of the lens. Rays 1, 2, and 3 come to a focus at the tip of the image S′. In the diagram, the film is 0.8 cm away from the image S′. As a result, ray 1 has diverged 4 mm from ray 3 before it hits the film, while ray 2 has only diverged 1.2 mm. What would have been a point on the image becomes a circle of radius 4 mm if ray 1 is allowed to reach the film. If the size of the aperture is decreased so that ray 1 is blocked out, but ray 2 is allowed to reach the film, the circle has a radius of only 1.2 mm. The image of the farther object is in better focus on the film when the size of the aperture is decreased. The smaller the diameter of the aperture, the less blurred the background becomes. However, as the depth of field is increased, the shutter must be open longer. And if the object being photographed is moving quickly, a blurred image can result. The amount of light available also limits the depth of field.

FIGURE 11.41 The longer the shutter is open, the greater the depth of field.

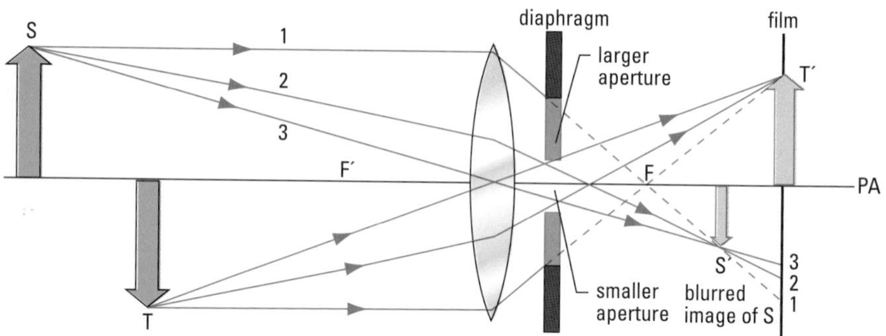

FIGURE 11.40 The smaller the aperture, the greater the depth of field. If the camera is focussed on T, the image of S is in sharper focus when the aperture is smaller.

Section 11.4 Review

Understanding Concepts

1. What is the difference between the functions of the shutter and the diaphragm of a camera?

Applying Inquiry/ Communication Skills

2. Research fish-eye lenses. How are they designed to provide a wide field of view?
3. Look at the specifications for a wide-angle lens and a regular lens. How are they similar? How are they different?
4. Write a consumer report on the kinds of compound lenses made for cameras. In your report indicate the diameter of the lenses, the range of focal lengths, their cost, and the function of each.

Making Connections

5. A wide-angled lens has a focal length of 28 mm. What range of motion must the focussing ring have to enable this lens to focus an object 50 cm from the lens?

11.5 The Eye

Key Understandings

When you have completed this section, you will be able to:

- explain why the eye uses a converging lens
- predict, using ray diagrams and algebraic equations, the image position and characteristics of a converging contact lens
- evaluate the effectiveness of eyeglasses, contact lenses, and laser surgery with regard to human perception of light

Our eyes are our windows to the world. Without them we would experience eternal darkness. That is why it is important to look after them and to have periodic eye examinations (Figure 11.42). What are the parts of the eye, and how do they work together? How can technological devices or procedures be used to improve vision? What is meant by the "power" of a lens?

FIGURE 11.42 An optometrist uses equipment with several lenses to test your eyesight.

Parts of the Eye

Figure 11.43 is a sketch of a section of the human eye. The eye is a sphere about 3 cm in diameter. Light enters the eye through the convex **cornea**. Because of its curvature and high refractive index (1.38) compared to air (1.00), about 70% of the refraction of light takes place at the front surface of the cornea. A person under water without goggles has poor vision because light entering the cornea directly from water (n = 1.33) is refracted very little. Goggles, which create an air space in front of the eye, correct this problem.

Light leaving the cornea travels through the **aqueous humour** (liquid) to the **lens**. The convex jelly-like lens contains minute transparent fibres. These fibres slide over one another when the **ciliary muscle** contracts and relaxes to change the shape of the lens. The lens is connected to the ciliary muscles by the **suspensory ligaments**. A coloured **iris** in front of the lens controls the size of the **pupil**. Fully open, the pupil has a diameter of about 8 mm; when contracted, its diameter is 2 mm. The pupil can vary the intensity of light reaching the retina by a factor of 16. Chromatic aberration occurs in the human eye. As a result, blue light is bent the most and red light the least by the cornea and lens. Fortunately, under normal circumstances, your brain compensates for this chromatic aberration.

Light leaving the lens passes through the **vitreous humour** (which helps maintain the shape of the eye) and reaches the **retina**, the light-sensitive lining of the cavity of the eye. The retina contains two types of light-sensitive cells: rods and cones. **Rods** are sensitive to dim light, do not register colour, and are more numerous farther away from the fovea. The **fovea** contains only **cones** and is the most sensitive area for bright light and colour. Cones require a greater intensity of light than rods in order to be stimulated. Thus, we lose our ability to sense colour in dim light. The concentration of cones

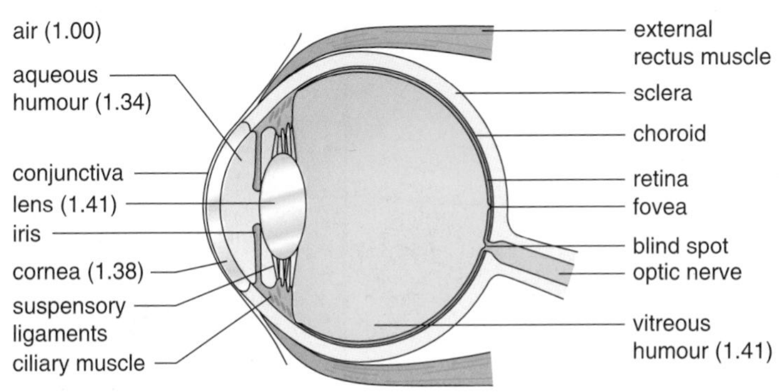

FIGURE 11.43 Parts of the human eye

decreases as the distance from the fovea increases. A small area near the optic nerve is called the **blind spot** because it contains no photoreceptors.

The image formed on the retina is inverted. The **optic nerve** carries the electrical information from the rods and cones to the brain. Fortunately, the image from the retina is re-inverted by the brain.

Discovering Physics — *Measuring the Diameter of Your Blind Spot*

Work in groups of three with one person being the experimenter, one the measurer, and the third the recorder. Rotate roles. You will need a metre-stick for this activity.

1. Copy the following table into your notebook.

Eye Open	Disappearance Distance Δd_1 (cm)	Reappearance Distance Δd_2 (cm)	Calculated Diameter of Blind Spot w (cm)
right			
left			

2. Draw a large dark dot and a star separated by a distance $\Delta s = 12$ cm.
3. Position the dot in front of your right eye at arm's length.
4. Close your left eye and move the dot slowly toward your face. When the star first disappears, measure and record the perpendicular distance from your eye to the paper Δd_1.
5. Move the paper closer to the eye. When the star re-appears, measure and record the perpendicular distance from your eye to the paper Δd_2.
6. Close your right eye and position the star in front of your left eye. Repeat the procedure.

Figure 11.44 shows the geometry involved in estimating (for the right eye) the width of the blind spot. The width of the blind spot w is given by the equation

$$w \cong r\left[\tan^{-1}\left(\frac{\Delta d_2}{s}\right) - \tan^{-1}\left(\frac{\Delta d_2}{s}\right)\right]$$

where r is the distance between the retina and the optical centre of the lens (1.7 cm).

- Use a calculator to estimate the width of the blind spot for each eye.
- Is the width the same for each eye?
- Is the width the same for different people?
- What are the sources of error in the activity?
- Refer to Figure 11.44 and derive the equation for the width of the blind spot. Show your work.

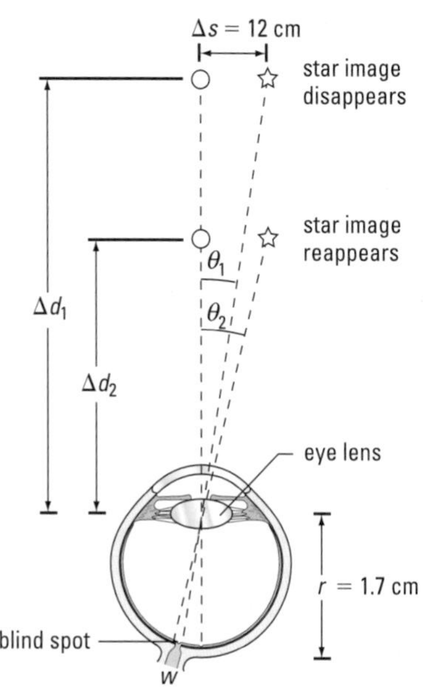

FIGURE 11.44

Accommodation

Recall that in the case of the camera, the image is focussed by adjusting the distance of the lens from the film. This is done differently in the eye. **Accommodation** is the process of changing the focal length of the lens to adjust for near and far objects. Accommodation is controlled by nerve signals from the retina. The ciliary muscle and suspensory ligaments adjust the shape of the lens to focus the images of near or far objects on the retina. When the ciliary muscle and eye are relaxed, the suspensory ligaments stretch the lens, making it flatter. This is how the image of a distant object is focussed. The **far point** of an eye is the location of the farthest object on which a fully relaxed eye can focus. Rays entering the eye are parallel and the principal focus is at the retina, as shown in Figure 11.45a). The closer the object, the more the ciliary muscle contracts, allowing the lens to become shorter and fatter. The more convex the lens, the shorter the focal length and the more the light rays are refracted. This is shown in Figure 11.45b). The near point at which most adults can focus is assumed to be 25 cm for normal vision. However, children with normal vision can focus on objects as close as 7 cm from the eye.

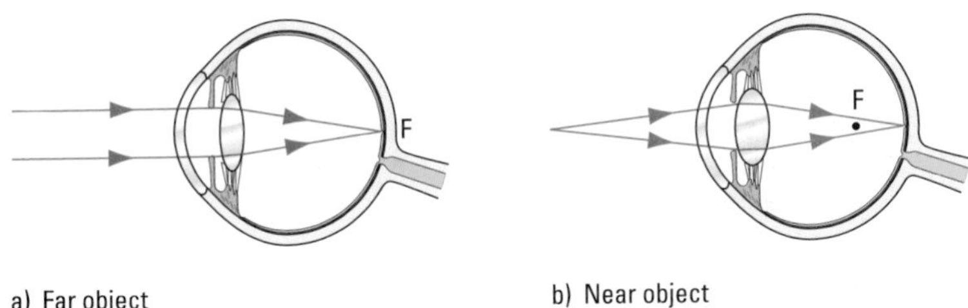

FIGURE 11.45 During accommodation, the lens changes shape to focus the image on the retina as the object distance changes.

Technological Devices Improve Vision

Myopia, or **nearsightedness**, is the inability of the eye to focus light from distant objects onto the retina—either the eyeball is too long or the convex lens is curved too much. As a result, the light focusses in the vitreous humour in front of the retina, and the image on the retina is blurred, as shown in Figure 11.46a). Myopia is corrected by wearing glasses or contact lenses that have diverging meniscus lenses. The lens refracts the rays before they reach the cornea. This enables the lens of the eye to focus the image on the retina, as shown in Figure 11.46b).

WEBLINK

To see simulations of how various eye defects can be corrected with lenses, go to **www.pearsoned.ca/physics11**.

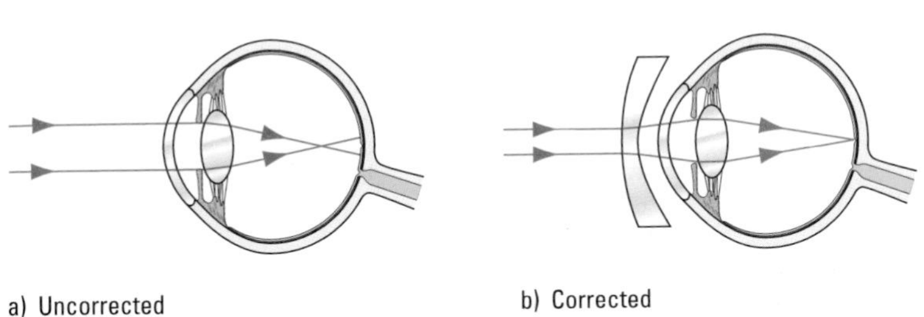

FIGURE 11.46 Correcting myopia (nearsightedness)

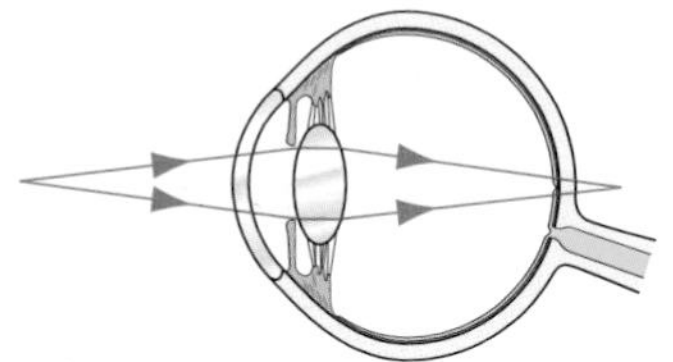

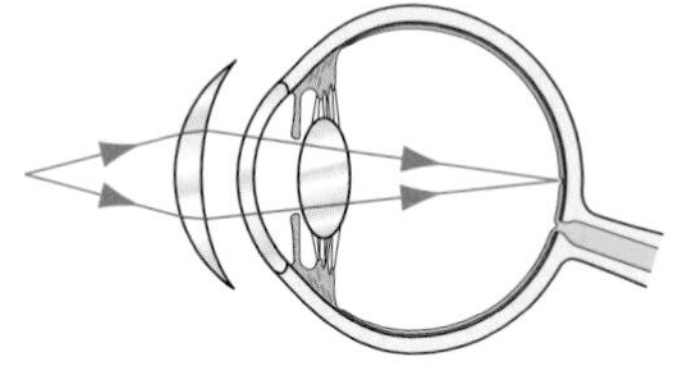

FIGURE 11.47 Correcting hyperopia (farsightedness)

Hyperopia, or **farsightedness**, is the inability of the eye to focus light from near objects onto the retina—either the lens is too flat or the eyeball is too short. This causes the light to focus behind the retina, as shown in Figure 11.47a). Hyperopia is corrected by using a converging meniscus lens to refract the rays before they reach the cornea. The eye lens can then refract the rays enough to focus the image on the retina, as in Figure 11.47b).

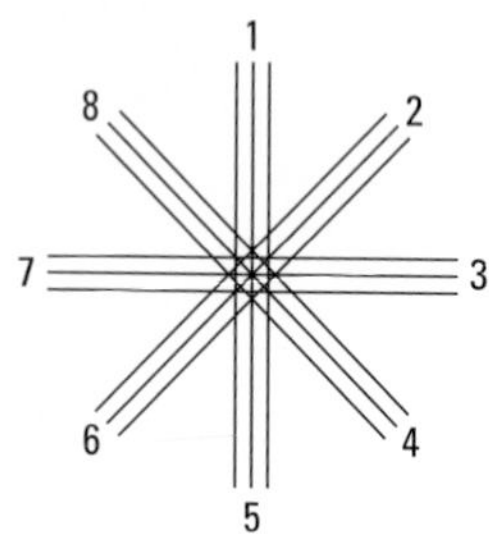

FIGURE 11.48 A test for astigmatism

Astigmatism is the inability of the eye to focus light in different planes at the same time. A common test for this is to look at a system of crossed lines (Figure 11.48). For an astigmatic eye, only the lines in one plane are in focus at a given instant. The eye accommodates continually in an attempt to bring the others into focus, causing eye fatigue. Astigmatism is due to different curvatures of the cornea (or sometimes the lens) in different planes. This defect is corrected by using a lens that has a cylindrical curvature, as shown in Figure 11.49.

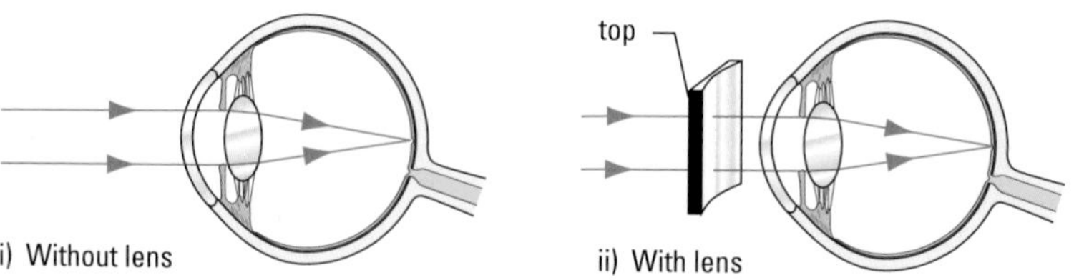

a) Top view of the eye. The concave cylindrical lens is straight in this plane and does not refract the rays.

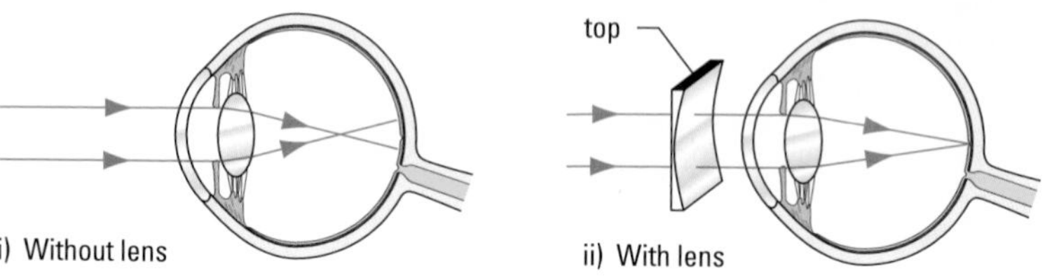

b) Side view of the eye. The concave cylindrical lens diverges the rays in this plane.

FIGURE 11.49 Correcting astigmatism using a cylindrical concave lens

The Power of a Lens

Opticians refer to the **optical power** P of a lens instead of its focal length. When two or more lenses are used, the optical power of the combination is the sum of the individual powers. The power of a lens, expressed in diopters D, is the reciprocal of the focal length in metres.

$$P \text{ (diopters)} = \frac{1}{f \text{ (metres)}}$$

Optical power is positive for converging and negative for diverging lenses. For example, a diverging lens of focal length -50 cm has an optical power of $1/(-0.50 \text{ m})$, or -2.0 D. The higher the optical power of a lens, the shorter its focal length.

EXAMPLE 6 NUMERICAL

A nearsighted person can focus on objects no farther than 20 cm from the eye. What power of contact lens is needed to enable the eye to focus on distant objects clearly?

Given

d_o = infinity

d_i = 20 cm from the eye

Required

P

Analysis

- A contact lens rests on the cornea.
- The contact lens must produce a virtual image of an object at infinity, 20 cm in front of the lens. Therefore, the image distance is negative.
- If d_o is very large, then $1/d_o \approx 0$

Solution

$$\frac{1}{f} = \frac{1}{d_o} + \frac{1}{d_i}$$

$$= 0 + \frac{1}{-20 \text{ cm}}$$

$$= 0.050 \text{ cm}^{-1}$$

$$f = -20 \text{ cm}$$

$$P = \frac{1}{f}$$

$$= \frac{1}{-0.20 \text{ m}}$$

$$= -5.0 \text{ D}$$

Statement

The power of the lens is −5.0 D. The negative sign indicates that it is a diverging lens.

INSIGHT

When using the lens equation, image and object distances must be measured from the lens, not the eye. A contact lens rests on the eye, but eyeglasses are worn some distance from the eye.

PRACTICE PROBLEMS

1. A nearsighted person wears contact lenses having a power of −2.5 D. What is the far point for this person?
2. A farsighted person wears contact lenses of power +1.5 D to read a computer screen 40 cm away.
   a) What is the person's near point without contact lenses?
   b) What focal length of contact lenses does the person need to read a book 25 cm away?
3. A farsighted person has a near point that is 50.0 cm from her or his eyes. Wearing glasses enables her or him to read print at a distance of 30.0 cm. See Figure 11.50.
   a) Find the focal length of eyeglass lenses if they are worn 2.0 cm away.
   b) Calculate the power of the lenses.

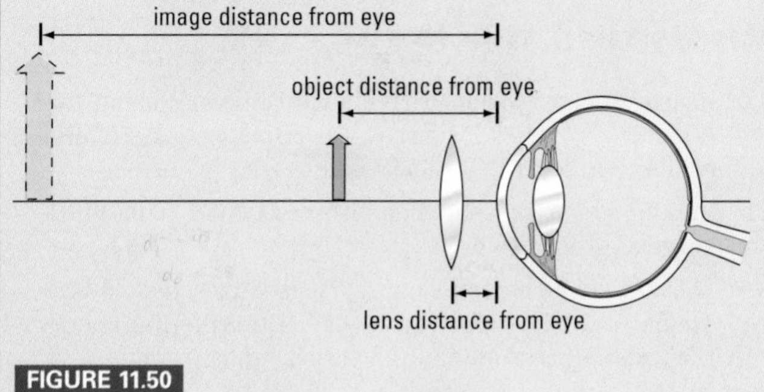

FIGURE 11.50

Evaluating Laser Vision Correction

Decision-Making Skills

- Defining the Issue
- Developing Assessment Criteria
- Researching the Issue
- Analyzing Data and Information
- Proposing a Course of Action
- Justifying the Course of Action
- Communicating Your Proposal

BACKGROUND INFORMATION

Laser vision correction uses an excimer laser to adjust the focal length of the eye by changing the curvature of the cornea. Excimer lasers apply ultraviolet light of wavelength 193 nm to vaporize tiny amounts of tissue from the cornea. The process of removing tissue from the cornea is called ablation. The cornea is a five-layer structure (Figure 11.51).

There are two ways that the laser can be used to ablate tissue and provide a refractive correction (Figure 11.52). One technique is called photorefractive keratectomy (PRK). In the PRK process, the epithelium is removed using chemicals, then the laser is used to ablate some stroma tissue just below the epithelium.

Another technique is called LASIK. Here, the epithelium is left intact. An instrument called a microkeratome is used to cut a thin flap of tissue that includes the epithelium from the front surface of the cornea. This flap is folded back exposing the stroma. Once the stroma layer is ablated with the laser, the flap is returned to its original position over the remaining stroma.

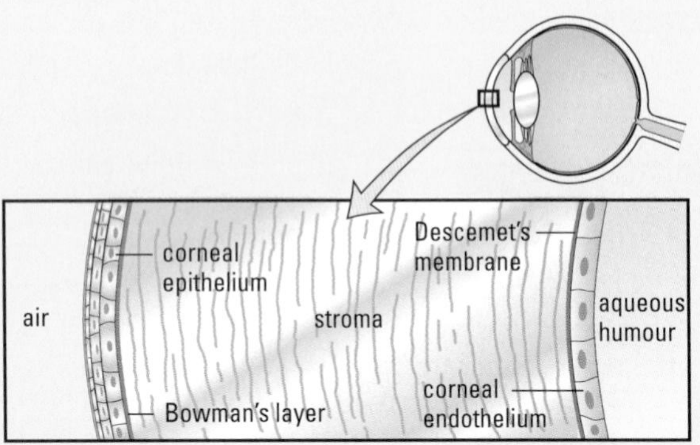

FIGURE 11.51 The cornea has five layers. Tissue is removed from the front of the stroma.

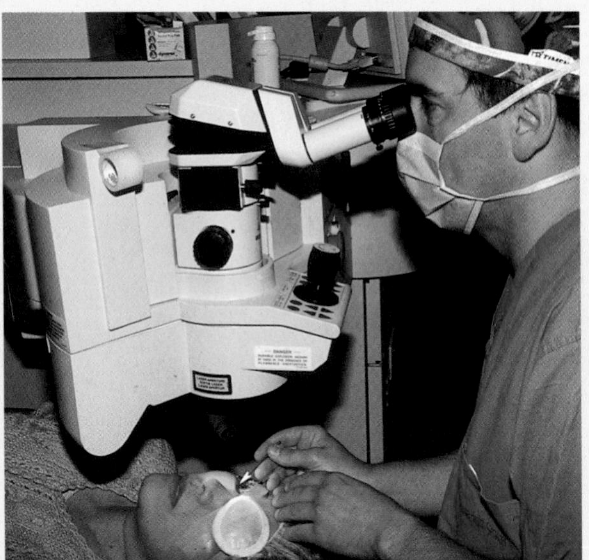

FIGURE 11.52 Laser surgery to correct an eye defect

Analyzing the Issue

1. Research laser vision correction technology using the Internet and other resources. Describe the types of disorders that laser eye sugery is intended to correct.
2. Identify the risks and benefits associated with these surgical procedures.
3. Laser vision correction surgery is advertised in the media (i.e. television, radio, etc.). Describe the effects that media promotion of the surgery may have.
4. Propose a course of action for assessing whether laser vision correction surgery would be apporpriate for you.
5. Debate the question, "Is laser vision correction surgery safe?" Consider the social, technological, and economic factors that may affect your position.

Section 11.5 Review

Understanding Concepts

1. Where does most of the refraction take place for the eye?
2. Explain the process called accommodation.
3. Calculate the power of the following lenses:
   a) $f = 20$ cm
   b) $f = -40$ cm
4. A farsighted eye can focus on an object no closer than 1.5 m away. Calculate the power and kind of contact lens required to enable this eye to focus on print 30 cm away.

Applying Inquiry/ Communication Skills

5. Draw diagrams to illustrate myopia and hyperopia.
6. Draw diagrams to show how to correct for myopia and hyperopia.
7. Explain why a person swimming under water without goggles has poor vision while one swimming with goggles has ordinary vision.
8. Research how an eagle's eye differs from a human eye to enable it to distinguish more clearly between two distant objects. Submit a report on your findings.
9. If you wanted to use a friend's eyeglasses as a magnifying glass, would you ask someone who is nearsighted or farsighted?
10. Write an explanation of how the human eye works, for two readers:
    - your science teacher who understands scientific terms; and
    - your friend who is several grades behind you

WEBLINK

Exciting careers exist in the fields of medical optics. Find out about these careers and what qualifications are necessary to enrol in courses leading to these careers. Summarize your findings in a chart. Begin your research at **www.pearsoned.ca/physics11.**

Investigation 1 (Section 11.1)

Inquiry Skills

- Initiating and Planning
- Applying Technical Skills
- Using Tools, Materials, Equipment
- Conducting and Recording
- Analyzing and Interpreting
- Concluding and Communicating

Images Formed by a Converging Lens

Suggest some ways to measure the focal length of a converging lens. One method is to direct parallel rays toward the lens, find the focal point with a screen, and measure the distance from the centre of the lens to the focal point. The rays from a distant source reaching a thin lens of small diameter are considered to be parallel. How do you think the characteristics of an image will change as the object is brought closer to a converging lens? Make predictions before doing the activity.

Problem

What are the characteristics of the images formed by a converging lens as the object changes position?

Materials

- optical bench
- converging lens
- object (light source)
- paper screen

Caution: When using a candle as the light source, tie back long hair, secure loose clothing, and avoid sudden movements.

Experimental Design

1. Design and implement a procedure to determine the focal length of your converging lens.
2. Design and implement a procedure using the equipment shown in Figure 11.53 to determine the image distance d_i and the image characteristics (kind, attitude, and magnification) for the following object distances d_o: $2.5f$, $2.0f$, $1.5f$, $1.0f$, and $0.50f$. You will have to use the zero parallax method to find the position of any virtual images.
3. Create a data table to record your measurements and the image characteristics.

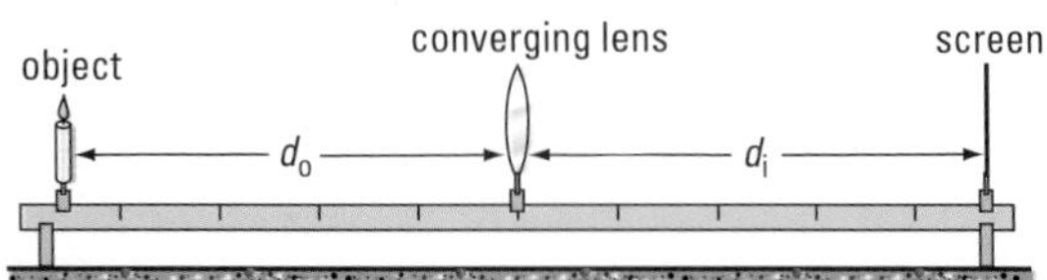

FIGURE 11.53 The images formed by a converging lens

Analyzing and Interpreting

1. As the object moved from $2.5f$ toward the principal focus F′, what happened to:
   a) the size of the image?
   b) the location of the image?
   c) the attitude of the image?
2. Why was no image formed when the object was at $1.0f$?
3. a) Describe the characteristics of the image when the object is between the principal focus F′ and the lens.
   b) Where was this image with reference to the lens and the object?
   c) Why was it impossible to focus the image on the screen?

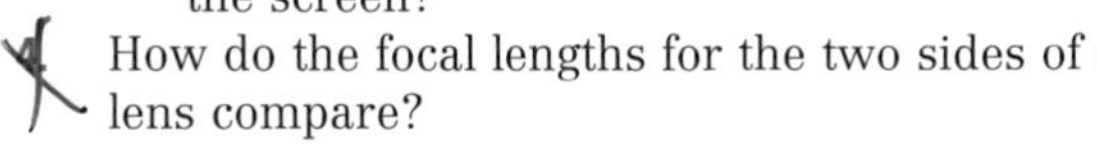

4. How do the focal lengths for the two sides of a lens compare?

Concluding and Communicating

5. Where must the object be placed with reference to the principal focus to produce
   a) a real image?
   b) a virtual image?
6. A projectionist wishes to produce an image of an object that is the same size and inverted. Where should the object be placed with reference to the focal point?
7. When you look through a magnifying glass are you seeing a real or a virtual image? How do you know?

Extending

8. Use black tape to cover the top half of the converging lens. Predict what the image of an object will look like for this lens. Write down your prediction and reasoning before doing the experiment. Set up the equipment as shown in Figure 11.53. Place the object at $2f$ and catch the image on a screen. Describe the image. What characteristic of the image has changed as a result of covering the top half of the lens? Explain the results.

Investigation 2 (Section 11.3)

Inquiry Skills

- Initiating and Planning
- Applying Technical Skills
- Using Tools, Materials, Equipment
- Conducting and Recording
- Analyzing and Interpreting
- Concluding and Communicating

Properties of Telescopes

In this activity you will be constructing and examining a Keplerian and a Galilean telescope.

Problem

What are the differences between Galilean and Keplerian telescopes?

Materials

- long–focal-length converging lens
- short–focal-length converging lens
- short–focal-length diverging lens
- two lens holders
- optical bench
- screen
- screen support

Caution: Never look directly at the Sun through a telescope.

Procedure

1. Mount a converging lens with a long focal length at one end of the optical bench. This is the objective lens of both telescopes.
2. Use the screen and a distant object to find the principal focus of the objective lens.
3. Mount a diverging lens, with a short focal length, halfway between the objective lens and its principal focus, as shown in Figure 11.54. This is to be the eyepiece for the Galilean telescope.

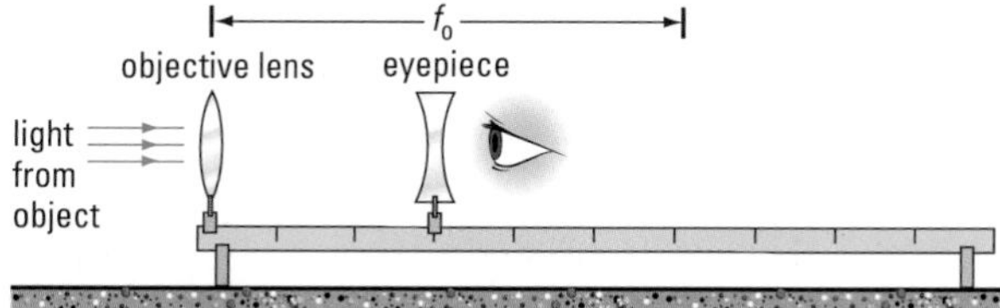

FIGURE 11.54 A model of a Galilean telescope

4. Draw a series of vertical, equally spaced, black lines on a card. Draw a line across the top to indicate which direction is up. Position the card at the far end of the room.
5. Keep both eyes open and place one eye in front of the eyepiece.
6. Look at the lines both through the telescope and with the unaided eye.
7. Compare the attitude of the object and the image.
8. Estimate how many spaces seen with the unaided eye fit into one space seen through the telescope. This represents the magnification.
9. Remove the diverging lens.
10. Determine the focal length of the short–focal-length converging lens. Use it as the eyepiece of the Keplerian telescope.
11. Mount the eyepiece on the optical bench so that the distance between the objective lens and the eyepiece is slightly less than the sum of their focal lengths (i.e. their focal lengths overlap slightly), as shown in Figure 11.55.
12. Repeat steps 5, 6, 7, and 8.

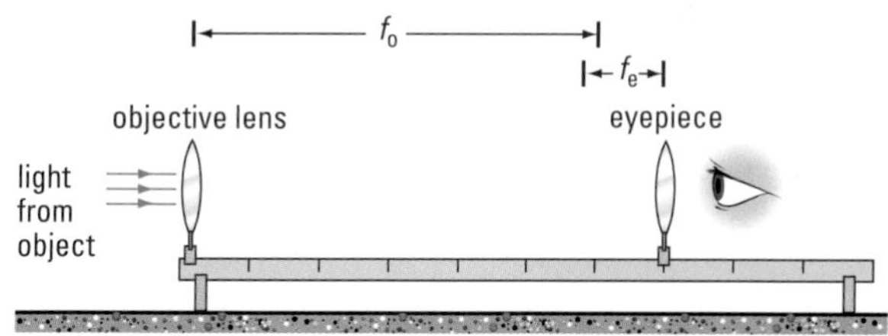

FIGURE 11.55 A model of a Keplerian telescope

Analyzing and Interpreting

1. Compare the attitude of the images in the two telescopes.
2. Which telescope produces the greater magnification?
3. Which telescope produces the brighter image? Why?

Concluding and Communicating

4. Draw ray diagrams to show how each telescope forms a magnified image.
5. Which telescope would you use for opera glasses and why?
6. Which telescope w [illegible] use for studying the stars and why?

Extending

7. Draw a ray diagram showing how a third converging lens might be used to obtain an erect final image with the Keplerian telescope. Ask your teacher for an appropriate lens and try it.

Design & Build

Need

FIGURE 11.56

A company that makes telescopes wishes to use the lens from a one-time–use camera and a Fresnel lens to construct a Keplerian telescope. You are the engineer and designer working on the project. Your teacher represents the company and will receive your final project.

Proposal

Construct a Keplerian telscope and assess its quality. Design a box with a lid to hold the Keplerian telescope.

Materials

- carriage template
- cardboard
- coloured markers
- Fresnel lens
- lens (from one-time–use camera)
- ruler
- glue
- tape
- scissors

Specifications

The Keplerian telescope must be carefully assembled and must have a magnification of about 3×. The assembled Keplerian telescope must fit into a box with a lid. The information and visuals on the outside of the box must explain how to use the telescope and how the telescope works. Technical details such as the focal length of each lens, the power of each lens (in diopters), and the overall magnification must be included.

Plan

Packaging is an important component of any marketing plan. Draw up plans for the box. Show all dimensions of the box, and determine the layout and the information to go on the outside of the box.

Construction

a) Build the Carriage of the Telescope
Use the template shown in Figure 11.57 to make the carriage for the lenses. Enlarge the template to fit on one-half of a standard manila folder.

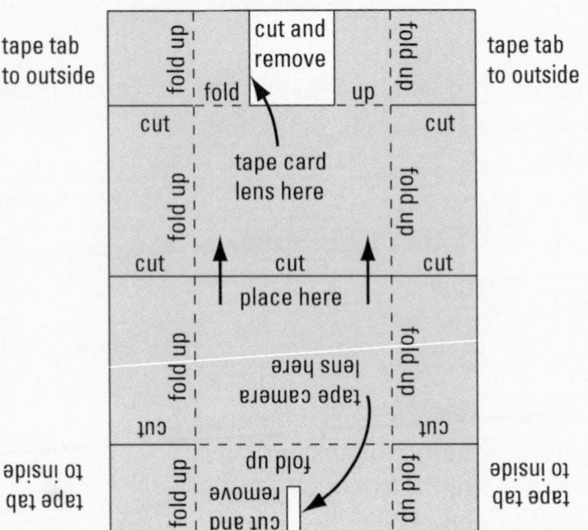

FIGURE 11.57

b) Attach the Lenses to the Carriage
Locate the short–focal-length lens from the one-time–use camera and the Fresnel lens. Measure the focal length of each lens. Insert the camera lens into one end of the carriage and the Fresnel lens into the other, and attach with tape.

c) Investigate the Telescope
Look through the camera lens, and slide the carriage back and forth to focus on a distant object. Determine the magnification of the telescope. Compare this magnification with that calculated using the equation $m = \frac{f_o}{f_e}$. When you have a distant object in focus, measure the distance between the lenses and compare it with the sum of the focal lengths.

d) Assemble the Box
Add the diagrams and instructions to the outside of the box so they are readable when the box is assembled. Assemble the box and insert the telescope.

Evaluation

Have peers use your Keplerian telescope and assess its quality. Have them assess the design of the box and the clarity of the diagrams and instructions on the outside. Write a report that includes your own assessment of the telescope and the box, as well as the assessments of your peers. Submit the box and the report to your teacher.

CHAPTER SUMMARY

Key Terms

angle of deviation
astronomical telescope
chromatic aberration
compound microscope
condensing lens system
converging lens
diverging lens
eyepiece
far point
field lens
focal length
Galilean telescope
hand magnifier
image distance
Keplerian telescope
lateral displacement
linear magnification
magnifying glass
near point
object distance
objective lens
optical centre
projector
terrestrial telescope

Key Equations

$$\frac{1}{d_o} + \frac{1}{d_i} = \frac{1}{f}$$

$$m = \frac{h_i}{h_o} = -\frac{d_i}{d_o}$$

$$m = -\frac{N(L - f_e)}{f_o f_e}$$

$$m_t = m_o \times m_e$$

Essential Understandings

- Algebraic equations can be used to determine the characteristics and locations of images formed by curved lenses.
- Converging and diverging lenses are used in a variety of technological devices.
- A lens is a transparent object designed to control the path of light.
- A converging lens causes rays parallel to the principal axis to converge to a real principal focus.
- A diverging lens causes rays parallel to the principal axis to appear to diverge from a virtual principal focus.
- The three rays commonly used to find an image are: a ray parallel to the principal axis, a ray through the optical centre of the lens, and a ray directed toward the principal focus F'.
- The characteristics of the image formed with a converging lens depend on the position of the object.
- The attitude and kind of image formed with a diverging lens are constant, but the size and position depend on the position of the object.
- A key difference between the camera and the eye is the means of focussing on an object at different optical distances.
- A convex lens acts as a magnifying glass if the object is located inside the principal focus.
- A compound microscope has a converging lens with a short focal length next to the object, and a magnifying glass next to the eye.
- In a slide projector and a movie projector, the object is placed outside the principal focus of the converging projection lens.
- The Keplerian telescope is similar to a microscope except the objective lens has a long focal length.
- A Galilean telescope uses a diverging lens as an eyepiece.
- Chromatic aberration is the inability of a single lens to focus light of different colours to the same point.

Consolidate Your Understanding

1. Look back to your answer for the Checkpoint on page 401. What answer would you give now? Explain why each of the other answers is incorrect.
2. Use a ray diagram to explain what the photographer would see on the film if a regular lens were used, but with an opaque card placed in front of the upper half of the object.
3. Create a concept map to be used as a study map for lenses and optical instruments. Consult the Key Terms provided above, and include as many terms as possible in your concept map. Include two key equations and an example problem involving each equation. Show a model solution using the GRASS strategy.
4. Describe the change in size, kind, and attitude of the image produced by a converging lens as the object is moved from infinity to halfway between the focal point of the lens and the optical centre. Draw one ray diagram to show how to locate a real image and draw another ray diagram to show how to locate a virtual image. Indicate the location of the object to produce each of these images.

CHAPTER 11 REVIEW

Understanding Concepts

1. Where must a source of light be placed with reference to a converging lens to produce the kind of beam leaving a searchlight?
a) as far from the lens as possible
b) at 2F′
c) between 2F′ and F′
d) at F′
e) at 0.5F′

2. Most of the refraction of light for an eye in air takes place at the boundary between
a) the air and the cornea
b) the air and the lens
c) the cornea and the aqueous humour
d) the aqueous humour and the lens
e) the lens and the vitreous humour

3. An object is placed 20 cm from a converging lens of focal length 25 cm. The optical power of the lens in diopters is
a) +25 D   b) −5.0 D   c) +5.0 D
d) −4.0 D   e) +4.0 D

4. Suppose that f_o is the focal length of the objective lens of a Keplerian telescope, and f_e is the focal length of the eyepiece. When the telescope is properly focussed, the intermediate image is
a) more than f_e away from the eyepiece
b) f_e away from the eyepiece
c) less than f_o away from the objective lens
d) close to f_o away from the objective lens
e) more than f_o away from the eyepiece

5. Suppose a candle is the only source of light in a room. After the candle is lit, an image produced by a converging lens appears on the screen as shown in Figure 11.58.

FIGURE 11.58

If the top half of the lens is covered with black tape, how will the appearance of the image on the screen be affected?

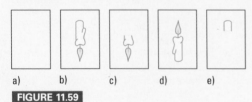

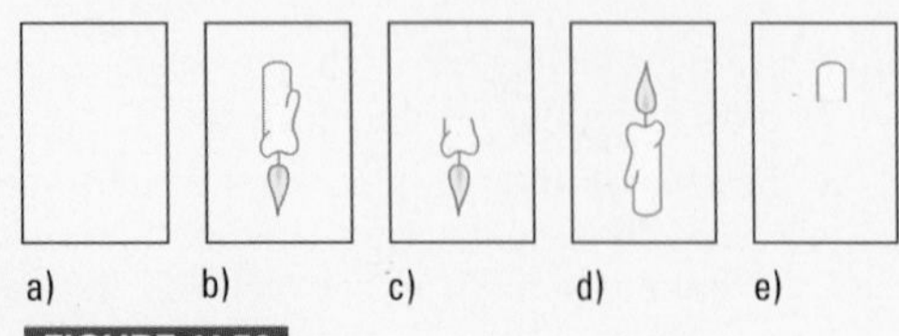

FIGURE 11.59

6. Does a block of glass with parallel sides have a focal length? Explain.

7. How will the size of the angle opposite the base of a triangular prism affect the angle of deviation of the light?

8. An observer looks at the letter K through the side of a large test tube filled with water. Describe the change in the image of K as it is brought closer to, and finally in contact with, the test tube. Try it!

9. a) Where must a painting be placed to produce a real image 15 cm from a thin lens of focal length 10 cm?
b) What is the magnification?

10. A tourist wishes to photograph a 6.0-m tall giraffe from a distance of 50 m. What focal length of lens is required if the image is to fill a 24-mm slide?

11. A photographic enlarger produces images 5× the size of the object. The maximum distance from the negative to the print paper is 72 cm. What is the focal length of the lens in the enlarger?

12. A figurine is placed 20.0 cm in front of a converging lens of focal length 30.0 cm. Draw a ray diagram to scale and use it to find:
a) the image distance
b) the magnification

13. How is an erect image produced by a terrestrial telescope?

14. The objective lens of a compound microscope of focal length 0.50 cm is separated from an eyepiece of focal length 4.0 cm by a distance of 16 cm. Calculate the magnification of this compound microscope if the microbiologist using it has a near point of 30 cm.

15. A Keplerian telescope has the following specifications: $f_o = 980$ mm and $f_e = 5.00$ mm.
a) What is the magnification of the telescope?
b) What is the approximate length of the telescope?

16. An entomologist with a near point of 24 cm achieves a magnification of 250× with a compound microscope. The focal length of the objective lens is 0.35 cm and of the eyepiece is 4.0 cm. What is the distance between the lenses in the microscope?

17. Why does chromatic aberration occur in converging and diverging lenses but not in curved mirrors?

18. Use a diagram to show how to position three convex lenses of focal lengths 16 cm, 5.0 cm, and 1.0 cm to form a simple terrestrial telescope. How far apart should the objective lens and the eyepiece be? Why?

19. Two lenses, whose focal lengths are 30 mm and 50 mm, are used to build an astronomical telescope. Which lens should be the objective and why?

20. Two astronomical telescopes have identical eyepieces, but telescope A is twice as long as telescope B. Which telescope has the greater magnification and why?

21. A film 40-mm square is used to record a scene 3.0 m from the camera. The lens of the camera has a focal length of 80 mm.
a) How far from the film should the lens be placed?
b) What were the dimensions of the scene being filmed?

22. What angle of lens must be used on a camera to capture the whole rainbow? Explain why using a diagram.

23. A macroscopic lens has a converging lens contained in a barrel whose length can be increased to accommodate the additional lens-to-film distance needed to take a picture of a close object. A certain macro lens has a focal length of 50.0 mm, and the barrel can be adjusted to provide a lens-to-film distance of 250 mm. How close can the object be located in front of the lens?

24. A photographer has a camera with interchangeable lenses. One has a focal length of 35.0 mm and the other has a focal length of 200 mm. A picture is taken of a 2.00-m tall horse from a distance of 8.00 m. Calculate the image height on the film produced by the
a) 35.0-mm lens
b) 200-mm lens

25. The image of Mount Everest on a slide is 15 mm tall. It is being projected onto a screen 15.0 m from the lens of the projector using a 120-mm lens. What is the size of the image of Mount Everest on the screen?

26. A certain patient with myopia cannot focus objects farther away than 16 cm.
a) What focal length of contact lens is needed to correct the eye?
b) What is the optical power of the contact lens?

27. A certain hyperopic eye cannot see objects clearly when they are closer than 50 cm from the eye. How close can this eye see clearly when a contact lens of power +4.0 D is worn?

28. A person wearing contact lenses of power +2.4 D can focus on newsprint 24 cm from the eye. How far from the eye must the newspaper be placed if the person removes both contact lenses?

29. When used by an agronomist, the magnification yielded by a compound microscope is 198×. What is the agronomist's near point if the eyepiece of focal length 3.2 cm is separated from the objective lens of focal length 0.40 cm by a distance of 19 cm?

30. A student reads print 7.5 cm from his or her eyes using a reading glass having a focal length of 10 cm. If the magnification is 4.0×, what is the student's near point?

31. Explain why objects viewed in dim light are best seen by looking off to the side of the object.

32. A full Moon is being photographed through a lens whose focal length is 50.0 mm. The Moon has a diameter of 3.48×10^6 m and is 3.85×10^8 m from Earth. What is the diameter of the Moon's image on the film?

Applying Inquiry/ Communication Skills

33. Each of the diagrams in Figure 11.60 shows an object O, image I, and lens. Reproduce the diagrams in your notebook and use ray diagrams to locate the principal focus and focal length of each lens.

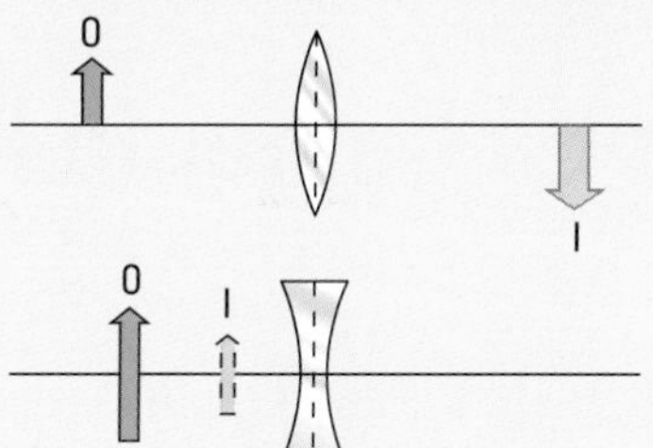

FIGURE 11.60 Locate F and *f* in each case.

34. In Figure 11.61 a parallel beam of sodium yellow light travelling in air enters each box from the left. Sketch the glass shape that could be in each box.

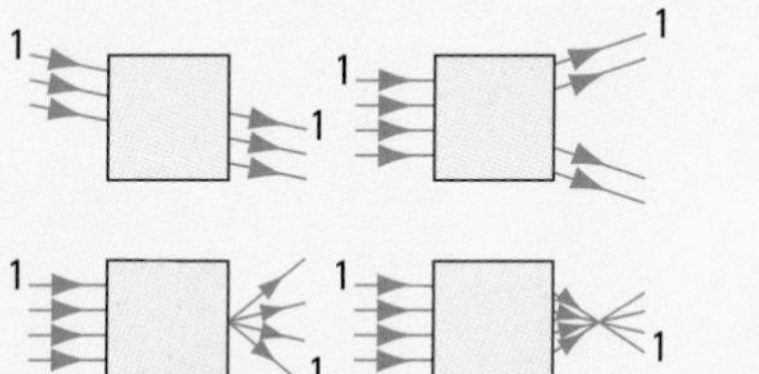

FIGURE 11.61 What shape is in each box?

35. Use a diagram to show how to position two convex lenses of focal length 16.0 cm and focal length 1.0 cm to form an astronomical telescope. How far apart should the lenses be? Why?

36. Is the liquid in a thermometer wider or narrower than it appears? Explain.

37. A working refractive optical instrument has two converging lenses separated by 15.0 cm. The focal lengths of the lenses are 0.60 cm and 4.5 cm. Is the instrument a compound microscope or an astronomical telescope? Why?

Making Connections

38. A photograph of a zebra is taken from a distance of 100 m with a 50-mm lens. A second picture is taken from a distance of 50 m with the same lens. What is the ratio of the height of the image in the second picture to the height in the first picture?

39. A camper is using a converging lens of focal length 10.0 cm to ignite dry leaves. The diameter of the Sun is 1.40×10^9 m and its distance from Earth is 1.50×10^{11} m.
a) What is the area of the Sun's image on the leaves?
b) If 0.550 W of sunlight pass through the lens, what is the intensity of sunlight on the leaves?

40. Extension tubes permit the distance between the film and the lens in a camera to be increased. When are they used and why?

41. The distance from the lens to the retina in a certain normal eye is 18 mm. What range of focal lengths does the eye have if the nearest point of distinct vision is 18 cm?

Preparing for a Career in Physics

In this, and other classes, you've been considering many things about your future. One of these is how to prepare yourself for the career of your choice. Let's assume that career is in physics or another science. So what can you do about it now?

FIGURE 1 Ask yourself these questions: Do I understand what I've been learning? Can I apply it to solve problems? Be honest. Marks won't reveal if you've skimmed over one or two key concepts. It's your responsibility to seek help when you need it. The reward is more than better grades. You'll move into new areas of study with confidence.

FIGURE 2 What courses should you take next year? Don't rely on university calendars alone. Talk to teachers and guidance staff. Go to several university Web sites and see what they require for entry into their programs. What other courses do they recommend?

FIGURE 3 Visit universities. Call (or email) the faculty of science and make an appointment with an undergraduate adviser. You can also arrange a tour with an upper-year student studying in the specific area that interests you.

Applying Yourself

Doing career research and checking out universities, while keeping up your grades, can seem a lot to do, but wait. There's more! You will be completing application forms for many things in the coming year, from job applications to applying for scholarships. They will seem to come at you from every direction. Some examples are listed below.

- *Part-time and summer jobs.* Most employers offering part-time or summer jobs will ask you to complete an application form as well as supply a résumé.
- *Contests and competitions.* Participating in certain contests or competitions can count toward your admission requirements for a university program. While your teacher may apply for these on behalf of your entire class, sometimes you'll have to apply to compete on your own. (Hint: Check with both the math and science departments in your school.)
- *Science fair.* Entering a local or regional science fair will gain you experience and knowledge, with the bonus that you could win significant recognition for your work. Plan ahead and consult with your school's science department to find out the entry requirements and deadlines.
- *Scholarships.* There will be application forms to complete for most scholarships.
- *University admission.* You will need to complete forms when applying to the universities of your choice.

Preparing for Your Application

So how do you get ready to fill out all of these application forms? By preparing in advance a folder or envelope containing the information you are likely to need. It can be stressful finding all of these things at the last minute, not to mention disastrous if you can't find them at all. Fortunately, you can gather most ahead of time.

1. Take time to gather the information or prepare the documents ahead of time. Put together your application preparation kit.
   - *Current résumé.* Keep several copies of your résumé ready to attach to application forms. You will also find that the information listed on your résumé will help you complete forms quickly and accurately.
   - *Course transcript.* The only time you will be asked for an official copy of your transcript is when you apply to university or for a scholarship. No one else needs to know your marks. Your school office will provide transcripts to you when you need them.
   - *Letters of reference.* Collect them as soon as you can, rather than at the last minute. If you have teachers, employers, coaches, and so on, who know you well, ask each to write a letter for you. Keep the originals and make copies, so you can send these letters with more than one application. Even if you don't get letters, be sure to have contact information for people who are willing to provide references on your behalf. This should include the correct spelling of their full names, job titles, and how they can be reached during business hours. (Hint: Members of your own family are usually not acceptable as references.)
   - *Timetable.* Deadlines are everything. Do not miss an opportunity to apply for a contest, course, or potentially valuable scholarship. Make a list of important dates for whatever you plan to apply for and do in the coming year.

Looking Outward

A little organization goes a long way. Imagine you've just heard about a great part-time job, but the person hiring is heading out of town and wants applicants to come in as soon as possible today, after school. You are sure the job will go quickly. Are you worried? No! Because you are prepared. You don't have to rush home to type and print out a résumé. You don't have to take time to phone anyone you can think of to ask for a reference. You can simply pick up your résumé and list of references (or letters) on the way to the interview.

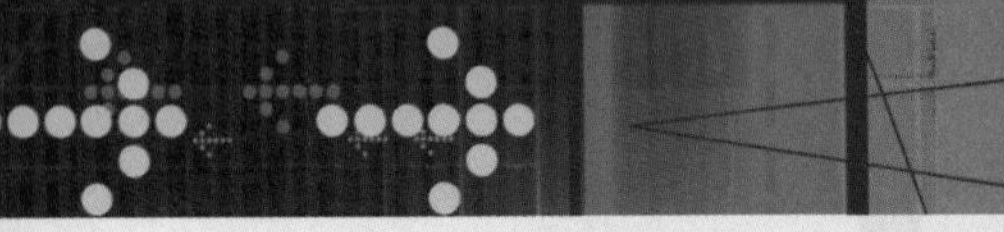

Presentation of Vision Correction Technology

Background Information

Fortunately, with some form of ocular assistance, older people can retain good eyesight well into their 80s. But as people age their eyesight deteriorates and their eyes require more medical attention. Senior citizens generally need brighter light for most tasks. Certain eye disorders and diseases occur more frequently. Presbyopia, a gradual decline in the ability to focus on near objects, starts at age 10 and affects nearly everyone by age 40. This can be corrected with eyeglasses, contact lenses, or possibly laser eye surgery. Floaters—tiny specks that float in the humours of the eye—occur in middle age and increase with age. Although normal and usually harmless, a sudden change in the number of floaters accompanied by light flashes can signal eye problems. Eye diseases common in older people are conjunctivitis, corneal diseases and conditions, cataracts, glaucoma, and retinal disorders, such as macular degeneration, diabetic retinopathy, and retinal detachment.

Using drugs, eyeglasses, or contact lenses can help most people with visual impairments. Low-vision aids stronger than eyeglasses such as telescopic glasses, light-filtering lenses, and magnifying glasses, along with a variety of electronic devices, also help. But there are many alternatives to consider, and it is important for people to have the information they need to make the best decision about treatment.

FIGURE 1

SCENARIO

You are a member of a research/presentation team hired by a seniors groups to research and assess various technologies and procedures. You will present your findings to the seniors group in a presentation format of your choice. In your presentation, you will explain the most common eye diseases affecting seniors and how these diseases and disorders affect vision. You will then describe the technology devices and procedures that can treat them.

Part A: Vision Defects and Corrective Options

1. Form a group of 3 or 4 members. Research vision ailments that most affect senior citizens and assess the effectiveness of technological devices available to correct the defect. Use newspapers, journal articles, books, and the Internet to obtain information.

   Your research should include the following:
   - cause(s)
   - early symptoms
   - long-term vision effects
   - incidence expressed as a percentage at age 55 and in 5-year increments
   - early correction or treatment
   - longer-term correction or treatment

2. Propose criteria for assessing the different methods of treatment available. For example, you can focus your assessment on the treatments affecting the most frequently experienced disorders.

Part B: Prepare a Presentation

3. Summarize the results of your research and organize the information into a presentation. This should include a risk/benefit analysis of treatments, as well as cost information.

4. Consider the audience (i.e. senior citizens) for your presentation. Select the most effective methods to communicate what the audience needs to understand about the information you are providing.

Part C: Recommendations

5. On what factors did you base your recommendations to the seniors group? Which two factors do you feel are most significant? Explain.

6. Write a one-page report to propose a funding model to a provincial health association to ensure that all senior citizens have access to the treatment they need.

UNIT 4 REVIEW

Understanding Concepts

1. A light ray travelling through the centre of curvature of a converging mirror hits the surface of the mirror. It will be reflected
   a) through the centre of curvature C
   b) through the vertex V
   c) along the principal axis PA
   d) through the principal focus F
   e) parallel to the principal axis PA

2. In an experiment similar to the one conducted by Michelson, the speed of light is known to be v and the rotating mirror has N faces. The distance from the rotating mirror to the stationary mirror is Δd. What is the correct equation for determining the frequency of the rotating mirror?
   a) $f = \dfrac{vN}{2\Delta d}$
   b) $f = \dfrac{2v\Delta d}{N}$
   c) $f = \dfrac{v\Delta d}{2N}$
   d) $f = \dfrac{v}{2\Delta dN}$
   e) $f = \dfrac{2\Delta dN}{v}$

3. The index of refraction of light in ruby is 1.52. If the speed of light in a vacuum is 3.0×10^8 m/s, the speed of light in ruby is:
   a) 1.52×10^8 m/s
   b) 1.97×10^8 m/s
   c) 3.00×10^8 m/s
   d) 4.56×10^8 m/s
   e) 4.92×10^8 m/s

4. The critical angle for zircon immersed in water is 44°. Total internal reflection occurs when light is incident on
   a) the water-to-zircon interface at an angle of incidence of 44°.
   b) the water-to-zircon interface at an angle of incidence less than 44°.
   c) the water-to-zircon interface at an angle of incidence greater than 44°.
   d) the zircon-to-water interface at an angle of incidence less than 44°.
   e) the zircon-to-water interface at an angle of incidence greater than 44°.

5. Where must an object be placed with reference to a converging lens to produce an inverted image the same size as the object?
   a) 2.5F′ b) 2.0F′ c) 1.5F′
   d) 1.0F′ e) C

6. Four statements pertaining to a diverging lens are listed below.
   I) The image is virtual.
   II) The image is erect.
   III) The image is smaller.
   IV) The lens is convex.

   Which of the statements are correct?
   a) I and II only
   b) II and III only
   c) I, II, and III only
   d) II, III, and IV only
   e) I, II, III, and IV

7. The part of the eye that adjusts the image to be focussed on the retina as an object changes position is the
   a) cornea
   b) iris
   c) lens
   d) optic nerve
   e) retina

8. An object is placed 20 cm from a diverging lens of power −4.0 D. The focal length of the lens is
   a) 0.25 cm
   b) −0.25 cm
   c) 25 cm
   d) −25 cm
   e) −20 cm

9. The image formed by a magnifying glass is
   a) virtual, larger, and located at F′
   b) real, larger, and located at F′
   c) virtual, larger, and located at 2F′
   d) real, larger, and located at the near point
   e) virtual, larger, and located at the near point

10. Four statements describing the difference between a Galilean and a Keplerian telescope are:
    I) The Galilean telescope is shorter than the Keplerian telescope.
    II) The final image is erect in the Galilean telescope and inverted in the Keplerian telescope.
    III) The eyepiece has a positive focal length in the Galilean telescope and a negative focal length in the Keplerian telescope.
    IV) The objective lenses are converging lenses in both the telescopes.

    Which of the statements are correct?
    a) I and II only
    b) II and III only
    c) I, II, and III only
    d) II, III, and IV only
    e) I, II, and IV only

11. A 1.7-m tall person is standing 1.0 m from a vertical plane mirror.
    a) What is the minimum length mirror needed to see from the top of the head to the shoes?
    b) If the person moves back 1.0 m farther from the mirror, will a different length mirror be needed? Explain.

12. What kind of mirrors are used in a car headlight and why? Use a sketch to support your answer.

13. A beam of monochromatic yellow light travels from air into glass at a 90° angle to the surface. Describe the

change in the following properties of the light as it travels in the glass:

a) speed
b) wavelength
c) frequency
d) period

14. Medium X has a critical angle of 30° and medium Y has a critical angle of 26°. In which medium does light travel more slowly? Explain.

15. Describe three ways to recombine the light from a prism into white light.

16. A parallel beam of light is incident at an obtuse angle θ to a glass block with parallel sides. Describe the direction and nature of the beam in the glass block. Prove that the emergent ray is parallel to the incident ray.

17. Compare the lens of a camera and the lens of a healthy young eye. How are they similar? How are they different?

18. An observer looks at a distant letter F through a large glass sphere. Describe the changes in the image as the letter F is brought closer to, and finally in contact with, the sphere.

19. Describe the characteristics of the final image produced by a compound microscope.

20. What role does the converging mirror serve in the slide projector?

21. Compare the attitude of the object and the attitude of the image for a slide projector.

Applying Inquiry/ Communication Skills

22. An erect arrow of length 2 cm is located 4 cm in front of a vertical plane mirror. A person standing to one side of the arrow is viewing the image of the arrow in the plane mirror. Draw a scale diagram showing where the image is located. Include rays to show how an eye sees the top and bottom of the arrow.

23. The Canadian Motor Vehicle Safety Standard specifies that wing mirrors on motor vehicles cannot have a radius of curvature less than 890 mm or greater than 1800 mm. Design a procedure to determine the focal length of a diverging mirror on a car. Do the experiment, and see if the mirror falls within the legal range.

24. Design an experiment using a pinhole camera to verify the relationship $m = -\frac{d_i}{d_o}$ where m is the magnification (the ratio of the size of the image to the size of the object), d_i is the distance of the image from the pinhole, and d_o is the distance of the object from the pinhole.

25. The rear window of an SUV is 1.4 m wide and located 2.0 m from the inside rearview mirror of the vehicle. The driver's eyes are 0.4 m from the mirror. What is the minimum width of a plane mirror needed to make full use of the rear window?

26. A 20-cm tall dog is standing 30 cm from a diverging mirror of focal length 60 cm. Draw a scale ray diagram to determine the characteristics of the image including its location.

27. A van is equipped with a wing mirror of focal length 0.65 m. A car in the passing lane is 6.5 m from the mirror.

a) Determine the apparent size of the passing car compared with its actual size.
b) Explain why the passing car appears to be farther away than its actual distance.

28. A plane mirror and a converging mirror, separated by a distance of 10.0 cm, are facing each other. The converging mirror has a focal length of 4.0 cm. A 2.0-cm tall object is placed 5.0 cm in front of the plane mirror. Assume that light from the object is reflected first from the plane mirror and then from the converging mirror.

a) Draw a ray diagram to scale to determine the position of the image that light reflected from the plane mirror to the converging mirror produces. Specify this distance relative to the centre of curvature of the converging mirror.
b) Apply the mirror equations to determine the height of this image.

29. A ray of light in water travels toward the water–air interface at an angle of incidence of 45°. The critical angle for water is 49°. Draw a ray diagram to scale to show the path of the light ray. Label all rays, angles, and media.

30. Calculate the speed of light in a vacuum if the speed of light in lucite is 1.97×10^8 m/s and its refractive index is 1.52.

31. Red light travels from air into diamond with an angle of incidence of 25° and an angle of refraction of 10°. Calculate the wavelength of red light in diamond if its wavelength in air is 650 nm.

32. Use an accurate scaled ray diagram to determine the location, characteristics, and size of the image for each of the following situations.

a) A converging lens has a focal length of 20 cm. A 10-cm object is placed 25 cm from the focal point.
b) A diverging lens has a focal length of 30 cm. A 15-cm object is placed 35 cm from the optical centre of the lens.
c) A converging lens has a focal length of 40 cm. A 12-cm object is placed 25 cm from the optical centre of the lens.

33. Draw a labelled diagram to show how a magnifying glass is used to see a specimen.

34. Two lenses having focal lengths of 30 cm and −5.0 cm are used to build a Galilean telescope.

a) Which lens should be the eyepiece and why?
b) Show where the lenses should be situated with reference to one another and to the focal points.

35. A compound microscope has an objective lens with a magnification of 100× and an eyepiece with a magnification of 10×. What is the magnification of the combination?

36. A magnifying glass with a focal length of 10 cm is used by a stamp collector with a near point of 25 cm. Calculate the object distance and the maximum magnification.

37. A certain myopic patient cannot focus on objects farther away than 18 cm.
a) What focal length of contact lens is needed to correct the vision?
b) What is the optical power of the contact lens?

38. Where must a beetle be placed with reference to a thin diverging lens having a focal length of 8.0 cm to produce an image one-third its normal size?

39. A person wearing contact lenses of power 2.5 D can focus on print 25 cm from the eye. How far from the eye must the text be placed if the person removes both contact lenses?

40. A Galilean telescope is built using an objective lens of focal length 1350 mm and an eyepiece lens of focal length −150 mm. Calculate:
a) the magnification of the telescope
b) the approximate length of the telescope

41. A photographer wishes to photograph a rainbow. On viewing the rainbow through the viewfinder (Figure 1), The photographer is disappointed to find that the camera lens does not have a wide enough angle to photograph the whole rainbow. Can the entire rainbow be photographed by moving closer or farther away? Explain.

FIGURE 1

42. Research the cause and correction of cataracts. Interview someone who has had a successful cataract operation. Submit a report of your findings.

43. A refractometer is a device for measuring the index of refraction of a transparent material. Find out how a refractometer works, and what uses are made of the measurements. Submit a report of your findings.

44. Look up the definition of resolution. Research the factors that affect the resolution of a lens. Find out the importance of resolution in astronomy. Submit a report of your findings.

Making Connections

45. A converging mirror of focal length 20 cm is used to produce an image of a distant object on a white screen. The screen is replaced by a small plane mirror that makes an angle of 45° with the principal axis. The plane mirror is moved to a distance 15 cm from the converging mirror.
a) Can the reflected image be caught on a screen? Explain with the aid of a ray diagram.
b) Will the reflected image be inverted or upright? Explain.
c) If the small plane mirror were replaced with a small concave mirror, what would be the characteristics of the image? Explain.

46. A sheet of ice 0.40-m thick is floating on top of a layer of water 15 m thick. A beam of light strikes the ice at 90° and reaches the bottom in a time t. How far would the light have travelled in the same time in a vacuum?

47. Two watch glasses are glued together to form an air lens. The air lens is submerged in water. If a parallel beam of light is directed toward it, will the lens act as a converging or a diverging lens? Why?

48. The length of the barrel of a macroscopic lens can be increased to enable it to focus on near objects. A certain macro lens has a focal length of 50.0 mm. The barrel can be lengthened to provide a lens to film distance of 200 mm. How close can the object be located in front of the lens?

49. A photographer has a camera with a 35.0-mm lens. A picture is taken of a 3.0-m giraffe from a distance of 10.0 m. Calculate the height of the image on the film produced by the lens.

50. Spectra are used in the studies of chemistry and astronomy. Spectra are used to identify elements and compounds both on Earth and on distant stars. Research in the library and on the Internet how spectra are used and the difference between emission and absorption spectra. Submit a 750-word report of your findings.

51. A swimmer is located 4 m below the surface in a crystal-clear lake. Use a scale diagram to determine the diameter of the swimmer's window to the world above the water.

52. How does the apparent depth of a stone beneath the surface of a lake change as an observer above the surface moves horizontally away from the stone? Explain, using a sequence of diagrams.

53. Sir Isaac Newton published his lens and magnification equations long before Karl Friedrich Gauss. Newton's equations are $S_iS_o = f^2$ and $\frac{h_i}{h_o} = \frac{f}{S_o} = -\frac{S_i}{f}$ where S_o is the extra focal object distance measured from the focal point F′ and S_i is the extra focal image distance measured from F. Solve Example 1 Numerical on page 414 using Newton's equations and compare the results to Gauss's equations. Which equations do you prefer? Why might one set of equations be more popular than the other?

54. What kind of radiant energy do low light sensors harness? Why are low light vision sensors so important to the military, to security forces, and to homeowners wishing to detect poorly insulated regions of their homes?

Problem Solving

53. A converging parabolic mirror is used to produce a real image of a distant object. A small plane mirror with its reflecting surface facing the parabolic mirror is positioned between the parabolic mirror and the image. The plane mirror makes an angle of 45° with the principal axis.
    a) Draw a ray diagram showing the image formed by the plane mirror.
    b) Is the image formed by the plane mirror real or virtual? Explain.
    c) If the small plane mirror is replaced by a small diverging mirror, would the final image be real or virtual? Explain.

54. Material 1 is a solid with a higher index of refraction than material 2, which is a liquid. Prove, mathematically, that the critical angle of material 1, immersed in material 2, is $\sin \theta_c = n_2/n_1$.

55. Describe the image Newton saw on the wall after white light was passed through a prism.

56. Describe the experiment Newton performed to find out if the prism was adding something to the white light.

57. What is the range of wavelengths (in nanometres) in the visible spectrum?

58. If the speed of light in air is 3.00×10^8 m/s, calculate the number of faces on Michelson's rotating mirror if it has a frequency of 500 Hz and the stationary mirror is 50 km away.

59. The critical angle for a stone immersed in ethanol is 45.5°. What is the index of refraction of the stone?

60. A light pipe in air will totally internally reflect light if its angle of incidence is at least 40.0°. If the light pipe is placed in water, what is the smallest angle of incidence for total internal reflection?

61. What objective lens is needed with an eyepiece of magnification 10× to produce a total magnification of 900×?

62. A magnifying glass with a focal length of 10 cm is used by a biologist to comfortably view an object 8.0 cm from the eye.
    a) Calculate the near point of the eye.
    b) Determine the linear magnification.

63. A compound microscope yields a magnification of 1000× with an eyepiece of magnification 15×. What is the magnification of the objective lens?

64. Compare and explain the difference in the appearance of stars to astronauts above Earth's atmosphere and to astronomers on the surface of Earth.

65. A ray of light in air is incident on a film of water at an angle of incidence of 40°. The film of water is 5.0 cm thick and is floating on a concentrated sugar solution having an index of refraction of 1.45. Draw a ray diagram to scale showing the path of light until after it enters the sugar solution. Label all angles.

66. A ray of light enters a rectangle of Plexiglas at an angle of incidence of 45° as shown in Figure 2. Use a scale ray diagram to determine the path of light until it leaves the Plexiglas. At what angle does the light leave the Plexiglas?

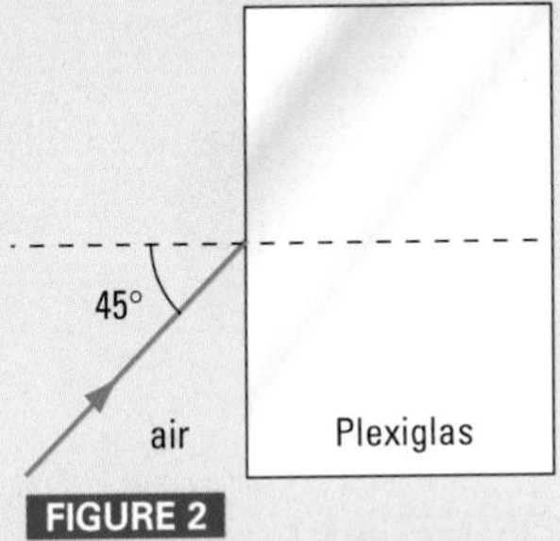

FIGURE 2

67. A transparent material floats on the surface of water. Suppose light is shone from the water toward the boundary it makes with the material. Explain how a measurement of the critical angle in water can be used to determine the index of refraction of the material above it.

68. Explain the formation of the secondary rainbow. Why is it seen at a greater angle above the horizon than the primary rainbow?

69. Design and carry out a procedure to compare the focal length of a convex lens in air and in water. Compare the experimental value with that predicted by the lensmaker's equation.

70. a) What role does the converging mirror play in the slide projector?
    b) What is the function of the condenser lenses?
    c) Why must the light incident on the slide consist of parallel rays?
    d) Explain why the slide has to be inserted into the slide projector upside down.

71. A silk flower is placed 40 cm from a thin diverging lens of focal length 20 cm. Calculate:
    a) the image distance
    b) the magnification

72. An amateur astronomer decides to build a Keplerian telescope from discarded eyeglass lenses. The lenses have the following refractive powers: 10 D and 1.4 D.
    a) Which lens should be used as the eyepiece?
    b) What should the distance be between the lenses?
    c) What is the magnification of the telescope?

73. Figure 3 shows parallel light rays travelling in water incident on a concave lens filled with air. Copy it into your notebook and draw in the path of the rays through the lens.

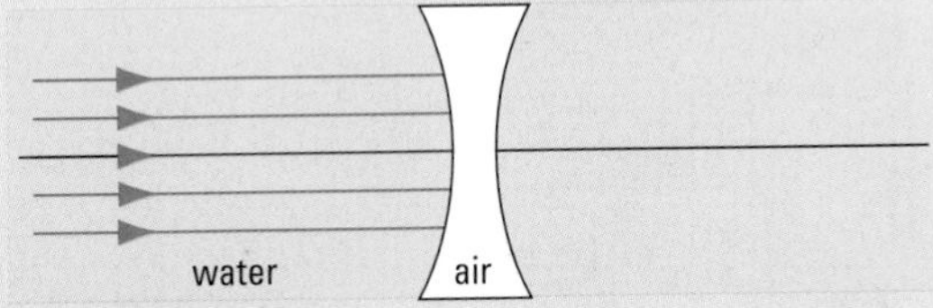

FIGURE 3 Will this beam converge or diverge after passing through the air lens?

UNIT

5

Electricity and Magnetism

OVERALL EXPECTATIONS

By the end of this unit, you will be able to:

- demonstrate an understanding of the properties, physical quantities, principles, and laws related to electricity, magnetic fields, and electromagnetic induction
- carry out experiments or simulations, and construct a prototype device to demonstrate characteristic properties of magnetic fields and electromagnetic induction
- identify and describe examples of domestic and industrial technologies that were developed on the basis of the scientific understanding of magnetic fields

Think about the chaos that would result from an electrical failure in a big city. People would be trapped in subway cars and elevators. Traffic lights would stop working and gasoline pumps would be useless. In homes, stores, factories, and farms, machines that rely on electricity would grind to a halt.

What would your life be like without computers, credit cards, VCRs, and all the objects in your home that use electricity? Electricity is an integral part of our daily lives and yet we tend to take it for granted. Where does it come from? How is it generated? How does it get to your home? How is it converted into the sound that blasts from your speakers, the heat that toasts your bread, or the hot air that dries your hair?

All these things depend on the interactions between electric charges and magnetic fields. Studying electromagnetism helps you understand how devices such as electromagnets, motors, generators, transformers, and even computer disks operate. This unit demonstrates that anyone can understand these things, predict their behaviour, and control them by simply understanding and applying a few basic scientific principles and concepts.

PHYSICS HEADLINES

- **Cell Phones and Vending Machines**

New vending machines being tested by soft-drinks manufacturer will allow you to purchase products without putting money in the machine. Dialing a phone number on the vending machine from your cell phone enables you to buy a product without opening your purse or wallet. The charges appear on your phone bill.

- **The Maglev Train MLX01**

Japan's Maglev MLX01 is the world's fastest train, reaching a top speed of 550 km/hr on a test track. It cruises comfortably at 500 km/hr. Because of this speed, the train is equipped with air brakes, similar to a fighter jet.

- **What to Wear**

Researchers in Belgium are designing clothes that will take incoming calls and monitor heart-beat, blood pressure, and temperature. It could keep track of your keys and credit cards and tell you when they go missing. Developers think that eventually the clothes could even judge the wearer's mood.

- **Switched Off?**

Electronic gear, even switched off, is really on stand-by—TVs, answering machines, VCRs, computers—in some areas accounting for 10% of all electricity used.

PREVIEW

ACHIEVEMENT TASK

At the end of this unit you will be asked to complete a task involving the design of an electrical system in order to animate a window display (see page 588).

CHAPTER 12

Electric Charge, Current, and Potential Difference

SPECIFIC EXPECTATIONS

By the end of this chapter, you will be able to:

- define and describe the concepts and units related to electricity and magnetism (12.1, 12.2)
- describe the two conventions used to denote the direction of movement of electric charge in an electric circuit, recognizing that electric current is the preferred convention (12.1)

The Van de Graaff generator shown in Figure 12.1 is a machine for separating and accumulating large quantities of electric charge. Negative charge is stored on the globe and concentrates at the pointed end of a conductor attached to the sphere. This stream of electrons causes the glowing particles in the flame to move sideways as they rise. Although the amount of charge leaving the Van de Graaff generator is difficult to measure, there are ways to measure the rate of flow of charge and the energy it possesses.

How are electrons and the unit of charge related? What is electric current and how is it calculated? What is electric potential difference, and how is it measured? How do series and parallel circuits differ?

In this chapter, you will investigate the concepts and units related to electric charge, electric current, electric potential, and electric potential difference. You will examine the conventions used to denote the direction of movement of an electric charge through a conductor. You will learn to solve

FIGURE 12.1 A Van de Graaff generator can produce a large electric charge.

various electrical problems including how to calculate the amount of electric current contained in a lightning bolt. Finally, you will use Kirchhoff's laws to solve problems involving electrical circuits. You can use this information to protect yourself in a lightning storm, but it has far more uses than that. The basic principles of electricity in this chapter can be used to explain everything from the safest way to boost a dead car battery to how a photocopier works.

Discovering Physics

An Air Analogy for an Electric Circuit

In this activity, you will study the flow of air through a tube containing cotton wool to see if this can act as analogy to illustrate the current and potential difference characteristics of an electric circuit. (An analogy is a similarity between things that are alike in some ways, but otherwise different.)

You will need: plastic tubing (100 cm), a manometer U tube, 2 one-hole rubber stoppers, glass tubing (4-cm diameter), 2 glass T-tubes, cotton wool, a beaker, and some ethyl alcohol.

Caution: Disinfect the end of the plastic tubing with ethyl alcohol before you blow into it.

1. Assemble the apparatus as shown in Figure 12.2. Pack the cotton wool loosely in the large glass tubing. Use coloured water in the manometer.
2. Place one end of the plastic tubing in a beaker of water.
3. Disinfect the other end with the ethyl alcohol and place it in your mouth. Blow softly and steadily into the end of the plastic tubing. Observe the number of bubbles that rise in the beaker and any changes in the levels of the coloured water in each side of the manometer.
4. Repeat, but this time blow hard and steadily.

- Compare the rate of flow of air bubbles when you blow softly and hard. What does the rate of flow of air bubbles measure?
- Compare the difference in height of the water in the two arms of the manometer when you blow softly and hard. What does the manometer measure?
- Create an analogy for an electric circuit for the following characteristics of your air circuit:
  a) force with which you blow
  b) cotton wool
  c) manometer
  d) air bubbles
  e) molecules in the air bubbles
  f) rate of flow of air bubbles through the water
  g) difference in height of the columns of water in each arm of the manometer
- What weakness is there in this analogy for an electric circuit?

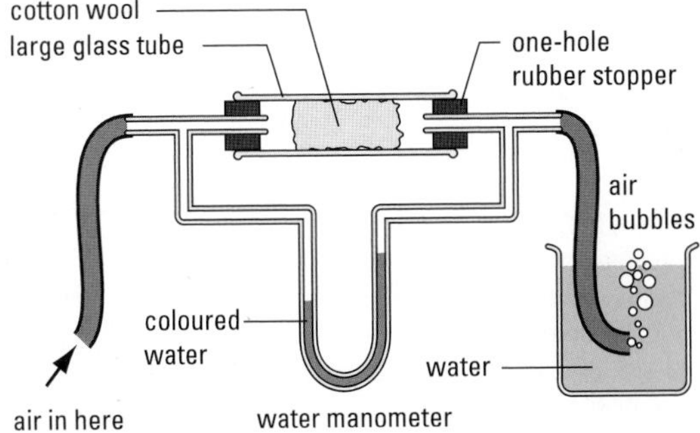

FIGURE 12.2 An air analogy for an electric circuit

CHECKPOINT

A simple electric circuit contains a bulb connected to a battery by means of a switch. When the switch is closed, how much of the current leaving the battery returns to the battery?

a) None; the bulb uses up all of the current.
b) Some; the bulb uses up most of the current.
c) Most; the bulb uses up a small amount of the current.
d) All; the bulb uses up no electric current.

Explain your answer.

12.1 Electric Charge and Electric Current

Key Understandings

When you have completed this section, you will be able to:

- define and describe the concepts and units related to electric charge and electric current
- describe the two conventions used to denote the direction of movement of electric charge in an electric circuit, recognizing that electric current is the preferred convention
- solve problems involving electric current, quantity of charge, and time
- solve problems involving charge, number of electrons that flow in a conductor, elementary charge, electric current, and time

Thunderclouds become charged due to friction between water droplets and ice crystals in the clouds as air currents move them around. As a result, the cloud becomes positively charged at the top and negatively charged at the bottom. The clouds often appear anvil shaped. A flash of lightning occurs when the air rapidly conducts a huge number of electrons. This movement of charge constitutes an electric current. What is the difference between electric charge and electric current?

The Nature of Electric Charge

Benjamin Franklin (1706–90), an American statesman and scientist, was the first person to recognize that there were two kinds of charges and to call them positive and negative. His theory of electricity explained electric charges about a century and a half before electrons were discovered. He hypothesized that a lightning discharge was an electrical charge moving through air, and he performed an experiment with a kite to verify this theory. He also observed that charge concentrates at a point and can more readily escape from pointed objects. Franklin designed the first lightning rod based on this principle.

WEBLINK

Over 100 lightning bolts strike Earth every second. Find out about lightning and write a report about what to do and not do during a thunderstorm to protect yourself from injury. Begin your research at **www.pearsoned.ca/physics11.**

Discovering Physics *An Invisible Flow*

Use a metal coat hanger to make a spiral with a pointed end. Set the spiral on top of the globe of the Van de Graaff generator as shown in Figure 12.4. Turn on the Van de Graaff generator and charge the globe. Light a candle and bring the flame of the candle near the pointed end of the spiral. Observe what happens.

- What evidence do you have that charge is escaping from the pointed end of the conductor?
- How is this principle used in the design of lightning rods?
- Can you explain how lightning rods protect buildings?

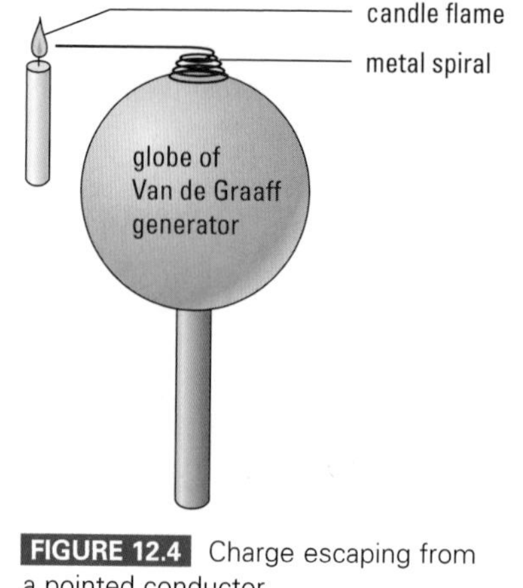

FIGURE 12.4 Charge escaping from a pointed conductor

INSIGHT

A Van de Graaff generator can be designed so that its globe builds up a positive charge instead of a negative one. Will the effect of a positive charge on the candle flame differ from that of a negative charge?

Although the kite experiment showed that lightning is a discharge of static electricity, it was an extremely dangerous thing to do. Others who have tried to repeat the experiment have lost their lives. In Benjamin Franklin's experiment, a long hemp cord was used to attach the kite at one end to a metal key at the other. Franklin used a dry silk cloth to hold the cord. A hemp cord becomes a very good conductor of electricity when wet. The dry silk cloth may have acted as an insulator to prevent Franklin from getting a shock from the lightning strike. Franklin was very fortunate.

Electric charge has many practical uses. Researchers have found a way to give pollen an electric charge and improve pollination. When sprayed on plants, about five times as much charged pollen sticks to flowers as uncharged pollen, increasing fertilization.

INFOBIT

Because over 100 lightning strikes hit Earth every second, many golf courses have installed early warning systems. These systems can detect a thunderstorm several kilometres away, giving golfers enough time to reach shelter. Fortunately, over 60% of all lightning discharges go from one cloud to another without ever hitting the ground.

The Coulomb

Current electricity is electric charge that moves from one place to another. In most electric circuits it is the electrons that move. We might try to measure electric charge by counting the number of electrons that move past a point, but this is impractical because the number is so large. Instead, a unit of charge, the **coulomb**, is used. The coulomb is equivalent to the charge of many electrons.

One coulomb (1 C) is equal to the charge on an object with an excess or deficiency of 6.24×10^{18} electrons. The **elementary charge, *e***, is the magnitude of the charge on an electron or proton. You can easily derive the value of one elementary charge in terms of the coulomb:

$$1\text{ C} = 6.24 \times 10^{18}\text{ elementary charges}$$

Therefore,

$$\text{one elementary charge} = \frac{1\text{ C}}{6.24 \times 10^{18}}$$

$$e = 1.60 \times 10^{-19}\text{ C}$$

If Q is the quantity of charge on an object in coulombs and N is the number of elementary charges, then

$$Q = Ne$$

Electrons have a negative charge. You can decide whether the charge is positive or negative by determining whether there is an excess or deficiency of electrons.

EXAMPLE 1 **NUMERICAL**

When an ordinary household light bulb is turned on, approximately 5.5×10^{-1} C of charge moves through the filament each second. Assume that only electrons move through a solid, how many electrons is this?

Given

$Q = -5.5 \times 10^{-1}$ C

$e = -1.60 \times 10^{-19}$ C

Required

N

INSIGHT

For an excess of electrons, e and Q are negative. For a deficit of electrons, e and Q are positive.

PRACTICE PROBLEMS

1. An electric heater, when it is switched on, has 14.6 C of charge moving through its heating element each second. How many electrons is this?
2. In every second 5.2×10^{18} electrons pass through the filament of an electric light bulb. How many coulombs is this?

Analysis

- Since there is an excess of electrons, both Q and e are negative.
- $Q = Ne$
- Therefore, $N = Q/e$.

Solution

$$N = Q/e$$
$$= \frac{-5.5 \times 10^{-1}\ \text{C}}{-1.60 \times 10^{-19}\ \text{C}}$$
$$= 3.4 \times 10^{18}$$

Statement

In one second about 3.4×10^{18} electrons will flow through the light bulb.

WEBLINK

The distribution of charge on a hollow conductor led to a method of shielding sensitive equipment from static electricity. Find out how shielding works and how sensitive equipment is protected. Begin your research at **www.pearsoned.ca/physics11.**

INFOBIT

When snow gets blown around it picks up an electric charge. As wind blown crystals hit a snowpack, particles of opposite charge attract each other and stick together to form an overlapping formation of snow along a ridge. This overhang can contribute to an avalanche.

Discovering Physics — *Where Does Charge Reside?*

Where does the charge accumulate on a hollow conductor? You will need a charged Van de Graaff generator, an uncharged metal leaf electroscope, a hollow conductor with a hole in its top, and a proof plane (Figure 12.5). (A proof plane is a small conductor attached to an insulating handle.)

1. Charge the hollow conductor by holding it by its insulating stand and touching the conductor to the globe of a charged Van de Graaff generator.
2. Make sure the proof plane is neutral, then touch it to the inside of the hollow conductor.
3. Bring the proof plane near the knob of a metal leaf electroscope. Is there any evidence of a charge on the proof plane?
4. Again make sure the proof plane is neutral. Now touch the proof plane to the outside of the hollow conductor. Is there any evidence of a charge on the proof plane?
   - Based on your observations, can you suggest why sensitive equipment such as computer memory is often shielded by enclosing it in a metal case or a wire cage?
   - Investigate the distribution of charge on various shapes of conductors. Do you notice any pattern that would let you predict how charge is distributed on other shapes?

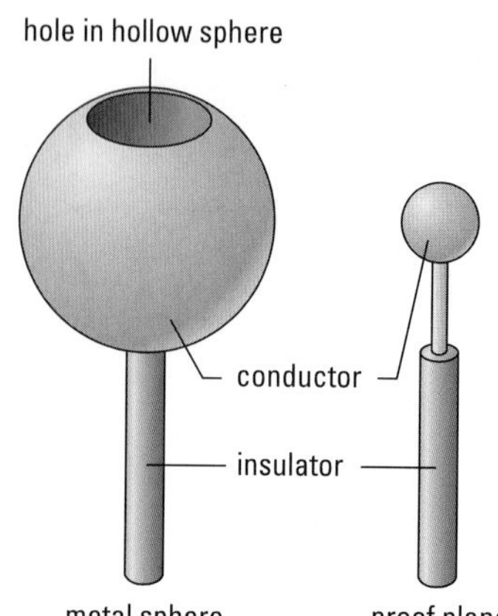

FIGURE 12.5 A hollow metal sphere and a proof plane

Coulomb's Law

Charles Coulomb (1736–1806), a French scientist, discovered how the force of attraction or repulsion between two fixed charged objects depends on the sizes of the charges and the distance between the objects. His findings are summarized in **Coulomb's law:**

The magnitude of the electric force between any two charged objects is directly proportional to the product of the charges on the objects and inversely proportional to the square of the distance between their centres.

Coulomb's law can be written in equation form as

$$F_e = \frac{k\, Q_1 Q_2}{\Delta d^2}$$

where F_e is an electrical force of attraction or repulsion, k is a proportionality constant, Q_1 and Q_2 are point charges, and d is the distance between the charges. Note the similarity between this equation and Newton's law of universal gravitation.

An example of a practical use of charge is the photocopier. In a typical photocopier, a metal drum or belt is coated with a light sensitive material know as a "photoconductor." The photocopier then coats this photoconductor with electrons and these electrons remain in place until the light strikes the photocopier. When this happens, portions of the photoconductor which did not receive enough light retain their electrons and their static charge while the illuminated portions of the photoconductor lose their charge. The static charges which remain, obeying Coloumb's law, are able to attract positively charged black toner particles. Because of the attractive electrostatic forces, these toner particles remain on the drum until they are deposited on copier paper which has been charged negatively. The black toner particles thus stick to the copier paper and are heat fused in place to produce the lasting image on the paper.

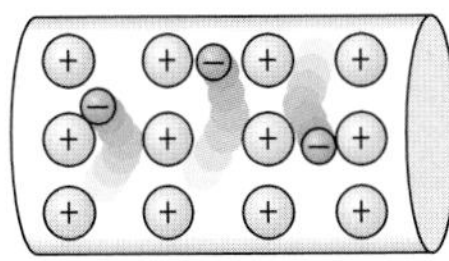
a)

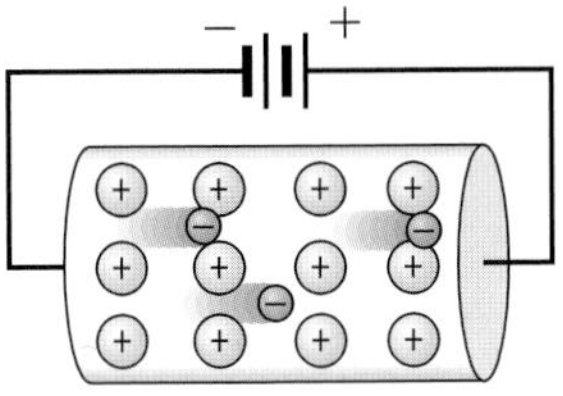

b)

FIGURE 12.6 When an energy source is connected between the ends of a conductor, electrons move through a conductor from atom to atom in an ordered way, pushed by the excess of electrons at the negative end of the battery.

a) Electrons drifting in random motion
b) Electrons in ordered motion

Electric Current

In a conductor, such as a metal wire, there are many electrons that are free to move randomly. In the absence of an electric current, the same number of electrons move in one direction as in the opposite direction, on average. However, when an electric current flows in the conductor, there is a net flow of electrons in one direction (Figure 12.6b)).

An **electric current** may be thought of as the number of electrons flowing past a given point in one second. The symbol for electric current is I. Q represents the quantity of charge that flows past a given point in the conductor and Δt represents the time taken for the charge to pass. Thus,

$$I = \frac{Q}{\Delta t}$$

The SI unit for electric current is the **ampere** (A), named in honour of André Marie Ampère, a French mathematician and physicist. Like the metre and the second, the ampere is an SI base unit, and the coulomb is derived from it:

$$1\text{ A} = \frac{1\text{ C}}{1\text{ s}}$$

INFOBIT

Electrons actually drift quite slowly through a conductor. Their speed is estimated to be only a few millimetres a minute. However, a lamp goes on as soon as you close the switch. Can you explain why?

By rearranging this equation, we can see that a coulomb is an ampere second:

$$1\ \text{C} = 1\ \text{A·s}$$

When a current of one ampere flows in a conductor for one second, one coulomb of charge passes any point along the conductor.

We know that one coulomb is equivalent to the charge on 6.24×10^{18} electrons. Hence, a current of one ampere involves 6.24×10^{18} electrons passing a given point in a conductor every second.

EXAMPLE 2 — CONCEPTUAL

Thunderclouds become charged due to friction between the water droplets and the air currents passing through them. The bottom of the cloud usually becomes negatively charged and induces a positive charge on Earth beneath it.

A flash of lightning occurs when the air breaks down and rapidly conducts a huge number of electrons. Suppose a lightning stroke carries 5.0 C of charge in the 2.0×10^{-2} s it takes to reach the ground. What is the current carried by the lightning stroke?

Reasoning and Solution

The electric current in amperes is the number of coulombs of electric charge that pass a point in one second. Hence,

$$I = \frac{Q}{\Delta t}$$

$$= \frac{5.0\ \text{C}}{2.0 \times 10^{-2}\ \text{s}}$$

$$= 2.5 \times 10^{2}\ \text{C/s}$$

$$= 2.5 \times 10^{2}\ \text{A}$$

This lightning stroke carried a current of 2.5×10^{2} A.

CHALLENGE

A typical lightning flash lasts a quarter of a second and the peak current is about 15 kA. Determine the quantity of charge in coulombs transferred by this lightning stroke.

Recall that the symbol for the charge on an electron is e, and N represents the number of electrons. The formula $Q = Ne$ can be combined with the formula for electric current $I = \frac{Q}{\Delta t}$ to solve problems as shown in the following numerical example.

EXAMPLE 3 NUMERICAL

It takes 15 h for a current of 50 mA to recharge the nickel-cadmium cells a portable CD player. How many electrons flow through the cells during this time?

Given
$I = 50$ mA

$\Delta t = 15$ h

Required
N

Analysis

- Change mA to A
- Change h to s
- $e = 1.60 \times 10^{-19}$ C
- $Q = Ne$
- Therefore, $N = \frac{Q}{e}$ (equation 1)
- $I = \frac{Q}{\Delta t}$
- Therefore, $Q = I\Delta t$ (equation 2)
- Substituting for Q from equation 2 into equation 1 gives $N = \frac{I\Delta t}{e}$

Solution

$I = 50 \times 10^{-3}\text{A} = 5.0 \times 10^{-2}$ A

$$\Delta t = 15 \text{ h} \times 60 \frac{\text{min}}{\text{h}} \times 60 \frac{\text{s}}{\text{min}}$$

$$= 5.4 \times 10^{4} \text{ s}$$

$$N = \frac{I\Delta t}{e}$$

$$= \frac{5.0 \times 10^{-2} \text{ A} \times 5.4 \times 10^{4} \text{ s}}{1.60 \times 10^{-19} \text{ C}}$$

$$= 1.69 \times 10^{22} \frac{\text{A·s}}{\text{C}}$$

$$= 1.69 \times 10^{22} \frac{\text{A·s}}{(\text{A·s})}$$

$$= 1.7 \times 10^{22}$$

Statement
During the recharging process 1.7×10^{22} electrons flow through the nickel-cadmium cells.

INSIGHT

Including the units with the numerals in equations helps keep track of the units of the final answer.

PRACTICE PROBLEMS

1. A current of 0.82 A flows through an electric lamp for 10 min. In that time, how much charge passes a given spot in the filament expressed in
   a) coulombs?
   b) electrons?
2. While starting the car on a cold winter day, a car battery delivers a charge of 12 kC for 0.50 min.
   a) How many electrons is this?
   b) What is the current in the starter motor (and in the battery) in amperes?

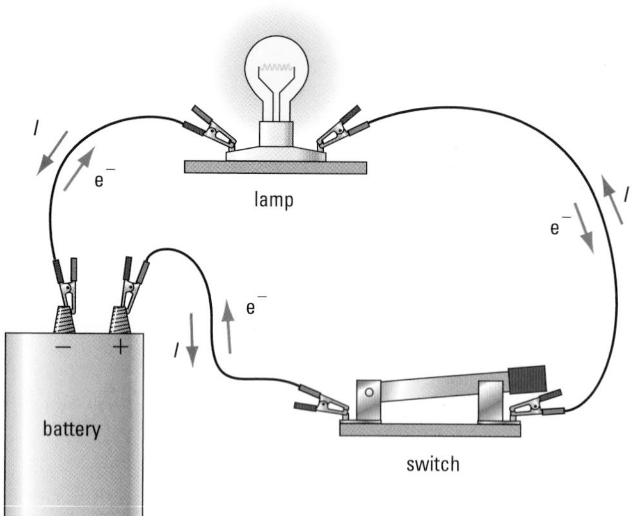

FIGURE 12.7 Electron flow and conventional current—this text uses conventional current (labelled *I* in the diagram).

Current Conventions

A convention is a custom or practice that most people agree to follow, such as shaking hands with the right hand or using SI metric units. There are two conventions for describing the flow of electric current. In the **electron flow convention**, the electric current is shown leaving the negative terminal of a cell or battery, moving through the circuit, and entering the positive terminal. This is the direction in which electrons move through the circuit. Thus, the electron flow convention corresponds to what actually happens in circuits containing solid conductors.

In the traditional convention, called **conventional current**, electric current is assumed to leave the positive terminal of the cell or battery, move through the circuit, and enter the negative terminal. The conventional current direction originated with Benjamin Franklin. He thought that the positive terminal had an excess of electricity and the negative terminal had a deficiency of electricity. He assumed that electricity flowed from the region of excess to the region of deficit. It does not matter which of the two conventions we follow as long as we use it consistently. Since almost all technical applications use conventional current, we will use it in this text. Figure 12.7 shows both conventions on the same circuit.

INFOBIT

In liquids and gases, there is often movement of positive charge. For example, both positive and negative ions carry the flow of charge in plasma, electrolysis, and lightning.

Measuring Electric Current

An **ammeter** is the instrument used to measure electric current. Since electric current is the rate of flow of charge past a point, the meter must be connected at that point. The circuit is disconnected and the meter inserted in series shown in Figure 12.8. The negative terminal of the ammeter must be able to be traced back to the negative terminal of the source (and vice versa).

WEBLINK

Plasma is a highly ionized gas containing nearly equal numbers of positive and negative ions. A plasma is highly conducting. Find out more about plasmas and write a paragraph explaining where they exist and how they conduct. Begin your research at **www.pearsoned.ca/physics11.**

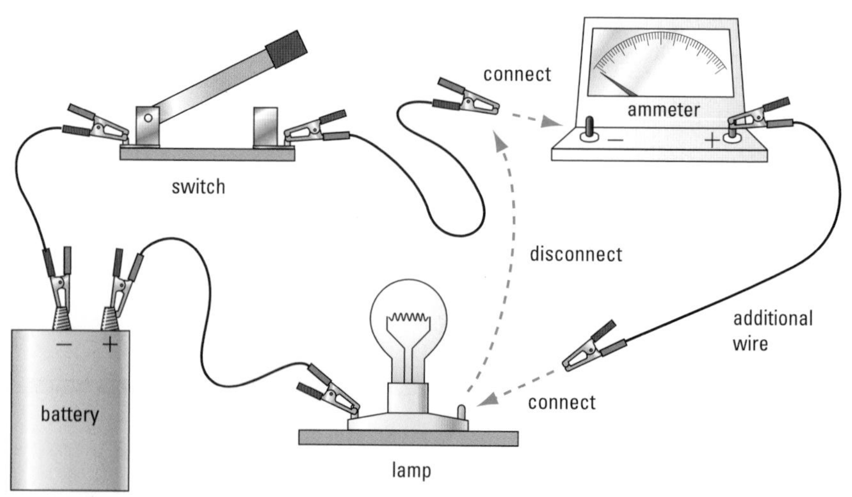

FIGURE 12.8 Connecting an ammeter

Section 12.1 Review

Understanding Concepts

1. How many elementary charges are there in two coulombs?
2. What is the charge on an object that has
   a) a deficiency of 20 electrons?
   b) an excess of 1.0×10^4 electrons?
   c) a deficiency of 2.0×10^{19} electrons?
3. The capacitor in a single-use camera stores a charge of about -4.0×10^{-2} C. How many excess electrons are stored in the capacitor?
4. If 2 C of charge pass a given point in a wire in 0.5 s, what current flows in the wire?
5. a) Suppose that your calculator requires 0.20 mA to operate and will be on for 2.0 min while you solve this problem. What quantity of charge will flow during this time?
   b) How many electrons will flow through the battery of the calculator during the 2.0 min?

Applying Inquiry/ Communication Skills

6. Do an Internet search on lightning. Find out how much charge is transferred during a lightning flash and the amount of electric current that flows.
7. Benjamin Franklin invented the first lightning rods in the late 1700s. Find out how lightning rods work and why they are pointed. Draw a labelled diagram showing a building made of wood and a lightning rod system.
8. You want to connect an ammeter to compare the current leaving a battery with the current returning. Draw a diagram that includes a battery, two ammeters, a bulb, and connecting wires. Label the polarity of the battery and the polarity of the two connected ammeters.

Making Connections

9. Find out why, in all technical and trade applications of electricity and electronics, conventional current is used instead of the electron flow convention. To understand why, research how charge is carried in ionic solutions, plasmas, and in semiconductors.
10. An automotive catalogue lists three qualities of car batteries rated in "cold-cranking amperes." One is rated at up to 1000, another at up to 750, and the third at up to 540. What does this information tell us? Which battery is the smallest in size? Which battery contains more lead to recycle?

12.2 Electric Potential Difference

Key Understandings

When you have completed this section, you will be able to:

- define and describe the concepts and units related to electric potential and electric potential difference
- solve problems involving work done (or energy used), charge, and electric potential difference

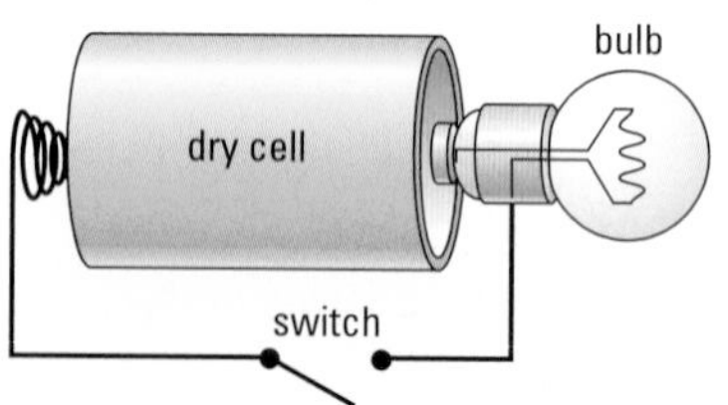

FIGURE 12.9 A flashlight converts electric energy to light energy at the press of a switch.

Press the switch on a flashlight and a flow of charge transfers energy from the flashlight battery to the bulb, producing light (Figure 12.9). How does charge transfer energy? How much energy does each unit of charge carry? How can we calculate the work done by the moving charge?

Electric Potential Difference

In physics, a field is a region where a force acts. You are familiar with the gravitational field near Earth's surface. Similarly, there is an electric field near every charged object.

Near Earth, gravitational potential energy depends on the distance from the centre of Earth. We usually measure only differences in gravitational potential energy, that is, the work done in moving a mass between two points. **Gravitational potential** is defined as the energy possessed by a unit mass at the new location.

Just as the gravitational potential of a mass depends on its distance from the centre of Earth, the **electric potential** of a charge in an electric field depends on its distance from another charged object.

We usually measure only differences in electric potential. The **electric potential difference** is the change in electric potential when a charge is moved between two points in an electric field. Electric potential difference is determined by measuring the work done in moving a unit charge between the two points.

EXAMPLE 4 CONCEPTUAL

During periods of low demand, surplus electrical energy can be used to pump water to a higher elevation. During high-demand periods, the water is released to turn turbines and generate electricity (Figure 12.10). Suppose a pump raises 1.0×10^6 kg of water 30 m. What is the change in gravitational potential energy of the water and what is the change in gravitational potential of a unit mass of water at this height? ($g = 9.8$ N/kg)

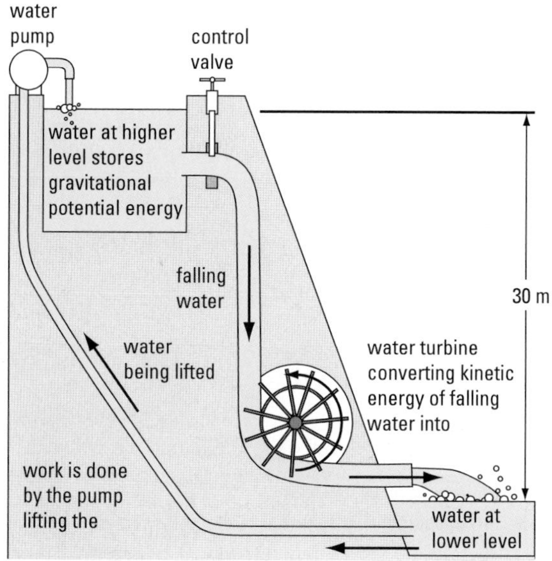

FIGURE 12.10

Reasoning and Solution

The work done in raising the water equals the change in gravitational potential energy. This depends on the mass of water and the height to which it is elevated. Hence

$$\begin{aligned} E_G &= mg\Delta h \\ &= 1.0 \times 10^6 \text{ kg} \times 10 \text{ N/kg} \times 30 \text{ m} \\ &= 3.0 \times 10^8 \text{ N·m} \\ &= 3.0 \times 10^8 \text{ J} \end{aligned}$$

The change in gravitational potential of the raised water ΔU, is the change in gravitational potential energy per unit mass at this new height. This can be calculated by dividing the total change in gravitational energy of the water by its mass.

$$\begin{aligned} \Delta U &= \frac{\Delta E_G}{m} \\ &= \frac{3.0 \times 10^8 \text{ J}}{1.0 \times 10^6 \text{ kg}} \\ &= 300 \text{ J/kg} \\ &= 3.0 \times 10^2 \text{ J/kg} \end{aligned}$$

The change in gravitational potential of the raised water is 3.0×10^2 J/kg.

CHALLENGE

To what elevation must a unit mass of water be raised to change its gravitational potential by 2.80×10^2 J/kg? What is the maximum amount of energy each kilogram of water can deliver if allowed to flow back to its initial level?

If E is the energy used and W the work done in moving a charge Q between two points, then the potential difference V is given by

$$V = \frac{E}{Q} \quad \text{or} \quad V = \frac{W}{Q}$$

We can use this equation to find the units for potential difference. Substituting the units for work and energy (J), and quantity of charge (C = A·s), into the equation, we obtain J/C or J/(A·s). Since potential difference is an important property in electricity, we use a special unit, the **volt** (V). The volt is named in honour of Alessandro Volta, the Italian physicist who made the first battery.

There is a potential difference of one volt between two points in a circuit if one joule of work is done in moving one coulomb of charge between the two points (Figure 12.11).

There is also a potential difference of one volt between two points if one joule of energy is required to supply a current of one ampere for one second between the two points.

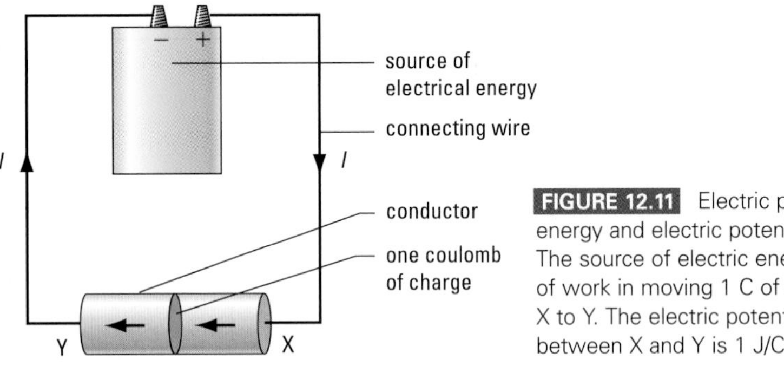

FIGURE 12.11 Electric potential energy and electric potential difference. The source of electric energy does 1 J of work in moving 1 C of charge from X to Y. The electric potential difference between X and Y is 1 J/C = 1 V.

EXAMPLE 5 NUMERICAL

Suppose the globe of a Van de Graaff generator has a large positive charge. A small metal ball has a positive charge of 1.6×10^{-8} C, so the globe repels the ball. Assume that an average force of 6.0×10^{-3} N is needed to move the ball 8.0 cm closer to the Van de Graaff generator (Figure 12.12). How much work is done and what is the change in the electric potential of the ball?

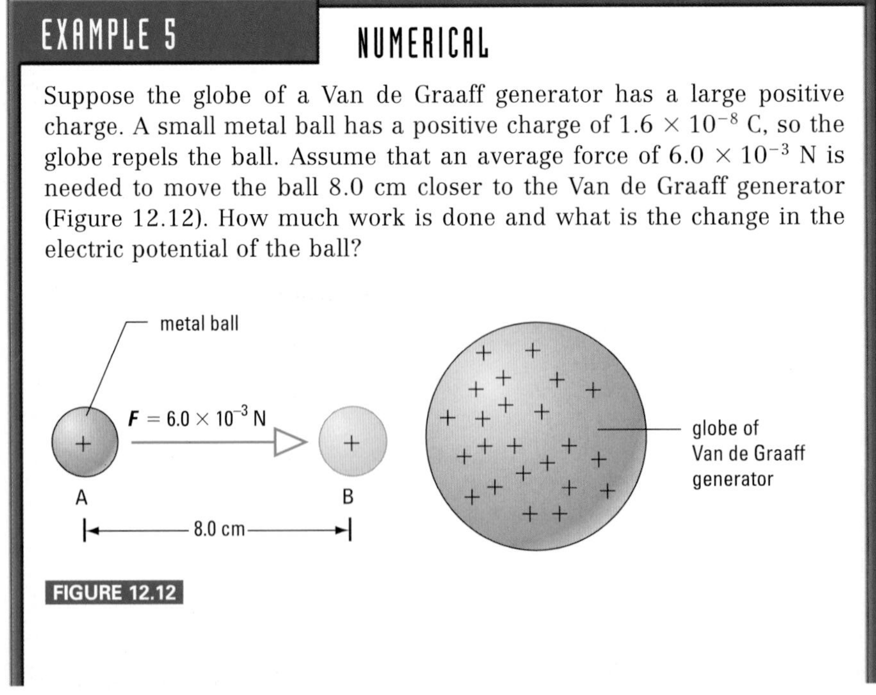

FIGURE 12.12

Given
$Q = 1.6 \times 10^{-8}$ C
$F = 6.0 \times 10^{-3}$ N
$d = 8.0$ cm

Required
W
V

Analysis

a) The work done in moving the ball from A to B can be calculated by multiplying the average force needed in newtons by the displacement of the ball in metres.

Use the equation $W = Fd$

b) The change in the electrical potential is the work done divided by the charge moved.

Use the equation $V = \dfrac{W}{Q}$ and the work calculated in a) to calculate the change in potential.

Solution

a) $$\begin{aligned} W &= Fd \\ &= 6.0 \times 10^{-3}\text{ N} \times 8.0\text{ cm} \\ &= 6.0 \times 10^{-3}\text{ N} \times 8.0\text{ cm} \times \frac{1.0\text{ m}}{100\text{ cm}} \\ &= 48 \times 10^{-5}\text{ J} \\ &= 4.8 \times 10^{-4}\text{ J} \end{aligned}$$

b) $$\begin{aligned} V &= \frac{W}{Q} \\ &= \frac{4.8 \times 10^{-4}\text{ J}}{1.6 \times 10^{-8}\text{ C}} \\ &= 3.0 \times 10^{4}\text{ J/C} \\ &= 3.0 \times 10^{4}\text{ V} \end{aligned}$$

Statement
The work done in moving the charged metal ball between A and B is 4.8×10^{-4} J. The change in electrical potential of the charged metal ball is 3.0×10^{4} V.

INSIGHT

In accordance with Coulomb's law, the force required to move the metal ball increases as it gets closer to the charge on the Van de Graaff generator. For this reason, we use an average of the force for our calculations.

INFOBIT

An electrical discharge requires a potential difference of about 30 kV per centimetre to jump between two spheres in dry air. If a spark jumps 1 mm when you reach for a doorknob after walking across a carpet, you are getting a 3-kV shock!

PRACTICE PROBLEMS

1. Suppose the work done in moving the metal ball between A and B in the above numerical example is 6.5×10^{-4} J. Calculate the size of the repulsive force.
2. Suppose the change in electrical potential of the charged ball in being moved from A to B remains 3.0×10^{4} V. Explain why the change in electrical potential should stay the same. What charge is now on the small metal ball?

Alessandro Volta

Alessandro Giuseppe Antonio Volta (1745–1827) was born in Como, Italy. His family was not wealthy, but young Volta was tall, handsome, friendly, and well liked. Electricity was a new and popular topic in Volta's time and Volta liked to experiment. His inventions opened up new areas of work in physics and chemistry, but he is most remembered for inventing the first electric battery in 1800.

One form of his battery consisted of a chain of bowls containing salt water. Each bowl was connected to the next by a bridge. One half of the bridge was made of silver, and the other half was made of zinc. Volta made a more compact form of the battery by stacking cells made from disks of silver, zinc, and cardboard moistened with a salt solution. This "Voltaic pile" produced an electric current when a wire was attached to the top and bottom of the stack. In his honour, the derived unit for electric potential difference is called the volt.

WEBLINK

Before he invented the first battery, Volta invented the electrophorus, the forerunner of the modern electrical capacitor. Find out about the design and use of electrical capacitors. Submit a report, including a labelled diagram of an electrolytic capacitor. Begin your research at **www.pearsoned.ca/physics11.**

EXAMPLE 6 NUMERICAL

The current flowing through a flashlight bulb is 0.50 A and the potential difference across the filament is 2.4 V. How much work is done in moving the charge in two seconds?

Given

$I = 0.50$ A

$\Delta t = 2.0$ s

$V = 2.4$ V

Required

W

Analysis

- $V = \frac{W}{Q}$ therefore, $W = Q \times V$
- To calculate the work done, we need the quantity of charge transferred.
- Find the quantity of charge transferred using $Q = I \times \Delta t$.

Solution

$$\begin{aligned} I &= 0.50 \text{ A} \\ &= 0.50 \text{ C/s} \\ Q &= I\Delta t \\ &= 0.50 \text{ C/s} \times 2.0 \text{ s} \\ &= 1.0 \text{ C} \\ W &= QV \\ &= 1.0 \text{ C} \times 2.4 \text{ V} \\ &= 2.4 \text{ C·V} \\ &= 2.4 \text{ C·}\frac{\text{J}}{\text{C}} \\ &= 2.4 \text{ J} \end{aligned}$$

Statement

The work required to move the electric charges through the filament of the flashlight bulb is 2.4 J.

PRACTICE PROBLEMS

1. A person walking across a carpet on a dry day does 2.4 J of work in accumulating a charge of 1.2×10^{-3} C on her body. What is the potential difference between her hand and the metal doorknob?
2. A school's Van de Graaff generator transfers 1.0×10^{-9} coulombs of charge through a potential difference of 90 kV. How much has the potential energy of the charge increased?

Measuring Electric Potential Difference

A **voltmeter** is used to measure the potential difference between two points in a circuit. The voltmeter must be connected at the two points between which the potential difference is to be measured (Figure 12.13). The voltmeter must be connected in parallel, and the negative terminal of the voltmeter must be able to be traced back to the negative terminal of the source.

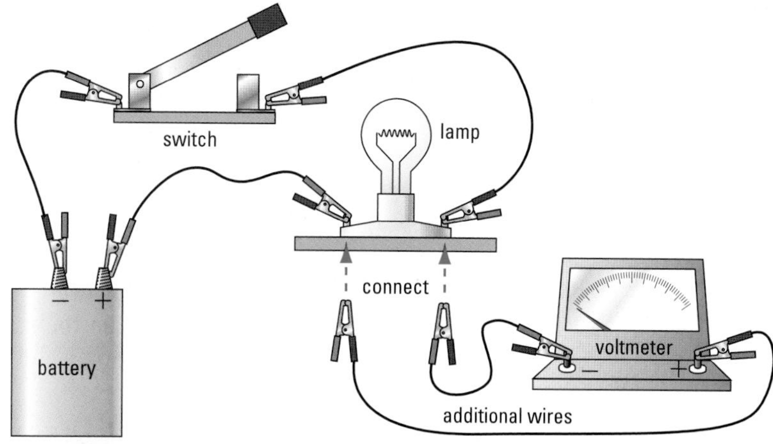

FIGURE 12.13 Connecting a voltmeter

Discovering Physics — *A Water Analogy for an Electric Circuit*

With a partner create an analogy for an electric circuit based on the apparatus shown in Figure 12.14. You will need: two cylinders, two rubber stoppers, a pinch clamp, a solution of water and food colouring, and plastic tubing.

1. Set up the apparatus as shown in Figure 12.14. Add enough of the coloured water solution to half fill each cylinder.
2. Close the pinch clamp and raise one cylinder about 10 cm higher than the other. (You have given the raised water some gravitational potential energy, creating a gravitational potential difference between the water on the two sides.)
3. Observe and record what happens when you open the pinch clamp a little.
4. Open it completely. Record your observations.
5. Raise the water on one side twice as far as before and open the pinch clamp a little. Observe and record what happens.
6. Work with a partner to create an analogy for an electric circuit based on this apparatus. Consider the ways that the two systems are alike. Identify the parts of the apparatus that could represent parts of an electric circuit. (For example, what could the pinch clamp correspond to in an electric circuit?)

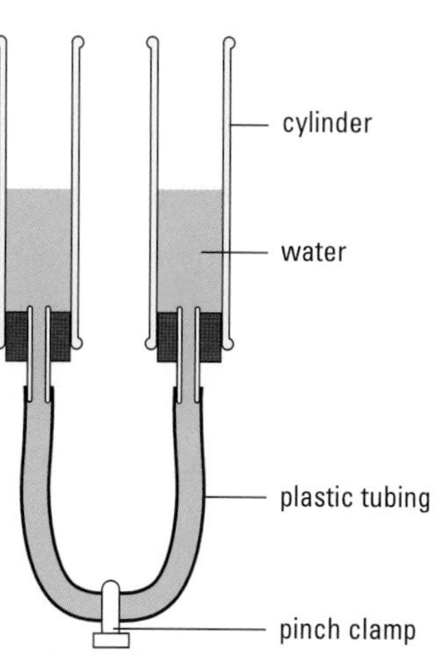

FIGURE 12.14 Water analogy for current and potential difference

WEBLINK

To explore water analogies for current and for potential difference, go to **www.pearsoned.ca/physics11.**

Conditions for Current Flow

For an electric current to flow, two conditions are necessary. First, there must be a **circuit,** a continuous pathway along which electric charge can flow. Second, a potential difference must exist. For example, the globe on the top of a Van de Graaff generator may hold a quantity of charge at an electric potential of 100 kV with reference to the ground. The ground is assumed to have an electric potential of zero volts. If a wire is connected between two points on the surface of the globe, no charge will flow because there is no potential difference between them. However, there is an electric potential difference between the globe and ground, so the static electric charge on the Van de Graaff will flow as an electric current if the wire connects the globe to the ground.

Schematic Circuit Diagrams

Every time you plug in an appliance or flick on a switch you complete an electrical circuit. **Schematic circuit diagrams** use symbols to show circuit components and their connections. Lines between electric components represent conducting pathways (usually wires). Figure 12.15 shows the symbols used to represent some common components. An electric current can flow in either direction through many components, such as resistors, light bulbs, and switches. However, most instruments to measure electric current and electric potential difference must be connected so that the current flows through them in a particular direction. You will need to know how to determine the direction of current flow and how to read a circuit diagram in order to connect circuits correctly.

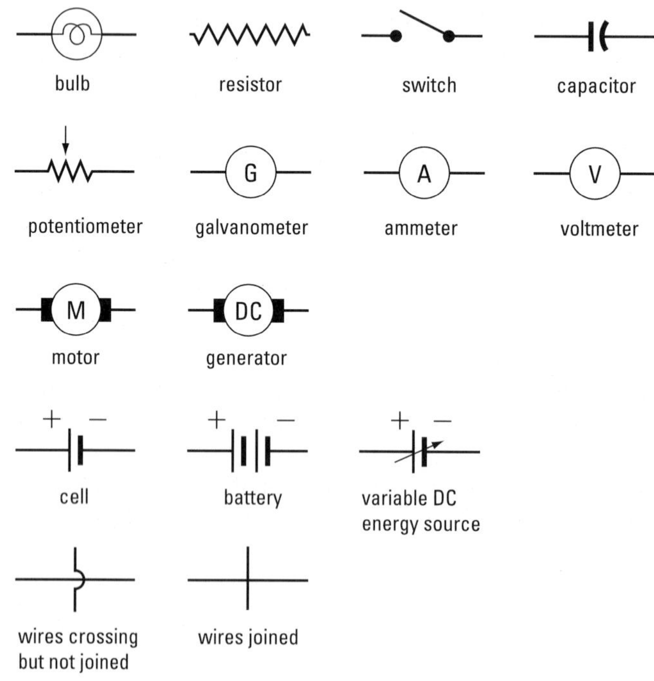

FIGURE 12.15 Symbols representing some electrical components

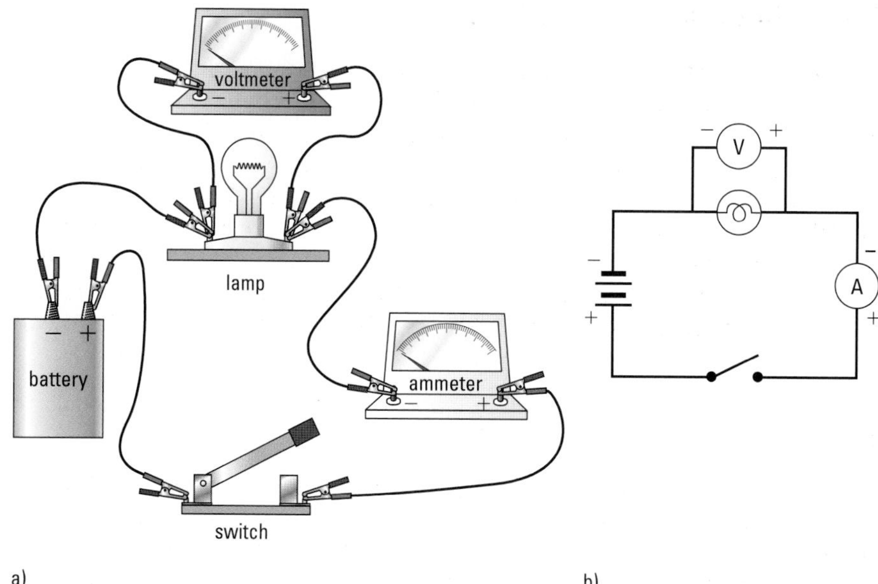

FIGURE 12.16 A simple circuit represented both technically and schematically.

A schematic circuit diagram is shown in Figure 12.16. When drawing a schematic circuit diagram, use the following strategy:

1. Draw the symbol for the cell, battery, or other energy source on the left side of the page. Place the positive terminal down and label the positive terminal + and the negative terminal −.
2. Draw the symbol for the ammeter on the right side of the page with its positive terminal down. Label the positive and negative terminals.
3. Draw the symbol for the voltmeter near the top of the page with its positive terminal toward the right of the page. Label the positive and negative terminals.
4. Draw the load, such as the light bulb or resistor below the voltmeter.
5. Draw the symbol for the switch below the load. Show the switch open.
6. Draw a line from the negative terminal of the energy source to the load. Add a line connecting the other side of the load to the negative terminal of the ammeter. Then draw a line connecting the positive side of the ammeter to the switch and another line connecting the other terminal of the switch to the positive terminal of the energy source.
7. Connect the negative terminal of the voltmeter to the side of the load connected to the negative terminal of the energy source. Connect the positive terminal to the other side of the load.
8. Check that you have a complete circuit and that the polarity of both meters is correct. Check also that the voltmeter is connected in parallel and the ammeter is connected in series.

Section 12.2 Review

Understanding Concepts

1. a) Summarize in a diagram, the differences and similarties between gravitational potential and electrical potential.

   b) The change in gravitational potential energy of a 50-kg mass raised to the top of a wall is 3.0×10^2 J. What is the gravitational potential at the top of the wall with reference to ground? Write a similar question involving electrical potential.

2. a) Show that three different yet equivalent units or sets of units can be used for electric potential difference.

   b) In your own words, define a volt.

3. Suppose that a 9.0-V battery delivers 4.0 C of charge.

   a) How much work is done on the charge by the battery?

   b) How long was the battery used if the current was 1.5 A?

4. In a lightning flash lasting 0.15 s, 25 C of charge pass from one cloud to another through a potential difference of 3.0×10^7 V.

   a) What is the electric current in the discharge?

   b) How many elementary charges move in the discharge?

   c) How much energy is dissipated?

5. What two conditions are necessary for an electric current to flow?

6. Describe the key difference between connecting an ammeter and a voltmeter in a circuit.

7. Sketch how you would connect meters to measure the current through L_2 and the potential difference across it. Show the polarity of the cell and of each meter.

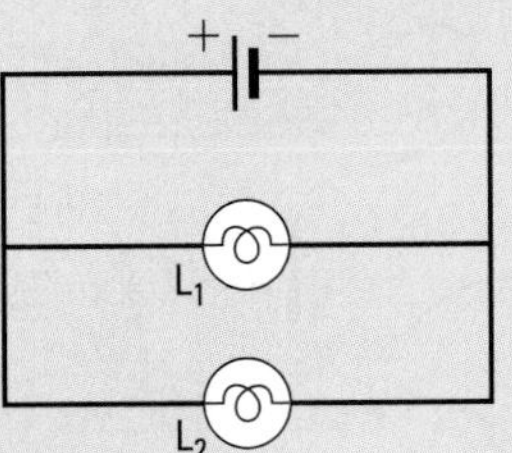

FIGURE 12.17

8. a) Draw a circuit diagram showing an electric cell, a light bulb, and a switch.

   b) Show how an ammeter could be connected to measure the current through the bulb. Also, add a voltmeter connected to measure the potential difference across the bulb. Label the positive and negative terminals of both meters.

Applying Inquiry/ Communication Skills

9. Suppose you want to connect a voltmeter to compare the potential difference across a battery with the potential difference across a load to which the battery is connected. Draw a diagram of the battery and the two voltmeters. Label the polarity of the battery and the polarity of the two connected voltmeters.

Making Connections

10. A consumer purchases an AA dry cell with a voltage rating of 1.5 V for use in a toy and a D dry cell of the same voltage rating for use in a flashlight. What is similar about the two dry cells? What is different? Why does one cost more than the other?

11. Which portable power source would you purchase, one that will start all types of vehicles or one at twice the price that can start a car or run selected 120-V electrical appliances? Outline your reasons.

12.3 Kirchhoff's Current and Voltage Laws

Key Understandings

When you have completed this section, you will be able to:

- state Kirchhoff's current and voltage laws
- use Kirchhoff's laws to solve problems involving series, parallel, and series–parallel circuits

We use electric circuits every day. Press the switch on a flashlight and a simple series circuit produces light. Switch on a radio and parallel circuits fill the room with sound. Turn the ignition key in a car (Figure 12.18) and starter-motor, fuel-pump, and ignition circuits bring the engine to life. Scientists have discovered simple laws that describe what is happening in both series and parallel circuits. Let us find out what the laws are and how to use them.

FIGURE 12.18 The ignition switch of a car controls the starter-motor, fuel-pump, and ignition circuits.

Kirchhoff's Current Law

Electrical connections can be made in two ways: series and parallel. At a **series connection**, current can flow along one path only. All the current passes through a component that is connected in series. Ammeters must always be connected in series so that all the current passes through the meter. At a **parallel connection** current can flow along two or more pathways. Voltmeters must always be connected in parallel. When you measure the potential difference between two points, most of the current passes between the two points, but a small amount goes through the voltmeter.

Investigation

Refer to page 479, Investigation 1.

The charge that makes up the electric current is conserved. Since charge in a series circuit can only flow along one pathway, the electric current at all points is the same. At a series connection

$I_t = I_1 = I_2 = I_3 = ...$ (in series)

where I_t is the total current in an electric circuit, and I_1, I_2, I_3 ... represent the current passing through components in series with the energy source (Figure 12.19).

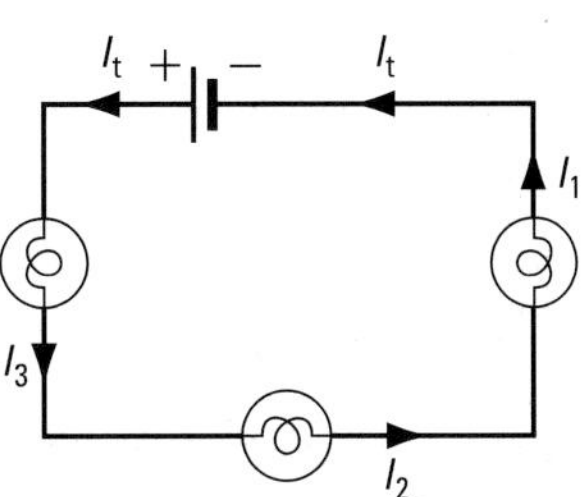

FIGURE 12.19 Current flow in a series circuit

At a parallel connection, the total current flowing into the connection must equal the sum of the currents flowing out of the connection (Figure 12.20). Thus, at a parallel connection

$I_t = I_1 + I_2 + I_3 + ...$ (in parallel)

These two equations were first discovered by Gustav Robert Kirchhoff, a German physicist. **Kirchhoff's current law** states:

At any junction in an electric circuit, the total current flowing into the junction is equal to the total current flowing out of the junction.

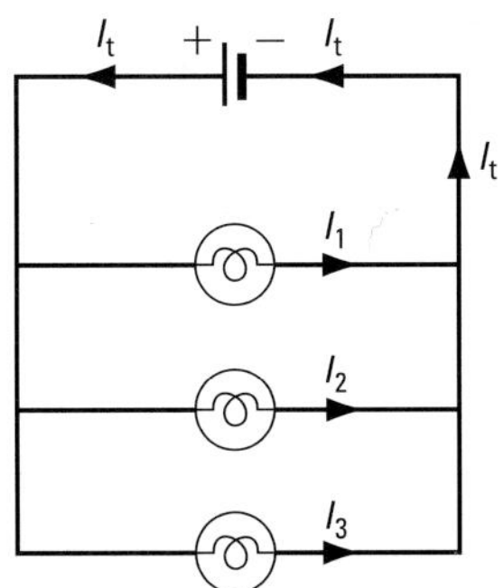

FIGURE 12.20 Current flow in a parallel circuit

WEBLINK

Kirchhoff was involved in the invention of the first spectroscope. He discovered that each chemical element produced its own spectrum. Find out more about Kirchoff and spectra. Draw a labelled diagram showing the construction of a spectroscope, and include a paragraph explaining its operation. Begin your research at **www.pearsoned.ca/physics11.**

EXAMPLE 7 CONCEPTUAL

Figure 12.21 shows a series connection of two different bulbs (X and Y), a switch, and four ammeters, A_1, A_2, A_3, and A_4. If the reading of ammeter A_1 is 0.50 A when the switch is closed, what are the readings on the other ammeters?

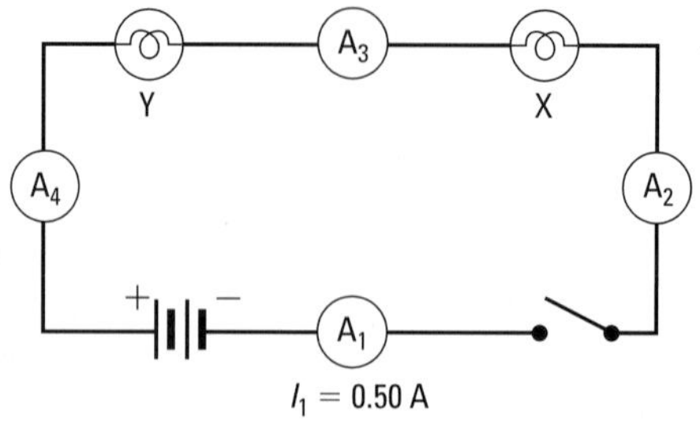

FIGURE 12.21

CHALLENGE

What will the reading be if the lamps X and Y are interchanged? Will the reading stay the same, increase, or decrease if one of the lamps is removed and the circuit is reconnected? Explain your answers.

Reasoning and Solution

Since the two bulbs, four meters, and the switch are all connected in series, the current is the same at every point in the circuit. Therefore, $I_t = I_1 = I_2 = I_3 = I_4 = 0.5$ A. The current entering each bulb is the same as the current leaving it. Current is never consumed.

EXAMPLE 8 CONCEPTUAL

Figure 12.22 shows a parallel connection of two different bulbs (X and Y), a switch, and four ammeters, A_1, A_2, A_3, and A_4. When the switch is closed, ammeter A_1 reads 0.50 A and A_2 reads 0.20 A. What are the readings on the other two ammeters?

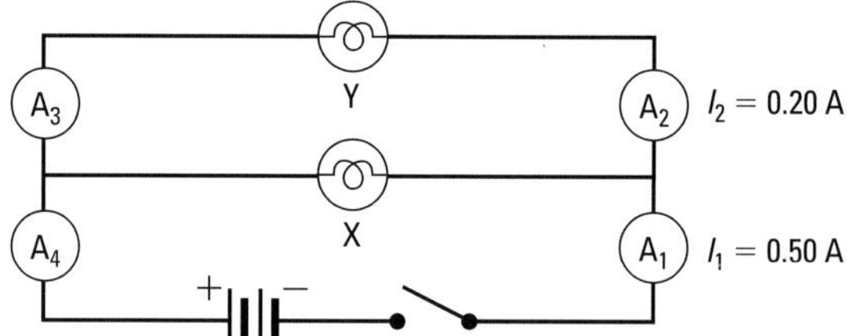

FIGURE 12.22

CHALLENGE

What will happen to the readings if the two bulbs are interchanged? What will happen to the reading on ammeter A_1 if bulb X is unscrewed? Explain your answers.

Reasoning and Solution

The current flowing through ammeter A_1 divides: 0.30 A goes through lamp X and 0.20 A goes through lamp Y. Since current is conserved, 0.30 A exits lamp X and 0.20 A exits lamp Y. The current passing through A_3 joins the current from lamp X making a total current of 0.50 A that passes through A_4. The readings on the four meters are $A_1 = A_4 = 0.50$ A and $A_2 = A_3 = 0.20$ A.

Kirchhoff's Voltage Law

Kirchhoff also investigated the potential difference in circuits. He found that the total potential difference V_t in a series circuit is equal to the sum of the potential differences across the components:

$$V_t = V_1 + V_2 + V_3 + \ldots \text{ (in series)}$$

This relationship is a result of the law of conservation of energy. A cell increases the energy of electrons between its terminals. Thus, there is an increase in potential difference across the terminals of the cell. The change in potential difference across a cell is given a positive sign. In the circuit, some electric energy is used by each component. Thus, there is a decrease in potential difference across electric components. The change in potential difference across a component is given a negative sign. The increase in energy given to electrons by the cell must equal the total decrease in energy as the electrons pass through the circuit. Hence, the increase in potential difference across the cell must equal the sum of the decreases in potential differences across each component connected in series.

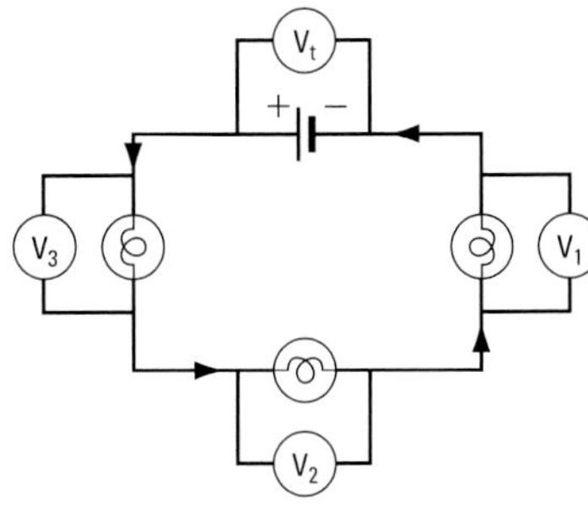

FIGURE 12.23 Potential difference in a series circuit.

EXAMPLE 9 CONCEPTUAL

A battery producing a potential difference of 6.0 V is connected to two light bulbs connected in series. If the drop in potential across one bulb is 2.0 V, what is the drop in electrical potential across the other bulb?

Reasoning and Solution

The increase in electrical potential produced by the battery is equal to the decrease in the electrical potential as the charge travels through the loads. Hence,

$$V_t = V_1 + V_2 \text{ (in series)}$$

$$\begin{aligned} \text{Therefore, } V_2 &= V_t - V_1 \\ &= 6.0 \text{ V} - 2.0 \text{ V} \\ &= 4.0 \text{ V} \end{aligned}$$

The drop in electrical potential across bulb 2 is 4.0 V.

CHALLENGE

Three different bulbs are connected in series. The drops in electrical potential across the bulbs are 2.0 V, 4.0 V, and 3.0 V. What potential difference does the battery produce?

The law of conservation of energy can also be applied to parallel connections of components, such as the light bulbs shown in Figure 12.24. Current flowing toward a parallel connection must divide and flow along more than one pathway. Components in parallel connections are usually joined to a common junction by short wires (for example, AB, BC, DE, and EF). It takes very little work to move charges along such good conductors. Hence, the potential difference across the wires is almost zero and can be ignored. As a result, the potential differences across components in parallel must be equal. Therefore,

$$V_t = V_1 = V_2 = V_3 = \ldots \text{ (in parallel)}$$

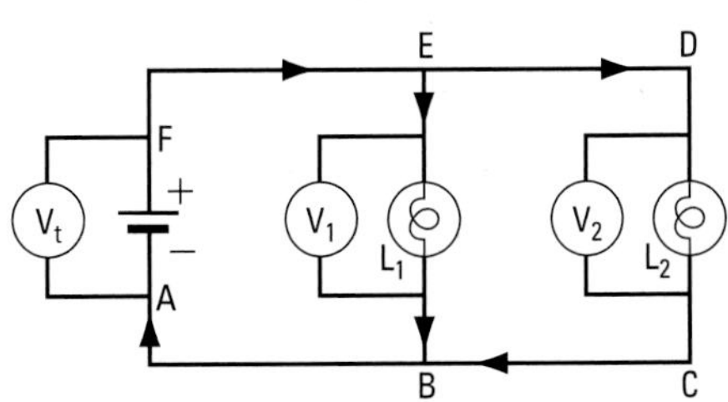

FIGURE 12.24 Voltmeters in the circuit would all measure the same value because $V_t = V_1 = V_2$.

CHALLENGE

A 6-V battery is connected to a light bulb L_1 that is connected in series to a parallel connection of two light bulbs L_2 and L_3. If the drop in electrical potential across bulb L_1 is 3 V, what is the drop in electrical potential across each of the other two bulbs? Explain your answer using the law of conservation of energy.

EXAMPLE 10 CONCEPTUAL

A battery is connected to two different light bulbs L_1 and L_2 connected in parallel. The drop in electrical potential across L_2 is 6.0 V. What is the drop in electrical potential across bulb L_1 and the increase in electrical potential across the battery?

Reasoning and Solution

Since energy is conserved, $V_t = V_1 = V_2$ (in parallel). But $V_2 = 6.0$ V. Therefore, $V_t = 6$ V and $V_1 = 6$ V. There will be an increase in electrical potential across the battery of 6 V and a decrease in electrical potential across each bulb of 6 V.

Kirchhoff's voltage law summarizes the potential difference relationships for both series and parallel circuits. It states:

The algebraic sum of the potential differences around any closed pathway or loop must equal zero.

There is an increase in the potential difference across the terminals of a source of electric current and a decrease in the potential difference across components like light bulbs. Kirchhoff's voltage law says that around any closed loop the sum of the increases must equal the sum of the decreases. This is just a different way of stating the law of conservation of energy.

Note that when two bulbs are in parallel with a cell, as in Figure 12.24, you can consider two loops. One loop includes the cell and bulb L_1. So $V_t = V_1$. The second loop includes the cell and L_2. Hence, $V_t = V_2$. Combining these results means that all potential differences in this circuit must be equal. Figures 12.25 and 12.26 summarize Kirchhoff's laws as they apply to simple series and parallel circuits.

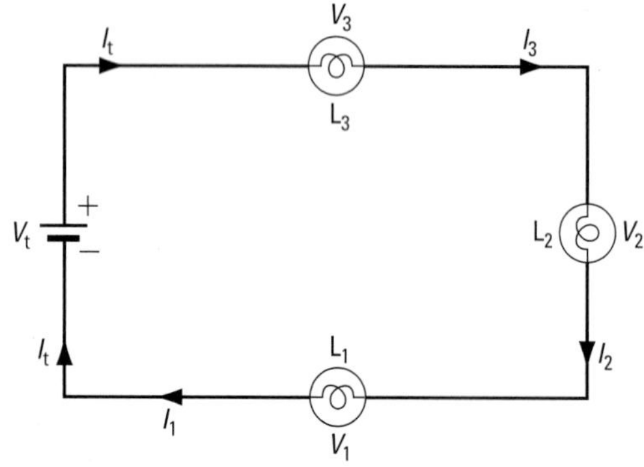

FIGURE 12.25 In a series circuit $I_t = I_1 = I_2 = I_3$ and $V_t = V_1 + V_2 + V_3$

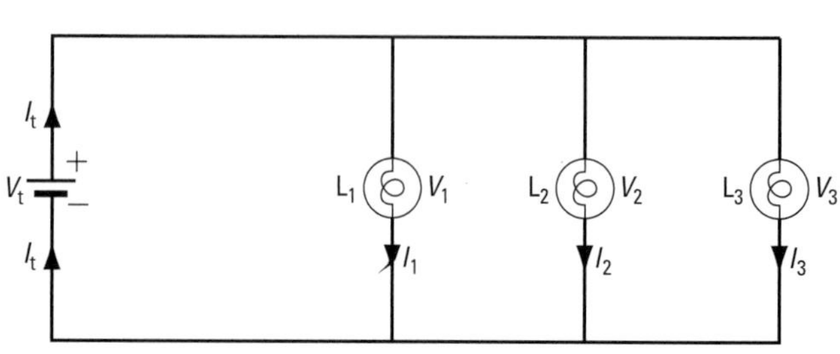

FIGURE 12.26 In a parallel circuit $I_t = I_1 + I_2 + I_3$ and $V_t = V_1 = V_2 = V_3$

EXAMPLE 11 NUMERICAL

Figure 12.27 shows a parallel connection of three bulbs.

a) Determine the unknown quantities V_t, V_2, V_3, and I_3.
b) Are the three identical?

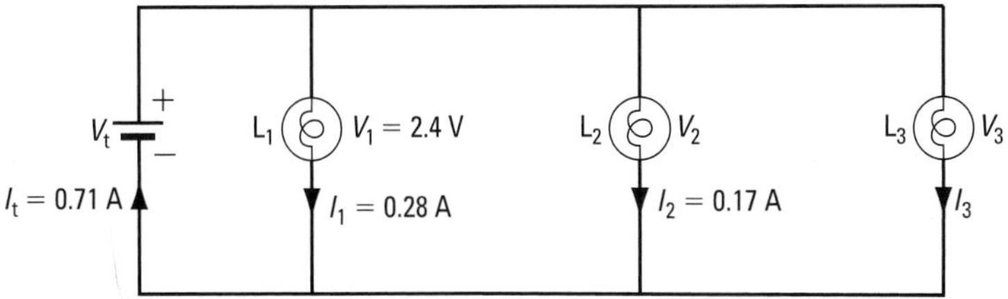

FIGURE 12.27

Investigation
Refer to page 480, Investigation 2.

Given
V_1, I_t, I_1, and I_2

Required
potential differences V_t, V_2, and V_3
current I_3

Analysis
- Use Kirchhoff's voltage law to determine V_t, V_2, and V_3.
- Use Kirchhoff's current law to determine I_3.
- Compare currents in the bulbs to see if they are the same.

Solution
In a parallel connection, the potential differences are equal. Therefore,

$$V_1 = 2.4 \text{ V} = V_t = V_2 = V_3$$

In a parallel connection, the total current is the sum of the currents through each pathway:

$$I_t = I_1 + I_2 + I_3$$

Therefore, $I_3 = I_t - I_1 - I_2$

$$= 0.71 \text{ A} - 0.26 \text{ A} - 0.17 \text{ A}$$

$$= 0.26 \text{ A}$$

Bulbs L_1 and L_3 may be identical because the flow of current through them is almost the same (within experimental error). However, bulb L_2 is different because the current is much less than in the others.

Statement
a) In this circuit, the potential differences V_t, V_2, and V_3 are all equal to 2.4 V. The current I_3 is equal to 0.26 A.
b) Bulbs L_1 and L_3 may be the same type, but bulb L_2 is different from the other two.

PRACTICE PROBLEMS

1. Suppose the given values in Figure 12.27 are changed to $I_t = 0.84$ A, $V_1 = 3.2$ V, $I_1 = 0.30$ A, and $I_2 = 0.30$ A.
   a) Calculate the unknown quanities V_t, V_2, and V_3 and I_3.
   b) Are the three bulbs identical? Explain.
2. Suppose the given values in Figure 12.27 are: $V_t = 4.5$ V, $I_1 = 0.33$ A, $I_2 = 0.40$ A, $I_3 = 0.15$ A.
   a) Calculate the unknown quantities V_1, V_2, and V_3 and I_t.
   b) How do you know that each of the three bulbs is different?

Series–Parallel Combinations

Most practical electric circuits make use of both series and parallel connections. The following numerical example shows how Kirchhoff's laws are applied in series–parallel combinations.

EXAMPLE 12 NUMERICAL

Figure 12.28 shows a series–parallel combination of different light bulbs. Determine the currents I_1 and I_2 and the potential differences V_1 and V_3.

Given
I_t, I_3, V_t, and V_2

Required
I_1, I_2, V_1, and V_3

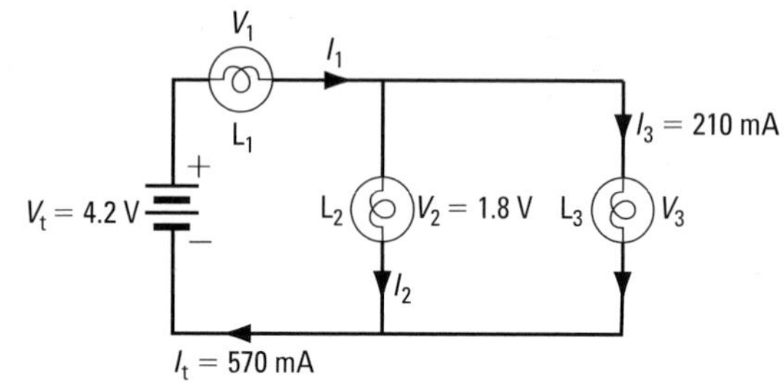

FIGURE 12.28

Analysis

- Use Kirchhoff's current law to determine I_1 and I_2.
- Use Kirchhoff's voltage law around the parallel loop to find V_3.
- Apply the same law to find the value of V_1.

Solution
L_1 is in series with the cell. Therefore, $I_1 = I_t = 570$ mA.

570 mA enters the parallel connection and 210 mA leaves along one path. Therefore, (570 – 210) mA flows along the other path:

$I_2 = I_1 - I_3 = 360$ mA

The potential difference across the parallel connection is 1.8 V. Therefore,

$V_3 = V_2 = 1.8$ V

Consider the loop containing L_1, L_2, and the cell. The increase in potential difference across the cell is 4.2 V. The sum of the decreases in the loop must equal 4.2 V. Therefore,

$4.2 \text{ V} = 1.8 \text{ V} + V_1$

$V_1 = (4.2 - 1.8) \text{ V} = 2.4 \text{ V}$

Statement
The voltage across L_1 is 2.4 V, and the voltage across L_3 is 1.8 V. The current through L_1 is 570 mA and the current through L_2 is 360 mA.

PRACTICE PROBLEM

Figure 12.29 shows a series–parallel combination of five identical light bulbs. Determine the currents I_1, I_3, I_4, and I_5 and the potential differences V_1, V_2, and V_3.

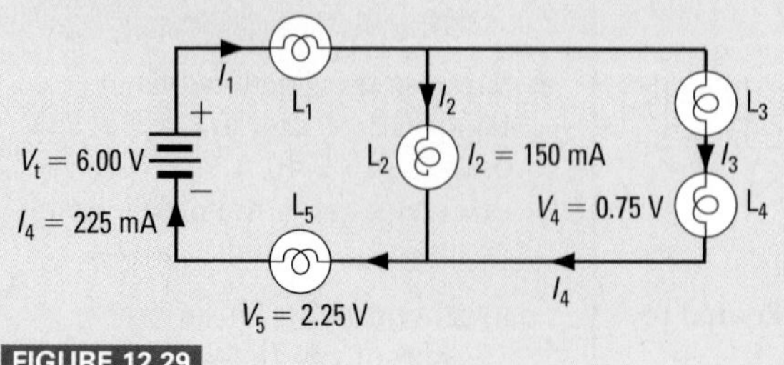

FIGURE 12.29

Connecting Cells in Series and in Parallel

We can connect the cells making up batteries in series or in parallel (Figure 12.30). Figure 12.30a) shows that when we connect opposite terminals of cells together they are in series. A parallel combination of cells has like terminals connected together as in Figure 12.30b). Kirchhoff's current and voltage laws apply to cells connected in series and in parallel as the following numerical example shows.

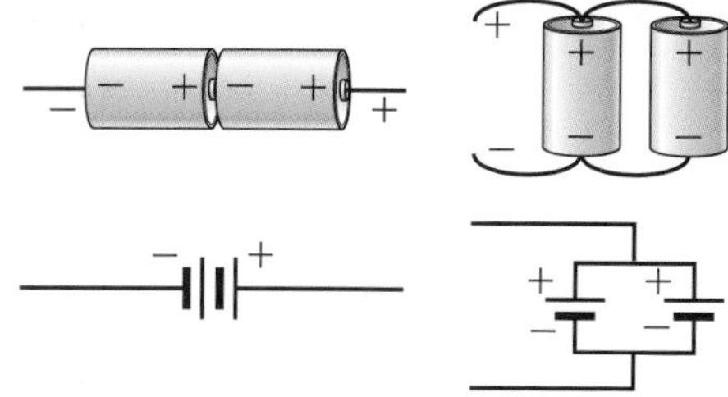

FIGURE 12.30 Cells in series and in parallel
a) Series
b) Parallel

EXAMPLE 13 NUMERICAL

Figure 12.31 shows two arrangements of identical cells. Each cell is 1.5 V and, if connected by itself to a light bulb, would produce a current of 400 mA.

a) What is the potential difference V_t in each circuit?
b) What is the current in each cell in the parallel combination?
c) Show how V_t and I_t could be measured.

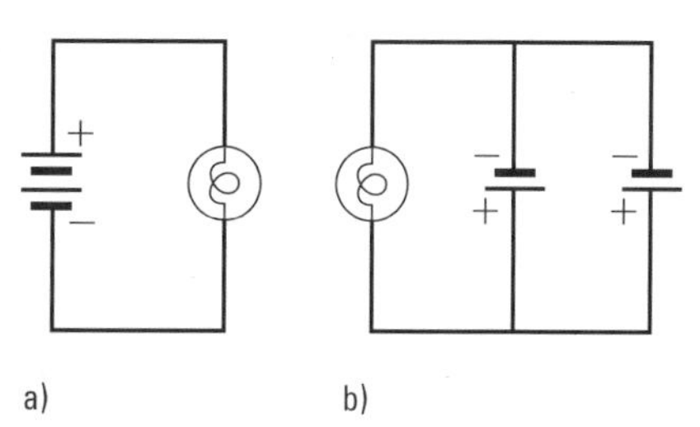

FIGURE 12.31

Given

$I = 400$ mA when $V = 1.5$ V

Required

a) V_t for each combination.
b) I_1 and I_2, the currents through the cells in the parallel combination
c) Show how V_t and I_t could be measured.

Analysis

- Figure 12.31a) shows a series combination of cells.
- In series combinations, $V_t = V_1 + V_2 + V_3 + ...$
- Figure 12.31b) shows a parallel combination of cells.
- In parallel combinations, $V_t = V_1 = V_2 = V_3 = ...$ and $I_t = I_1 + I_2 + I_3 + ...$
- Voltmeters should be connected in parallel and ammeters in series.

Solution

a) For the series combination,

$$V_t = 1.5 \text{ V} + 1.5 \text{ V} = 3.0 \text{ V}$$

For the parallel combination,

$$V_t = 1.5 \text{ V}$$

WEBLINK

To explore current and potential difference in series and parallel circuits, go to **www.pearsoned.ca/physics11.**

b) $I_t = 400$ mA

$$\text{Therefore, current through each cell} = \frac{400 \text{ mA}}{2}$$

$$= 200 \text{ mA}$$

c) The meters should be connected as shown in Figure 12.32.

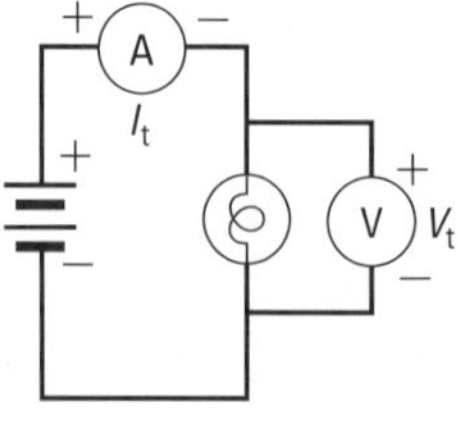

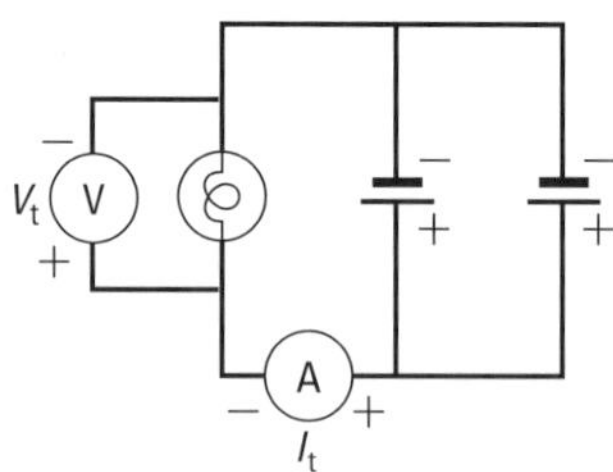

a) b)

FIGURE 12.32

Statement

a) The total potential difference is 3.0 V in the series combination shown in Figure 12.32a) and 1.5 V in the parallel combination shown in Figure 12.32b).

b) The current through each cell in the parallel combination is 200 mA.

c) In both circuits the total potential difference can be measured by connecting a voltmeter across the load and the total current can be measured by connecting an ammeter between the load and the battery.

PRACTICE PROBLEM

Two identical 1.2-V cells are connected in series with two identical light bulbs. If each cell were connected alone to one of the bulbs it would produce a current of 240 mA. Draw a circuit diagram showing the connection. Show where a voltmeter would be connected to read the total drop in electrical potential across the two bulbs and where an ammeter would be connected to read the current entering the bulbs. Label the polarity of each meter and show the direction of conventional current flow. What is the potential difference V_t and current I_t when the two cells are connected to the two bulbs?

FIGURE 12.33 Boosting a car battery

Have you ever seen someone turn the key in the ignition of a car and find the battery dead? Fortunately, you can boost the dead battery by connecting it in parallel to a fully charged battery—a very practical application of a parallel circuit. However, the process is not as simple as it looks and has some hidden dangers. So, what is the correct and safe way to connect the two batteries?

The like terminals of the two batteries must be connected together, but there is a serious hazard if the batteries are connected directly. Because the fully charged battery has a greater potential difference than the dead one, there is usually a spark when the last cable is connected and when the first cable is removed. These sparks can ignite hydrogen gas produced by chemical reactions within the battery. People have been blinded by the sulfuric acid that splashes from the exploding battery.

You can prevent an explosion by following this procedure: Connect the red booster cable clamps to the positive terminals of both batteries. These terminals are usually marked "pos" or "+." Next, attach one end of the black booster cable to the negative terminal ("neg" or "−") on the live battery. Now proceed carefully. Connect the other end of the black booster cable to a clean part of the engine, well away from the battery to avoid any leaking hydrogen. When you remove the booster cables, disconnect the negative clamp connected to the engine first. During the boosting procedure, the car with the live battery should be switched off to avoid any possibility of damaging its electrical system.

Caution: In some vehicles, the positive terminal rather than the negative terminal of the battery is connected to the engine. To prevent damage to the vehicle, check which terminal is grounded to the engine before you connect the booster cables.

WEBLINK

Batteries come in many forms. Find out about modern batteries and how and why they are recycled. In a chart, summarize the main types of batteries, their uses, their costs, and how they are recycled. Begin your research at **www.pearsoned.ca/physics11.**

Section 12.3 Review

Understanding Concepts

1. Four ammeters—A_1, A_2, A_3, and A_4—are placed in a circuit containing two different light bulbs and a switch as shown in Figure 12.34. When the switch is closed, A_3 reads 250 mA, and A_2 reads 350 mA. Note that the current read by A_3 is I_3.
   a) With the switch closed, what are the readings on A_1 and A_4?
   b) Assume that the cell supplies a constant voltage. If the switch is opened, what readings would you expect on the ammeters?

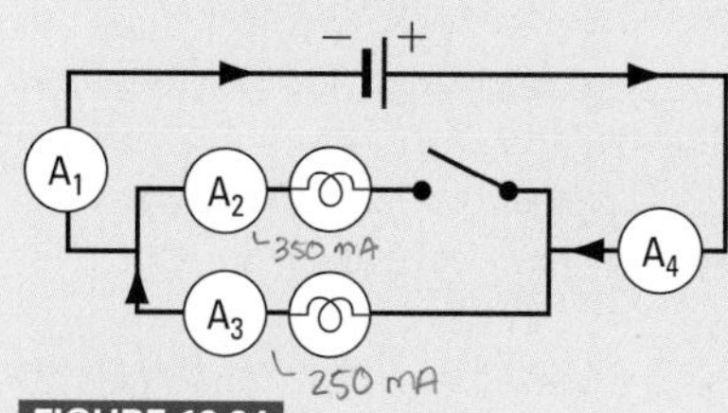

FIGURE 12.34

2. Refer to Figure 12.35.
   a) Identify the positive terminal of the cell and each meter connection.
   b) If voltmeter V_t shows 4.8 V, what will be the reading on V_2?
   c) If all bulbs are identical and ammeter A_2 reads 200 mA, what will be the reading on each of the other ammeters?

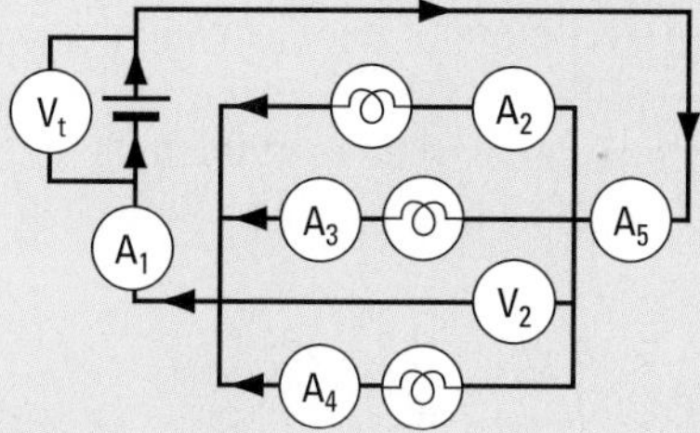

FIGURE 12.35

3. Refer to Figure 12.36. What will be the potential difference across L_2 and the current flowing through it?

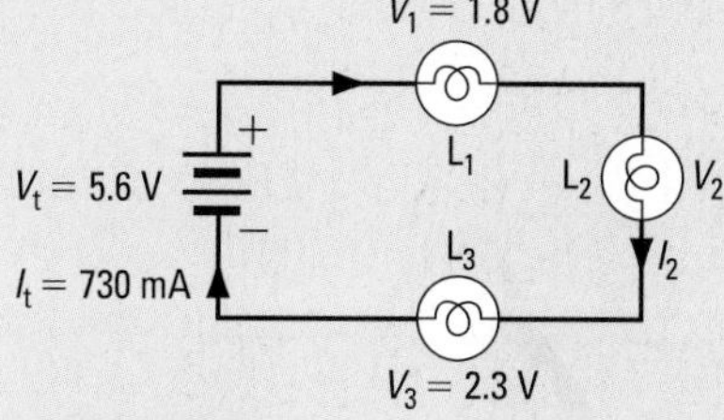

FIGURE 12.36

4. Seven identical bulbs are arranged in the circuit shown in Figure 12.37. If I_3, representing the current through L_3, is 300 mA, what is the current through each of the other bulbs?

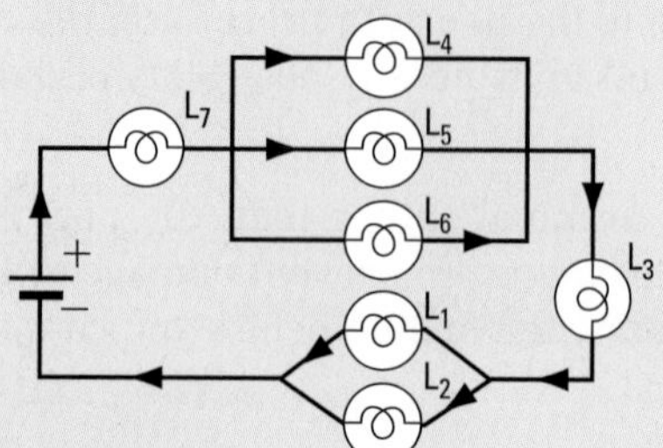

FIGURE 12.37

5. Describe how cells are connected in series. Use a diagram in your answer.

6. Describe how cells are connected in parallel. Use a diagram in your answer.

7. Suppose that three 1.5-V DC cells power a flashlight. Compare a series and a parallel combination with respect to
   a) the brightness of the bulb
   b) how long the bulb will stay lit

Applying Inquiry/ Communication Skills

8. In which circuit would identical 1.5-V bulbs glow longer, when connected in series to a 1.5-V dry cell, or when connected in parallel to an identical 1.5-V dry cell? How much longer? Explain. Then do an experiment to test your prediction.

Making Connections

9. The energy used to power an electric car is stored in a battery pack. While the car is being driven, the battery pack pushes electric charges through the electric motors that turn the wheels. With use, the potential difference of the battery pack decreases and the current passing though the motors decreases. Explain how this process is reversed.

10. Find out why electric cars are not yet replacing cars powered by fossil fuels. Make a summary of the advantages and disadvantages of electric cars.

Investigation 1 (Section 12.3)

Inquiry Skills

- Initiating and Planning
- Applying Technical Skills
- Using Tools, Materials, Equipment
- Conducting and Recording
- Analyzing and Interpreting
- Concluding and Communicating

Properties of a Series Circuit

Problem

What are the potential difference and current characteristics in a series circuit?

Materials

- ammeter
- switch
- 3 identical light bulbs
- 8 connector leads
- variable power supply
- voltmeter

Caution: Your teacher will tell you the maximum electrical potential difference to use so as not to burn out the light bulbs. Be careful connecting the meters.

Experimental Design

1. Connect the power supply, the switch, and the three light bulbs in series as shown in Figure 12.38.

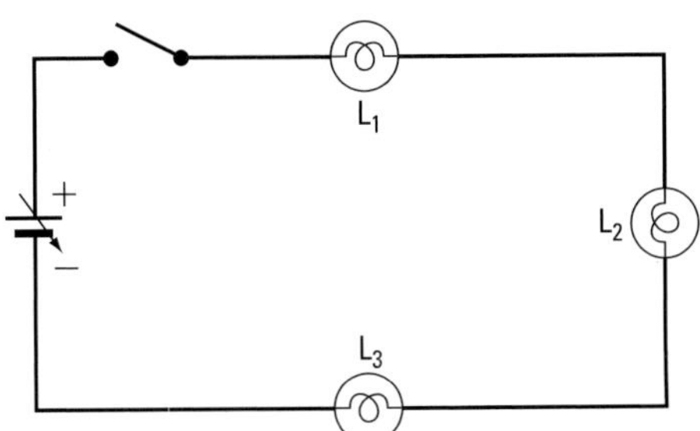

FIGURE 12.38 Series circuit

2. Design a procedure to determine the effect of opening and closing the switch, unscrewing one of the bulbs, and placing a wire across the terminals of one of the bulbs.
3. Design a procedure to determine the relationship between the potential difference across the power supply V_t and the potential differences V_1, V_2, and V_3 across the bulbs.
4. Design a procedure to determine the relationship between the current flowing through the power source I_t, and the currents I_1, I_2, and I_3 flowing through each of the bulbs.
5. Design a procedure to determine the relationship between the potential difference across the power supply V_t and the current flowing through it, I_t.
6. Check all procedures with your teacher before staring the experiments. Design tables to record the data from steps 1, 2, and 3 above.

Analyzing and Interpreting

1. A switch is used in a circuit to turn electric current off and on. Explain the effect that operating the switch has on the circuit.
2. What happens to the current when a break occurs in the circuit? Why does this happen?
3. a) How is a lighted bulb affected when a wire is connected across it?
   b) Why does this happen?

Concluding and Communicating

4. Examine your data table for step 3. Write an equation to show how the total potential difference across the circuit is related to the potential differences across the bulbs.
5. Examine your data table for step 4. Write an equation to show how the total current in the circuit is related to the current through each bulb.
6. Why will one bulb connected to a battery glow brighter than three identical bulbs connected in series to the same battery?

Extending

7. Replace one of the bulbs with a bulb that is dimmer. Predict how the potential difference and current for the replacement bulb will compare with those for the original bulb. Then do an experiment to test your prediction. Explain the results.

Investigation 2 (Section 12.3)

Inquiry Skills

- Initiating and Planning
- Applying Technical Skills
- Using Tools, Materials, Equipment
- Conducting and Recording
- Analyzing and Interpreting
- Concluding and Communicating

Properties of a Parallel Circuit

Problem

What are the potential difference and current characteristics in a parallel circuit?

Materials

- ammeter
- switch
- 3 identical light bulbs
- 10 connector leads
- variable power supply
- voltmeter

Caution: Your teacher will tell you the maximum electrical potential difference to use so as not to burn out the light bulbs.

Procedure

1. Connect the three bulbs in parallel across the power supply as shown in Figure 12.39. Adjust the power supply to give a potential difference of 6.0 V (or that specified by your teacher).

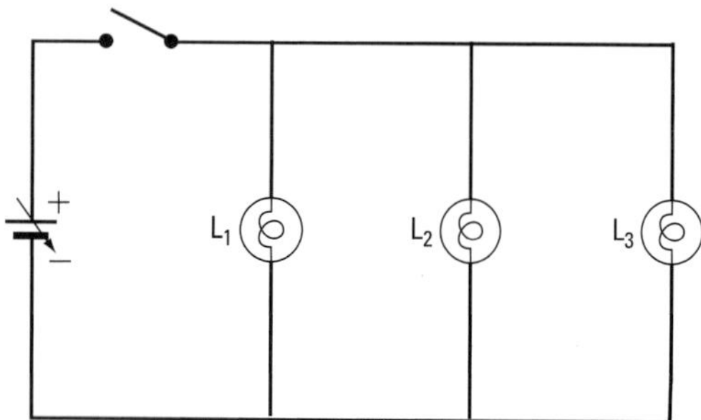

FIGURE 12.39 A parallel circuit

2. Close the switch and verify that all the bulbs are working.
3. Unscrew one of the bulbs. Record your observations regarding any change in the brightness of the remaining bulbs.
4. Unscrew another bulb and again record your observations regarding any change in the brightness of the remaining bulb.
5. Re-install the two bulbs you unscrewed. Measure the total potential difference across the power supply and the potential difference across each of the bulbs. Record your results in a table.
6. Repeat step 5 with the power supply set at 4.5 V, then 3.0 V, and finally 1.5 V.
7. Reset the power supply to 6.0 V. Measure the total current in the circuit and the current through each of the bulbs. Record your results in a table.
8. Repeat step 7 with the power supply set at 4.5 V, then 3.0 V, and finally 1.5 V.

Analyzing an Interpreting

1. a) How does removing one bulb from a parallel circuit differ from removing one bulb from a series circuit? Explain the result in terms of the path along which the electrons flow.
   b) What happens to the brightness of the bulbs left on in the parallel circuit when first one and then a second bulb is unscrewed?
2. a) In a parallel circuit, how many pathways exist for the electric current?
   b) Is a voltmeter connected in series or in parallel? Explain.

Concluding and Communicating

3. Examine your data table for steps 5 and 6. Write an equation showing how the total potential difference across the circuit is related to the potential differences across each bulb.
4. Examine your data table for steps 7 and 8. Write an equation showing how the total current in the circuit is related to the current through each bulb.
5. Why will one bulb connected to the battery glow with the same brightness as three identical bulbs connected in parallel to the same battery?
6. Will the three identical bulbs connected in parallel still glow as brightly as a single bulb if the battery is weak? Why or why not?

Extending

7. Replace one of the bulbs with a dimmer one. Predict how the potential difference across the replacement bulb and the current through it will compare with those for the original bulb. Then do an experiment to test your prediction. Explain the results.

CHAPTER SUMMARY

Key Terms

ammeter
ampere
battery
cell
circuit
circuit diagram
conventional current
coulomb
Coulomb's law
current electricity
electric current
electrical potential
electrical potential difference
electron flow convention
elementary charge
Kirchhoff's voltage law
Kirchhoff's current law
law of conservation of energy
parallel connection
series connection
volt
voltage
voltmeter

Key Equations

$Q = Ne$

$I = \dfrac{Q}{\Delta t}$

$F_e = \dfrac{kQ_1Q_2}{d^2}$

For a series circuit:

$I_t = I_1 = I_2 = I_3 = \ldots$ and $V_t = V_1 + V_2 + V_3 + \ldots$

For a parallel circuit:

$I_t = I_1 + I_2 + I_3 + \ldots$ and $V_t = V_1 = V_2 = V_3 = \ldots$

Essential Understandings

- According to the electron flow convention, electrons flow from the negative terminal of a source of electrical energy through the circuit to the positive terminal.
- According to the conventional current flow, positive charge flows from the positive terminal of a source of electrical energy through the circuit to the negative terminal.
- At a series connection electric current flows along one pathway. At a parallel connection electric current flows along two or more pathways.
- Kirchhoff's current law states that at any connection in an electric circuit, the total current flowing into the connection is equal to the total current flowing out of the connection.
- Kirchhoff's voltage law states that the algebraic sum of the potential differences around any closed pathway or loop must equal zero.
- A battery, consisting of cells connected in series, produces a total potential difference equal to the sum of potentials produced by each cell. The total current is the same as the current passing through any one of the cells.
- The potential difference produced by a battery consisting of identical cells connected in parallel is the same as the potential difference across any one of the cells. The total current is equal to the sum of the currents produced by each cell.

Consolidate Your Understanding

1. Look back to your answers for the Checkpoint on page 451. What answer would you give now? Explain why each of the other answers is incorrect.

   Suppose ammeters could be connected in series in the middle of the filament of a light bulb and in the middle of a battery. Would the ammeters register any current? Explain.

2. Create a concept map to be used as a study map for electric charge, current, and potential difference. Consult the Key Terms provided above, and include as many terms as possible in your concept map. Include two Key Equations and an example problem involving both. Show a model solution using the GRASS strategy.

3. Write a paragraph explaining the similarities and differences between electric current and electrical potential difference. Write the equation and units of each. Explain why many people confuse the two concepts.

CHAPTER 12 REVIEW

Understanding Concepts

1. An object has a positive charge of 1.2×10^{-11} C. Since a coulomb equals the charge on 6.24×10^{18} electrons then the object has
   a) a deficit of 7.5×10^{7} electrons
   b) an excess of 7.5×10^{7} electrons
   c) a deficit of 7.5×10^{29} electrons
   d) an excess of 7.5×10^{29} electrons
   e) a deficit of 5.2×10^{29} electrons

2. When the potential difference is 100 V, a steady current flows in a circuit for 60 s. A total of 60 kJ of energy is converted into heat. What is the current in the circuit?
   a) 0 mA b) 0.10 A c) 0.50 A
   d) 1.0 A e) 10 A

3. How much energy is required to move 2.0 C of charge through a potential difference of 5.0 V?
   a) 0.40 J
   b) 2.5 J
   c) 3.0 J
   d) 7.0 J
   e) 10 J

4. What is the potential difference between two points in a circuit if 6.8 J of work is done while supplying a current of 20 mA for 2.0 min?
   a) 0.17 V
   b) 2.8×10^{-3} V
   c) 2.8 V
   d) 6.0 V
   e) 1.7×10^{2} V

5. Five identical cells are available, each of which produces a potential difference of 2.0 V and a current of 0.50 A when connected alone in a certain circuit. If a battery made by connecting the cells together in series is used in the circuit, what are the total current and total potential difference?

	Total Current (I)	Total Potential Difference (V)
a)	0.10 A	0.50 V
b)	0.50 A	1.0 V
c)	1.0 A	2.0 V
d)	2.5 A	5.0 V
e)	2.5 A	10 V

6. The two light bulbs L_1 and L_2 shown in Figure 12.40 are different. I_c and V_c refer to the cell. Which one of the following potential difference relationships is correct?
   a) $V_c = V_1$
   b) $V_c = V_1 + V_2$
   c) $V_c = V_1 + V_2 + V_3$
   d) $V_2 = V_3$
   e) $V_c = V_1 = V_2 = V_3$

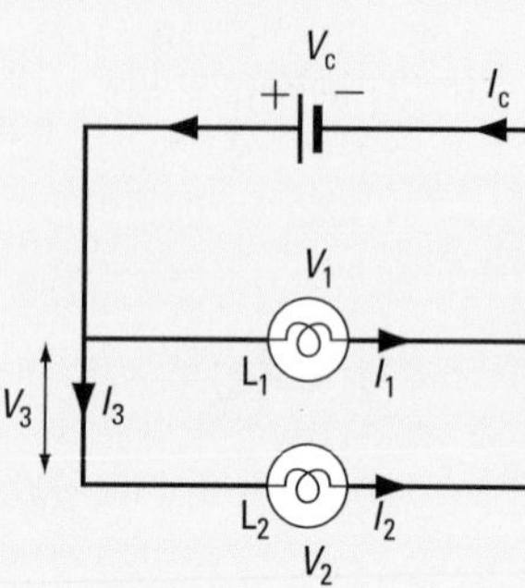

FIGURE 12.40 A circuit with two light bulbs

7. a) Name the unit of electric charge and describe how it is related to an excess or deficit of electrons.
   b) Describe the elementary charge.

8. a) Where does charge reside on a hollow conductor?
   b) What use is made of this information?

9. a) Define electric current.
   b) What are the units of electric current and what instrument is used to measure current?

10. a) Name and describe the two different conventions for electric current.
    b) Which convention are we using in this text?

11. a) Where is the greatest concentration of charge on an irregular-shaped conductor?
    b) How did Benjamin Franklin make use of this fact?

12. a) Define field.
    b) Where is an electric field located?

13. Does the potential difference of a cell provide a force, a source of energy, or both? Give reasons for your answer.

14. Distinguish between the terms "potential difference" and "current" as they apply to electric circuits.

15. A circuit diagram in a text shows an arrow leaving the positive side of an electrical source to indicate the direction of current flow. Explain this apparent contradiction with the direction of electron flow.

16. State Kirchhoff's current law and use an example to explain it.

17. State Kirchhoff's voltage law and use an example to explain it.

18. a) Why do all the lights go out when any one bulb burns out in a string of decorative lights connected in series?
    b) How could you find out which bulb was burned out?

19. A fuse is used to protect a circuit by limiting the amount of current that can flow. Should fuses be connected in series or in parallel with the circuits they protect? Explain.

20. Refer to Figure 12.40. When one bulb is connected across a single cell, it glows with a normal brightness. Match each circuit in Figure 12.41 with a description of the bulb brightness from the list below. All the cells are identical. Each description may be used once, more than once, or not at all.

i) Normal brightness
ii) Dimmer than normal
iii) Brighter than normal
iv) No glow at all
v) Bulb probably destroyed

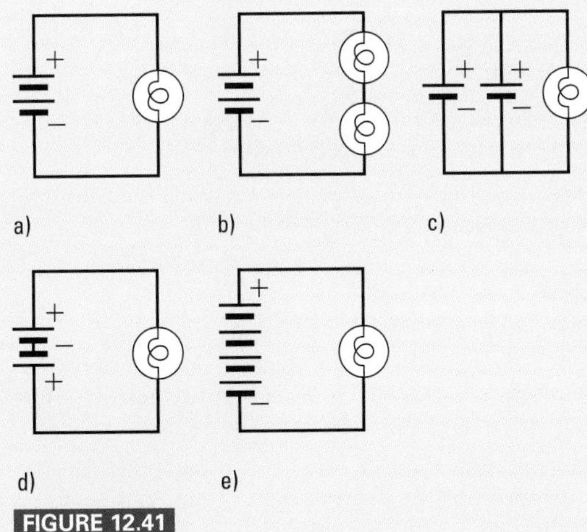

FIGURE 12.41

Applying Inquiry/ Communication Skills

21. A charge that produces a large lightning bolt is about 10 C. Explain by referring to electrons why this is such a large charge. How many AA cells is this equivalent to?

22. Coulomb's law is similar to Newton's law of universal gravitation in some ways and different from it in other ways. Make a table summarizing the similarities and differences.

23. Draw schematic circuit diagrams showing:
a) a cell, a bulb, and a switch connected in series.
b) a cell connected to a parallel combination of two bulbs. Show how meters could be connected to measure the current leaving the cell and the potential difference across both bulbs. Include in your diagram the polarity of the terminals of the meter connections.
c) two cells connected in parallel to form a battery. The battery is in series with one bulb that is connected to a parallel combination of two others.

24. Suppose you are given one cell, as many connecting wires as necessary, and three identical light bulbs.
a) How many different circuits can you design?
b) For each one draw the circuit diagram.
c) Suppose you connect one bulb to the cell and record its brightness. Explain what will happen to the brightness of the bulb if the other two are connected
i) so that all three are in series
ii) so that all three are in parallel

25. Explain why a bulb lights almost at the same time as the switch is closed even though charge flows very slowly in a circuit.

Making Connections

26. Figure 12.42 shows a light pith ball covered with aluminum foil supported by an insulating thread. The pith ball is suspended midway between the globe of a charged Van de Graaff generator and a neutral conductor connected to ground. The pith ball swings back and forth between the charged globe and the neutral conductor. Explain why.

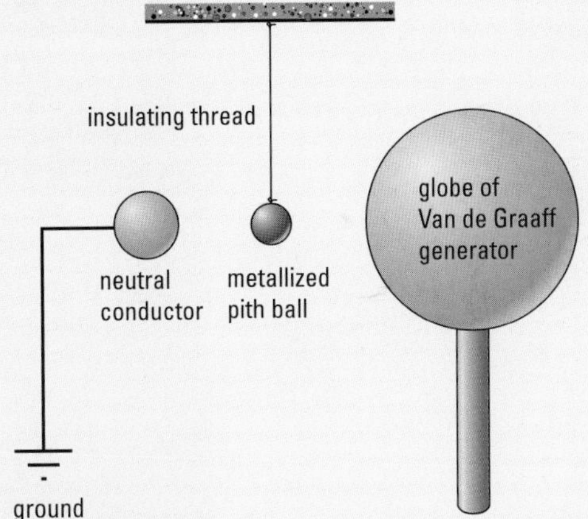

FIGURE 12.42

27. a) Explain why street lights are connected in parallel.
b) List two other situations where parallel connections would be an advantage.

28. a) Design a system to protect a golf course clubhouse from lightning.
b) Why don't you see lightning rods on ordinary houses?

29. Why can a bird perch on two feet on a high-voltage line without being electrocuted, but a cow experiences an electric shock by touching an electric fence that operates on a 6-V battery?

CHAPTER 13

Electrical Resistance, Power, and Energy

SPECIFIC EXPECTATIONS

By the end of this chapter, you will be able to:

- define and describe the concepts and units related to electricity (13.1, 13.2, 13.3)

The incandescent light bulb produces a convenient, inexpensive source of light. An incandescent light bulb contains a thin wire, called a filament, inside a glass bulb (Figure 13.1). When you turn on a switch, electrical energy causes the filament to emit heat and light. Light bulbs come in dif-

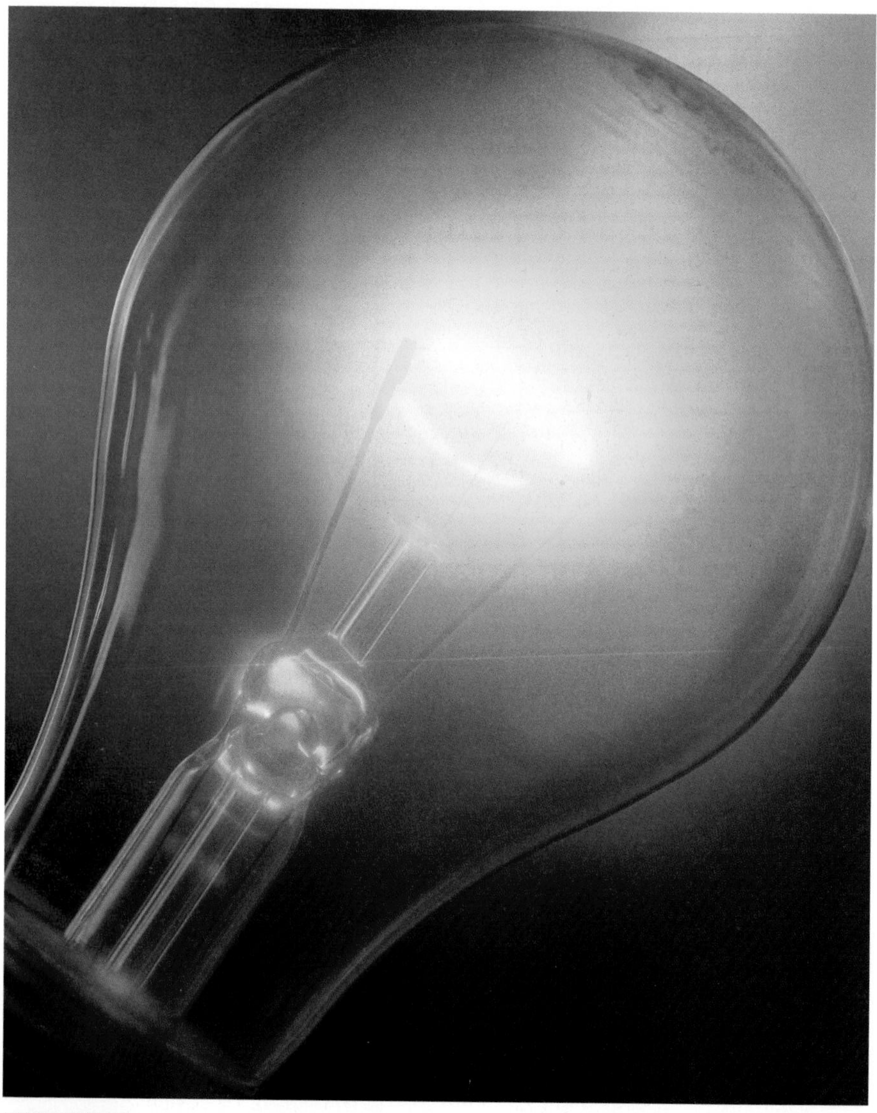

FIGURE 13.1 Incandescent lights are available with a wide range of power ratings. How is power rating related to resistance?

ferent powers. If you examine some at home, you might see them marked 60 W or 100 W. Why is electrical energy transformed into heat and light in the filament rather than in some other part of the circuit? How does a 60-W bulb differ from a 100-W bulb? Does it cost much more to use a 100-W instead of a 60-W bulb? Do we pay for power or energy?

In this chapter we will investigate electrical resistance. This important property will help us answer these and other questions. What is electrical resistance and how is it measured? What is equivalent resistance and how is it calculated? What do we pay for on our electric bills, energy or power, or both?

Discovering Physics

Different Light Bulbs, Different Connections

In this activity you will experiment with connecting two light bulbs with different ratings in different ways and observe the brightness of the bulbs. Later in the chapter you will be able to explain your observations in terms of electrical resistance and electrical power.

You will need a 6.0-V battery, a 3.5-V bulb and holder, a 6.0-V bulb and holder, connecting wires, and a switch.

1. Record the voltage rating written on the base of the bulbs. Keep track of their location during the activity.
2. Connect the circuit shown in Figure 13.2. Make sure the two bulbs are connected in series as shown.
3. Close the switch and record the brightness of the bulbs.
4. Repeat steps in the experiment but connect the two bulbs in parallel as shown in Figure 13.3. Before you close the switch, predict which bulb will glow more brightly.
   - Which of the two bulbs glowed more brightly when they were connected in series?
   - Which of the two bulbs glowed more brightly when they were connected in parallel?
   - Discuss the results with other students and try to come up with an explanation. Use terms like energy, series connection, parallel connection, electrical resistance, electrical energy, and electrical power.

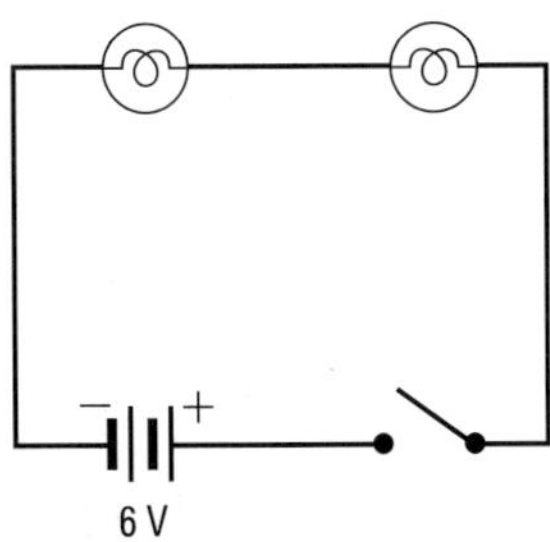

FIGURE 13.2 Different bulbs connected in series

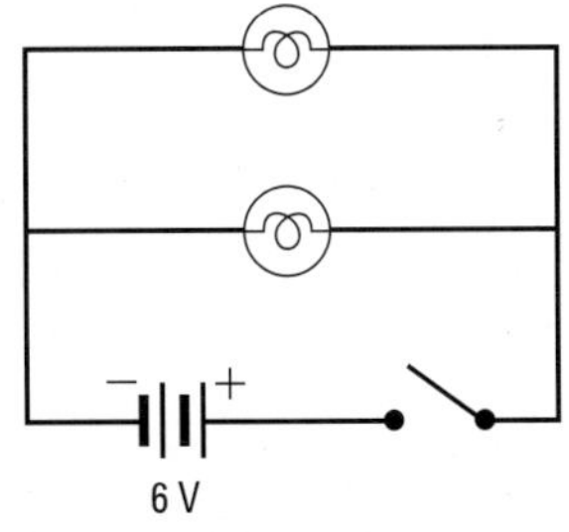

FIGURE 13.3 Different bulbs connected in parallel

CHECKPOINT

A series circuit contains a battery, a bulb, and two resistors R_1 and R_2 whose resistance can be increased or decreased. The bulb is located between the two resistors. While the bulb is lit, R_1 is decreased and R_2 is kept the same. What will happen to the brightness of the bulb?

a) It increases.
b) It decreases.
c) It remains the same.
d) It is impossible to predict unless the resistances of R_1 and R_2 are known.

Draw a schematic diagram for the circuit and explain your answer.

13.1 Resistance and Ohm's Law

Key Understandings

When you have completed this section, you will be able to:

- define and describe the concepts and units related to resistance and conductance
- state Ohm's law
- state the compound unit of resistance and its alternative name
- solve problems involving potential difference, electric current, and resistance
- describe the four factors that affect the resistance of a cylindrical conductor
- describe and solve problems involving resistivity

In 1878, Thomas Edison set out to produce light from electricity. Sir Joseph Wilson Swan, an English physicist and chemist, had devised an incandescent bulb in 1860 using a carbon filament. But Swan could not obtain the necessary vacuum to keep it working for an extended period of time. Edison spent $50 000 and a year experimenting to confirm that platinum wire would not work as the filament. His motto was "genius is one percent inspiration, and ninety-nine percent perspiration." He persevered and found the answer in 1879. A scorched cotton thread had the necessary resistance and produced light for 40 continuous hours in a nearly perfect vacuum.

Resistance and Ohm's Law

INFOBIT

Henry Cavendish (1731–1810), an English chemist and physicist, discovered the relationship between voltage and current about 50 years before Ohm did. However, Cavendish did not publish his results!

The filament of an electric light bulb impedes the flow of electric current. The filament has a property called **resistance**. Increasing the resistance in a circuit decreases the current that flows. **Conductance** is a measure of how easily current can flow through a material. Conductance is the inverse of resistance, so a large resistance means a small conductance. We can investigate the resistance of a material by varying the potential difference across it and measuring the electric current passing through it. For a metal at constant temperature, a graph of the results would look like Figure 13.5a). The graph has a constant, positive slope and a y-intercept of zero. The graph shows that if potential difference V is doubled, then current I also doubles. V and I are directly proportional. Georg Simon Ohm discovered this relationship in 1827. **Ohm's law** states:

The potential difference across a conductor is directly proportional to the current flowing through it.

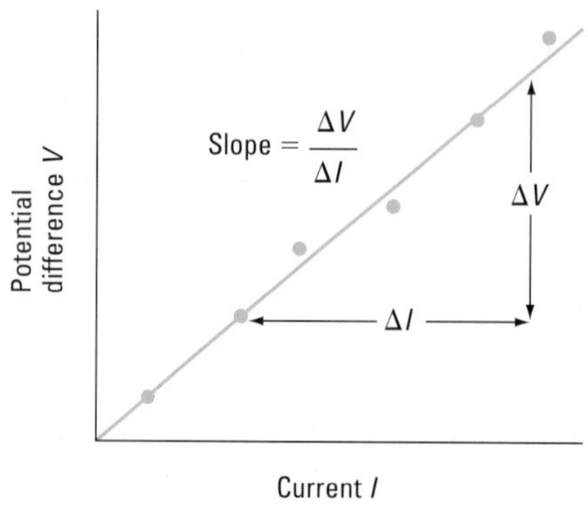

a) Ohmic resistor

Potential difference V

Current I

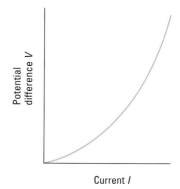

b) Non-ohmic resistor

FIGURE 13.4 Potential difference against current for ohmic and non-ohmic materials

Ohm's law holds true for a metallic conductor at a constant temperature. Materials that obey Ohm's law are said to be **ohmic**, and materials that do not obey Ohm's law are said to be **nonohmic**. The resistors used in electronics are very nearly ohmic. As Figure 13.4 b) shows, the resistance of a nonohmic material can change dramatically as the current through it increases. Often, this change in resistance is the result of a temperature change of the material by the current.

Mathematically, the proportionality between potential difference and current for ohmic resistors can be written as:

$$V \propto I$$

So, $V = \text{constant} \times I$.

The proportionality constant is the slope of the graph. It is called resistance and is given the symbol R. Hence

$$V = R \times I$$

This equation summarizes Ohm's law. Rearranging the equation,

$$R = \frac{V}{I}$$

Investigation

Refer to page 513, Investigation 1

INFOBIT

In 1827 it was not possible to go to the hardware store and buy resistance wires of various diameters. Fortunately, Ohm learned how to draw out wires while helping his father, who made his living as a mechanic.

Units of Resistance

The unit for potential difference is the volt and the unit for current is the ampere. Substituting these units into the equation for Ohm's law gives the compound unit for resistance, the volt per ampere. However, in honour of Ohm's work, the volt per ampere is called an **ohm**. The symbol for an ohm is Ω, the Greek letter omega. Thus,

$$1\ \Omega = 1\ \frac{V}{A}$$

The resistance of a conductor is 1 Ω is if a potential difference across it of 1 V produces a current of 1 A through it.

Discovering Physics — *Examining a Bulb Filament*

Have you ever looked closely at a light bulb filament? Ask your teacher for a cavity slide, a 3.2-V bulb, a 6.0-V bulb, dissecting scissors, tweezers, two plastic bags, clear adhesive tape, a compound microscope, and a 100-g mass.

Caution: You must wear safety goggles.

Place each bulb inside a plastic bag and gently break the glass envelopes using the mass as a hammer. Do not touch any of the broken glass with your bare hands. Use the scissors to cut the filaments loose and use the tweezers to lift them out of the broken glass and place them in the cavity of the slide. Tape the filaments into position on the cavity slide and record which filament is from which bulb. Place the cavity slide on the stage of the microscope and view the filaments using the 100X lenses.

Can you see any differences between the two filaments? Which one do you think is likely to resist the flow of current more? Record your observations and come back to them after you have studied the factors affecting electrical resistance. You should then be able to explain which filament has the greater resistance and why.

EXAMPLE 1 CONCEPTUAL

Electrical resistance is a property of a load that hinders the motion of electric charge and converts electrical energy into other forms of energy such as heat and light. The larger the electrical resistance, the smaller the electric current allowed to pass and the greater the drop in electric potential. Calculate the resistance of a load if a potential difference of 70 V across it produces a current of 0.28 A.

Reasoning and Solution

The resistance of a load can be calculated by dividing the potential difference across the load by the electric current passing through it.

$$R = \frac{V}{I}$$

$$= \frac{70\ \text{V}}{0.28\ \text{A}}$$

$$= 2.5 \times 10^2 \frac{\text{V}}{\text{A}}$$

$$= 2.5 \times 10^2\ \Omega$$

The resistance of this load is $2.5 \times 10^2\ \Omega$.

CHALLENGES

Calculate the potential difference across a load of resistance $1.5 \times 10^2\ \Omega$ that passes a current of 0.27 A.

What will happen to the current through a load if the resistance is doubled while the potential difference stays the same? Explain.

Resistors

You will see **resistors** if you look inside almost any electronic device, such as a radio, CD player, or computer monitor. Resistors are often cylinders about 1 cm long, with a wire at each end (Figure 13.5). Resistors limit the current in a circuit. The resistance of a resistor and its tolerance are usually indicated by a series of coloured bands on the body of the resistor (see Table 13.1). For example, a resistor marked red-red-black-silver has a resistance of 22 Ω ±10%. The **tolerance** is stated as a percentage and gives the allowable variation in the value of the resistance. For example, a resistor might have a resistance of 10 Ω with a tolerance of ±10%. Since 10% of 10 Ω is 1 Ω, the resistance is designed to be between 9 Ω and 11 Ω.

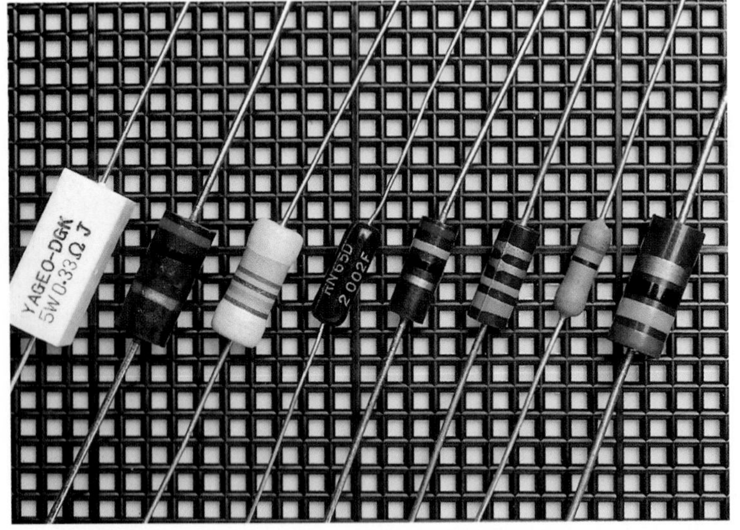

FIGURE 13.5 Resistors

TABLE 13.1 Resistor Colour Codes

Colour	Black	Brown	Red	Orange	Yellow	Green	Blue	Violet	Grey	White	Gold	Silver	No colour
Number	0	1	2	3	4	5	6	7	8	9			
Multiplier	× 1	$\times 10^1$	$\times 10^2$	$\times 10^3$	$\times 10^4$	$\times 10^5$	$\times 10^6$	$\times 10^7$	$\times 10^8$	$\times 10^9$	× 0.1	× 0.01	
Tolerance											5%	10%	20%

Variable Resistors

Sometimes a smooth steady change in current is required rather than a step-by-step change that we would get by connecting various fixed resistors. For example, a sewing machine or model racing car needs a continuously variable speed control. The adjustable part in these speed controls is a **variable resistor**. A typical circuit consists of a power source, a switch, a motor, and a type of variable resistor called a potentiometer (Figure 13.6).

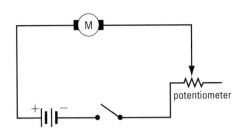

FIGURE 13.6 A potentiometer can be used to vary current in a circuit.

A potentiometer can be used to vary current in an electric circuit. It consists of a coil of resistance wire and a sliding contact point. The contact point can be moved to various places along the coils, changing the length of resistance wire in the circuit. The longer the resistance wire, the larger the resistance. The larger the resistance, the smaller the electric current and the slower the motor turns. To save space, the coils are often formed into a doughnut shape. The sliding contact is rotated along the surface of the doughnut by a knob.

Potentiometers have many uses in electronics, for example, they are widely used to control the volume in stereos and the power circuit in dimmer switches.

Short Circuit

A pathway that contains almost no resistance is called a **short circuit**. This can happen if a good conductor, such as a copper wire, is connected across the terminals of a cell (Figure 13.7). Since there is very little resistance in the circuit, the current will be large. Figure 13.8 shows a short circuit across a light bulb. In this case, the bulb does not light because most electrons flow through the short circuit.

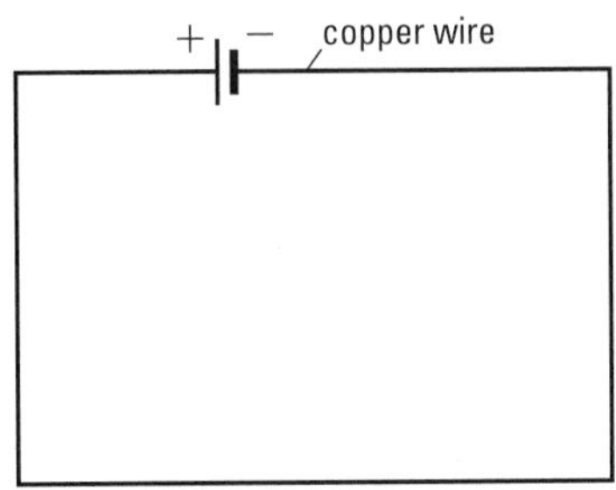

FIGURE 13.7 A short circuit across a cell: The copper wire will heat up. Why?

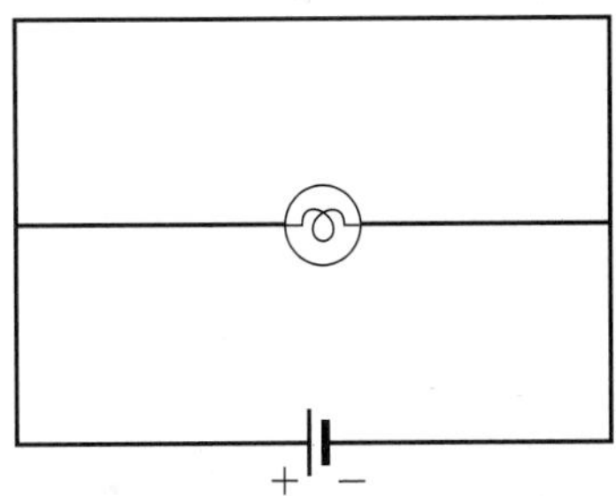

FIGURE 13.8 A short circuit across a light bulb: The bulb will not light, and the wire causing the short circuit will heat up.

Factors Affecting Electrical Resistance

Resistors of different values often look identical on the outside except for the colour bands. If they appear the same, how can they have different values?

Resistors are usually made in one of two ways: a fine wire is wrapped around an insulating core; or a mixture of carbon and other materials is moulded into a cylindrical shape. The resistance R of a cylindrical wire depends on four factors: length, cross-sectional area, temperature, and resistivity.

- **Length** The longer a wire, the greater the resistance. In fact, if the length is changed by a certain factor, the resistance will change by the same factor. The resistance of a wire is directly proportional to its length. Thus

  $R \propto L$

- **Cross-sectional area** The cross-sectional area A of a cylindrical wire is given by the equation

  $A = \pi r^2$, where r is the radius.

A thicker wire has a greater radius, and therefore a greater cross-sectional area than a thin wire. The resistance of a wire decreases if it has a larger cross-sectional area. The resistance is inversely proportional to the cross-sectional area.

$$R \propto \frac{1}{A}$$

Wires that carry larger currents are made to have a low resistance. For example, the wires connected to an electric stove are thicker than those connected to a kettle. This is because the electric stove often draws a higher current than the kettle. The thicker wires to the stove have less resistance.

- **Temperature** In general, the resistance of a metal increases as its temperature increases. Semiconductors, such as carbon, germanium, and silicon, behave in the opposite way to metals. As the temperature of a semiconductor increases, its resistance decreases, although it never becomes zero.
- **Resistivity** A silver or gold wire has a lower resistance than an iron wire of the same size. This characteristic property of a material is called its resistivity. The **resistivity**, ρ, of a material is the resistance a cylinder of the material would have if it were 1 m long, with a cross-sectional area of 1 m^2. Because resistance varies with temperature, resistivities are specified for a certain temperature, usually 20°C. Table 13.2 shows the resistivities of some materials.

INFOBIT

Lord Kelvin (1824–1907), a Scottish mathematician and physicist, discovered in 1854 that the resistance increases when a wire is stretched and decreases when it is compressed. Today, this fact is used to monitor the forces on robotic arms. What other uses can you think of?

TABLE 13.2 Resistivities of Some Materials at 20°C

Metals		Semiconductors		Insulators	
Material	Resistivity ρ ($\Omega \cdot m$)	Material	Resistivity ρ ($\Omega \cdot m$)	Material	Resistivity ρ ($\Omega \cdot m$)
Silver	1.6×10^{-8}	Carbon	3.5×10^{-5}	Mica	$10^{11} - 10^{15}$
Copper	1.7×10^{-8}	Germanium	0.5*	Rubber (hard)	$10^{13} - 10^{16}$
Aluminum	2.6×10^{-8}	Silicon	20–2300*	Teflon	10^{16}
Tungsten	5.6×10^{-8}			Wood (maple)	3×10^{10}
Iron	9.7×10^{-8}				
Nichrome	100×10^{-8}				

* Values depend on purity

The resistance of a wire of constant temperature is given in terms of the resistivity, length, and cross-sectional area by the equation:

$$R = \frac{\rho \cdot L}{A}$$

Therefore,

$$\rho = \frac{R \cdot A}{L}$$

Substituting units into the equation, resistivity has units of

$$\frac{\Omega \cdot m^2}{m} = \Omega \cdot m$$

Superconductors

A few metals and other materials lose all resistance at very low temperatures and become **superconductors**. Since it has no resistance, a superconducting wire can carry an electric current without losing any energy as heat. Superconductivity was first discovered in 1911 by Heike Kamerlingh-Onnes, a Dutch physicist. He found that certain metals, such as lead and mercury, become superconducting at a temperature of a few degrees above absolute zero (0 K or −273.15°C). The only way to achieve such low temperatures is to use liquid helium, which boils at 4 K. But liquid helium is costly to buy and requires expensive refrigeration. As a result, scientists have tried to find materials that become superconducting at higher temperatures.

In 1986, a discovery was made that may have a great impact on your life. K. Alex Müller, working for IBM in Switzerland, and his colleague J. Georg Bednorz discovered a new superconducting material. Müller's and Bednorz's discovery caused considerable excitement because they had achieved superconductivity at 35 K and because their material—a ceramic—was completely different from those tried before. Ceramics are a class of materials commonly used in pottery and dishes. No one else had thought that such materials could become superconducting. For their breakthrough, Müller and Bednorz were awarded the 1987 Nobel Prize for physics.

With the realization that ceramics can become superconducters, the race was on to achieve superconductivity at even higher temperatures. The next breakthrough was the discovery of a material that is superconducting at temperatures above 77 K, the boiling point of liquid nitrogen. When produced in large quantities, a litre of liquid nitrogen costs less than a litre of milk. Furthermore, liquid nitrogen can be kept in insulated containers, eliminating the need for expensive refrigeration. Now scientists are searching for room-temperature superconductors. Such materials could be used to make superconducting chips for a new generation of faster and more energy-efficient computers.

Superconductors are already being used to produce extremely powerful magnets for particle accelerators and medical diagnostic scanners. Superconductors may also help in the development of magnetic levitation vehicles, which are suspended just above the ground by magnetic repulsion. Japanese researchers have built an experimental magnetically levitated train that can travel smoothly and relatively quietly at speeds of up to 500 km/h.

WEBLINK

Superconductors lose all resistance at very low temperatures. Researchers are continuing the search for materials that have very low resistance at temperatures close to outside temperatures. Write a half-page report about this research and uses for superconductors. Begin your research at **www.pearsoned.ca/physics11.**

FIGURE 13.9 Researchers are searching for room-temperature superconductors.

Exploration Using a Graphing Calculator

Resistance of Copper Wire

Household wiring and extension cords are made using copper wire. In Canada, the diameter of wire is specified according to the American wire gauges (AWG). As the gauge number increases, the wire diameter decreases. Building codes require a minimum of 14-gauge (diameter $= 1.63 \times 10^{-3}$ m) for lighting circuits and 12-gauge (diameter $= 2.05 \times 10^{-3}$ m) for most baseboard heater circuits. A full-size clothes dryer needs a cable with 10-gauge wire (diameter 2.59×10^{3} m). Most extension cords have 18-, 16-, or 14-gauge wire. Let us explore the relationship between the resistance R and the diameter d of different gauges of copper wires at 20°C.

From Table 13.2 the resistivity of copper wire at 20°C is 1.7×10^{-8} Ω·m. For a 100-m length, the equation for resistance becomes

$$R = \frac{\rho L}{A} = \frac{1.7 \times 10^{-8} \times 100 \text{ m}}{A} = \frac{1.7 \times 10^{-6}}{A}$$

Since $A = \pi\left(\frac{d}{2}\right)^2$, the resistance expressed in terms of the diameter is

$$R = \frac{4 \times 1.7 \times 10^{-6}}{\pi d^2} = \frac{2.2 \times 10^{-6}}{d^2}$$

Use the graphing calculator to plot resistance against diameter for wire ranging from 26-gauge (0.41×10^{-3} m) to 10-gauge (2.59×10^{-3} m).

Discussion

1. What does the shape of the curve tell you about the relationship between the resistance and the diameter of copper wire?
2. As the diameter of the copper wire increases, what happens to its resistance?
3. Using the graph, determine the resistance of 100 m of
   a) 10-gauge copper wire
   b) 14-gauge copper wire
   c) 26-gauge copper wire
4. Why do cables for electric baseboard heaters use 12-gauge wire, whereas circuits for lights require only 14-gauge wire?
5. Find out what gauge of wire is used for
   a) telephone lines
   b) TV cables
   c) high-voltage transmission lines

EXAMPLE 2 NUMERICAL

What is the resistance of an aluminum wire 90 cm long with a diameter of 2.0 mm?

Given

$\rho = 2.6 \times 10^{-8}\ \Omega \cdot m$ (Refer to Table 13.2.)

$L = 90$ cm

$d = 2.0$ mm

Required
R

Analysis

- Convert L and d to metres.
- For a circle, radius $r = \dfrac{\text{diameter}}{2}$ and area $A = \pi r^2$
- $r = \dfrac{\rho \cdot L}{A}$

Solution

$L = 90 \text{ cm} = 0.90 \text{ m}$

$d = 2.0 \text{ mm} = 2.0 \times 10^{-3} \text{ m}$

$r = \dfrac{d}{2} = \dfrac{2.0 \times 10^{-3} \text{ m}}{2} = 1.0 \times 10^{-3} \text{ m}$

$A = \pi r^2 = 3.14 \times (1.0 \times 10^{-3} \text{ m})^2$

$= 3.14 \times 10^{-6} \text{ m}^2$

$R = \dfrac{\rho \cdot L}{A} = \dfrac{2.6 \times 10^{-8} \ \Omega \cdot \text{m} \times 0.90 \text{ m}}{3.14 \times 10^{-6} \text{ m}^2}$

$= 7.5 \times 10^{-3} \ \Omega$

Statement
The resistance of the wire is $7.5 \times 10^{-3} \ \Omega$.

PRACTICE PROBLEMS

1. Tungsten is used for filaments in incandescent lamps. What is the resistance of a tungsten filament 5.0 cm long with a diameter of 0.76 mm?
2. In an experiment performed to determine the resistivity of modelling clay (Figure 13.12) the following readings were obtained: $V = 2.5$ V, $I = 17$ mA, $A = 3.15 \times 10^{-4} \text{ m}^2$, and $L = 15$ cm. What was the resistivity of the modelling clay?

Discovering Physics — *Resistivity of Modelling Clay*

In this activity, you will use your results to calculate the resistivity of modelling clay. You will need: an ammeter, a voltmeter, a 6-V battery, brass rods, connecting leads, a switch, and two or more different colours of modelling clay. Roll out cylinders of modelling clay of the same diameter but different colours. Roll out another set of cylinders having the same colour but different diameters. Connect the circuit shown in Figure 13.10 with one of the cylinders bridging the two brass rods. Close the switch and immediately measure the current I flowing through the cylinder and the potential difference V between two points separated by a distance L. Measure the diameter d of the cylinder. Repeat this procedure for the other cylinders of modelling clay.

Design a suitable table for recording colour, length L, cylinder diameter d, current I, and potential difference V and record your data. Calculate the resistivity.

- How does diameter affect the resistance of the modelling clay cylinder?
- Does colour have any effect on resistance?
- How consistent were the values for the resistivity of each colour of modelling clay? Can you explain any variations?
- Do different colours have the same resistivity?

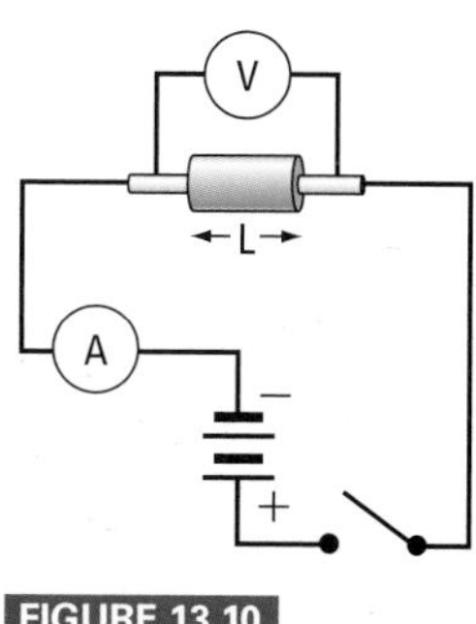

FIGURE 13.10

Section 13.1 Review

Understanding Concepts

1. State Ohm's law in your own words.

2. Prove that 1 Ω is equivalent to

   $1 \frac{J}{C \cdot A}$

3. A technician measures a current of 220 mA through the resistor when a potential difference of 4.65 V is placed across it.

   a) What should the technician calculate the resistance to be?

   b) If the resistor has a resistance of 22 Ω ±10%, is the value calculated within the accepted range?

4. If the potential difference across the nerve of a frog is 85 mV and its resistance is 2.5×10^2 Ω, what current will flow through the nerve?

5. List four factors that affect the resistance of a cylindrical wire and describe how a change in each one will affect the wire's resistance.

6. If all other factors remained the same, what change in resistance would result if the radius of a wire were doubled?

7. a) Do you think the filament of a 60-W light bulb has a large or small resistance? State your reasons.

   b) Estimate the filament's length, cross-sectional area, and the resistivity.

8. If a light bulb contains a tungsten filament that is 1.0×10^{-2} m in diameter and 0.75 m long, what is its resistance at 20°C?

Applying Inquiry/ Communication Skills

9. How do you think the resistance of the filament of a low-voltage incandescent light bulb changes with temperature? Make a prediction by sketching a graph of potential difference against current. Then design and do an experiment to check your prediction.

Making Connections

10. Human hands have a resistance of about 1.0×10^5 Ω when dry and 1.5×10^3 Ω when wet. When a current of about 1.2 mA passes through the body a person will feel a tingle. The person will lose muscular control at current of about 20 mA.

    a) Suppose the person touches a 120-V wire. Describe the difference in what happens with dry hands and with wet hands.

    Caution: Do not try this.

    b) Will the person lose muscular control by short-circuiting a 12-V car battery? If not, what will happen? Discuss.

13.2 Resistors in Series and Parallel

Key Understandings

When you have completed this section, you will be able to:

- apply Kirchhoff's laws and Ohm's law to series and parallel circuits and derive expressions for the equivalent resistance of each kind of circuit
- apply Kirchhoff's laws and Ohm's law to series, parallel, and series–parallel combination circuits to calculate the potential difference, current, and resistance at various points in the circuit

Loads such as light bulbs and resistors can be connected in either series or parallel. Often it is useful to know the value of the single resistor that would have the same resistance to the source as the separate resistors. This is called the **equivalent resistance** of the circuit. As more and more resistors are connected in series, what happens to the equivalent resistance? What if they are connected in parallel?

Equivalent Resistance of a Series Combination of Resistors

Practical circuits usually contain several components, each having a resistance. What is the equivalent resistance R_t of components connected in series. Kirchhoff's potential difference law for a series combination of components is

$$V_t = V_1 + V_2 + V_3 + ...$$

Using Ohm's law and substituting for V ($V = IR$) we obtain

$$I_tR_t = I_1R_1 + I_2R_2 + I_3R_3 + ...$$

Since Kirchhoff's current law states that in a series circuit the current through each component is the same, we can write I_t instead of I_1, I_2, I_3.

Thus

$$I_tR_t = I_tR_1 + I_tR_2 + I_tR_3 + ...$$

Simplifying,

$$I_tR_t = I_t(R_1 + R_2 + R_3 + ...)$$

Therefore,

$$R_t = R_1 + R_2 + R_3 ... \quad \text{(in series)}$$

The relationships for potential difference, current, and resistance in series combinations are summarized in Figure 13.11.

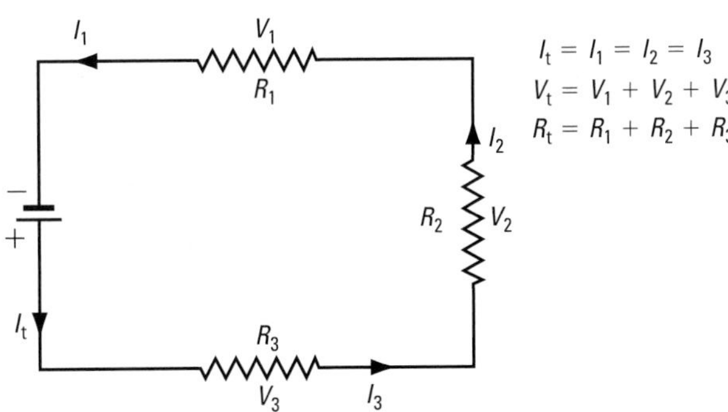

FIGURE 13.11 The characteristics of a series combination of three resistors

INFOBIT

The electrical resistance across a layer of dry skin is about 40 kΩ. However, the resistance across the internal organs of your body is much smaller, about 100 Ω. If you touch the terminals of a 9-V battery, with your thumbs, the current encounters three resistances in series: skin on your left thumb, internal organs, and skin on your right thumb. The total resistance is over 80 kΩ. Use the formula $I = \frac{V}{R}$ to see that the current flow through your body is less than 0.125 mA. However, even low voltages can cause dangerous currents if probes are inserted through the skin because the probes bypass the high resistance of the skin.

Discovering Physics — *Sensing Series Resistance*

Use the materials in this set up to make a model that you can use to think about a series connection of resistors. You will need: a glass of water, 6 hollow plastic coffee stirrers, and 2 medium-diameter drinking straws.

Tape four coffee stirrers in series using masking tape to make an airtight connection (Figure 13.12). Tape one coffee stirrer in series with one drinking straw. Start with the single coffee stirrer. Place the end about 2 cm below the water and gently blow bubbles. Repeat with a single drinking straw, then with the series connection of coffee stirrers, and finally with the series connection of the coffee stirrer and the drinking straw, blowing with the same effort each time.

- How does resistance vary with the number of coffee stirrers connected in series?
- When the coffee stirrer and drinking straw are connected in series, which affects the resistance the most?
- Is air blown through a series connection of coffee stirrers a good analogy for electrons travelling through a series connection of resistors? Discuss.

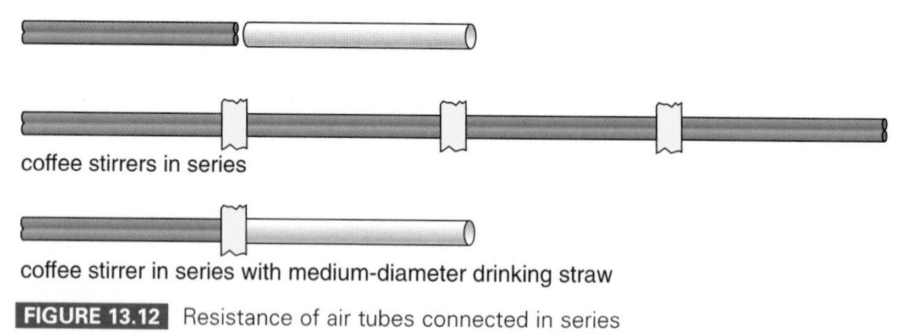

FIGURE 13.12 Resistance of air tubes connected in series

EXAMPLE 3 — CONCEPTUAL

Suppose that a string of decorative lights consists of 12 identical bulbs connected in series. If each bulb has a resistance of 15 Ω, what is the equivalent resistance?

Reasoning and Solution

The equivalent resistance of a series connection of resistors is equal to the sum of the individual resistances: $R_t = R_1 + R_2 + R_3 + \ldots$ If two identical resistors are connected in series the resisitance doubles. If twelve are connected in series it increases by a factor of 12. Therefore,

$$R_t = 12 \times 15\ \Omega$$
$$= 180\ \Omega$$

The equivalent resistance of the 12 lights connected in series is 180 Ω.

CHALLENGE

Three resistors connected in series have an equivalent resistance of 121 Ω. The resistance of two of the resistors are 15 Ω and 84 Ω, respectively. What is the resistance of the third resistor?

EXAMPLE 4 CONCEPTUAL

Knowing how to calculate the equivalent resistance of a series connection of resistors enables us to determine the values of other variables in the circuit including potential differences and currents. In Figure 13.13, $V_t = 6.4$ V and $V_1 = 3.8$ V. If $I_t = 0.65$ A, calculate the values of V_2, R_2, and the equivalent resistance of the circuit R_t.

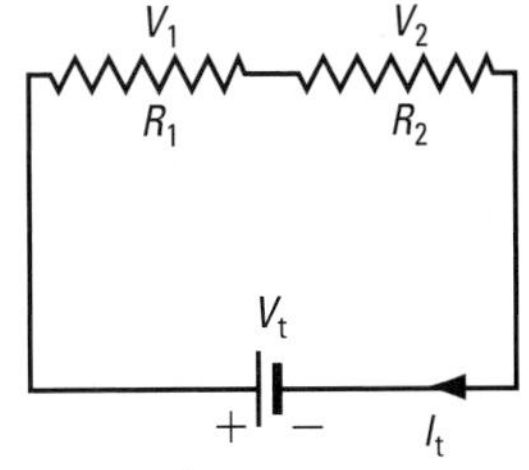

FIGURE 13.13

Reasoning and Solution

Since the total potential difference in a series circuit is equal to the sum of the potential differences across the components,

$$V_t = V_1 + V_2$$

Therefore $V_2 = V_t - V_1$

$$= 6.4 \text{ V} - 3.8 \text{ V}$$

$$= 2.6 \text{ V}$$

According to Ohm's law, the ratio of the drop in potential across a load to the current flowing through it is equal to the resistance of the load. Hence,

$$R_2 = \frac{V_2}{I_2}$$

$$= \frac{2.6 \text{ V}}{0.65 \text{ A}}$$

$$= 4.0 \ \Omega$$

The total resistance of a circuit is equal to the total potential difference divided by the total current. Hence,

$$R_t = \frac{6.4 \text{ V}}{0.65 \text{ A}}$$

$$= 9.8 \ \Omega$$

The potential difference across V_2 is 2.6 V, the resistance of R_2 is 4.0 Ω, and the equivalent resistance R_t is 9.8 Ω.

INSIGHT

The equivalent resistance for resistors connected in series is always larger than any of the resistances in the combination.

CHALLENGE

Refer to Figure 13.15. Given the values $V_2 = 22$ V, $V_1 = 33$ V, and the current passing through resistor R_1 equals 2.2 A, determine the potential difference V_t, the current I_t, the values of resistors R_1 and R_2, and the total resistance R_t.

Equivalent Resistance of a Parallel Combination of Resistors

Many circuits contain components connected in parallel. Let us see how to find the equivalent resistance R_t of a parallel combination of components. Kirchhoff's current law for a parallel combination of components is

$$I_t = I_1 + I_2 + I_3 +$$

Using Ohm's law and substituting for I ($I = V/R$), we obtain

$$V_t/R_t = V_1/R_1 + V_2/R_2 + V_3/R_3 + \ldots$$

Investigation

Refer to page 514, Investigation 2

$I_t = I_1 + I_2 + I_3$
$V_t = V_1 = V_2 = V_3$
$\frac{1}{R_t} = \frac{1}{R_1} + \frac{1}{R_2} + \frac{1}{R_3}$

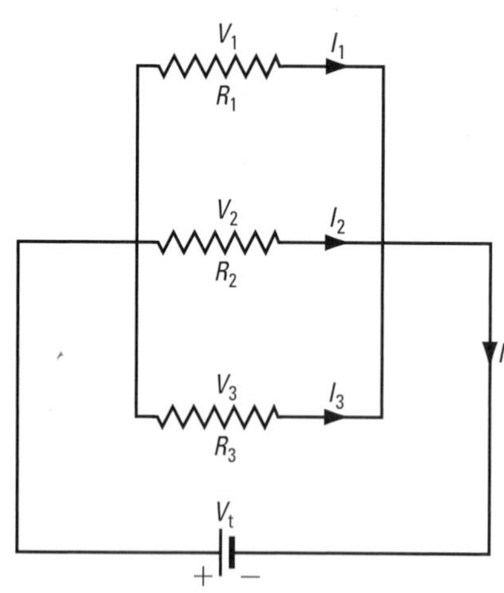

FIGURE 13.14 The characteristics of a parallel combination of three resistors

Kirchhoff's potential difference law for a parallel combination of components is

$$V_t = V_1 = V_2 = V_3 = \ldots$$

Therefore,

$$\frac{V_t}{R_t} = \frac{V_t}{R_1} + \frac{V_t}{R_2} + \frac{V_t}{R_3} + \ldots$$

Simplifying, we obtain

$$\frac{1}{R_t} = \frac{1}{R_1} + \frac{1}{R_2} + \frac{1}{R_3} + \ldots$$

The relationships for potential difference, current, and resistance in parallel combinations are summarized in Figure 13.14.

Discovering Physics — *Sensing Parallel Resistance*

How is the resistance of air tubes affected when the air tubes are connected in parallel? Try this to find out. You will need: a glass of water, 6 hollow plastic coffee stirrers, 2 medium-sized drinking straws, and masking tape.

Cut the drinking straws to the same length as the coffee stirrer. Tape four coffee stirrers in parallel using masking tape. Tape one coffee stirrer in parallel with the medium-diameter drinking straw (Figure 13.15). Start with the single coffee stirrer. Place the end about 2 cm below the water and gently blow bubbles. Repeat with the drinking straw, the parallel connection of coffee stirrers, and the coffee stirrer connected in parallel with the drinking straw.

- How does resistance vary with the number of coffee stirrers connected in parallel?
- When a coffee stirrer and a drinking straw are connected in parallel, which affects the resistance the most?
- Is resistance to blowing air through a parallel connection of coffee stirrers a good analogy for resistance to electrons travelling through a parallel connection of resistors?

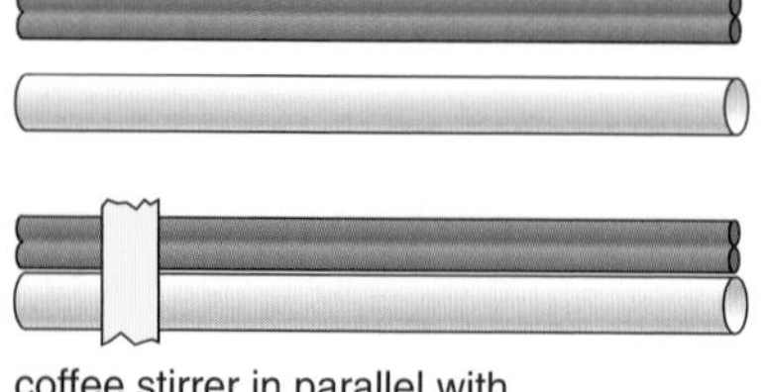

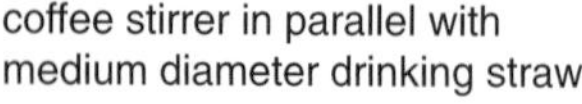

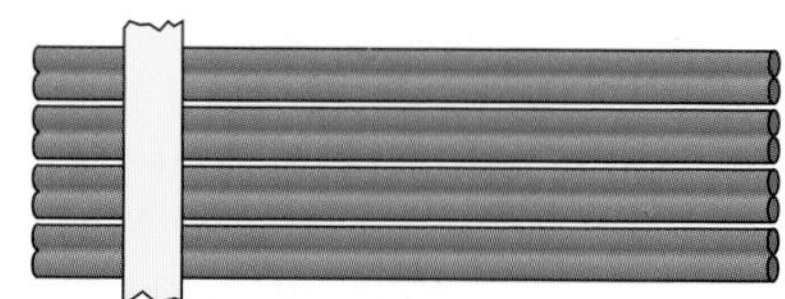

FIGURE 13.15 Resistance of air tubes connected in parallel

EXAMPLE 5 CONCEPTUAL

Resistors can be connected in parallel to obtain an equivalent resistance smaller than any of the individual resistors. What is the equivalent resistance of a combination containing a 20-Ω and a 30-Ω resistor in parallel?

Reasoning and Solution

The equivalent resistance of two resistors connected in parallel can be calculated as follows:

$$\frac{1}{R_t} = \frac{1}{R_1} + \frac{1}{R_2}$$

$$= \frac{1}{20\ \Omega} + \frac{1}{30\ \Omega}$$

$$= \frac{3 + 2}{60\ \Omega}$$

$$= \frac{5}{60\ \Omega}$$

Therefore,

$$R_t = \frac{60\ \Omega}{5}$$

$$= 12\ \Omega$$

The equivalent resistance of a 20-Ω and a 30-Ω parallel combination is 12 Ω.

CHALLENGE

The equivalent resistance of three resistors connected in parallel is 5.0 Ω. Two resistors have resistances of 15 Ω and 20 Ω, respectively. What is the resistance of the third resistor?

INSIGHT

Do not forget to take the reciprocal of the result after combining the reciprocals of the resistances.

EXAMPLE 6 CONCEPTUAL

When equal-sized resistors are connected in parallel it is easy to find the equivalent resistance, as this problem demonstrates. What is the equivalent resistance of a parallel connection of four resistors, each having a value of 40 Ω?

Reasoning and Solution

Substituting into the equation for the equivalent resistance of resistors connected in parallel, we obtain

$$\frac{1}{R_t} = \frac{1}{R_1} + \frac{1}{R_2} + \frac{1}{R_3} + \frac{1}{R_4}$$

$$= \frac{1}{40\ \Omega} + \frac{1}{40\ \Omega} + \frac{1}{40\ \Omega} + \frac{1}{40\ \Omega}$$

$$= \frac{4}{40\ \Omega}$$

Therefore, $R_t = \frac{40\ \Omega}{4}$

$$= 10\ \Omega$$

When four identical 40-Ω resistors are connected in parallel, the total resistance is 10-Ω. What pattern do you see?

CHALLENGE

The equivalent resistance of five identical resistors connected in parallel is 15 Ω. What is the resistance of each resistor?

INSIGHT

The equivalent resistance of resistors connected in parallel is always less than the value of any of the resistances in the combination.

The solution to this last numerical example suggests an interesting relationship. If a number (N) of resistors, each having the same value R, are connected in parallel, the equivalent resistance is $R_t = \frac{R}{N}$. See if you can prove this relationship.

EXAMPLE 7 CONCEPTUAL

A trilight bulb can be switched so that it has a power of 50 W, 100 W, or 150 W. The bulb is connected to the standard wall outlet and receives only one voltage, 120 V. How can one bulb produce three levels of illumination without being connected to three different potential differences? How can a single switch produce this effect?

Reasoning and Solution

Figure 13.16 shows the schematic diagram of the circuit showing two filaments and a four-position switch with two sets of contacts. The four-position switch is usually built into the lamp socket

When the switch is in the first position, contact A is closed and contact B is open. Energy reaches only the 50-W filament, resulting in the lowest level of illumination. When the switch is in the second position, contact B is closed and contact A is open. Energy reaches only the 100-W filament, resulting in the middle level of illumination. When the switch is in the third position, contacts A and B are both closed and the 50-W and 100-W filaments are connected in parallel to the 120-V source, resulting in the highest level of illumination. When the switch is in the fourth position, both contacts are open and the light is off. Only one level of illumination will be possible if either the 50-W or the 100-W filament burns out.

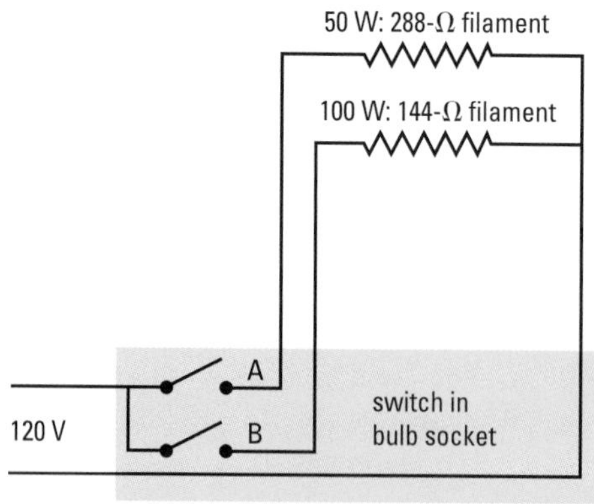

FIGURE 13.16 Circuit diagram of a trilight bulb showing two filaments and a four-position switch

CHALLENGES

Calculate the resistance of the trilight bulb in Figure 13.16 when the filaments are connected in parallel.

Calculate the current through the trilight bulb when

a) only the 50-W filament is connected
b) only the 100-W filament is connected
c) both filaments are connected (Do this in two ways.)

Current in Series and Parallel Circuits

Two resistors can be connected either in series or in parallel. The effective resistance of the two combinations will be different, and this will affect the current, as the following numerical example shows.

EXAMPLE 8 NUMERICAL

Two resistors of 10 Ω and 40 Ω are to be connected to a 100-V supply. Calculate the total current in the circuit if the resistors are connected in series. Compare this with the value when they are connected in parallel.

Given

$R_1 = 10\ \Omega$

$R_2 = 40\ \Omega$

$V_t = 100\ \text{V}$

Required

a) I_t (series connection)

b) I_t (parallel connection)

Analysis

a) Use the equation $R_t = R_1 + R_2$ to find the equivalent resistance of the series connection and $I_t = \frac{V_t}{R_t}$ to calculate the current in the circuit.

b) Use the equation $\frac{1}{R_t} = \frac{1}{R_1} + \frac{1}{R_2}$ to find the equivalent resistance of the parallel connection and $I_t = \frac{V_t}{R_t}$ to calculate the current in the circuit.

Solution

a) Series

$$R_t = R_1 + R_2 = 10\ \Omega + 40\ \Omega = 50\ \Omega$$

$$\text{Therefore, } I_t = \frac{100\ \text{V}}{50\ \Omega} = 2.0\ \text{A}$$

b) Parallel

$$\frac{1}{R_t} = \frac{1}{R_1} + \frac{1}{R_2} = \frac{1}{10\ \Omega} + \frac{1}{40\ \Omega} = \frac{4+1}{40\ \Omega} = \frac{5}{40\ \Omega}$$

$$R_t = \frac{40\ \Omega}{5} = 8.0\ \Omega$$

$$\text{Therefore, } I_t = \frac{100\ \text{V}}{8.0\ \Omega} = 12.5\ \text{A} = 12\ \text{A}$$

Statement

When connected in series, the total current through the combination is 2.0 A. When connected in parallel, the total current through the combination is 12 A. A larger current flows in the parallel circuit than in the series circuit.

INSIGHT

As more and more loads are connected in parallel, the total current in the main circuit gets larger and larger. Can you explain how a household circuit could become overloaded?

PRACTICE PROBLEMS

1. A 5.0 Ω resistor and a 20 Ω resistance are connected to a 100 V source. Calculate the current in the series circuit.
2. If the same two resistors are connected in parallel what current flows?

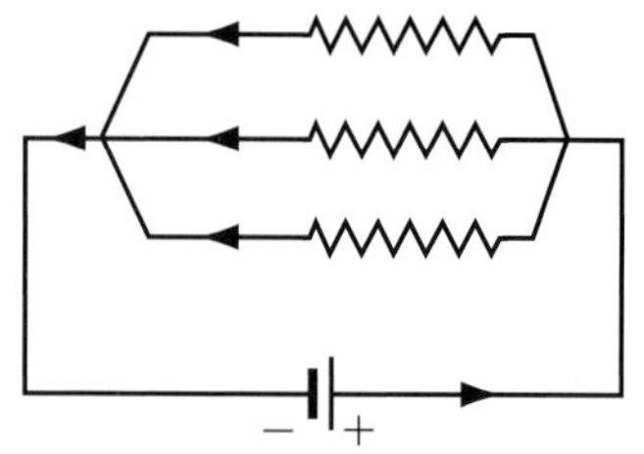

FIGURE 13.17 Current through parallel pathways

The results of this numerical example might seem odd, since a much larger current flows in the parallel circuit than in the series circuit. However, the total resistance of a parallel combination is always less than the smallest resistance in any pathway of the combination. If the applied voltage remains constant, the total current in a parallel combination is always more than if the same resistors were connected in series.

Consider what happens when current flows into a parallel junction such as the one shown in Figure 13.17. The resistance is less than it would be with just a single pathway. The more parallel pathways there are to carry the current in an electric circuit, the larger the total current flow for a given potential difference. Since the total resistance R_t of a circuit is given by $R_t = V_t/I_t$, a smaller resistance results in a larger current.

Series–Parallel Combinations of Resistors

Complex circuits contain both series and parallel combinations. We can analyze complex circuits if we break them down into simpler steps. Here is a strategy that can help solve these problems.

1. Identify resistors that are connected in series and draw a box around each series combination.
2. Calculate the single equivalent resistance that can replace each series connection.
3. Identify resistors that are connected in parallel and draw a box around each parallel combination.
4. Calculate the single equivalent resistance that can replace each parallel combination.
5. Draw a new schematic circuit diagram by replacing the resistors in the boxes with the equivalent resistances.
6. Repeat steps 1–5 until the complex circuit is simplified to a single equivalent resistance.
7. Use the final equivalent resistance and the potential difference of the source to calculate the current in the main part of the circuit.
8. The drops in electrical potential across resistors and the currents in parallel paths can now be calculated beginning with the series resistances in the main circuit.

EXAMPLE 9 NUMERICAL

What is the equivalent resistance of the circuit shown in Figure 13.18?

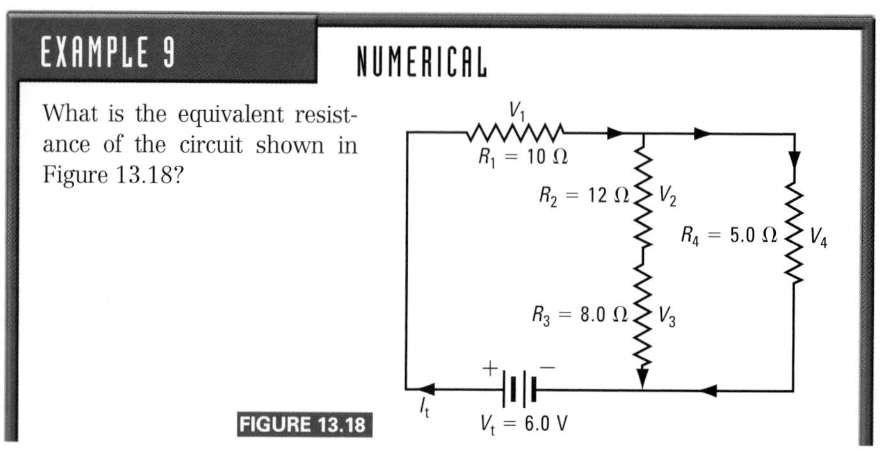

FIGURE 13.18

Given

R_1, R_2, R_3, R_4, and V_t

Required

R_t

Analysis

- Draw a box around the series connection R_2 and R_3 in Figure 13.19 a). Note that you should not draw a box around R_2, R_3, and R_4 because it would enclose both a series and a parallel connection.

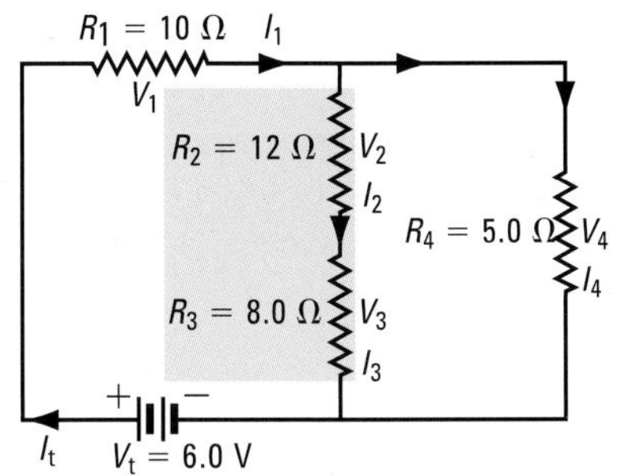

a)

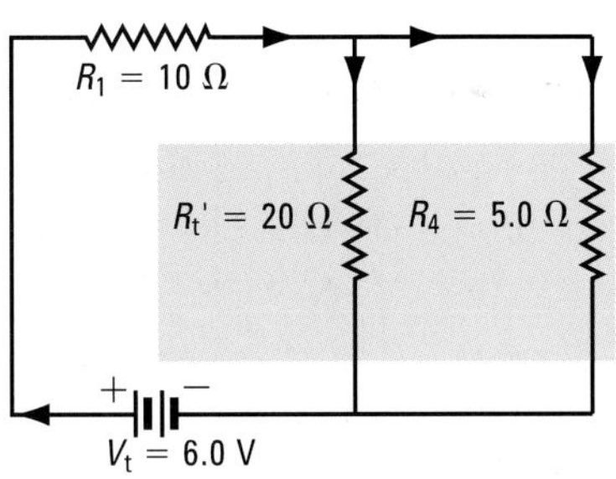

b)

V_1

$R_1 = 10\ \Omega$

$R_t'' = 4.0\ \Omega$

I_t $V_t = 6.0$ V

c)

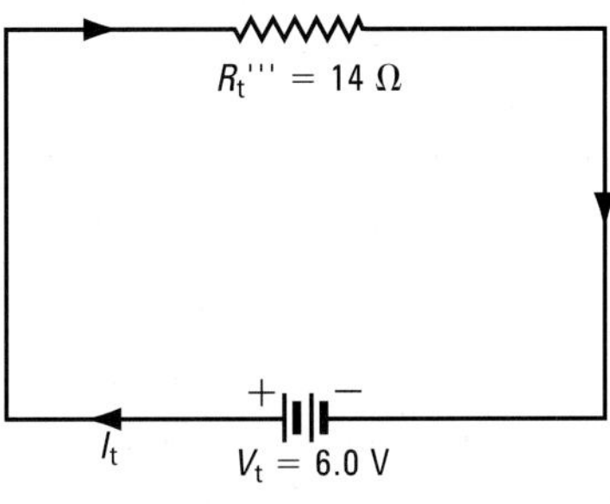

d)

FIGURE 13.19 Steps for determining equivalent resistance

- Find the equivalent resistance R_t' for this series combination using $R_t' = R_2 + R_3$
- Draw a box around R_t' and R_4. See Figure 13.19 b).
- R_t' and R_4 are in parallel, therefore, find the equivalent resistance using

$$\frac{1}{R_t''} = \frac{1}{R'} + \frac{1}{R_4}$$

- Draw a box around R_t'' and R_1. See Figure 13.19 c).
- R_t'' is in series with R_1; therefore, find the equivalent resistance using $R_t''' = R_t'' + R_1$
- Draw the final schematic diagram showing R_t'''. See Figure 13.19 d).

PRACTICE PROBLEM

1. What is the equivalent resistance of the circuit shown in Figure 13.20?

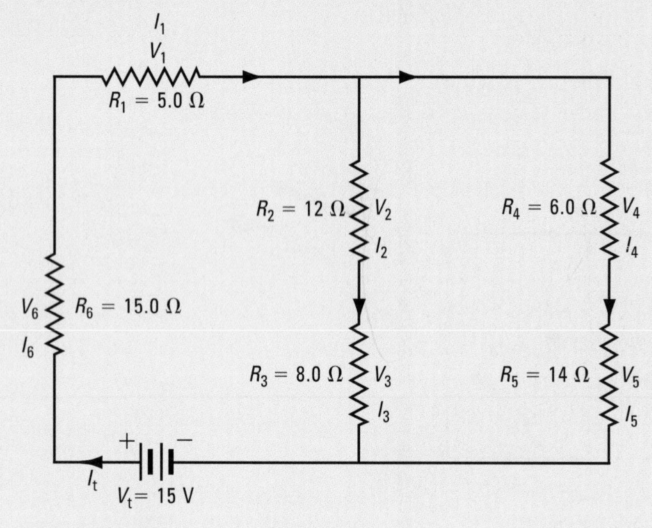

FIGURE 13.20

Solution

For resistors R_2 and R_3,

$$R_t' = R_2 + R_3$$
$$= 12\ \Omega + 18\ \Omega$$
$$= 20\ \Omega$$

For resistors R_t' and R_4,

$$\frac{1}{R_t''} = \frac{1}{R_t'} + \frac{1}{R_4}$$
$$= \frac{1}{20\ \Omega} + \frac{1}{5.0\ \Omega}$$
$$= \frac{1+4}{20\ \Omega} = \frac{5}{20\ \Omega}$$
$$R_t'' = \frac{20}{5}\ \Omega = 4.0\ \Omega$$

For resistors R_t'' and R_1,

$$R_t''' = R_t'' + R_1$$
$$= 4.0\ \Omega + 10\ \Omega$$
$$= 14\ \Omega$$

Statement

The equivalent resistance of the circuit is 14 Ω.

Section 13.2 Review

Understanding Concepts

1. What is the effective resistance when resistors having values of 10 Ω, 25 Ω, and 30 Ω are connected in series?
2. Six identical lights are connected in series to a 100-V supply. If the total current flowing is 750 mA, calculate
   a) the potential difference across each bulb
   b) the resistance of each bulb
   c) the equivalent resistance of the string of lights
3. What is the total resistance of a parallel connection of two resistors if one has a resistance of 60 Ω and the other has a resistance of 20 Ω?
4. Six identical lights are connected together in parallel. Each bulb has a resistance of 25 Ω. The lights are to be connected to a 10-V supply.
   a) What is the total resistance of the lights?
   b) What is the total current in the main circuit?
   c) What is the current through each bulb?
5. A parallel combination of three identical resistors has a total resistance of 12 Ω. What is the value of each resistor?
6. Two resistors are connected in parallel. The total resistance of the combination is known to be 6.0 Ω. If one of the resistors is 10 Ω, what is the value of the other?

7. Figure 13.21 shows a circuit containing three resistors and a switch. Find
   a) the total resistance and the total current when the switch is open
   b) the total resistance and the current through the 10-Ω resistor with the switch closed

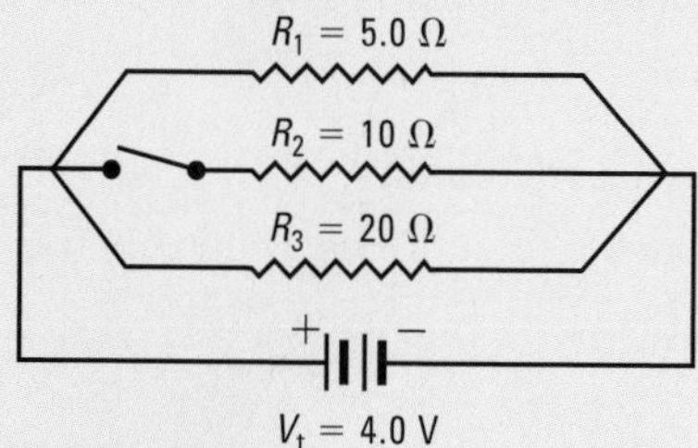

FIGURE 13.21

8. Use Figure 13.20 opposite and the value obtained for the equivalent resistance in the practice problem to calculate the current flowing in the main circuit, the potential difference across each resistor, and the current flowing through each resistor.

Applying Inquiry/ Communication Skills

9. A person connects a 6.0 V battery in series with a 10 Ω resistor and two 10 Ω resistors connected in parallel. In a second circuit the person connects an identical 6.0 V battery to two 10 Ω resistors connected in series.
   a) Draw schematic diagrams for the circuits.
   b) In which circuit will the current passing through the battery be greater? Explain using equations.
   c) Design an experiment to check your prediction.

Making Connections

10. If too many loads are connected in a household circuit, the current rating of the circuit can be exceeded. Explain why adding more resistances to the circuit increases the current rather than decreasing it.
11. What is the function of a fuse or circuit breaker? How does it work?

13.3 Electric Power and Energy

Key Understandings

When you have completed this section, you will be able to:

- define electric power and describe the concepts and units related to energy and power
- solve problems involving power, electric current, potential difference, and resistance
- solve problems involving power, energy, and duration of power use
- determine the cost of operating an electrical device

Appliances designed to change electrical energy into thermal energy consume energy at a much greater rate than most electric motors. Baseboard heaters have power ratings from 250 W to 3000 W. A 1200-W hair dryer consumes energy at a rate about 12 times that of a 100-W incandescent bulb. Water-pump motors for homes range in power from 200 W to 1000 W. What is power and how is it calculated? What is the relationship between power and energy?

FIGURE 13.22 A hair dryer gobbles up energy at a great rate but only for a short period of time.

Electric Power

The specified power of electric motors, hair dryers, light bulbs, and other electrical devices depends on the rate at which they use electric energy. **Power** P is the energy E used per unit time:

$$P = \frac{E}{\Delta t}$$

The work done, or energy used E, in moving unit charge Q between two points that have a potential difference V between them is given by

$$E = Q \cdot V$$

Substituting for E into the formula for power we obtain

$$P = \frac{Q \cdot V}{\Delta t}$$

but $\frac{Q}{\Delta t} = I$

Therefore,

$$P = IV$$

Thus, the power rating of an electrical device can be determined by multiplying the current flowing through it by the voltage across it. The unit for current is the ampere (A) and the unit for potential difference is the volt (V). We can get the unit for power by substituting these units into the equation for power:

units for power = ampere volt (A·V)

The derived unit for power is the **watt**, W. One watt is the power rating of an electrical device or energy source if one ampere flows through it when there is a potential difference of one volt across it. Table 13.3 shows some typical power ratings of electrical devices.

TABLE 13.3 Typical Power Ratings of Some Common Appliances

Appliance	Typical Power Rating (W)
Electric guitar	0.075
Radio alarm clock	5
Curling iron	15
Light bulb	60
Colour TV	155
Refrigerator	200
Vacuum cleaner	500
Toaster	1000
Hair dryer	1000
Kettle	1500
Clothes dryer	5800

EXAMPLE 10 CONCEPTUAL

Calculate the power of a resistor that has a potential difference of 5.5 V across it and a current of 820 mA flowing through it.

Reasoning and Solution

Since we are given the electrical current and the potential difference, substitute as shown below and solve for power.

$$P = I \cdot V$$

$$= 0.820 \text{ A} \times 5.5 \text{ V}$$

$$= 4.51 \text{ A·V}$$

$$= 4.5 \text{ W}$$

The power of the resistor is 4.5 W.

CHALLENGE

A 60-W bulb is connected to a 120-V source. What electric current flows through the bulb?

Other Relationships for Electric Power

Although many devices are labelled with their power ratings, we sometimes have to calculate the power using potential difference, current, and/or resistance. Start with the equation $P = I \cdot V$, and substitute for I and V using the equation for Ohm's law.

Substituting $V = I \cdot R$

$$P = I \times (I \cdot R)$$

$$P = I^2 R$$

Substituting $I = \frac{V}{R}$

$$P = \frac{V}{R} \times V$$

$$P = \frac{V^2}{R}$$

FIGURE 13.23 A clothes dryer can consume energy at a great rate.

EXAMPLE 11 CONCEPTUAL

A hot-glue gun rated at 75 W is plugged into a 120-V source. What is the resistance of the glue gun, and how much current passes through it?

Reasoning and Solution

Sometimes we know the power of an appliance and want to know its resistance. This can be determined as shown in a). To determine how much current is passing, use $P = I \cdot V$ as shown in b).

Solution

a) $P = \frac{V^2}{R}$

Therefore, $R = \frac{V^2}{P} = \frac{120\ \text{V} \times 120\ \text{V}}{75\ \text{W}} = 192\ \Omega$

b) $P = I \cdot V$

Therefore, $I = \frac{P}{V} = \frac{75\ \text{W}}{120\ \text{V}} = 0.625\ \text{A}$

The glue gun has a resistance of $1.9 \times 10^2\ \Omega$ and passes a current of 0.63 A.

CHALLENGE

A 1500-W electric heater connected to a potential difference of 120 V passes a current of 13.6 A. Calculate the resistance of the heater using Ohm's law and using the equation $P = I^2R$ and compare the values.

EXAMPLE 12 CONCEPTUAL

A student discovered that a 100-W bulb glowed more brightly than a 60-W bulb when the two were connected in parallel to a wall socket source. However, when the same bulbs were connected in series to the same source the intensities reversed; the 60-W bulb glowed more brightly than the 100-W bulb. Why?

Reasoning and Solution

In a parallel circuit, the potential difference across the branches is the same as the potential difference of the source. Therefore, the potential difference across the 100-W bulb is equal to the potential difference across the 60-W bulb. The equation power $P = V^2/R$ can be used to compare the resistance of the two filaments. Since the 100-W bulb has a greater power than the 60-W bulb when both are connected to the same potential difference, the filament of the 100-W bulb must have a smaller resistance than the filament of the 60-W bulb.

In a series circuit, the current is the same throughout the circuit. Therefore, the current in the 100-W bulb is equal to the current in the 60-W bulb when they are connected in series to the same source. The equation $P = I^2R$ can be used to compare the power of the two bulbs when connected in series. The resistance stays relatively constant from one circuit to the other. Since the resistance of the 60-W bulb is larger than the 100-W bulb, the 60-W bulb should glow more brightly than the 100-W bulb when connected in series. This explains the reversal of intensities when the connections are changed.

CHALLENGES

1. What is the resistance of the 100-W and the 60-W bulbs when connected in parallel to a 120-V source?
2. Determine the current when the bulbs are connected in series to the same 120-V source.
3. Determine the power of the bulbs when connected in series.

INFOBIT

In Canada, the power rating for most small appliances is based on the appliance being connected in parallel to a 120-V source. Large appliances such as stoves usually have a power rating based on a voltage of 240 V.

Electrical Energy

Often the power rating of an appliance is marked on the bottom or the back of the appliance, along with the voltage it requires and a Canadian Standards Association (CSA) approval number (Figure 13.24). Many appliances, such as hair dryers and toasters, convert much of the electrical energy supplied into heat energy. The energy used by a device can be determined from its power rating and the length of time that it is used:

FIGURE 13.24 Most appliances have a label listing their voltage and their current or power.

$$\text{power} = \frac{\text{energy}}{\text{time}}$$

Therefore,

$$\text{energy} = \text{power} \times \text{time or } E = P\,\Delta t$$

Since $P = IV$,

$$E = IV\,\Delta t$$

Energy is measured in joules (J), power in watts (W), and time in seconds (s).

$1\text{ J} = 1\text{ W} \times 1\text{ s} = 1\text{ W·s}$

However, the joule is a very small amount of energy. The work done on an apple when you pick it up off the ground and put it into your pocket is equal to about one joule. The practical unit of electrical energy is the megajoule, which equals 1×10^6 J.

Another large unit of energy used at the present time is the **kilowatt hour**, which is equal to 3.6 MJ. One kilowatt hour (kW·h) is the energy used to operate a device rated at one kilowatt for one hour. This unit is easier to use in calculations because the electrical energy consumed can be found by multiplying the power rating in kilowatts by the time of use in hours. The cost of 1 kW·h of electric energy is called the **unit cost**. In Ontario, this unit cost is roughly 7¢ per kW·h in most areas. If you had a perfectly efficient machine, you could lift 3.6 million apples from the floor to counter height for about 7¢.

EXAMPLE 13 NUMERICAL

Calculate the energy in kW·h used to operate a 40-W bulb for 30 min.

Given

$P = 40$ W

$\Delta t = 30$ min

Required

E (in kW·h)

Analysis

- Convert P to kW.
- Convert Δt to h.
- E (kW·h) = P (kW) × Δt (h)

Solution

$$P = 40\text{ W} \times \frac{1\text{ kW}}{10^3\text{ W}}$$

$$= 4.0 \times 10^{-2}\text{ kW}$$

$$\Delta t = 30\text{ min} = 0.50\text{ h}$$

$$E = P \cdot \Delta t$$

$$= 4.0 \times 10^{-2}\text{ kW} \times 0.50\text{ h}$$

$$= 2.0 \times 10^{-2}\text{ kW·h}$$

Statement

A 40-W light bulb uses 2.0×10^{-2} kW·h of energy when on for 30 min.

PRACTICE PROBLEMS

1. A factory has a separate energy meter to measure the energy used by a large electric motor. After using the motor for 300 min the meter reading has changed by 3.0 kW·h. What is the power of the motor in watts?
2. How long in minutes will it take a 1500-W electric heater to consume 4.50 kW·h of energy?

FIGURE 13.25 A domestic electricity meter

The Cost of Electricity

We pay for electrical energy, not electric power. The company supplying electrical energy uses a meter to determine how much energy (in kW·h) has been used. Figure 13.25 shows a typical home electricity meter. The total cost of the energy used is found by multiplying the energy used (kW·h) by the unit cost (¢/kW·h)

total cost = energy used × unit cost

EXAMPLE 14 NUMERICAL

Estimate the cost of watching television for 3.0 h. A typical colour TV has a power consumption of 150 W. Use a unit cost of 8.0¢/kW·h.

Given
$P = 150$ W

$\Delta t = 3$ h

unit cost = 8¢/kW·h

Required
total cost

Analysis
- Convert W to kW.
- The energy used is $E = P\Delta t$
- Total cost = energy used × unit cost

Solution
$P = 150$ W = 0.150 kW

$E = P\Delta t$

= 0.150 kW × 3 h

= 0.45 kW·h

Total cost = energy used × unit cost

= 0.45 kW·h × 8¢/kW·h

= 3.6¢

Statement
The cost of watching television for 3 h is about 3.6¢

PRACTICE PROBLEMS

1. A vacationer uses three 1500-W heaters to warm a cottage for seven days. The heaters are on for 25% of each day. If electricity in the area costs 20¢/kW·h, what is the cost of warming the cottage?
2. The cost of electricity for running all the machines and appliances in a large workshop for 30 d is $120.00. If energy costs 7.9 ¢/kW·h in that area, what was the average rate of energy use by the shop in kilowatts?

Electricity Generation for the Future

Decision-Making Skills

- Defining the Issue
- Developing Assessment Criteria
- Researching the Issue
- Analyzing Data and Information
- Proposing a Course of Action
- Justifying the Course of Action
- Communicating Your Proposal

BACKGROUND INFORMATION

Power for the People

Ontario's demand for electricity is huge, ranging from 14 000 MW to a peak of about 24 500 MJ. The Ontario Power Generation company (OPG) provides approximately 85% of Ontario's electricity. OPG operates a total of 80 stations, which generate electricity using nuclear power, hydro-electric power, and fossil fuels.

Ontario's nuclear stations provide about 40% of all electricity in Ontario. Hydro-electric and fossil fuel generation make up the rest. Although hydro-electric generation is a relatively clean way to generate power, nuclear power and the burning of fossil fuel are not. It is estimated that fossil fuel pollution (nitrogen oxide) results in 1900 deaths each year in Ontario. And nuclear power is not without its problems. Where to put dangerous nuclear waste, which remains radioactive for hundreds or even thousands of years, is one such problem.

FIGURE 13.28

OPG is planning to spend $250 million on special catalytic reduction burners in fossil-fuel stations that will reduce the amount of toxic emissions.Environmentalists suggest instead that cleaner natural gas burners should be the goal, even though they are more expensive to run. Environmentalists want to see "green energy", generating power from wind, solar cells, biomass gas, and small hydro-electric generators investigated more thoroughly.

Analyzing the Issue

1. Identify the different stakeholders who are affected by decisions on energy production in Ontario.
2. In two groups, research different sources of energy described in the scenario and make a PMI chart for each energy source. One group should focus on fossil fuels and the other on "green energy" sources.
3. On what criteria should Ontario base its investment policy for future energy resources? Why do you think so?
4. Plan a debate between environmentalists and the Ontario Power Generation company. Argue the social, environmental, economic, and political impacts of the decision to adapt fossil fuel stations. Has Ontario made the right choice for our future?

Section 13.3 Review

Understanding Concepts

1. An 800-W hair dryer is plugged into a 120-V wall socket. What current will it draw?
2. A toy truck uses a 1.5-V cell. If the toy operates at a power of 120 mW, what is its resistance?
3. A small electric motor has a resistance of 4.5 Ω. If the motor operates using 670 mA of current, what is its power?
4. A 60-W bulb is left on for 10 min. What is the total cost if the utility company charges 8¢/kW·h? What is the cost if a 15-W fluorescent lamp is used instead?
5. A coin-operated clothes dryer is rated at 5.0 kW and runs for 12 min when 50¢ is inserted. Assuming a unit cost of 9.0¢/kW·h, how much is left for the owner after energy costs?
6. A typical bill for electricity is $35.00 for a month. At 7.0¢/kW·h, how much energy in kW·h is used?
7. A typical nuclear electric power plant has a power of 1.0 GW. If all the energy produced in a day's operation were sold at a unit cost of 10¢/kW·h, how much money would the plant earn?

Applying Inquiry/ Communication Skills

8. Look at the power rating or the current rating of three electrical appliances in your home that operate on 120 V AC. Calculate the resistance of each appliance.

Making Connections

9. List all the electrical appliances in your home in a table and record their power rating. Estimate the time for which each is used in a month. Calculate the cost for each and a total for the month. How would you save money if you wanted to reduce your bill?
10. Electrical power companies sell electrical energy. "The more energy they sell, the more money they make." Do you agree or disagree with this statement? Explain.
11. What measures is your local electric power company taking to encourage consumers to conserve electrical energy? Are they working? How could they be improved?
12. Which devices in your home have the greatest power? Which consume the most energy in a month? A person makes a claim that the device with the greatest power does not necessarily consume the most energy. Can this be true? Explain.
13. An electric power company representative from the United States claims that institutional customers, including schools, all commercial customers, and all industrial customers pay for both power and energy. Explain why these customers pay for something they do not use. Is this the case in Ontario?

Inquiry Skills

- Initiating and Planning
- Applying Technical Skills
- Using Tools, Materials, Equipment
- Conducting and Recording
- Analyzing and Interpreting
- Concluding and Communicating

Investigation 1 (Section 13.1)

Ohm's Law for a Resistor

Problem

What is the relationship between the potential difference across a resistor and the current flowing through it? Before you start, sketch what you think a graph of potential difference against current will look like.

Materials and Cautions

- ammeter
- switch
- 6 connecting leads
- voltmeter
- variable power supply
- several different resistors

Caution: Review the procedure for connecting and using electric meters and have your teacher check the circuit before plugging in the power supply.

Procedure

1. Set up a table for recording your measurements.
2. Record the colour bands on the resistor.
3. Connect the circuit as shown in Figure 13.25.

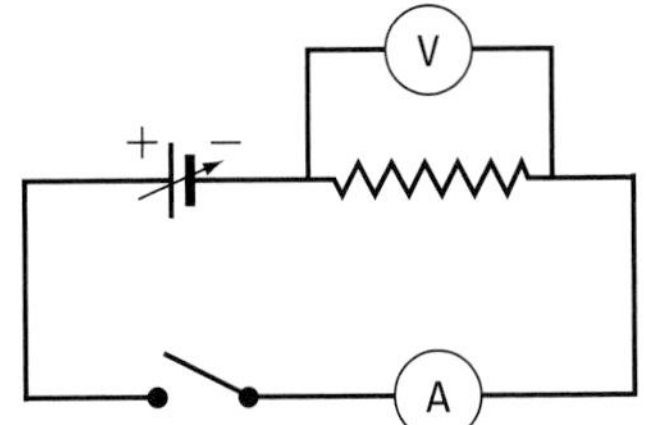

FIGURE 13.25 Ohm's law for a resistor

4. Adjust the power supply to give a potential difference of about 1.5 V. Close the switch. Record the readings on the voltmeter and ammeter.
5. Open the switch. Repeat step 4 using 3.0 V, 4.5 V, and finally 6.0 V.
6. If time permits, replace the resistor you have been using with a different one and repeat steps 2–5.

Analyzing and Interpreting

1. Plot voltage against current for each resistor.
2. Draw the line of best fit for each resistor.
3. Determine the y-intercept and the slope for each graph. Be sure to include units.
4. Describe the graph of potential difference against current. Does the graph pass through the origin? What would it mean if the graph did not pass through the origin?
5. When the potential difference is doubled, what change occurs in the current? What relationship between voltage and current does this suggest?

Concluding and Communicating

6. The general equation for a straight line is $y = mx + b$. Find the equation for your data.
7. Determine the resistance and tolerance of the resistor(s) you used from the colour bands (see Table 13.1). Is the value you found from the equation for each resistor within the tolerance for the resistor? If not, can you explain why?
8. Table 13.4 lists measurements of potential difference and current for a piece of Nichrome wire. Plot a graph of potential difference against current manually or by using a graphing calculator or spreadsheet program. Determine if the Nichrome wire is ohmic or nonohmic.

Extending

9. Replace the resistor with a flashlight bulb. Take potential difference and current readings starting when the bulb is dim and continuing until it is shining brightly. Plot a graph of potential difference against current and compare the graph with that for the resistor. Account for the difference.

TABLE 13.4 Potential Difference and Current for Nichrome Wire

Potential Difference V (V)	Electric Current I (mA)
0	0
0.50	0.72
1.0	1.25
1.5	1.67
2.5	2.30
4.5	3.00
6.0	3.33

Investigation 2 (Section 13.2)

Inquiry Skills

- Initiating and Planning
- Applying Technical Skills
- Using Tools, Materials, Equipment
- Conducting and Recording
- Analyzing and Interpreting
- Concluding and Communicating

Resistors in Parallel

How do you think the equivalent resistance R_t of a parallel combination of resistors relates to the individual resistances R_1, R_2, and R_3? Write a prediction in your notebook. Then design and do an experiment to test your prediction.

Problem

What is the relationship between the resistance of each resistor in a parallel combination and the equivalent resistance of the combination? Predict how R_t of a parallel combination will relate to the individual resistances R_1, R_2, and R_3.

Materials and Cautions

- ammeter
- switch
- 3 resistors
- 9 connecting leads
- 6.0-V power supply
- voltmeter

Caution: Review the procedure for connecting and using electric meters and have your teacher check the circuit before plugging in the power supply.

Experimental Design

1. Draw a circuit diagram showing three resistors connected in parallel with the DC power supply.
2. Review Kirchhoff's laws and decide what measurements must be made to verify these laws for your circuit.
3. Write out a set of procedures to obtain the required measurements.
4. Design a data table to record your measurements.
5. When your teacher has approved your procedure, carry out the experiment.

Analyzing and Interpreting

1. How well do your measurements verify Kirchhoff's current law?
2. How well do your measurements verify Kirchhoff's voltage law?

Concluding and Communicating

3. How does the total resistance of the circuit compare with the individual resistances? What relationship does this suggest between the total resistance and the resistance of each resistor?
4. Do your calculations support the prediction you made before starting the experiment? Why or why not?
5. If you had several resistors all connected in parallel, would the total resistance be very small or very large? Explain.

Extending

6. Suppose you connect two resistors R_1 and R_2 in series to a parallel combination of two resistors R_3 and R_4. Develop an equation to calculate the equivalent resistance R_t of the combination. Ask your teacher for four resistors and test the validity of your equation.

CHAPTER SUMMARY

Key Terms

conductance
equivalent resistance
kilowatt hour
nonohmic
ohm
ohmic
Ohm's law
power
resistance
resistivity
resistor
short circuit
superconductor
tolerance
unit cost
watt

Key Equations

$V = IR$

$\rho = \frac{R \cdot A}{L}$

$P = \frac{E}{\Delta t} = IV = I^2R = \frac{V^2}{R}$

$E = P\,\Delta t = IV\,\Delta t$

Energy cost = energy used × unit cost

The characteristics of a parallel connection of components are

- $V_t = V_1 = V_2 = V_3 = \ldots$
- $I_t = I_1 + I_2 + I_3 + \ldots$
- $\frac{1}{R_t} = \frac{1}{R_1} + \frac{1}{R_2} + \frac{1}{R_3} + \ldots$

The characteristics of a series connection of components are

- $V_t = V_1 + V_2 + V_3 + \ldots$
- $I_t = I_1 = I_2 = I_3 = \ldots$
- $R_t = R_1 + R_2 + R_3 + \ldots$

Essential Understandings

- Ohm's law states that the potential difference across a conductor is directly proportional to the current flowing through it.
- An ohmic conductor is one that obeys Ohm's law.
- Four factors affect the resistance of a resistor: length, cross-sectional area, temperature, and the type of material used.
- The resistivity of a material is a characteristic property of the material which corresponds to the resistance of a 1-m long cylinder with a cross-sectional area of 1 m^2.
- The practical unit of electrical energy is the kilowatt hour (kW·h). The total cost of electrical energy is found by multiplying the energy used in kW·h by the unit cost in cents per kW·h.

Consolidate Your Understanding

1. Look back to your answer for the Checkpoint on page 485. What answer would you give now? Explain why each of the other answers is incorrect

   A circuit contains a battery and a bulb connected in series to a parallel connection of two resistors, R_1 and R_2, whose resistance can be increased or decreased. What changes will take place in the circuit if R_1 is increased by the same amount as R_2 is decreased? Consider potential difference and current at different locations as well as bulb brightness.

2. Create a concept map to be used as a study map for electrical resistance, power, and energy. Consult the Key Terms provided above, and include as many terms as possible in your concept map. Include two Key Equations and an example problem involving both. Show a model solution using the GRASS strategy

3. Construct a chart to summarize the differences between a series circuit and a parallel circuit. Include criteria such as definitions, current characteristics, potential difference characteristics, resistance characteristics, and uses. Explain your chart to a parent or guardian and identify any implications it has for his or her daily life.

CHAPTER 13 REVIEW

Understanding Concepts

1. The graphs in Figure 13.26 show potential difference V plotted against current I for various conductors. Which one of the graphs shows an ohmic conductor?

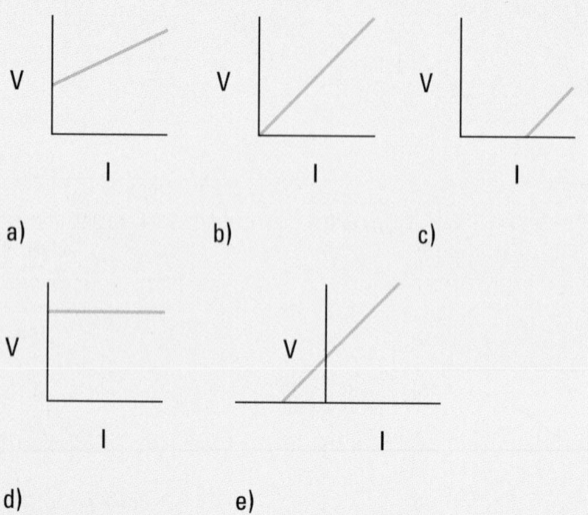

FIGURE 13.26

2. Figure 13.27 shows part of an electric circuit that contains a 10-Ω resistor. It is required that the total resistance between X and Y be 16 Ω. Which of the following combinations of resistors could be inserted between P and Q to achieve the desired resistance?
   a) two 8.0-Ω resistors in parallel
   b) a 10.0 Ω and a 6.0-Ω parallel combination
   c) a series resistance of 4.0-Ω in parallel with two 4.0-Ω resistors
   d) a parallel combination of 48 resistors, each having a value of 6.0-Ω
   e) a 12-Ω and a 24-Ω parallel combination

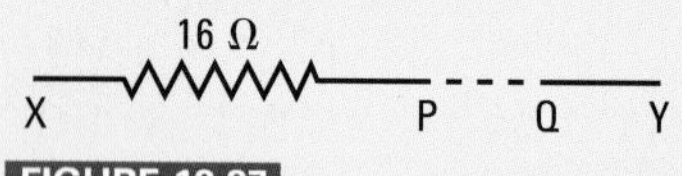

FIGURE 13.27

3. Figure 13.28 shows two identical 1.5-V cells connected to resistors of 3 Ω and 6 Ω. All components are connected in series. What will be the current through the 6-Ω resistor?
   a) 1/3 A
   b) 1/2 A
   c) 1 A
   d) 2 A
   e) 3 A

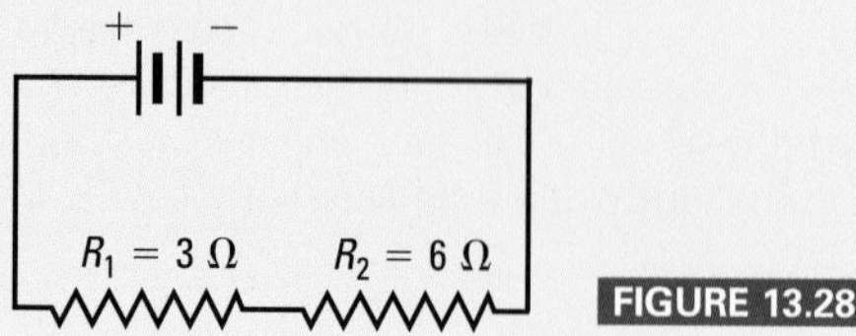

FIGURE 13.28

4. Choose from the descriptions below the one that would consume the most electrical energy.
   a) a 60-W bulb left on for 80 h
   b) a TV rated at 220 W that is on for 5 h
   c) a 8-kW stove used for 3 h
   d) a 1.5-kW heater operating for 10 h
   e) a 200-W refrigerator operating for 40 h
5. What is the cost of using a refrigerator continuously for one day if it is rated at 100 W and the unit cost is 6.00¢/kW·h?
   a) 0.600¢
   b) 2.40¢
   c) 14.4¢
   d) $1.44
   e) $6.00
6. a) Explain why a current loses most of its electrical potential energy when travelling through the filament of a light bulb but very little when travelling through connecting leads.
   b) Name the SI unit of resistance.
7. a) How does the potential difference of the battery compare with the potential difference across each resistor in a series circuit?
   b) How does the current in the main part of the circuit compare with the current flowing through each resistor in a series connection?
   c) How is the equivalent resistance related to the resistance of each separate resistor in a parallel connection?
8. a) How does the potential difference of the source compare with the potential difference across each resistor in a parallel connection of resistors?
   b) How does the current in the main circuit compare with the current flowing through each resistor in a parallel connection of resistors?
   c) Why is the equivalent resistance of three resistors connected in parallel less than the resistance of the smallest resistor in a parallel connection of resistors?
9. a) Define power in terms of energy and time, and give an example.
   b) Write three equations for power in terms of potential difference, current, and resistance.
   c) What is one difference between energy and power?
10. a) Write the equation for determining the energy consumed in terms of power and elapsed time.
    b) What are the two possible units for energy from this equation?
11. a) Write the equation for determining the energy consumed in terms of potential difference, current, and time.
    b) What is the unit of energy from this equation?

Applying Inquiry/ Communication Skills

12. A graph of potential difference against current is shown in Figure 13.29.
    a) What does the slope of the graph represent?
    b) What is the slope of the graph?
    c) What are the units of the slope of the graph?
    d) What unit has replaced these two units?
    e) Draw a schematic diagram showing the circuit used to collect the data for this graph. Label the polarity of the battery and the meters.
    f) Draw a pictorial diagram for the same circuit. Show the polarities of the terminals of the meters and the battery.

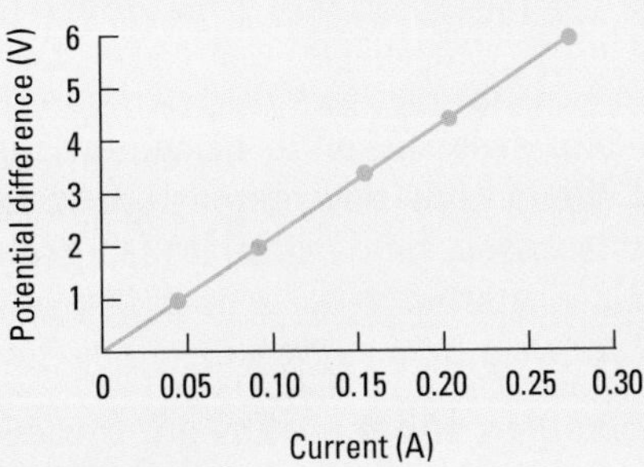

FIGURE 13.30

13. A variable power supply was connected to a resistor, and current readings were taken for various potential differences. These data are summarized in Table 13.5.
    a) Plot a voltage against current graph for the data with voltage on the y-axis.
    b) Describe the graph in terms of slope and where it intercepts the x- and y-axes.
    c) What does the shape of the graph tell us about the resistance of the resistor?
    d) What is the resistance of this resistor? State the answer using two different kinds of units.

TABLE 13.5 Data for a Resistor

Potential Difference V (V)	0.00	0.60	1.0	2.0	4.0	8.0	16
Current I (A)	0.00	0.03	0.05	0.10	0.20	0.40	0.80

14. A student wants to use a voltmeter, an ammeter, and a battery to measure the equivalent resistance for two resistors connected in series. Draw a schematic diagram to show the set-up. Show the polarities of the meters and the source.

15. A pictorial diagram showing a set-up to measure the equivalent resistance of a circuit is shown in Figure 13.31. Draw the schematic circuit diagram for the circuit. Show all polarities.

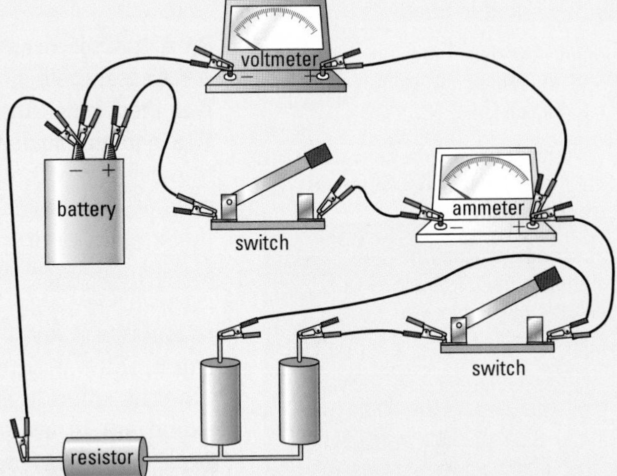

FIGURE 13.31 Draw the schematic diagram for this circuit.

16. A student is told that a particular bulb is rated at 2.0 V. The power of the bulb is not known.
    a) Draw a schematic diagram showing a circuit that could be used to determine the energy consumed by the bulb in 20 min.
    b) In a paragraph, describe all the equipment needed and the procedure. Indicate any safety precautions to be taken.

Making Connections

17. How is the motion of water molecules through a narrow pipe similar to the motion of electrons through a narrow filament of a light bulb?

18. What will happen if an appliance made to operate on 120 V in North America is plugged into a 240-V supply in Europe?

19. You look at the back of an electric kettle and read that its power is 1500 W.
    a) In a short paragraph, explain how you can calculate the electrical resistance of the heating element in the kettle and the amount of current flowing through it when it is connected.
    b) Determine the electrical resistance and the current using the GRASS problem-solving strategy.

20. The average refrigerator consumes more energy in a year than the average range and oven, although the power of the refrigerator is about one-twentieth that of the range and oven. Why?

CHAPTER 14

Magnetism

SPECIFIC EXPECTATIONS

By the end of this chapter, you will be able to:

- define and describe the concepts and units related to electricity and magnetism (14.1, 14.3)
- describe the properties, including the three-dimensional nature, of magnetic fields (14.1)
- describe and illustrate the magnetic field produced by an electric current in a long straight conductor and in a solenoid (14.2)
- analyze and predict, by applying the right-hand rule, the direction of the magnetic field produced when electric current flows through a long straight conductor and through a solenoid (14.2)
- analyze and describe the operation of industrial and domestic technological systems based on principles related to magnetic fields (14.4)

Magnetic forces have intrigued people for centuries. The early history of magnetism abounds with legends. One story tells us that magnetism was discovered by a shepherd named Magnes. He supposedly became stuck to the ground when the nails in his boots and the iron tip of his staff came into contact with an outcrop of magnetic rock, or magnetite. Another legend speaks of an ancient Chinese king whose fortress was equipped with magnetic doors to prevent assassins from entering with concealed knives.

Magnets have been used as playthings and as a part of toys. Albert Einstein recalled that, as a child, he had been fascinated by compasses.

Today we are surrounded by magnetism. The power supplies for electronic devices such as answering machines and calculators use magnetism

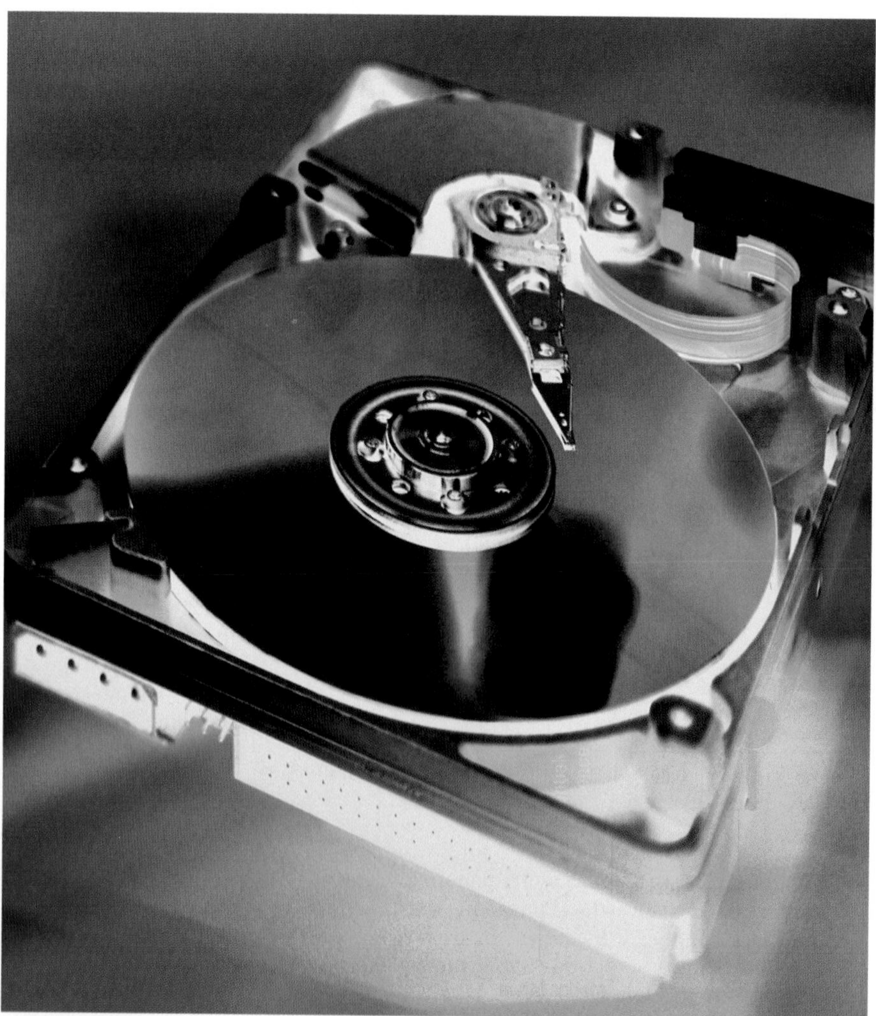

FIGURE 14.1 A computer hard drive uses magnetism to store data.

to produce safe voltages. Electric motors, cassette tapes, computer disks, credit cards, and pass cards involve magnetism. The latest high-speed trains are lifted off the tracks to reduce friction and are propelled forward by means of magnetic forces.

Our study of magnetism begins with the properties of magnets and how they affect the space around them. Then we will examine the relationship between magnetism and electric current.

Discovering Physics

Mapping Magnetic Fields

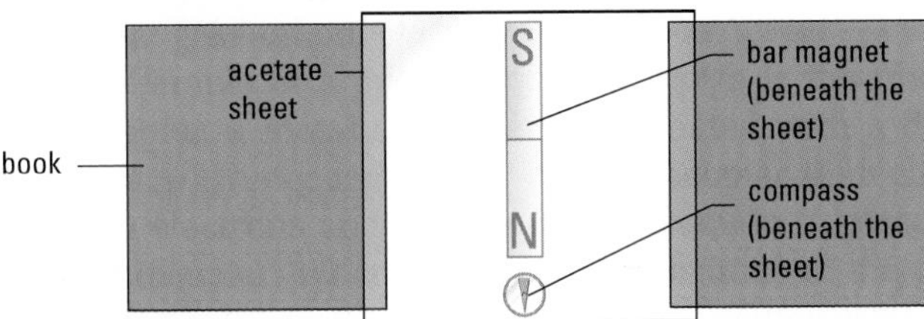

FIGURE 14.2

What are the magnetic fields around magnets like? Since magnetic fields are invisible, this question could be hard to answer. However, if you place iron filings in a magnetic field they become magnetized. These tiny magnets tend to line up in the direction of the field. Their pattern shows the shape of the magnetic field.

Try this method for mapping a magnetic field.

Caution: Be careful not to spill the iron filings.

1. Cover a bar magnet with a clear acetate sheet. Support the sheet at the sides so that it is relatively flat (Figure 14.2).
2. Sprinkle iron filings uniformly over the acetate, then tap it gently.
3. Sketch the pattern of magnetic field lines indicated by the iron filings. Indicate on the sketch the location of the north and south poles of the bar magnet, if its poles are labelled.
4. Move a magnetic compass around the acetate sheet and note on your sketch which direction the compass points at locations all around the magnet.
5. Try this mapping procedure with several magnets of different shapes, such as horseshoe or ring magnets.

- Is there a relationship between the shapes of the magnets and the shapes of the magnetic fields?
- Do the patterns for the different magnets have any elements in common?
- Does the compass needle point the same way around all the magnets?
- Predict the shape of the magnetic field and the directions a compass will point near a refrigerator magnet. Check your prediction experimentally.

CHECK**POINT**

Compass needles point north because

a) the magnetic field is stronger at the North Pole due to the density of the Canadian Shield
b) Earth's molten core acts like an electromagnet with its pole near the North Pole
c) an ancient meteor impact left a major deposit of magnetic iron near the North Pole
d) compass needles are attracted to the North Star (Polaris), the closest star to us
e) they respond to tidal forces created by the Moon

State a reason for your choice.

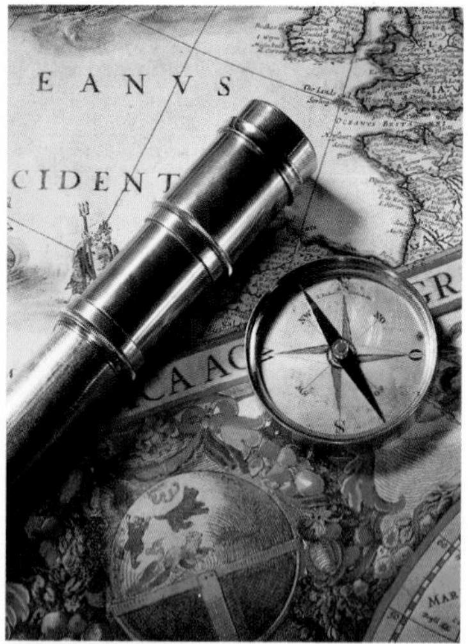

FIGURE 14.3

14.1 Magnetic Poles, Fields, and Forces

Key Understandings

When you have completed this section, you will be able to:

- describe the properties, including the three-dimensional nature, of magnetic fields
- describe the magnetic field around a bar magnet
- describe a magnetic pole and state the law of magnetic poles
- given a labelled magnet, apply the law of magnetic poles to identify the poles of another magnet
- describe how some animals or birds may use Earth's magnetic field

From ancient times magnetism has fascinated people. How could pieces of rock attract and repel each other? Why would a suspended lodestone always swing to point north? Many people suspected that they must be pointing to mountains of lodestone in the far north.

Magnetic Poles

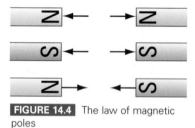

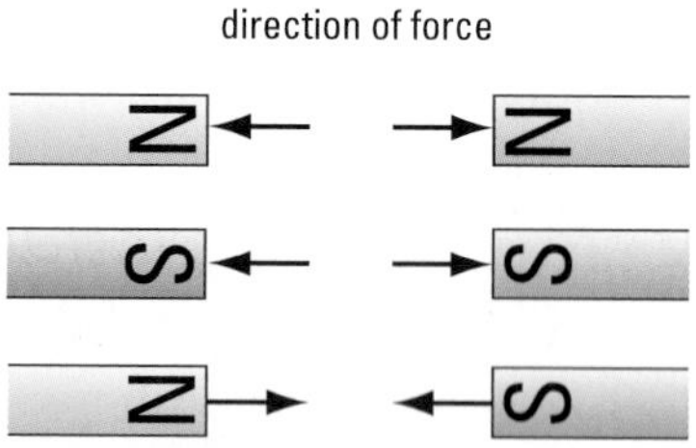

direction of force

N ← → N

S ← → S

N → ← S

FIGURE 14.4 The law of magnetic poles

Naturally occurring magnets made of **magnetite** (Fe_3O_4) are called **lodestones**. Early compass makers shaped lodestones so that one end always pointed toward Earth's geographic north and the other toward the geographic south. These ends became known as the north-seeking and the south-seeking poles of the **magnet**. Later these names were shortened to the **north pole** and the **south pole**. A **compass** is simply a magnet that is allowed to rotate horizontally to point north and south.

A number of important properties of magnetic poles have been discovered. First, when you try to place two magnets together, they will attract if a north pole is next to a south pole and they will repel if two north poles or two south poles are together (Figure 14.3). This interaction is summarized as the **law of magnetic poles**:

Similar magnetic poles repel while opposite magnetic poles attract.

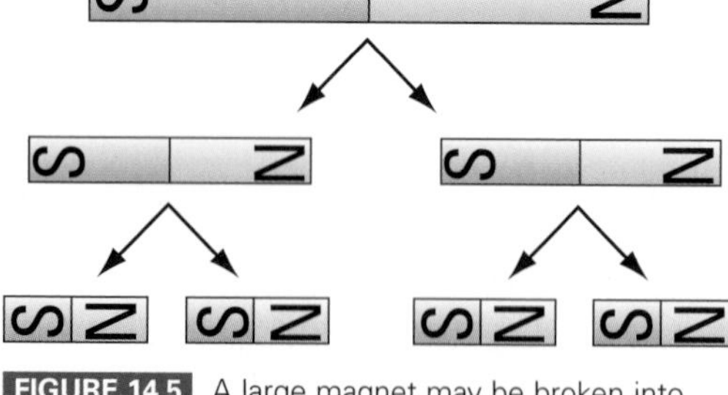

FIGURE 14.5 A large magnet may be broken into many smaller magnets.

Second, the magnetic field about a magnet is strongest at the poles. Third, the north pole and the south pole of the same bar magnet are, in general, equally strong. Fourth, if you cut a magnet in two, each half possesses a north pole and a south pole (Figure 14.5). Cutting up the pieces of the magnet simply produces an increased number of smaller but weaker magnets. Since each piece possesses two poles, it appears that poles always come in pairs—you cannot have a north pole without a corresponding south pole. However, some theories suggest the possibility of an isolated pole. Physicists are currently investigating whether such **monopoles** could actually exist.

Properties of the Magnetic Field

The space around a magnet in which a magnetic force can be detected is called a **magnetic field**. To examine the field around a bar magnet, we must use a substance that can be influenced by the field. Such a substance is said to be magnetic. Most substances are magnetic, but only to an extremely small extent. However, iron, nickel, cobalt, and most of their alloys respond strongly to a magnetic field, as do the rare metals dysprosium and gadolinium. Such elements and alloys are called **ferromagnetic**. The name indicates that these elements share similar magnetic properties with iron (*ferrum* in Latin).

INFOBIT

The magnetic pole in the far north must be a south pole since it attracts all the tiny north poles on compasses. Thus, the geographic North Pole is a magnetic south pole, and the geographic South Pole is a magnetic north pole.

Lines of Magnetic Force

A pattern of lines appears when a bar magnet is covered with a sheet of clear acetate and iron filings are sprinkled on the sheet (Figure 14.6). These lines, which arc from pole to pole, follow imaginary **lines of magnetic force**. The lines are closest together at the poles (where the magnetic field is the strongest) and tend to spread out farther away from the poles.

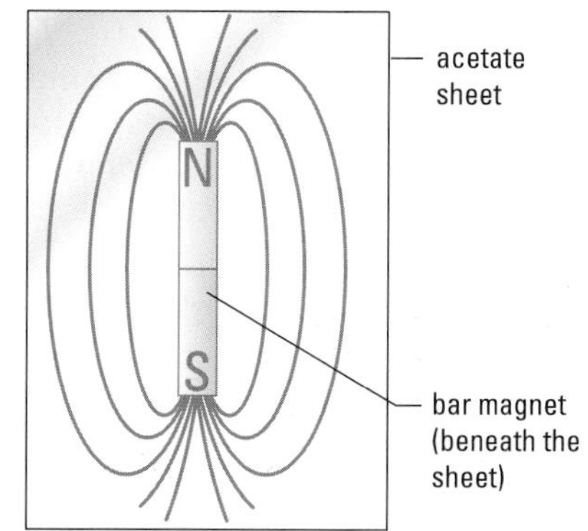

FIGURE 14.6 When iron filings are sprinkled on the acetate sheet they will line up along the lines of magnetic force.

When a tiny compass is placed upon a line of magnetic force, we find that the compass needle always points along the line. The north pole of the compass is directed away from the north pole of the bar magnet and toward its south pole (Figure 14.7). **The direction of a line of force is defined as the direction in which the north pole of a compass points when placed along that line**. The lines appear to loop out from the north pole and arc around to the south pole outside the magnet. Therefore, the lines inside the magnet must travel from the south pole to the north pole (Figure 14.8). Although these lines are usually drawn on a flat sheet, they actually arc through all the space around the magnet. The lines of force form complete loops that surround the magnet in three dimensions.

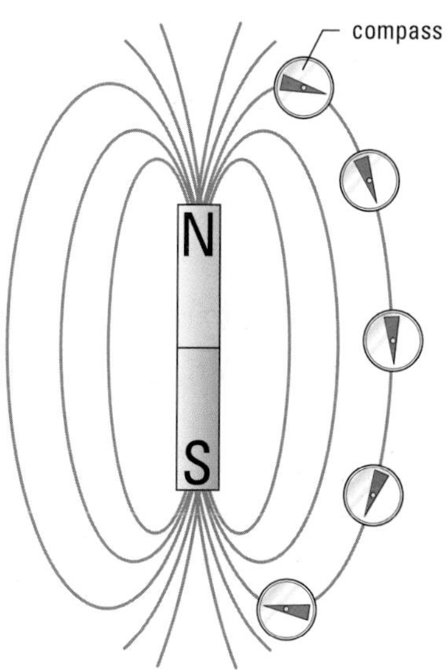

FIGURE 14.7 Compass needles in a magnetic field point in the direction of the field.

It is important to realize that lines of force are simply our way of picturing the magnetic field. Like lines of longitude and latitude, discrete lines of force do not actually exist. However, the concept of a line of force is useful. We can represent strong fields by drawing lines of force close together. The direction of a line of force is shown by placing arrowheads along it. The arrows point from the north pole to the south pole outside the magnet and from the south pole to the north pole inside the magnet. Magnetic lines of force never cross each other (Figure 14.9). If they did, the magnetic force at the intersection point would be acting in two different directions at once!

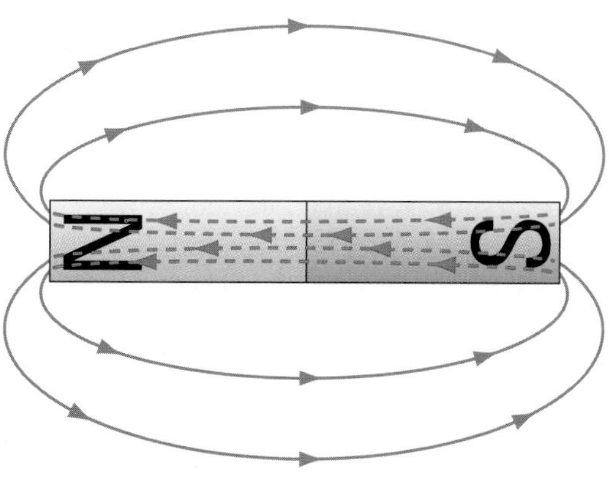

FIGURE 14.8 The lines of force inside a magnet are directed from south to north.

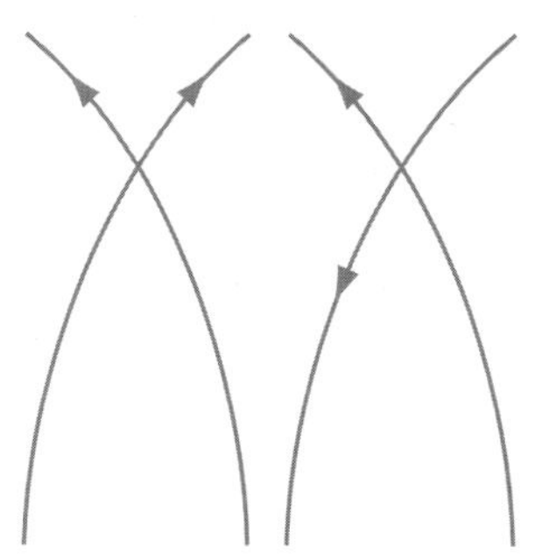

FIGURE 14.9 Why can't lines of force intersect?

WEBLINK

The magnetic field around a planet, its magnetosphere, is distorted by the outpouring of protons and electrons from the Sun in the solar wind. Find out more about the shape and size of the magnetosphere around Earth and Jupiter. Draw a diagram showing the shape of these fields around either planet. Begin your research at **www.pearsoned.ca/physics11.**

INSIGHT

Like poles repel each other and opposite poles attract, similar to the way that like charges repel and opposite charges attract. However, north and south poles are not positive and negative charges. Can you think of ways in which magnetic poles and electric charges differ?

Discovering Physics — *Distorted Fields, Attractions, and Repulsions*

How is the magnetic field of a magnet affected by metal or another magnet nearby? Can we use the shapes and directions of magnetic fields to predict magnetic attraction and repulsion?

Use iron filings, an acetate sheet, and a compass to investigate the fields produced when

1. two north poles face each other as in Figure 14.10 a)
2. two south poles face each other as in Figure 14.10 b)
3. a north pole faces a south pole as in Figure 14.10 c)
4. pieces of various metals are placed midway between a north pole and a south pole as in Figure 14.10 d)
5. a keeper is placed across the poles of a horseshoe magnet as in Figure 14.10 e)
6. two bar magnets are placed side by side, first with their like poles adjacent to each other and then with the north pole of one magnet beside the south pole of the other (Figure 14.11).

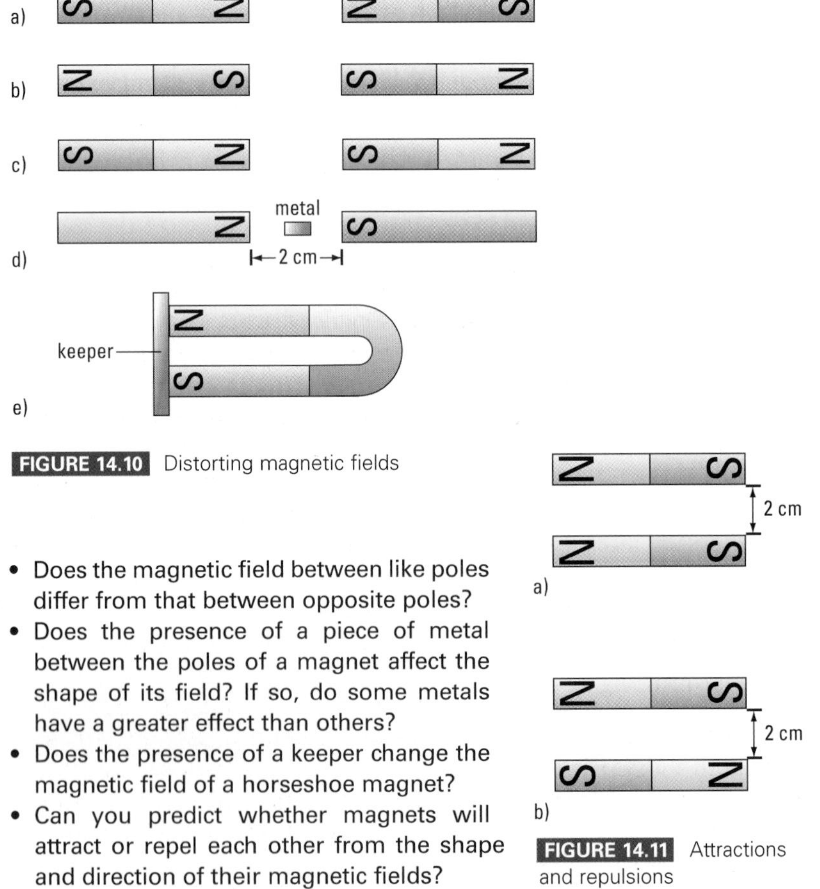

FIGURE 14.10 Distorting magnetic fields

- Does the magnetic field between like poles differ from that between opposite poles?
- Does the presence of a piece of metal between the poles of a magnet affect the shape of its field? If so, do some metals have a greater effect than others?
- Does the presence of a keeper change the magnetic field of a horseshoe magnet?
- Can you predict whether magnets will attract or repel each other from the shape and direction of their magnetic fields?

FIGURE 14.11 Attractions and repulsions

Predicting Magnetic Forces

Lines of force can be used to predict how different magnetic fields will interact with each other. For instance, lines of force that act in the same direction indicate an intensified field. On the other hand, lines of force acting in opposite directions indicate a diminished field.

The fields shown in Figure 14.13a) could come from two bar magnets lying side by side with like poles together, as shown in Figure 14.12a). Since like poles repel, **parallel fields indicate repulsion**. The two bar magnets shown in Figures 14.12b) will produce the opposite fields as shown in Figure 14.13b). Opposite poles attract, and so **opposite fields indicate attraction**.

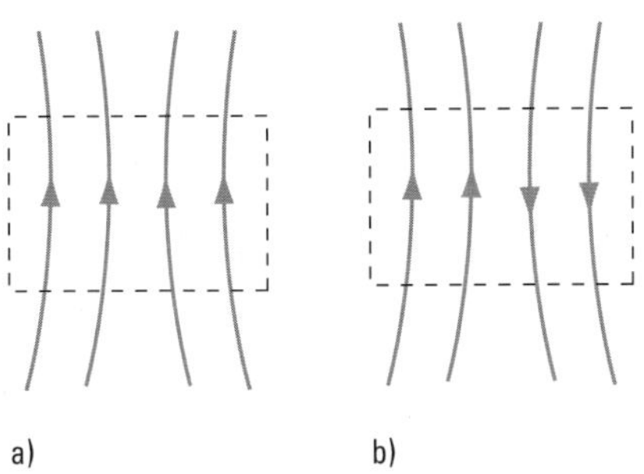

FIGURE 14.12 Interacting magnetic fields

a) Parallel fields reinforce each other

b) Opposite fields diminish each other

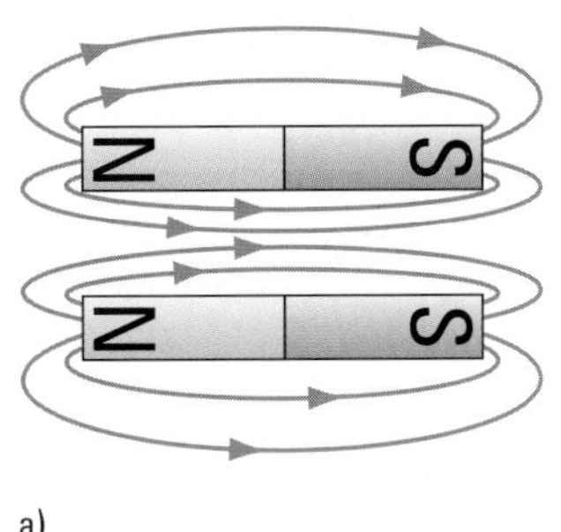

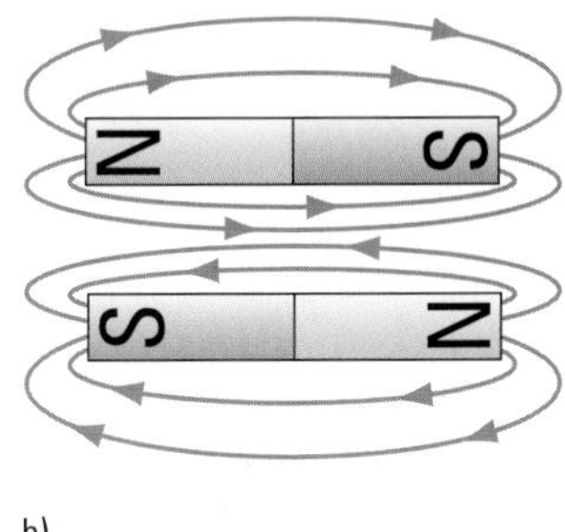

FIGURE 14.13 Predicting magnetic forces

a) Parallel fields repel

b) Opposite fields attract

Uses of Magnetic Fields

Research into the uses of magnetic fields has yielded some remarkable technologies, from a simple navigational compass to the complex workings of medical imaging machines. By the end of the twentieth century a non-invasive technique emerged that provided doctors with an incredible understanding of the working of the human body. At the same time it represented an enormous improvement in their ability to diagnose internal problems. This technique became known as magnetic resonance imaging or MRI. It uses a strong magnetic field to cause atoms such as hydrogen to emit tiny radio signals. These signals vary according to the nature of the molecule in which the hydrogen atom is found. In this way, doctors can obtain scans of the body in which they not only see the internal structure, they can determine to a large extent the chemical nature of these structures.

Humans may not be the only species to use Earth's magnetic field for navigation. Some species seem to have internal compasses. Magnetite has been found in some of the cells of many creatures. Some scientists theorize that some migrating birds sense Earth's magnetic field and use it to determine north and south. Magnetic cells have also been found in such diverse creatures as honeybees and whales.

There are even bacteria that possess magnetite. In this case, the magnetic force may guide them to the location of the food-laden bottom of a body of water. In the Northern Hemisphere, the bacteria follow the magnetic field down into the silt. What might happen to these bacteria if they were transported to the Southern Hemisphere?

WEBLINK

A recent medical innovation known as magnetic resonance imaging (MRI) is improving our ability to obtain internal images of our bodies and to understand our own biochemistry. Prepare a poster or computer presentation on this technique showing how it works and what information it can provide. Begin your research at **www.pearsoned.ca/physics11.**

WEBLINK

Recently we have learned much about the behaviour of birds during migration and their ability to navigate. Write a half-page report on the navigation abilities of birds. Begin your research at **www.pearsoned.ca/physics11.**

Section 14.1 Review

Understanding Concepts

1. a) How are the poles of a magnet named?
   b) Sketch the magnetic field around a bar magnet.
   c) Where is the magnetic field around a magnet the strongest?
   d) How is this shown in your sketch?
2. State the law of magnetic poles.
3. Identify the poles labelled A, B, C, D, E, F, G, H in Figure 14.14.
4. In which direction do magnetic lines of force point:
   a) outside the magnet?
   b) inside the magnet?
5. Which type of magnetic pole is located near the geographic North Pole?
6. To which geographic pole do the magnetic lines of force point?

Making Connections

7. Molten rock seeps out from the interior of Earth at an extremely slow rate and spreads out to form the ocean bottom. In a region where the ocean floor spreads at a rate of 2.1 cm/year, bands of rock, 4.8 km apart on the ocean floor, were found to be magnetized in opposite directions. What does this information indicate about Earth's magnetic field?

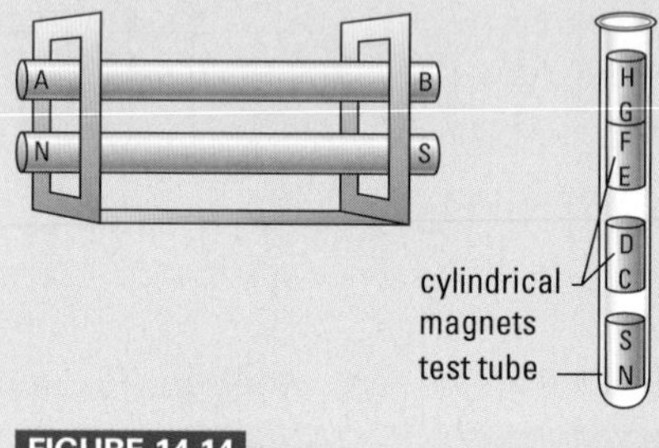

FIGURE 14.14

WEBLINK

Animations of physical processes often help us to understand them better. Search the Internet for animations of the formation of the magnetic field around a current-carrying conductor. Draw a series of diagrams to summarize these animations. Begin your research at **www.pearsoned.ca/physics11.**

FIGURE 14.15 An electromagnetic crane

14.2 Magnetic Field Around a Current-Carrying Conductor

Key Understandings

When you have completed this section, you will be able to:

- describe and illustrate the magnetic field produced by an electric current in a long straight conductor and in a solenoid
- analyze and predict, by applying the right-hand rule, the direction of the magnetic field produced when electric current flows through a long straight conductor and through a solenoid
- describe the factors that affect the strength of these magnetic fields
- describe the construction of an electromagnet
- describe the factors that contribute to the strength of an electromagnet
- describe Earth's magnetic field

As the electromagnetic crane in Figure 14.15 demonstrates, we can produce strong magnetic fields by wrapping electrically insulated wire into a tight coil and passing large electric currents through it. Obviously there is some link between an electric current and a magnetic field. How does the current affect the strength of the field? Is there any relation between the direction of the current and the direction of the magnetic field?

Discovery of Electromagnetism

In 1820, a Dutch physicist, Hans Christian Oersted, accidentally discovered electromagnetism. Prior to his discovery scientists believed that electricity and magnetism were separate phenomena. Indeed, on the day of the discovery, Oersted had just finished demonstrating that an electric current in a wire had no effect on a nearby magnetic compass. To do this, he placed a wire at right angles to a stationary compass needle. Because of Earth's magnetic field, the needle pointed north. When he passed a current through the wire the needle did not change direction.

After the demonstration, some students gathered around the apparatus to have a closer look. By chance, the wire was oriented north and south parallel to the needle when the current was turned on again. Much to Oersted's surprise, when the current flowed through the wire the compass needle instantly swung away from north. This event placed Oersted's name in the annals of science.

FIGURE 14.16 A patrol aircraft equipped to detect submarines

Since then, the magnetic forces produced by electricity—**electromagnetism**—have been intensely studied and applied. Electromagnets, motors, generators, transformers, computer disks, magnetic tapes, metal detectors—all employ electromagnetism. Patrolling aircraft (Figure 14.16) use it to detect submarines hidden beneath the ocean's surface.

Oersted's discovery of the magnetic field around an electric current triggered immediate investigation of this effect by other scientists. One of these was André Marie Ampère. Less than a week after Oersted's discovery, Ampère had determined how the shape of the magnetic field was related to the direction of the electron flow.

Ampère's rule tells us that:

- The magnetic field around a straight, current-carrying conductor is circular with the conductor located at the centre.
- Viewed from above, when the current flows down the wire (into the page), the magnetic field is clockwise. Conversely, when the current flows up the wire (out of the page), the magnetic field is counterclockwise.

In Figure 14.17, an X indicates that the current is flowing away from you, or into the page. A dot indicates that the current flow is toward you, or out of the page. The cross and dot convention is easy to remember if you simply

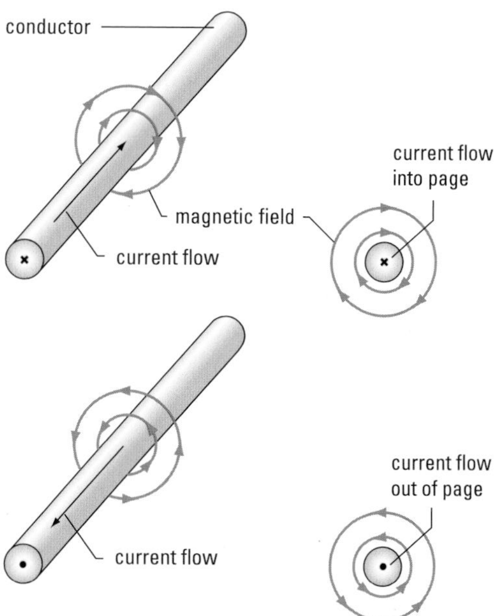

FIGURE 14.17 Magnetic field around a straight, current-carrying conductor

picture an arrow in flight. If it is flying away from you, you see the feathers somewhat like a cross. If it is coming toward you, then you see the point of the arrow. (Note, conventional current is used in this book, as explained in Chapter 12.)

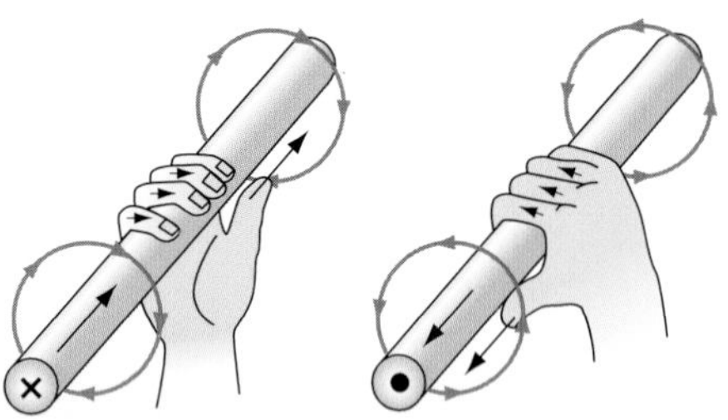

FIGURE 14.18 Right-hand rule for a straight conductor

Right-Hand Rule for a Straight Conductor

The **right-hand rule for a straight conductor** enables us to predict the direction of the field about a straight conductor (Figure 14.18). To apply this rule, mentally **grasp the conductor with your right hand so that the thumb points in the direction of the current. Your fingers then wrap around the conductor in the same direction as the magnetic field.** This same relationship can be used to predict the direction of the current if you know the direction of the magnetic field.

Factors Affecting the Strength of the Magnetic Field

In an experiment using iron filings, the magnetic field lines close to the wire appear quite distinct. Farther out, however, the lines are fuzzier. This indicates that the strength of the magnetic field decreases as the distance from the wire increases.

The strength of the magnetic field also depends on the size of the current. A larger current produces a stronger magnetic field. When the current is zero, there is no magnetic field.

Investigation

Refer to page 538, Investigation 1.

Magnetic Field around a Coiled Conductor

From Straight Conductor to Loop Imagine a straight conductor in which the current is flowing toward the right. The right-hand rule for a straight conductor allows us to predict that the magnetic field about that conductor would be as indicated in Figure 14.19a).

Now, suppose the conductor is bent into a loop, as shown in Figures 14.19b) and c), and then rotated 90° as shown in d). Inside the loop, the lines of force point to the left as we see in Figure 14.19d) and e). Outside, the lines of force arc around from the left side of the loop and re-enter on the right. In this way, the loop is acting as an extremely short bar magnet with its north pole at the left and its south pole at the right in Figure 14.19e).

INFOBIT

Subway systems use huge currents, sometimes over 5000 A. Such currents can generate intense magnetic fields. If you ever carry a compass on a subway, you will see the needle bounce around with every change in the current.

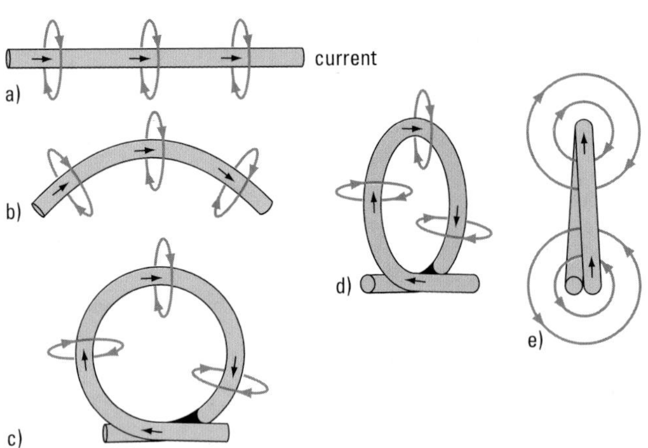

FIGURE 14.19 Magnetic fields
a) Straight conductor
b) Curved conductor
c) Loop
d) Loop, rotating the left side toward you
e) Side view of loop

From Loop to Helix If we continue to coil the conductor, we will have a series of loops that form a **coil** or **helix** (Figure 14.20). The fields of the loops all add together, and the helix acts as a bar magnet with its north pole on the left and its south pole on the right.

But what happens to the fields between the loops? To answer this question, picture a cross-section of the helix as the loops are being added as shown in Figure 14.21. Note that the fields inside the loops point consistently to the left. The fields above and below the loops point to the right. However, the fields between the loops act in opposite directions and so cancel. The net effect is shown in Figure 14.21d).

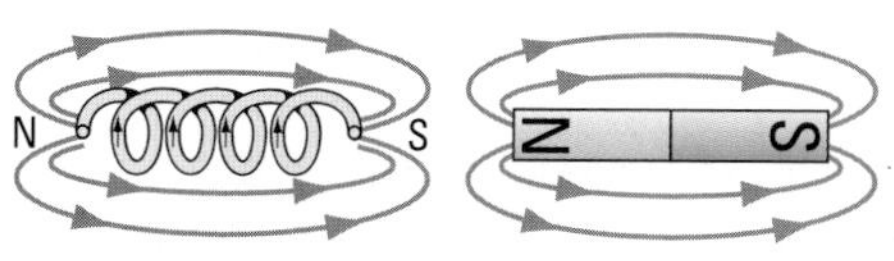

FIGURE 14.20 The magnetic field around a helix resembles that of a bar magnet.

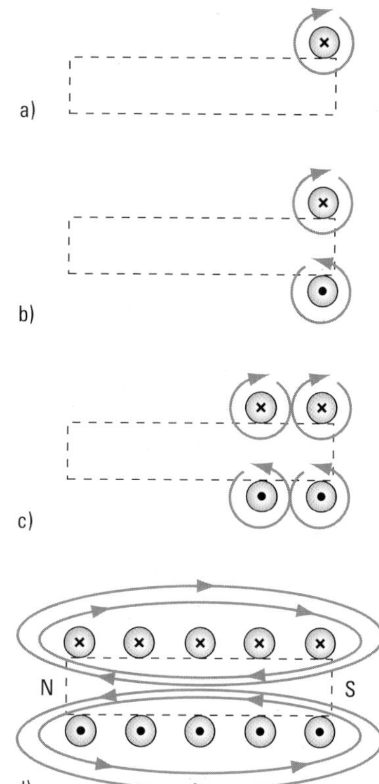

FIGURE 14.21 The magnetic fields between the loops of a helix cancel each other out.

Right-Hand Rule for a Current-Carrying Helix

It is not necessary to go through all this reasoning every time we wish to predict the direction of the magnetic field produced by a current through a helix. The location of the north pole of any current-carrying helix can be easily determined using the **right-hand rule for a helix**. To apply the rule, mentally **grasp the helix with your right hand so that your fingers wrap around the helix in the same direction as the current. Your thumb points toward the north pole of the helix**, as shown in Figure 14.22.

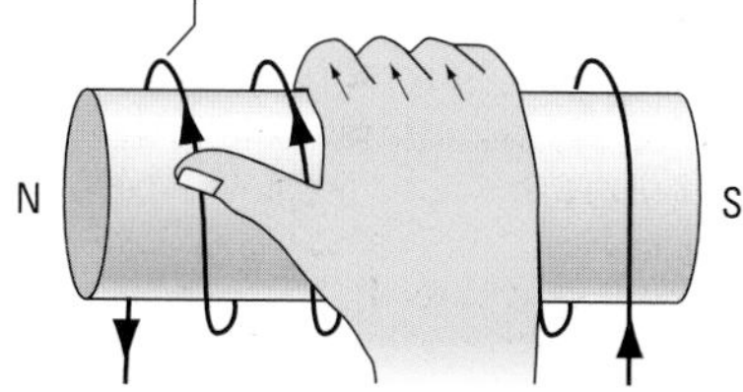

FIGURE 14.22 Right-hand rule for a helix

The Electromagnet

There is an enormous increase in the strength of the magnetic field about a helix when a ferromagnetic core is inserted. A helix that contains a core is called an **electromagnet**. The strength of an electromagnet depends on several factors (Figure 14.23).

Current in the Helix The strength of the electromagnet varies directly with the current as Figure 23a) shows. This can be expressed by

$$F \propto I \quad \text{or} \quad \frac{F_1}{F_2} = \frac{I_1}{I_2}$$

where F is the force exerted by the electromagnet in newtons and I is the current in amperes.

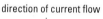

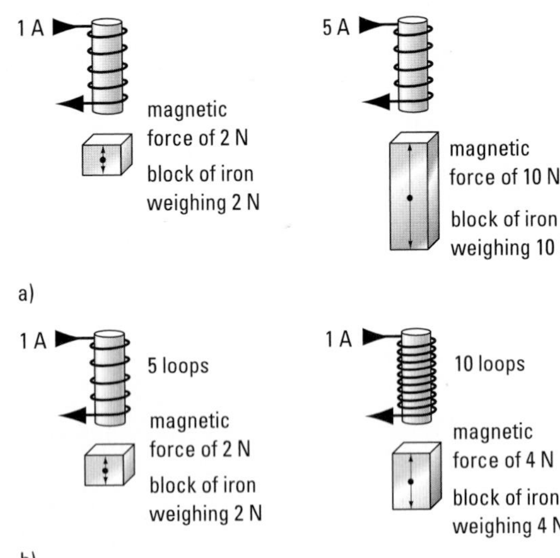

FIGURE 14.23 Strength of the magnetic field produced by an electromagnet

Refer to page 539, Investigation 2

Number of Turns per Unit Length The strength of the electromagnet varies directly with the number of **turns** (or loops) per unit length of the helix as we see in Figure 14.23b). This is expressed by

$$F \; \alpha \; N \qquad \text{or} \qquad \frac{F_1}{F_2} = \frac{N_1}{N_2}$$

where F is the force exerted by the electromagnet in newtons and N is the number of turns in the helix per unit length, for example, per centimetre.

Permeability of the Core **Relative permeability** is the factor by which the strength of the field increases due to the presence of the **core**. Because it is a ratio, relative permeability has no units. For nonmagnetic metals such as copper and aluminum, the relative permeability is 1.0. Table 14.1 shows permeabilities of some common core materials.

TABLE 14.1 Permeabilities of Some Core Materials

Substance	Maximum Relative Permeability
Pure iron	2×10^5
Mild steel	2×10^3
Silicon iron (Fe 96.2%, Si 3.8%)	1.4×10^6
Permalloy (Fe 21.5%, Ni 78.5%)	1×10^5
Superalloy (Fe 16%, Ni 79%, Mo 5%)	1×10^6

EXAMPLE 1 NUMERICAL

A lifting electromagnet, such as that shown in Figure 14.24, can suspend a weight of 2.0×10^4 N when a current of 15 A flows through it. What current is required to suspend a weight of 5.0×10^4 N?

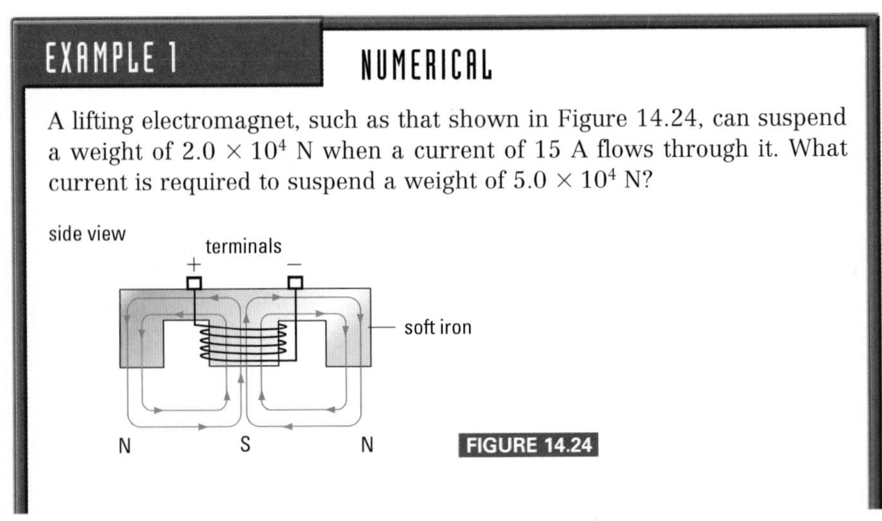

FIGURE 14.24

Given
F_1, F_2, and I_1

Required
I_2

Analysis

- Use the equation $\frac{F_1}{F_2} = \frac{I_1}{I_2}$
- Re-arrange to solve for I_2

Solution

$$I_2 = I_1 \times \frac{F_2}{F_1}$$

$$= \frac{15 \text{ A} \times 5.0 \times 10^4 \text{ N}}{2.0 \times 10^4 \text{ N}}$$

$$= 38 \text{ A}$$

Statement
The current required to lift a weight of 5.0×10^4 N is 38 A.

PRACTICE PROBLEMS

1. An electromagnet with 100 turns/cm can exert a force of 250 N on an iron block. How much force could be exerted on that block if the number of turns is increased to 420 turns/cm and the current remains the same?
2. An electromagnet with 80 turns/cm and a current of 0.20 A can exert a force of 33 N on a steel lever. What force could be exerted on that same lever if the number of turns is increased to 120 turns/cm and the current is decreased to 0.10 A?

Earth's Magnetic Field

It is convenient to imagine that a huge bar magnet runs along the axis of rotation of Earth as shown in Figure 14.25. There are, however, problems with making an analogy between Earth and a bar magnet. First, the magnetic poles are not located exactly at the geographic poles. The "magnetic north" is in fact near Resolute, Nunavut, about 1600 km away from the geographic North Pole (Figure 14.26). The south magnetic pole is similarly located about l600 km away from the geographic South Pole. Second, the magnetic poles are not directly opposite each other and they continually move (although, extremely slowly). Third, geological evidence indicates clearly that Earth's north and south poles have reversed a number of times.

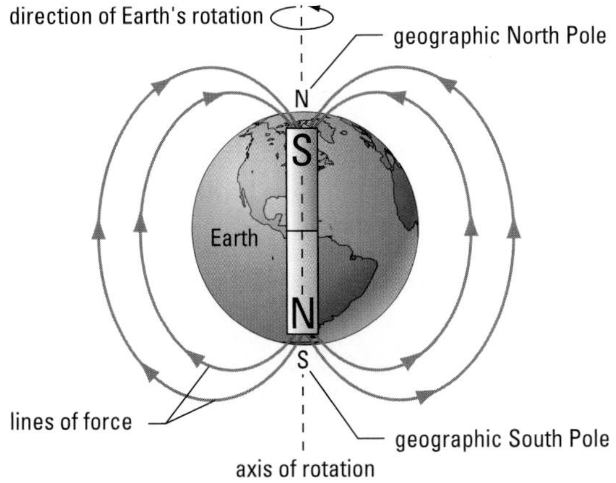

FIGURE 14.25 Early model of Earth's magnetic field

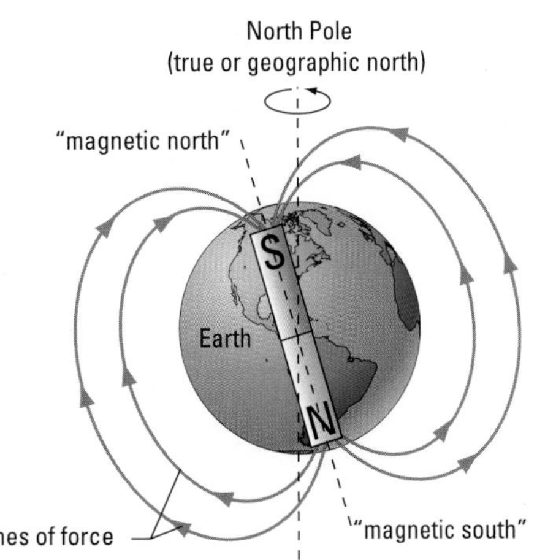

FIGURE 14.26 Magnetic and geographic poles do not coincide.

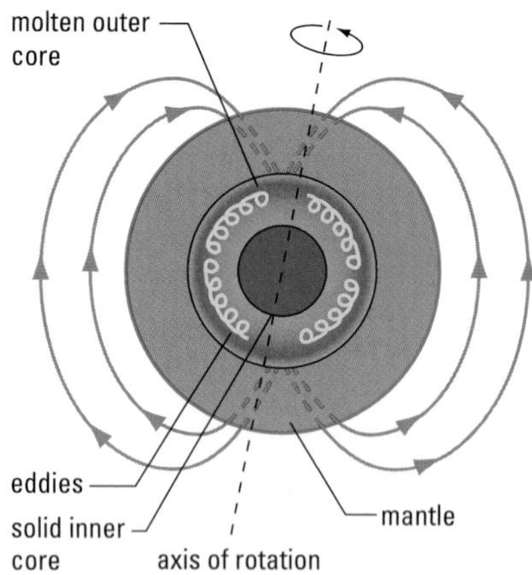

FIGURE 14.27 Modern model for Earth's magnetic field

A modern theory is that Earth's magnetic field is produced by the circulation of charged atoms (or ions) in large eddies in Earth's molten outer core (Figure 14.27). The large-scale movement of these charged particles would create a magnetic field much as an electric current does in a helix. The circling motion of the eddies could be driven by thermal convection and by Earth's rotation about its axis.

Minor variations in Earth's magnetic field are often due to the presence of ore bodies under the surface. However, there are other local magnetic fluctuations that cannot be explained this way. In the early nineteenth century scientists became aware that Earth's magnetic field was changing. In 1840, Britain began a study of these changes and set up observatories to monitor the magnetic changes at various locations around the world. The strongest field known at the time was near Toronto, Ontario, so an observatory was built there. In 1881, the original wood building was replaced by a stone building that stands on what is now the campus of the University of Toronto (Figure 14.28).

INFOBIT

Christopher Columbus may have been the first to realize that the compass needle does not point exactly north. As his famous voyage progressed, the needle pointed farther and farther away from geographic north. Columbus hid this fact from his crew believing that they might panic and try to turn back.

FIGURE 14.28 The Toronto observatory building

Section 14.2 Review

Understanding Concepts

1. Describe the shape of the magnetic field around a straight current-carrying conductor.
2. How does the strength of the magnetic field vary as the distance from the conductor increases?
3. Make a sketch of the conductors in Figure 14.29 showing the direction of the magnetic field around each conductor for the current directions indicated.

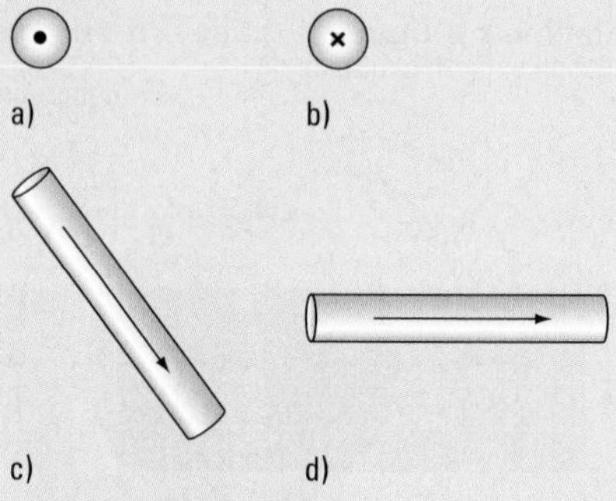

a) b)

c) d)

FIGURE 14.29 What is the shape and direction of the magnetic fields?

4. For each of the helices shown in Figure 14.30, identify which end is the north pole.

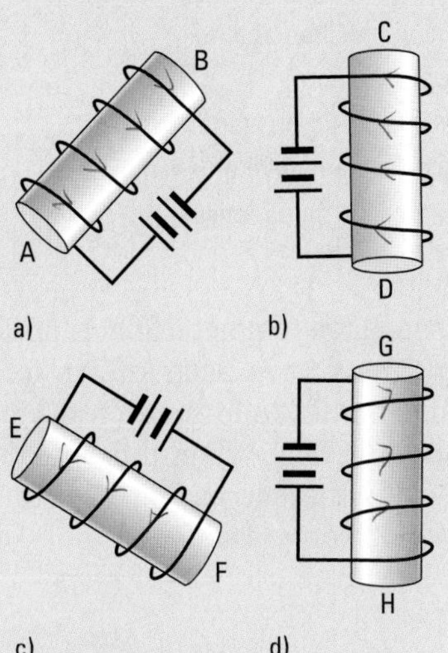

FIGURE 14.30 Which ends are the north poles?

5. For each of the helices shown in Figure 13.31, state whether the current is from X to Y or from Y to X.

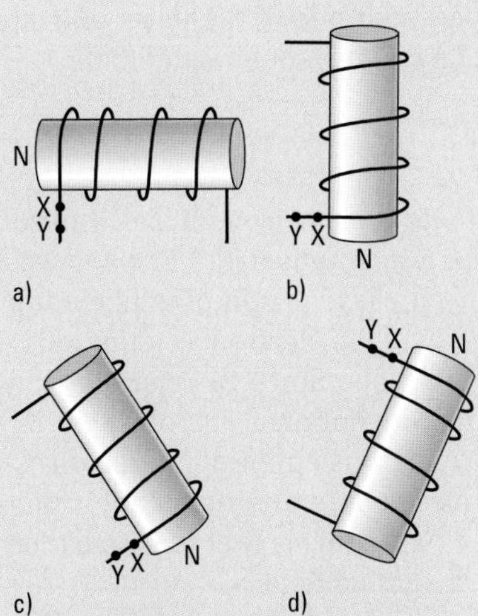

FIGURE 14.31 In which direction does the current flow?

6. Distinguish between the terms "helix" and "electromagnet."

7. a) What three factors affect the strength of an electromagnet?
   b) How do each of these factors affect the strength?

8. An electromagnet can lift a weight of 100 N when the current through it is 3.5 A. What weight could it lift if the current becomes 2.0 A?

9. An electromagnet that contains 500 turns/cm can lift a weight of 800 N. If the current and core are to remain the same, how many turns per centimetre would be required in order to lift a weight of 1200 N?

Applying Inquiry/ Communication Skills

10. Outline a controlled experiment to determine how the magnetic field around a straight, current-carrying conductor varies with distance from the conductor.

11. Describe the procedure in an investigation to show the shape of the magnetic field of a magnet using iron filings.

Making Connections

12. Find out what evidence we have to suggest that Earth's magnetic field has reversed itself in the past. How often has it happened? What effect could such a charge have on our society?

WEBLINK

Industrial electromagnets come in many different shapes and range in size from very small ones to colossal ones capable of lifting trucks. Prepare a poster that could be used as an advertisement for a company which produces a complete range of electromagnets. Begin your research at **www.pearsoned.ca/physics11.**

FIGURE 14.32 An ancient Chinese compass

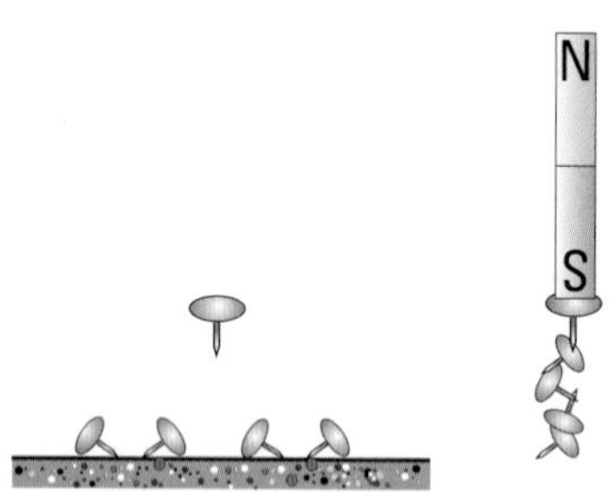

FIGURE 14.33 Why does the large tack become magnetized?

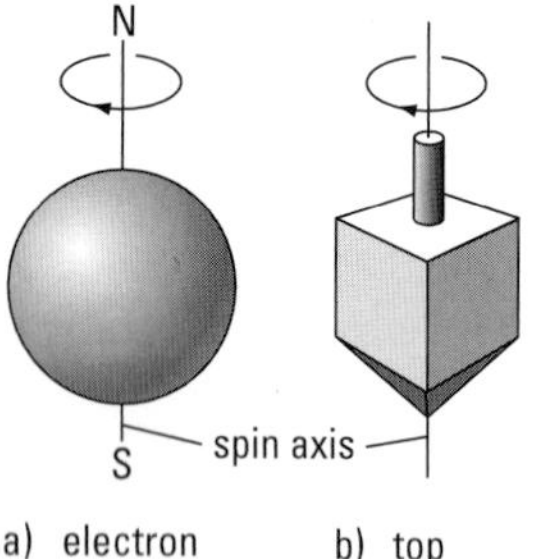

FIGURE 14.34 The spinning electron behaves like a tiny current-carrying loop.

INFOBIT

Cow magnets are cylindrical magnets that are placed into a cow's stomach. Their purpose is to attract and hold any bits of iron or steel such as fence wire and nails that the cow might ingest and so prevent damage to the cow's digestive tract.

14.3 Ferromagnetism

Key Understandings

When you have completed this section, you will be able to:

- state the meaning of the term "ferromagnetism"
- identify the three most common ferromagnetic elements
- explain the concept of induced magnetism and give an example of it
- describe and apply the domain theory of ferromagnetism

From the work of Oersted and Ampère we see that a magnetic field is produced by an electric current. And yet, natural magnets have been known for centuries. In ancient times, the Chinese would mount lodestone on a block of wood, which was often carved in the shape of a fish. When this was floated on water it behaved like a compass. Where is the current in that chunk of lodestone? Why can an unmagnetized block of iron attract either pole of that floating compass?

Induced Magnetism

A steel tack does not normally attract other tacks. However, when the pole of a magnet touches a tack, other tacks will cling to it (Figure 14.33).

Ferromagnetic substances such as steel (which usually consists mainly of iron) become magnetized in the presence of a magnetic field. This phenomenon is known as **induced magnetism**. In most cases, the magnetism disappears when the original field is removed. However, if you take a steel needle and stroke it several times in the same direction with one of the poles of a strong permanent magnet, the needle will retain its magnetism for some time.

Ferromagnetism

What is it that allows ferromagnetic elements such as iron, nickel, and cobalt to become magnetized when placed within a magnetic field? The answer lies with the electrons in the atoms. Picture each electron spinning like a top, as shown in Figure 14.34. Now imagine the spin of the electron as a tiny, current-carrying loop with a north pole and a south pole. Since the electron carries negative charge this spin is equivalent to conventional current flow in the opposite direction. In most elements, the electrons spinning in one direction are almost completely paired up with electrons spinning in the opposite direction. The magnetic field of one of the pair cancels that of its partner. As a result, the atom is left with little or no magnetic field.

Discovering Physics *Making Magnets*

Try lifting steel tacks or nails with a magnet as shown in Figure 14.33. How could you compare the strength of the north and south poles of the magnet? Now take a steel needle and stroke it several times in the same direction with the pole of a strong magnet. How could you determine if the needle is magnetized and, if so, which end is north?

However, the pairing is not always complete. For instance, in the case of iron, four electrons in each atom are unpaired. Their magnetic fields do not cancel and the atom is left with an overall magnetic field. Because these atoms exert magnetic forces on other nearby iron atoms, they tend to form clumps in which all the atomic magnetic fields point in the same direction. These clumps are called **domains**. A typical domain measures 0.1 mm along a side and contains about 10^{17} atoms. Each domain acts like a tiny bar magnet, as shown in Figure 14.35.

The random thermal motion of the atoms tends to keep the domains oriented at random, as Figure 14.35a) and b) shows. However, in the presence of an external magnetic field, the domains whose magnetic fields closely match the direction of the external field grow, as we see in Figure 14.35c) and d). This occurs when atoms in nearby domains react to the magnetic force exerted by both the growing domain and the external field. Eventually the whole piece of iron becomes a single domain.

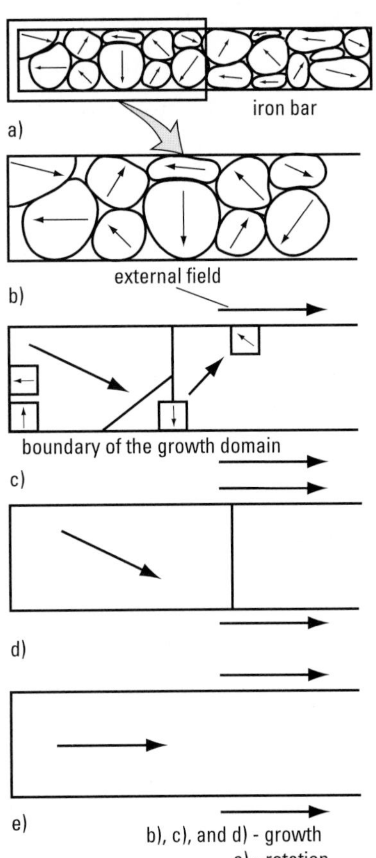

FIGURE 14.35 The domain theory: Each domain acts like a tiny bar magnet.

In Figure 14.35d) we see that the magnetic field of that domain does not yet line up exactly with that of the external field. Because of this, the atoms in the domain are pushed around until their fields match the direction of the external magnetic field, shown in Figure 14.35e). The piece of iron is now a magnet. This explanation, based on the formation and growth of domains, is called the **domain theory** of magnetism.

Pure iron stays magnetized only in an external magnetic field. This property makes iron useful as the core in a lifting electromagnet whose field must vanish quickly when the current stops flowing. On the other hand, hardened steel contains carbon atoms mixed in with the iron atoms. This tends to lock the domains in position. As a result, when the external field ceases, the steel keeps its magnetism. Consequently, hardened steel is used to make **permanent magnets**. Such magnets are often used in electric meters, electric motors, audio speakers, toys, compasses, and refrigerator note clips.

When a magnet is heated, the atoms gain kinetic energy. Because this motion is random, it decreases the precise orientation of the atoms. Consequently, the magnet loses its magnetism. The temperature above which a solid substance can no longer be magnetized is known as the **Curie temperature** (Table 14.2). It is named after Pierre Curie, who was one of the first to study this effect. Which material in Table 14.2 would be most easily demagnetized by heating?

TABLE 14.2 Curie Temperatures of Several Metals

Metal	Curie Temperature
Iron	770°C
Cobalt	1131°C
Nickel	358°C
Gadolinium	16°C

Section 14.3 Review

Understanding Concepts

1. What is a magnetic domain?
2. When an external magnetic field is present, what happens to
   a) a domain whose field is close in direction to that of the external field?
   b) a domain whose field is not close in direction to that of the external field?
   c) the metal if it is composed of a single domain whose magnetic field is close in direction to that of the external field?
3. Use the domain theory to explain the following:
   a) when a bar magnet is cut in half, both halves are weaker magnets with a north and south pole.
   b) when a bar magnet is hammered, it loses much of its magnetism.

Making Connections

4. Why is hardened steel not suitable as a core in lifting electromagnets?
5. When a steel ship is built, it usually possesses a permanent magnetic field. This field is attributed to the hammering and pounding that the steel undergoes during the construction.
   a) Why does this happen?
   b) What could be done to counter this effect?
6. Why is gadolinium rarely used for making magnets?

WEBLINK

Scanners that sense magnetic fields are used in store anti-theft systems and in airport security systems. Find out how they work and draw a labelled diagram showing how one of these systems works. Begin your research at **www.pearsoned.ca/physics11.**

14.4 Electromagnets in Action

Key Understandings

When you have completed this section, you will be able to:

- understand and explain the operation of electromagnetic devices such as relays, doorbells, and solenoid switches

Electromagnets play many roles in our daily life. If you dismantle a door bell or buzzer, you will likely find an electromagnet inside. Various relays and circuit breakers also employ electromagnets. We shall examine a few of these devices in detail.

Relays

When you push a button and an elevator begins to move, you have activated a **relay**. A relay is a remote-control switch. By closing a switch in a low-voltage circuit, you cause a switch in a higher-voltage circuit to close. Figure 14.36 shows the relationship between the essential parts. The **armature** in an electromagnetic device is the part which is moved by magnetic forces. In a relay the armature is usually made of iron or steel.

When the switch in the low-voltage circuit is closed, current flows through the coil. The resulting magnetic field exerts an attractive force on the armature, pulling it to the left. The contacts meet, allowing current to flow in the 120-V circuit.

When the switch in the low-voltage circuit is opened, current no longer flows through the coil. The magnetic field around the coil collapses and the

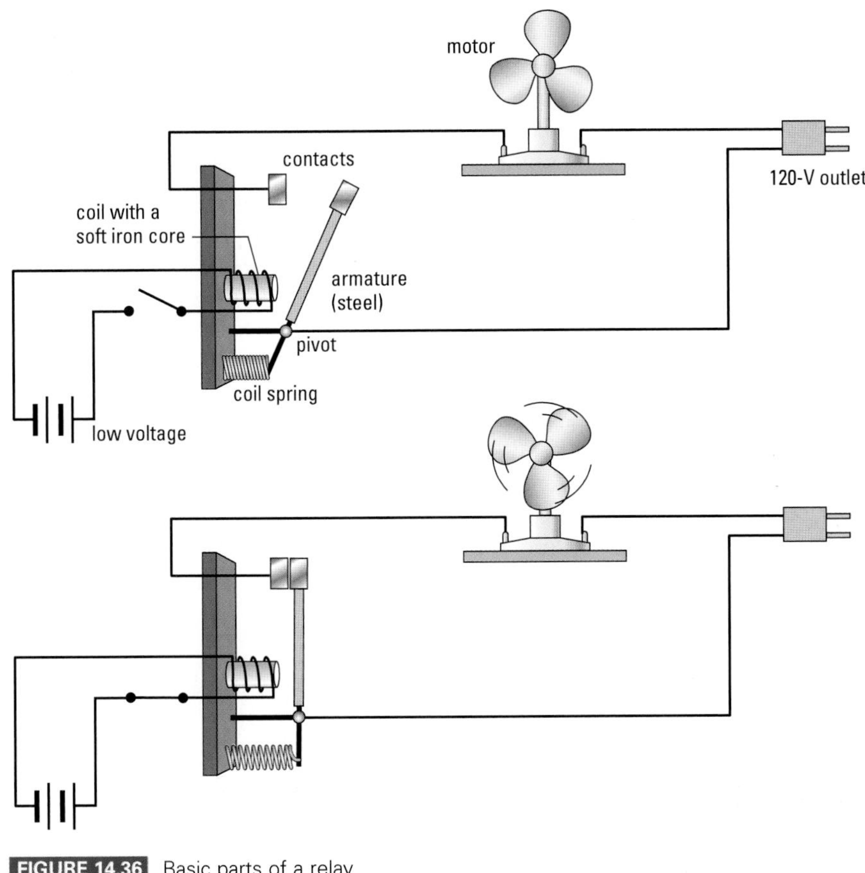

FIGURE 14.36 Basic parts of a relay

spring causes the armature to swing to the right. The contacts separate, and current stops in the 120-V circuit.

Relays are often used to control heating or cooling in our homes. In these circuits, a thermostat opens or closes the low-voltage switch depending on temperature.

Door Chimes

The electromagnet in door chimes acts much as the one in a relay. When the switch is closed by pushing the doorbell button, current flows through the coil, creating a magnetic field. The armature is attracted toward the left, and the hammer strikes the left chime cylinder. When the doorbell button is released, current stops flowing and the magnetic field around the coil disappears. The spring then pulls on the armature causing the hammer to strike the second chime, as shown in Figure 14.37.

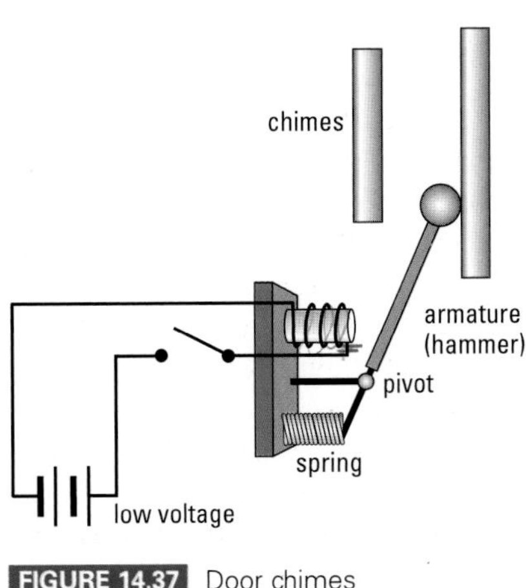

FIGURE 14.37 Door chimes

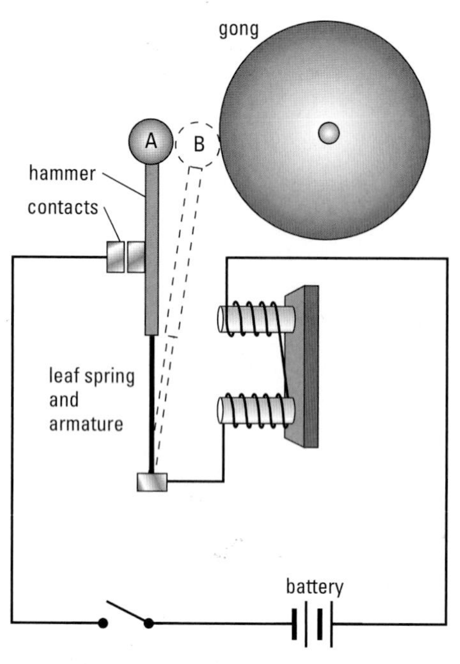

FIGURE 14.38 An electric bell

Electric Bell or Buzzer

When the switch is closed, current flows through the coils, creating a magnetic field. This field pulls the armature to the right as shown in Figure 14.38. The hammer travels from A to B, striking the gong. At the same time, the contacts separate. Current stops flowing and the magnetic field ceases. The spring pulls the armature and hammer back to A. The contacts meet and the cycle repeats.

If there is no hammer and gong, the armature vibrates rapidly back and forth, creating a buzzing sound.

Solenoid Switch

Imagine that an iron core has been partly inserted into a coil. When the current is turned on, the magnetic field pulls the core into the coil (Figure 14.39). This action can be used to close or open a switch. Because electromagnets are also called **solenoids**, this type of switch is referred to as a **solenoid switch**. Solenoids can also be used to operate mechanical devices such as valves or counters.

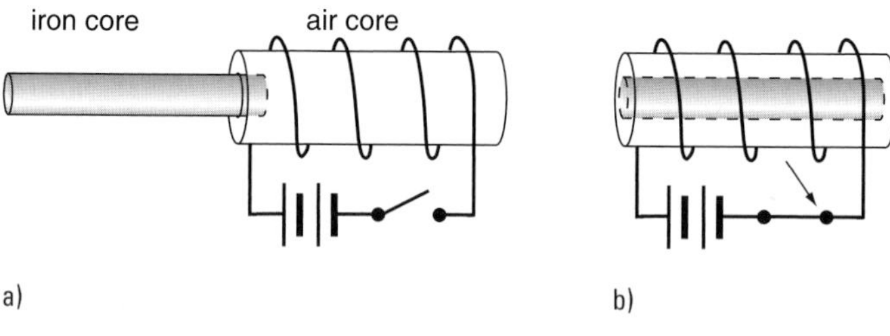

FIGURE 14.39 A solenoid mechanism

a) Iron core partially inside the coil

b) Iron core pulled into the coil

Section 14.4 Review

Understanding Concepts

1. If a thermostat connected to a furnace acts as a switch in a low-voltage circuit, does it close when the temperature rises or falls? Explain your choice.
2. What is the purpose of the soft iron core in the coil of the relay switch?
3. How will the sound of the chimes change if
   a) the voltage is increased?
   b) the spring is made stronger?
4. Why does the armature in the chimes not vibrate repeatedly back and forth like the buzzer?

Applying Inquiry/ Communication Skills

5. Draw a circuit to show how a solenoid can be used as a relay. Explain your diagram.

Making Connections

6. A circuit breaker is a switch that automatically opens when the current becomes too great. Describe how a solenoid could be used as a circuit breaker.

Maglev Trains

Decision-Making Skills

- ▶ Defining the Issue
- Developing Assessment Criteria
- ▶ Researching the Issue
- ▶ Analyzing Data and Information
- ▶ Proposing a Course of Action
- ▶ Justifying the Course of Action
- ▶ Communitcating Your Proposal

BACKGROUND INFORMATION

Imagine a train ride in which you race across the countryside at speeds approaching 500 km/h. Such high-speed trains are already operating in Japan and Germany and may soon be used in mainland China. They rely upon magnetic fields to lift the train off the tracks (to reduce friction) and so are known as "maglevs." Magnetic fields are also used to propel the trains forward.

Maglev trains show great promise. They can transport people rapidly from city to city, which could be extremely useful in a sprawling country such as Canada. Because they are entirely run on electricity, they release no pollutants (although the source of the electricity may do so). However, they are expensive to set up and cannot run on existing tracks. They may also have severe environmental impacts. The decision of whether or not to create a maglev system is not easy.

FIGURE 14.40

Analyzing the Issue

1. Create a web to show the stakeholder groups who are affected by the possibility of integrating maglev trains into the Canadian transportation system.
2. Research the costs/benefits that have resulted from prototype use of maglev trains in Europe. What impact should that research have on Canadian consideration of the train?
3. What conflict could be created between the industrial sector and the general population by proceeding with a Canadian prototype of a maglev train?
4. Recommend a course of action to Transport Canada on our future consideration of this method of transportation. Role play a symposium being held with industry, agriculture, and community groups to discuss the feasibility of a Canadian study on the cost-benefits of maglev trains.

Investigation 1 (Section 14.2)

Inquiry Skills

- Initiating and Planning
- Applying Technical Skills
- Using Tools, Materials, Equipment
- Conducting and Recording
- Analyzing and Interpreting
- Concluding and Communicating

Magnetism and Current

Problem

What are the shape and direction of the magnetic field around a current-carrying conductor?

Materials

- cardboard (4 cm × 4 cm with a 0.5-cm hole in the centre)
- straight stiff conducting wire
- 2 retort stands
- small compass
- switch
- 3 connector leads
- 3 test-tube clamps (jaws insulated)
- iron filings
- power supply (DC)

Caution: Wire may get hot. Do not touch the wire or terminals after the switch has been closed.

Procedure

1. Assemble the apparatus as shown in Figure 14.40, leaving the switch open. Connect the leads so the current will flow up the wire.

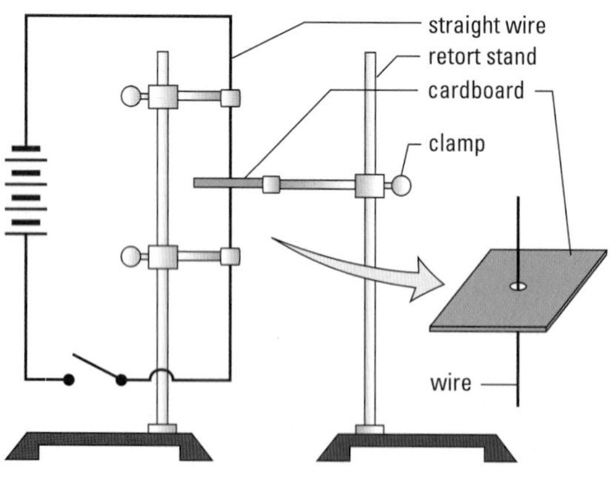

FIGURE 14.40 Magnetism and current

2. Sprinkle iron filings uniformly on the cardboard. Close the switch for a couple of seconds and tap the cardboard gently. Then open the switch.
3. Sketch the pattern of the iron filings, then remove the filings.
4. Place the compass on the cardboard close to one side of the wire. Close the switch for a couple of seconds and observe the direction in which the compass points. Indicate this direction on your drawing. Repeat for three other locations about the wire.
5. Reverse the connection of the leads to the power supply and repeat steps 2–4.

Analysing and Interpreting

1. Describe the shape of the magnetic field aroud a current-carrying conductor. Is the pattern affected by the direction of current flow?
2. What is the direction of the magnetic field around a current-carrying conductor? Is the field's direction affected by the direction of current flow?

Concluding and Communicating

3. Do your results confirm the right-hand rule for a straight conductor?
4. Does a magnetic field around a straight conductor possess a north pole and a south pole? Discuss.

Extending

5. How could you make the magnetic field around a straight conductor stronger? Give reasons for your answer. Devise a method to test your hypothesis.

Investigation 2 (Section 14.2)

Inquiry Skills
- Initiating and Planning
- Applying Technical Skills
- Using Tools, Materials, Equipment
- Conducting and Recording
- Analyzing and Interpreting
- Concluding and Communicating

The Strength of the Magnetic Field of a Helix

Helices are used extensively to produce magnetic fields. They are found in motors, generators, solenoid switches, industrial electromagnets, and are used in an enormous range of applications from magnetic resonance imaging (MRI) to new propulsion systems. So it is important to be able to predict the fields produced by helices in order to design such equipment.

In this activity you will investigate the effect of varying the current through the helix, changing the number of turns per unit length of the helix, and inserting a permeable core into the helix.

Problem

How can the strength of the magnetic field produced by a helix be changed?

Materials

- ammeter
- 2 helices of equal length but different numbers of turns
- iron core
- 3 connecting leads
- variable DC power supply

The method used to measure the strength of the magnetic field will depend on the equipment available in the class room.

(a) If a data logger probe is available, you will need a computer, an interface, and a magnetic field sensor.
(b) If no probe is available, a magnetic compass and protractor can be used. The compass needle will point north unless acted upon by a second magnetic field. By measuring the amount that the needle is deflected from north, you can determine the strength of the second magnetic field relative to Earth's field.

Caution: Review how to correctly connect the ammeter and power supply into the circuit. Make sure that the current never exceeds the rated limit for the coils, the ammeter, or the power supply.

Experimental Design

1. As a small group decide how you will connect one of the helices to the power supply and the ammeter. Draw a circuit diagram to show your arrangement.
2. a) If you are using the magnetic probe and the data logger, find out the correct steps in its use. The type of field that you will be investigating is "axial."
   b) If you are using the compass method for determining the strength of the magnetic field, decide how you will measure the amount by which the field of the helix pulls the needle away from north. The graph in Figure 14.41 allows you to convert the angle of deflection into magnetic field strength. It assumes that the second field acts at right angles to Earth's field.

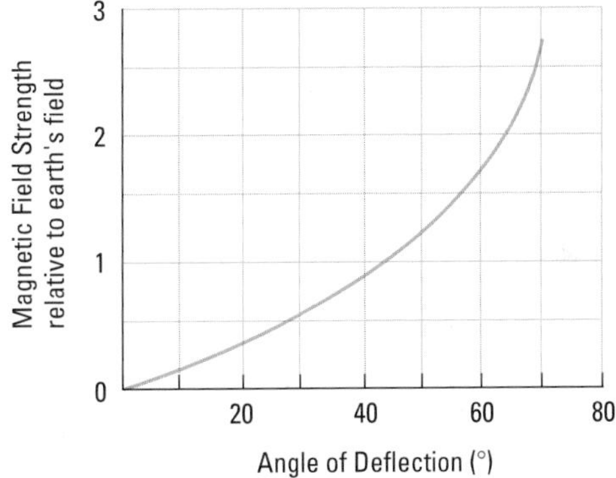

FIGURE14.41 Conversion between angles of deflection and relative field strength

Part A Effect of Current

3. Make a prediction about how an increase in current will affect the strength of the magnetic field of the helix.
4. Write up the steps that will allow you to determine how a change in current affects the strength of the magnetic field of the helix. How many different current values do you intend to set? How many trials do you intend to run in order to check the consistency of your data?

What factors must remain constant during this part of investigation? Decide how you will organize and display your data.

5. Once the teacher has approved the procedure, set up the equipment. When the connections have been checked by the teacher, run the investigation.

Part B Effect of the Number of Tums per Unit Length

6. Make a prediction about how an increase in the number of turns per centimetre will affect the strength of the magnetic field of the helix. (Note: If the helices are of equal length, then you can simply compare the total number of turns on each helix.)
7. As you did in Part A, write up the steps that will allow you to determine how a change in the number of turns per centimetre affects the strength of the magnetic field of the helix. What factors must remain constant during this part of investigation?
8. Once the teacher has approved the procedure, set up the equipment. When the connections have been checked by the teacher, run the investigation.

Part C Effect of an Iron Core

9. Make a prediction about how the presence of an iron core inside the helix will affect the strength of the magnetic field.
10. As you did in Part A, write up the steps that will allow you to determine how the insertion of a core will affect the strength of the magnetic field of the helix. What factors must remain constant during this part of the investigation?
11. Once the teacher has approved the procedure, set up the equipment. When the connections have been checked by the teacher, run the investigation.

Analyzing and Interpreting

1. For a constant number of turns per unit length in the helix, how does the magnitude of the current affect the strength of the magnetic field?
2. For a constant current, how does the number of turns per unit length affect the strength of the magnetic field?
3. How does the presence of an iron core affect the strength of the magnetic field?

Concluding and Communicating

4. List the factors that affect the strength of the magnetic field of a helix and indicate how they affect the field.
5. Describe three ways for increasing the strength of the magnetic field produced by a helix.

Extending

6. Using the technique for measuring the magnetic field from this activity, investigate how the strength of the magnetic field varies with distance from the end of the helix.

CHAPTER SUMMARY

Key Terms

armature
coil
core
domain theory
electromagnet
electromagnetism
ferromagnetic
helix
induced magnetism
lines of magnetic force
law of magnetic poles
magnetic field
magnetic pole
north pole
permanent magnet
relative permeability
relay
solenoid switch
south pole

Key Equations

For an electromagnet,

$$F \propto I \quad \text{or} \quad \frac{F_1}{F_2} = \frac{I_1}{I_2}$$

$$F \propto N \quad \text{or} \quad \frac{F_1}{F_2} = \frac{N_1}{N_2}$$

Essential Understandings

- Similar magnetic poles repel while opposite poles attract.
- Magnetic fields are strongest at or near the poles of a magnet.
- Magnetic lines of force indicate the strength and interaction of magnetic fields. They point north to south outside a magnet and south to north inside a magnet.
- The right-hand rules can be used to predict the direction of the magnetic field around conductors: For a straight conductor, your fingers curve in the direction of the field when your thumb points in the direction of the current; for a coiled conductor, your thumb points toward the north pole when your fingers curve in the direction of the current.
- The strength of an electromagnet is affected by the amount of current, the number of turns per unit length, and the relative permeability of the core.
- Induced magnetism occurs when a substance becomes magnetized while in the presence of a magnetic field.
- Ferromagnetism is explained by the domain theory.

Consolidate Your Understanding

1. Look back to your answer to the Checkpoint question on page 519. Do you still agree with your answer, or do you wish to change it? Give reasons for your decision. Now take one of the wrong answers and explain why it is incorrect.

If eddies in Earth's molten core are carrying positive ions with them, which way must they be circling to produce Earth's magnetic field? Describe the direction as it would be seen from above the geographic North Pole.

2. Draw a web diagram beginning in the centre with the statement, "A magnetic field is created by charges in motion." Extend outwards from the centre by identifying effects and applications. Use as many of the Key Terms above as possible.

3. Draw diagrams from this chapter to illustrate the right hand rules. Choose one of the applications of electromagnets mentioned in this chapter and make a bulleted list of the sequence of effects that occur when the switch is closed. Try explaining this to a student who has not studied electromagnetism.

CHAPTER 14 REVIEW

Understanding Concepts

1. Which of the following rows represents the direction of the lines of force for a magnet?

	Inside the Magnet	Outside the Magnet
a)	toward the N pole	toward the N pole
b)	toward the S pole	toward the S pole
c)	do not exist	toward the S pole
d)	toward the N pole	toward the S pole
e)	toward the S pole	toward the N pole

2. Pole X attracts pole Y. Pole Y repels pole Z. Pole Z repels a north pole. Which of the following describes poles X, Y, and Z, respectively?
a) south, north, north
b) north, south, south
c) south, north, south
d) north, south, north
e) north, north, north

3. On the side of a current-carrying conductor closest to you the lines of magnetic force are directed straight upward. In which direction is the current?
a) upward
b) downward
c) to the right
d) to the left
e) toward you

4. If the direction of the current in a conductor is downward, what is the direction of the magnetic field on the side of the conductor farthest away from you?
a) upward
b) downward
c) to the right
d) to the left
e) away from you

5. For which of the diagrams shown in Figure 14.42 is the relation between the directions of the current and the magnetic field correct?

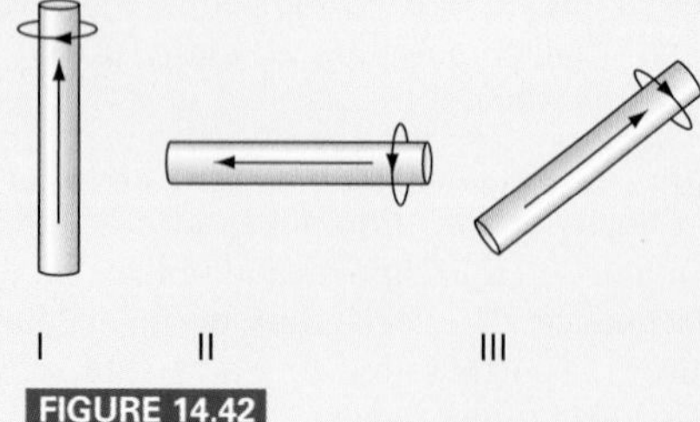

FIGURE 14.42

a) I only
b) II only
c) III only
d) I and II only
e) II and III only

6. For which of the helices shown in Figure 14.43 is the north pole at the right?

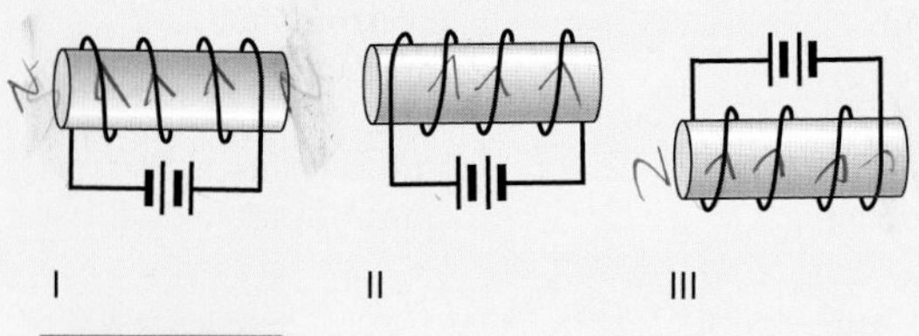

FIGURE 14.43

a) I, II, and III
b) I only
c) II only
d) III only
e) none of them

7. For which of the helices shown in Figure 14.44 is the relation between the polarity of the battery and the position of the north pole correct?

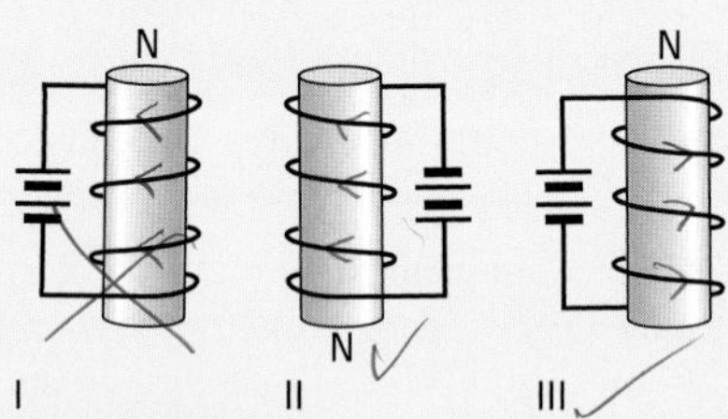

FIGURE 14.44

a) I only
b) II only
c) III only
d) I and II only
e) II and III only

8. How is the difference between a strong magnetic field and a weak magnetic field illustrated with lines of force?

9. State the right-hand rule for a straight conductor.

10. Explain the difference between a loop and a helix.

11. Describe three ways for decreasing the strength of an electromagnet.

12. What is a magnetic domain?

13. If an electromagnet can exert a force of 50 N when the current is 1.5 A, what is the force if the current becomes 2.5 A?

14. An electromagnet is created by wrapping 80 turns of wire around an iron nail. When the current is 0.400 A, the electromagnet can exert a maximum force of 2.00 N on a pair of steel pliers. How many turns have to be added (using the same length) to increase the force on the pliers to 8.00 N for the same current and distance?

15. An electromagnet can exert a force of 600 N on a metal block. If the current through the electromagnet must be reduced to one-quarter of its initial value,
 a) what would the force become?
 b) what must happen to the number of turns per centimetre if the strength of the magnet is to remain at 600 N?

16. An electromagnet contains 2000 turns in its length. A current of 2.5 A provides a lifting force of 100 N.
 a) What current would be required to provide a lifting force of 300 N?
 b) If the current is 2.5 A, how many turns would be required to provide a lifting force of 600 N?

Applying Inquiry/ Communication Skills

17. Three magnets are placed as shown in Figure 14.44. Draw this diagram in your notes and sketch how the magnetic fields would likely appear.

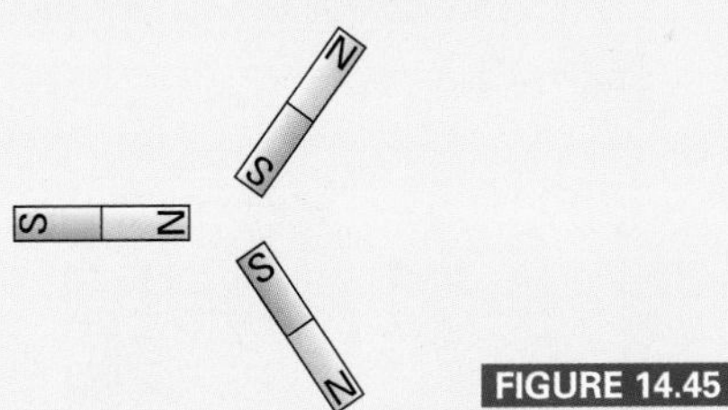

FIGURE 14.45

18. In liquids and gases, both negative and positive charges can flow. If the flow actually consists of negative charges,
 a) explain why the rule for predicting the direction of the magnetic field about that flow is called the left-hand rule
 b) state what the rule would be

19. Explain why a liquid cannot become a permanent magnet.

20. Explain why it is impossible for two lines of force to cross.

21. Copy Figure 14.46 into your notes. Indicate on your diagrams the lines of force and their direction both outside and inside the magnets.

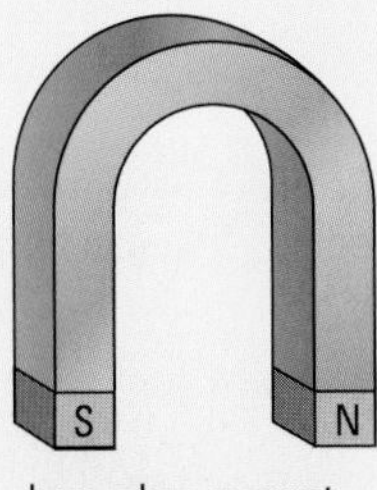

horseshoe magnet

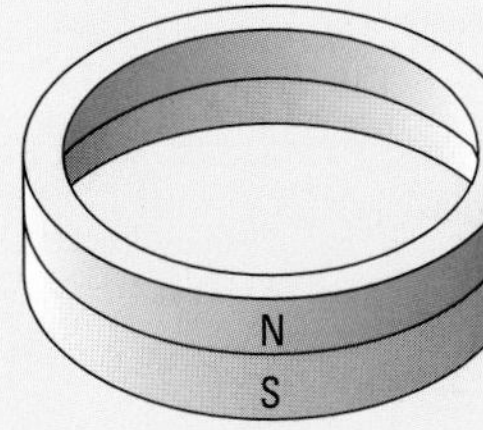

ring magnet

FIGURE 14.46

22. In an experiment to measure the magnetic force between two disk magnets, the following data were obtained:

Separation between Magnets, *d* (cm)	Force *F* (N)
1.0	2.0
1.5	0.40
2.0	0.12
2.5	0.051
3.0	0.025

Using a graphing calculator,
 a) plot the scatter points with force on the y-axis and separation on the x-axis
 b) find the equation relating force in newtons and separation in centimetres as a power function in the form, $F = kd^n$
 c) What are the units for "k"?
 d) At what separation would the force be (i) 0.25 N and (ii) 0.10 N?

23. Write an equation for F_2 in terms of F_1, I_1, I_2, N_1 and N_2, where F_1 is the initial force I_1 is the initial electric current, and N_1 is the initial number of turns. F_2, I_2, and N_2 represent the final values of these quantities.

24. a) Describe three separate ways by which you could increase the strength of an electromagnet 10 times.
 b) If you made all three changes, by what factor would the strength of the electromagnet increase?

Making Connections

25. Would you expect the casing of an "antimagnetic" watch to have a low or high relative permeability? Explain your answer.

26. Explain why compasses do not work properly near the magnetic poles of Earth.

27. Design a way of using a compass and a helix to measure the current in a circuit.

28. Why is an electromagnet more useful in a junkyard than a permanent magnet?

29. Investigate the electric appliances in your home to find out which ones use an electromagnet. Make a list.

CHAPTER 15

Motors and Generators

SPECIFIC EXPECTATIONS

By the end of this chapter, you will be able to:

- define and describe the concepts and units related to electricity and magnetism (15.1, 15.4)
- state the motor principle, explain the factors that affect the force on a current-carrying conductor in a magnetic field, and, using the right-hand rule, illustrate the resulting motion of the conductor (15.1)
- analyze and describe electromagnetic induction in qualitative terms, and apply Lenz's law to explain, predict, and illustrate the direction of the electric current induced by a changing magnetic field, using the right-hand rule (15.4)
- compare direct current (DC) and alternating current (AC) in qualitative terms, and explain the importance of alternating current in the transmission of electrical energy (15.5, 15.7)
- explain, in terms of the interaction of electricity and magnetism, and analyze in quantitative terms, the operation of transformers (15.6)
- conduct an experiment to identify the factors that affect the magnitude and direction of the electric current induced by a changing magnetic field (Investigation 15.1)
- construct, test, and refine a prototype of a device that operates using the principles of electromagnetism (Design and Build)
- analyze and describe the operation of industrial and domestic technological systems based on principles related to magnetic fields (15.3, 15.7)
- describe the historical development of technologies related to magnetic fields (15.5)
- identify and describe examples of domestic and industrial technologies that were developed on the basis of the scientific understanding of magnetic fields (15.2, 15.3, 15.4, 15.5, 15.6)
- describe the historical development of technologies related to magnetic fields (15.4, 15.5)

Once it was known that magnetism and electricity were linked, scientists began to explore this link more closely and inventors tried to find novel uses for the effect. So the study of electromagnetism progressed rapidly. André Ampère was the first to notice that when two conductors lie side by side and carry currents in the same direction, the conductors are attracted to each other. However, when the currents are in opposite directions, the conductors repel. This interaction forms the basis for all electric motors and many propulsion systems.

FIGURE 15.1 How does this subway train convert electrical energy into motion?

Today's average North Americans enjoy many conveniences. We light our rooms by flicking a switch. We regulate the temperature of our homes in summer and winter. Hot and cold water are always available, and orchestras and actors play for our amusement while we watch from home. We can also communicate instantly over huge distances.

All of these conveniences depend on a steady flow of electrical energy. The ability to generate and transmit electrical energy has had a profound effect on our culture, lifestyle, and standard of living.

Why do current-carrying conductors experience a force in a magnetic field?

What relation exists between the magnetic field, the current, and the force?

If an electric current can produce a magnetic field, can a magnetic field be used to produce an electric current?

How do generators provide electrical energy?

What role do transformers play in the distribution of electrical energy?

What are the advantages of alternating current?

If the high voltages of transmission lines are so dangerous, why not transmit the energy at a lower, and much safer, voltage?

Discovering Physics

Motor or Generator?

A flow of electric current produces a magnetic field. Can a magnetic field produce a flow of current? Try using a coil and a permanent magnet to find out.

Most small battery-powered motors have a magnet mounted on the motor frame and a coil wrapped around the motor shaft. So the motor from a toy or a device such as a portable tape recorder will likely have just the parts you need. Check that the motor you are using does have a permanent magnet.

1. Connect a sensitive voltmeter across the terminals of your motor. If the voltmeter is an analogue type with an adjustable zero, set the zero in the middle of the scale.
2. Try turning the motor shaft at different speeds.

- Is there any sign that current is being produced? What happens if you spin the motor shaft in the opposite direction?
- Do you notice any pattern in how the speed and direction of rotation affect what you observe? Can you suggest why such patterns might occur?
- Would the motor you are using make a good generator? Why or why not?
- Where would it be useful to have a motor that could also be used as a generator?

CHECKPOINT

Electrical transmission lines operate at a high voltage to

a) keep birds and animals off the transmission lines
b) prevent terrorists from cutting the lines
c) reduce corrosion of the transmission lines
d) keep ice from forming on the transmission lines
e) reduce the power loss due to resistance in the transmission lines

15.1 The Motor Principle

Key Understandings

When you have completed this section, you will be able to:

- state the motor principle
- state the right-hand rule for electromagnetic force
- predict the direction of the electromagnetic force on a current-carrying conductor in an external magnetic field
- explain how the galvanometer uses the motor principle
- list the basic parts of the galvanometer and state their functions
- describe how a basic galvanometer can be used to measure voltages and large currents

FIGURE 15.2 The motor principle explains the relationship between Earth's magnetic field and the northern lights.

Current-carrying conductors can exert forces on each other through their magnetic fields. This concept is the key to how an electric motor converts electrical energy into kinetic energy. How can we design motors for maximum efficiency and power? Can the electromagnetic forces between conductors be used for other applications?

Forces on a Conductor in a Magnetic Field

Imagine a current-carrying conductor in an external magnetic field that runs perpendicular to it (Figure 15.3). The "X" in the centre of the conductor indicates that the current flows away from you, into the page. Using the right-hand rule for a straight conductor, the field produced by the current is clockwise as shown. Thus, the magnetic fields are in opposite directions on the left side of the conductor and in the same direction on the right side. As a result, the conductor will be *attracted* to the *left* and *repelled* from the *right*. Figure 15.4 shows the pattern for repulsions. The conductor is pushed to the left and the external magnet is pushed to the right (Figure 15.5).

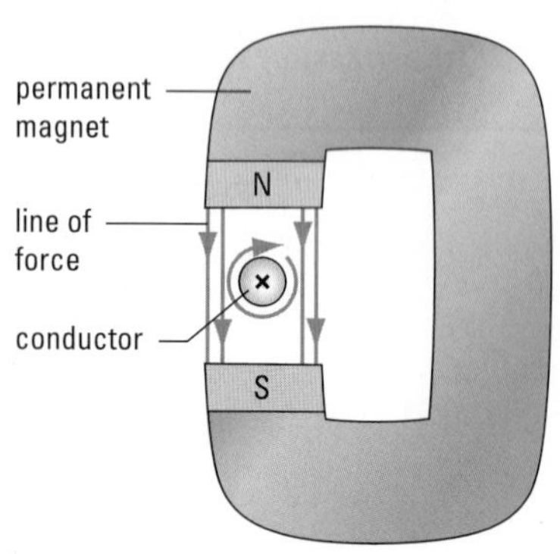

FIGURE 15.3 A conductor in an external magnetic field

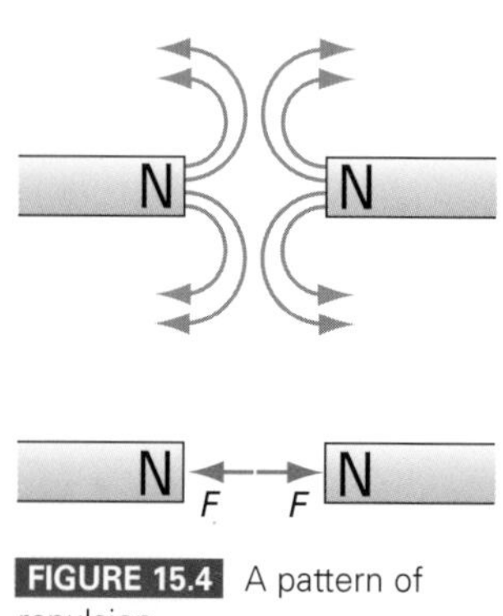

FIGURE 15.4 A pattern of repulsion

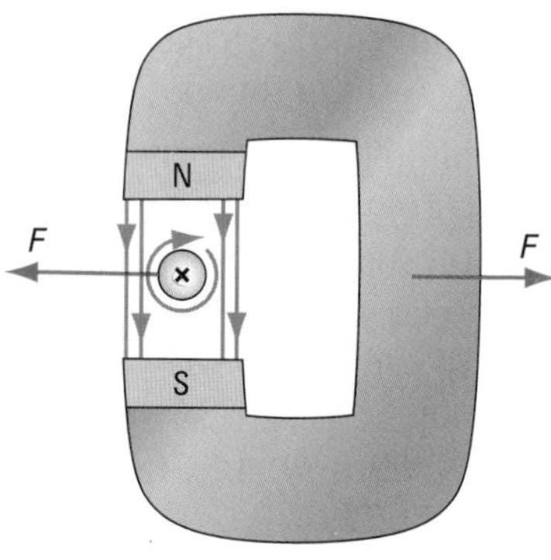

FIGURE 15.5 The conductor is repelled to the left in the permanent magnetic field.

The Motor Principle

The fact that a magnetic field exerts a force on a moving charge is called the **motor principle**. This principle states: **When a current-carrying conductor is located in an external magnetic field perpendicular to the conductor, the conductor experiences a force that is perpendicular to both itself and the external magnetic field.** The magnitude of this electromagnetic force depends on the amount of current and the magnitude of the external magnetic field (its flux density, B):

$F \propto I$ and $F \propto B$

The SI unit of magnetic field is the **tesla** (T). Imagine a charge of one coulomb moving at a speed of one metre per second perpendicular to a magnetic field. If the electromagnetic force acting on that charge is one newton, then the magnetic flux density is one tesla. In terms of base units, the tesla is equal to a kilogram per ampere per second squared:

$1\ \text{T} = 1\ \text{N/(C·m/s)} = 1\ \text{kg/(A·s}^2\text{)}$. The tesla is about ten thousand times the strength of Earth's magnetic field. As a result, a smaller unit, the gauss (G), is commonly used. A gauss is one ten-thousandth of a tesla ($1\ \text{G} = 10^{-4}\ \text{T}$).

WEBLINK

Northern lights glow when charged particles, guided by Earth's magnetic field, stream down through the atmosphere near the poles. Write a newspaper-style account of northern lights. Include their causes and the range of effects seen in them. Begin your research at **www.pearsoned.ca/physics11**.

EXAMPLE 1 NUMERICAL

When a current of 4.0 A passes through a conductor in a magnetic field, the electromagnetic force is 5.0 mN. What current will provide a force of 3.5 mN in this magnetic field?

Given

$I_1 = 4.0\ \text{A}$, $F_1 = 5.0\ \text{mN}$, and $F_2 = 3.5\ \text{mN}$

Required

I_2

Analysis

$$\frac{I_2}{I_1} = \frac{F_2}{F_1}$$

therefore $I_2 = I_1 \times \dfrac{F_2}{F_1}$

Solution

$$I_2 = 4.0\ \text{A} \times \frac{3.5\ \text{mN}}{5.0\ \text{mN}}$$
$$= 2.8\ \text{A}$$

Statement

The required current will be 2.8 A.

INSIGHT

Since the forces on the right side of the equation appear as a ratio, it is not necessary to convert them from mN to N as the units will cancel out. To make sure, include the units in your work.

PRACTICE PROBLEMS

1. A conductor in a magnetic field experiences an electromagnetic force of 7.5 mN when the current is 0.60 A. If the current is changed to 0.25 A, what will the electromagnetic force become? Assume that the magnetic field remains constant.
2. A current-carrying conductor in a magnetic field experiences an electromagnetic force of 38 μN. If the force on the conductor drops to 10 μN with no change in current, how has the magnetic field changed?

WEBLINK

A mass spectrometer uses a magnetic field to deflect ions into a detector. The amount of their deflection allows us to find their mass with great precision and speed. Find out more about this device and prepare a table listing various occupations and the role that the mass spectrometer plays in that occupation. Begin your research at **www.pearsoned.ca/physics11**

Refer to page 580, Investigation 1.

Discovering Physics — *Electromagnetic Force*

What is the relationship between electric current and electormagnetic force? Use a retort stand to suspend a light metal bar between the poles of a strong horseshoe magnet as shown in Figure 15.6. Preferably, the metal bar should not contain iron or nickel. Use clamps with insulated jaws to hold the suspension wires and connect them in series with a switch, variable resistor, and a battery or a rugged DC power supply.

Caution: This circuit can produce high currents. It should be turned on only for a few seconds at a time. Check with your teacher.

Close the switch briefly with the variable resistor at several different settings and note any motion of the metal rod. What happens if you turn the power on with the magnet flipped over so that its poles are reversed?

Do your observations suggest any relationship between the amount of current and the size of the electromagnetic force? Are the directions of the current, the magnetic field, and the electromagnetic force related? Can you suggest a method for predicting which way a current-carrying wire will move in a magnetic field?

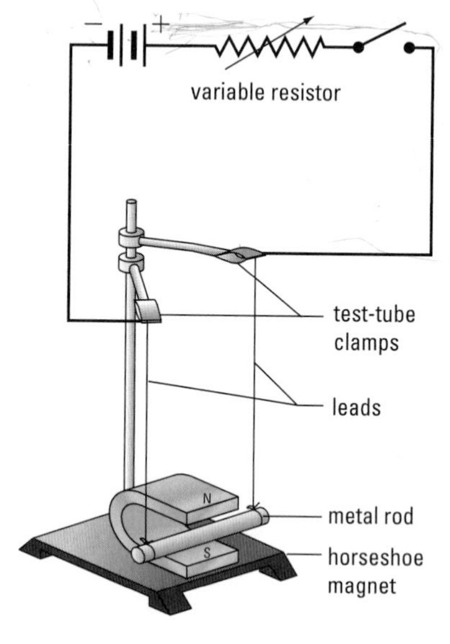

FIGURE 15.6 Demonstrating the motor principle

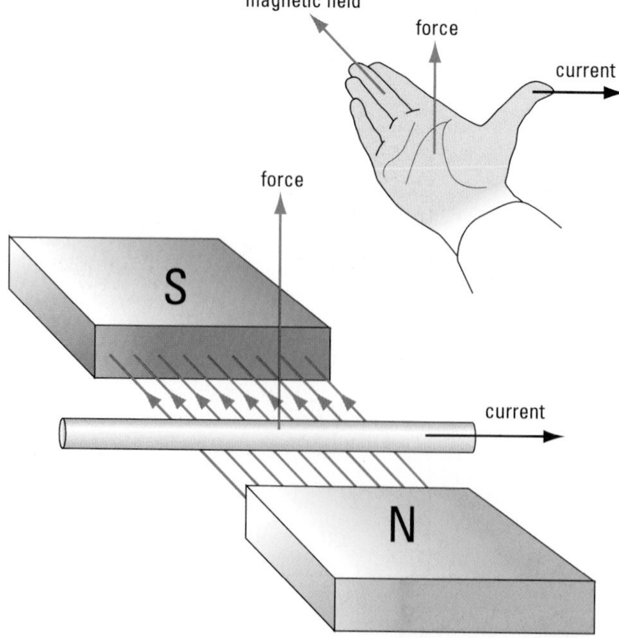

Right-Hand Rule for Electromagnetic Force

The direction of the force on the conductor can be predicted using the **right-hand rule for electromagnetic force:**

Hold out your right hand so that your thumb points in the direction of the current and your fingers point in the direction of the external magnetic field. Then, the force on the conductor is directed outward from the palm of your hand (Figure 15.7).

The direction of the electromagnetic force on a conductor depends on only two factors: the direction of the current and the direction of the perpendicular external magnetic field.

FIGURE 15.7 The right-hand rule for electromagnetic force

The Galvanometer

Many everyday devices use electromagnetic forces. One of the simplest applications is in meters. All sorts of meters, from electricity meters to speedometers, are based on the electromagnetic force. Until the development of digital measuring instruments almost all of the meters in science classes used the electromagnetic force to push a pointer across a scale.

The **galvanometer** is the heart of many electric meters including ammeters, voltmeters, and ohmmeters. A galvanometer consists of a helix suspended between the poles of a permanent magnet. However, to understand the operation of this device, it is easier to consider a single loop rather than a helix.

In Figure 15.8 a single loop is shown mounted so that it can rotate about a vertical axis. When current flows up the conductor from B to C there is an electromagnetic force exerted on the segment BC, as predicted by the motor principle. This electromagnetic force pushes the conductor BC out of the page. Check this by using the right-hand rule for electromagnetic force.

Similarly, since the current flows down from D to E, the electromagnetic force on this segment is directed into the page. These two electromagnetic forces tend to rotate the loop counterclockwise (viewed from above). Since the current that flows across the top and bottom of the loop is moving parallel to the external magnetic field, these parts of the loop experience no electromagnetic force.

Because a helix is made up of many loops it rotates in the same direction as a single loop, but the force on a helix is greater for the same amount of current. So a galvanometer uses a helix for increased response to a given current (Figure 15.9). The permeable core acts to concentrate the strength of the magnetic fields of both the permanent magnet and the helix.

The two springs attached to the shaft serve two functions. First, they provide a connection for the current to flow in and out of the meter. Second, they limit the amount of rotation of the helix. When a current passes through the helix, it rotates until the restoring force exerted by the springs balances the electromagnetic force. If the amount of current increases, the electromagnetic force increases and the helix rotates farther. The pointer, which is attached to the shaft, moves farther across the scale. When a galvanometer is manufactured, its scale is calibrated so that the pointer indicates the amount of current flowing through the helix. The galvanometer is so sensitive that it can measure currents in the microampere (10^{-6} A) range.

INFOBIT

Ampère's discovery of the force between parallel current-carrying wires led to a method for measuring current. One ampere is equal to the current that will produce a force of 2.0×10^{-7} N/m when flowing through two parallel wires one metre apart.

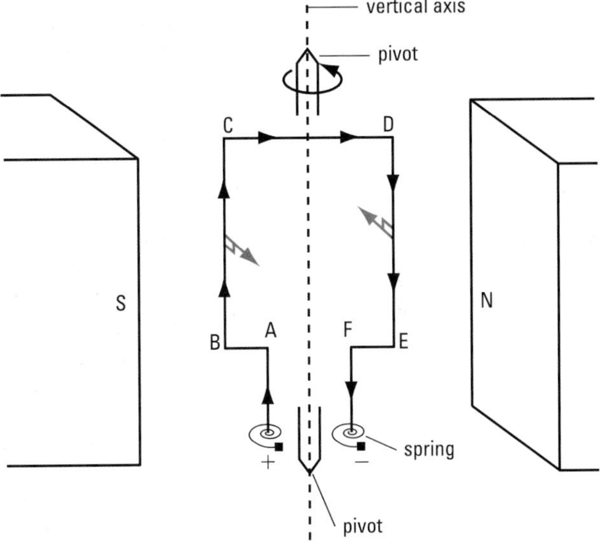

FIGURE 15.8 A loop in a permanent magnetic field rotates when a current passes through it.

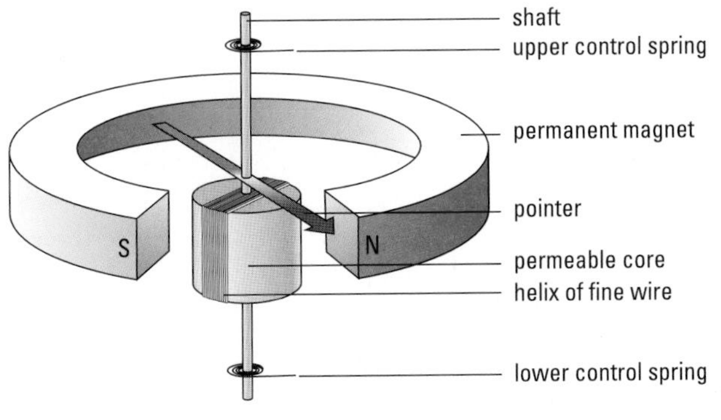

FIGURE 15.9 The galvanometer

The Ammeter

To measure currents in the ampere range (as opposed to the microampere range) an **ammeter** is used because the galvanometer is too sensitive. Most currents to be measured would cause the fine wire in the helix of a galvanometer

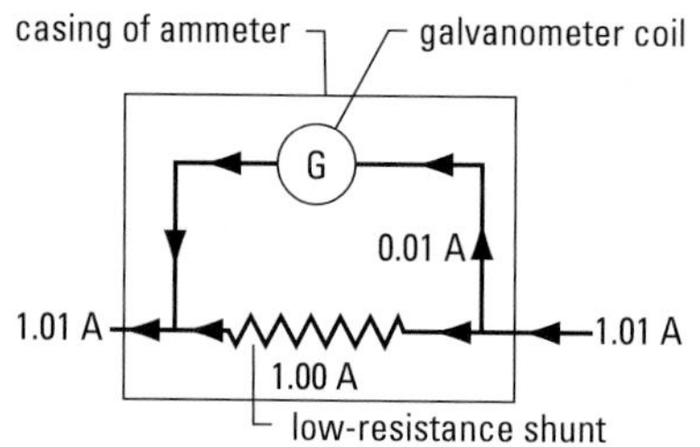

FIGURE 15.10 Using the galvanometer as an ammeter

to heat up and melt. So to convert the galvanometer into an ammeter a low-resistance device called a **shunt** is connected in parallel with a galvanometer coil (Figure 15.10).

If the resistance of the shunt is 1/100 of the resistance of the galvanometer coil, then 100 times as much current will pass through the shunt as will pass through the coil. For example, if 0.01 A passes through the galvanometer coil, then 1.00 A passes through the shunt. The total current entering the meter is 1.00 A + 0.01A or 1.01 A. Changing the sensitivity of the meter simply involves changing the resistance of the shunt (Figure 15.11).

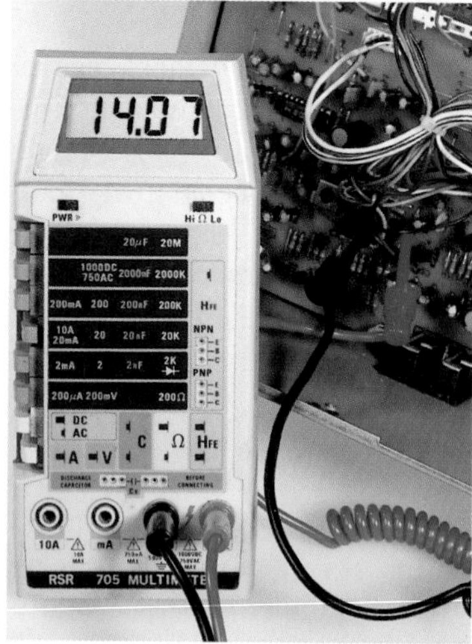

FIGURE 15.11 A multimeter

EXAMPLE 2 NUMERICAL

A galvanometer contains a coil with a resistance of 45.0 Ω and a maximum deflection current of 25.0 μA. How would the galvanometer be used in an ammeter with a range of 0–15.0 mA?

Given

$R_{coil} = 45.0\ \Omega$

$I_{coil} = 25.0\ \mu A$

$I_{total} = 15.0\ mA$

Required

R

Analysis

- The ammeter is placed in series in the circuit, so the full 15.0-mA current must pass through the meter.
- Since only 25.0 μA can pass through the coil at full deflection, the rest must pass through the shunt.
- Since the coil and the shunt are in parallel, $V_{shunt} = V_{coil}$.
- $I_{shunt} = I_{total} - I_{coil}$
- Calculate the resistance of the shunt using $R = V/I$.

Solution

$$V_{shunt} = V_{coil} = I_{coil} \times R_{coil}$$
$$= 25.0 \times 10^{-6}\ A \times 45.0\ \Omega$$
$$= 0.001\ 12\ V$$

$$I_{shunt} = I_{total} - I_{coil} = 15.0\ mA - 0.025\ mA$$
$$= 14.98\ mA \text{ (carrying one extra digit)}$$
$$= 0.014\ 98\ A$$

$$R_{shunt} = \frac{V_{shunt}}{I_{shunt}}$$
$$= \frac{0.001\ 12\ \text{V}}{0.014\ 98\ \text{A}}$$
$$= 0.0748\ \Omega$$
$$= 74.8\ \text{m}\Omega$$

Statement
The galvanometer requires a 74.8-mΩ shunt in parallel to the coil in order to measure currents up to 15 mA

PRACTICE PROBLEMS

1. An ammeter contains a coil with a resistance of 30.0 Ω and a maximum deflection current of 60.0 μA. Determine the resistance of the shunt if the maximum current to be measured is 0.100 A.
2. What shunt would allow the same ammeter to measure currents up to 15.0 mA?

The Voltmeter

The **voltmeter** is a device used to measure the electric potential difference between two points in a circuit. A voltmeter is constructed from a galvanometer as shown in Figure 15.12. There is no need for a shunt since a voltmeter is always connected in parallel with another element in a circuit (such as a resistor or battery), which provides an alternate path for the current. We only need to make it easier for the current to flow through the element rather than through the galvanometer coil. We do this by connecting a resistor in series with the coil of the galvanometer. The size of the resistance selected is such that very little current will pass through the fine wire of the coil during the measurement of potential difference.

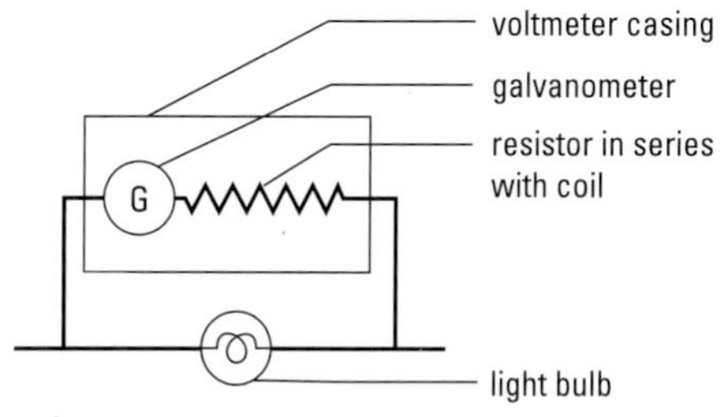

FIGURE 15.12 Using a galvanometer in a voltmeter

If the potential difference across the circuit element increases, the potential difference across the coil also increases. This in turn causes a larger current to flow through the coil. Consequently, the coil rotates farther and the pointer attached to the coil moves farther across the scale. The voltmeter is calibrated by the manufacturer so that the needle indicates the potential difference on the scale. In a multirange voltmeter, a selector switch or terminal connection adds larger resistances in series as higher-voltage scales are chosen (Figure 15.13).

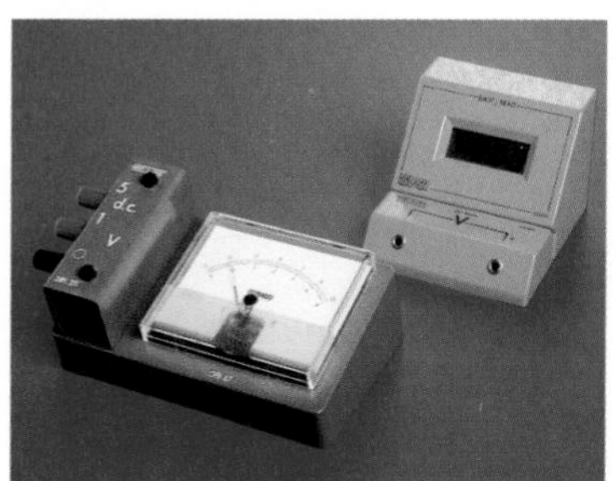

FIGURE 15.13 Voltmeters

EXAMPLE 3 NUMERICAL

A galvanometer contains a coil with a resistance of 50.0 Ω and a maximum deflection current of 30.0 μA. How would this galvanometer be used in a voltmeter with a range of 0–0.100 V?

Given
$R_{coil} = 50.0\ \Omega$ $\quad I_{max} = 30.0\ \mu\text{A}$ $\quad V_{max} = 0.100\ \text{V}$

Required
$R_{resistor}$

Analysis

- Calculate the maximum potential difference across the coil.
- Calculate the corresponding potential difference across the series resistor by subtraction.
- Calculate the value of the series resistance from the potential difference and the current.

Solution

$$V_{coil} = I_{coil} \times R_{coil}$$
$$= 30.0 \times 10^{-6}\ \text{A} \times 50.0\ \Omega$$
$$= 0.00150\ \text{V}$$

$$V_{resistor} = V_{max} - V_{coil} = 0.100\ \text{V} - 0.00150\ \text{V}$$
$$= 0.0985\ \text{V (carrying one extra digit)}$$

$$R_{resistor} = \frac{V_{resistor}}{I_{resistor}}$$
$$= \frac{0.0985\ \text{V}}{30.0 \times 10^{-6}\ \text{A}}$$
$$= 3283\ \Omega$$
$$= 3.3\ \text{k}\Omega$$

Statement

You would have to add a 3.3-kΩ resistor in series with the coil to measure voltages up to 100 mV.

PRACTICE PROBLEMS

1. A voltmeter contains a coil with a resistance of 80.0 Ω and a maximum deflection current of 60.0 μA. What is the value of the series resistor that would allow the voltmeter to measure up to 0.500 V?
2. What series resistor would allow the same voltmeter to read up to 10.0 mV?

Section 15.1 Review

Understanding Concepts

1. For each of the diagrams in Figure 15.14, determine the direction of the electromagnetic force on the conductor.

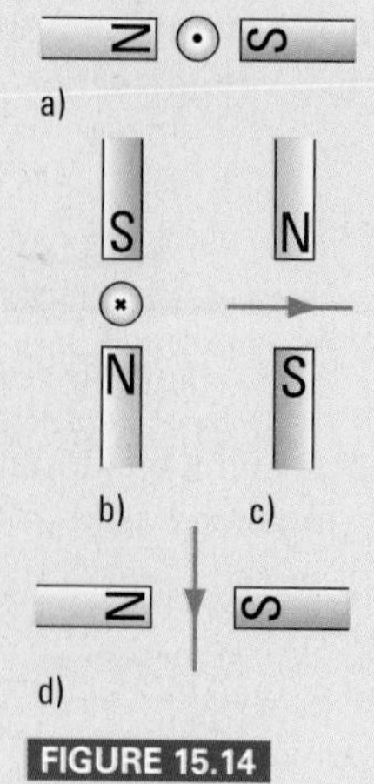

FIGURE 15.14

2. Each diagram in Figure 15.15 shows a loop located between the poles of a permanent magnet. For

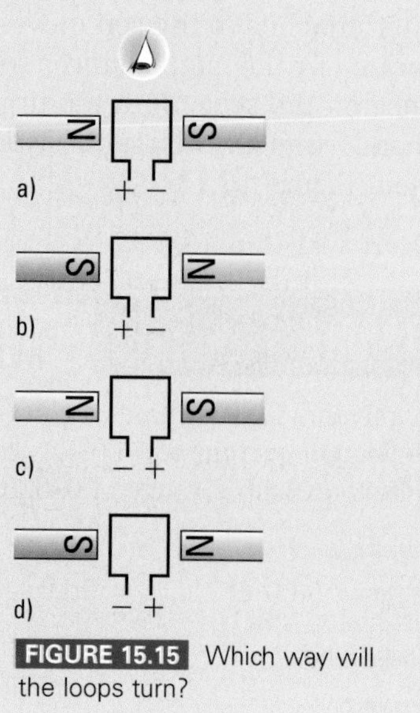

FIGURE 15.15 Which way will the loops turn?

each diagram, decide if the loop will rotate clockwise or counter-clockwise as seen by the eye in the diagram. Explain your reasoning.

3. A force of 7.0 N acts on a conductor that is carrying a current of 12 A in a magnetic field. If the current is reduced to 2.0 A while the field is kept constant, what would the force become?

Applying Inquiry/ Communication Skills

4. A galvanometer contains a coil with a resistance of 60.00 Ω and a full-scale deflection current of 40.00 μA. How would you adapt this galvanometer for use in
   a) a voltmeter with a full scale reading of 1.000 V?
   b) an ammeter with a full scale reading of 25.00 mA?

5. Explain the function in the galvanometer of
   a) the helix
   b) the core
   c) the permanent magnet
   d) the control springs

6. How does the helix in a galvanometer indicate how much current is passing through it?

7. Explain the function of
   a) the shunt in an ammeter
   b) the series resistor in a voltmeter

Making Connections

8. Examine the devices around your home and make a list of the ones that have an electric motor.

9. What is a car alternator?

15.2 The Direct Current Motor

Key Understandings

When you have completed this section, you will be able to:

- list the parts of a DC motor and describe their function
- describe how a DC motor operates
- describe how several factors affect the operation of a DC motor

When you walk into a toy store you find yourself surrounded by motors. These motors provide the movement in such toys as robots, cars, model trains, and boats. What causes the rotation in these motors? If electric leads are connected to the rotating parts, why do they not become twisted as the motor runs?

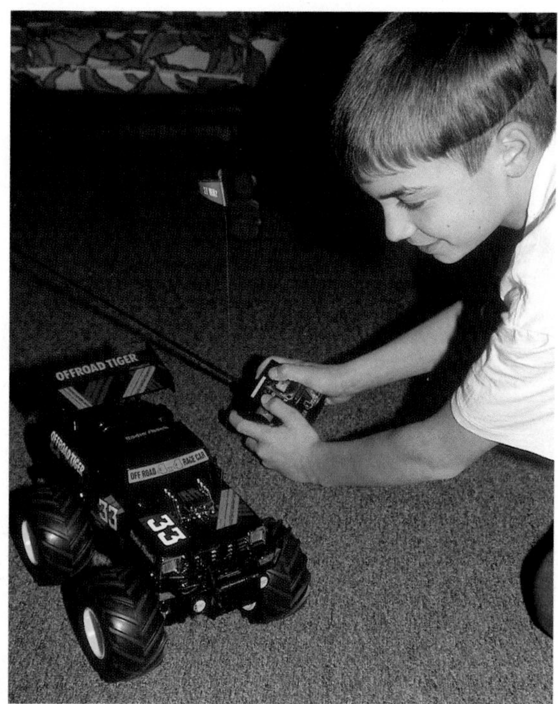

FIGURE 15.16 One of the numerous uses for direct-current motors

Basic Operation of the DC Motor

The **direct current motor** consists of a helix wound on a permeable core, external magnets, and a device called a **split-ring commutator** that allows current to flow in and out of the coil even while the coil is rotating. **Direct current** (DC) means that the current flows in one direction only.

To understand how the motor operates, picture a single loop located between two opposite magnetic poles similar to the one in Figure 15.17a). Each side of the loop is connected directly to a segment of the split-ring commutator, as illustrated in Figure 15.17b). These segments are insulated from each other. For most of the time, each segment of the split ring is in contact with a carbon block called a **brush**. This brush allows current to flow from an external circuit through the commutator to the loop. The right-hand rule for electromagnetic force predicts that the right half of the loop (CD) will be pushed downward while the left half of the loop (AB) will be pushed upward. This produces a clockwise rotation of the loop, as viewed from the commutator end in Figure 15.17c).

As the loop rotates, the split-ring commutator is carried around with it. Note that the ring segment slides past the carbon brush but stays in contact with it. In this way, the current can flow in one end of the loop and out the other end without the external leads having to twist with the rotation. Springs hold the brushes firmly against the commutator.

In Figure 15.17d), the loop is shown in the vertical position. The commutator has rotated far enough so that the carbon brushes are now in contact

WEBLINK

To explore the DC motor further, go to **www.pearsoned.ca/physics11**

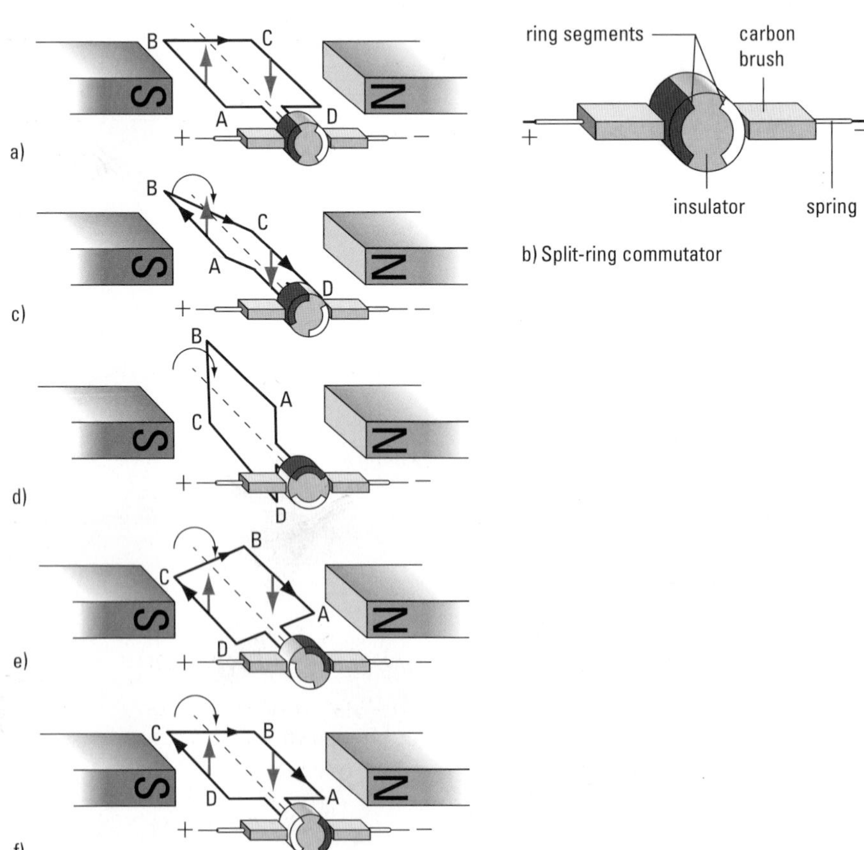

FIGURE 15.17 The basic DC motor

with the insulation that separates the two halves of the split ring. No current flows through the loop, so no electromagnetic forces act on it. However, because of its inertia, the loop keeps rotating.

The split rings come in contact with the brushes once again, as we see in Figure 15.17e). At this position, AB, which was connected to the positive brush, is now touching the negative brush. The current reverses, causing the electromagnetic force to reverse. As a result, AB is pushed downward while CD is pushed upward. This maintains the clockwise rotation of the loop shown in Figure 15.17f). The process repeats itself as long as the motor is connected to the source of direct current.

From Rotating Loop to Electric Motor

To convert this rotating loop into a DC motor, a helix consisting of many turns wound onto a permeable core replaces the single loop. This combination of core with helix is called an **armature** or **rotor**. Since the force causing the rotations of a single helix is *zero* twice during each cycle, DC motors usually contain a number of different helices recessed into slots in a common core (Figure 15.18). Each helix is attached to its own commutator segments. Multiple helices enable the force acting on the rotor to be continuous. Electromagnets can be used in place of permanent magnets, as shown in Figure 15.19. These electromagnets are called **field windings**.

The speed of this motor is very sensitive to the amount of current through it. As the current increases, the force on the rotor increases due to an increase both in the current in the helix and in the strength of the field windings. In Figure 15.19, the field windings are connected in series with the loop. Parallel connections are also possible.

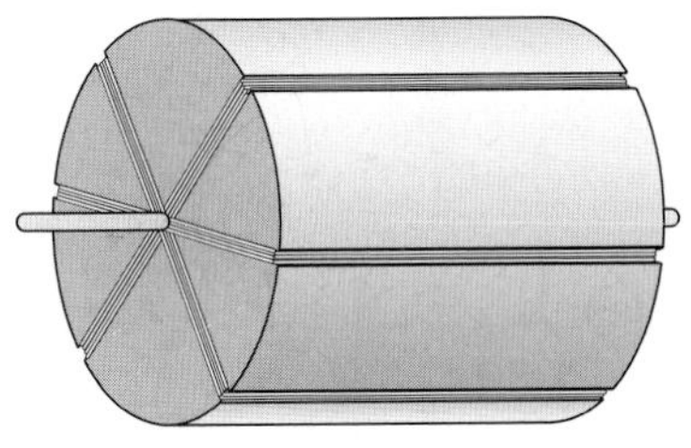

FIGURE 15.18 An armature or rotor with three helices (field windings)

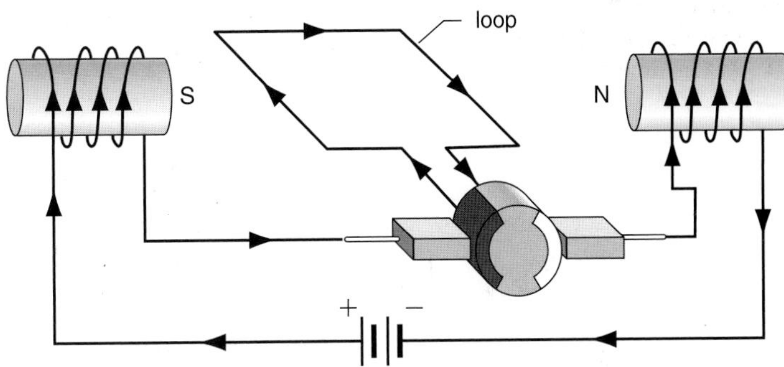

FIGURE 15.19 Electromagnets can be used in a DC motor in place of permanent magnets.

Section 15.2 Review

Understanding Concepts

1. a) For a DC motor, why must the direction of the current in the helix periodically be reversed?
   b) In a rotor with one helix, how often does the current reverse during each complete rotation?
   c) Explain how the split-ring commutator and brushes cause the direction of the current to reverse when necessary.
2. If there are six different helices on the rotor, how many breaks must there be in the split-ring commutator?
3. What is the advantage of using field windings in place of a permanent magnet?

Applying Inquiry/ Communication Skillls

4. In what ways is a DC motor similar to a galvanometer? In what ways is it different? Illustrate your answer by means of a graphic organizer such as a Venn diagram.

WEBLINK

Many plans are available for building a model motor. You can find some on the Internet. Choose one and build a working model. Begin your research at **www.pearsoned.ca/physics11**.

15.3 The Motor Principle in Action

Key Understandings

When you have completed this section you will be able to:

- apply the motor principle to explain the operation of audio speakers, TV picture tubes, railguns, and the curvature of comet tails

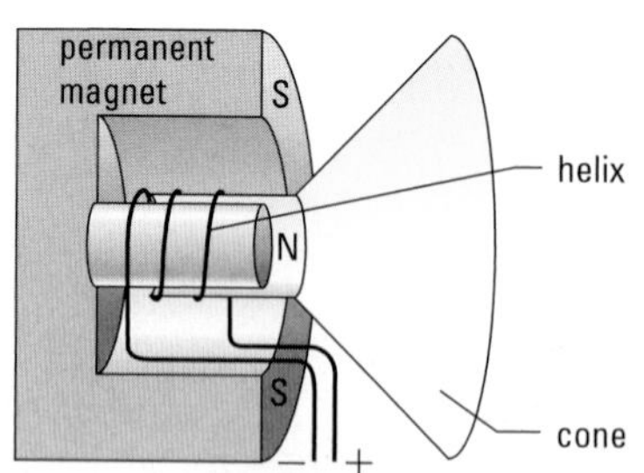

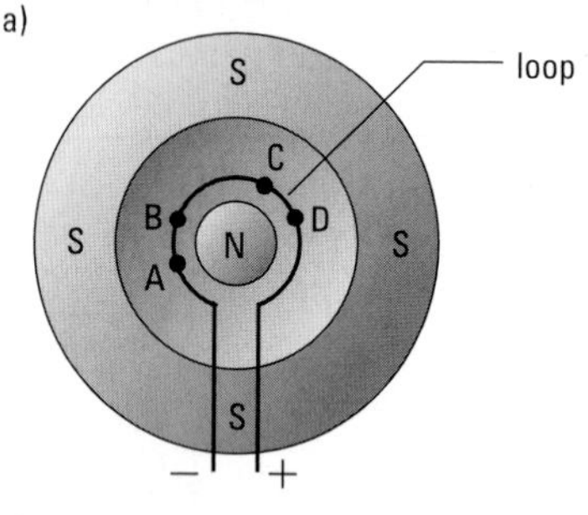

FIGURE 15.20 Diagram of the main components of an audio speaker

a) Side view showing helix

b) Front view showing single loop

Although the motor principle finds major applications in electric motors, there are many other situations involving this principle that have very little to do with motors. You will find it applied in audio speakers, television sets, the futuristic railgun, and the glowing wisps of comet tails.

Audio Speaker

An audio speaker contains a helix located within the field of a permanent magnet, as shown in Figure 15.20a). A **cone**, often made of stiffened paper, is attached to the helix and moves when the helix moves. Figure15.20b) shows one loop of the helix as seen from the front of the speaker. The north pole of the permanent magnet is located inside the loop. The south pole forms a continuous ring around the outside of the loop.

Imagine that current from an amplifier is flowing counter-clockwise around the coil. In one part of the loop, the current flows from B to A. The magnetic field in that region points to the left, from north to south. The right-hand rule for electromagnetic force allows us to predict that the segment will feel an inward force. Similarly, all other segments, such as CD, will be pushed inward. Since the speaker cone is attached to the coil, the cone will move inward, creating a rarefaction in front of it. When the current in the coil reverses direction the speaker moves outward, compressing the air in front of it. In this way, sound waves are produced in step with the variations in the current through the speaker.

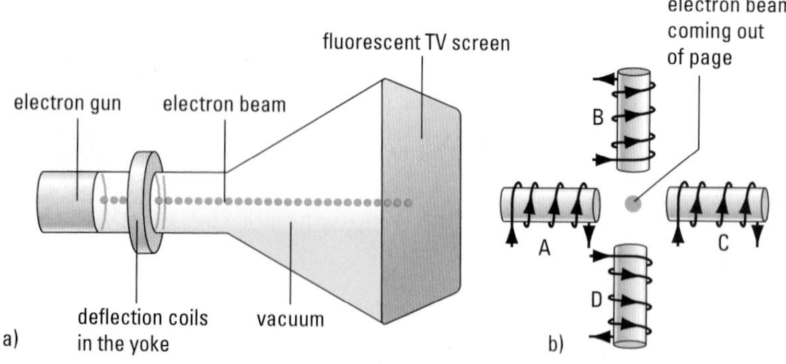

FIGURE 15.21 Magnetic deflection in a TV picture tube

a) Parts of a picture tube

b) Deflection coils

Television Scanning

The fluorescent screen of a television or computer monitor glows when struck by a beam of electrons from an **electron gun** located at the back of the picture tube. In most North American televisions these electrons scan across the screen fast enough to form 525 horizontal lines in 1/30 of a second. These lines produce the picture across the television screen (Figure 15.21a).

The electron beam is moved across the screen by means of the magnetic fields produced by **deflection coils** in the **yoke** (Figure 15.21b). Once again, the right-hand rule for electromagnetic force can be used to predict the direction in which the electron beam will be pushed by its interaction with the magnetic fields.

EXAMPLE 4 **CONCEPTUAL**

A magnetic field will exert a force on a moving charge in accordance with the motor principle. If current flows through the deflection coils as shown in Figure 15.21b), in which direction will the electron beam be pushed?

Analysis and Solution

- Using the right-hand rule for a current-carrying helix on coils A and C, we find that the right end of coil A is a south pole while the left end of coil C is a north pole. Thus, the magnetic field across the electron beam is directed from C to A.
- A flow of electrons *out* of the page is equivalent to a conventional current flow *into* the page.
- The right-hand rule for electromagnetic force indicates that the beam will be pushed upward.
- Similarly, the magnetic field between B and D will push the electron beam to the right.
- The combined effect of all four coils will be to push the beam toward the top right corner of the television screen.

INSIGHT

The scanning action of the electron beam can provide a stroboscopic effect with television screens and computer monitors. Move a pencil or ruler rapidly in front of the screen to observe this effect.

CHALLENGE

How should the currents in the deflecting coils be changed in order to place the electron beam in the middle of the bottom of the screen?

Railguns

A **railgun** is an electromagnetic accelerator that is in the laboratory-research stage of development. Someday a railgun may launch space probes. The main advantage of a railgun is that it provides virtually all of the probe's kinetic energy—the probe would not need to carry fuel, except perhaps for steering. Also, since electrical energy would be used instead of chemical energy, solar cells might be able to power a railgun at a space station or on the Moon.

A railgun is essentially a loop with one end free to move. This end is the projectile. In Figure 15.22, the projectile is shown as a slab that can slide

INFOBIT

Some experimental railguns are capable of accelerating a projectile by as much as 5×10^6 g. In one millisecond a projectile can be accelerated to a speed of 10 km/s—faster than a bullet.

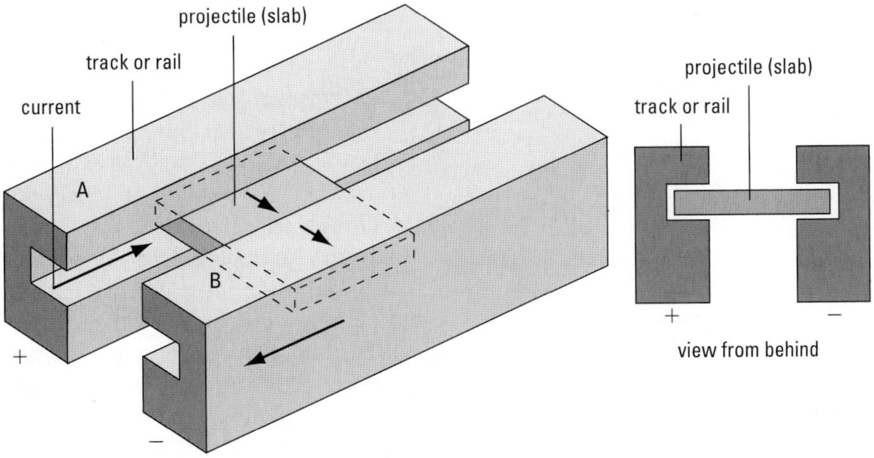

WEBLINK

Railguns are also being considered as a Star Wars type weapon. Find out about the research into railguns, and prepare a report outlining the basic physics behind the railgun and its possible applications. Begin your research at **www.pearsoned.ca/physics11**

FIGURE 15.22 The current through a railgun

along grooves in a fixed track. Current flows in through track A, across the slab, and out through track B. The current through the tracks creates a magnetic field that is directed downward in the gap between the tracks. The electromagnetic force between this magnetic field and the current through the slab pushes the slab along the track in the direction away from the current-carrying part of the rails.

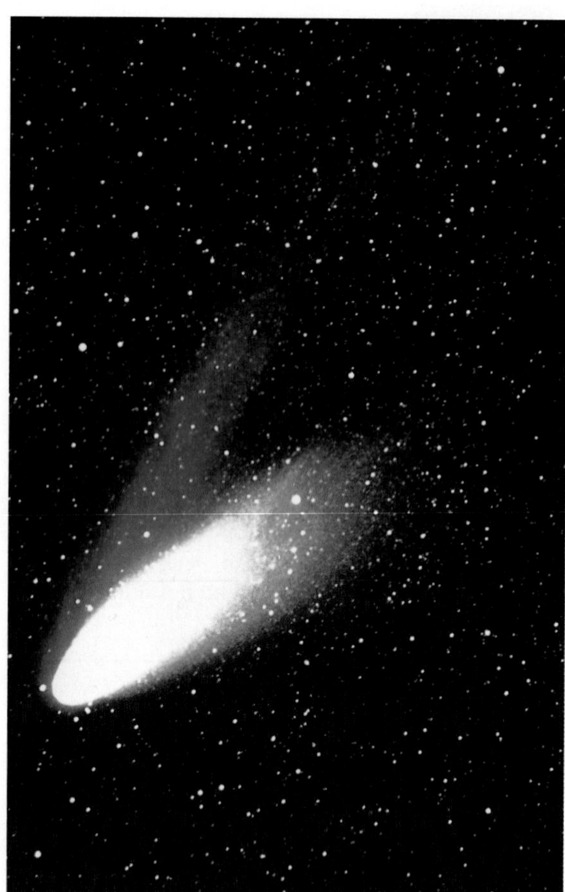

FIGURE 15.23 A comet has two tails.

Comet Tails

A comet is a collection of ice and rubble that follows a large, elongated orbit about the Sun. When the comet comes close to the Sun, the radiation and solar wind cause the ice to change into an extremely tenuous vapour. The solar wind pushes this vapour outward from the Sun to form the **comet tail** (Figure 15.23). We can see the tail because the particles and radiation from the Sun cause the atoms in the tail to glow.

However, careful observation reveals that comets actually have two tails. One always points straight out from the Sun and consists of neutral atoms and molecules. The other is curved. The curvature is due to the motion of the comet through the Sun's magnetic field. The curved tail contains atoms that have lost one or more electrons due to solar radiation and are now positive ions. The motion of these ions represents a current within a magnetic field. The Sun's magnetic field pushes those charged particles away from the uncharged particles in the comet's main tail, forming a second tail, as can be seen in Figure 15.23.

WEBLINK

Comets present us with a beautiful, glowing sight in the night sky. Find out more about comets on the Internet. Download some comet photos and assemble them into a computer presentation for the class. Begin your research at **www.pearsoned.ca/physics11**

Section 15.3 Review

Understanding Concepts

1. If the current in the helix of a speaker oscillates at 500 Hz, what will be the frequency of the sound produced by the speaker?
2. Why are coils A and C in Figure 15.21 referred to as the vertical deflecting coils even though they are arranged horizontally? Would your explanation also account for coils B and D being referred to as the horizontal deflecting coils even though they are arranged vertically?
3. In which directions should the deflection currents flow in Figure 15.21 (page 556) to place the electron beam
   a) at the bottom right corner of the TV screen
   b) at the centre of the top of the screen

Assume that you are looking into the screen as you look at the page.

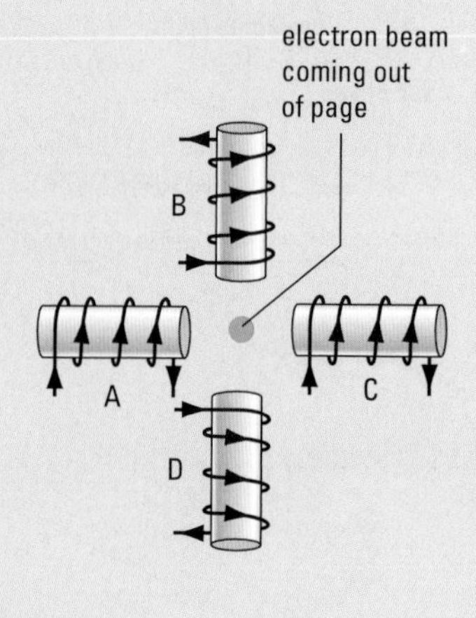

FIGURE 15.24

Applying Inquiry/ Communication Skills

4. What would happen to the direction of motion of the projectile in a railgun if the current were reversed?
5. How would a comet have to be moving if it has only one tail while in the Sun's magnetic field?

Making Connections

6. Outline two ways by which the final speed of the projectile in a railgun can be increased.

15.4 Electromagnetic Induction

Key Understandings

When you have completed this section, you will be able to:

- describe the method and results of Faraday's induction experiment
- state the conditions necessary for induction of a potential difference
- list the factors that affect the magnitude of an induced potential difference
- state Lenz's law
- explain, with reference to the law of conservation of energy, why the induced current cannot aid the inducing action
- apply Lenz's law to predict the direction of an induced current or potential difference

Electric motors can provide us with a way of converting electric energy into motion. These are not, however, the only devices that link motion and electrical energy. Generators perform the opposite task—converting motion into electrical energy. Without this conversion, many of our electric motors would be useless. How is this conversion accomplished? Is it a different effect from the motor principle, or simply another aspect of it?

Discovery of Electromagnetic Induction

After Oersted's discovery of the magnetic field about an electric current and Ampère's investigation of this effect, scientists began to wonder if a magnetic field could, in turn, produce an electric current. On August 29, 1831, an English scientist, Michael Faraday, succeeded in proving this hypothesis. He wrapped two helices around the same iron ring. One helix was connected to a battery and the other to a galvanometer (Figure 15.25).

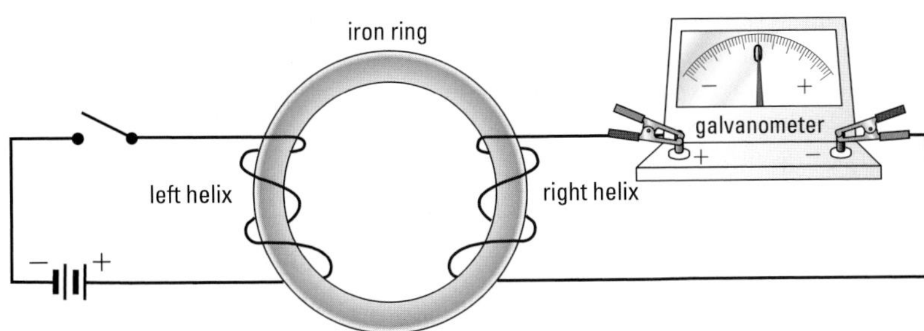

FIGURE 15.25 Faraday's apparatus

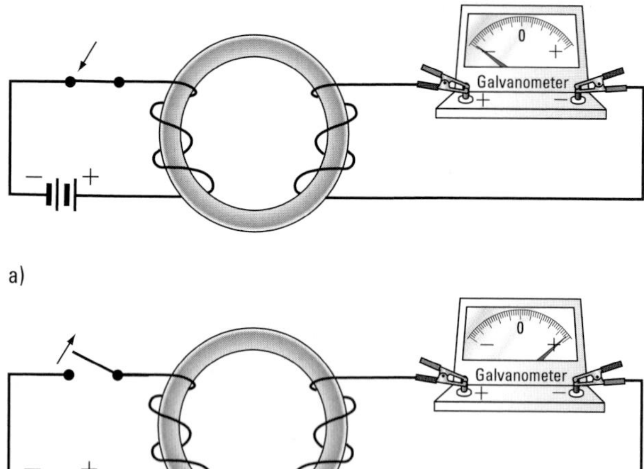

FIGURE 15.26 Induction occurs while the magnetic field about a conductor is changing.

a) Closing the circuit

b) Opening the circuit

Faraday believed that when a current flowed through the helix on the left, the magnetic field it created would be channelled to the right-hand helix by means of a permeable iron ring. He closed the switch, but no steady current registered on the galvanometer. However, the galvanometer registered a brief surge of current in the right-hand helix, then the needle returned to zero. This current appeared only during the actual closing of the switch and again when the switch was opened in the left-hand circuit.

Faraday had discovered the method for inducing an electric current by means of a magnetic field. A current can only be induced when the magnetic field about a conductor is changing. This occurs when the circuit is being closed or opened. Note that the current when opening the switch is opposite in direction to that when closing the switch (Figure 15.26).

INFOBIT

Joseph Henry in the United States had discovered the same effect somewhat earlier than Faraday. However, Faraday investigated the effect in greater detail and published his findings earlier than Henry. As a result, Faraday received credit for the discovery.

Magnitude of Electromagnetic Induction

Faraday observed electromagnetic induction because a current was indicated by his galvanometer. But, a current begins to flow in a circuit only if there is a gain in energy by the charge within the circuit. Such a gain in energy is a positive electric potential difference. Thus, the **induced current** is a result of the **induced potential difference**. Both cases are known as **electromagnetic induction**. The induced potential difference, V, varies directly with the number of turns in the helix, N. This is expressed by

$$V \propto N \qquad \text{or} \qquad \frac{V_1}{V_2} = \frac{N_1}{N_2}$$

In addition, the induced potential difference, V, varies directly with the rate at which the magnetic field (B) is changing:

$$V \propto \frac{\Delta B}{\Delta t}$$

Note that it is the rate at which the field is changing, and not the actual magnitude of the field, that is important. Since motion is relative, changing the field around a conductor is equivalent to moving the conductor through the magnetic field.

Discovering Physics ***Electromagnetic Induction***

Connect a galvanometer or very sensitive ammeter in series with a helix. Try moving a permanent magnet in and out of the core of the coil. What do you observe? Experiment with different factors. Does the speed with which the magnet moves make a difference? Does the type of pole have any effect? Is there any difference between inserting a pole into a helix and withdrawing that same pole?

EXAMPLE 5 NUMERICAL

When a bar magnet is inserted into a helix containing 200 turns, a maximum potential difference of 30 mV is induced. If the same magnet were inserted at the same speed into a helix with 1000 turns, what maximum potential difference would be induced?

Given
$V_1 = 30$ mV
$N_1 = 200$ and $N_2 = 1000$

Required
V_2

Analysis
$$\frac{V_2}{V_1} = \frac{N_2}{N_1}$$
therefore $V_2 = V_1 \times \frac{N_2}{N_1}$

Solution
$$\begin{aligned} V_2 &= V_1 \times \frac{N_2}{N_1} \\ &= 30 \text{ mV} \times \frac{1000}{200} \\ &= 150 \text{ mV} \\ &= 0.15 \text{ V} \end{aligned}$$

Statement
A maximum potential difference of 0.15 V would be induced in a helix with 1000 turns.

PRACTICE PROBLEMS

1. When a bar magnet is inserted into a coil containing 400 turns, a maximum induced potential difference of 20 mV is produced. If the speed of the magnet remains the same, what number of turns would be required to produce a maximum induced potential difference of 15 mV?
2. When a bar magnet is inserted into a coil containing 600 turns, a maximum induced potential difference of 72 mV is produced. If the speed of the magnet remains the same, what maximum potential difference would be induced if the number of turns is decreased to 100?

EXAMPLE 6 NUMERICAL

When a bar magnet is inserted into a coil at 10 cm/s, the maximum potential difference is 18 mV. If the magnet is now inserted at 15 cm/s, what will be the maximum potential difference?

Given
voltage $V_1 = 18$ mV

velocities of the magnet $v_1 = 10$ cm/s and $v_2 = 15$ cm/s

Required
V_2

Analysis
In problems like this one, we will assume that the rate of change of the magnetic field can be indicated by the rate of change of position of the magnet, which is the velocity of the magnet.

PRACTICE PROBLEMS

1. When a bar magnet is withdrawn at 8.0 cm/s from a coil, the maximum induced potential difference is 25 mV. How fast should the magnet be removed to produce a maximum induced potential difference of 15 mV?
2. What would be the maximum induced potential difference if the bar magnet in the previous question were withdrawn at 24 cm/s?

$V \alpha v$ or $\frac{V_2}{V_1} = \frac{v_2}{v_1}$

and

$V_2 = V_1 \times \frac{v_2}{v_1}$

Solution

$$V_2 = V_1 \times \frac{v_2}{v_1}$$

$$= 18 \text{ mV} \times \frac{15 \text{ cm/s}}{10 \text{ cm/s}}$$

$$= 27 \text{ mV}$$

Statement

The maximum potential difference will be 27 mV.

INFOBIT

At 2:44 a.m. on March 13, 1989, a flood of charged particles from the Sun slammed into Earth's magnetic field, inducing wild voltage swings in Quebec's power grid. Across the province, transformers overloaded and circuit breakers began tripping. In 90 s, the whole system crashed. It took nine hours to restore power throughout the province.

Lenz's Law

For over a decade after Faraday and Henry had discovered electromagnetic induction, scientists puzzled over the question of how to predict the direction of the induced current or potential difference. This problem was solved in 1843 by a German physicist, Heinrich Lenz. He discovered that **the magnetic field of an induced current always opposes the change in magnetic field that is causing the induced current**. This is now known as **Lenz's law**.

For example, when a north pole approaches a helix, the induced current forms a second north pole which repels the first, as we see in Figure 15.27a). If the north pole of a bar magnet is moved away from the helix, then the induced current sets up a south pole to attract the bar magnet and again opposes the motion of the magnet, as Figure 15.27b) shows.

Lenz's law is a direct application of the law of conservation of energy. The induced current must have received energy in order to begin to flow. This induced current can then transfer energy into forms such as light or heat. But energy cannot be created from nothing. The energy is provided by the action causing the induction. That is, if you push a bar magnet through a loop of conducting wire, the energy that you expend in moving the bar magnet is transferred to the conducting loop which is seen in the induced current in the loop.

Imagine what could happen if Lenz's law were not correct. If an experimenter begins to move the north pole of a bar magnet toward the helix

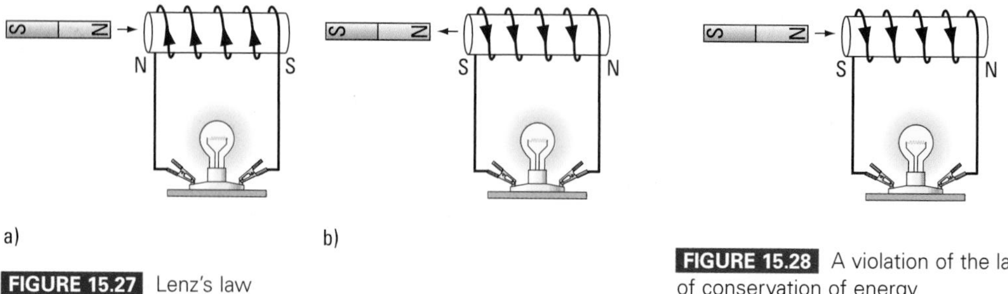

FIGURE 15.27 Lenz's law

FIGURE 15.28 A violation of the law of conservation of energy

(Figure 15.28), the helix would form a south pole. If there were no friction, the attraction of the south pole for the north pole would pull the magnet into the coil, while at the same time forming an induced current which would light the bulb. Energy would have been produced without any corresponding energy input. By the law of conservation of energy, this can never happen. So Lenz's law must be correct.

Magnetic Recording

Cassette recorders, VCRs, credit cards, computer hard drives, and floppy disks all store information on a magnetic medium. Current flows through a specially designed coil to record the information by magnetizing tiny segments on the tape, disk, or magnetic stripe. When another coil is passed over the magnetized segments, they induce a small current in the coil, reproducing the recording current. Although the physical recording process in all these devices is similar, they use two radically different ways of processing information.

Tape Recorders A reporter snaps a cassette into her recorder, holds her microphone in front of the winning gymnast, and tapes his words of victory and joy. While the gymnast speaks, the microphone converts the air pressure variations of the sound waves into corresponding variations in an electric current. These tiny current fluctuations are amplified and fed to an electromagnetic coil called a recording head (Figure 15.29). Because the current is changing, the magnetic field produced by the coil likewise changes.

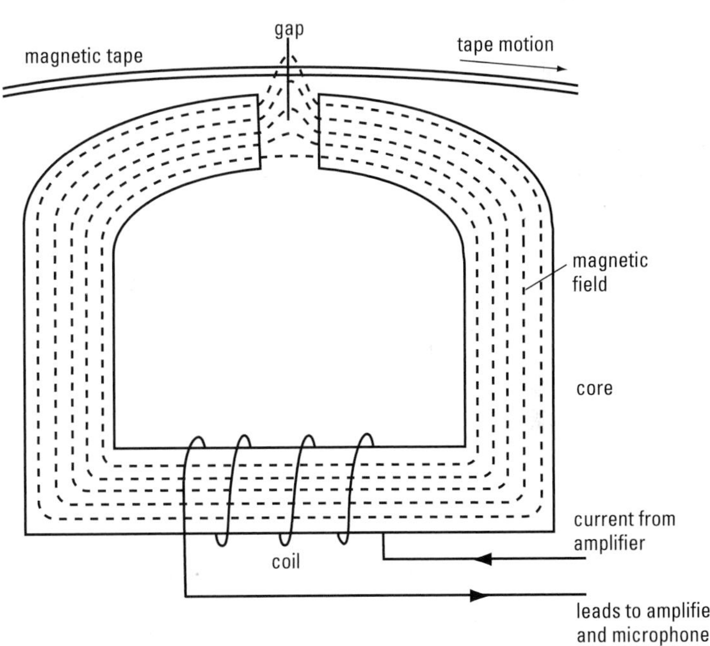

FIGURE 15.29 An electromagnet used as a recording head

This magnetic field is almost entirely contained within the core, but it spreads out slightly at the gap. When the magnetic tape passes by the gap, the tape becomes magnetized. The amount and direction of the magnetization depend on the field of the coil. Consequently, the variation in magnetism along the tape mimics the variation in the air pressure of the original sound waves. This is known as an **analogue process** because the voltage, current, or magnetism in the circuit closely parallels the original signal. In contrast, a **digital** recording converts the amplified signal into a stream of binary numbers (ones and zeros) by constantly measuring or **sampling** the signal. The numbers are recorded onto tape or a disk by magnetizing the tape for a one and leaving it unmagnetized for a zero.

Later, the reporter plays back the tape. The magnetized tape runs past a coil called the playback head. In many tape recorders the recording head is also used as the playback head. As the tape passes by the gap in the head, the varying magnetic field from the tape induces a correspondingly varying current in the coil. When this current is amplified and fed to a speaker, it reproduces the original sound waves and the words of victory and joy are heard again.

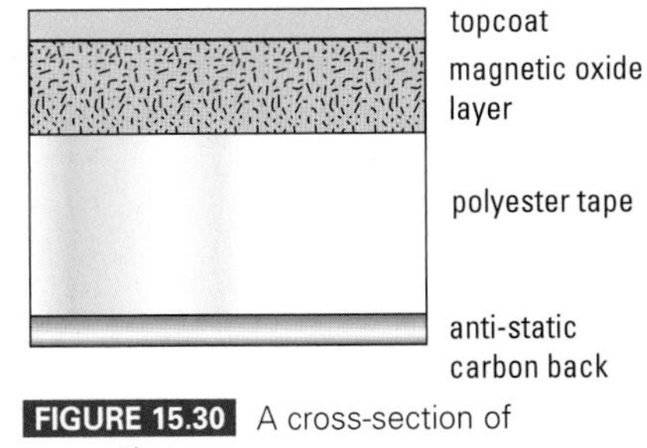

FIGURE 15.30 A cross-section of magnetic tape

Discovering Physics *Slow Magnets*

How can you slow down a falling magnet?

Hold a cardboard or plastic tube upright over a soft surface. Drop a cylindrical magnet through the tube and time how long it takes to fall. Now repeat this drop using a copper tube of about the same size as the nonmetallic tube. How do the drop times compare? Can you explain the difference?

If a "smart pulley" is available, connect the magnet to it as shown in Figure 15.31. The counterweight slows down the acceleration of the magnet, allowing more careful observations and comparisons. Now try the two drops again. Compare the two by plotting velocity against time for both of them on the same set of axes.

- How do the graphs compare?
- Did either drop reach terminal velocity?

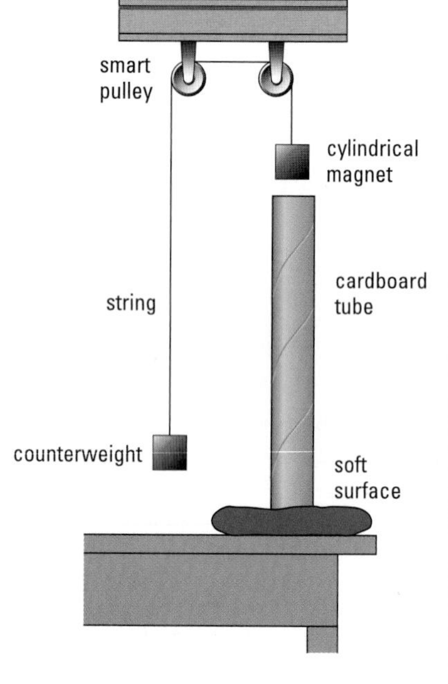

FIGURE 15.31 Analyzing the motion of slow magnets

Storing Information on Floppy Disks When working with computers, floppy disks are sometimes used to store information or transfer it between computers. They are called floppy disks because they contain a magnetic disk made of a flexible material, in contrast to a hard drive, which uses magnetic material coated onto a rigid platter.

Magnetic storage of data on disks requires four key components (Figure 15.32). The first is the magnetic disk itself. The second is a read/write head.

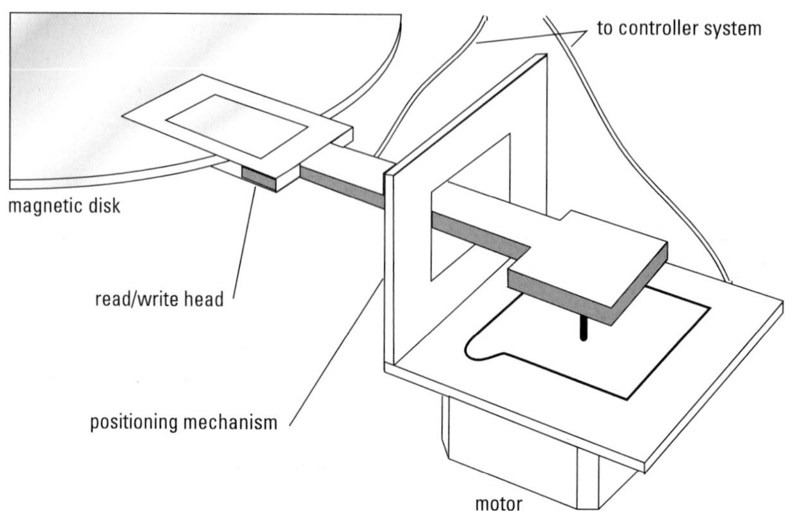

FIGURE 15.32 Magnetic disk drive: A motor positions a read/write head over a magnetized track on a spinning disk.

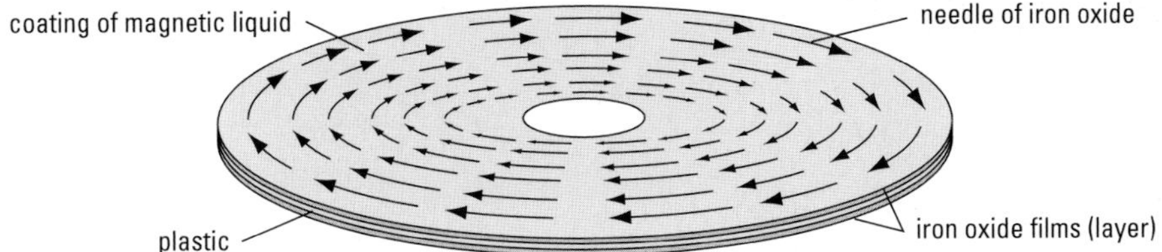

FIGURE 15.33 The alignment of particles (needles) of iron oxide on a blank floppy disk

This head both reads data off and writes data onto the surface of the disk. The third component is a motorized positioning mechanism. This aligns the head properly over the disk. The fourth is an electronic link to transfer information between the disk and the computer.

A floppy disk is a thin sheet of plastic coated on each side with a film of iron oxide. Iron oxide is a magnetic material that consists of needle-like particles approximately one-millionth of a metre in length. Each needle is a tiny bar magnet. The overall magnetization in any region of the field is the sum of the fields of the individual particles.

When the disk is manufactured, the needles are aligned by rotating the disk in a magnetic field before the iron oxide film dries. This process leaves the needles aligned with the plane of the disk and approximately parallel to its circumference, as shown in Figure 15.33.

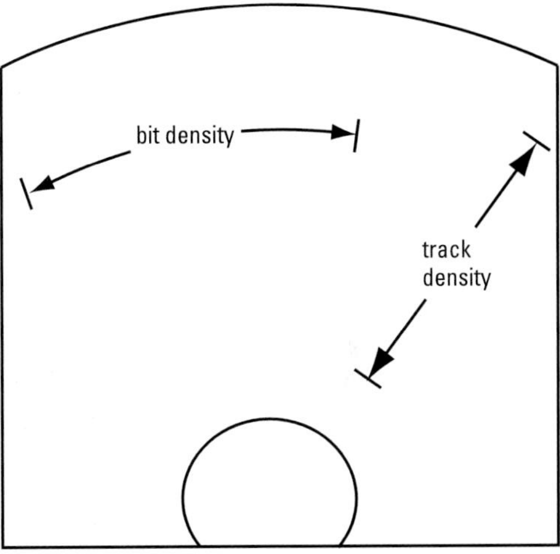

FIGURE 15.34 Disk storage capacity is determined by the number of tracks per surface and the number of bits per track.

The read/write head converts electric impulses into magnetic fields and vice versa. An electric impulse in the head can reverse the north and south poles at the ends of the needles and so changes their magnetization. The magnetization of the needles takes place along concentric tracks on the disk's surface. Two factors determine the disk's storage capacity (Figure 15.34). One is the number of tracks on the surface or track density. On the 90-mm floppy disks, there are five tracks per millimetre.

The other factor affecting the disk's storage capacity is the number of iron oxide needles per millimetre along the track, which affects the bit density, number of ones and zeros that can be stored along the track (each one or zero is a bit). A typical 90-mm floppy disk has a bit density of 700 bits per millimetre.

WEBLINK

More information could be coded into computer memories if the process did not involve magnetizing small particles of iron oxide on disks. What other processes could be used to store information? Could it be stored at the molecular level? Search for some of the latest proposals for information storage. Prepare a table listing some of the proposals along with their advantages and disadvantages. Begin your research at **www.pearsoned.ca/physics11**.

Discovering Physics *Erasing a Tape*

To test whether sound is recorded in a magnetic form on a cassette tape, try the following activity. Record about a half-minute of music onto a blank cassette and then play it back to check it. Remove the cassette from the tape recorder. Then rewind the tape by hand while holding a magnet close to the exposed surface of the tape. Play the tape again. How does the quality of the sound heard now compare with that of the original? Why did this change occur?

Cellular Telephones and Electromagnetic Radiation

Decision-Making Skills

- Defining the Issue
- Developing Assessment Criteria
- Researching the Issue
- Analyzing Data and Information
- Proposing a Course of Action
- Justifying the Course of Action
- Communitcating Your Proposal

BACKGOURND INFORMATION

We live immersed in a sea of electromagnetic radiation, and many people are concerned about exposure to this radiation. Some studies have suggested a link between leukemia in children and exposure to radiation from high-voltage transmission lines. Other studies have looked at the possibility of harm due to radiation from television sets, computer monitors, and microwave ovens.

Recently, with the explosive growth in the use of cellular telephones, attention has been directed to concerns about the radio waves they emit. Cell phones use frequencies in the range of 835 MHz. Radiation from cell phones has certainly been shown to affect aircraft flight electronics, electronic hospital equipment, and even pacemakers. In addition, the emissions from cell phones occur close to the head of the user and so have more potential for harm than emissions from most other devices.

FIGURE 15.35 Some people think that the use of cell phones is dangerous

But is there really a problem? A number of people believe there is and, as a result, several lawsuits have been initiated in which cell phone users are seeking compensation for developing brain cancer due to repeated use of cell phones. However, these cases may be difficult to prove. Is there solid evidence of danger from cell phones? What types of studies can be used as evidence? These are questions currently occupying scientists, lawyers, and legislators.

Analyzing the Issue

1. In groups, research electromagnetic radiation. Complete a risk/benefit analysis to summarize your research.
2. In your opinion, do the risks of electromagnetic radiation outweigh the benefits? Why do you think so?
3. Identify and describe other technologies in society that produce electromagnetic radiation.
4. Plan and carry out a debate to hear both sides of the argument regarding the safety hazards of using cellular phones. Identify the question for debate. Select a representative from each research group to be a member of one of the debating teams.
5. At the end of the debate, the class will be polled again. The winning team will be decided by the number of students who have been convinced to change their position.
6. At the end, each team should analyze its presentation. What were its strengths and weaknesses? Which points in the opposition's presentation were easiest to counter and which were harder? Did any points raised by your opponents surprise you?

Section 15.4 Review

Understanding Concepts

1. At which point in his experiment did Faraday notice an induced current?
2. What is the necessary condition for electromagnetic induction?
3. a) What two factors affect the magnitude of the electromagnetic induction in a helix?
   b) How do each of these factors affect the magnitude of the electromagnetic induction?
4. When a student inserts a magnet into a coil at 5.0 cm/s, he observes an induced potential difference of 30 mV. How fast should he move the magnet to produce an induced potential difference of 90 mV?
5. A student inserts a magnet into a helix containing 200 turns and observes a potential difference of 40.0 mV. If the student then inserts the same magnet at the same rate into a helix with 800 turns, what will be the magnitude of the potential difference?
6. State Lenz's Law.
7. Explain why an induced current cannot aid the inducing action.
8. For each of the inducing actions in Figure 15.36 predict
   a) which of the poles formed on the helix is the north pole
   b) whether the induced current will flow from X to Y, or from Y to X

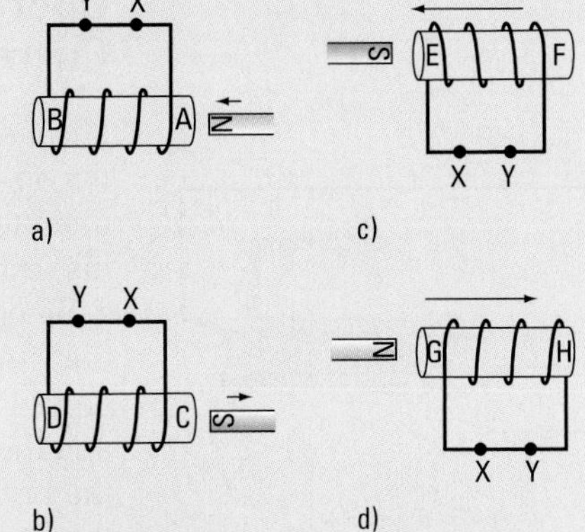

FIGURE 15.36 Label the poles and the current for each helix.

Making Connections

9. Explain why a speaker can be used as a microphone.
10. Why does exposing a credit card to a strong magnetic field make the card unreadable?

15.5 Alternating Current Generators

Key Understandings

When you have completed this section, you will be able to:

- name the main parts of an alternating current generator and state the function of each
- explain the production of the induced potential difference in an alternating current generator
- explain the reversal of the induced potential difference during each revolution of the armature
- explain the difference between direct and alternating current

FIGURE 15.37 A wind-up radio contains a hand-cranked generator

When you turn on the lights in your home, the bulbs receive electrical energy that began its journey in a distant generating station. In such a station, energy from oil, coal, moving water, or atomic nuclei is converted into

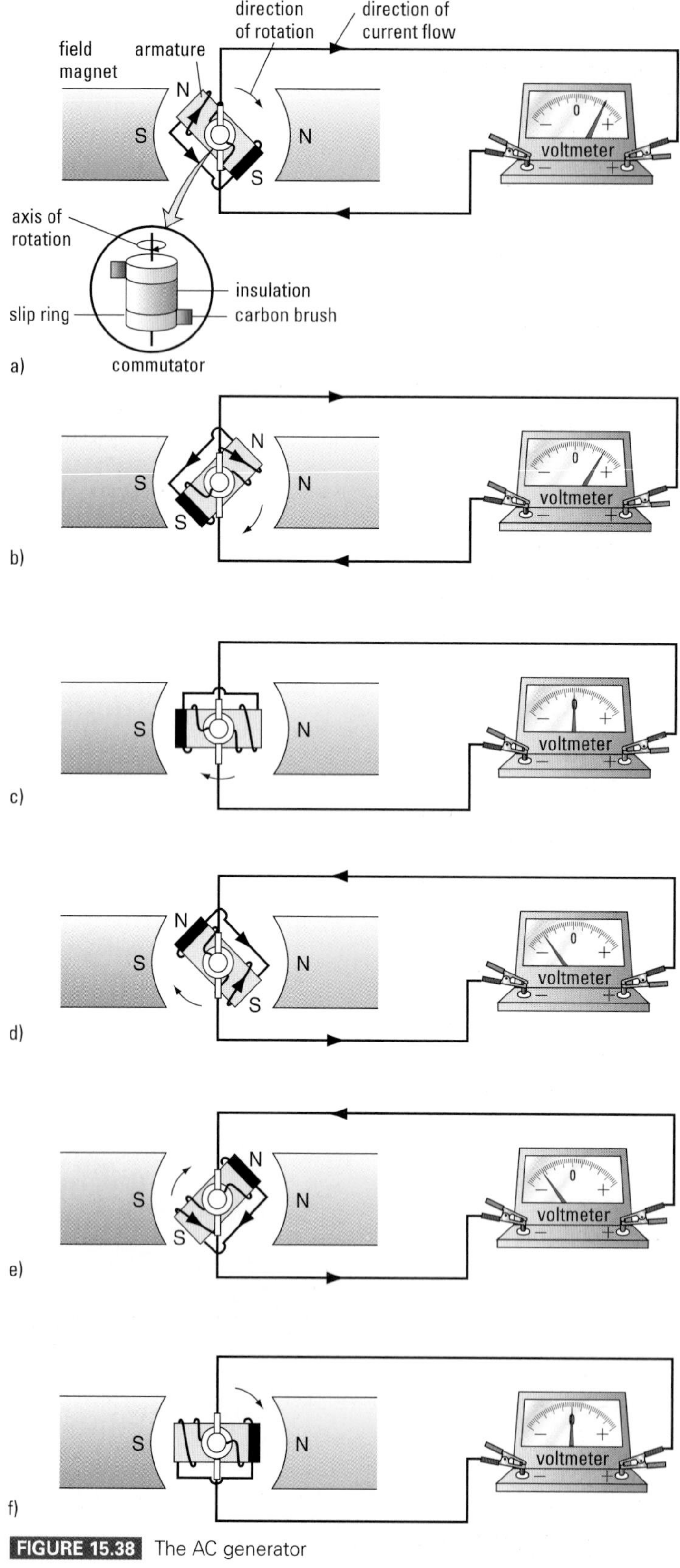

FIGURE 15.38 The AC generator

kinetic energy in a turbine. A **generator** then converts this kinetic energy into electrical energy, which comes to our homes as alternating current. Why do generators produce alternating current and how does it differ from the current we have discussed in previous chapters?

Operation of the Alternating Current Generator

Michael Faraday built the first electric generator in 1831. It consisted of a copper disk mounted with its rim between the poles of a horseshoe magnet. When the disk was rotated, a potential difference was produced between the rim and the shaft of the disk. Current then flowed when sliding contacts connected the rim and the shaft to an external circuit. A year later, the French inventor Hippolyte Pixii constructed the first generator that used a coil between magnetic poles. Basically, modern generators are improved versions of this design.

The essential parts of an alternating current generator are illustrated in Figure 15.38. An **armature**, consisting of a coil of wire wrapped around a permeable core, is spun between the poles of a **field magnet**. The ends of the coil are each attached to a separate ring of metal, called a slip ring, such as the one shown in Figure 15.38a). These **slip rings** allow current to flow from the rotating armature to an external circuit.

Remember that a potential difference can be induced in a coil by changing the magnetic field about the coil. In the generator, this change is produced by spinning the coil in the magnetic field. For large generators, steam-driven or water-driven turbines spin the coil. The motion of the coil, relative to the magnetic field, induces a potential difference.

In Figure 15.38a), the coil is shown rotating clockwise. Lenz's law states that the induced current will produce a magnetic field to oppose this motion. As a result, the coloured end of the armature becomes a south pole. The attraction between this south pole and the north pole of the field magnet opposes the rotation.

In Figure 15.38b), the coloured end of the armature is approaching a south pole. The

Discovering Physics — *Blurred Vision?*

Turn on a vertical showcase bulb and use a convex lens to form a greatly magnified image of the filament on a screen. Now bring the pole of a strong magnet up close behind the bulb. If you have a horseshoe magnet, place it around the bulb so that the poles are in front of and behind the filament. What happens to the image? Can you suggest an explanation for what you observe?

coloured end remains a south pole and the repulsion between the two south poles opposes the motion of the armature.

In Figure 15.38c), the coloured end is directly opposite the field pole. For a moment the armature is neither approaching nor moving away from that pole. With no change of magnetic field, there is no induced potential difference.

However, as the coloured end of the armature begins to move away from the field pole, it becomes a north pole. The attraction between the north pole of the armature and the south pole of the field magnet opposes this motion. For the coloured end of the armature to become a north pole, the current must reverse itself in both the coil and the external circuit, shown in Figure 15.38d). This periodic reversal of the current is the reason it is called **alternating current** (AC).

To keep opposing the motion, the coloured end stays as a north pole until it reaches the position shown in Figure 15.38f). As before, when the coloured end is directly opposite the field pole, no induction occurs.

We can see that the induced current reverses itself whenever the axis of the helix lines up exactly with the poles of the field magnet. At these times, the induced potential difference and the current are both zero. In addition, the induced potential difference and the current are greatest when the axis of the helix is perpendicular to the magnetic field lines. It is here that the coil is moving the fastest, relative to the external field. Figure 15.39 shows the variation of the induced potential difference with time and with the position of the armature.

The graph in Figure 15.39 shows the key feature of alternating current that distinguishes it from direct current. In direct-current circuits, the current flows only in one direction and the voltage always has the same polarity. In alternating-current circuits, the direction of the current and the polarity of the voltage change repeatedly. Also, we have to use an equivalent or effective value for calculations with alternating voltages and currents. The formula linking the effective voltage and the peak voltage is $V_{\text{effective}} = \frac{V_{\text{peak}}}{\sqrt{2}}$. Similarly, $I_{\text{effective}} = \frac{I_{\text{peak}}}{\sqrt{2}}$.

In North America the current from generating plants alternates with a frequency of 60 Hz. Because the current becomes zero and then reverses itself twice during each cycle, the time between reversals is 1/120 s. Consequently electric lights flicker somewhat 120 times a second. This flicker is too fast for our eyes to detect.

WEBLINK

To look at a simulation of rotating armature in a generator, go to **www.pearsoned.ca/physics11**.

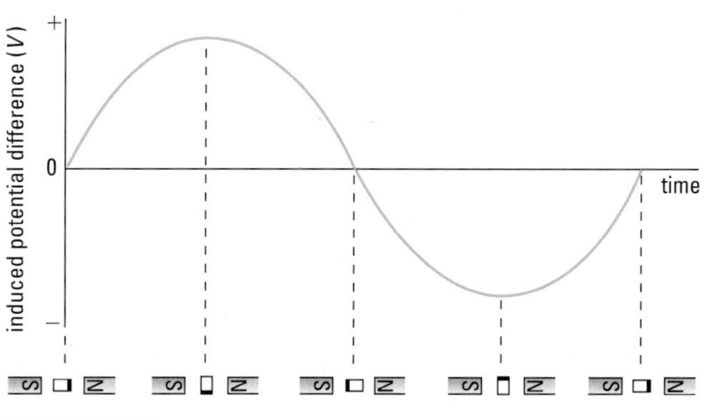

FIGURE 15.39 The generation of alternating current

Battle of the Currents

In 1882, in the financial district of New York City, Thomas Edison and his associates set up the first direct-current power station. However, Edison had no means of stepping the voltage in his distribution system up or down. Long-distance transmission would require a copper wire as thick as your arm to avoid large power losses and voltage drops. Edison and his associates decided that this problem could be solved by having a power station every couple of kilometres. Although the voltage of alternating current could be changed easily, no practical AC motors or generators were available.

Born in 1856, Nikola Tesla arrived in New York City in 1884 with four cents in his pocket and an ingenious design for alternating-current motors and generators. Tesla worked with Edison for a while, but Edison had built his business on direct-current power and was aggravated by any talk of alternating current.

When Tesla left to produce AC equipment, Edison and his associates at General Electric tried to discredit Tesla's work. To show how "dangerous" alternating current was, they electrocuted animals in public demonstrations and suggested using AC to execute prisoners on death row.

Despite competition from General Electric, Tesla and the George Westinghouse Company won a contract to light the 1893 World Exposition in Chicago using large alternating-current generators of Tesla's design.

After this success, Tesla and Westinghouse were immediately awarded a contract to harness the energy from Niagara Falls. In 1896, three 3.7-MW AC generators—the largest generators of their time—began feeding power into a 22 kV transmission line. Tesla's designs began to be widely used, and AC became the standard for power distribution.

The electrical age had begun, thanks to a man whose contributions are often overlooked.

WEBLINK

The hydro-electric plants at Niagara Falls have helped to fill the energy needs of Ontario for many years. Research their history and development and draw an illustrated timeline of this development. Begin your research at **www.pearsoned.ca/physics11**.

Discovering Physics — *Fast Flicker*

Can you devise a way to detect the flicker in a light bulb connected to 60-Hz power? If a data logger is available, try connecting a light sensor to the interface and computer. Make sure that the sampling rate is fast enough to register events that are happening 120 times per second. Can you think of any other methods? Is the flicker more apparent with some types of bulbs than with others?

Section 15.5 Review

Understanding Concepts

1. What conditions are necessary to produce an induced potential difference?
2. Explain the operation of the slip rings.
3. Why is the induced potential difference zero twice during each cycle of rotation?
4. Why does the induced potential difference reverse itself during the rotation of the armature?

Inquiry and Communication

5. What changes could you make in the design or operation of an AC generator to provide
   a) a higher frequency alternating current?
   b) a higher induced potential difference?

Making Connections

6. If the current from the AC generator shown in Figure 15.39 alternates at 100 Hz, at what rate would a light bulb connected to the generator flicker?

15.6 The Electric Transformer

Key Understandings

When you have completed this section, you will be able to:

- name the basic parts and describe the operation of a transformer
- solve problems involving potential difference, current, and number of turns in the primary and secondary coils of a transformer
- describe the operation and applications of step-up and step-down transformers

Often the potential difference or current that we receive from our electric utility is not directly usable for many devices. The picture tube in a computer monitor or television set requires a much higher potential difference, while most computers use a much lower potential difference, usually 5 or 12 V. An arc welder requires both low voltages and large currents.

The device that changes the potential difference and current to the amounts we need is called a transformer. In this section we will find out how these useful devices work.

A basic **transformer** is a simple device containing no moving parts. It consists of two coils of wire wrapped around a permeable **core** (Figure 15.40). This core is usually soft iron, which can concentrate a magnetic field and yet allow the field to change rapidly. The coil that receives alternating current from an external circuit is called the **primary coil**. The coil in which a potential difference is induced is called the **secondary coil**. The basic transformer is similar to Faraday's apparatus for demonstrating electromagnetic induction.

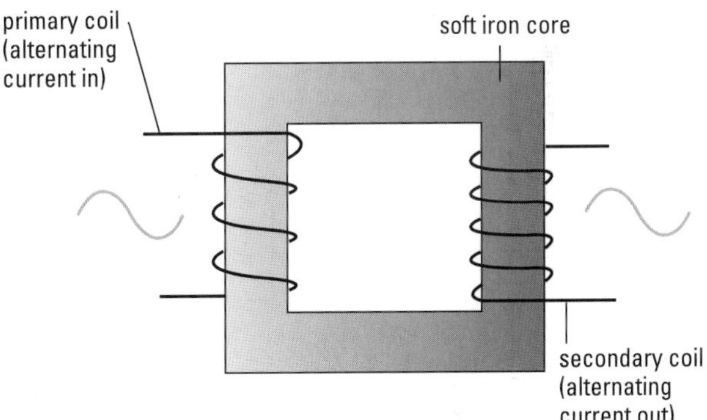

FIGURE 15.40 Basic parts of a transformer

The primary coil receives alternating current. While current flows through it, a magnetic field is set up that is carried to the secondary coil by the core. Since the current in the primary coil is changing, its magnetic field is also changing. This changing magnetic field induces a potential difference in the secondary coil.

Figure 15.41 shows a graph of an alternating current supplied to the primary coil, along with diagrams of the induced current and magnetic fields in the secondary coil at four points in the cycle. At point A the current in the primary coil is increasing. Therefore, the magnetic field due to that current is also increasing. According to Lenz's law, the secondary coil must set up a field that opposes this increase in magnetic field. Thus, the induced current must produce a north pole opposite the north pole of the primary coil. The directions of the induced current and magnetic field are illustrated in Figure 15.41.

At C the current in the primary coil is decreasing. This causes the primary magnetic field to decrease. The secondary coil now tries to maintain the existing magnetic field. Note that both the secondary magnetic

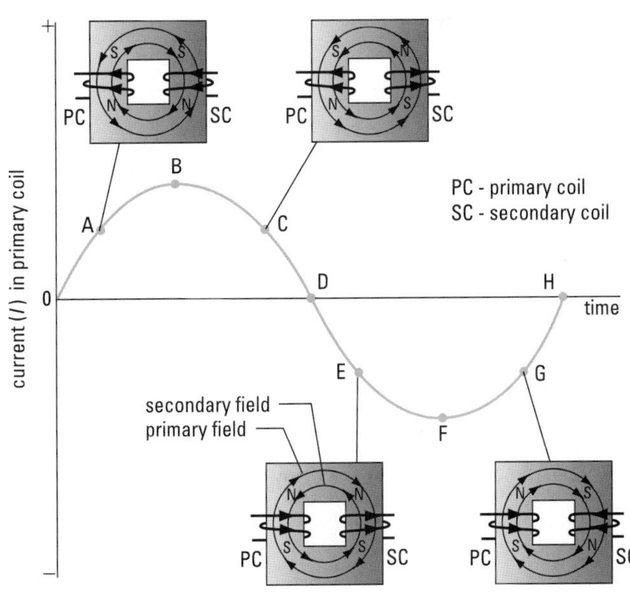

FIGURE 15.41 Induction in a transformer

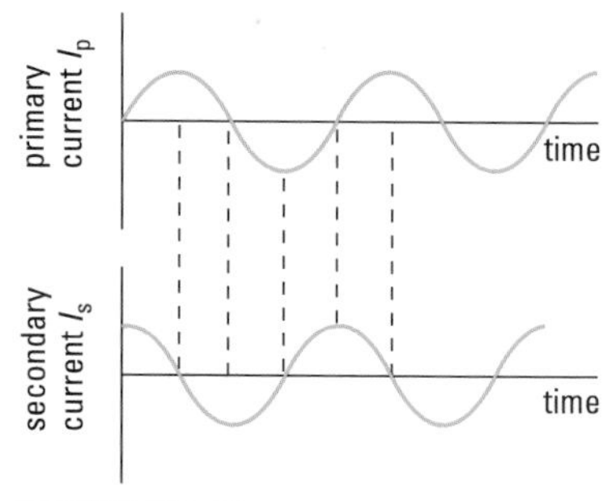

FIGURE 15.42 The secondary current is out of phase with the primary current.

field and the secondary electric current have reversed. The same process occurs at E and G. At E the secondary field opposes the increase in the primary field. At G the secondary field attempts to maintain the primary field while the primary current is decreasing in value.

At B and F the primary current is neither increasing nor decreasing. As a result, the primary field is not changing. Since the field remains constant, no electron flow is induced in the secondary coil. The opposite effect occurs at D and H. Here the primary current (and field) is undergoing the most rapid change, as indicated by the steepness of the slope of the current–time graph. Thus, the induced current in the secondary coil is the greatest where the slope of the primary current–time graph is steepest.

The relationship between the primary and secondary currents is shown in Figure 15.42. Note that the two currents are out of phase with each other. When the value of the primary current is at a maximum, the values of the induced secondary potential difference and current are zero.

Step-Up and Step-Down Transformers

The magnitude of the induced potential difference depends on both the rate of change of the magnetic field and the number of turns in the secondary coil relative to the number of turns in the primary coil. If there are more turns in the secondary coil than in the primary coil, the potential difference in the secondary coil is greater than the potential difference in the primary coil. This type of transformer is called a **step-up transformer** because it increases the potential difference. If there are fewer turns in the secondary coil than in the primary coil, the induced potential difference in the secondary coil is less than that of the primary coil. This type of transformer is called a **step-down transformer**.

In general, the potential difference relationships can be expressed by

$$\frac{V_s}{V_p} = \frac{N_s}{N_p}$$

Investigation

Refer to page 581, Investigation 2

where V_p and V_s are the potential differences in volts across the primary and secondary coils, respectively, and N_p and N_s are the numbers of turns in the primary and secondary coils, respectively. $\frac{N_s}{N_p}$ is called the **turns ratio**.

A second relationship can be developed from the law of conservation of energy. From Chapter 13, we know that electrical energy can be expressed as

$$E = VI\Delta t$$

where E is the energy exchanged in joules
V is the potential difference in volts
I is the current in amperes
Δt is the time interval in seconds

Assuming no losses of energy through heating and radiation, in any given time the amount of energy lost by the primary coil must equal the amount of energy gained by the secondary coil:

$$E_p = E_s$$

$$V_p I_p \Delta t = V_s I_s \Delta t$$

therefore

$$V_p I_p = V_s I_s$$

or

$$\frac{V_p}{V_s} = \frac{I_s}{I_p}$$

Comparing with the first relationship for V_s/V_p gives:

$$\frac{I_s}{I_p} = \frac{N_p}{N_s}$$

Note that the turns ratio is equal to the voltage ratio and to the *inverse* of the current ratio. Figure 15.43 shows the relationship between the corresponding variables in the primary and secondary coils for step-up and step-down transformers. In all problems we will assume that there is negligible energy loss in the transformer and that the formulas above apply.

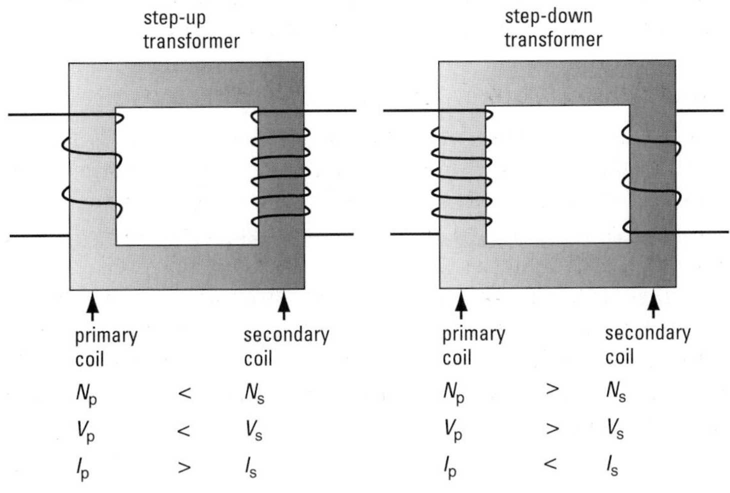

primary coil		secondary coil	primary coil		secondary coil
N_p	$<$	N_s	N_p	$>$	N_s
V_p	$<$	V_s	V_p	$>$	V_s
I_p	$>$	I_s	I_p	$<$	I_s

FIGURE 15.43 Step-up and step-down transformers

WEBLINK

The construction of a transformer is seems to be very simple as it consists of only two coils and a soft iron core. Are the transformers that you see on hydro poles and in hydro yards really that simple? Find out and prepare a diagram to explain the construction of a heavy-duty transformer. Begin your research at **www.pearsoned.ca/physics11**

EXAMPLE 7 NUMERICAL

A step-down transformer contains 2000 turns on the primary coil and 200 turns on the secondary coil. If the potential difference and current in the primary coil are 30.0 V AC and 0.700 A, what are the values for the potential difference and current in the secondary coil?

Given
$N_p = 2000$ and $N_s = 200$
$V_p = 30.0$ V and $I_p = 0.700$ A

Required
V_s and I_s

Analysis

$$\frac{V_s}{V_p} = \frac{N_s}{N_p}, \text{ so } V_s = \frac{V_p \times N_s}{N_p}$$

$$\frac{I_s}{I_p} = \frac{N_p}{N_s}, \text{ so } I_s = \frac{I_p \times N_p}{N_s}$$

Solution

$$V_s = \frac{V_p \times N_s}{N_p}$$

$$= \frac{30.0 \text{ V} \times 200}{2000}$$

$$= 3.00 \text{ V}$$

$$I_s = \frac{I_p \times N_p}{N_s}$$

$$= \frac{0.700 \text{ A} \times 2000}{200}$$

$$= 7.00 \text{ A}$$

Statement

The potential difference is 3.00 V AC and the current is 7.00 A in the secondary coil.

PRACTICE PROBLEMS

1. A transformer has 250 turns on the primary coil and 1000 turns on the secondary coil.
   a) If the primary voltage is 120 V AC, what will the secondary voltage be?
   b) If the primary current is 0.40 A, what will the secondary current be?
2. A transformer has 500 turns on the primary coil. If it is being used to step an input of 120 V AC down to 12 V AC, how many turns should be on the secondary coil?

INSIGHT

The second part of this solution could have been done using the previously calculated value for potential difference and the formula. $\frac{I_s}{I_p} = \frac{V_p}{V_s}$.

However, if the calculation for potential difference had been incorrect, then the answer based upon it would have also been incorrect. Decide if your answers seem reasonable. For example, if there are more windings on the primary coil than on the secondary coil, expect the potential difference to decrease and the current to increase. If it doesn't, then check your work.

From the numerical example above we can see that as the potential difference decreases, the current increases. This relationship is consistent with the law of conservation of energy. At first glance, it might seem that transformers violate Ohm's law. However, remember that the input and output windings are in two separate circuits that are linked by electromagnetic induction instead of by conductors.

Transformers in the Home

Step-down transformers are common in the home. Doorbells and small electric motors, such as the ones in some toys and humidifiers, use step-down transformers. Adapters for electronic equipment such as keyboards and scanners are also step-down transformers. In fact, most plug-in electronic equipment contains at least one transformer. Step-up transformers are less common, but they are used in televisions, computer monitors, and in many furnace-ignition circuits.

Section 15.6 Review

Understanding Concepts

1. At what instant during the cycle of the primary alternating current is the induced potential difference:
   a) greatest?
   b) zero?
2. By how much of a cycle are the primary and secondary currents out of phase?
3. For a step-up transformer, which coil has the larger
   a) number of turns?
   b) potential difference across it?
   c) current through it?
4. Repeat Question 3 for a step-down transformer.
5. A transformer consists of a primary coil of 100 turns and a secondary

Design & Build

Audio Speaker Kit

You have been asked to help demonstrate the properties of sound to elementary school students. The school is not well equipped for teaching science and so you wish to let the students build some of the supplies themselves. One such item could be an audio speaker. Not only would it illustrate the need for a vibrating source for sound, it would emphasize an application of electrical energy and magnetism.

Proposal

Design a speaker which can be easily constructed and taken apart for instructional purposes. Include a booklet or manual which would include design plans, instructions for building the speaker, and an outline of investigations that could be done with the speaker.

Materials

Any materials for the speaker should be readily obtained from around the house or purchased inexpensively at local electronics or electrical stores.

The leads should consist of thin insulated wire such as #22 or #24 gauge wire.

A resistor of about 4 Ω to 6 Ω should be included in series with the speaker to prevent shorting out any device to which the speaker might be connected such as a signal generator or a tape or CD player.

Specifications

1. Design a speaker that
   - consists of readily obtained materials
   - will produce a range of audible frequencies
   - can be easily assembled and taken apart
   - can be easily modified
2. Choose the materials to use in the speaker. For example, what will act as the speaker cone? If you are using an electromagnet, what will act as the core? How will you make the speaker cone pulse in step with the alternating current in the electromagnet?

HINT: Speakers have been built out of margarine tubs. When a small magnet was glued to the middle of the lid, the lid acted as the cone.

3. Provide an instruction manual for this speaker kit. It is to explain how the speaker is to be constructed. Write in clear enough language that a student in grade 7 or 8 could follow the instructions. Include good diagrams. Also outline various investigations that could be accomplished with this speaker and how it could be connected to a tape or CD player.

Caution: Do not connect this speaker to a 120-V outlet.

Design

1. In your group brainstorm various designs that could be used. You may wish to develop designs for different-sized speakers that could respond better to different frequency ranges.
2. Choose one or more designs that you wish to investigate. Provide an initial sketch of each design and make a list of all materials required.
3. Have the teacher check your proposal before continuing with the project.

Construction

a) Assemble the materials and build the speaker or speakers. Test them by connecting them to the output of a tape or CD player. (Make sure that the resistor has been included in series.)

b) If you are satisfied with the results, develop a series of investigations that could be done with the speaker(s).

c) Prepare an instruction manual to go along with your speaker kit.

d) Demonstrate your speaker kit to the rest of the class and provide a display of your instruction manual.

Evaluation

Assess your design after your presentation. Does the speaker work? Can it be used for sound investigations? How might you improve the design? If possible, try this kit out with a few elementary school students and obtain their comments.

Investigation 1 (Section 15.1)

Inquiry Skills

- Initiating and Planning
- Applying Technical Skills
- Using Tools, Materials, Equipment
- Conducting and Recording
- Analyzing and Interpreting
- Concluding and Communicating

Producing an Induced Potential Difference

A potential difference can be induced by changing the magnetic field around a conductor. This can be done by inserting one pole of a bar magnet into the air core of a coil. How do you think the induced potential difference will be affected by:

a) reversing the direction of the motion of the magnetic pole?
b) inserting the opposite pole?
c) changing the speed of the magnet?
d) moving the coil instead of the bar magnet?
e) using a coil with more turns?

Make predictions. Then do the activity to check your predictions.

Problem

What factors affect the magnitude of the potential difference produced during electromagnetic induction?

Materials

- bar magnet
- voltmeter (with millivolt range)
- electric leads
- 2 helices, each with a different number of turns

Procedure

1. Hold the bar magnet stationary inside one of the helices.
2. Connect the voltmeter to the helix and observe the deflection of the needle. Record the maximum reading.
3. Connect the voltmeter to the helix with the least number of turns.
4. Slowly insert the north pole of the bar magnet as shown in Figure 15.49. Record the sign and value of the maximum reading.

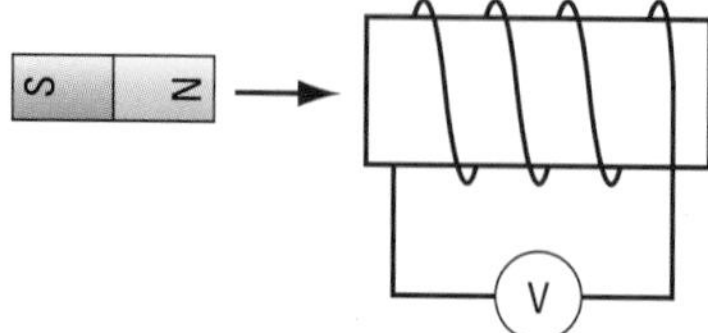

FIGURE 15.49 Observing an induced potential difference

5. Withdraw the north pole slowly from the helix. Record the sign and value of the maximum reading.
6. Repeat steps 4 and 5 using instead the south pole of the bar magnet.
7. Repeat steps 4 and 5, but this time moving the magnet quickly.
8. Repeat steps 4 and 5, but this time holding the bar magnet steady and moving the helix.
9. Connect the helix with the larger number of turns to the voltmeter. Take care to connect it exactly as the first helix was connected. Quickly insert the north pole of the bar magnet into the helix.

Analyzing and Interpreting

1. Was any potential difference produced when the magnet was stationary?
2. When all other factors remained constant, how was the magnitude of the induced potential difference affected by:
   a) the type of pole inserted or withdrawn?
   b) the direction of motion of the pole in or out of the coil?
   c) the speed of the magnet?
   d) moving the helix instead of the bar magnet?
   e) the number of turns in the helix?
3. Which of the above factors affected the direction of the induced potential difference?

Concluding and Communicating

4. What conditions must be met in order to produce an induced potential difference?
5. What factors affect
   a) the magnitude of the induced potential difference
   b) the direction of the induced potential difference?
6. What type of device is likely to use electromagnetic induction?

Extending

7. How can this apparatus be used to demonstrate that motion is relative? Investigate other ways by which the external magnetic field can be changed and determine the effect on the induced potential differences.

Investigation 2 (Section 15.6)

Verifying Transformer Relationships

Inquiry Skills

- Initiating and Planning
- Applying Technical Skills
- Using Tools, Materials, Equipment
- Conducting and Recording
- Analyzing and Interpreting
- Concluding and Communicating

Transformers are electrical devices used to change the potential difference in a circuit. Many electronic devices need a potential difference that is much lower than the 120 V AC supplied by household circuits. In some cases, such as for television picture tubes and fluorescent lighting, the potential difference must be increased.

In this activity, you will investigate how the potential difference and current coming out of a transformer relate to the number of turns on the coils within the transformer. Make a prediction about how the potential difference and current will vary across a transformer if the number of turns on the secondary coil is greater than the number on the primary coil.

Problem

What are the potential difference and current relationships for the transformer?

Materials and Cautions

- 2 AC ammeters
- AC power supply
- 2 AC voltmeters
- 2 coils (with different numbers of turns)
- iron core which can link the coils
- 2 resistors
- switch (which may be included in the power supply)

CAUTION: Use only the low potential differences specified by your teacher. Do not touch any terminals while the switch is closed. To prevent overheating, close the switch for only the time required to take measurements.

Experimental Design

1. Draw a circuit diagram for a circuit with which you could measure the primary potential difference and current and also the secondary potential difference and current. Include resistors in both the primary and secondary circuits to prevent short circuits.
2. Write the steps for a method in which you can measure the primary potential difference and current and also the secondary potential difference and current. Be sure to include a transformer set-up in which the secondary coil has the higher number of turns (a step-up transformer) and one in which the primary coil has the higher number of turns (a step-down transformer). Decide how you will organize and present your data. How many different readings will you take with each arrangement of coils? Make sure that you are recording the number of turns on each coil.
3. After the teacher has approved the circuit diagram and the steps of your procedure, assemble the circuit.
4. Have the teacher check the circuit before you perform the investigation.

Analyzing and Interpreting

1. How did the primary and secondary potential differences compare
   a) when the secondary coil had the greater number of turns?
   b) when the primary coil had the greater number of turns?
2. How did the primary and secondary currents compare
   a) when the secondary coil had the greater number of turns?
   b) when the primary coil had the greater number of turns?
3. Using the formula $P = VI$ compare the power generated in the secondary coil to that lost in the primary coil.

Concluding and Communicating

4. a) What happens to the potential difference and current in a step-up transformer?
   b) What happens to the potential difference and current in a step-down transformer?
5. Power represents the rate at which energy is being exchanged or transformed. Do the powers in the primary and secondary coils represent energy gains or losses? Discuss.
6. According to law of conservation of energy, the powers in the two coils should be the same.

a) How close are they to each other? Express this as an efficiency

$$\text{efficiency} = \frac{\text{secondary power}}{\text{primary power}} \times 100\%$$

b) If the two powers are not the same, suggest reasons for the difference.

7. For each type of transformer, how does the
   a) ratio of potential differences compare with the ratio of turns on the coils?
   b) ratio of currents compare with the ratio of turns on the coils?
   c) ratio of potential differences compare with the ratio of currents?

Extending

8. Is the rate of energy loss in a transformer affected by the total number of turns in the primary and secondary coils? Make a hypothesis, giving reasons for your prediction. Then design and perform an experiment to test your hypothesis. To simplify your analysis, use the same number of turns in the primary and secondary coils.

CHAPTER SUMMARY

Key Terms

alternating current
armature
brush
cone
deflection coils
direct current
direct current motor
electromagnetic induction
field magnet
field windings
gauss
generating station
generator
induced current
induced potential difference
primary coil
rotor
secondary coil
slip-ring
split-ring commutator
tesla
transformer
transmission line
turbine
turns ratio

Key Equations

For the electromagnetic force, $F \alpha I$ and $F \alpha B$

For electromagnetic induction, $V \alpha N$ and $V \alpha \frac{\Delta B}{\Delta t}$

For a transformer, $\frac{V_s}{V_p} = \frac{N_s}{N_p}$, $\frac{V_p}{V_s} = \frac{I_s}{I_p}$, and $\frac{I_s}{I_p} = \frac{N_p}{N_s}$

Essential Understandings

- The motor principle states that when a current-carrying conductor is placed in an external magnetic field that is perpendicular to the conductor, there is a force on the conductor that is perpendicular to both the conductor and the external magnetic field.
- The right-hand rule for electromagnetic force states that if you place your right hand so that your thumb points in the direction of the current and your fingers point in the direction of the external magnetic field, then the force on the conductor is directed outward from the palm of your hand.
- The size of the force on the conductor is affected by the amount of current in the conductor and the strength of the perpendicular magnetic field.
- The force exerted on a current-carrying conductor in an external magnetic field forms the basis of all electric motors.
- Factors affecting the operation of a DC motor include the number of turns on the armature, the strength of the field magnet, and the magnitude of the current through the helix.
- The operation of speakers, TV picture tubes, and railguns and the behaviour of comet tails can be explained by using the motor principle.
- A potential difference is induced in a conductor when there is a relative motion between the conductor and an external magnetic field.
- The size of the induced potential difference in a helix depends on the number of turns in the helix and the rate of change of the magnetic field.
- Lenz's law states that the magnetic field of an induced current always opposes the change in the magnetic field that is causing the induced current.
- When a coil moves relative to a magnetic field, a potential difference is induced in the coil. This induction is the basis of an AC generator.
- A transformer, through electromagnetic induction, changes the magnitude of an alternating potential difference and current.
- All large-scale generation of electrical energy in the world is accomplished with turbine generators, the key difference being the primary energy source used to drive the turbines.
- Increasing the potential differnce at which electrical energy is transmitted can substantially reduce the power loss due to heating in the transmission line.

Consolidate Your Understanding

1. Look back at your answer to the Checkpoint question on page 547. Do you still agree with your answer or do you wish to change it? Give reasons for your choice.

   Which choice or choices of answer might be correct if electrical transmission occurred at low voltages (potential differences)? Explain your answer.

2. Draw two graphic organizers side by side. Begin the left-hand one with a rectangle containing the words, The Motor Principle. Begin the right-hand one with a rectangle containing the words, Electromagnetic Induction. Extend outwards from each rectangle by indicating factors, effects, and applications. Then use coloured lines to show parallel links between the two charts.

CHAPTER 15 REVIEW

Understanding Concepts

1. Who first discovered the magnetic induction of an electric current?
   a) Ampère
   b) Faraday
   c) Henry
   d) Lenz
   e) Oersted
2. Which of the diagrams in Figure 15.50 represents a correct relation between the directions of the current, the external magnetic field, and the force on the conductor?
   a) I and II only
   b) I and III only
   c) II and III only
   d) I, II, and III
   e) none of the diagrams

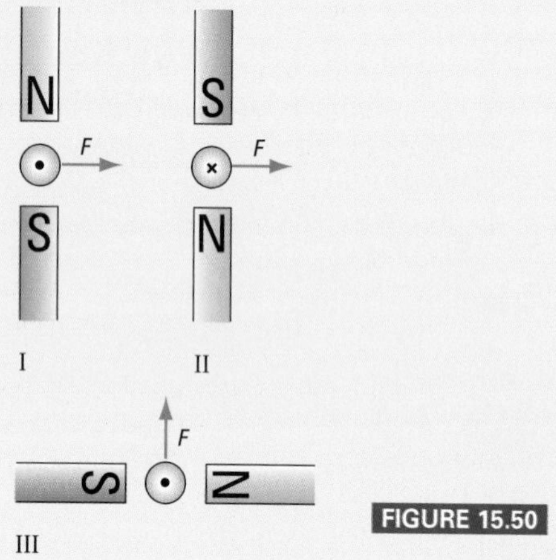

FIGURE 15.50

3. Which of the following affects the magnitude of an induced potential difference in a solenoid (helix)?
   I. number of turns in the solenoid
   II. rate of change of the magnetic field
   III. strength of the magnetic field
   IV. resistance of the wire used in the solenoid

   Choose your answer from the following:
   a) I and II only
   b) I and III only
   c) I and IV only
   d) II and III only
   e) II and IV only
4. Generating plants use step-up transformers before the electrical energy is transmitted across the country in order to:
   a) reduce the resistance
   b) increase the current in the lines
   c) reduce the potential difference in the lines
   d) reduce the power loss in the lines
   e) keep birds from perching on the lines
5. a) What are the essential parts of a galvanometer?
   b) What is the function of each part?
6. In a direct current motor, what is the function of
   a) the field windings?
   b) the rotor?
   c) the split-ring commutator?
7. Why are the brushes in a DC motor usually spring loaded (attached to compressed springs)?
8. In a television set, what is the function of
   a) the electron gun?
   b) the deflection coils?
9. What is the function of the cone in a speaker?
10. Why is a helix attached to the cone of a speaker?
11. List three important parts of the AC generator and state their functions.
12. Compare the transformations of energy in the electric motor and the generator.
13. What is the frequency of alternating current in North America?
14. What is the relationship between the turns on the primary and secondary coils for
    a) a step-down transformer?
    b) a step-up transformer?
15. What is the relationship between the potential differences and current in the primary and secondary coils of
    a) a step-down transformer?
    b) a step-up transformer?
16. Which type of transformer is used for
    a) a television picture tube?
    b) a doorbell?
17. What potential difference is provided to homes in Canada?

Applying Inquiry/ Communication Skills

18. Design a device that would use the motor principle to compare magnetic field strengths.
19. Sketch a graph of current against time for segment AB of the DC motor shown in Figure 507 (page 554). Assume the rotation rate is 100 rev/s. Show at least five complete revolutions of the loop, beginning with it oriented as shown in Figure 15.17a).
20. a) Explain how deflection coils control the vertical motion of the electron beam in a television set.
    b) How would the operation of the coils be different if the gun fired protons instead of electrons? Assume that the protons travel at the same speed as did the electrons. (Protons have a positive charge and nearly 2000 times the mass of electrons.)

21. A stream of electrons and hydrogen nuclei is travelling through a vacuum as shown in Figure 15.51. Both types of particles are travelling with the same speed and direction. When either type strikes the fluorescent face, a flash of light is emitted. Each electron has a single negative charge and each hydrogen nucleus has a single positive charge. Explain the technique you would use to:
    a) separate the hydrogen nuclei from the electrons
    b) demonstrate that the hydrogen nucleus is much more massive than an electron

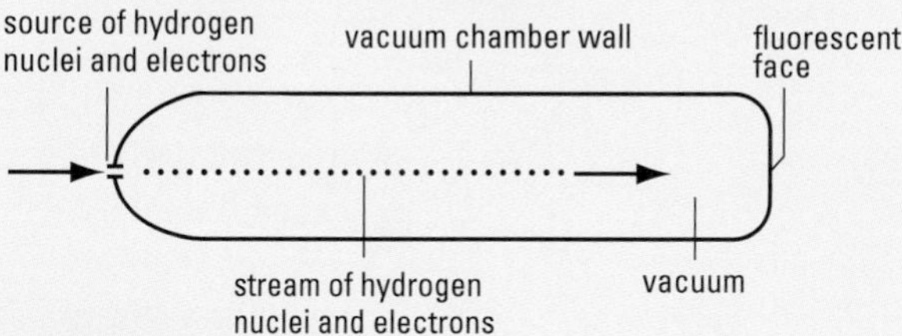

FIGURE 15.51

22. Describe how the slip rings of an AC generator could be modified to produce a DC generator. Draw a sketch to show how the current produced from such a generator would vary during two cycles of the armature.

23. Compare the electric motor and the AC generator using an organizer such as a Venn diagram.

Making Connections

24. An ohmmeter is a device that measures resistance when connected across an unknown resistor. Basically, it is a galvanometer being used as an ammeter.
    a) What must be known in order to find resistance?
    b) Why does an ohmmeter require batteries?
    c) Why does a zero deflection of the pointer indicate infinite resistance, and full-scale deflection indicate effectively zero resistance?

25. Explain why you must always begin readings on the maximum scale of a multi-range meter.

26. Above the Arctic Circle a proton is heading north parallel to the ground. Which way will it be deflected by Earth's magnetic field? Assume that the field is nearly perpendicular to the ground.

27. On a cold day, which power line should birds sit on to keep their feet warmest—the line leading into or out of a step-down transformer? Explain your answer.

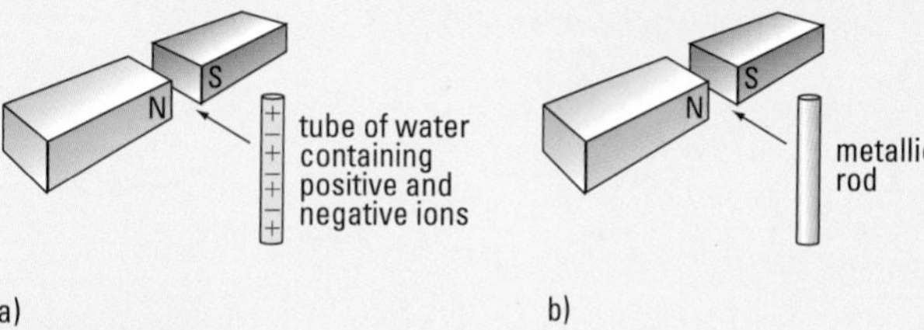

FIGURE 15.52

28. Imagine that a long tube of water contains positive ions and negative ions. It is moved between magnetic poles as shown in Figure 15.52. Use the right-hand rule for electromagnetic force to predict the direction
    a) in which the positive ions will tend to move
    b) in which the negative ions will tend to move
    c) of the resulting current if the charged ions can move.

29. Imagine that a long metallic rod replaces the tube of water in question 27. Its motion is shown in Figure 15.52b).
    a) Sketch Figure 15.52b) into your notes.
    b) Draw the lines of magnetic force between the magnetic poles, indicating their direction on the diagram.
    c) Indicate the direction of the circular field around the rod that would oppose the motion of the rod (Lenz's law).
    d) Using the right-hand rule for a straight conductor, predict the direction of the current in the rod that would create the circular field.
    e) How does your prediction of current direction based upon the right-hand rule for electromagnetic force compare with your direction based upon Lenz's law for induced currents?
    f) Are electromagnetic force and electromagnetic induction completely different concepts? Discuss.

30. Figure 15.53 shows the structure of a laboratory induction coil.

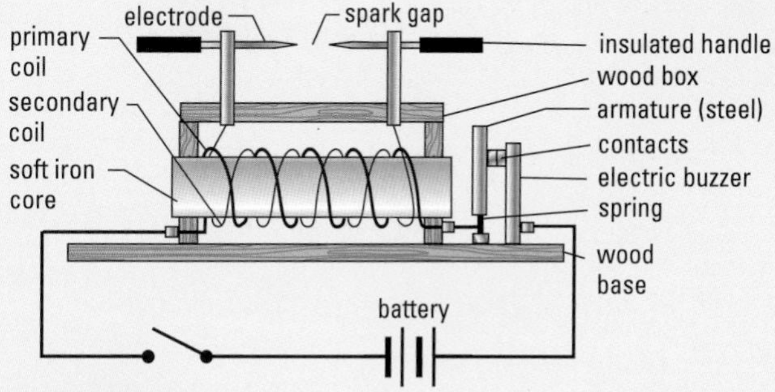

FIGURE 15.53

    a) Explain why the armature vibrates when the switch is closed.
    b) How does this design produce a large potential difference across the secondary coil?

After Class

You've learned about some of the many career choices available to someone interested in physics. You've explored how your skills can give you ideas about what type of career might suit you. Perhaps you've done some research about a career or two over the Internet and started collecting what you'll need when applying for jobs, scholarships, and courses. What comes next? How could you continue your career explorations after this class is over?

FIGURE 1 Summer work experience develops skills and adds to your résumé.

Is It Summer Break?

1. Prepare for your summer break before it begins by obtaining as much information as you can from your school's guidance and science departments. Here are some examples:
   - any important dates for applications, contests, etc., especially any occurring early in the coming fall
   - any forms or applications that can be completed over the summer or which must be submitted by the end of June
   - letters of reference from teachers who know you and your work particularly well (Ask *before* the last day of class.)
   - registration information for courses offered during the summer in a field of interest to you. These may be at your school, other schools in your community, or at universities and science centres. (You may need to apply a few months ahead. If you are interested, but the deadline for this year has passed, see if the course is offered at another time or location. Also, be aware that many courses and camps charge tuition fees.)
   - your science department's guidelines about science fair experiments if you plan to begin during the summer. (You may be able to sign out equipment as well.)

2. If you wish to continue using the Internet to research your career and educational options, but don't have access at home, find out how you can do this before leaving school. Here are some possibilities:
   - public libraries
   - a relative or family friend
   - a local computer store or Internet café (these offer the use of a computer and Internet access on their premises, usually for a fee)

- take a computer course on using the Internet (these courses may include a certain amount of time for personal research.)
- consult the communications technology teacher in your school for more ideas

Taking Charge

Have you considered taking a correspondence course that can count toward a future degree or improve your grades? These are offered by many institutions. Perhaps you can do this during the summer.

3. Obtain information from your school guidance department or by contacting the specific institution. Ask yourself these questions:
   - What do you want to achieve by taking this course? You should have a clear, defined goal in mind. For example, if you need high school calculus for the university degree you wish to pursue, but your high school isn't offering it at a time that suits your timetable, you might want to see if a correspondence or summer calculus course is available.
   - Realistically, will you complete the course? It's up to you to find the time and the motivation. Are you working full-time over the summer? Will you be away from home for significant lengths of time? Think about whether you need a classroom setting and peers in order to keep going. Many students do.
   - What prerequisites does the course require? There are usually high school courses you need to have first. Will you need Internet access or equipment such as a video cassette player and television?
   - How much does the course cost? (Don't forget the cost of equipment and books.) How reputable is the institution offering the course? Don't hesitate to ask questions and compare your options. Before making any commitment, be sure any course you plan to take for credit or toward a degree is recognized by your school and/or universities.

If It Isn't Summer Break?

4. Go over the suggestions for what you could do over the summer. Which of these could you start during your next term of high school? For each, what would be the advantage(s) of making an early start? What are the possible disadvantage(s)?
   - If you will be going into science at university, what courses will you need to take next year? What additional courses would be useful? (For example, if you are looking at careers in physics, and want to become an entrepreneur, you may wish to learn more about marketing, economics, or law.)
   - Many contests are run during the spring term. Find out about these, as well as science fair opportunities.

Looking Outward

You are on a journey, not rushing to a finish line. The career choices you are considering now may turn out to be ones you pursue—or you may change your mind and go in a completely different direction. That's fine. The key is to take charge of your own career search, find information about what interests you, and be ready for the opportunities ahead.

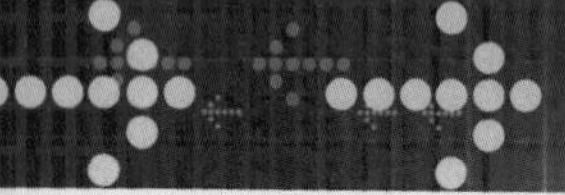

Designing a Window Display

Background Information

Many of the things you see around you work because of the principles of electromagnetism. Motors and generators are an integral part of everyday life, providing movement, light, and sound. This activity will highlight a few of these applications, especially those in which electromagnetic principles are used to produce and control motion.

SCENARIO

The manager of a hardware store has asked you to add life to a window display. It portrays a street scene in a small village. The ten houses have windows but no lights. The waterwheel of a mill dips into a tiny river but does not turn and the sails of a windmill remain still. The deck of a lift bridge across the same river is free to go up and down, but sits motionless.

It is your task to add as much light and motion to this scene as you can, using materials that you find around the store. To make it as portable as possible, it will run off six D-cell batteries. There are no electromagnets or motors, but the store does have

- miniature light bulbs rated at 1.5 V and 40 Ω
- sockets for the miniature light bulbs
- D-batteries rated at 1.5 V and 18 000 mA·h (four of these may be used for the lighting, one for the bridge and one for the waterwheel and windmill).
- electrical wire
- spools of magnet wire
- tiny button magnets
- electrical tape
- epoxy glue
- cardboard and balsa wood
- thin strips of copper
- nails and needles
- standard hardware tools—pliers, scissors, saws, soldering equipment, drills and so on
- multimeters which can act as ammeters or voltmeters

You may also bring any common item that you might find around the home, but you may not bring motors or electromagnets. Think carefully how you can complete this task with the materials you have.

Part A: Research and Planning

1. Working in a small group of three or four students, brainstorm possible ways to
   - connect the light bulbs and four of the D-cell batteries
   - make the waterwheel and the sails of the windmill turn around
   - make the bridge go up and down
2. Do some research. You can find a number of suggestions for constructing motors on the Internet.

Part B: Design

3. Prepare a design to show your proposal. Along with the design, provide a set of notes to explain why your design should work.
4. Once the design has been approved by your teacher, prepare schematic diagrams to show:
   - how you would determine the electrical power used by the waterwheel
   - how you would determine the resistance of the device used to raise the bridge

Part C: Costs and Considerations

5. Calculate the expected life of the D-cells.
6. Estimate the total cost of your proposal. Assume that you will have to use a whole spool of magnet wire.
7. If possible, build a working model of the waterwheel, windmill, and lift bridge.

Part D: Communicate Your Design

8. If you have constructed and tested the devices, prepare a demonstration of your animated display. If it is too difficult to bring these items into class, you could bring in a videotape showing the lighting of the village and the various devices in action. At the same time, prepare a presentation, possibly as a poster or computer-aided display. Include graphics to illustrate how the various electromagnetic devices work.

FIGURE 1

UNIT 5 REVIEW

Understanding Concepts

1. What current will pass through a 100-mΩ resistor if the potential difference across it is 2.00 V?
a) 0.200 A
b) 20.0 A
c) 5.00 A
d) 100 A
e) 2.00 kA

2. Three resistors with values of 2.0 Ω, 3.0 Ω, and 4.0 Ω are connected in parallel. What is the effective resistance of the combination?
a) 0.80 Ω
b) 0.92 Ω
c) 1.1 Ω
d) 9.0 Ω
e) 24 Ω

3. What is the power loss across a 50.0-Ω resistor if a potential difference of 20.0 V exists across it?
a) 2.50 W
b) 8.0 W
c) 20.0 W
d) 312 W
e) 1.00 kW

4. For which of the coils in Figure 1 are the poles indicated correctly?
a) I and II
b) III and IV
c) I and III
d) II and IV
e) II and III

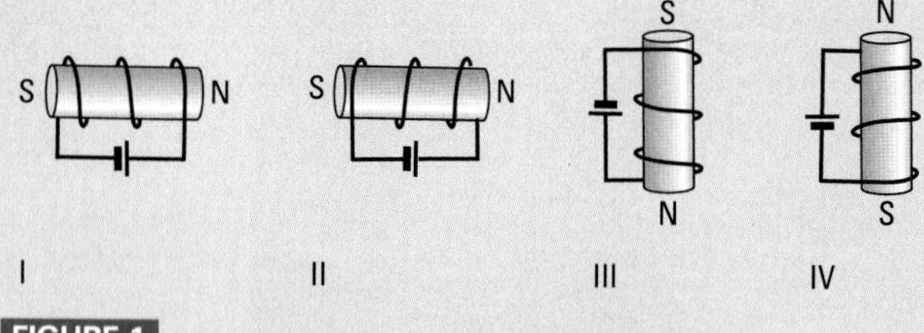

FIGURE 1

5. Two coils are arranged as shown in Figure 2. Current flows into the page through a conductor indicated by the circle. In which direction will the electromagnetic force act on the conductor?
a) toward helix X
b) toward helix Y
c) to the right
d) to the left
e) up, out of the page

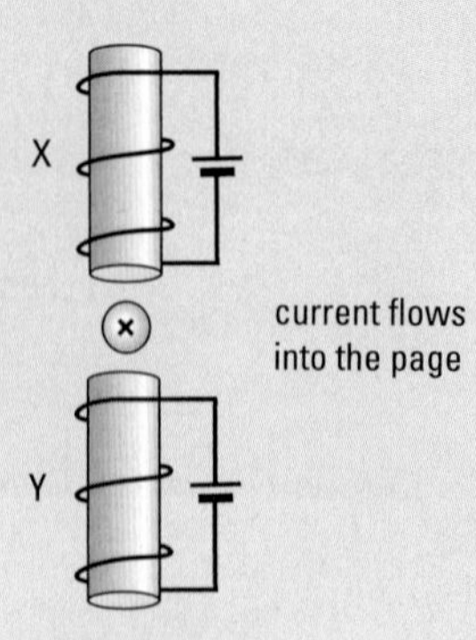

FIGURE 2

6. In Figure 3, a south pole is being withdrawn from a helix. Which pole will be created at the left side of the helix and which way will the induced current flow between X and Y?
a) south, X to Y
b) south, Y to X
c) north, X to Y
d) north, Y to X
e) There is no induced current.

FIGURE 3

7. A transformer converts 120.0 V AC to 12.00 V AC. If there are 200 turns on the primary coil, how many are on the secondary coil?
a) 12
b) 20
c) 100
d) 1200
e) 2000

8. a) State Ohm's law.
b) What factor must be held constant for Ohm's law to be valid?

9. What are the basic units for
a) the volt?
b) the ampere?
c) the ohm?

10. Which magnetic pole is located in the Antarctic? Explain how you know.

11. What is the direction of the lines of magnetic force inside a magnet?

12. Which scientist discovered the magnetic field around an electric current?

13. In a DC motor, what is the function of
a) the split-ring commutator?
b) the helix?
c) the field magnets?

14. a) Why is a shunt needed in an ammeter?
b) Why does a shunt not work in a voltmeter?

15. Who was the first scientist to make an electric generator?

16. Which two scientists discovered electromagnetic induction?

17. Wire is coiled around a vertical cardboard tube. State two ways of inducing a south pole at the upper end of the coil.

18. A transformer has the following characteristics:

Primary Coil	Secondary Coil
115 V AC	28.3 V AC
3.5 A AC	12.5 A AC

Determine the efficiency of the transformer.

19. A 50-g toy monkey takes a current of 40 mA from a 1.5-V battery. If it is 83% efficient, how high could it climb in 20s?

Potential Difference V (V)	Current I (A)
0.00	0.00
0.50	2.97
1.00	4.50
1.50	5.74
2.00	6.82
2.50	7.80
3.00	8.70

Applying Inquiry/ Communication Skills

20. A student determined the following potential difference and current characteristics for a non-ohmic resistor (one that does not follow Ohm's law)
    a) Draw a graph of current (y-axis) against potential difference.
    b) Using a graphing calculator, find the relationship between current and potential difference in the form $I = aV^b$

21. Design an experiment to determine how the strength of a magnetic field varies with distance from a long, straight current-carrying conductor.

22. Draw a circuit that could be used to measure the resistance of a light bulb.

23. Draw a circuit that could be used to measure the power loss across a resistor.

24. Research the relationship between Earth's magnetosphere and the Northern Lights.

25. Research the life of Michael Faraday and present a brief biography of him to your class.

26. Construct a simple DC motor and demonstrate its operation in class.

27. Design an experiment to:
    a) measure the power input to a DC motor
    b) measure the power output of the same DC motor (possibly by making it lift a known mass)

    How would you determine the efficiency of the motor from this experiment?

28. A conductor which is carrying an alternating current is surrounded by an alternating magnetic field. How could you use a helix and a sensitive AC voltmeter to measure the current in the conductor without touching the conductor?

Making Connections

29. a) Explain why a DC motor can be used as a generator.
    b) How might this ability be useful in an electric automobile?

30. In a particle accelerator, a stream of positive nuclei must be deflected upwards and to the left. The deflection coils are shown in Figure 4.

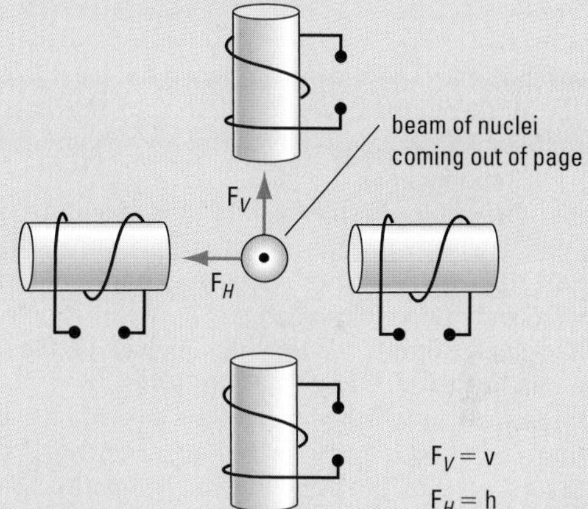

FIGURE 4

    a) Copy Figure 4 into your notes and show how the batteries could be connected to provide the required deflection.
    b) What change should you make if the deflection is not far enough to the left?
    c) If a stream of negative ions now comes out of the page, which way would they be deflected?

31. How might you use a generator and a galvanometer to measure
    a) the rate of revolution of a spinning pulley wheel?
    b) the speed of a bicycle or car?

32. A normal heart beats in response to regularly timed electric impulses. When these impulses cannot be provided naturally, a cardiac pacemaker may be necessary. Research the physics of such a pacemaker.

33. A ground fault interrupter is a safety device included in some electric devices and circuits. Sketch a diagram of a ground fault interrupter and explain its operation. Describe one instance where a ground fault interrupter would be preferred over a fuse or circuit breaker.

34. Investigate the factors that must be taken into account when a decision is to be made about the route of a new high-voltage transmission line.

35. Investigate and present a report on the use of the induction coil in the automobile.

36. There are advantages and disadvantages for all major methods of generating electrical energy on a large scale. Research three of the major types of electrical generation and complete a chart as shown:

Method of Generation	Advantages	Disadvantages	Steps Taken to Overcome Disadvantages
e.g. coal-fired plant			

37. Research the lives and contributions of at least five scientists or inventors who contributed to the development of our knowledge of electricity and magnetism. In your portfolio include:
   - point form notes on the scientists or inventors
   - a timeline showing the major developments in the study and application of electricity and magnetism, along with references showing how the people you have chosen fit into the timeline. Include on the timeline major world events.
   - a videotape in which you play the role of one of the other people (not the letter-writing scientist). As that scientist, give an interview in which you discuss your work, its importance, and possible future application.

38. Dry skin has a resistance of about 0.10 MΩ, while the resistance of wet skin might be around 300 Ω. Calculate the current flowing when a person touches a 100-V source with dry hands. Compare this with the current flowing if the hands are wet.

39. If the monthly electricity bill for a household is $25, how much energy in kW·h was used? Assume a unit cost of 8.0¢/kW·h.

40. An 18-gauge extension cord can safely carry a maximum current of 10 A.
   a) Will a 15-A fuse protect the extension cord?
   b) Could a 1200-W hair dryer be used with the extension cord?
   c) What is the maximum power rating of an appliance that could be safely connected to the extension cord?

Problem Solving

41. When the potential difference across three identical cells connected in series is measured, the voltmeter appears as in Figure 5. What is the potential difference across
   a) the battery?
   b) one cell?

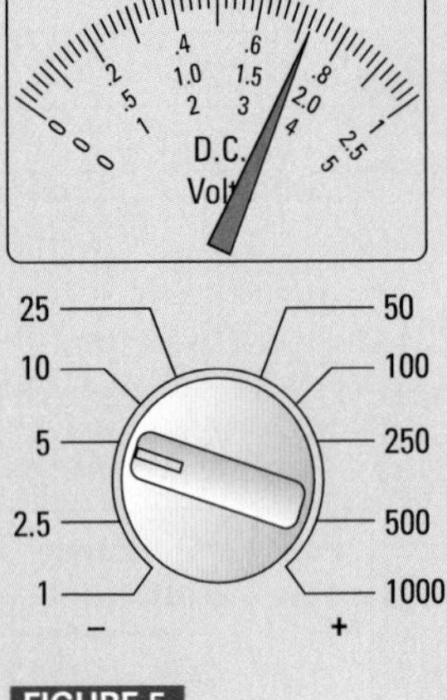

FIGURE 5

42. The element of an electric kettle operates with a potential difference of 120 V across it. How much work is required to move each electron through the element?

43. Calculate the energy expended by a 9.0-V power supply that provides a current of 300 mA for 2.5 min.

44. A current of 80 mA passing through the body could be fatal. If you accidentally touched a 120-V supply, would a skin resistance of 100 kΩ be high enough to save you from a shock which would be lethal?

45. Calculate the effect on the current in a circuit if the potential difference is doubled and the resistance is halved.

46. A typical 60-W light bulb converts only 5 % of the electrical energy it receives into light. How much electrical energy is converted into light in 1.0 h?

47. Refer to Figure 6.
   a) What is the total resistance of the circuit?
   b) What current flows through the 2-Ω resistor?
   c) What is the potential difference across the 15-Ω resistor?
   d) What is the power dissipated by the 30-Ω resistor?

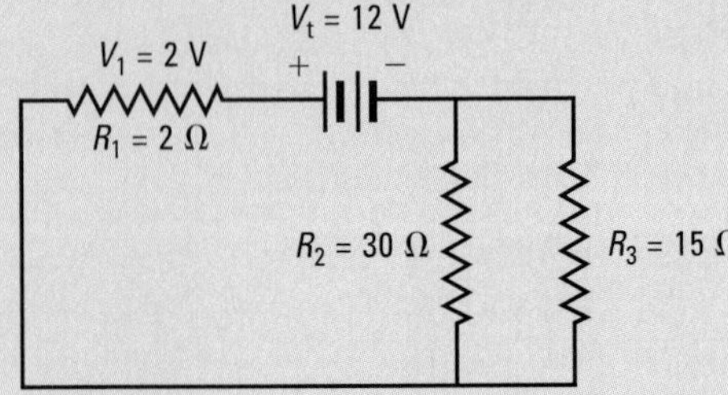

FIGURE 6

48. The manufacturer of a 90-W halogen outdoor spotlight claims that it produces the same light as an ordinary 150-W spotlight.
a) Explain this claim.
b) What current passes through the halogen spotlight when it is operating?
c) What are the resistances of the halogen spotlight and a regular 150-W spotlight?

49. Your school is staging an evening outdoor event. The student in charge of lighting asks you how many spotlights can be connected in parallel in a circuit that has a 15-A circuit breaker.
a) How many 150-W regular spotlights can be connected?
b) How many 90-W halogen spotlights can be connected?

50. A large home heated by electricity consumes 9000 kW·h of electrical energy in a two-month period in the winter. If the unit cost is 9.4¢/kW·h, what is the electrical energy bill for the two months?

51. Draw Figure 7 in your notes and sketch the direction of the magnetic field lines around each conductor. The arrows represent the direction of current flow.

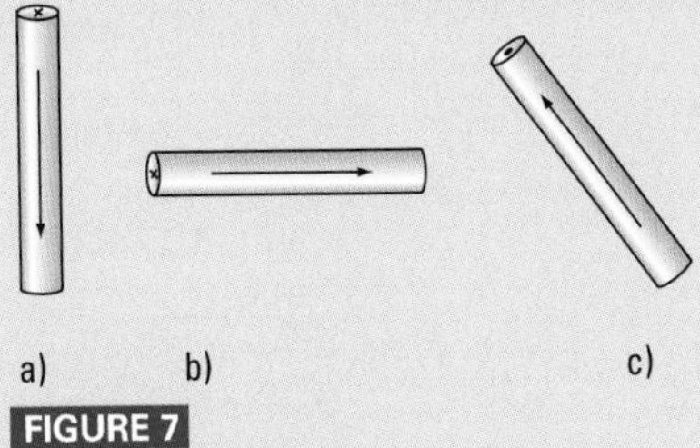

FIGURE 7

52. Locate and label the north and south poles for each of the electromagnets shown in Figure 8.

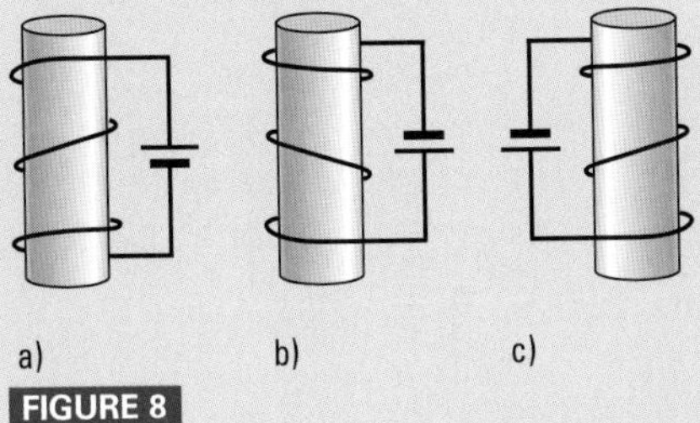

FIGURE 8

53. An electromagnet can exert a force of 600 N on a metal block. If the current through the electromagnet must be reduced to one-quarter of its initial value,
a) what would the force become?
b) what must happen to the number of turns per centimetre if the strength of the magnet is to remain at 600 N?

54. An electromagnet contains 2000 turns in its length. A current of 2.5 A provides a lifting force of 100 N.
a) What current would be required to provide a lifting force of 300 N?
b) If the current is 2.5 A, how many turns would be required to provide a lifting force of 600 N?

55. When a certain electromagnet contains 1000 turns in its length and carries a current of 10 A, it can exert a force on an iron block of 2000 N. If the electromagnet is rewound such that it contains 5000 turns in the same length and carries a current of 25 A, what force could it exert on the block?

56. a) Describe three separate ways by which you could increase the strength of an electromagnet 10 times.
b) If you made all three changes, by what factor would the strength of the electromagnet increase?

57. An AC generator is rotating at 10 Hz. Sketch a graph of induced current against time for 4 cycles.

58. A transformer has 100 turns on the primary coil and 1000 turns on the secondary coil. If the primary voltage and current are 115 V and 2.00 A, respectively, determine the secondary voltage and current.

59. A transformer is to decrease a potential difference from 115 V AC to 9.0 V AC. If the primary coil has 500 turns, how many should be on the secondary coil?

60. A generating plant provides a town with electrical energy at the rate of 4.0 MW and a potential difference of 800 kV. If the transmission line has a resistance of 2.4 Ω, what is the rate of energy loss in the transmission lines?

Appendix

A. Science and Safety

Doing science and learning science occur in the classroom, in the laboratory, and in the field. Safe practices are essential when students are actively learning science in all environments. Familiarity with the potential hazards makes it possible to take proper precautions and develop a safe learning environment.

Before every investigation, you should review all safety precautions and understand their importance. If you are unsure of any procedure or safety instructions, ask your instructor before you proceed.

The Canadian Hazardous Products Act requires chemical manufacturers to include all hazard symbols and the degree of hazard. You may recognize the household product symbols shown on the products in the photograph. These symbols indicate hazard(s), precaution, and first-aid treatment.

Hazardous Product and WHMIS Symbols

The household hazardous symbols indicate the type of danger and the degree of danger. They appear in either a triangle (which means "caution"), a diamond (which means "warning"), or an octagon (which means "danger").

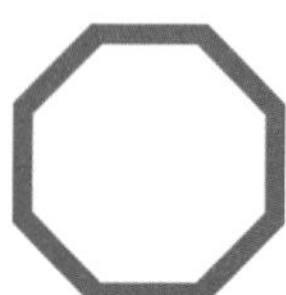

Below are some of the more common symbols.

Flammable Hazard: Materials could ignite (catch on fire) if exposed to flames, sparks, or friction.

Explosive Hazard: The materials or equipment could explode.

Toxic Hazard: The material is very poisonous and could have immediate and serious effects.

Corrosive Hazard: The material may corrode ("eat away at") clothing, skin, or other materials.

Biological Hazard: Be alert to the possibility of poisoning or infection from microscopic and other organisms.

Electrical Hazard: Be alert to the possibility of an electric spark or shock.

Many of the chemical products used in Canadian schools are manufactured in the United States. To standardize the labelling systems, WHMIS (the Workplace Hazardous Materials Information System) was developed. The symbols belonging to this system appear on materials and products used both in workplaces and our schools.

The WHMIS Symbols

compressed gas	**dangerously reactive material**	**oxidizing material**	**poisonous and infectious causing immediate and serious toxic effects**	**flammable and combustible material**	**biohazardous infectious material**	**corrosive material**	**poisonous and infectious causing other toxic effects**

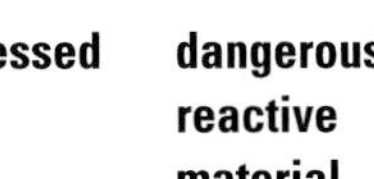

Laboratory Safety

Approach all investigations, especially in the laboratory, with maturity. Before you begin, read the instructions carefully, noting all safety precautions. In addition, your teacher may provide other safety reminders and rules pertaining to the laboratory activity. It is your responsibility to inform your teacher of medical conditions such as possible allergies to materials used (e.g. latex) or by-products of the activity. Inform your teacher if you wear contact lenses.

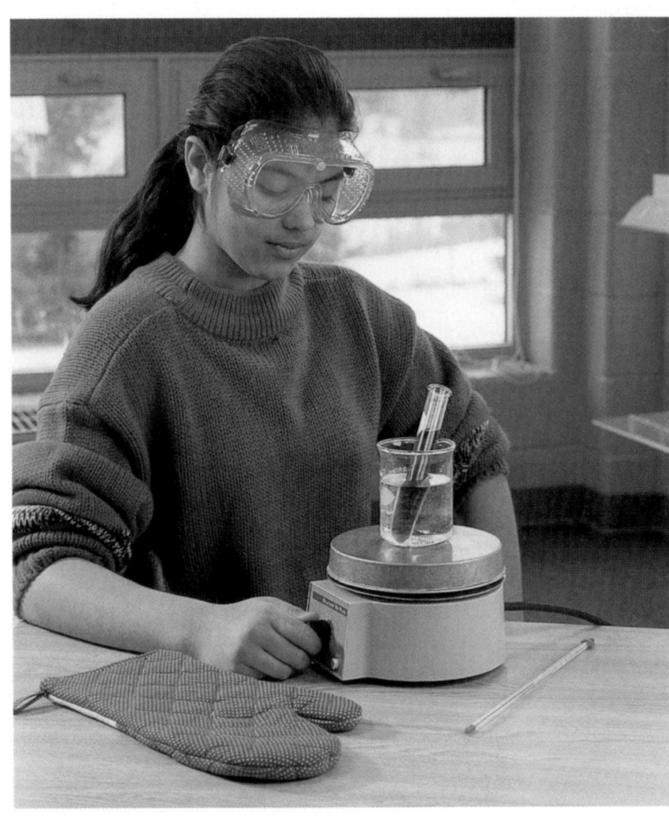

1. **Precautions and Safety Equipment**
   a) Identify all safety equipment in the laboratory.
   b) Know the location of and how to operate safety equipment, including the fire extinguisher, fire blankets, eyewash fountains, sand, and the first-aid kit.
   c) Wear appropriate laboratory apparel, which includes safety goggles, rubber gloves, and lab aprons.
   d) Tie back long hair and secure any loose clothing.

2. **Precautions with Burners or Hot Plates**
   a) Never leave any burner or hot plate unattended.
   b) Before connecting a burner, make sure the gas supply valve is completely closed. Open it only slightly just before lighting the burner.
   c) If the flame keeps going out, turn off the gas before you seek your teacher's help.

d) Ensure the use of Borosilicate (e.g. Pyrex) for heating substances.

e) Use tongs or holders to handle hot glassware or objects.

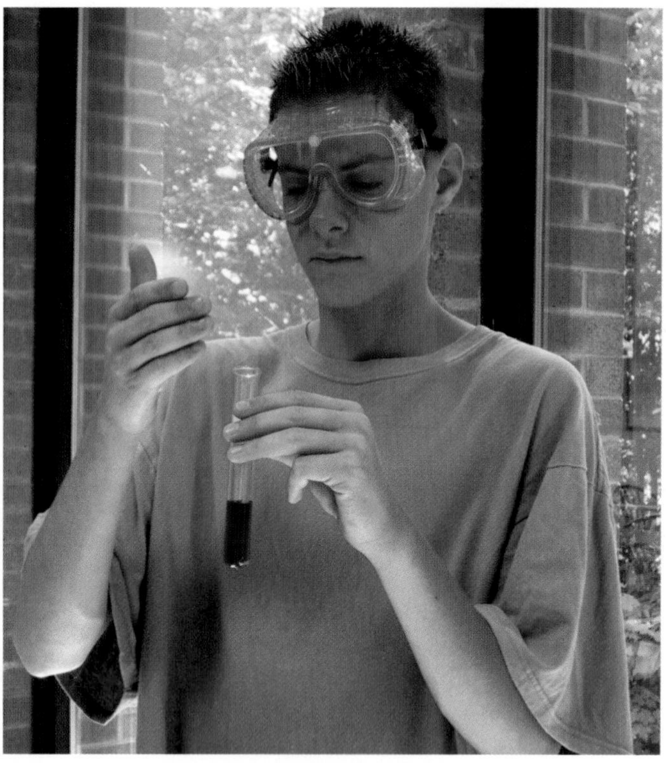

3. **Precautions with Glassware**
   a) Check for any chipped, cracked, or broken glassware.
   b) Ensure the glassware is clean before and after use.
   c) Use only equipment specified in the laboratory instructions unless advised otherwise by your teacher.

4. **Precautions with Chemicals**
   a) Never smell, touch, or taste substances in the laboratory without your teacher's instruction.
   b) Do not inhale fumes directly. Instead, wave the air above the substance toward your nose.
   c) Take materials only from labelled containers.
   d) Dilute acids by adding only ACID to WATER.
   e) Never return unused chemicals to stock bottles or containers.

5. **Precautions with Live or Preserved Specimens and Micro-organisms**
   a) Treat all animals (invertebrates and vertebrates) gently.
   b) Put on rubber gloves and mount all specimens before dissection.
   c) Always cut specimens away from you.
   d) Dispose of all dissected specimens as instructed by your teacher.
   e) Follow all instructions for cleaning the microbiology lab. Use aseptic techniques. When finished, use disinfectants and paper towels, and wipe your lab bench surfaces.
   f) Ensure you wash your hands and the lab surface with proper disinfectants.

6. **Precautions with Electromagnetic Radiation Light Sources**
   a) Never look directly into an intense, visible ultraviolet (UV), or infrared (IR) light source. Intense light can harm the retina. UV and IR radiation are absorbed by the cornea and eye contents, and can cause burning and overheating or other damage.
   b) Never look directly into the beam of an operating laser, even one with a low power. The eye focusses the laser light onto the retina, resulting in a power density of about 50 times that of direct sunlight. This can cause pinpoint burns to the retina.
   c) Guard against stray reflections and turn the laser off when not in use.

7. **Precautions with Electrical Sources**
   a) Do not use 110-V AC equipment if it has a damaged plug (e.g. missing the ground pin) or a frayed cord.
   b) Keep water and wet hands away from electrical cords.
   c) Do not touch a person in contact with live electrical currents. Disconnect the power source first. Then give artificial respiration, if necessary, and treat burns.
   d) Make sure electrical cords are not placed where someone could trip over them. When unplugging an electrical device, always disconnect the cord from the socket by pulling the plug, not the cord.
   e) Never attempt to recharge a non-rechargeable battery. Always exercise caution in handling any batteries: allowing them to discharge quickly, through a short circuit for instance, can generate dangerous amounts of heat in the wires and in the batteries themselves, and some kinds of batteries could even explode.
   f) Never cut open batteries. Their contents can be corrosive and poisonous.

8. **Other Precautions and Accident Procedures**
   a) All accidents (including breakage and spillage) or injuries must be reported to your teacher.
   b) With your teacher's help and supervision, clean up all spills and broken glassware.
   c) If a chemical splashes into your eyes or on your body, wash at the eyewash for several minutes or add copious amounts of cool water immediately. Ensure your teacher is notified.
   d) At the end of all lab activities, ensure the lab bench is clean.
   e) Put all cleaned apparatus away.
   f) Ensure your hands are washed before you leave the lab.

9. **For Any Independent Investigation**
   a) Before you begin, obtain approval from your teacher for all procedures.
   b) Carefully discuss the apparatus and the procedure with your instructor.
   c) Learn the appropriate safety measures for your work.
   d) Never work without your teacher's supervision and never work alone.

B. The Inquiry Process

Initiating and Planning

Notice a scientific problem or issue, ask a question, and formulate a plan to solve it.
I wonder if? I wonder why?
How can I find out?

Applying Technical Skills

Use your skills to put your plan into practice.
Did I set up the photogate in the proper position?

Using Tools, Materials, and Equipment

Use suitable tools and materials appropriately.
Would spherical objects be the best ones to drop?

Conducting and Recording

Conduct your study in a controlled manner and observe/record appropriate results.
Did I control all of the variables?
Are my results recorded clearly and accurately?

Analyzing and Interpreting

Use various tools to analyze results and figure out what they mean.
Should I use a graph or a calculation to examine these results?
What do my results mean?

Concluding and Communicating

Make a decision about the experimental results and communicate them.
Do my results support my conclusion?
Will others be able to understand my work?
Would they be able to repeat my work?

Why do apples fall from trees? What causes foot-and-mouth disease? Why do different types of wood burn to produce different amounts of heat? What causes leaves to change colours? How can I capture an image on film? Why did the bacteria die in this Petri plate?

All of these are questions asked by scientists as they observe parts of the world around them. While an answer to the last question might be "Let's just throw out this plate's results," a scientist named Alexander Fleming might have asked, "What factors existed in this culture plate to kill these bacteria?" It turns out, Fleming had discovered a mould, called *Penicillium notatum,* that has a lethal effect on many harmful organisms. As a result of Fleming's discovery, Oxford researchers Howard Florey and Ernst Chain were able to isolate the active component *penicillin*. Today, penicillin is produced by drug companies to help fight infections and diseases.

Fleming approached the problem from a scientific perspective, using a structured approach to examine the world and answer his questions. This approach is called the **Inquiry Process**. It is a logical reasoning process used to solve problems through observation and measurement, experimentation and research, and analysis and dissemination. It attempts to explain phenomena by examining cause and effect in a controlled situation. Scientists use experiments as a key part of their scientific work. Working scientifically involves being precise and accurate when making and interpreting observations and formulating conclusions based on them. It is also important to communicate the results of experimental work clearly to other scientists. The flowchart on this page outlines some of the steps involved in the inquiry process.

Initiating and Planning

A scientist notices an event or occurrence and attempts to explain it. If a reasonable explanation does not exist, the scientist may take further steps. He or she will develop a question that can be answered through various means. The question should point to a structured approach to finding the answer or explanation through an experiment, a model, or research. The scientist will make a prediction (hypothesis) of the answer based on his or her scientific knowledge and experience. A plan must then be devised for gathering information and drawing appropriate conclusions.

Question: Do objects with different masses fall at different accelerations?

Hypothesis: Heavier objects will accelerate more quickly than lighter objects.

One scientific plan would be to conduct an experiment. A sequence of steps (method) must be determined to describe how the experiment is to be conducted. The design of the method is essential to ensure that consistent and valid results are obtained. The method should be geared toward collecting data specific to the hypothesis and should identify what tools, equipment, and materials would be necessary. Care should be taken to control as many variables as possible, otherwise results will be difficult to interpret correctly. Any safety considerations should also be included in the method. In addition, the method should be written to allow others to reproduce the experiment.

Method

1. Measure a height of 1.5 m above the floor.
2. Set the photogate 0.50 m above the floor to get a drop height of 1.0 m.
3. Start the timer and simultaneously drop the sphere from the 1.5-m height such that it passes through the gate of the sensor.
3. Record the time it takes for each sphere to reach the sensor when released.
4. Calculate the final velocity of each sphere from the diameter of the sphere and the time it takes for the sphere to pass through the photogate. The average velocity in passing through the photogate is equal to the instantaneous velocity at mid-gate.

The method should also clarify the size and shape of the spheres to be used (they should be the same to avoid air resistance affecting the results), and the number of trials to ensure accurate and reliable results that are reproducible.

Applying Technical Skills

To conduct an experiment on falling objects (e.g., spheres), you would need to control a number of variables that may affect the results. So it is important to use proper technical skills—for example, properly positioning the photogate and the release point—in applying a method to ensure that variables are indeed controlled. Proper application of technical skills would ensure the spheres have the same initial velocity, which in turn would ensure the validity of the data. Determining the best way to observe results is also a technical decision that could affect the accuracy and interpretation of the data.

Using Tools, Materials, and Equipment

In a laboratory, using tools, materials, and equipment safely and correctly is essential to ensure a secure environment for all. Safety is everyone's responsibility. If you see a fellow student struggling to use equipment properly, it is your responsibility to offer assistance or notify the lab supervisor (your teacher). A review of specific safety considerations and proper use of apparatus may be necessary at the outset of an experiment. Working responsibly includes knowing what to do and when to ask for help.

Materials

2 spheres of different mass but equal size and shape; (e.g., Ping-Pong ball and lead sphere)
photogate
metric tape
sensitive timer

Conducting and Recording

While performing an experiment, use your scientific and technical skills to follow the identified method, gathering and recording both qualitative and quantitative observations in your lab notes. The critical functions of lab notes are to state what was done and what was observed. The greatest flaw found in lab notes, even with experienced scientists, is that they are often unreadable. Hard as it is to believe, even the author of a particular notebook might not understand his or her own notes after a few years. The problem is not usually one of legibility, but rather of poorly labelled entries and incomplete descriptions. Writing in complete sentences, indicating units of measurement, and noting possible sources of error are excellent ways to ensure a high-quality record of the experiment.

A table is one method to present results. Tables offer an organized structure to present experimental results/data. It is apparent from the quantitative observations provided here that the final velocities of the two types of spheres are similar but not identical. The data can be manipulated through graphing or calculations to find further relationships.

Observations

Table B.1: Time and Final Velocity for Spheres Dropped from Rest through a 1-m Height

Trial	Lead Sphere Final Velocity v_2 (m/s) [down]	Elapsed Time Δt (s)	Ping-Pong Ball Final Velocity v_2 (m/s) [down]	Elapsed Time Δt (s)
1	4.4	0.45	4.2	0.46
2	4.3	0.45	4.1	0.46
3	4.6	0.44	4.3	0.48

Analyzing and Interpreting

A collection of numbers or a list of observations is not sufficient to address your hypothesis. It is necessary to use appropriate analysis tools to find meaning in your experimental results. The tools may include a graphical representation of results, a calculation, a comparison to known data, and an identification of patterns or trends. Often visual representations of data simplify the identification of relationships that exist in the data.

Analysis

Assuming uniform acceleration, the acceleration can be calculated using the relationship $\vec{v}_2 = \vec{v}_1 + \vec{a}\Delta t$. For an initial velocity of zero. The equation can be simplified and rearranged to $\vec{a} = \frac{\vec{v}_2}{\Delta t}$. The average acceleration for the first trial for the lead sphere can be calculated as follows:

$$\vec{a} = \frac{\vec{v}_2}{\Delta t}$$

$$= \frac{4.4 \text{ m/s [down]}}{0.45 \text{ s}}$$

$$= 9.8 \text{ m/s}^2 \text{ [down]}$$

Table B.2 shows the rest of the calculated values for acceleration.

Table B.2: Calculated Acceleration for Spheres Dropped Through a 1-m Height

Trial	Average Acceleration $\vec{a}$ (m/s²) [down]	
	Lead Sphere	Ping-Pong Ball
1	9.8	9.1
2	9.6	8.9
3	10	9.0

Once a value has been calculated for each trial, an average may be calculated for each sphere using the relationship $\vec{a}_{av} = \frac{\vec{a}_1 + \vec{a}_2 + \vec{a}_3}{3}$. The results for the two spheres are as follows.

For the lead sphere:

$$a_{av} = \frac{\vec{a}_1 + \vec{a}_2 + \vec{a}_3}{3}$$

$$= \frac{9.6 \text{ m/s}^2 \text{ [down]} + 9.8 \text{ m/s}^2 \text{ [down]} + 10 \text{ m/s}^2 \text{ [down]}}{3}$$

$$= 9.8 \text{ m/s}^2 \text{ [down]}$$

For the Ping-Pong ball:

$$a_{av} = \frac{\vec{a}_1 + \vec{a}_2 + \vec{a}_3}{3}$$

$$= \frac{9.1 \text{ m/s}^2 \text{ [down]} + 8.9 \text{ m/s}^2 \text{ [down]} + 9.1 \text{ m/s}^2 \text{ [down]}}{3}$$

$$= 9.0 \text{ m/s}^2 \text{ [down]}$$

Concluding and Communicating

Use your completed analysis to draw conclusions that support or refute your hypothesis. Your conclusion should be written in such a manner that it is clearly linked to your analysis and results. Any errors noted should be addressed, indicating their effect on the observed results.

Your overall inquiry process should be organized in order to communicate your results. Regardless of the form they take, the information and ideas should be communicated with a high degree of clarity and precision using the correct terminology, symbols, conventions, SI units, and number of significant figures. It may be necessary to use technology to support the communication of your inquiry process. You may choose to use computers or media tools to enhance your work.

Conclusions

When an object is falling, it will accelerate. This acceleration seems to be greater for a heavier mass than for a lighter one of the same shape. Other factors such as air resistance may affect the acceleration of an object as it falls. The experiment should be repeated in a vacuum to eliminate the effect of air resistance.

You can use the following Inquiry Process Checklist to guide your work.

Inquiry Process Checklist

Purpose

- ☐ poses a question
- ☐ question can be answered by following an inquiry process

Hypothesis

- ☐ hypothesis specifically predicts the answer to the question stated in the purpose

Method

- ☐ written in logical steps
- ☐ reproducible by other scientists
- ☐ data collected are connected to the hypothesis
- ☐ variables controlled where necessary
- ☐ diagram included where appropriate

Inquiry Skills

- ☐ demonstrate knowledge of proper use of tools, materials, and equipment
- ☐ use apparatus properly
- ☐ use apparatus safely
- ☐ help others to work safely and properly

Conducting and Recording

- ☐ follow method
- ☐ qualitative observations written with adequate detail
- ☐ quantitative observations include appropriate units and significant figures
- ☐ use tables/charts to organize results
- ☐ note errors or discrepancies

Analyzing and Interpreting

- ☐ include a visual representation of results
- ☐ calculations where necessary; clearly organized, units shown

Conclusion

- ☐ link hypothesis with results
- ☐ hypothesis supported or refuted
- ☐ error analysis

Overall

- ☐ spelling and grammar correct
- ☐ written in clear, precise language
- ☐ scientific terms used correctly
- ☐ neat presentation
- ☐ technology used where necessary

C. The Decision-Making Process

The *Mir Space Station* was officially built to conduct studies and experiments of interest to science and the Soviet economy. It was the culmination of the Soviet space program's efforts to maintain a long-duration human presence in space. The permanently manned space station regularly hosted two or three cosmonauts who performed scientific and technical experiments, along with recording real data on life in space. The experiments ranged from those involving space life sciences, microgravity, and space technology, to Earth observations and sciences, and space sciences. *Mir* was originally designed to have a 5-year lifetime in space, but the final crew left the station in August 1999—more than 13 years after the first component had been launched. After 86 331 orbits, *Mir*'s Russian Space Agency controllers were faced with the challenge of ending the station's years in space.

The situation of the *Mir Space Station* typifies the many different issues facing science and scientists today. Some of these issues are ethical in nature, requiring analysis of one's beliefs and values. Others require a consideration of safety. This type of issue and the questions it raises require that an informed decision be made. Some decisions are easier than others. How does one make an informed decision and analyze its validity? Scientists often use an approach called the **Decision-Making Process** as they strive to make prudent choices. The flowchart on this page outlines this process.

Defining the Issue

The issue should be articulated using a brief statement or question. For example, space safety is the issue from the above example and the broad question might be: "How can we safely return the *Mir Space Station* to Earth?"

Developing Assessment Criteria

Establish assessment criteria prior to the in-depth research and analysis of the issue. This will facilitate an objective decision-making process. Some possible criteria include cost, social implications, precedents, norms, environmental impact, and/or feasibility. In this example, one might base a decision on the suitability of the target location for pieces of debris to impact.

Defining the Issue

Identify an issue and its context.
Is this ethical? Is this acceptable?
What are the options and which one is better?

Developing Assessment Criteria

Establish criteria to use as the basis for making a final decision.
On what criteria will I base my decision?
What factors are important in making this decision?

Researching the Issue

Find as much information as possible to make an informed decision.
What sources of information can I use?
Are my sources reliable?
Have I considered all aspects of the issue?

Analyzing Data and Information

Select the relevant information, organize it, manipulate it, and examine it.
How can I best present the information?
What method should I use to analyze the data?

Proposing a Course of Action

Make a decision.
Have I considered all of the relevant factors?
Have I put the possible courses of action in the right order?

Justifying the Course of Action

Determine whether the information supports your decision.
Is there enough data supporting my decision to allow others to reach the same conclusion?
What will I do if my proposed course of action is turned down?
Check for the consequences or impact of the decision.
What are the consequences of this decision?
Have I weighted the consequences in an appropriate way?

Communicating Your Proposal

Decide how you will communicate your findings.
Who is my intended audience?
How will I communicate my findings?
What visuals will I include in my work?

Researching the Issue

To make an informed decision, identify and describe all related factors. A researcher might consult journals, articles, the Internet, experts, available data, past practice, or precedents to find information, impacts, factors, norms, and connections to other fields. Relevant ethical, moral, and social perspectives should be noted. If relevant information is overlooked, the wrong decision may be reached. For example, the following questions might arise in the case of the *Mir Space Station*:

- *preferred re-entry location*: How easy will it be to collect the surviving debris from this location?
- *safety*: Will there be a risk to human inhabitants?
- *orbit decay*: Will we need to correct for the natural decay of *Mir*'s orbit?
- *trajectory*: How will controllers steer the orbit into exactly the right position with respect to Earth?
- *re-entry issues*: How may the rush through rarified air during re-entry affect *Mir*?
- *costs*: How much will it cost and how are we going to fund the re-entry project?
- *human factors*: How will those closely involved with *Mir* feel during its re-entry?

Analyzing Data and Information

Organize the information in a structured manner to facilitate analysis. Methods for organizing information might be a chart comparing pros and cons, a cost–benefit analysis, a consequences or responsibilities chart, statistical analysis, graphical representation, or a flowchart to illustrate the issue.

Use the assessment criteria to analyze the organized information. Consider the relative importance of the factors and weigh them accordingly within the decision-making process. For example, the size and location of the target re-entry impact point is essential for the safety of Earth's inhabitants.

Proposing a Course of Action

Taking into account all available research and its analysis, choose an objective course of action. For example, the team recommended a mid-January 2001 return near 47° South, 140° West longitude based on the station's projected velocity and orbit.

Justifying the Course of Action

Your course of action should be directly supported by your analysis of the research. To justify your course of action it is necessary to evaluate its effect or impact on society. The evaluation can be conducted from two perspectives.

1) the validity of the decision in comparison to the data and criteria *(Did you make the best decision possible with the available information and financial resources?)*

2) the impact and effect of a decision over an extended period of time *(How has the course of action helped in our understanding of orbits and bringing materials back to Earth? Were there unforeseen consequences?)*. This analysis could be accomplished through public polls, expert analysis, or a study of success rates. The method of analysis will depend on the scope of the issue. The argument presented should appeal to the reader's intellect through logic and reason.

Communicating Your Proposal

Any good research project requires clear communication of the work and results. The communication should summarize the goal, the process, and the recommendations of the work in a succinct and concise manner. Regardless of the form used for communication, there are key components to include: an introductory statement of the issue, an accurate and precise description of relevant background information and the research undertaken, an analysis of the information, and a conclusion clearly supported by the analysis and data.

There are various ways to communicate your work, both orally and in writting. A number of forms of communication are outlined in the table below. The form used should be supported by visual aids to enhance the communication. In addition, the tone and perspective of the work should be matched to its intended audience. For example, an editorial may contain more personal views than a news report.

Forms of Communication

Oral	Written
debate	editorial
presentation (e.g. town meeting, school council)	position paper
radio spot	poster
TV spot	pamphlet or brochure

You can use the following Decision-Making Process Checklist to guide your work.

Decision-Making Process Checklist

Issue

- ☐ clearly articulated as a statement or question

Assessment Criteria

- ☐ clearly identified
- ☐ enables objective, fact-based decision making

Research

- ☐ relevant factors identified
- ☐ factors described in detail and seriated
- ☐ a variety of sources used

Analysis

- ☐ appropriate method(s) used
- ☐ easily interpreted
- ☐ weighted according to relative importance ▶

Decision
- ☐ objective course of action chosen
- ☐ supported by data

Evaluation
- ☐ predicted possible impact or consequence of decision
- ☐ checked validity of decision with respect to data

Communication (Overall)
- ☐ information presented clearly and precisely
- ☐ spelling and grammar correct
- ☐ scientific terms used correctly
- ☐ approach appropriate to intended audience
- ☐ content appropriate to intended audience
- ☐ structure of content appropriate to form of communication
- ☐ use of technology enhances presentation

D. Problem Solving

Solving Numerical Problems

A significant amount of effort in physics is spent in solving problems that have a numerical component. Often these problems seem more difficult than they really are because they involve physics concepts, principles, and/or laws as well as mathematical operations. Research into the problem-solving abilities of professionals and novices shows that professionals have logical procedures they follow when solving problems while novices who are having difficulty do not. The more methods the problem-solver can apply, the more adept he/she is at problem solving.

The approach we use in Numerical Problems throughout the text follows five basic steps. These steps are easy to remember and apply because combined, the first letters of the key words spell GRASS. The flowchart on the facing page outlines the GRASS approach to solving numerical problems. A description of the five steps and their application to a problem is provided below.

Step 1: List what is Given

The first step in solving numerical problems involves answering the question, "What information are we given?" This is sometimes referred to as *data extraction*. To answer this question, read the problem carefully, study the information given, and represent physical quantities and numerical data with appropriate symbols, units, and directions (if necessary). Write the data in standard form to the correct number of significant figures (Appendix H).

Step 2: List what you are Required to find

The second step involves answering the question, "What am I required to find?" To answer this question, identify what the problem is asking you to do. Be sure to note the units requested and, for vector quantities, the direction. Answering this question will point you in the right direction and prevent you from being distracted by irrelevant information.

Step 3: Analyze the problem carefully

The third step requires a careful analysis of the problem. To analyze the problem you must break it down into a series of logical steps. If possible, begin by sketching a diagram. Many physics problems lend themselves to a diagram and the diagram often provides the key to solving the problem. Then write down all the relationships you know involving the givens and the required. Also, write down any assumptions that must be made in order to solve the problem. An assumption is anything that must be taken for granted. Next, start with what you are trying to find, and answer the question, "What additional information do I need to calculate the unknown?" This may be a constant that you have to look up in a reference book or from a table of constants given in a text.

Step 4: Work out the Solution

The fourth step requires you to find the solution to the problem. This is the reverse of analysis and is sometimes referred to as *synthesis*. It involves putting together the elements of the parts to form a whole. The parts identified during the analysis stage must be organized and sequenced to form the solution. In physics, this often involves substituting appropriate data into an equation. We recommend rearranging the equation to solve for the unknown before substituting the data. Always be on the lookout for errors in the mathematical computations, and check that the answer has the correct number of significant figures and that units are included, if appropriate.

Step 5: Write the concluding Statement

The numerical answer should be stated in a form that answers the original question. Since the original question was a sentence, the statement of the final answer should also be a complete sentence. Physical quantities should include units and directions, if appropriate.

Step 1: Identify the Given Data

Read the problem carefully, extract the data, represent physical quantities with appropriate symbols and units, and write the data in standard form to the correct number of significant figures.

↓

Step 2: List what is Required

Identify what the problem is asking you to do and identify the units of the final answer.

↓

Step 3: Analyze the Problem

Draw a sketch, write down possible relationships, list assumptions, look up any constants needed, identify any inconsistent units, look up any unit conversions required, identify any red herrings in the given data, note the least number of significant digits in the given data, and note any directions if vector quantities are involved.

↓

Step 4: Work out the Solution

Perform the necessary unit conversions, substitute appropriate data into the relationship, simplify the results, check the math calculations, check the significant figures of the final answer, and check the direction of the final answer for vector quantities.

↓

Step 5: Write the concluding Statement

Write the answer to the original problem in a complete sentence to the correct number of significant figures and with units (and directions) indicated. Check that the original question has been answered.

EXAMPLE PROBLEM Numerical

The general equation that summarizes the relationship between the stretch of an elastic spring x and the force F applied is $x = k \cdot F$, where k is the proportionality constant for the spring. On Earth, the force of gravity on a 1.0-kg object is 9.8 N (to two significant figures). An experimenter hangs an 800-g mass from the end of an elastic spring. If the proportionality constant of the spring is 3.0 cm/N, how many cm will the spring stretch under this load?

Given

1.0 kg = 9.8 N (two significant figures)

m = 800 g = 8.00×10^2 g (three significant figures)

$k = 3.0 \frac{\text{cm}}{\text{N}}$ (two significant figures)

Required

Stretch x, in cm

Analysis

Sketch a diagram showing the set-up.

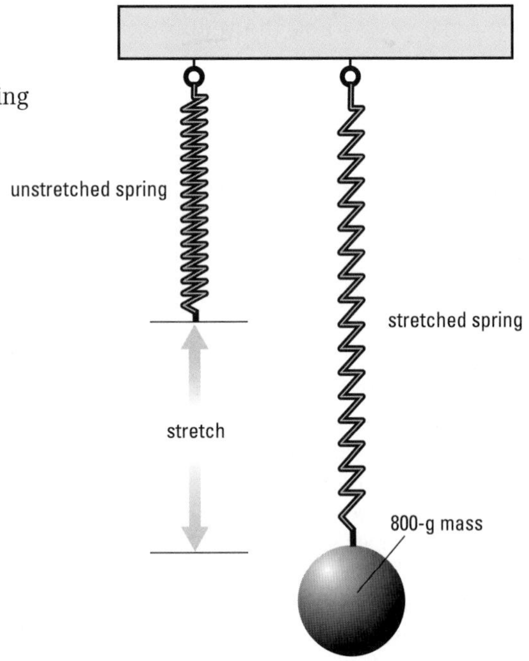

- Defined equalities are perfectly accurate; hence 1000 g = 1 kg is perfectly accurate and can be expressed to any number of significant figures (e.g., three significant figures).
- Since the least accurate data given have two significant figures, the answer can have two significant figures.
- Convert the mass m in grams to a force F in newtons.
- Assume that the stretch is within the elastic limit of the spring and hence its behaviour for the attached mass can be correctly described by the given equation.
- Substitute the appropriate data into the equation $x = k \cdot F$

Solution

$$m = 8.00 \times 10^2 \text{ g} \times \frac{1.0 \text{ kg}}{1000 \text{ g}} = 8.00 \times 10^{-1} \text{ kg (three significant figures)}$$

$$F = 8.00 \times 10^{-1} \text{ kg} \times \frac{9.8 \text{ N}}{1.0 \text{ kg}} = 7.8 \text{ N (two significant figures)}$$

$$x = k \cdot F$$

$$= 3.0 \frac{\text{cm}}{\text{N}} \times 7.8 \text{ N}$$

$$= 23 \text{ cm (two significant figures)}$$

Statement

The spring will stretch 23 cm when the 800-g mass is attached. The answer is expressed to two significant figures because the least accurate data used in its determination have two significant digits.

You can use the following Numerical Problem Checklist to guide your work.

Numerical Problem Checklist

Given

- ☐ read problem carefully
- ☐ extract data
- ☐ represent physical quantities with appropriate symbols
- ☐ include units with physical quantities
- ☐ include directions where needed
- ☐ write the numerical data in standard form
- ☐ show the correct number of significant figures

Required

- ☐ identify what the problem is asking for
- ☐ identify units of the final answer
- ☐ identify direction of the final answer (for vector quantities)

Analysis

- ☐ draw a sketch
- ☐ write down possible relationships
- ☐ list viable assumptions
- ☐ identify constants needed
- ☐ identify inconsistent units
- ☐ identify unit conversion factors needed
- ☐ identify red herrings
- ☐ note the least number of significant figures in the given data
- ☐ note directions (for vector quantities)

▶

Solution

- ☐ perform unit conversions
- ☐ look up constants needed
- ☐ rearrange the equation to solve for the unknown
- ☐ substitute data into the rearranged equation
- ☐ simplify the mathematics
- ☐ check the mathematical calculations
- ☐ check the number of significant figures
- ☐ check the direction (if required)

Statement

- ☐ write the final answer in a complete sentence
- ☐ check that units are included with numerals
- ☐ check accuracy of significant figures
- ☐ check accuracy of direction (if required)
- ☐ check that the original question has been answered and that the answer seems realistic

Solving Conceptual Problems

Students in introductory physics courses frequently lack skill in solving qualitative problems as well as quantitative ones. Some of the conceptual examples in the text are entirely qualitative in nature. The emphasis in conceptual examples is on how to apply physics concepts to explain natural phenomena. The focus is on real-world situations that are related to the concepts, principles, and laws under study. Conceptual examples often deal with misconceptions that the learner brings to physics from everyday experiences. For example, some students believe that mass and weight are identical concepts and that both mass and weight would decrease if an object were transported to the Moon. Many conceptual examples involve higher-order thinking skills, including analysis, synthesis, and evaluation. The subheadings used in conceptual examples are Background, Reasoning and Solution.

EXAMPLE PROBLEM Conceptual

Engineers are designing an electric-powered vehicle of mass m to be used to travel along the level on the Moon's surface. The gravitational field intensity on the Moon is 1.6 N/kg, about $\frac{1}{6}$ that on Earth (9.8 N/kg). As a result, the weight of the vehicle on the Moon is less than on Earth. Suppose the vehicle is tested on Earth and is able to accelerate horizontally with an acceleration of $\vec{a}$. If the same vehicle is used on a similar surface on the Moon, will the horizontal acceleration be less than, the same as, or greater than on Earth?

Reasoning and Solution
The acceleration of the vehicle can be determined using Newton's Second Law and the equation $\vec{a} = \frac{\vec{F}_{net}}{m}$ where $\vec{F}_{net}$ is the unbalanced force.

Assume that air resistance is negligible on Earth compared to the Moon. Since the surfaces are described as being identical, the rolling friction on the tires will be identical in the two locations. We can assume that the same electric motor will exert the same force on the tires in the two locations. As a result, the net horizontal force on the vehicle will be the same on Earth and on the Moon. Since mass depends only on the quantity of matter in the object, and not its location, the mass of the vehicle on the moon and on Earth will be identical. Since the net force and the mass will be the same, Newton's second law predicts that the horizontal accelerations on the Earth and the Moon will be identical. But that will not be true if the vehicle accelerates up identical slopes in the two locations. Can you explain why? If air resistance could not have been ignored, how would the results have been affected? If the force of gravity affected friction (i.e., the normal force), how would this affect the results?

E. Using Graphic Organizers

Graphic organizers are effective tools that can help you learn. They enable you to problem solve and think critically through analyzing similarities and differences, inferring sequences, and establishing cause-and-effect relationships. They generate discussion and negotiation of ideas, extend comprehension of a concept, theme, or topic, and lead to organized representation and presentation of understandings. You can use them to brainstorm, demonstrate what you know, and organize your thoughts before planning a presentation or writing a report or essay. The following chart outlines a number of graphic organizers, their intended purposes, and how to use them as you study science.

Type of Graphic Organizer	Purpose	Method
Concept Map concept — connector — descriptor	Used to clarify relationships and linkages between concepts, events, or ideas	Brainstorm ideas and link together from "big to small" with arrows and linking words.

Type of Graphic Organizer	Purpose	Method
Venn Diagram Different Same Different	Used to visualize similarities and differences between two or more ideas, topics, or concepts	Brainstorm traits common to both topics and list in the overlapping section of the two circles. Repeat for unique traits and list in the non-overlapping sections.
Web Diagram Main Idea	Used to clarify concepts and ideas by clustering them	Cluster words and/or information around a central object, concept, or idea.
Pie Chart	Used to estimate the relationship of parts to the whole	Estimate/research the importance or amount of proportionate time of each aspect of an event in relation to the whole.
Flowchart/Sequence Chart	Used to map out your thinking about an issue or to organize ideas for an essay or report	Brainstorm aspects of the whole event. Select important aspects and put them into sequential order.
Ranking Ladder	Used to rank ideas in order of importance	Brainstorm ideas and rank them in order from least important (bottom rung) to most important (top rung).

Type of Graphic Organizer	Purpose	Method
Fishbone Diagram	Used to identify cause-and-effect relationships	Identify a problem to be solved. List the "effect" at the head of the fish. Brainstorm "possible causes" in each bone. Rank the causes and circle the most probable ones (provide justification).
Right-Angle Diagram	Used to explore the implications of ideas and reflect on applications of those ideas	Identify an event and show it on the horizontal arrow. Brainstorm traits and list them to the right of the horizontal arrow. Expand on one trait and list details about it along the vertical arrow. Describe social impacts of that trait below the vertical arrow.
Target Diagram	Used to weigh the importance of facts and ideas	Brainstorm facts and ideas. Rank their importance and place the most important facts/ideas centrally and the least important ones toward the outer rings.
Agree/Disagree Chart (Agree | Disagree)	Used to organize data to support a position for or against an idea or decision	List a series of statements relating to a topic or issue. Survey agree-disagreement before discussion. Survey again after discussion/research.
PMI (Plus, Minus, Interesting) Chart (Plus | Minus | Interesting)	Used to summarize the positive and negative aspects of a topic or issue, as well as identify interesting aspects of the topic for possible further research	Sort ideas or information about a topic or issue in a three-column chart that has the following headings: Plus (+), Minus (-), and Interesting.
Gathering Grid	Used to make distinctions between ideas or events	Gather information on a number of ideas or events and arrange it on a grid. Each idea or event is assigned to a separate row. Analyze the information according to selected criteria in each specific column.
Concept Hierarchy Diagram	Used to identify and sequence the subordinate concepts needed to understand a higher-order concept	Place the higher-order concept at the top of a page. Then consider the question, "What concepts do I need to understand before the I can grasp the higher-order concept?" The same question is then asked for each of the subordinate concepts identified and a hierarchy of connected concepts is created.

F. Graphing Techniques

Physicists make extensive use of graphs to convey information and to help determine how one physical quantity is affected by another. To review simple graphical analysis techniques, we will use the data for an experiment similar to that performed by Robert Hooke in 1678. Hooke's experiment was designed to answer the question, "How does the stretch of an elastic material, such as a spring, vary with the force applied to it?" Hooke hung masses on a spring, and measured the amount by which the spring stretched from its starting position.

The Data Table

A data table is the most practical way to record quantitative data. Table F.1 shows the data from an experiment similar to that performed by Hooke. Note that the name of each variable, the symbol, and the unit of measurement are recorded at the top of each column. The unit is enclosed in round brackets and directions are included in square brackets.

TABLE F.1

Applied Force F (N) [down]	Stretch ΔL (cm)
0	0
1.0	4.0
2.0	9.0
3.0	14
5.0	22
7.0	32
9.0	44
10	51

The Title of the Graph

Figure F.1 shows a sample graph for Hooke's experiment. Every graph needs a title to describe what it is about. We place the title at the top of the graph or in a box on a clear area above the graph.

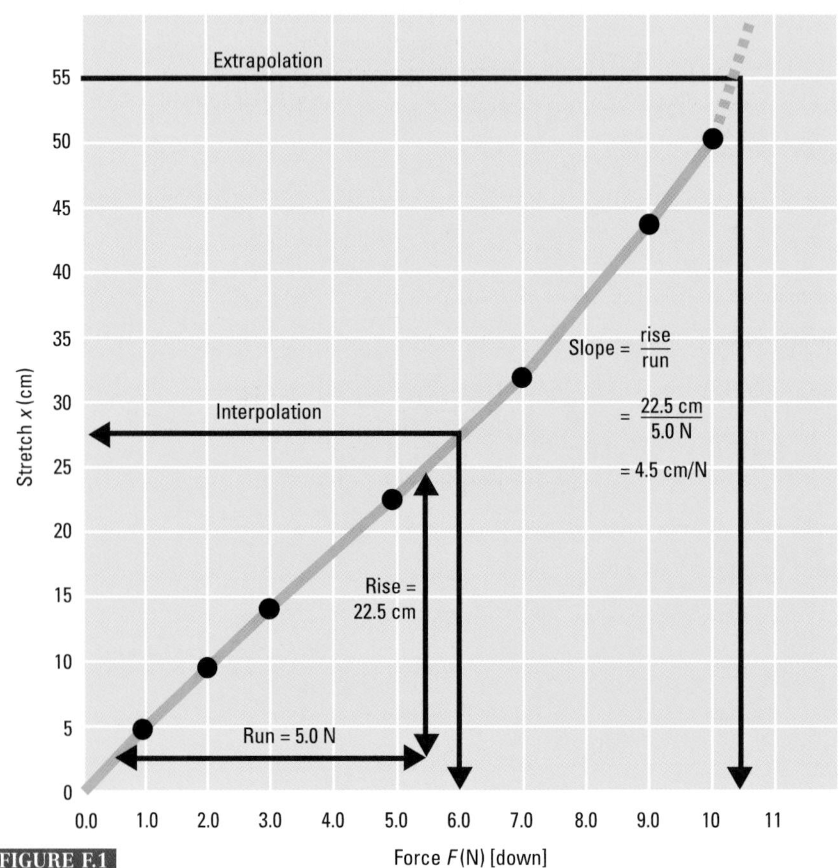

FIGURE F.1

The Axes of the Graph

In physics, we usually plot the independent variable on the horizontal x-axis and the dependent variable on the vertical y-axis. The variable that we change intentionally is called the *independent variable*. Force was the independent variable in Hooke's experiment, since he chose to change the force by changing the mass suspended from the spring. The variable that the experimenter observes and measures is called the *dependent variable*. Since Hooke measured the stretch corresponding to each force, the dependent variable in Hooke's experiment was the amount the spring stretched from its initial length.

We label each axis with the name, symbol, and unit of the variable being plotted, as shown in Figure F.1. The graphs in this text have origins of (0, 0). Scales are chosen for each axis to spread the measured values across the graph paper without making the plotting difficult and without wasting too much graph paper. The scale on each axis usually has equal divisions and each division represents a whole number.

The maximum value of the applied force in Figure F.1 is 10 N. The graph paper has 12 major horizontal divisions, so it is convenient to use only 10 of them to plot the force. Each major vertical division has been made to represent 5.0 cm.

Plotting the Data

Use a pencil to plot the data points. Mark the data points with a small visible dot. Then draw a small circle around each data point. The diameter of the circle should not exceed two small-scale divisions or 2 mm, whichever is smaller. This circle shows that all measured data points have some error. The circles are not meant to accurately show the size of the error. In some cases, a data point has no error, so no circle is drawn. In Figure F.1, (0, 0) is such a point because zero force results in zero stretch.

In this text, we assume that all measured quantities have an error no larger than plus or minus one-half of the smallest division on the measuring instrument. For example, suppose a line is measured to be 45.5 mm using a ruler calibrated in millimetres. Then the error is no larger than plus or minus 0.5 mm. With experience, people can read instruments to plus or minus a tenth of the smallest division. Figure F.2 shows this for a ruler calibrated in centimetres. An experienced person would probably record a measurement of 6.6 cm or 6.7 cm.

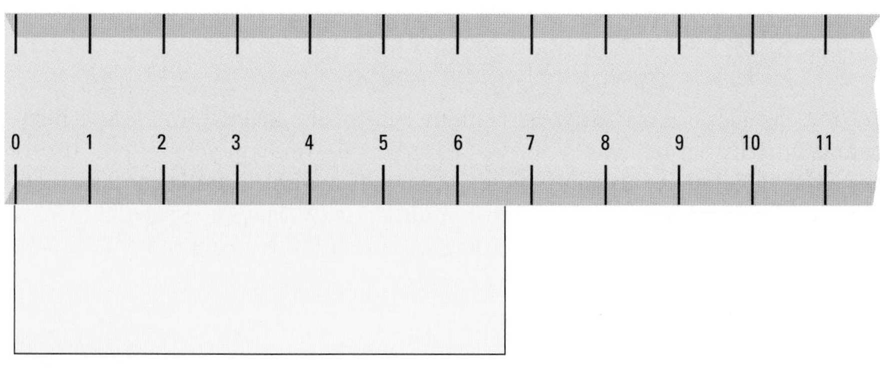

FIGURE F.2

Drawing the Line of Best Fit

Once all of the data points and error circles have been plotted, a line of best fit is drawn. A line of best fit is a line that shows the trend of the points. Do not try to have the curve or straight line go through all the dots since most data points have some error. The scatter of the data points from the smooth line indicates the extent of the errors in the data.

Where a point is far off the line, a serious error may have been made. If this occurs, measure the data for that point again. If the same result is obtained, a factor other than those under investigation may be the cause. Notice that the last two data points in Figure F.1 are far off the straight line and that the line has been curved to account for this trend.

Interpolating from the Graph

Interpolation is the process of finding intermediate values between the known or measured points. To interpolate, locate the given value of the variable on its axis. Draw a straight line perpendicular to this axis to intersect the graph. Draw a line at the intersection point perpendicular to the second axis. Read the value of the second variable from this axis.

There is some risk of inaccuracy involved in interpolation, since it is assumed that the trend of the line continues between the measured points. This assumption is not always valid. Figure F.1 shows the process of interpolating the value of the stretch corresponding to a force of 6.0 N. From the graph, what is the interpolated value for the stretch? Is this value valid?

Extrapolating from the Graph

Extrapolation is the process of finding values beyond the limits of the known or measured values. However, there is a considerable risk of inaccuracy because we are assuming that the trend of the curve continues outside the range of the data. When the line is extended, a dotted line is used to show that the extension is little more than guesswork. Figure F.1 shows the process of extrapolating the curve to find the value of the force needed to yield a stretch of 55 cm. From the graph, what is the extrapolated value for the force? How valid is the value?

Calculating the Slope

If the line of best fit is straight, we can find the slope of the line. The *slope* of the line is defined as the ratio of the rise to the run. Thus

$$\text{slope} = \frac{\text{rise}}{\text{run}}$$

To find the slope, draw any convenient run on the graph. A *run* is a horizontal line drawn below the curve of the graph, touching the curve at one end. The calculations are simplified if the run is a whole number and as large as possible. Then draw in the corresponding rise. A rise is a vertical line joining the free end of the run to the curve. A run of 5.0 N (from 0.5 N to 5.5 N) is shown in Figure F.1. The rise is 22.5 cm (from 2.5 cm to 25 cm). The slope is calculated as follows:

$$\text{slope} = \frac{\text{rise}}{\text{run}}$$

$$= 22.5 \text{ cm}/5.0 \text{ N}$$

$$= 4.5 \frac{\text{cm}}{\text{N}}$$

Notice that the slope in this example has units. This is true for many slopes in physics.

Writing the General Equation of the Line

If the trend of the curve is a straight line through the origin, the plotted variables are directly proportional to each other. As one variable doubles, the other doubles, and vice versa. The general equation for a straight line passing through the origin is $y = mx$, where y is the variable on the vertical axis, x is the variable on the horizontal axis, and m is the slope of the line.

Figure F.1 shows a straight line for a force between 0 and 7.0 N. For this range, the stretch is directly proportional to the applied force. This can be written as $x \alpha F$, where α means "is proportional to."

The general equation for the straight-line portion of Figure F.1 is $x = k \cdot F$, where x is the stretch, F is the applied force, and k is the slope of the graph.

Writing the Specific Corresponding Equation

The general equation shows the relationship between the variables symbolically. For example, $x = k \cdot F$. The specific corresponding equation replaces the symbol for the proportionality constant k with its numerical value. The value of the proportionality constant is equal to the slope of the line. Since the slope of the line is 4.5 cm/N, the specific corresponding equation in our example is

$$x = 4.5 \frac{\text{cm}}{\text{N}} \cdot F$$

Using the Specific Corresponding Equation

It is often more convenient to interpolate or extrapolate using the specific corresponding equation than from a graph. For example, we could use the equation to determine the value of the stretch for a force of 6.0 N. Try it and see if you get a stretch of 27 cm. The equation can only be used to extrapolate if the trend of the graph is a straight line beyond the plotted points. This is not the case in Figure F.1, since the line curves for forces greater than 7.0 N. For example, for a stretch of 55 cm, the force needed according to the equation is 12 N. But interpolation yields a value of about 10.4 N—a significant difference.

TABLE G.1 Period Versus Mass for a Vibrating Spring Pendulum

Period *T* (s)	Attached Mass *m* (kg)
0.20	0.02
0.31	0.05
0.44	0.10
0.63	0.20
0.77	0.30
0.89	0.40
0.99	0.50
1.18	0.70
1.33	0.90
1.40	1.00

G. Using the Graphing Calculator

Graphing calculators make the process of plotting and interpreting graphs easy and efficient. Data from an experiment can be entered into the calculator and displayed as a scatterplot. The calculator can help us determine the function that best fits a given scatterplot. The information provided for this function can also be used to write the equation that best describes the relationship between the two plotted variables.

The graphing calculator can also be used to help us explore the graph of a given equation or relationship. It can be used to interpolate values between the plotted points or to extrapolate values beyond the plotted points. These uses make the graphing calculator a very powerful laboratory tool.

Lines and Curves of Best Fit

Let's see how a graphing calculator can be used to graph data and determine the relationship between two variables. We will use data from an experiment performed to answer the question: "How does the period of vibration of an elastic spring depend on the mass attached to the end?" Different masses were attached to the end of a spring suspended from a vertical support. For each mass, the spring was caused to vibrate by pulling downward on the mass, stretching the spring, and releasing it. The period of vibration of each mass was measured. The data for the period of the pendulum corresponding to each attached mass is summarized in Table G.1.

Let's use the graphing calculator to plot the data, and to calculate and graph the equations of functions that might be used to model the situation. Plot a graph with mass *m* on the *x*-axis and period *T* on the *y*-axis. The screens and keystrokes below are for the TI-83 Plus calculator.

FIGURE G.1

Display a Scatterplot

1. Clear RAM and the screen to make sure no equations are already selected in the Y= list. To do this, press **2nd** **MEM** . **7** . **1** . **2** . **CLEAR** .
2. Define the viewing window by entering values of X and Y so that the data will appear on and almost fill the screen. For our data, X corresponds to mass and Y to period. Press **WINDOW** . Suitable range values are X_{min} = 00, X_{max} = 1.00 and Y_{min} = 0.00, Y_{max} = 1.5. You can simply type over the existing signs and numerals. For negative signs, make sure that you use the negative symbol at the bottom of the calculator instead of the minus sign at the side.
3. Enter the data from the table in the list editor. List the values to be plotted on the *x*-axis in list 1 and the *y*-axis in list 2. Press **STAT** **1**, and enter the mass values in the first column and the corresponding period values in the second column, as shown in Figure G.1.
4. Define the statistical plot. Press **2nd** **Y=** **1**. In the menu that appears, press **ENTER** to make sure for Plot 1 that **On** is selected in the first line, the **first graph type** is selected in the second line, and lists **L1** and **L2** appear in the third and fourth lines, as shown in Figure G.2.
5. To add a second set of data on the same set of axes, toggle up to the top line and right to Plot 2. Press **ENTER** . Repeat the steps above—only for the

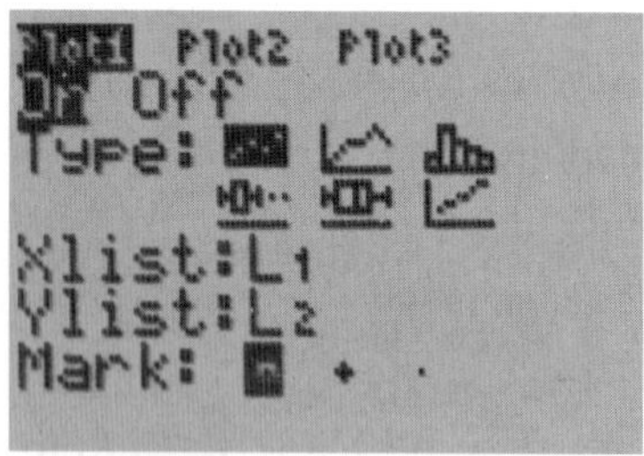

FIGURE G.2

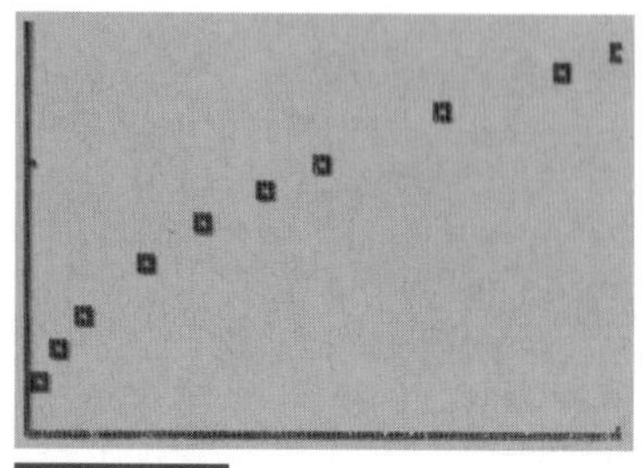
FIGURE G.3

Y list press 2nd LIST and choose L3 instead of L2 from the list. Press ENTER.

6. Graph the data as a scatterplot. Press GRAPH to graph the data, as shown in Figure G.3.

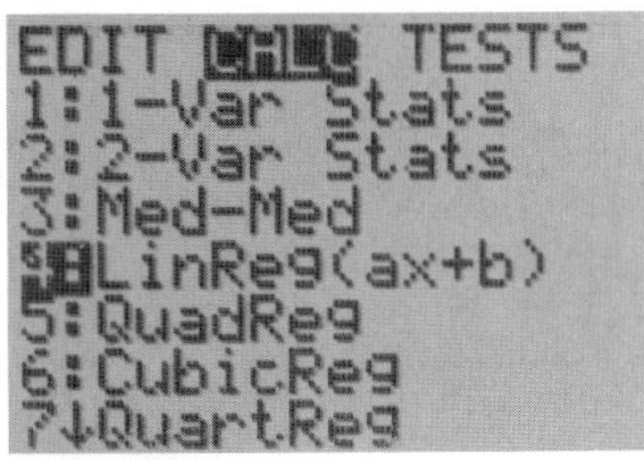

FIGURE G.4

Determine the Best-Fit Curve

To fit a curve to data, the first step is to select a suitable type of function. This involves comparing patterns in the plotted points (the scatterplot) with features of a particular function. For the above graph, as mass m becomes larger, the period T becomes larger. This suggests a linear relationship. But it may also be a power relationship. Let's determine which function best fits the scatterplot.

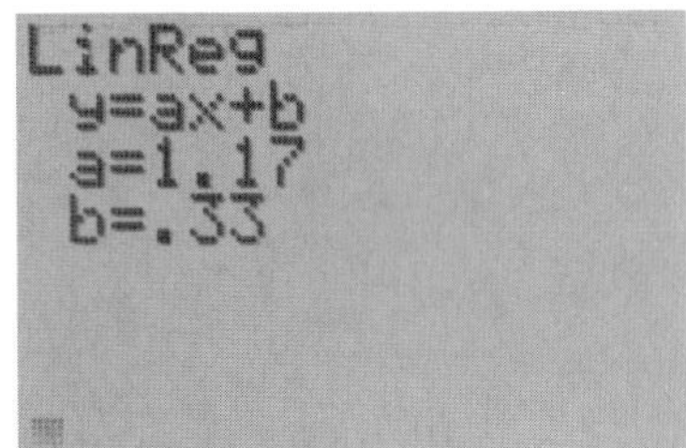

FIGURE G.5

7. Choose the desired function type from the STAT CALC menu. Press STAT > to obtain the menu shown in Figure G.4 (you must scroll down to see it all). Let's see if the scatterplot corresponds to a linear regression. Scroll down to LinReg(ax+b), the fourth line in the menu. To select this type of function, press ENTER. ALPHA ENTER. The screen in Figure G.5 shows the calculated results for the function y = a + xb. These calculations are called a *regression*.

Graph the Curve of the Regression

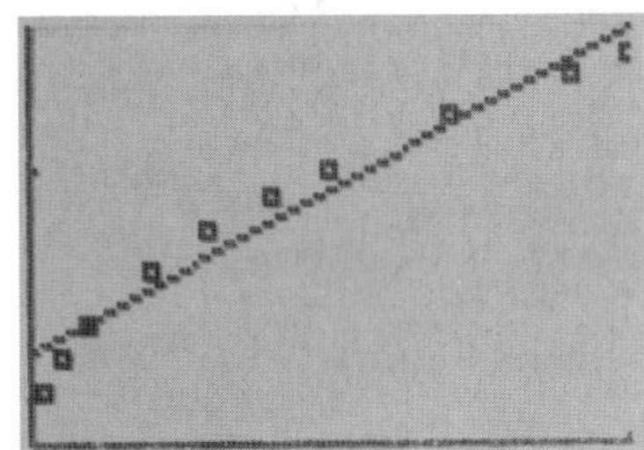
FIGURE G.6

8. To graph the curve of the regression, we will enter the equation of the regression directly into the calculator. Press Y= CLEAR VARS 5 > > 1.

9. Graph the equation of the regression that comes closest to the plotted points. Press GRAPH. The screen shows the graph of the regression superimposed on the scatterplot of the original data (Figure G.6). Our choice of the linear regression does not seem to fit the scatterplot perfectly. The points of the scatterplot seem to form a curve rather than a straight line.

   To try the power regression, repeat steps 7, 8, and 9 but select PwrReg, $y = ax^b$ in step 7. The results for the power regression are shown in Figure G.7. Figure G.8 shows the graph of this function superimposed on the scatterplot. The power regression fits the plotted points almost perfectly. The function that best fits the data is a power regression.

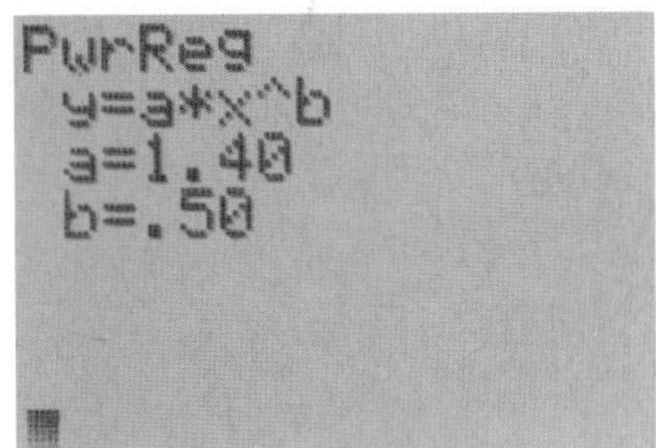

FIGURE G.7

Write the Equation of the Matching Function

10. The calculated results for the power regression shows that the function that best describes the plotted points is $y = 1.4x^{0.5}$. Another way of writing this is $y = 1.4\sqrt{x}$ or in terms of period and mass $T = 1.4\sqrt{m}$. The period of a vibrating spring pendulum is directly proportional to the square root of the mass. This explains the curve in the plotted points. If the mass doubles, the period increases but does not double. In order for the period to double, the mass must increase by a factor of 4. You can check this out by referring to Table G.1. Look at what happens when the period of the attached mass increases by a factor of 9.

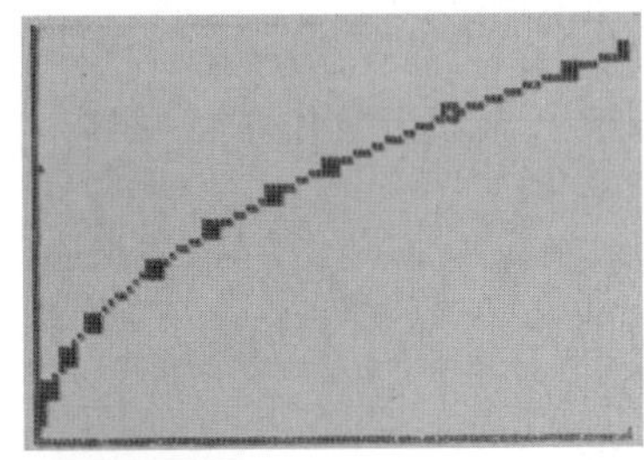
FIGURE G.8

Equations, Graphs, and Graphical Analysis

The equation for the period of a string pendulum is $T = 2\pi\frac{\sqrt{l}}{\sqrt{g}}$ where T is the period of the pendulum, l is the length of the pendulum, and g is the force

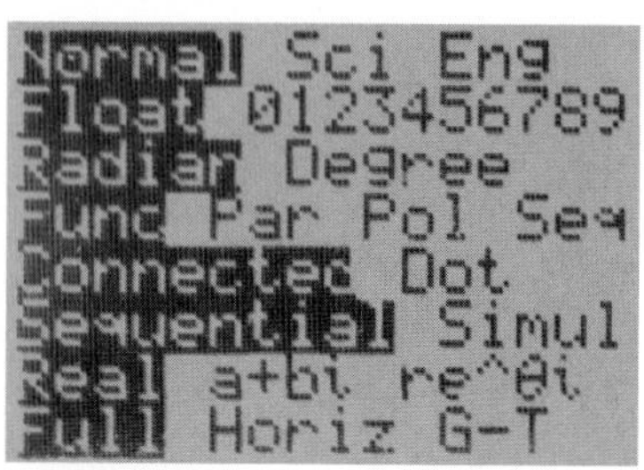

FIGURE G.9

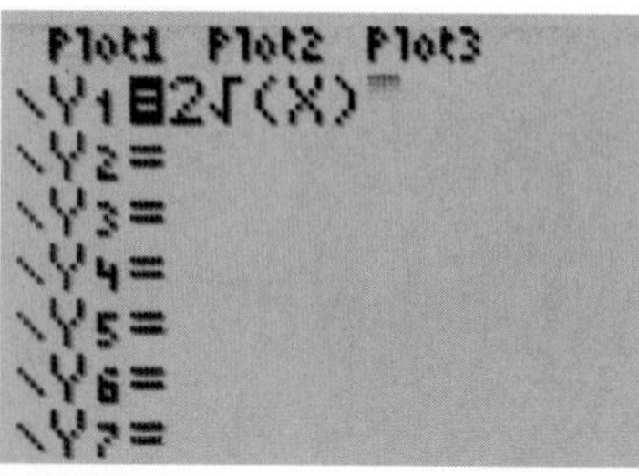

FIGURE G.10

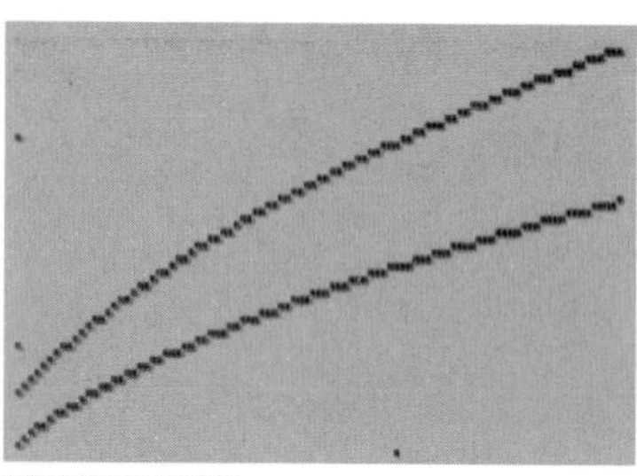
FIGURE G.11

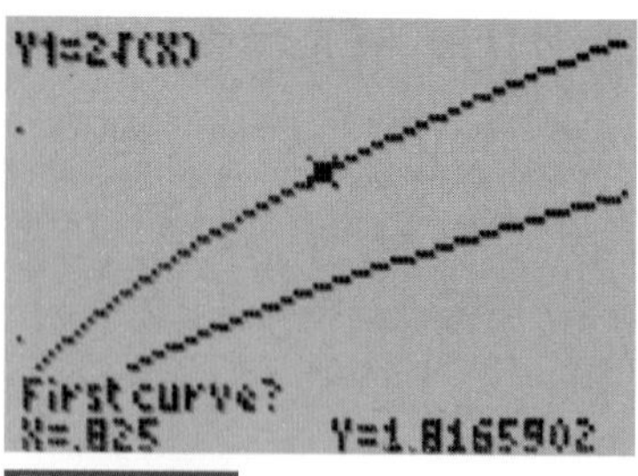

FIGURE G-12

of gravity to mass ratio of the celestial object. On Earth, this equation simplifies to $T = 2\pi\frac{\sqrt{l}}{\sqrt{9.8}}$ or $T = 2\sqrt{l}$ since g has a value of about 9.8 N/kg. Use your graphing calculator to plot a graph of the period T on the y-axis (with a range of 0.50 s to 2.5 s) and length l on the x-axis (with a range of 0.15 m to 1.5 m).

Drawing the Curve

1. Clear RAM. Press 2nd MEM. Press 7. Press 1. Press 2.
2. Press MODE and select NORMAL from the menu shown in Figure G.9.
3. Press WINDOW and enter $X_{min} = 0.15$, $X_{max} = 1.5$, and $Y_{min} = 0.50$, $Y_{max} = 2.5$.
4. Press Y= and enter for Y_1 the equation $y = 2\sqrt{x}$ (Figure G.10) where y corresponds to the period T, and x to the length of the string pendulum.
5. Press GRAPH and you will see the curve for the string pendulum.
6. Suppose you want to plot the graphs for another different equation on the same axis. For example, the equation for the period of a spring pendulum is $T = 2\pi\frac{\sqrt{m}}{\sqrt{k}}$, where T is the period of the pendulum, m is the mass of the attached object, and k is the elastic constant of the particular spring. This equation can be simplified to $T = 1.4\sqrt{m}$ by selecting a spring with a spring constant of 20 N/m. In other words, it takes a force of 20 N to stretch the spring 1.0 m. If we want to graph this equation on the same axis as the equation for a string pendulum, we can press Y= and enter for Y_2 the equation $y = 1.4\sqrt{x}$.
7. Press GRAPH and you will see the two curves in the same window (Figure G.11).

Reading Coordinates of the Curves (Interpolation)

8. Press 2nd CALC and select 5:intersect. You will then see the equation for one of the curves, and the values of x and y displayed for the location of the cursor (Figure G.12). You can use the ▶ and ◀ keys to toggle the curve and read values of y corresponding to specific values of x.
9. To read values from a different curve, use the ▲ and ▼ keys to toggle between the two curves.
10. If you need to set the value of x to one decimal place and obtain the corresponding value of y, press ZOOM 4 2nd CALC and reselect 5:intersect.

H. Accuracy and Significant Digits

Accuracy

Physicists are interested in how closely a measurement agrees with the accepted value. This is an indication of the quality of the measuring instrument and the technique of the user. *Accuracy* is a means of describing how closely a measurement agrees with the accepted or actual size of a quantity being measured. The difference between an observed value (or the average of observed values) and the accepted value is called the *error*. The size of the error is an indication of the accuracy. Thus, the smaller the error, the greater the accuracy.

The *percent error* is determined by subtracting the accepted value from the measured value, dividing this by the accepted value, and multiplying by 100. Thus,

$$\text{percent error} = \frac{(\text{measured value} - \text{accepted value})}{\text{accepted value} \times 100\%}$$

EXAMPLE PROBLEM

The density of copper is measured to be 8650 kg/m^3. The accepted value for the density is 8900 kg/m^3. What is the percentage error?

$$\text{Percent error} = \frac{(\text{measured value} - \text{accepted value})}{\text{accepted value} \times 100\%}$$

$$= \frac{(8650\ \text{kg/m}^3 - 8900\ \text{kg/m}^3)}{8900\ \text{kg/m}^3 \times 100\%}$$

$$= -2.800\%$$

The negative percentage error indicates that the measured value is low by 2.800%.

Significant Digits

The accuracy of a measurement is indicated by the number of significant digits. *Significant digits* are those digits in the numerical value of which we are reasonably sure. When we are expressing a physical quantity as a number, how many significant digits should we give it? These rules should help you decide:

- Numbers obtained by counting are considered to be exact and contain an infinite number of significant digits. For example, if there are 12 stopwatches in a classroom, there are not 11 stopwatches, or 13 stopwatches, or 12.35 stopwatches. There are exactly 12.000... stopwatches. The zeros may be extended to as many decimal places as necessary in calculations.
- Numbers obtained from definitions are considered to be exact and contain an infinite number of significant digits. For example, 1 m = 100 cm, 1 kW·h = 3600 kJ, and π = 3.141 592 654 are all definitions of equalities. π has an infinite number of decimal places, as do numbers in equations such as $C = 2\pi r$.

- All of the digits from one to nine (1, 2, 3, ... 9) are significant, so 424.7 m or 0.424 7 km each have four significant digits.
- All zeros to the left of the first non-zero digit are not significant. For example, 1.4 kg and 0.001 4 kg each have two significant digits.
- Zeros between other non-zero digits are significant. Therefore, 501.009 s has six significant digits.
- Any zero to the right of a non-zero digit is significant. Therefore, the mass of an object written as 2000 kg has four significant digits. If the mass is a stated value, not a measured value, we can indicate that we know it to four significant digits by using scientific notation and writing the mass as 2000×10^4 kg.
- Unless otherwise noted, assume that all physical quantities in this text are measured. Therefore zeros to the right of numerals one to nine are significant.

I. Rounding Off Numbers

When making measurements, or when doing calculations, never keep more digits in the final answer than in the least accurate number in the calculation. For example, $0.6 + 0.32 = 0.9$, not 0.92. The procedure for dropping off digits is called *rounding off*. The procedure for rounding off digits is as follows:

- When the first digit discarded is less than five, the last digit retained is left the same. Notice that we start rounding off at the digit immediately after the last digit we are retaining. For example, 14.248 1 kg rounded to three digits is 14.2 kg, since the fourth digit (4) is less than five.
- When the first digit discarded is greater than five, or if it is a five followed by at least one digit other than zero, we increase the last digit retained by one. Therefore, 7.836 1 km rounded to three digits is 7.84 km, and 4.255 01 s rounded to three digits is 4.26 s.
- When the first digit discarded is five followed by zeros or no digits, we increase the last digit by one if it is odd, or leave it unchanged if it is even. This is sometimes called the *Even-Odd Rule* and is equivalent to rounding the last digit to the nearest even digit. For example, 3.475 m rounded to three digits is 3.48 m, and 3.485 m rounded to three digits is also 3.48 m.
- Consider numbers that are exact counts to be perfectly precise. For example, the average mass of three cars having masses of 1000 kg, 1250 kg, and 1165 kg is (1000 kg + 1250 kg + 1165 kg)/3 or 1133 kg. The denominator (3) in this example is an exact count, and therefore the answer includes four significant digits.
- Consider fractions and defined equalities to be perfectly precise. The fraction $\frac{1}{2}$ in the equation $E_k = \frac{1}{2mv^2}$ does not influence rounding off. Neither does the defined equality 10 mm = 1 cm.

J. Mathematical Operations with Data

The Weakest Link Rule

When performing calculations with data, it is important that we give the answer no more accuracy than the accuracy of the least accurate data. This is called the *Weakest Link Rule*, which is a reference to the saying, "A chain is no stronger than its weakest link." Two different methods of determining the weakest link are used, depending on whether the mathematical operation involved is multiplication and division, or addition and subtraction.

Multiplication and Division When we either multiply or divide measurements and then round off, our final answer should contain the same accuracy as the measurement used in the calculation having the least number of significant digits.

The answer to the Example Problem is rounded to two significant digits because the radius is given to only two significant digits. Since π is a constant, we used it to three significant digits, which is one more than the least accurate measurement in the calculation.

EXAMPLE PROBLEM

A cylinder has a height of 120 cm and a radius of 2.4 cm. Calculate the volume of the cylinder.

The formula for the volume of a cylinder is

$$\begin{aligned} V = \pi r^2 h &= 3.14 \times (2.4\ \text{cm})^2 \times 120\ \text{cm} \\ &= 2\,170.368\ \text{cm}^3 \\ &= 2.2 \times 10^3\ \text{cm}^3 \text{ (rounded to two significant figures)} \end{aligned}$$

The cylinder has a volume of 2.2×10^3 cm^3.

Addition and Subtraction When we add or subtract measurements and round off, our final answer should be as precise as the least precise of the measurements used in the calculation. Precision is indicated by the number of decimal places in a measurement.

Steps to Solving Problems with Significant Digits

The following steps will help identify the significant digits in the answer:

- Solve the problem.
- Decide what mathematical function(s) was/were involved.
- Accordingly, decide which Weakest Link Rule applies:
    a) For multiplication and division, identify the least accurate number (with the least number of significant digits).
    b) For addition and subtraction, identify the least precise number (with the least number of decimal places).
- Look at the answer and decide how many significant digits or decimal places it should have.
- Round off the answer.

K. Exponential Notation and Standard Form

Exponential Notation

Exponential notation makes use of powers of ten to write large and small quantities and to convey the number of significant digits. The first part of the number is called the *coefficient*, and the power of ten is the *exponent*. The radius of Earth may be written in exponential notation to three significant digits as 638×10^4 m, 63.8×10^5 m, 6.38×10^6 m, or 0.638×10^7 m. The diameter of a typical atom may be expressed to one significant digit as 1×10^{-8} cm or 0.1×10^{-7} cm.

Standard Form (Scientific Notation)

Any measurement that consists of a coefficient multiplied by a power of ten is expressed in exponential notation. Both 6.38×10^6 and 0.638×10^7 are in exponential notation. Standard form is a special kind of exponential notation. The number is in standard form only when the first digit in the coefficient is between 1 and 9. This means that 6.38×10^6 is expressed in standard form and 0.638×10^7 is not.

Standard form enables us to show the correct number of significant digits. Remember that any zero to the right of the decimal point is significant. Therefore, if all four digits in the measurement 3400 J are significant, then it would be written in standard form as 3.400×10^3 J. However, if only two digits are significant, it would be 3.4×10^3 J.

The results of all calculations should always be expressed in standard form, unless you are told otherwise. This involves moving the decimal point and changing the exponent until the coefficient is between 1 and 9. The exponent is decreased by one for each position the decimal point in the coefficient is moved to the right, and increased by one for each position the decimal point is moved to the left. For example:

a) $$500 \times 10^4 = 5.00 \times 10^2 \times 10^4 = 5.00 \times 10^{2+4} = 5.00 \times 10^6$$

b) $$0.068 \times 10^{-3} = 6.8 \times 10^{-2} \times 10^{-3} = 6.8 \times 10^{-3+(-2)} = 6.8 \times 10^{-5}$$

Exponential Notation and Mathematical Operations

Multiplication The product of exponential numbers is determined by multiplying the coefficients and adding the exponents. For example:

$$(3.0 \times 10^2)(4.0 \times 10^{-6}) = (3.0 \times 4.0)(10^2 \times 10^{-6}) = 12 \times 10^{2+(-6)} = 12 \times 10^{-4} = 1.2 \times 10^{-3}$$

Division We can divide exponential numbers by dividing the coefficients normally and subtracting the exponent of the bottom number from the exponent of the top number. For example:

$$\begin{aligned}\frac{3.3 \times 10^5}{6.6 \times 10^{-2}} &= \frac{3.3}{6.6} \times \frac{10^5}{10^{-2}} \\ &= 0.50 \times 10^{5-(-2)} \\ &= 0.50 \times 10^{5+2} \\ &= 0.50 \times 10^7 \\ &= 5.0 \times 10^6\end{aligned}$$

Addition and Subtraction When the Exponents are the Same When the exponents are the same, add or subtract the coefficients normally and keep the exponent of the result the same as the original exponents. For example:

$$\begin{aligned}(2 \times 10^{-4}) + (3 \times 10^{-4}) - (1 \times 10^{-4}) &= (2 + 3 - 1) \times 10^{-4} \\ &= 4 \times 10^{-4}\end{aligned}$$

Addition and Subtraction When the Exponents are Different If the exponents are different, convert the numbers to a form in which all exponents are the same. Move the decimal point so that all have the same exponent as the largest number in the group. Then add or subtract the coefficients normally and keep the exponent of the result the same as the largest exponent. For example:

$$\begin{aligned}&(1.00 \times 10^{-3}) - (2.00 \times 10^{-4}) + (400 \times 10^{-5}) \\ &\quad = (1.00 \times 10^{-3}) - (0.200 \times 10^{-3}) + (4.00 \times 10^{-3}) \\ &\quad = (1.00 - 0.200 + 4.00) \times 10^{-3} \\ &\quad = 4.80 \times 10^{-3}\end{aligned}$$

L. Precision and Reading Instruments

The degree of accuracy of any instrument depends on two things: first, on the precision of the measuring instrument; and second, on the skill and care of the user.

Being precise means being sharply defined. The precision of a measuring instrument depends on its degree of fineness and the size of the unit being used. Using an instrument with a more finely divided scale allows us to take a more precise measurement.

Any measurement that falls between the smallest division on the measuring instrument is an estimate. We should always try to read any instrument by estimating tenths of the smallest division. For a ruler calibrated in centimetres, this means estimating to the nearest tenth of a centimetre or to 1 mm. Using this procedure, we find that the length of the object in Figure L.1 is 6.7 cm. We are certain of the 6, but the 0.7 is an estimate. In reality, it could easily be 0.6 or 0.8. It is unlikely, however, that it would be 0.5.

Figure L.2 shows the measurement of the same object using a ruler calibrated in millimetres. The reading estimated to the nearest tenth of a millimetre appears closest to 6.74 cm. We might be tempted to record the length as either 6.7 cm or 6.8 cm. This would be wrong. We can tell that the length is between the two divisions. The estimated digit is always shown when recording the measurement. The estimated digit in this reading is 0.04 cm.

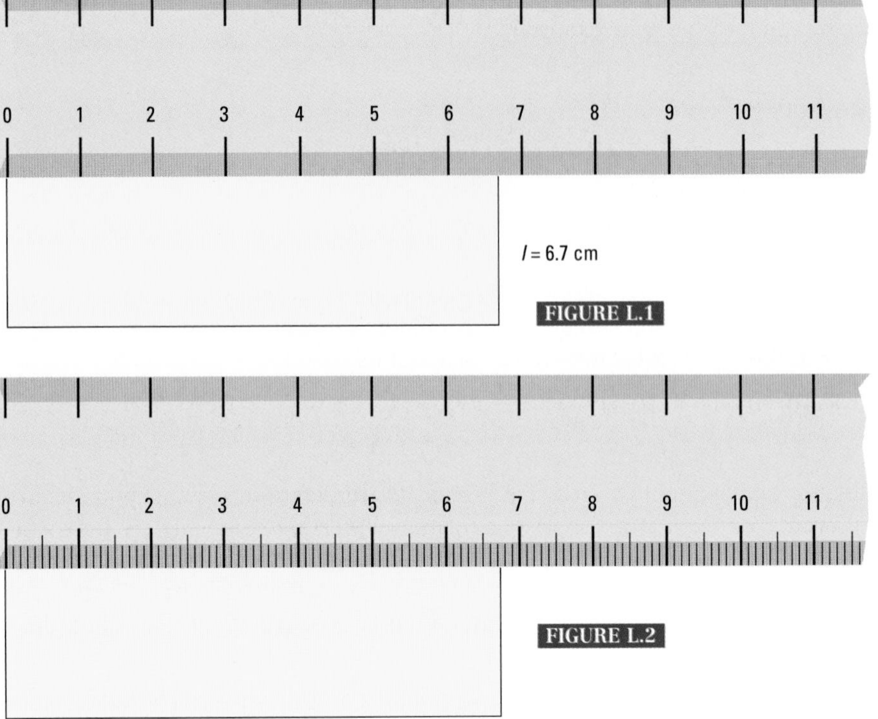

FIGURE L.1

FIGURE L.2

Figure L.3 shows a different object being measured with a ruler calibrated in centimetres. The length falls exactly on the 6-cm mark. Should the length be recorded as 6 cm or 6.0 cm? Remember that with a centimetre ruler we can estimate to tenths of a centimetre. With this ruler we can therefore distinguish readings of 5.9 cm and 6.1 cm. The object is right on a division mark, so the estimated digit is zero-tenths of a centimetre. Zero-tenths is indicated by 0.0 and the correct reading is 6.0 cm, not 6 cm.

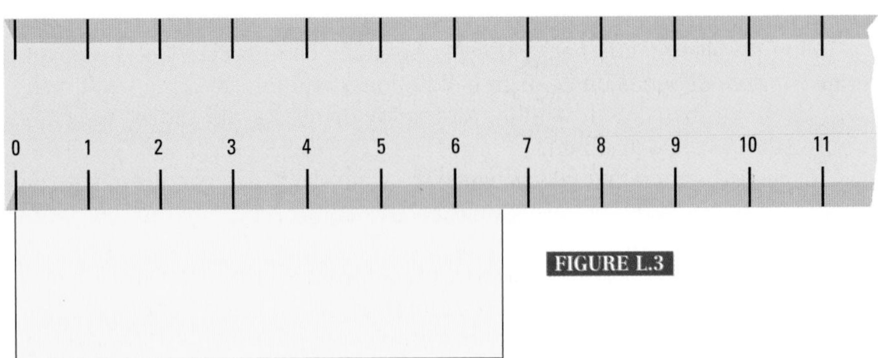

FIGURE L.3

Indicating the Precision of Measured Quantities

The *precision* of a measurement is indicated by the number of decimal places. For example, 2.861 cm is more precise than 581.86 cm even though the latter contains more digits. This is because the three decimal places in 2.861 make it precise to the nearest one-thousandth of a centimetre, while the two decimal places in 581.86 make it precise to the nearest one-hundredth of a centimetre.

M. Reference Tables

Table M.1 Metric Prefixes

Prefix	Symbol	Factor	Multiplier
giga	G	1 000 000 000	$= 10^{9}$
mega	M	1 000 000	$= 10^{6}$
kilo	k	1 000	$= 10^{3}$
hecto	h	100	$= 10^{2}$
deca	da	10	$= 10^{1}$
		1	$= 10^{0}$
deci	d	0.1	$= 10^{-1}$
centi	c	0.01	$= 10^{-2}$
milli	m	0.001	$= 10^{-3}$
micro	µ	0.000 001	$= 10^{-6}$
nano	n	0.000 000 001	$= 10^{-9}$

Table M.2 Table of Fundamental Quantities

Quantity	Quantity Symbol	Unit	Unit Symbol
Length	*l*	metre	m
Mass	*m*	kilogram	kg
Time	*t*	second	s
Electric current	*I*	ampere	A
Absolute temperature	*T*	kelvin	K
Amount of substance	*n*	mole	mol
Luminous intensity	*I*	candela	cd

Table M.3 Derived Quantities

Quantity	Quantity Symbol	Unit	Unit Symbol	Derivation
Area	*A*	square metre	m^2	—
Volume	*V*	cubic metre	m^3	—
Speed, velocity	*v*	metre per second	m/s	—
Acceleration	*a*	metre per second squared	m/s^2	—
Frequency	*f*	hertz	s^{-1}	—
Density	*ρ*	kilogram per cubic metre	kg/m^3	—
Force	*F*	newton	N	$kg{\cdot}m/s^2$
Pressure	*p*	pascal	Pa	N/m^2
Energy, work	*E, W*	joule	J	N·m
Power	*P*	watt	W	J/s
Heat capacity	*C*	joule per kelvin	J/K	—
Specific heat capacity	*c*	Joule per kilogram kelvin	J/(kg·K)	—
Electric charge	*Q*	coulomb	C	A·s
Electric potential	*V*	volt	V	J/C
Resistance	*R*	ohm	Ω	V/A
Activity	*A*	becquerel	Bq	s^{-1}
Absorbed dose	*D*	gray	Gy	J/C

Table M.4 Numerical Constants

Name	Symbol	Value
Fundamental Physical Constants		
Absolute zero	0 K	-273.15°C
Speed of light	c	2.9979×10^{8} m/s
Change on an electron	e	1.602×10^{-19} C
Gravitational constant	G	6.673×10^{-11} N·m²/kg²
Coulomb's constant	k	9.0×10^{9} N·m²/C²
Atomic mass unit	u	1.661×10^{-27} kg
Rest mass of an electron	m_o	9.110×10^{-31} kg
Rest mass of a proton	m_p	1.673×10^{-27} kg
Rest mass of a neutron	m_n	1.675×10^{-27} kg
Constants for Earth		
Standard atmospheric pressure	atm	1.013×10^{5} Pa
Acceleration due to gravity (sea level, at equator)	g	9.78049 m/s²
Mass	m_e	5.98×10^{24} kg
Radius (mean)	r_e	6.38×10^{6} m
Duration of year	T_y	3.16×10^{7} s
Constants for the Moon		
Mass of Moon	m_m	7.36×10^{22} kg
Radius (mean)	r_m	1.74×10^{6} m
Period of orbit	T_o	2.36×10^{6} s

Table M.5 Nuclide Masses

Nuclide	Mass ($\times 10^{-27}$ kg)
$^{0}_{-1}e$	0.000 909 68
$^{1}_{0}n$	1.674 383 9
$^{1}_{1}H$	1.672 989 5
$^{2}_{1}H$	3.343 24
$^{3}_{1}H$	5.006 643
$^{3}_{2}He$	5.006 609 8
$^{4}_{2}He$	6.644 3
$^{6}_{3}Li$	9.985 099 2
$^{86}_{36}Kr$	142.660 4

Nuclide	Mass ($\times 10^{-27}$ kg)
$^{93}_{36}Kr$	154.26
$^{95}_{42}Mo$	157.610 36
$^{139}_{56}Ba$	230.607 2
$^{140}_{56}Ba$	232.25
$^{139}_{57}La$	230.584 56
$^{235}_{56}U$	390.172 9
$^{236}_{92}U$	391.835 86
$^{238}_{92}U$	395.164 33
$^{239}_{94}Pu$	396.826 57

Table M.6 Natural Sines, Consines, and Tangents

Angle	Sine	Cosine	Tangent
1°	0.0175	0.9998	0.0175
2°	0.0349	0.9994	0.0349
3°	0.0523	0.9986	0.0524
4°	0.0698	0.9976	0.0699
5°	0.0872	0.9962	0.0875
6°	0.1045	0.9945	0.1051
7°	0.1219	0.9925	0.1228
8°	0.1392	0.9903	0.1405
9°	0.1564	0.9877	0.1584
10°	0.1736	0.9848	0.1763
11°	0.1908	0.9816	0.1944
12°	0.2079	0.9781	0.2126
13°	0.2250	0.9744	0.2309
14°	0.2419	0.9703	0.2493
15°	0.2588	0.9659	0.2679
16°	0.2756	0.9613	0.2867
17°	0.2924	0.9563	0.3057
18°	0.3090	0.9511	0.3249
19°	0.3256	0.9455	0.3443
20°	0.3420	0.9397	0.3640
21°	0.3584	0.9336	0.3839
22°	0.3746	0.9272	0.4040
23°	0.3907	0.9205	0.4245
24°	0.4067	0.9135	0.4452
25°	0.4226	0.9063	0.4663
26°	0.4384	0.8988	0.4877
27°	0.4540	0.8910	0.5095
28°	0.4695	0.8829	0.5317
29°	0.4848	0.8746	0.5543
30°	0.5000	0.8660	0.5774
31°	0.5150	0.8572	0.6009
32°	0.5299	0.8480	0.6249
33°	0.5446	0.8387	0.6494
34°	0.5592	0.8290	0.6745
35°	0.5736	0.8192	0.7002
36°	0.5878	0.8090	0.7265
37°	0.6018	0.7986	0.7536
38°	0.6157	0.7880	0.7813
39°	0.6293	0.7771	0.8098
40°	0.6428	0.7660	0.8391
41°	0.6561	0.7547	0.8693
42°	0.6691	0.7431	0.9004
43°	0.6820	0.7314	0.9325
44°	0.6947	0.7193	0.9657
45°	0.7071	0.7071	1.0000
46°	0.7193	0.6947	1.0355
47°	0.7314	0.6820	1.0724
48°	0.7431	0.6691	1.1106
49°	0.7547	0.5661	1.1504
50°	0.7660	0.6428	1.1918
51°	0.7771	0.6293	1.2349
52°	0.7880	0.6157	1.2799
53°	0.7986	0.6018	1.3270
54°	0.8090	0.5878	1.3764
55°	0.8192	0.5736	1.4281
56°	0.8290	0.5592	1.4826
57°	0.8387	0.5446	1.5399
58°	0.8480	0.5299	1.6003
59°	0.8572	0.5150	1.6643
60°	0.8660	0.5000	1.7321
61°	0.8746	0.4848	1.8040
62°	0.8829	0.4695	1.8807
63°	0.8910	0.4540	1.9626
64°	0.8988	0.4384	2.0503
65°	0.9063	0.4226	2.1445
66°	0.9135	0.4067	2.2460
67°	0.9205	0.3907	2.3559
68°	0.9272	0.3746	2.4751
69°	0.9336	0.3584	2.6051
70°	0.9397	0.3420	2.7475
71°	0.9455	0.3256	2.9042
72°	0.9511	0.3090	3.0777
73°	0.9563	0.2924	3.2709
74°	0.9613	0.2756	3.4874
75°	0.9659	0.2588	3.7321
76°	0.9703	0.2419	4.0108
77°	0.9744	0.2250	4.3315
78°	0.9781	0.2079	4.7046
79°	0.9816	0.1908	5.1446
80°	0.9848	0.1736	5.6713
81°	0.9877	0.1564	6.3138
82°	0.9903	0.1392	7.1154
83°	0.9925	0.1219	8.1443
84°	0.9945	0.1045	9.5144
85°	0.9962	0.0872	11.4301
86°	0.9976	0.0698	14.3007
87°	0.9986	0.0523	19.0811
88°	0.9994	0.0349	28.6363
89°	0.9998	0.0175	57.2900
90°	1.0000	0.0000	

GLOSSARY

A

acceleration $\vec{a}$, rate of change of velocity; calculated as change in velocity divided by elapsed time

acceleration due to gravity $\vec{g}$, the common acceleration of all objects near the surface of a planet

accommodation process of changing the focal length of the eye lens to adjust for near and far objects

achromatic lens converging lens combined with a diverging lens to minimize chromatic aberration

acoustical resonance vibration involving sound waves (See resonance.)

acoustics study of sound

action force force exerted by one object on another object

actual mechanical advantage AMA, ratio of the actual force required to perform work, without using a simple machine, to the force required with the machine

alternating current AC, current that continually reverses its direction. (Compare direct current.)

ammeter instrument used to measure electric current

ampere A, SI unit for electric current. When a current of one ampere flows in a conductor for one second, one coulomb of charge passes any point along the conductor

amplitude maximum displacement of a vibrating object from its rest position

analogue process data are manipulated by variable physical quantities (compare digital process)

angle of deviation angle between the incident ray and the emergent ray

angle of incidence i, angle between an incident ray and the normal

angle of reflection r, angle between a reflected ray and the normal

angle of refraction R, angle between the refracted ray and the normal

antinodal lines imaginary lines along which continual constructive interference occurs

antinodal point point in a standing wave that vibrates with maximum amplitude due to continual constructive interference

antinodes antinodal points

anvil a tiny bone in the middle ear which connects the hammer and the stirrup. It helps to transmit vibrations from the eardrum to the inner ear.

aqueous humour clear liquid located between the cornea and the lens in the human eye

armature coil plus iron core which spins in an electric motor or generator; the moving ferromagnetic arm in devices such as electric bells

astigmatism inability of the eye to focus light in different planes at the same time

astronomical telescope optical instrument with two converging lenses: an objective lens and an eyepiece; also called a Keplerian telescope

attitude orientation of an image relative to the object (for example, erect or inverted)

audible region part of the sound spectrum detectable by humans; ranges from about 16 Hz to 20 kHz

auditory canal part of the ear. Hearing begins with the passage of a sound wave down the auditory canal.

auditory nerve part of the auditory system that transmits electric impulses from the inner ear to the brain

average acceleration $\vec{a}_{av}$, overall change in velocity divided by the time interval. This may represent the combination of different accelerations into one equivalent acceleration. (See acceleration.)

average velocity $\vec{v}_{av}$, overall displacement divided by elapsed time. This may represent the combination of different velocities into one equivalent velocity. (See velocity.)

B

beam bundle of light rays

beat full cycle of loudness variation from loud to soft to loud due to alternating constructive and destructive interference from two sound waves

beat frequency rate of production of beats

bel B, unit of sound intensity

blind spot small area in the eye near the optic nerve that contains no photoreceptors

bridge device that anchors the strings at one end of a musical instrument; transmits the energy to the soundbox

brush device made of carbon in a basic DC motor that allows the current to flow from an external circuit through a commutator to a loop

C

calorimeter container used to measure the amount of heat exchanged

centre of curvature C, centre of the sphere or cylinder from which a mirror is made

chemical energy potential energy stored in molecules

chromatic aberration phenomenon in which an image viewed through a single lens appears with coloured fringes; due to the difference in the refractive index of the lens for different colours

ciliary muscle contracts and relaxes to change the shape of the lens in the eye

circuit pathway for an electric charge

circuit diagram diagram that uses conventional symbols to show circuit components and their connections

cochlea main part of the inner ear containing cilia and nerves which respond to different auditory frequencies

coefficient of kinetic friction μ_k, ratio of the magnitude of force of friction to the magnitude of the normal force when one surface slides past another. (See kinetic friction.)

coefficient of static friction μ_s, magnitude of the minimum force needed to start an object moving divided by the magnitude of the normal force

coil conductor shaped in a series of loops; also called a helix

collinear along the same straight line

collinear forces forces that act along the same straight line

comet tail long tail of dust and gas that forms and becomes visible when a comet approaches the Sun

compass magnet that is allowed to rotate horizontally to point north, south, east, and west

compound microscope arrangement of two converging lenses to increase the magnification of close objects

compression C, region created when longitudinal waves, which are vibrating parallel to the direction of travel, move closer to each other than normal

concave mirror curved mirror that causes parallel rays to come to a principal focus; also called converging mirror

condensing lens system lens system in slide and movie projectors that refracts the light from the light source and directs a parallel beam of light of uniform intensity toward the object

conductance property of a material that describes how easily current can flow through it. Conductance is the inverse of resistance, so a large conductance means a small resistance.

cone in an audio speaker, often made of stiffened paper and attached to the helix; moves when the helix moves

constant acceleration $\vec{a}$, acceleration which remains the same in magnitude and direction; provides equal velocity changes in equal time intervals; produces a straight line on a velocity-time graph

constant velocity $\vec{v}$, velocity which remains the same in magnitude and direction; provides equal displacements in equal time intervals; produces a straight line on a displacement-time graph. (See also uniform motion.)

constructive interference effect resulting from two or more waves pushing a medium in the same direction

conventional current one of two conventions for describing the flow of electric current: electric current is assumed to leave the positive terminal of the cell or battery, move through the circuit, and enter the negative terminal; see also the electron flow convention

converging beam one in which the rays get closer together until they meet

converging lens a lens which will cause an incident beam of parallel rays to converge; a lens which is usually thickest in the middle

converging mirror causes parallel rays to come to a principal focus; also called concave mirror

convex mirror causes parallel rays to spread farther apart from a principal focus; also called diverging mirror

core substance about which a helix is looped to create an electromagnet. Some examples of materials used as cores are iron, steel, and permalloy.

cornea part of the eye through which light enters

coulomb C, unit of charge equal in value to 6.24×10^{18} elementary charges. (See elementary charge.)

Coulomb's law the magnitude of the electric force between any two charged objects is directly proportional to the product of the charges on the objects and inversely proportional to the square of the distance between their centres

crest region of a transverse wave which is above the rest position

critical angle θ_c, angle of incidence that creates an angle of refraction of 90°

Curie temperature temperature above which a solid substance can no longer be magnetized

current electricity electric charge that moves from one place to another. In most electric circuits it is the electrons that move.

cycle repeated pattern of motion; also called a vibration

cylindrical mirror double-sided curved mirror as if sliced from a cylinder

D

deceleration movement of an object that is slowing down; also called negative acceleration

decibel dB, one-tenth of a Bel, a measure of sound intensity

deflection coils electromagnets used to deflect a stream of charged particles, such as the electron beam in a television picture tube.

depth of field range of object distances for which the image is in acceptable focus

destructive interference effect resulting from two or more waves pushing the medium in opposite directions

diaphragm camera mechanism that controls the size of the aperture

diffraction spreading out of a wave as it passes through an opening, or the bending of a wave around an object

diffuse reflection reflection in which an incident parallel beam is scattered in different directions when reflected from an irregular surface; also called irregular reflection

digital process a process in which data are sampled and their magnitudes expressed as binary numbers

direct current DC, current flows in one direction only. (Compare alternating current.)

direct current motor motor that utilizes a direct current; consists of a helix wound on a permeable core, external magnets, and a split-ring commutator

dispersion separation of white light into its composite colours

displacement $\Delta\vec{d}$ change in position of an object; a vector quantity equal to the area beneath a velocity–time graph

diverging beam a beam in which the rays are spreading away from each other; a beam whose cross-sectional area is increasing

diverging lens a lens which will cause an incident beam of parallel rays to diverge from a virtual principal focus; a lens which is usually thinnest in the middle

diverging mirror causes parallel rays to spread farther apart from a principal focus; also called convex mirror

domain any of the clumps of atoms of uniform magnetization in a ferromagnetic substance; a typical domain measures 0.1 mm along a side and contains about 10^{17} atoms

domain theory theory of ferromagnetism involving formation and modification of domains, regions acting like tiny magnets

Doppler effect phenomenon in which a) waves in front of a moving source have a higher frequency and shorter wavelength than if the source were at rest and b) waves behind a moving source have a lower frequency and longer wavelength than if the source were at rest

dynamics branch of mechanics dealing with the causes of changes in motion

E

echoes reflection of sound waves

efficiency ratio of the useful work done by a machine to the amount of energy expended to operate the machine; usually expressed as a percent

elastic energy energy stored in an object when it is forced out of its normal shape

electric current I, the rate of flow of electric charge; usually measured in amperes (A). 1 A = 1 C/s (See coulomb.)

electric potential the potential energy of a unit charge due to its location in an electric field

electric potential difference V, change in electric potential when a charge is moved between two points in an electric field; determined by measuring the work done in moving a unit charge between the two points

electrical energy E_e, energy associated with moving electrical charges

electromagnet helix surrounding a ferromagnetic core whose magnetic field is induced by an electric current; also called a solenoid

electromagnetic force combination of the electric force between two charged particles at rest and the magnetic force produced when charged particles move

electromagnetic induction production of an electric current using a changing magnetic field

electromagnetism magnetic forces induced by electricity

electron flow convention one of two conventions for describing the flow of electric current. The electric current is shown leaving the negative terminal of a cell or battery, moving through the circuit, and entering the positive terminal. (See conventional current.)

electron gun device that produces a beam of electrons, for example, at the back of a television picture tube

electroweak force combination of the electromagnetic and the weak nuclear forces

elementary charge e, magnitude of the charge on an electron or proton

energy E, ability to do work

equilibrium position position from which amplitude of a vibrating object is measured; also called rest position

equivalent resistance R_t, the value of the single resistor which provides the same resistance as a combination of resistors

Eustachian tube keeps the air in the middle ear at atmospheric pressure

eyepiece lens in a telescope that is closest to the eye

F

far point location of the farthest object on which a fully relaxed eye can focus

farsightedness inability of the eye to focus light from near objects onto the retina; also called hyperopia

ferromagnetic property describing a substance that responds strongly to a magnetic field

field lens third lens in a terrestrial telescope used to produce an erect image

field magnet magnet used to provide the external magnetic field in devices such as motors and generators

field winding an electromagnet acting as a field magnet. (See electromagnet.)

first harmonic the lowest frequency mode and simplest pattern for a standing wave. (See fundamental standing wave.)

first overtone the second lowest frequency mode formed by adding a complete loop to the fundamental standing wave. (See fundamental standing wave.)

fixed end unmoving part of material used to form wave; for example, the end of a rope held steady

fixed point position from which, when reflected, a wave reverses phase

fluid friction force of friction that resists the motion of an object through a fluid

focal length f, distance from the optical centre of a lens to the principal focus, measured along the principal axis

focal plane surface on which all the principal focal points for a lens fall

focal point P, when rays are reflected from a smooth surface or refracted through a lens, the point at which the rays of light converge, or from which they diverge, or appear to diverge

force $\vec{F}$, push or a pull on an object; a vector quantity

force of friction force that acts opposite to the direction an object is moving or is tending to move. (See friction.)

force of gravity force of attraction between any two masses in the universe

fossil fuels substances used as fuel, derived from living matter from previous time periods; for example, coal

fovea most sensitive area for bright light and colour in the eye; contains cones only

free-body diagram vector diagram showing all the forces acting simultaneously on an object

free end position at which the points in the medium are free to move. A wave remains erect when reflecting at a free end.

free point position from which, when reflected, a wave keeps the same phase

frequency f, number of cycles per unit of time

friction force that opposes motion when one surface moves or tends to move with/across another. See also static friction, rolling friction, and kinetic friction.

fulcrum fixed point on a lever about which the lever rotates

fundamental standing wave the simplest and lowest frequency standing wave. (See standing wave.)

G

Galilean telescope optical instrument with a converging objective lens and a diverging lens as the eyepiece

galvanometer instrument used to detect and measure the amount and direction of small electric currents

gauss G, unit of magnetic field strength smaller than the tesla; a gauss is one ten-thousandth of a tesla

generating station a building in which generators convert energy, such as thermal energy provided by burning fossil fuels, or the kinetic energy of running water into electric energy

generator device that converts kinetic energy into electrical energy

geothermal energy heat energy obtained from Earth's interior

gigajoule GJ, one billion joules; 10^9 J

gravimeter instrument used to measure variations in Earth's gravitational field

gravitational field intensity $\vec{g}$, ratio of the force of gravity to mass at a specific location; $\vec{g} = \frac{\vec{F}_G}{m}$

gravitational potential energy E_g, energy that an object has as a result of its distance from a celestial body like Earth

gravity force of attraction between objects that have mass; the weakest of the four fundamental forces

H

hammer tiny bone in the middle ear which connects the eardrum to the anvil and helps transmit sound waves into the inner ear

hand magnifier converging lens used to provide enlarged images of an object; also called a magnifying glass

harmonic standing wave pattern whose frequency is a whole number multiple of the fundamental frequency; also known as a partial

helix conductor shaped in a series of loops; also called a coil

hertz Hz, basic unit for frequency; one hertz equals one per second

hyperopia inability of the eye to focus light from near objects onto the retina; also called farsightedness

I

ideal mechanical advantage IMA, theoretical mechanical advantage of a simple machine in which friction is ignored. (See actual mechanical advantage.)

image distance d_i, distance from the optical centre of a lens where an image of an object is formed

image height h_i, height of an image produced using a lens; if the image is inverted, by convention the height is negative

incident ray ray of light approaching a reflecting surface

inclined plane a simple machine consisting of a ramp; used to raise or lower a load using forces smaller than those needed to lift the load vertically

index of refraction n, ratio of the speed of monochromatic light in a vacuum to its speed in a medium

induced current current created using a magnetic field

induced magnetism phenomenon of ferromagnetic substances becoming magnetized in the presence of a magnetic field. In most cases, the magnetism disappears when the original field is removed.

induced potential difference electric energy per unit charge produced by means of a changing magnetic field about a conductor

inertia property of an object that resists change in its state of rest or motion

infrasonic adjective describing frequencies lower than 16 Hz

infrasound sound at frequencies below 16 Hz

instantaneous acceleration $\vec{a}_{inst}$, acceleration at a specific instant of time

instantaneous velocity $\vec{v}_{inst}$, velocity of an object at a specific instant of time

intensity I, amount of energy passing each second through a unit area

interference effect resulting from the passage of two like waves through each other such as two transverse waves or two longitudinal waves

irregular reflection behaviour describing incident rays reflected in many different directions; also called diffuse reflection

J

joule J, work done by a force of one newton applied through a displacement of one metre in the direction of the force; one joule equals one newton·metre

K

Keplerian telescope optical instrument with two converging lenses: an objective lens and an eyepiece; also called an astronomical telescope

kilojoule kJ, one thousand joules; 10^3 J

kilowatt hour kW·h, common unit for electric energy based on the relation $\Delta E = P \cdot \Delta t$ where power is measured in kilowatts and time in hours;
1 kW·h = 3.6 MJ

kinematics branch of mechanics that describes the motion of an object without considering the cause

kinetic energy E_k, energy of a moving object

kinetic friction force of friction that opposes the sliding of one surface over another

Kirchhoff's current law at any connection in an electric current, the total current flowing into the connection is equal to the total current flowing out of the connection

Kirchhoff's voltage law the algebraic sum of the potential differences around any closed pathway or loop must equal zero

L

latent heat Q_l, heat needed to cause a change in state but not a change in temperature

lateral displacement amount of sideways displacement between an incident ray and the final emerging ray

Law of conservation of energy energy cannot be created or destroyed; it can be changed from one form to another, but the total amount of energy in the universe stays constant

law of magnetic poles similar magnetic poles repel while opposite magnetic poles attract

law of the lever when there is more than one torque applied to a lever, it will balance if the sum of the clockwise torques is equal to the sum of the counterclockwise torques

law of universal gravitation the force of gravity between two masses in the universe is directly proportional to the product of the masses and inversely proportional to the square of the distance between their centres

laws of reflection the angle of reflection is equal to the angle of incidence; and the incident ray, normal, and reflected ray all lie on the same plane

laws of refraction the ratio $\sin i / \sin R$ is a constant for a given colour of light and a given material (also called Snell's law); the incident ray and refracted ray are on opposite sides of the normal at the point of incidence, and all three lie in the same plane

Lenz's law the magnetic field of an induced current always opposes the change in magnetic field that is causing the induced current

lever simple machine; a rigid bar that can rotate about a fixed point. There are three classes of levers: first class (the fulcrum is between the load and the applied force), second class (the load is between the fulcrum and the applied force), and third class (the force is between the fulcrum and the load).

light form of radiant energy that the eye can detect

limiting static friction maximum value of the force of friction just before the object starts to move

linear magnification *m*, ratio of the size of an image to the size of the object

lines of magnetic force imaginary lines representing the direction and strength of a magnetic field. The direction of the field is indicated by the direction in which a north pole of a compass would point at that location in the field. The strength of the field is indicated by the spacing of the lines.

lodestone naturally occurring magnets, made of iron ore

longitudinal vibration vibration in which an object vibrates parallel to its long axis. (See vibration.)

longitudinal wave wave in which the medium vibrates parallel to the direction of travel of the wave

loop a vibrating region in a standing wave; extends between adjacent nodes

loudness measure of the response of the ear to sound

luminous objects produce their own light so they are seen by their own light; for example, the Sun

M

machine device that enables us to do work more easily than is otherwise possible

magnet object that provides a magnetic field

magnetic field space surrounding a magnet in which a magnetic force can be detected

magnetic pole a location on the surface of an object where the magnetic field is strongest

magnetite a naturally occurring magnetic mineral (Fe_3O_4)

magnification *m*, the change in size of an image relative to the size of the object; ratio of the size of the image to the size of the object. (See linear magnification.)

magnifying glass converging lens used to enlarge images; also called hand magnifier

magnitude size of something expressed quantitatively

mass *m*, amount of material in an object; the SI unit of mass is the kilogram

mass defect in a nuclear fission reaction, the difference in mass between the total mass of the reactants and the total mass of the products

mechanical resonance resonance that involves mechanical systems; for example, pendulums and springs

medium material through which waves travel; for example, air and water; waves move but the medium does not move along with the wave

megajoule MJ, one million joules; 10^6 J

method of mixtures calculation of the heat exchanged when substances are mixed

monopole theoretical object with only one magnetic pole

motor principle when a current-carrying conductor is located in an external magnetic field perpendicular to the conductor, the conductor experiences a force that is perpendicular to both itself and the external magnetic field

myopia inability of the eye to focus light from distant objects onto the retina; also called nearsightedness

N

natural frequency frequency at which an object vibrates when allowed to do so freely

near point minimum distance of an object at which the normal eye can focus. The near point for a normal eye is about 25 cm.

nearsightedness inability of the eye to focus light from distant objects onto the retina; also called myopia

negative acceleration movement of an object that is slowing down; described by a velocity-time graph which has a negative slope; also called deceleration

net force $\vec{F}_{\text{net}}$, total of two or more forces acting on an object; also called unbalanced force or the resultant force

newton N, SI unit for force; one newton equals one kilogram·metre per second squared

Newton's first law of motion every object will continue in a state of rest or with constant speed in a straight line unless acted upon by an external unbalanced or net force

Newton's second law of motion when a net force acts on an object, the object accelerates in the direction of the net force. The acceleration is directly proportional to the net force and inversely proportional to the mass.

Newton's third law of motion whenever one object exerts a force on a second object, the second object exerts a force that is equal in magnitude and opposite in direction on the first object

nodal lines imaginary lines or curves along which continual destructive interference occurs, thus consisting of nodal points

nodal point point on a wave that never vibrates between supercrests and supertroughs; also called a node

node See nodal point.

noise result of an irregular mixture of frequencies

non-collinear not along the same straight line

non-collinear forces forces that do not act along the same straight line

non-luminous objects do not emit their own light so they are seen by reflected light; most objects are non-luminous

non-ohmic adjective applied to substances that do not obey Ohm's law. (See Ohm's law.)

non-renewable energy energy that is used up faster than it is replaced

normal force $\vec{F}_{\text{n}}$, force acting at right angles to a surface

normal an imaginary line perpendicular to a surface at the point of incidence of a light ray

north pole of a magnet end of a magnet that points toward Earth's geographic north pole

nuclear energy energy stored in the nucleus of an atom

nuclear fuel source of the nuclear energy used to produce heat, such as the fuel rods in nuclear reactors

O

object distance d_o, distance of an object from the optical centre of a lens

object height h_o, height of an object from which an image is being formed

objective lens lens in a two or more lens system that is nearest the object

octave interval between two musical notes that have frequencies in the ratio of two to one; for example, a frequency of 512 Hz is one octave above a frequency of 256 Hz

ohm Ω, unit of measure for resistance; volt per ampere

ohmic an adjective indicating that the substance obeys Ohm's law

Ohm's law potential difference across a conductor is directly proportional to the current flowing through it

opaque medium one that does not transmit light

opposite magnetic fields magnetic fields whose directions are opposite. Such fields indicate attraction between the sources of the fields.

opposite phase property of objects that are always moving in opposite directions at the same time, or at rest and tending to move in opposite directions

optic nerve carries the electrical information from the rods and cones in the eye, to the brain

optical centre O, centre of a lens

optical illusion perception of a visual stimulus that represents what is perceived in a manner different from the way it is in reality

optical power P, power of a lens system, expressed in diopters D; the reciprocal of the focal length in metres

origin beginning of a vector; also called the tail

oscilloscope instrument that shows changes in electric voltages and currents in wave form on a screen

out of phase property of objects whose periodic motion is between the same and opposite phases

oval window part of the cochlea attached to the stirrup. Auditory vibrations enter the inner ear through the oval window.

overtone a standing wave mode with a higher frequency than the fundamental mode or pattern

P

parabolic mirror a mirror whose cross-section is a parabola

parallax apparent motion of an object or an image, which is nearby, with reference to a second object, which is farther away, caused by the change in position of the observer

parallel beam one in which the rays are parallel to each other

parallel connection electric circuit connection that provides the current with a choice of two or more paths. (See also series connection.)

parallel magnetic fields magnetic fields whose lines point in the same direction. Such fields indicate repulsion between the sources of the fields.

partial wave whose frequency is a whole-number multiple of the fundamental frequency; also called harmonic

particle model of light describes light as consisting of microscopic particles radiating away from the source

period T, time required to complete one cycle of a vibration

periodic motion pattern of motion repeating itself at regular intervals

permanent magnet object that keeps its magnetism

phase stage in a cycle

photosynthesis the process in which light (photo) energy is converted to chemical energy in green plants

pitch property of a tone that indicates how high or low it is on a musical scale and is determined by the frequency of the tone

plane a flat surface, real or imagined

point of incidence location where an incident ray strikes a surface

position location of an object relative to a reference point; a vector quantity since a direction must be specified

power P, rate at which work is done; SI unit is watt

primary coil coil in a transformer that receives the alternating current from an external circuit

principal axis PA, line drawn through the optical centre of a lens perpendicular to both surfaces

principal focus F, point where light rays parallel to the principal axis of a mirror or lens either come together or appear to diverge. There are many focal points depending on the orientation of the incident rays, but only one principal focus.

principle of heat exchange whenever two substances at different temperatures are mixed, the amount of heat lost by the hotter substance in cooling is equal to the amount of heat gained by the colder substance in warming

principle of superposition whenever two or more waves pass through each other, the resultant displacement at each point is the sum of all the individual displacements occurring at that point

projector instrument designed to focus an enlarged image of a scene onto a distant screen

pulley modified lever consisting of a grooved wheel that is free to turn in a frame called a block

pure note note that has no overtones; takes the basic wave shape

Q

quantum model of light describes light as consisting of microscopic particles called photons with wave properties; a combination of the particle and wave models of light

R

radiant energy energy that travels as electromagnetic waves

radius of curvature R, distance from the centre of curvature to a mirror

railgun a device which accelerates objects to high speeds using repulsion between magnetic fields produced by huge currents

rarefaction R, region created when longitudinal waves, which are vibrating parallel to the direction of travel, move farther from each other than normal

ray directed straight line representing the path followed by light

ray tracing method used to find the location and properties of an image by determining the paths of light rays coming from the object.

reaction force force exerted by an object when an action force is exerted on it

real image image formed when light comes directly from an image; can be captured on a screen

recomposition process of recombining the colours of the spectrum to form white light

rectilinear propagation term used to describe the fact that light appears to travel in straight lines through a uniform medium

reference coordinates drawing showing the points of a compass to show vector direction

reflected ray ray of light leaving a reflecting surface

reflection waves rebounding from a shiny surface

refracted ray ray of light transmitted from one medium into a new medium

refraction bending of light as it passes at an oblique angle from a material of one refractive index to a material of a different refractive index

regular reflection reflection in which an incident beam of parallel rays remains parallel after reflection; also called specular reflection

relative permeability factor by which the strength of a magnetic field increases due to the presence of a substance

relay remote-control switch

renewable energy energy that is replaced as fast or faster than it is used up; for example, wind energy

resistance property of a material that describes how much or how little the flow of an electric current is impeded. Increasing the resistance in a circuit decreases the current flow. Resistance is the inverse of conductance.

resistivity ρ, a proportionality constant used to calculate the resistance of a wire from knowledge of the wire's length, temperature, cross-sectional area, and type of material

resistor a device having resistance; sometimes used to limit the current in a circuit or to convert electric energy to light or heat

resonance transfer of the energy of vibration from one object to another having the same natural frequency

resonant frequency the frequency at which an object will resonate

resonant length length of an air column that will vibrate in step with (or resonate to) a given frequency

rest mass energy total energy of an object because of its mass

rest position position of an object or medium before it starts to vibrate

resultant force net force; also called the unbalanced force

retina light-sensitive lining of the cavity of the eye

reverberation back and forth reflection of sound

rich note note that contains several overtones in addition to the fundamental frequency; produces a more complex wave pattern than a pure note

right-hand rule for a helix when a helix is grasped with the right hand such that the fingers are wrapped around the helix in the same direction as the current, the thumb points toward the north pole of the helix

right-hand rule for a straight conductor when a conductor is grasped with the right hand such that the thumb points in the direction of the current, the fingers wrapped around the conductor are in the same direction as the magnetic field

right-hand rule for electromagnetic force If the fingers of the right hand point in the direction of the magnetic field, and the thumb points in the direction of the current, the force on the conductor acts outwards from the palm.

rods cells in the eye sensitive to dim light; they do not register colour

rolling friction force of friction that opposes the rolling motion of one surface over another

rotor helix consisting of many turns wound onto a permeable core

S

saddle device that raises the strings on a musical instrument

same phase property of objects that are either at rest or moving in the same direction at the same time

sampling process in which a variable quantity such as a wave is measured at specific time intervals

scalar quantity any physical quantity that can be completely described by a single numeral and the correct unit of measurement

secondary coil coil in a transformer in which a potential difference is induced

series connection electric circuit connection which provides only one path for electron flow. (See also parallel connection.)

shock wave strong compression wave produced as an aircraft exceeds the speed of sound

short circuit pathway in a circuit that contains almost no resistance

shunt low-resistance device connected between two points in an electric circuit that diverts part of the current

shutter camera mechanism that controls the length of time the light is let in

shutter speed time the shutter in a camera is open

silent point a point where sound waves from two or more sources continually undergo complete destructive interference resulting in a nodal point.

sliding friction force of friction that makes it difficult to slide one surface past another. (See kinetic friction.)

slip ring allows current to flow from the armature to an external circuit in an electromagnet

slope property of a line on a graph; determined by dividing the rise between two points on the line by the corresponding run

Snell's law first law of refraction: $\sin i / \sin R$ is a constant for a given colour of light and a given material

solenoid electromagnet

solenoid switch a switch whose operation is based on the motion of a core within a helix or solenoid

sonar system using echoes from sound waves to locate underwater objects; acronym for Sound Navigation and Ranging

sonic adjective indicating that the property relates to sound

sonic boom shock wave produced while an object travels at or faster than the speed of sound.

sound energy that travels as longitudinal waves containing regions of high and low pressure

soundboard the surface in a stringed instrument which enhances the ability of the vibrations from the string to be passed into the air because of its large surface area

soundbox box that amplifies sound through resonance

sound energy energy that is carried from molecule to molecule by longitudinal vibrations

south pole of a magnet end of a magnet that points toward Earth's geographic south pole

specific heat capacity c, quantity of heat needed to change the temperature of a unit mass of a substance through a unit change in temperature

specific latent heat l, quantity of heat required to change the state of a unit mass of a substance

specific latent heat of fusion l_f, quantity of heat required to melt one kilogram of a substance without changing its temperature

specific latent heat of vaporization l_v, quantity of heat needed to vaporize one kilogram of a substance without changing its temperature

spectrum band of colours that make up white light: red, orange, yellow, green, blue, and violet

specular reflection behaviour describing incident rays reflected as a parallel beam; also called regular reflection

spherical aberration inability of a spherical surface to reflect all rays travelling parallel to the principal axis through a common focal point, resulting in a principal focus that is a small fuzzy circle instead of a sharp point

spherical mirror double-sided curved mirror, as if sliced from a sphere

split-ring commutator device that allows current to flow in and out of a helix even while the helix is rotating

standing wave a stationary pattern of vibration consisting of nodes, antinodes, and loops; it is produced by interference from identical waves travelling in opposite directions

step-down transformer transformer in which there are fewer turns in the secondary coil, thereby producing a potential difference smaller than that in the primary coil

step-up transformer transformer in which there are more turns in the secondary coil, thereby producing a potential difference larger than that in the primary coil

stirrup tiny bone in the middle ear located between the anvil and the oval window of the cochlea; it transmits acoustic vibrations from the middle ear to the cochlea

strong nuclear force force that binds atomic nuclei together

subsonic adjective describing speeds slower than that of sound

superconductor material that loses all resistance at a very low temperature and can therefore carry an electric current without losing any energy as heat

supercrest wave crest resulting from constructive interference, which is larger than either individual crest involved in the interference

superposition addition of the displacements of waves

supersonic adjective describing speeds that are faster than sound

supertrough wave trough resulting from constructive interference, which is larger than either individual trough involved in the interference

suspensory ligament connects the lens to the ciliary muscle in the eye

T

tail beginning of a vector; also called the origin

tail-to-tip strategy a graphical method for adding vectors

tangent straight line that touches a curve at only one point and does not cross the curve

terminal point ending of a vector; also called the tip

terrestrial telescope optical instrument similar to a Keplerian telescope but with a third lens, called a field lens, designed to produce an erect final image

tesla T, SI unit of magnetic field strength

thermal energy sum of the potential energy and the kinetic energy possessed by the molecules of an object

tip ending of a vector; also called the terminal point

tolerance permitted variation, stated as a percentage, in the value of the resistance of a material

torque the turning effect of a force calculated by multiplying the magnitude of the force by its perpendicular distance from the fulcrum

total internal reflection phenomenon in which a light ray in a medium with a higher index of refraction cannot refract out into a medium with a lower index of refraction. As a result, it reflects inside the medium with the higher index of refraction.

transformer device that alters electric potential difference and current through electromagnetic induction

translucent medium one that transmits light but the light is scattered so objects cannot be seen clearly through it

transmission line cable used to transmit electrical energy from the generating station to the consumer

transparent medium one that transmits light so well that objects are seen clearly through them

transverse vibration a vibration in which an object moves perpendicular to its long axis. (See vibration.)

transverse wave a wave in which the medium vibrates at right angles to the direction of travel of the wave

trough region of a transverse wave found below the rest position

turbine device that converts the kinetic energy of moving water into rotational kinetic energy of a turbine shaft, which generates power

turns loops in a helix or coil

turns ratio number of turns in the secondary coil divided by the number of turns of the primary coil

tympanic membrane eardrum

U

ultrasonic adjective describing frequencies higher than 20 000 Hz

ultrasound sound at frequencies higher than 20 000 Hz

unbalanced force net force; also called the resultant force

uniform motion movement in a straight line covering equal displacements in equal times; also called constant velocity

universal gravitational constant G, constant used when writing the law of universal gravitation in an equation; $G = 6.67 \times 10^{-11}$ N·m²/kg²

universal wave equation $v = f\lambda$, where v is speed of the wave, f is the frequency, and λ is the wavelength; applies to all types of waves; for example, water waves, sound waves, and seismic waves

V

variable resistor device used to vary the current in a circuit. A potentiometer is a type of variable resistor.

vector quantity represented on a diagram as a line segment with an arrowhead at one end

vector quantity any quantity that is completely described by a numeral, a unit, and a direction

velocity $\vec{v}$, change in position of an object per unit time

vertex V, geometric centre of a mirror

vibration repeated pattern of motion; also called a cycle

virtual image an image from which light only appears to come; cannot be captured on a screen, but can be seen with the eye

vitreous humour the jelly-like fluid between the lens and the retina. It helps maintain the shape of the eyeball. Its index of refraction is 1.34.

volt V, the SI unit for electric potential difference or voltage; 1V = 1J/c

voltmeter instrument used to measure the electric potential difference between two points in a circuit

W

watt W, the SI unit of power. One watt represents the transfer or transformation of 1 joule of energy per second. 1 W = 1 J/s

wave disturbance that transfers energy through a medium by means of a series of vibrations

wave model of light describes light as consisting of transverse waves radiating away from the source

wavelength λ, the distance in a wave between adjacent points vibrating in phase with each other

weak nuclear force force responsible for some nuclei being radioactive

weight term used to describe the force of gravity that a celestial body exerts on a mass

work W, product of the magnitudes of the applied force and the displacement of the object in the direction of the force

yolk ferromagnetic material that connects two or more magnetic cores

Z

zero-parallax method way to locate an image using parallax

ANSWERS TO NUMERICAL QUESTIONS

UNIT 1

Chapter 1

Section 1.1

Example 2 Practice Problems

1. 7 km [W]
2. 2 km [S 45° W]

Example 3 Practice Problems

1. 3.2 km [S 72° W]
2. 540 m [S 5° E]

Section 1.1 Review

2. [S 40° W]
6. a) 75 km
   b) 69 km
   c) 69 km [S 66° E] of the start

Section 1.2

Example 4 Practice Problems

1. 7.1 km/h [S 53° W]
2. 13 km/h [N 18° E]

Section 1.2 Review

4. 80 km/h [E]
5. 5.1 m/s [home to second base]

Section 1.3 Review

4. 125 m
5. 60.0 s to 110 s
6. 5.00 m/s, 1.25 m/s, 0 m/s, −1.67 m/s, 0 m/s, −2.50 m/s
7. −0.50 m/s
8. 181 s

Section 1.4

Example 5 Practice Problems

1. a) 7.1 m/s² [forward]
   b) 1.3 m/s² [forward]
2. a) 6.0 km/h/s [forward] or −1.7 m/s² [forward]

Section 1.4 Review

5. 1.1 m/s² [N]
6. 2.0 m/s² [N]

Section 1.5

Example 6 Practice Problems

1. 18 m/s [down]
2. 10 m/s [down]

Example 7 Practice Problems

1. 4.0 m/s [down]
2. 2.9 m/s² [forward]

Example 8 Practice Problems

1. 32 m [down]
2. 53 m [forward]

Example 9 Practice Problems

1. 19 km/h/s [forward]
2. −56 km/h/s [forward]
3. 1.9×10^2 m [forward]

Section 1.5 Review

6. a) 1.0 m/s [W], 2.5 m/s [W], 0 m/s
7. a) 4.0 m/s² [W], 1.5 m/s² [W], 0 m/s, −4.5 m/s² [W]
   b) 8 m [W], 60 m [W], 54 m [W], 36 m [W]
   c) 168 m [W]

Section 1.6

Example 10 Practice Problems

1. 26 km/h [E]
2. 3.0 m/s [S]

Example 11 Practice Problems

1. 50 m [W]
2. 10 m [down ramp] from start

Example 12 Practice Problems

1. 15 m/s [E]
2. 7.5 s
3. 10 s

Example 13 Practice Problems

1. 66 m [down]
2. 9.5×10^2 m [up]

Section 1.6 Review

4. a) 22 m/s [E]
   b) 3.0 s
   c) 1.5 s
   d) 66 m [E]
5. a) 78 m [S]
   b) 4.3 m/s² [S]
   c) 13 m/s [S]
   d) 3.0 s
6. a) 4.0 m/s [W]
   b) 22 m/s [W]
   c) 3.0 s

Chapter 1 Review

1. a 2. a 3. d 4. b 5. b 6. b

20. 23 m/s [down]
21. 17 m/s [S]
22. a) 2.5 m/s [forward]
    b) 0.12 m/s² [forward]
23. 0.13 m/s²
24. 34 m [S 57° W]
29. b) 1.6×10^2 m [N]
    c) 9.0 km/h/s [S]

Chapter 2

Section 2.1

Example 2 Practice Problems

1. 2.0×10^3 N [up]
2. 16 N [left]

Example 3 Practice Problems

1. 12 N [N 36° E]
2. 2.80×10^2 N [S 75° E]

Section 2.1 Review

4. b) 300 N [forward]
5. b) 2 N [E]
7. b) 45 N[W 1° S]

Section 2.2

Example 6 Practice Problems

1. 2.0×10^{20} N
2. 2.0×10^8 kg

Section 2.2 Review

3. a) $\frac{1}{4}$ F
   b) $\frac{2}{4}$ F $= \frac{1}{2}$ F
4. a) On the Moon: $F_G = 1.62 \times 10^2$ N
   b) On Earth: $F_G = 9.80 \times 10^2$ N
   Comparison:
   $F_{Moon}/F_{Earth} = 0.165/1$

Section 2.3

Example 7 Practice Problems

1. 1.2×10^2 kg
2. 1.1×10^4N

Example 8 Practice Problems

1. a) 4
   b) 6.1×10^{-1} N/kg [down]
2. 16 N [down]

Section 2.3 Review

2. b) 2.51 : 1.00

3. 9.81 N/kg [down]

4. 3.8 N/kg

5. 1.7×10^2 N [down]

Section 2.4

Example 9 Practice Problems

1. 25 m/s [down]

2. a) 7.5 s
b) 15 s

Example 10 Practice Problems

1. 8.8 m/s [up]

2. a) 10 m [up]

Section 2.4 Review

2. 88 N [down]

3. 8.2 m/s^2 [down]

4. 9.0 kg

5. a) 2.4×10^2 m [down]
b) 69 m/s [down]

Chapter 2 Review

1. b **2.** e **3.** d **4.** c **5.** c

14. a) 7.8 m/s [down]
b) 3.1 m

15. a) 1.4/1

16. 15 m

17. 9.5 m

Chapter 3

Section 3.1

Example 1 Practice Problems

1. 1.8×10^3N; 0.67/1

2. 1.1×10^2 N

Example 2 Practice Problems

1. a) 0.60
b) 24 N

2. 4.6×10^{-2}

Section 3.1 Review

3. 2×10^3 N

4. 0.40

5. 2.1 N

Section 3.3

Example 3 Practice Problems

1. 49 N [forward]

2. 5.000×10^{-1} m/s [backward]

Example 4 Practice Problems

1. 74 kg

2. 5.3 m/s [E]

Example 5 Practice Problems

1. 1.3×10^4 N [up]

2. a) 29 N [down]
b) 12 N

Section 3.3 Review

5. 2.0 m/s^2 [S]

6. 1.6×10^3 kg

7. 7.51×10^2 N [S]

8. 5.0×10^{-1} N [N]

9. 15 N [forward]

Section 3.4

Example 6 Practice Problems

1. 11 N (one to the left and one to the right)

2. 2.2 m/s^2 [up]; 71 N [up]

5. 12 N

6. 12 N

Section 3.4 Review

5. 12 N [S], 12 N[N]

6. 4 N [S], 4 N

8. 5.0×10^{-1} N [N]

9. 15 N [forward]

Section 3.5

Example 8 Practice Problems

1. 16 m

2. 18 m

Example 9 Practice Problems

1. a) 2.0 m/s^2 [forward]
b) 2.0 s

2. 3.5 m/s

Section 3.5 Review

2. a) 5.0×10^{-1} m/s^2 [forward]
b) 36 cm
c) 6.0×10^{-1} m/s [forward]

3. a) 2.0×10^{-1} m/s^2 [W]
b) 6.3 s
c) 60 cm/s [W]

4. a) 4.6 m/s^2 [down]
b) 13 m/s [down]

Chapter 3 Review

1. c **2.** c **3.** b **4.** e **5.** d

7. 42 m/s [down]

8. a) −6.9 m/s^2
b) 1.2 s

15. a) 1.6 s
b) 11 m
c) 12 m

21. a) 16 m/s^2 [up]
b) 8.1×10^2 N [up]

24. 3.0×10^2 m/s

Unit 1 Review

1. b **2.** a **3.** d **4.** b **5.** a **6.** b
7. c **8.** b **9.** c **10.** b **11.** b
12. d **13.** a **14.** d **15.** d

20. 15 N [up]

27. 10 m [E]

34. 85 km/h; 65 km/h [N 23° E]

35. 7.0 m/s^2 [E]

36. 4.0 s

37. a) 10.2 m/s [forward]
b) 2.17×10^2 N

38. [S 89° E]

39. 5.8×10^5 N [down]

40. 24.8 N

41. 1.4 s

42. past home plate by 50.0 cm

43. a) 78.4 m
b) 70.4 m

44. 8.6 N [forward]

45. 1.5 t

46. a) 1×10^{-1} N [backward]
b) 8×10^{-1} m/s^2 [backward]
c) 9 s

47. a) 3.7×10^7 N [down]
b) 1.3×10^7 N
c) 3.4 m/s^2 [up]

48. 5.6×10^{-1} m/s^2 [forward]

49. 7.7×10^2 N [west]

50. 7.31×10^2 kg

51. 10 N [up]

52. 4 s

53. a) 5.3 m/s^2 [forward]
b) 4.8×10^2 N

54. 1.8×10^3 N [forward]

UNIT 2

Chapter 4

Section 4.1

Example 1 Practice Problems

1. 9.0 m

2. 3.8×10^2 N

Example 4 Practice Problems

1. 5.0×10^{-2} J

2. 2.0 J

Section 4.1 Review

1. c) 3.9×10^3 J

2. 1.4×10^3 J

3. 40 J

4. 2.8×10^3 J

5. a) 2.9×10^2 J
b) -2.9×10^2 J

6. 2.8 J

7. a) 20 J, 42 J, 6.0 J
c) Total work = 68 J

Section 4.2

Example 6 Practice Problems

1. 1.8×10^{-11} J

2. 2.3×10^{-28} kg

Section 4.2 Review

3. 3.0×10^{-11} J

10. 4.0 km

Section 4.3

Example 8 Practice Problems

1. a) 2.4×10^4 J
b) 2.4×10^4 J

2. a) 88 J
b) 81 J
c) −7.4 J

Section 4.3 Review

2. a) 1.2×10^4 J
b) 1.2×10^4 J

3. a) 4.5×10^2 J
b) 3.2×10^2 J
c) -1.3×10^2 J

4. a) 1.3×10^5 J, -3.2×10^5 J
b) -4.5×10^5 J

5. a) 1.2×10^6 J
b) 1.2×10^6 J

Section 4.4

Example 9 Practice Problems

1. 1.6 kJ

2. 14 m/s

Example 10 Practice Problems

1. 31.6 m/s

2. 3.5×10^5 J

Section 4.4 Review

2. 26 J

3. 1.8 m/s

4. 1.40×10^2 g

5. a) 3.2×10^2 J
b) 3.2×10^2 J
c) 6.4×10^2 J

Section 4.5

Example 11 Practice Problems

1. 5.6 m/s

2. 32 m

Section 4.5 Review

5. a) 2.5 m
b) 9.9 m/s

6. a) 6.3 m/s
b) 1.6 m

Chapter 4 Review

1. a **2.** c **3.** e **4.** b **5.** a

10. 2.0×10^2 N

11. 3.0 m [S]

12. 24 J

13. 2.43 m

14. 2.0 kg

19. a) 8.4 kJ
b) 17 kN

21. a) 5.6×10^6 kg
b) -2.6×10^9 J

22. a) 5 m
b) 1.2×10^1 m/s

33. b) 7.4×10^2 J
c) 1.0 m

Chapter 5

Section 5.1

Example 1 Practice Problems

1. 89%

2. 74%

Section 5.1 Review

2. a) 1.6
b) 73%

5. a) 2
b) 1.6
c) 80%

Section 5.2

Example 3 Practice Problems

1. 29 W

2. 2.4 s

Example 4 Practice Problems

1. a) 2.9×10^5 J
b) 7.3×10^3 W = 7.3 kW

2. 5.0×10^4 W = 50 kW

Section 5.2 Review

3. 1.2×10^8 J

4. 2.7 s

5. 6.9×10^4 W

6. 3.7×10^6 J

7. 4.5×10^2 kJ

Section 5.3

Example 5 Practice Problems

1. 1.6×10^6 J

2. 2.2×10^3 J/kg·K; ethylene glycol

Example 6 Practice Problems

1. 9.3×10^2 J/kg·K

2. 1.8 kg

Example 8 Practice Problems

1. 3.42×10^5 J

2. 4.8 kg

Section 5.3 Review

1. a) -1.3×10^5 J
b) −12 K
c) 4.0 kg

2. 8.94×10^2 J/kg·K

3. 4.1×10^2 J/kg·K

4. a) 1.1×10^6 J
b) 2.0×10^{-1} kg

5. 26 kJ/kg

6. 3.58×10^2 kJ

Section 5.4

Example 9 Practice Problems

1. 85.3 %

2. 2.6×10^6 J

Section 5.4 Review

4. 9.1×10^9 kg

6. a) 34 kW
b) 10 kW

Chapter 5 Review

1. e) **2.** e) **3.** b) **4.** d) **5.** e)

19. b) 25 W

20. 4.2 kJ/(kg·°C); 2.2 kJ/(kg·°C)

21. 3.90×10^2 J/kg·°C

23. a) 3.8 kW
b) 35 km/h

26. iron, 2.0 kg; aluminum, 3.0 kg

27. 10 t

28. 4.3 m

Unit 2 Review

1. c **2.** c **3.** c **4.** c **5.** c **6.** b **7.** e **8.** e **9.** d **10.** c **11.** b

26. 34 km

27. a) 3.3×10^2 W
b) 51 min

28. 7.6 MJ

29. 5×10^1 kg

30. 1.9×10^8 W

43. a) −3.0 kJ
b) +3.0 kJ

44. 1.5 m

45. 7.1×10^2 J

46. 32 m/s

47. 3.0 kg

48. 3.1 kJ

49. 2.3 kJ

50. a) 1.2×10^2 kJ
b) 20 g

51. a) 9.8×10^{-1} J
b) 4.9×10^{-1} J

52. 1.41 kJ

53. a) 47 J
b) 47 J
c) 26 m/s

54. 82 kJ; 1.2×10^2 kJ

55. 1.5

56. 45 kW

57. 81 km/h

58. 26°C

59. 1.4×10^2 g

60. a) 3.00×10^4 W
b) 4.5 kW
c) $75 000

61. 2.8×10^2 N

62. 2.3×10^2 W

63. 89 W

64. 4.9×10^2 kJ

65. a) 1.9×10^5 W
b) 6.7 m/s or 24 km/h

66. a) 6.6 kJ
b) 12 kJ
c) 2.2
d) 54%

67. 17 kg

68. 5.2×10^{-1} kg

69. 1.0 GW

UNIT 3

Chapter 6

Example 1 Practice Problems

1. 5.00×10^5 Hz or 500 kHz

2. 0.20 s

Section 6.1 Review

3. 96 cm

4. a) 1.5 s

5. a) 0.017 s
b) 1.2×10^2 times

#6 ?

Section 6.3 Review

3. 10 m

4. a) 6.0 m

Section 6.4

Example 2 Practice Problems

1. 210 km

2. 0.079 m or 7.9 cm

Section 6.4 Review

1. 85 m/s

2. 6.0×10^{-7} m

3. 5.00×10^{-4} Hz, 2.00×10^3 s or 33.3 min

4. 8.0 Hz

5. 3.00×10^{-3} s

7. a) 4.2×10^{-7} m
b) 48 times as large

Example 3 Practice Problems

1. 6.0 m

2. 12 m/s

Section 6.5 Review

2. a) 5 cm trough
b) 25 cm trough
c) pulse with zero amplitude

4. a) 3.00 m
b) 200 m/s

Chapter 6 Review

1. c **2.** a

11. 1.0×10^3 Hz

12. a) 3.9 s
b) 0.26 Hz

13. 20 s

14. 1.3×10^{-5} s

15. 2.8312×10^9

16. 360 m/s

17. 5.0×10^{17} Hz

18. 1.806×10^5 m

19. 6.00×10^{-11} m

20. 4.7×10^{-7} m

21. 15 m

22. 3.0 m

27. c) $T = 0.90\sqrt{h}$

29. b) 1.0 cm, 3.0 cm
c) 4.0 Hz, 1.3 Hz

30. 226 km

33. 22 min

34. 2.50×10^{-7} m

Chapter 7

Section 7.1 Review

4. a) 220 Hz
b) 110 Hz
c) 1024 Hz or 1.02 kHz
d) 4096 Hz or 4.10 kHz

Section 7.2 Review

1. 16 H to 20 kHz

2. 10 octaves

3. a) 0 – 16 Hz
   b) > 20 kHz

8. a) 1.0×10^8 pW/m^2
   b) 1.0×10^9 pW/m^2
   c) 1.0×10^{13} pW/m^2
   d) 1.0×10^{20} pW/m^2

Example 1 Practice Problems

1. 479 m
2. 0.574 s

Example 2 Practice Problems

1. 1.00×10^6
2. 781 m
3. 5.5×10^{-2} s

Section 7.3 Review

1. a) 333 m/s
   b) 352 m/s
   c) 313 m/s
   d) 322 m/s
2. 0.302 s
5. 0.39 km
6. 5.2 s

Section 7.4 Review

4. 4.0 Hz
5. 90 beats

Chapter 7 Review

3. d 4. a 5. b
13. 19°C
14. 3.3 s
15. 6 beats
16. 2×10^1 beats
17. 1.20 s
18. 3.31 m
19. a) 446 Hz or 434 Hz
    b) 446 Hz
20. 225 Hz
21. a) 1.339 m
    b) 0.225 m
    c) 0.346 m
    d) 3.980 m
22. 22 m to 0.018 m
23. 1.68 km
24. 403 m
25. 23°C
26. a) 993 m/s
    b) 883 m
27. 2.98 s
31. $v = 3.8 \times 10^{2-0.5}$
32. 1.0×10^5 pW/m^2
34. 2.5×10^3 pW
36. wavelength is 60 times larger than the opening
38. b) 3°C
41. 4×10^3 Hz
44. a) 4 times
47. a) 70 dB

Chapter 8

Section 8.1 Review

1. a) $2\frac{1}{2}\ \lambda$
2. 5.3 m
4. a) zero, 10 cm, 20 cm
   b) 5.0 cm, 15 cm, 25 cm
5. a) 1.5 cm, 4.5 cm, 7.5 cm
   b) zero, 3.0 cm, 6.0 cm

Section 8.2

Example 1 Practice Problems

1. 15 cm
2. a) 329 Hz
   b) E

Section 8.2 Review

3. $\frac{1}{2}\ \lambda$
4. 63.0 cm

Section 8.3

1. 167.5 Hz or 502.5 Hz
2. 0.0838 m or 8.38 cm

Example 3 Practice Problems

1. 0.0872 m or 8.72 cm
2. 421 Hz

Example 4 Practice Problems

1. 275 Hz, 550 Hz
2. 0.034 m or 3.4 cm

Section 8.3 Review

1. 30.0 cm, 90.0 cm, 150 cm
2. a) 3.2 m
   b) 1.1 m
   c) 0.64 m
3. a) 1
   b) 2
   c) 3
   d) 21
4. 15 cm, 30 cm, 45 cm
5. a) 1.2 m
   b) 60 cm
   c) 24 cm
7. a) 100 cm or 1.00 m

Example 5 Practice Problems

1. 0.150 m or 15.0 cm
2. 477 Hz

Chapter 8 Review

1. b 2. c 3. d 4. a 5. a
15. 1.00×10^3 m/s
16. a) 1.6 m
    c) 9.6 m/s
    d) 4.0 Hz
17. 20.0 cm
18. 53 cm
19. 391 Hz
20. 1.9 m
21. 68.0 cm
22. 22.7 cm
23. 0.60 m, 1.2 m
24. 0.45 m, 1.4 m
25. 88 cm
26. 50 cm
27. 334 m/s
28. 2.3 kHz
29. 1500 Hz, 2500 Hz
30. a) 4000 Hz, 6000 Hz
31. 0.196 m
34. b) $1\ \frac{3}{4}\ \lambda$
35. b) 363 Hz; 490 Hz
    c) 4 times
    d) $y = 63.2x^{0.5}$
38. 340 m/s
39. a) 60.0 cm
    b) 20.0 cm
    c) 12.0 cm
40. a) 587 Hz
    b) 1.76 kHz
    c) 2.94 kHz
41. a) 24 Hz
    b) first overtone
42. a) 2.6 m
    b) 65 Hz

Unit 3 Review

1. a **2.** a **3.** d **4.** e **5.** d **6.** b
7. c **8.** a **9.** c

20. 15 m

21. a) 1.5 m trough
b) total destructive interference
c) 5.5 m crest

19. 6.0 s

25. a) 342 m/s
b) −0.58%

28. 0.017 Hz

29. a) 7.5 Hz
b) 22.5 Hz

30. a) 77 cm crest
b) 13 cm crest
c) 13 cm trough
d) 77 cm trough

31. 2.4×10 beats

32. 443 Hz or 437 Hz

33. 0.087 s

34. 2664 m

35. 140 cm

36. a) 10 pW/m^2
b) 1.0×10^6 pW/m^2
c) 1.0×10^{11} pW/m^2

37. a) 358 m/s
b) 325 m/s

39. a) 4.0 m
b) 12 m/s

40. 450 m/s

41. a) 1.0×10^{-10} W/m^2
b) 1.0 W/m^2

42. 400 s

43. 36°C

44. a) 0.041 m
b) 1.6 m

45. 1.55 m

46. a) 10.0 m/s
b) 20.0 s
c) 1.60 m
d) 0.200 s
e) 8.00 m/s

47. 5.0×10^{-11} W/m^2

48. 68.6 Hz, 137 Hz, 206 Hz

49. 218 Hz, 436 Hz

50. 50 Hz

51. a) 3.0 cm
b) 1.0 cm

54. b) 1.7 m
c) 10 nW/m^2

59. 19.3 cm

62. a) 3.2 kHz

68. f = 23 kHz

69. 1.99 m

70. 3.0×10^2 m/s

71. a) 291 Hz
b) 582 Hz
c) 562 Hz

72. a) 500.0 Hz
b) 1000 Hz (no change)

73. 33°C

74. 4th harmonic

75. 1st overtone

76. –15 Hz (a drop of 15 Hz)

77. a) 1.5 m/s
b) 1.5 m/s in the same direction as the waves
c) 1.5 m/s in the opposite direction to the waves

78. 6 times

79. a) 392 Hz
b) G

80. 241 m

81. 179 km

82. 184 m

83. 40 beats

84. 434 Hz or 446 Hz

86. a) 392 Hz
b) G

87. 35.3 cm

88. 350 m/s

89. a) 0.579 m
b) 0.071 m

90. a) 0.174 m
b) 0.046 m

91. 293 kHz

UNIT 4

Chapter 9 Review

3. a

4. d

8. a) 1 m

17. (3, −3), (−3, 3), (−3, −3)

Chapter 10

Section 10.1

Example 1 Practice Problems

1. 2.9×10^2 Hz
2. 14 sides

Section 10.1 Review

1. 4.8×10^2 Hz
2. 1.33
3. 2.40×10^8 m/s
6. b) 2.99×10^8 m/s

Section 10.2

Example 2 Practice Problems

1. 1.97×10^8 m/s
2. 46°

Example 3 Practice Problems

1. 25°
2. 1.58; flint glass

Section 10.2 Review

2. 2.2×10^8 m/s
3. 18°
4. 32°
5. 1.1

Section 10.3

Example 4 Practice Problems

1. 61°
2. 1.7

Section 10.3 Review

4. 34°
5. 1.59
7. 24.4° (in air); 33.3° (in water)

Section 10.4

Example 5 Practice Problems

1. 12 cm
2. 1.5

Section 10.4 Review

2. a) 60 cm
b) 27 cm

Chapter 10 Review

1. a **2.** d **3.** c **4.** c **5.** a
8. 15°
9. 1.31; ice
11. 2.62×10^8 m/s
12. 73°
13. 21 m

14. **a)** 38.5° (red); 37.9° (violet)
b) 1.99×10^8 m/s (red); 1.96×10^8 m/s (violet)

18. **a)** 31.4°
b) 1.54

19. 33.3°

20. **a)** 24°

21. **a)** 1.1 m
b) 1.3 m

30. 14 m

Chapter 11

Section 11.2

Example 1 Practice Problems

a) −2.96 cm; virtual
b) 0.417×
c) 1.25 cm; erect

Section 11.2 Review

1. **a)** −15 cm
b) 0.33

4. **a)** 12 cm; −3.6 cm

5. **a)** −60 cm
b) 5.0×

6. **a)** 57 cm
b) 0.05×

Section 11.3

Example 2 Practice Problems

1. 1.5×

2. 1.25×; erect

Example 3 Practice Problems

1. **a)** 57×
b) 4.0×

2. -5.4×10^2×

Section 11.3 Review

2. 7.5 cm; 4.0×

4. -2.9×10^2×

6. **a)** −21.1×
b) 995 mm

8. **a)** 11×
b) 600 mm

Section 11.4

Example 5 Practice Problem

2.6 mm, inward

Section 11.4 Review

5. 1.7 mm; outward

Section 11.5

Example 6 Practice Problems

1. 40 cm

2. **a)** −99 cm
b) +33 cm

3. **a)** 0.67 m
b) 1.5D

Section 11.5 Review

3. **a)** +5.0 D
b) −2.5 D

4. +2.7 D (converging)

Chapter 11 Review

1. d **2.** a **3.** e **4.** d

5. b (fainter)

8. 20 cm

9. **a)** 30 cm
b) −0.50×

10. 20 cm

11. 10 cm

12. **a)** 60.0 cm
b) 3.0×

14. -1.8×10^2×

15. **a)** 196×
b) 985 mm

16. 19 cm

18. 37 cm

21. **a)** 82 mm
b) 1.5 m (square)

22. 84°

23. 62.5 mm

24. **a)** −8.8 mm
b) −51 mm

25. 1.9 m

26. **a)** −16 cm
b) −6.3 D

28. 57 cm

29. −16 cm

30. −30 cm

32. -4.5×10^{-1} mm

35. 17 cm

38. 2:1

39. **a)** 0.77 mm^2
b) 0.810 W/mm^2

41. 1.6 cm to 1.8 cm

Unit 4 Review

1. a **2.** d **3.** b **4.** e **5.** b **6.** c

7. c **8.** d **9.** e

11. 0.85 m

25. 24 cm or 0.24 m

26. $d_o = -20$ cm; $h_i = 13$ cm

27. 0.091 ×

28. **a)** 2.5 cm
b) −0.74 cm

30. 2.99×10^8 m/s

31. 267 nm

32. **a)** $d_i = 36$ cm; $h_i = -1.6$ cm
b) $d_i = 16$ cm; $h_i = 6.9$ cm
c) $d_i = 67$ cm; $h_i = 32$ cm

35. 1000×

36. $d_o = 7.1$ cm; m = 3.5×

37. **a)** −18 cm
b) −5.6 D

38. $d_o = 16$ cm

39. −67 cm

40. **a)** 9.00×
b) 1.20×10^3 mm

46. 21 m

48. 66.7 mm

49. 11 mm

51. 6.5 m

53. $S_o = 41.7$ cm; $m = 0.60$

59. 400 nm to 750 nm

60. 6.0 faces

61. 1.92

62. 58.5°

63. 90×

64. **a)** −40 cm
b) 5.0×

65. 67×

68. 45°

73. **a)** −13 cm
b) 0.33×

74. **b)** 81 cm
c) 7.1×

UNIT 5

Chapter 12

Section 12.1

Example 1 Practice Problems

1. 9.13×10^{19} electrons

2. 8.3×10^{-1} C

Example 3 Practice Problems

1. a) -4.9×10^{2} C
b) 3.1×10^{21} electrons

2. a) -7.5×10^{22} electrons
b) 4.0×10^{2} A

Section 12.1 Review

1. 1.25×10^{19} elementary charges

2. a) 3.2×10^{-18} C
b) -1.60×10^{-15} C
c) 3.2 C

3. 2.5×10^{17} electrons

4. 4 A

5. a) 24 mC
b) 1.5×10^{17} electrons

Section 12.2

Example 5 Practice Problems

1. 8.1×10^{-3} N

2. 2.1×10^{-8} C

Example 6 Practice Problems

1. 2.0×10^{3} V

2. 9.0×10^{-5} J

Section 12.2 Review

1. b) 6.0 J/kg

3. a) 36 J
b) 2.7 s

4. a) 1.7×10^{2} A
b) 1.6×10^{20} elementary charges
c) 7.5×10^{8} J

Section 12.3

Example 11 Practice Problems

1. 3.2 V; 0.24 A

2. 4.5 V; 0.88 A

Example 12 Practice Problem

$I_1 = 225$ mA, $I_3 = 75$ mA,
$I_4 = 75$ mA, $I_5 = 225$ mA,
$V_1 = 2.25V$, $V_2 = 1.50V$, $V_3 = 0.75V$

Example 13 Practice Problem

$V_t = 2.4V$; $I_t = 240$ mA

Section 12.3 Review

1. a) 600 mA
b) $I_2 = 0$, $I_1 = I_3 = I_4 = 600$ mA

2. b) 4.8 V
c) $I_3 = I_4 = 200$ mA,
$I_1 = I_5 = 600$ mA

3. $V_2 = 1.5V$; $I_2 = 730$ mA

4. $I_7 = 300$ mA; $I_1 = I_2 = 150$ mA,
$I_4 = I_5 = I_6 = 100$ mA

Chapter 12 Review

1. d **2.** e **3.** e **4.** c **5.** e **6.** a

13. a **14.** e **15.** e **16.** c **17.** b

18. d **19.** e **20.** a

21. $N = 6.25 \times 10^{19}$ electrons;
2 AA cells

26. 6.1×10^{-9} C

27. -1.5×10^{9} electrons

28. a) 5.0 s
b) 22 mA
c) 45 C

29. a) 20 J
b) 0.40 MC
c) 0.20 GV

30. 7.5 C

31. 1.3 J

32. $V_1 = 1.5$ V; $V_3 = 6$ V; $V_4 = 3$ V

33. $I_3 = 150$ mA; $I_5 = 90$ mA

34. a) 18 V
b) 6 V

35. 5×10^{-13} %

36. 26 mA

37. 4.8 mA

38. 1.6×10^{-17} J

39. 4.0×10^{2} J

40. a) $I_2 = I_3 = 150$ mA; $I_4 = 300$ mA
b) each meter reads 0
c) $I_2 = 0$; $I_3 = I_4 = 200$ mA

41. a) $I_2 = I_4 = I_5 = I_6 = 200$ mA;
$I_3 = 400$ mA
b) $I_2 = I_5 = I_6 = 300$ mA;
$I_3 = 600$ mA; $I_1 = 900$ mA
c) $I_2 = I_4 = I_5 = I_6 = 250$ mA;
$I_1 = 750$ mA

42. $V_1 = 7$ V; V3 = 5 V; $I_3 = 110$ mA;
$I_4 = 150$ mA

43. -2.6×10^{-7}

44. 9.05×10^{16} electrons

45. 15 s

46. a) 3.1×10^{-6} m^2
b) 3.1×10^{-6} m^3
c) 3.1×10^{23} electrons per metre
d) 6.3×10^{18} electrons
e) 2.0×10^{-5} m/s

47. 1.2×10^{5} V

48. $V_3 = 10$ V; $V_t = 30$ V
b) 80 C
c) 2.4 kJ

49. a) 1.20 A
b) L_1
c) I_1 and I_3 would increase slightly; $I_2 = 0$

Chapter 13

Section 13.1

Example 2 Practice Problems

1. 6.2×10^{-2} Ω

2. 3.1×10^{-1} Ω·m

Section 13.1 Review

3. a) 21.1 Ω

4. 3.4×10^{-4} A

6. $\frac{1}{4}$

8. 5.3×10^{-4} Ω

10. a) $I_{dry} = 1.2$ mA;
$I_{wet} = 80$ mA

Section 13.2

Example 8 Practice Problems

1. 4.0 A

2. 25 A

Example 9 Practice Problem

$R_t = 30$ Ω; $I_t = 0.50$ A

Section 13.2 Review

1. 65 Ω

2. a) 16.7 V
b) 22.2 Ω
c) 133 Ω

3. 15 Ω

4. a) 4.17 Ω
b) 2.40 A

c) 0.40 A

5. 36 Ω

6. 15 Ω

7. a) 4.0 Ω; 1.0 A
b) 2.9 Ω; 0.40 A

Example 13 Practice Problems

1. 600 W

2. 180 min

Example 14 Practice Problems

1. $37.80

2. 2.1 kW

Section 13.3 Review

1. 6.67 A

2. 19 Ω

3. 2.0 W

4. 0.080¢; 0.020¢

5. 41¢

6. 500 kW·h

7. $\$2.4 \times 10^6$

Chapter 13 Review

1. b 2. e 3. a 4. c 5. c

12. b) 2×10^1 Ω

13. d) 20 V/A or 20 Ω

Chapter 14

Section 14.1

3. A north — B south
C south — D north
E north — F south
G north — H south

7. time for magnetic reversal is 2.3×10^5 a

Section 14.2

Example 1 Practice Problems

1. 1.05×10^3 N

2. 25 N

Section 14.2 Review

4. a) B
b) D
c) F
d) G

5. a) Y to X
b) X to Y
c) X to Y
d) Y to X

8. 57 N

9. 750 turns/cm

Chapter 14 Review

1. d 2. a 3. d 4. c 5. c 6. d 7. e

13. 83 N

14. 240 turns

15. a) 150 N

16. a) 7.5 A
b) 1.20×10^4

Chapter 15

Section 15.1

Example 1 Practice Problems

1. 31 mN

2. 0.26 B_1

Example 2 Practice Problems

1. 0.0180 Ω

2. 0.120 Ω

Example 3 Practice Problems

1. 8.25 kΩ

2. 87 Ω

Section 15.1 Review

3. 1.2 N

4. a) 24.9 kΩ series resistor
b) 96.15 mΩ shunt

Section 15.2

2. 12

Section 15.3

1. 500 Hz

Section 15.4

Example 5 Practice Problems

1. 300

2. 12 mV

Example 6 Practice Problems

1. 4.8 cm/s

2. 75 mV

Section 15.4 Review

4. 15 cm/s

5. 160 mV

8. a) i) A is north, B is south
ii) C is north, D is south
iii) F is north, E is south
iv) H is north, G is south
b) i) Y to X — ii) Y to X
iii) Y to X — iv) X to Y

Section 15.5 Review

6. 200 Hz

Section 15.6

Example 7 Practice Problems

1. a) 480 V
b) 0.10 A

2. 50

Section 15.6 Review

2. $\frac{1}{4}$ cycle

5. a) 6.00 kV
b) 4.00×10^{-2} A

6. 52

7. b) 1500 W

Section 15.7

Example 8 Practice Problems

1. 1.0×10^7 W

2. 1.00 kW

Section 15.7 Review

3. a) from 27.6 kV to 4.16 kV
b) from 4.16 kV to 240 V

4. a) 21 W
b) 64 kW

Chapter 15 Review

13. 60 Hz

17. 220 V

Unit 5 Review

1. b 2. b 3. b 4. e 5. d

6. d 7. b

18. 88%

19. 2.0 m

20. b) $I = 4.5V^{0.6}$

38. $I_{dry} = 0.0010$ A or 1.0 mA
$I_{wet} = 0.33$ A
current increased by 330 times

39. 3.1×10^2 kW·h

40. **a)** no
b) yes, 10 A
c) 1200 W

41. **a)** 3.6 V
b) 1.2 V

42. 1.92×10^{-17} J

43. 405 J

44. 1.20 mA, safe

45. four times

46. 11 kJ

47. **a)** 12 Ω
b) 1 A
c) 10 V
d) 3.3 W

48. **b)** 0.75 A
c) 1.6×10^2 Ω, 96.0 Ω

49. **a)** 12
b) 20

50. $846

52. **a)** top is south
b) top is south
c) top is north

53. **a)** 150 N
b) multiplied by 4

54. **a)** 7.5 A
b) 1.20×10^4 turns

55. 25 kN

56. **b)** 1000 times

58. 1.15 kV, 0.200 A

59. 39 turns

60. 60 W

INDEX

M

N

O

P

Q

R

S

T

U

V

W

X

Y

Z

PHOTO CREDITS AND ACKNOWLEDGEMENTS

The publisher wishes to thank the following sources for photographs, illustrations, and other materials used in this book. Care has been taken to determine and locate ownership of copyright material used in this text. We will gladly receive information enabling us to rectify any errors or omissions in credits.

Photography

CH. 1 p. 2(top left) Dennis Kitchen/Stone, (top right) Adastra/FPG, (bottom) Richard Price/FPG, p. 4 Michael Lea/CP Picture Archive, p. 6 Magellan, p. 13 Eric Draper/CP Picture Archive, p. 15 Norm Piluke/Ivy Images, p. 16 Steve Niedorf Photography/Image Bank, p. 24 Ivy Images, p. 25 Peter Poulides/Stone, p. 30 Bill Ivy/Ivy Images, p. 31 First Light, p. 32 First Light, **CH. 2** p. 54 Joe McBride/Stone,p. 56 Ivy Images, p. 64 Charles Sykes/Visuals Unlimited, p. 66 M.M Lawrence/First Light,p. 68 Martine Mouchy/Stone, p. 71 Greg Adams/Stone, p. 73 NASA, p. 79 J. O'Brien/Ivy Images, **CH. 3** p. 90 Benelux Press B.V/ Photo Researchers, Inc., p. 92 Fred Chartrand/CP Picture Archive, p. 93 (top) Seguin Royal Mailship, (bottom) Jordi Blancafort/First Light, p. 98 (top) Mark E. Gibson/Visuals Unlimited, (bottom left) Michael Rosenfeld/Stone, (bottom right) Ivy Images, p. 99 Robert Brimson/FPG, p. 104 Kevin Frayer/CP Picture Archive, p. 106 A. Marsh/First Light, p. 113 Don Johnston/Stone, p. 115 G. Shelley/First Light, p. 118 Bill Ivy/Ivy Images, p.119 JohnO'Brien/SpectrumStock/Ivy Images, p. 120 Custom Medical Stock, p. 121 World Perspective/Stone, p. 133 Michael Rosenfeld/Stone **CH. 4** p.140 (left) Space Frontiers-TCL/Masterfile, (right) John Terence Turner-FPG/Masterfile p. 142 (top) Bill Ivy/Ivy Images, (bottom) Ryan Remiorz/CP Picture Archive, p. 144 Jeff Greenberg/Visuals Unlimited, p. 152 Michael Deyoung/First Light, p. 153 David Joel/Stone, p. 155 David Madison/Stone, p. 156 Steve Callahan/Visuals Unlimited, p. 157 Cosmo Condina, Stone p. 158 Bill Ivy/Ivy Images, p. 167 Thomas Kienzle/CP Picture Archive, **CH. 5** p. 178 Sandra Baker/Stone, p. 184 Angela Wyant/Stone, p. 187 Ivy Images, p. 201 M. George/Ivy Images, p. 204 (top) Pickering Nuclear Plant, p. 204 (bottom) Masterfile, p. 208 R. Garnett/Airscapes, p. 210 Warren Gretz/NREL, p. 212 Solar Design Associates Inc./NREL, p. 214 Cummins Power Generation Inc./NREL, p. 227 Loren Santow/Stone **CH. 6** p. 234 Bill Lisenby/First Light, p. 236 (top) Sarah Lawless/Stone (bottom) Tom Raymond/Stone, p. 241 (top) Bill Ivy/Ivy Images, (bottom) W. Fraser/Ivy Images, p. 242(top) CP Picture Archive, (bottom) Nicholas Pinturas, p. 243 First Light, p. 244 Bettman/CORBIS/Magma, p. 247 Lynette Cook/Science Photo Library/Photo Researchers, Inc., p. 250 (top) Toronto Police Department, (middle) Bettmann/CORBIS/Magma (bottom) Allan R. Moller/Stone p. 252 (top left) Marc Epstein/Visuals Unlimited, (top right) Bill Ivy/Ivy Images, (bottom) William Wright/Fundamental Photographs, p. 254 John K. Gates/Visuals Unlimited, p. 255 Bill Ivy/Ivy Images, **CH. 7** p. 264 (top) Carol Kohen/Image Bank, (bottom) Felix Clouzot/Image Bank, p. 267 NASA, p. 269 Adri Berger/Stone, p. 271 Stephen Krasemann/Stone, p. 272 (top left) Bruce Coleman/First Light, (top centre) John Warden/Stone, (top right) Daryl Torckler/Stone, (bottom) Bill Ivy/Ivy Images, p. 275 Bill Ivy/Ivy Images, p. 276 Ron Watts/First Light, p. 278 CORBIS/Magma, **CH. 8** p. 290 (top) Chad Elhers/First Light, (bottom) Mark Harmel/Stone, p. 292 Richard Nowitz/CORBIS/Magma, p. 297 J. Feingersh/First Light, p. 299 (top) Photodisc, (bottom) Jaume Gual/First Light, p. 300 Bill Ivy, Ivy Images, p. 301 David J. Brooks/Visuals Unlimited, p. 304 Tom Stewart/First Light, p. 306 Winston Fraser/Ivy Images, p. 307 Photodisc, p. 308 Bill Ivy/Ivy Images, p. 312 Ultratech, p. 319 John O'Brien/Ivy Images, Careers Picture???? p. 322 Bill Ivy/Ivy Images, **CH. 9** p. 328 Image Bank, p. 330 Gavriel Jecan/Stone, p. 332 (top) Corel Stock Photo Library, (bottom left) First Light, (bottom right) NASA, p. 338 Bill Ivy/Ivy Images, p. 339 (top) Baiba Morrow, (bottom) Stone, p. 343 (top) J. Bator/First Light, (centre) Ron Chappel, (bottom) Brian Stablyk/Stone, p. 346 Paul Silverman/Fundamental Photographs, p. 347 (left) NREL, (top right) Stone, (bottom right) Roger Ressmeyer/CORBIS/Magma, p. 350 (top) Visuals Unlimited, (bottom) Photodisc, p. 354 Bruce Berg/Visuals Unlimited, **CH. 10** p. 362 Ed Young, Science Photo Library/Photo Researchers, Inc., p. 364 Reuters New Media Inc./CORBIS/Magma, p. 368 Bettmann/CORBIS/Magma, p. 370 Corel Photo Library, p. 382 Image Bank, p. 390 Lester Lefkowitz/First Light, p. 391 Corel Photo Library, p. 392 Tom Skrivan/First Light, p. 393 David Olsen/First Light, **CH. 11** p. 400 Bill Kamin/Visuals Unlimited, p. 411 Ray Boudreau, p. 416 Bill Ivy/Ivy Images, p. 421 (top) Photodisc, p. 421 (bottom) Roger Ball/First Light, p. 426 Bill Ivy/Ivy Images, p. 427 Steve Chenn/CORBIS/Magma, p. 432 Bill Kamen/Visuals Unlimited, p. 436 John Bova/Photo Researchers, Inc., p. 440(top) Lito C. Uyan/CORBIS/Magma, (centre) Robet E Daemmrich/Stone, (bottom) Gratis Photo "Brock University, St. Catharines, Ontario, Canada www.brocku.ca", p. 442 Don Smetzer/Stone p. 446 D. Wiggett/First Light, **CH. 12** p. 448 Photo Disc p. 449 Masterfile, p. 450 Bill Ivy/Ivy Images, p. 460

Bill Ivy/Ivy Images, p. 469 General Motors of Canada, p. 476 Kim Fennema/Visuals Unlimited, **CH. 13** p. 484 R. Faris/First Light, p. 488 Charles D. Winters/ Photo Researchers, Inc., p. 491First Light, p. 505 Donna Day/Stone p. 507 Steve Callahan/Visuals Unlimited, p. 510 Schlumberger, p. 511 Photodisc, **CH. 14** p. 518 Peter Samuels/Stone, p. 520 First Light, p. 522 George Hall//Magma, p. 524 Wayne Decker/Fundamental Photographs, p. 530 University of Toronto Archives, p. 532 Keren Su/CORBIS/Magma, p. 537 Michael S. Yamashita/CORBIS/Magma **CH. 15** p. 544 Bill Ivy/Ivy Images, p. 546 First Light, p. 550 Paul Silverman/ Fundamental Photographs, p. 551 Martin F. Chillmaid/Photo Researchers, Inc., p. 553 Bill B./Visuals Unlimited, p. 558 NASA, p. 566 Nancy Richmond/Ivy Images, p. 567 Bill Ivy/Ivy Images,p. 575 NREL, p. 576 Bob Chambers/Ivy Images, p. 586 Jon Riley/Stone, p. 589 Corel Stock Photo Library.